C0-AUL-328

BRADFORD
COLLEGE
LIBRARY

# The Earth Sciences

Second Edition

**Arthur N. Strahler**
Columbia University

**Harper & Row, Publishers**
New York, Evanston, and London

*Photographs on front and back covers by Emily Harste*

*Endpapers courtesy Autometric Operation, Raytheon Company and U.S. Army Engineering Topographic Laboratories*



**The Earth Sciences,** Second Edition

 For information address Harper & Row, Publishers, Inc., 49 East 33rd Street, New York, N.Y. 10016.

LIBRARY OF CONGRESS CATALOG CARD NUMBER: 78-127335

# Contents

# Preface

THE SEVEN YEARS that have elapsed since publication of the First Edition of this book span an epoch of scientific exploration and discovery without parallel in our century. Developments in geology and solid-earth geophysics, in submarine geology and sedimentology, in space science, and in lunar and planetary geology have occurred during this period at an unprecedented rate. Consequently, the demands of a textbook revision have been heavy and have necessitated the writing of much new material and the preparation of many new illustrations. As I have pointed out in a statement closing Chapter 41, a significant trend in the last decade has been the bringing together of diverse branches of science and methods of investigation to solve new and complex problems in the earth sciences. This reunification of science seems to have reversed the drift toward fragmentation and compartmentalization that was for decades the price of increased scientific information.

The writing of the First Edition of this book was prompted by my conviction that a major redistribution of emphasis was long overdue in the introductory course offered as part of the general education of the college student by departments of geology throughout the United States. I stated then that the teaching of the full spectrum of the earth sciences should be recognized as the responsibility of each geology department within the fold of the natural sciences. Success of the First Edition has supported my conviction, although it is obvious that the weight of tradition has continued to impede the modernization of course content in many of our colleges and universities. The pressure, however, of new discoveries is forcing a reorganization of institutional departments; we now find unions of geologic, atmospheric, oceanographic, and space sciences to the accompaniment of a strong infusion of geophysics, geochemistry, and astronomy. It is to such unified programs of broad scope that the Second Edition of *The Earth Sciences* is directed.

Some of the major changes in content and emphasis in the Second Edition are as follows: Mineralogy and petrology are strengthened to the extent that three chapters replace a single chapter. Some basic geochemical information has been introduced into these and other chapters and includes element abundances, silicate structures, radioactivity, radiometric age determination, and oxygen-isotope analysis. To overcome what was pointed out as a weakness in the First Edition, historical geology and evolution of life are now developed at some length, with four chapters replacing what was a single chapter. In preparing this new material on earth history, I steered clear of the traditional approach in which each period is chronicled in detail in terms of paleogeography, stratigraphic sections and their fossil contents, and tectonic events; instead, the evolution of life in a changing environment is traced in broad strokes that apply principles of organic evolution. A new chapter devoted entirely to the Pleistocene and Holocene epochs concludes the book and brings together diverse disciplines and lines of evidence in interpreting the environment in which Man has evolved and lives today.

To review and interrelate major scientific discoveries of the past few years, discussions of planetary and lunar geology, early earth history, paleomagnetism, crustal spreading, continental drift, plate tectonics, the deep-sea sediment record, and other topics have been introduced.

The need to understand the nature of our sun as a star becomes increasingly apparent as lunar and planetary sciences bring the geologist into closer contact with the astronomer. The text material dealing with astronomy has been expanded by forming a new chapter reviewing stellar and galactic topics, placing our solar system in the context of the universe.

A substantial move in the direction of unification of the earth sciences has been made by introducing concepts of radiation, heat, and water balances of our planet. In explaining the operation of global systems of energy and mass transport and exchange, the oceans, atmosphere, and continental surfaces become interrelated areas of scientific inquiry.

Although the structure of the Second Edition follows the substantive-descriptive pattern, the nature and characteristics of energy systems are briefly presented in introducing and concluding many chapters. These explicit references to broad concepts may help to meet the reader's intellectual demands for increased relevance and meaning in the study of science.

In writing a book that spreads its content over the principles of many sciences, I have been keenly aware that my own field of authority is small indeed. I have, therefore, relied upon the generosity of scientific colleagues—each an authority in his own field—to review parts of the manuscript in order to eliminate as far as possible errors and misconceptions that existed in the text as it was first drafted. I acknowledge the aid of these authorities, without holding any of them responsible for flaws and weaknesses that persist in the text.

Professor Theodore G. Mehlin, Department of Astronomy, Williams College, had reviewed several of the chapters on astronomy in the First Edition. He also reviewed two of the largely-new chapters, *The Solar Family* and *Our Sun as a Star in Galaxy and Universe.*

Chapter 3, *Time,* was extensively revised with the assistance of Dr. William Markowitz, Wehr Professor of Physics at Marquette University and formerly Director of the Time Service Division of the U.S. Naval Observatory. William Danielson of the Talcott Mountain Science Center, Avon, Connecticut, reviewed the new paragraphs on sun-synchronous orbiting satellites in Chapter 8. Professor Edward P. Clancy, Department of Physics, Mount Holyoke College, recently the author of a fine popular book on tides, reviewed Chapter 9, *The Tide.* A beneficial reorganization in topics resulted.

Mrs. Irene Fischer of the U.S. Army Topographic Command updated material on ellipsoids and the geoid for Chapter 10, *The Earth's Figure and Gravity.* She made many valuable suggestions and furnished new information for illustrations. Professor William M. Kaula, Institute of Geophysics and Planetary Physics, University of California at Los Angeles, read the new text on satellite gravimetry in this same chapter.

Dr. Helmut H. Schmid, Director of the Geodetic Research and Development Laboratory of ESSA Coast and Geodetic Survey, assisted in preparing the new material on triangulation by orbiting satellite for Chapter 11. Material on geodetic surveys in this chapter had been reviewed for the First Edition by staff geodesists of the Coast and Geodetic Survey through the courtesy of its Deputy Director, Rear Admiral James C. Tison, Jr.

Professors J. Lamar Worzel and John E. Nafe of the Department of Geology and Lamont-Doherty Geological Observatory of Columbia University, reviewed chapters of Part I in the First Edition on the subjects of the earth figure and gravity, tides, and terrestrial magnetism.

Dr. Elmar R. Reiter, Professor of Atmospheric Science at Colorado State University and the author of a book on jet streams, reviewed Chapters 12, 15, and 19 dealing with the structure of the atmosphere and its motions. Professor Charles D. Thor, Maritime College of the State University of New York, had previously read chapters on meteorology in the First Edition.

Professor William D. Sellers, Institute of Atmospheric Physics, University of Arizona, reviewed Chapters 13 and 14, dealing with the radiation and heat balances, and parts of chapters 16 and 18 relating to the water balance. He very kindly made available to me a number of figures and data tables from his own book, *Physical Climatology.*

Professor Jerome Williams, U.S. Naval Academy, Annapolis, the author of a well-known textbook, *Oceanography,* reviewed Chapters 12, 16, and 17 dealing with various topics in physical oceanography. Professor William L. Donn, Department of Geology, The City College of New York, and Lamont-Doherty Geological Observatory of Columbia University, had previously reviewed the oceanographic material for the First Edition.

Dr. Martin Prinz, Institute of Meteoritics, University of New Mexico at Albuquerque, reviewed Chapters 20 and 21 dealing with minerals and igneous rocks. Professor Earle F. McBride, Department of Geology, University of Texas at Austin, reviewed Chapter 22, *The Sedimentary Rocks.*

Professor Charles L. Drake, Department of Earth Sciences, Dartmouth College, reviewed Chapters 23, 25, and 26 dealing with the earth's interior, crust, and tectonic forms. Professor Jack E. Oliver, Chairman of the Department of Geology, Columbia University, had read the First Edition chapter on the earth's interior.

Professor Bruce C. Heezen, Department of Geology and Lamont-Doherty Geological Observatory of Columbia University, reviewed Chapter 24, *The Ocean Basins and Their Sediments.* He generously allowed me to reproduce a number of his fine illustrations of submarine topography.

Professor A. G. W. Cameron, Belfer Graduate School of Science, Yeshiva University, reviewed the first part of Chapter 27, dealing with the origin of the solar system. Professor Mehlin also reviewed this material, in addition to the chapters previously mentioned. Professor Preston Cloud, Department of Geology, University of California at Santa Barbara, reviewed the second part of the same chapter. He generously permitted me to draw heavily upon the ideas in his publications and to use a number of his photographs.

Edwin D. McKee, Project Chief, Paleotectonic Map Section, U.S. Geological Survey, reviewed Chapter 28, *Principles of Stratigraphic Interpretation.* As the leading authority on stratigraphy of the Colorado Plateau areas used as examples in the text, his suggestions were much appreciated, together with his generosity in providing a number of the illustrations. Parts of this chapter were also reviewed for the First Edition by Professor Marshall Kay, Department of Geology, Columbia University.

Professor A. Lee McAlester, Department of Geology and Geophysics, Yale University, reviewed Chapters 29 and 30, and a part of Chapter 41, dealing with evolution of life throughout geologic time. He generously allowed me to draw heavily upon the information, concepts, and illustrations in his recent book, *The History of Life.*

Dr. John A. Wood, Smithsonian Institution Astrophysical Observatory, Cambridge, reviewed Chapter 31, *The Geology of Planetary Space.* Portions of this chapter were also read by Professor Bruce C. Heezen (tektites), Professor William M. Kaula (mascons), and Professors Theodore G. Mehlin and A. G. W. Cameron. Officials of NASA provided many new photographs of lunar and martian subjects.

Professor Stanley A. Schumm, Department of Geology, Colorado State University at Fort Collins, reviewed Chapter 36, *Systems of Fluvial Denudation.* Professor William C. Krumbein, Department of Geology, Northwestern University, also read portions of this chapter. Professor Sheldon Judson, Department of Geology, Princeton University, allowed me to use denudation data compiled by him and associates.

Professor William R. Farrand, Department of Geology and Mineralogy, University of Michigan at Ann Arbor, reviewed Chapter 41, an entirely new chapter on the Pleistocene and Holocene epochs. He had also read Chapter 40, *Glacial Processes and Forms,* as it appeared in the First Edition. Professor Wallace S. Broecker also reviewed Chapter 41. Various portions of this chapter were read by others whose investigations and hypotheses are discussed: David B. Ericson, Cesare Emiliani, and William L. Donn.

A large number of individuals to whom credit is due for suggesting corrections and changes are not listed by name but deserve the author's warm thanks. These include many who took time to write to the author, and particularly the more than 125 instructors whose opinions were obtained through a detailed questionnaire. Opinions and comments thus collected exerted a strong influence in shaping the Second Edition and have we trust, made the new work of greater practical value to instructors and students of the earth sciences.

**Arthur N. Strahler**

# Introduction

WHAT ARE *THE EARTH SCIENCES?* One helpful approach to understanding the scope of subject matter within the earth sciences is to consider the geographic or spatial regions which the phenomena occupy. Thus we have the solid earth, or *lithosphere,* with which the *geological sciences* are traditionally concerned; the *oceans,* obviously the subject of a group of *oceanographic sciences;* an inner layer of the *atmosphere* with which *meteorology* and *climatology* deal; and finally, an *outer atmosphere* grading imperceptibly into *interplanetary space,* with which the *space sciences* and *planetary sciences* are concerned.

The domain of molecules and smaller, elementary particles of matter is assumed to be studied elsewhere, in the physical sciences of modern chemistry and physics; the world of vast interstellar dimensions, in the science of astronomy. Moreover, the world of existing plant and animal life is largely left to be treated in the broad field of the life sciences, including zoology and botany.

From the standpoint of the scale of size of the spaces and objects concerned, it will be more meaningful for us to reverse the geographical order stated above and to consider first the earth as a single object in interplanetary space. Part One, therefore, treats the gross physical properties of the earth as a planet, its motions in space, and its relations to other objects and physical phenomena in the solar system.

Much knowledge that only a few decades ago was regarded as a part of astronomy has now become of interest in a broader, newer definition of earth-science investigation. Astronomers have been looking farther and farther away, toward the vast dimensions of interstellar space, whereas the earth scientists have been taking more and more interest in the moon and nearer planets as having points of direct comparison with the earth. Study of the composition, structure, and origin of these nearer celestial bodies can be thought of as simply an outward extension of the geological sciences. Studies of the surface forms, surface processes, and atmospheres of the moon and planets are extensions of corresponding branches of established terrestrial studies. Thus there are evolving rapidly the new fields of *planetology* and *space science,* in which the efforts of scientists trained in physics, chemistry, astronomy, and geology are being focused cooperatively upon study of the physical conditions to be encountered and the scientific problems to be investigated in Man's ventures into space travel.

Part One will emphasize the physical properties and physical phenomena of the earth as a single object—a globe—of more or less spherical shape. A number of fields within the earth science of *geophysics* enter here in studies of the earth's figure and gravity, the behavior of the earth as a magnet, and tidal phenomena. Within the geophysical field of *geodesy* is included the precision determination of position and elevation on the earth's surface.

Geophysics, broadly conceived, is the application of principles of physics to problems of the earth. In this sense geophysics pervades virtually all phases of the earth sciences. The adjective *geophysical* usually connotes the application of rigorously mathematical analysis to any physical phenomena of the earth. Other, more specific phases of geophysics relate to the investigation of the earth's crust and interior by indirect, instrumental observations. These phases are referred to below.

Part Two of the book treats the earth's atmosphere, at first viewed broadly with specific references to features of the upper atmosphere that fall into the realm of *aeronomy.* Then we take up *meteorology* and *physical climatology,* concerned particularly with the inner, or lower, atmosphere, in which weather phenomena and storms occur. We may think of meteorology as treating the physics of the atmosphere and of physical climatology as treating the exchanges of energy and water at the earth's surface. These sciences are regarded as geophysical because they apply principles of physics in a quantitative way to problems of the atmosphere.

Included in Part Two is the earth science of *oceanography.* Emphasis in this book is upon the physical aspects of oceanography, whereas the equally important field of biological oceanography has been left for treatment elsewhere, as a part of the biological sciences. Physical oceanography deals with the physical properties and circulation of ocean waters. The study of configuration of the ocean basins, the relief features of the floors, the nature of the sediments resting there, and the rock varieties and structures beneath the floors are more conveniently treated in Part Three as *submarine geology,* an oceanward extension of the various fields of geology.

Part Three is concerned with the solid earth, or lithosphere. Here we study the earth's interior composition and structure as deduced from classical studies of geophysics—particularly earthquake wave propagation—and considerations of distribution of density and heat within the earth. Geophysics and geology then meet in dealing with problems of the nature of the earth's crust, and of the form and distribution of the ocean basins and continents.

Historically the field of classical geology has served as a foundation for the earth sciences. Traditionally geology deals with interpretation of rocks lying near the earth's surface, where they are exposed for examination and can be sampled for chemical, physical, and biological analysis. Geology has long included *petrology,* the study of mineral composition, classification, and origin of rocks; *stratigraphy,* the study of rock strata in terms of relative age and environment of deposition; *tectonic* or *structural geology,* the study of rock deformation and mountain-building, and *vulcanology,* the science of volcanoes. *Paleontology,* the study of the record of life of the geologic past and its evolutionary development, is an important branch of historical geology that rests upon biological foundations. Currently the principles of geology are being extended into space in an effort to interpret the origin and history of the moon, the inner planets, and other objects of the solar system.

This book, because of its emphasis upon physical phenomena, gives only secondary attention to the important role of chemistry in the earth sciences. *Geochemistry* applies the principles of chemistry to problems of the natural substances of the earth and to all geologic problems in which chemical analysis will increase understanding of the processes in operation. In its dealing with the solid earth, geochemistry is closely interwoven with *mineralogy,* the traditional geological science of minerals. In making use of principles of radioactivity, geochemistry plays a leading role in determination of the ages of events in geologic time.

Part Four concerns that part of the solid earth most closely and continuously affecting man in his daily life. *Geomorphology* deals with the surface configuration of the lands and with the thin, but extremely complex, soil layer that mantles much of the earth's lands. The earth's topographic features, or *landforms,* develop in the zone of interaction between atmosphere and solid earth. The processes of rock decay and disintegration—with accompanying movement under the force of gravity and transportation under the action of flowing water, glacial ice, and winds—shape the landscape and prepare the surface layer for soil development. Of great importance in these processes is the role of water flowing over the ground surface, or in streams, and moving downward into the soil and rock. Here we include one part of the earth science of *hydrology.* In its broadest sense, hydrology traces the global movement and storage of water in gaseous, liquid, and solid states. Other aspects of hydrology are included elsewhere in meteorology, physical climatology, and oceanography.

How, on a national basis, are the earth sciences coordinated in the United States by a formal, representative body of scientists? The Division of Earth Sciences of the National Academy of Sciences (NAS) and its affiliated group, the National Research Council (NRC), may be regarded as our national (but not federal) coordinator of the many branches of the earth sciences. The National Academy of Sciences, a private nonprofit corporation, was establishd in 1863 by act of Congress to further science and to provide scientific advice to the federal government. In 1916 there was formed within the Academy the National Research Council, supported by the nation's scientific societies and designed to give more direct and effective advice to the government, and to serve science broadly. The Earth Sciences Division of the NAS–NRC gives representation to about sixteen societies, each representing some field or fields of the earth sciences. These individual societies represent the fields of geology, geography, geophysics, geochemistry, meteorology, and the more specific fields of surveying and mapping, photogrammetry, mineralogy, paleontology, and seismology. One of the included societies, the American Geophysical Union, was itself established by the NRC and lists the following as its component sections: geodesy; seismology; meteorology; geomagnetism and paleomagnetism; oceanography; volcanology, geochemistry, and petrology; hydrology; tectonophysics; planetology; solar–terrestrial relationships.

Thus, in answer to our opening question—"What are the earth sciences?"—we can refer to the Earth Sciences Division of the NAS–NRC, and be guided by the activities of scientists within its member societies and advisory committees.

A formal definition and statement of content of each subdivision of the earth sciences is given at an appropriate point in the text.

# ONE

# The earth as a planet

*View of the earth 240,000 statute miles away from Apollo 8.*
*Courtesy National Aeronautics and Space Administration.*

# 1

# The earth in its orbit

THE EARTH in its larger setting, as one of the nine known planets revolving in orbits about the sun, is the logical starting point for a study of the earth sciences. The history and composition of the earth and the operation of complex processes affecting its solid body, its atmosphere, and its oceans can be understood only through a study of the relations between earth and sun. We will place strong emphasis on the earth as a spherical body exposed to the radiant energy of the sun, for almost all processes operating at or near the earth's surface and the maintenance of all forms of life depend upon the quantities of solar energy received at various positions on the earth's surface and upon the daily and yearly variations in these quantities.

To understand the several theories of the earth's origin it will be necessary to learn something about the other members of the solar system. For inquiry into the age of the earth it will be necessary to look at the solar system as a part of a great galactic assemblage of stars, which in turn is but one of many galaxies. Thus much of the material in these early chapters is clearly a part of the science of astronomy; most of the scientific knowledge to be reviewed has been discovered and refined by astronomers. Astronomy is not itself regarded as one of the earth sciences, for, as the Introduction points out, the concern of astronomy is largely with the world of vast dimension. We shall limit our selection of astronomical topics to those which will help us understand what takes place on earth. Most of what we shall want to know of astronomy will deal with the very modest dimensions of distance and time in relation to the earth, in comparison to the vast dimensions in relation to the stars beyond the sun.

## Earth or sun at the center?

Early astronomical thought dealt largely with the solar system for the obvious reasons that without a telescope only the sun, moon, and planets could be seen to have relative motions among themselves and to show measurable diameters, whereas the stars seemed to be fixed pinpoints of light showing no motion with respect to one another. The idea that observable members of the solar system are discrete bodies in space, moving in a systematic manner with respect to one another, was accepted by the earliest astonomers of Greece and Egypt. The question of which of two bodies, earth or sun, was the fixed object about which the others revolved was disputed for perhaps 2000 years, to be settled only in the dawning years of modern astronomy.

The followers of Pythagoras, a Greek philosopher and mathematician who lived in the sixth century B.C., asserted as a principle of their philosophy that the earth rotates upon its axis and revolves in an orbit about the sun. Although they offered no scientific observations or reasoning to support their views, the Pythagoreans can be credited with first stating the *heliocentric theory* (from the Greek word *helios,* sun) of the solar system, in which the sun is at the center of planetary orbital motion. Not long thereafter a Greek astronomer, Aristarchus (about 310–250 B.C.), advanced the heliocentric theory in a systematic manner based on careful astronomical observations and calculations, but this was the last time for many centuries that the theory was to be supported.

The *geocentric theory* (from the Greek word *geos,* earth), which places the earth at the center of the universe, was put forward about the middle of the second century A.D. by Claudius Ptolemy, an astronomer and mathematician of Alexandria, who made use of the previously recorded astronomical observations of Hipparchus (180–110 B.C.). Called also the *Ptolemaic system* of astronomy, the geocentric theory describes the individual apparent paths of sun, moon, planets, and stars as complex systems of cyclic motions relative to a stationary (nonrotating) earth. It is possible in this way to represent the apparent motions of these bodies geometrically, but a good deal of ingenuity is required to cope with each new motion discovered by more precise measurements, and, moreover, the method fails completely to give any explanation of why the bodies move as they do.

Heliocentric theory was revived by the Polish astronomer Nikolaus Copernicus (1473–1543), who referred to Aristarchus' concepts of nearly eighteen hundred years earlier to develop what is now generally called the *Copernican theory* of the solar system. Based largely on the argument that it was a much simpler way to explain the known facts, Copernican theory placed the sun at the center of the solar system, with the planets revolving about the sun in a set of circular orbits. Bear in mind that the telescope was not yet invented, nor were the laws of gravitation and motion known. Absolute evidence of the earth's motions could not then be obtained by any available instrument.

Copernicus' contemporaries and successors were strongly divided on the merits of a heliocentric system. A powerful and scientifically accurate objection was brought against it a century later by Tycho Brahe (1546–1601), a distinguished Danish astronomer. He revived an old argument of Aristotle's to the effect that, if the earth revolves about the sun, being at one season at one side of its orbit and six months later on the opposite side, the stars would seem to change their positions annually in relation to the earth (the so-called "annual parallax," discussed later in this chapter). Brahe could detect no such change and concluded that the Copernican theory was impossible. Little did he realize the enormity of distances to the stars. The change in angle of star positions, which he rightly anticipated, were the Copernican theory valid, is so minute as to be completely undetectable to the naked eye. Only in recent times has the development of powerful telescopes permitted the effect to be measured.

Great strides in establishing the heliocentric theory came through the use of the first astronomical telescope by its inventor, the Italian scientist Galileo Galilei (1564–1642), who in 1610 discovered that there are moons revolving around the planet Jupiter. Although not constituting direct proof, the similarity in observed orbital motion of these moons and that required of the planets under Copernican theory could be regarded as evidence by analogy. Then Galileo discovered that Venus shows phases similar to those of the moon and, moreover, changes apparent size with phase (see Figures 5.5 and 5.6). Because the changes of phase are clearly the different proportions which we see of a spherical surface illuminated by the sun's rays, the only logical conclusion was that Venus revolves about the sun. Galileo was not free to support his own beliefs publicly, because Copernican theory was then regarded by church authorities as a religious heresy. He was compelled to recant his views and to retire into seclusion for his remaining years.

During this same period Johannes Kepler (1571–1630), using a long series of observations made by Tycho Brahe, discovered empirically the three fundamental laws of planetary motion which describe the Copernican theory. Their physical explanation was not understood until Isaac Newton (1642–1727) discovered the underlying laws of gravitation and motion, which he had formulated perhaps as early as 1665 and published in 1687 in a volume entitled *Mathematical Principles of Natural Philosophy.*[1] Despite such powerful supporting logic, opposition to Copernican theory persisted long beyond this time.

## Proofs of the earth's revolution around the sun

What direct and convincing proofs can be assembled to show that the earth actually moves in a more-or-less circular orbit around the sun? We must look beyond the mere reasonableness of the Copernican theory and its close agreement with Newtonian laws of gravitation and motion for some specific and independent evidence.

First consider the effect that the earth's orbital motion will have upon the light rays from a star as they are received on earth. The principle will be more easily

[1] *Philosophiae Naturalis Principia Mathematica.*

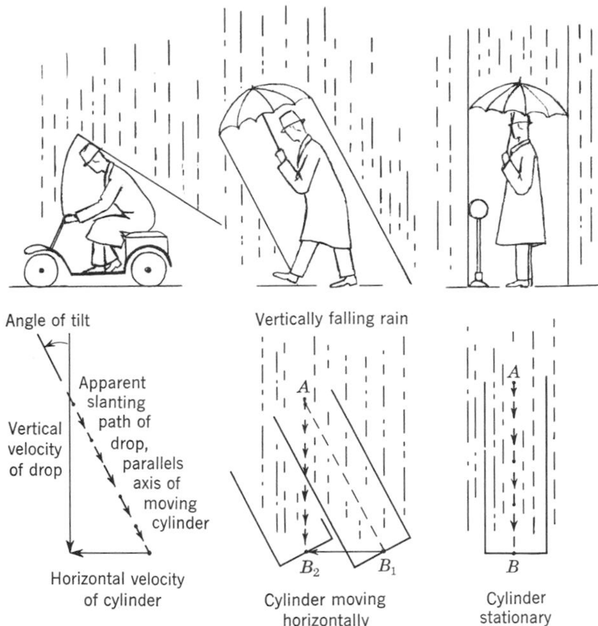


**FIGURE 1.1.** Principle of the aberration of starlight.

understood by a simple analogy. When the rain is falling vertically on a calm day, the paths taken by the drops appear vertical to a person standing still (Figure 1.1), and he will hold his umbrella directly above him. If he walks briskly along through the rain, the drops will seem to be traveling at an angle toward him, and he must tlit the umbrella forward in the direction of his motion to shield himself. Were he to move still faster on, say, a motor scooter, the drops would seem to be coming at him directly head-on, at a nearly horizontal attitude, requiring a windshield placed in front of him. Imagine, then, that this person wishes to collect the vertically falling drops on the bottom of a cylindrical vessel. When standing still, he would hold the cylinder vertical; when walking, he would tilt it forward to admit the drops directly; for still faster speeds he would tilt the cylinder until it was almost horizontal.

The behavior of light rays is closely analogous to that of the falling raindrops. If a telescope is to receive a star's rays parallel with the axis of the telescope tube and if the telescope is in rapid motion at some angle crossing the paths of the rays, it will be necessary to tilt the tube in the direction of transverse motion, as in the case of the cylinders in the lower half of Figure 1.1. (The triangles show the apparent path as the resultant effect of vertical and horizontal velocities.) In the case of light rays the degree of tilt would be minute, because the speed of light of 186,000 mi ($3 \times 10^5$ km) per second is vastly greater than the earth's linear velocity in orbit, about 18 mi (29 km) per second, resulting in an angle of only 20½ seconds of arc.

Because a telescope must always be tilted in the same direction as that in which the earth is moving, it will be tilted one way at one season of the year, and in the opposite direction during the opposite season; thus the position of each star appears to move annually through a tiny orbit. Depending upon the position of the star in the sky, this orbit will vary from a circle (for a star in a direction perpendicular to the plane of the earth's orbit), through an elliptical form, to a straight line (for stars directly in the plane of the earth's orbit). In all cases the long axis of the orbit will include an angle of 41 seconds, or twice the maximum tilt in each direction. This shift in a star's position is a phenomenon termed *aberration of light;* the apparent path of the star is called its *aberrational orbit.* Consider that two stars can have the same annual orbit of aberration only if they lie at exactly the same latitudinal position in the sky; hence virtually all stars have different orbits. Now, according to Ptolemaic (geocentric) theory it is the stars that are required to move in these orbits while the earth remains fixed. That the orbits of countless stars should move so systematically in terms of their positions in the sky would be most difficult to account for on a sound mechanical basis. According to Copernican (heliocentric) theory only the earth is moving; this movement, relative to fixed stars, produces the apparent aberrational orbits, a fact infinitely simpler to explain than the complex stellar motions required by the Ptolemaic theory.

The aberration of starlight was first discovered in 1727 by James Bradley, serving then as the English Astronomer Royal, and may be considered as the final stroke in settling the dispute concerning the relative motions of the earth and the heavenly bodies.

A second proof of the earth's revolution in an orbit about the sun is based upon the measurement of the degree to which the color spectrum of light is shifted by motions that increase or decrease the distances between light-emitting sources and the observer. The principle involved is familiar in the *Doppler effect* on sound waves, in which the pitch of a sound of fixed vibration period sounds higher as the emitting source is brought rapidly toward us and lower as it recedes from us. A very simple analogy may help to illustrate the principle. Suppose that we stand beside a long horizontal conveyer belt and place small objects, such as pebbles, on the belt at uniform intervals of time. If the belt speed is constant, the pebbles will be uniformly spaced. Now, if as we place the pebbles we also walk slowly in the direction in which the belt is moving, the pebbles will be spaced closer together; whereas if we walk in a direction opposite to the belt motion, again placing pebbles at the same intervals of time, they will be spaced farther apart on the belt.

Take now the case of a star emitting a given light spectrum. If the star is moving earthward, the frequencies of vibration constituting the light rays are all increased slightly, resulting in a slight change in the color, since the color is determined by the frequencies of light and these have been increased by the motion. If the star is moving away from the earth a reverse effect occurs, the frequencies of vibration being reduced. Such changes in the color spectrum can be studied by means of the *spectroscope,* an instrument which breaks up a light beam into its component colors (Figure 1.2). The phenomenon we are concerned with here is the shift in the color spectrum of the stars that is associated with the orbital motion of the earth. The same effect results whether the light source is in motion or the receiving point is in motion. Only the change in distance per

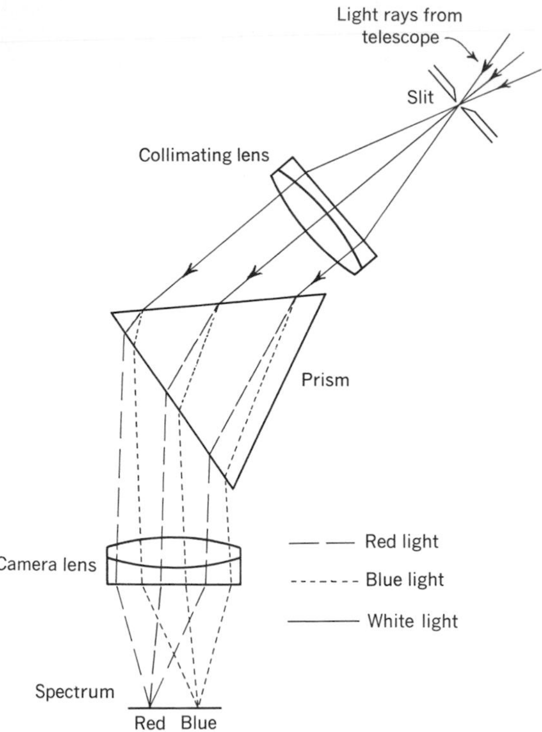


**FIGURE 1.2.** A slit spectograph focuses the image of a narrow spectrum upon a photographic plate. [After T. G. Mehlin (1959), *Astronomy,* New York, John Wiley & Sons.]

unit time is important. Thus, when the earth is in a part of its orbit where there is a component of motion away from a star, the star's spectrum is shifted slightly toward the red end. When the earth is at an opposite point in its orbit and is therefore moving toward the star, the spectrum is shifted toward the violet by an equal amount. Now, because all stars show spectral displacements consistent with the velocity and relative direction of motion required by an orbit around the sun, the only reasonable conclusion is that the earth's orbital motion is the single cause. According to the Ptolemaic (geocentric) theory all stars would be required to move away from the earth at one season and toward the earth at another, a fantastic requirement, which the supporters of that theory had no means of knowing about.

A third proof of orbital revolution lies in a phenomenon termed the *parallax of stars.*[2] It takes us back to Tycho Brahe's reasoning that, if the heliocentric theory is correct, as the earth moves across its great orbital distance each year the nearer stars should seem to change their apparent positions in relation to the more distant ones. Parallax, a word used in optics, means a difference in the apparent relative positions of objects when viewed from different points. This principle is illustrated in Figure 1.3 (the angles are greatly exaggerated). A near star, *A,* may appear very close to a distant star, *B,* when viewed in the spring. But as the earth moves in its orbit star *A* will seem to shift its location in the sky, so that in the autumn star *A* may be separated from star *B* by a very small angle. The closer the star is to us, the greater the parallax effect.

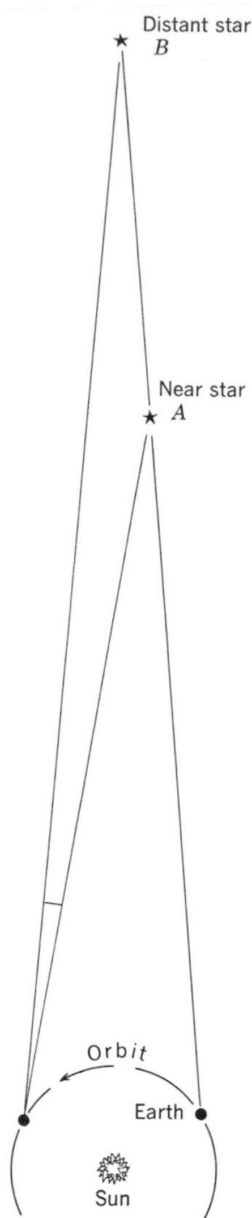


**FIGURE 1.3.** Principle of the orbital parallax of stars.

The parallax of the stars was first measured in 1838 by the Prussian astronomer Bessel, who discovered that a faint star in the constellation of Cygnus was displaced annually by 0.4 second of arc. Since then the trigonometric parallaxes of about 10,000 stars have been measured. Note that whereas the annual aberrational orbits of all stars are of the same length, 41 seconds of arc, the parallactic orbits are smaller for distant stars than for near ones, and even the largest parallactic orbits are very much smaller than the aberrational orbits. The parallax of the nearest known star to the sun, Alpha Centauri, is only 0.75 second of arc.

## Form of the earth's orbit

The orbit of the earth (and of each planet) is an *ellipse* (Figure 1.4), in which the sun occupies one *focus.* An ellipse has a longest diameter, the *major axis,* and a

[2] Also termed the *heliocentric parallax.*

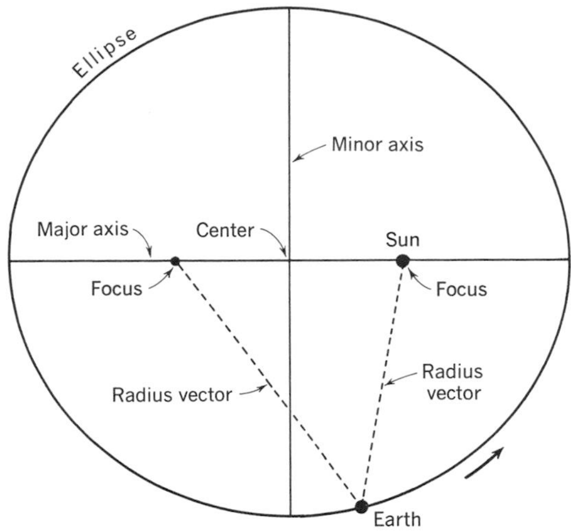


FIGURE 1.4. The orbit of every planet is an ellipse in which the sun occupies one focus.

shortest diameter, the *minor axis.* These two axes are at right angles to one another and intersect at the center of the ellipse. Along the major axis are two *foci* (plural of *focus*). Given any point on the ellipse, two straight lines known as *radius vectors* can be drawn, one to each of the two foci. A law of the geometry of the ellipse is that the sum of the two radius vectors remains a constant for all points on the ellipse. This law can be used in making a device for drawing ellipses, by using a loop of thread and two pins or thumbtacks on a drawing board (Figure 1.5). The *ellipticity,* or degree of flattening of the ellipse, may be varied by adjusting the spacing of the two foci in relation to the length of loop. As the two foci are brought closer to the center, the ellipse approaches a circle in form.

To the great German astronomer Johannes Kepler[3] (1571–1630) we owe the discovery of three laws of planetary motion, which bear his name. The first law simply states that the orbit of each planet is an ellipse, with the sun located at one focus of the ellipse. Kepler's second law states that a planet moves in its orbit about the sun at a varying velocity, such that the radius vector of the elliptical orbit sweeps over equal areas in equal

[3] Kepler became Tycho Brahe's assistant at the latter's observatory near Prague, Bohemia, in 1600. After Brahe's death in the following year, Kepler succeeded him and later became mathematician and astronomer to Emperor Rudolph II. Kepler formulated the planetary laws several years later, after intensive observation and calculation of the planetary orbits.

FIGURE 1.5. An ellipse is easily constructed using a loop of thread.

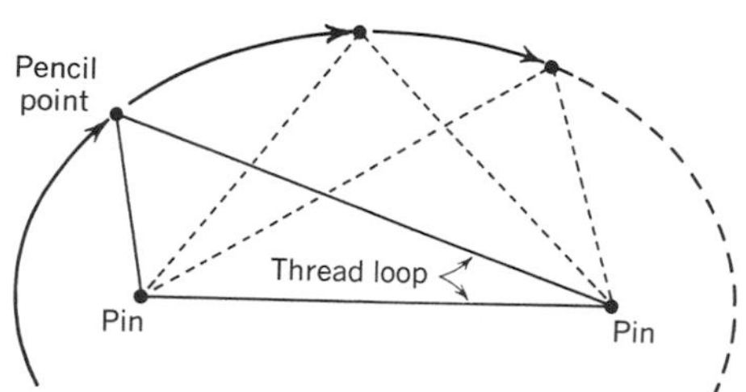


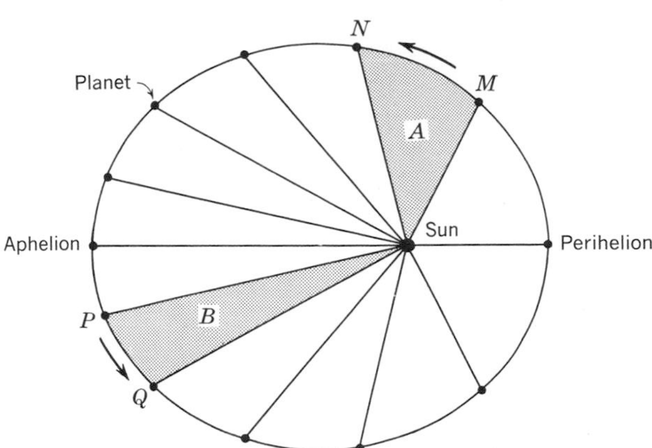


FIGURE 1.6. An ellipse divided into 12 equal areas.

times. This fact is illustrated in Figure 1.6, a greatly exaggerated ellipse, whose circumference has been divided into 12 segments representing 12 months (assumed exactly equal in time). The radius vectors enclose equal areas. Thus area *A* is equal to area *B.* In sweeping across area *A,* the radius vector must travel from *M* to *N,* a longer distance than from *P* to *Q;* hence it must travel at a greater average velocity between *M* and *N* than between *P* and *Q.*

It is obvious from Figure 1.6 that the earth in its orbit is nearest the sun when located at one end of the major axis of the ellipse, a position termed *perihelion* (from the Greek words *peri,* about or near; *helios,* sun); its most distant point is at the opposite end of the major axis, a position termed *aphelion* (from the Greek *ap,* away from; and *helios*). The earth is at perihelion about January 3, and at aphelion about July 4 each year. At perihelion the radius vector is about 91½ million mi ($147 \times 10^6$ km), at aphelion about 94½ million mi ($152 \times 10^6$ km), giving a mean value of about 93 million mi ($150 \times 10^6$ km) for the whole year.

It follows from Kepler's second law that the earth's velocity in its orbit must be continuously changing. From a maximum at perihelion the velocity diminishes to a minimum at aphelion, then increases again to the next perihelion. The average orbital velocity is about 66,600 mi (107,000 km) per hour, or about 18½ mi (29.6 km) per second. The varying orbital velocity of the earth affects the measurement of time by sun; also, the difference in distance to the sun from perihelion and from aphelion makes appreciable differences in the intensity with which solar radiation is received on the earth. Both topics are treated in later chapters.

## Division of the earth's surface

In order to proceed further with a study of the earth's motions, it wil be essential to understand the system of intersecting circles drawn upon the spherical surface of the earth for purposes of defining the locations of points on the globe and the directions of lines. This system is already familiar to most persons as the *geographic grid:* a network of east-west lines, the *parallels of latitude,* and north-south lines, the *meridians of longitude* (Figure 1.7).

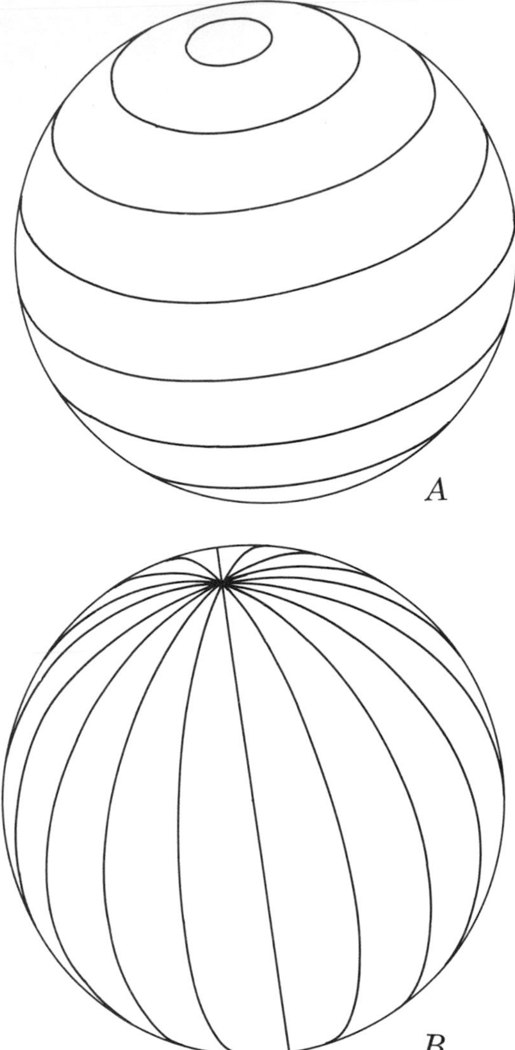


FIGURE 1.7. (*A*) Parallels. (*B*) Meridians.

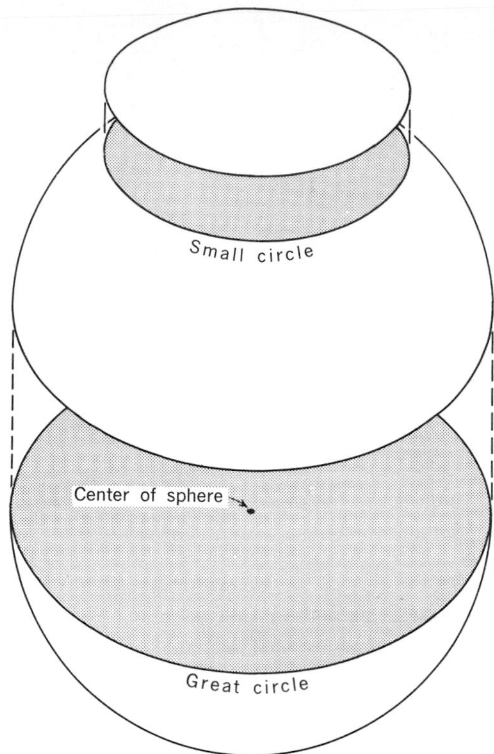


FIGURE 1.8. A great circle and a small circle.

The geographic grid makes use of two types of circles. If a sphere is cut exactly in half by a plane passed through its center, the surface intersection of the plane defines a *great circle* (Figure 1.8), the largest possible circle that can be inscribed on a given sphere. Should a plane be passed through a sphere in such a way that it does not pass through the center, the surface intersection is a *small circle.* Small circles can range in size from extremely tiny circles, approaching a point in smallness, to very large ones, which approach the diameter of a great circle, depending upon how near to the center the intersecting plane cuts through the sphere.

Great circles are important in many aspects of earth science and in applied fields, such as navigation and cartography. Because a plane may be passed through the center of a sphere in any possible orientation, the number of possible great circles that can be inscribed on the sphere's surface is infinite. This fact also means that a great circle may be found which will pass through any two surface points on a sphere; thus any two surface points may be joined by the arc of a great circle. Now, although the great circle is the largest possible circle that can be drawn on a sphere, the shorter arc of a great circle connecting any two points proves to be the shortest possible surface distance between them. This fact is of great importance in navigation and has led to the development of *great-circle sailing charts, so* constructed that any straight line drawn upon the map is a great-circle course (see Appendix I). An added fact of importance is that any two great circles bisect each other.

Great circles are needed in the earth sciences to plot the direction of surface travel of various kinds of waves generated from a point, to form hemispheres of darkness and light, or to find the opposite point, or *antipode,* with respect to any given point.

To find approximate great-circle arcs on a globe, stretch a string between the points, as shown in Figure 1.9, allowing the string to slip freely to a position such that its length is the shortest possible.

**Parallels and meridians** If we consider the earth as a rotating sphere, the appropriateness of the geographic grid becomes obvious. Rotation on an axis provides the earth with two fixed points of reference, the *geographic poles,* representing the points where the axis intersects the spherical surface (Figure 1.10). The one great circle lying in a plane perpendicular to the axis midway between the poles defines the *equator* (which is the longest of the parallels). Small circles, possible in infinite number, can be formed by passing planes through

**FIGURE 1.9.** A string stretched between two points on the globe forms a great-circle navigational course. (Photograph by A. N. Strahler.)

the earth in positions parallel with the equator, thus producing all other parallels of latitude.

Parallels are all true east-west lines. In the geographic grid *east* and *west* are defined as the directions taken by the parallel passing through any given point. Every parallel is parallel to every other parallel, therefore the distance separating any two parallels remains constant. Parallels are infinite in number, and it is possible to pass a parallel through any desired surface point on the globe.

The earth's axis and poles also provide the reference points for defining meridians, which are halves of great circles, produced by passing planes through both poles simultaneously (Figure 1.11). Of course, the earth's axis also lies in the plane of a meridian. For each meridian there is a corresponding opposite meridian; the pair together constitute a full great circle. An individual meridian comprises 180 degrees of arc, a half-circle; whereas a parallel comprises 360 degrees of arc, a full circle.

**FIGURE 1.10.** The equator and all other parallels lie in planes oriented at right angles to the earth's axis of rotation.

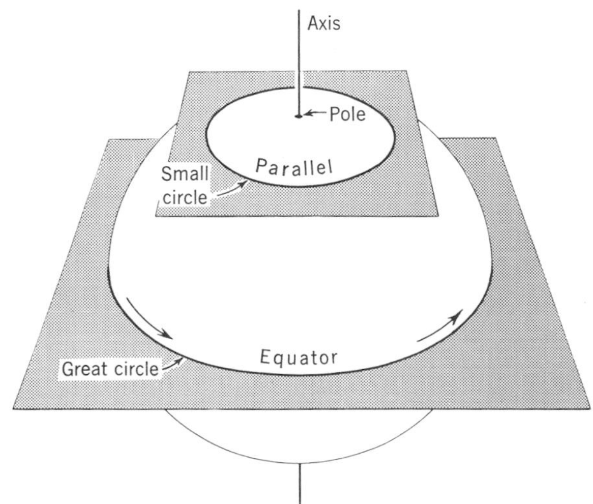


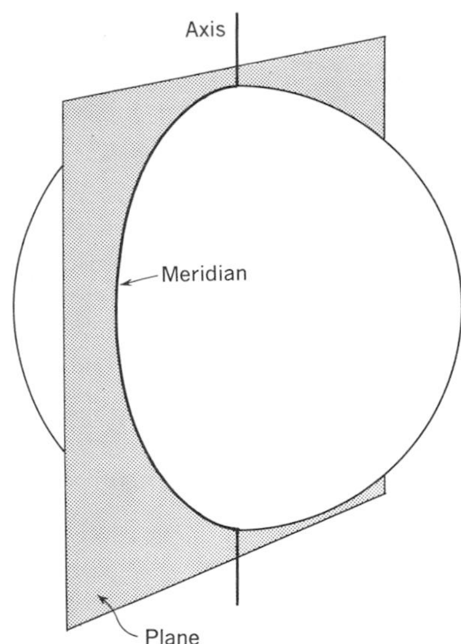


**FIGURE 1.11.** A plane passed through the earth's axis forms a meridian.

Because all meridians end at the poles, any two meridians are farthest apart at the equator, but converge poleward (Figure 1.7). Therefore the actual surface distance separating any two meridians decreases poleward, but the angular distance, or arc, between two meridians remains constant at all points (Figure 1.12), because this is the angle formed by the intersection of the two planes which form the two meridians.

Meridians are true north-south lines. *Geographic north* is defined as the direction taken by a meridian through a given point, aiming in the direction of the North Pole.

An important fact in the selection and reading of maps showing the data of the earth sciences is that the intersection of any parallel with any meridian is a true right-angle intersection.[4] Because both lines are circular, it would be more precise to say that the tangents to the curves at their points of intersection form right angles.

**Latitude and longitude** By measuring the arcs, or angular distances, along meridians and parallels with respect to one parallel and one meridian selected as the basic lines of reference, the location of any point on the globe can be uniquely stated in terms of the *geographic coordinates:* latitude and longitude.

The *latitude* of a place can be defined as the length of the arc of a meridian lying between that place and the equator (Figure 1.13). Latitude may also be thought of as the angle between the plane of the equator and the surface of an imaginary cone whose apex is at the earth's center and which cuts the earth along the given parallel[5] (Figure 1.12*A*). Latitude is stated in units of degrees and ranges from 0° at the equator to 90° N. at the North Pole (to 90° S. at the South Pole). Thus all

[4] In the language of mathematics the two sets of lines are said to constitute an *orthogonal family,* related by a simple law. Thus we can say "parallels are orthogonal with respect to meridians."
[5] Latitude so defined is termed *geocentric latitude* and is valid only for an earth assumed to be a sphere.

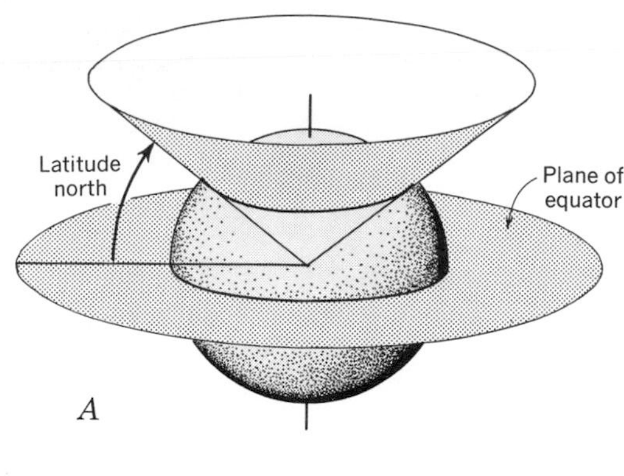


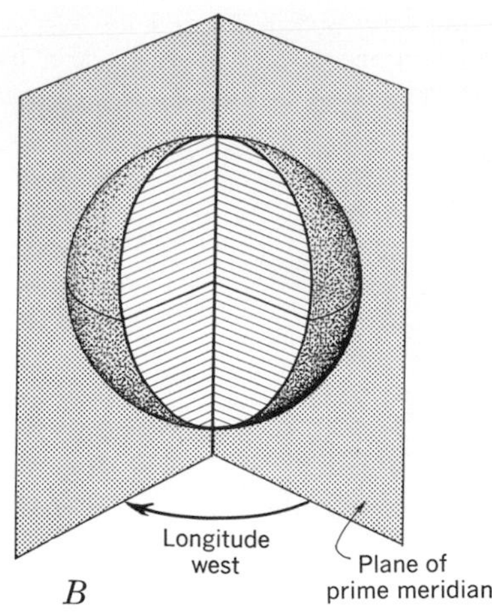


**FIGURE 1.12.** (*A*) Latitude can be thought of as the angle between a cone and a plane. (*B*) Longitude is the angle between two planes intersecting along the earth's axis.

latitude in the Northern Hemisphere must be designated as "north latitude" to distinguish it from the numerically equivalent "south latitude" of the Southern Hemisphere. Altogether, then, on the entire globe there are 180 degrees of latitude.

The *longitude* of a place may be defined as the length of the arc of a parallel between that place and the *prime meridian,* a meridian arbitrarily selected as the reference line (Figure 1.13). Longitude may also be thought of as the angle lying between the two planes that intersect along the earth's axis to produce the prime meridian and the meridian whose longitude is to be stated (Figure 1.12*B*). The prime meridian is given the longitude of 0°. Longitude is measured eastward and westward from the prime meridian to a maximum value of 180° at the meridian that lies opposite the prime meridian. Longitude measured eastward is described as "east longitude" to distinguish it from "west longitude," measured westward from the prime meridian. Thus the total number of degrees of longitude over the entire globe is 360, or twice as many as the total degrees of latitude.

**FIGURE 1.13.** The geographic grid of parallels and meridians. Point *P* has a latitude of 50° N. and a longitude of 75° W.

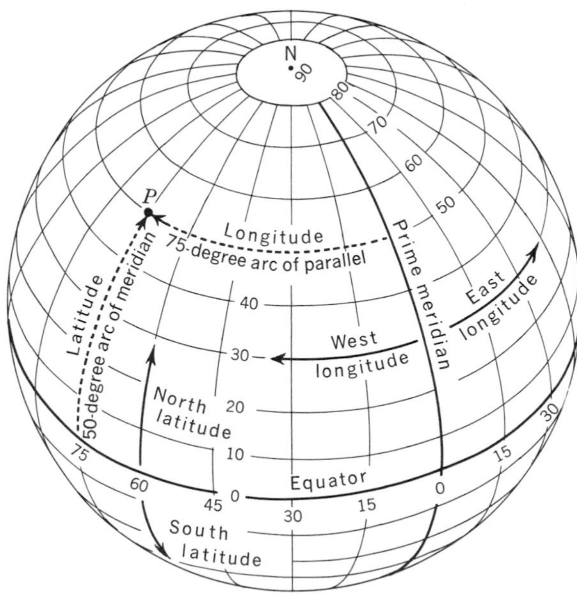


The prime meridian in world-wide use today is the *meridian of Greenwich,* chosen as that meridian passing through the former location of the Royal Observatory, at Greenwich, near London, England. Several of the European nations based their determinations of longitude upon their own nation meridians, commonly defined with respect to a key point in the capital city. Another prime meridian used in some of the older European map series is the *meridian of Ferro,* which passes through the western-most island of the Canary Islands. The meridian of Ferro, which has a value of 17°14′ west of the Greenwich meridian, was chosen so that all values of longitude in Europe would increase eastward, without any numerical duplication of east and west values. In the modern earth sciences the Greenwich meridian is accepted as the reference standard.

When the location of a point on the earth's surface is given in terms of latitude and longitude, the coordinates may be written

lat. 34°12′31″ N., long. 77°03′41″ W.

This may be read "latitude 34 degrees, 12 minutes, 31 seconds north, longitude 77 degrees, 3 minutes, 41 seconds west." Because of the awkwardness of calculating with minutes and seconds of arc, it is now common practice to state latitude and longitude in terms of the decimal parts of the degree. The above coordinates would thus become

lat. 34.2086° N., long. 77.0614° W.

The use of latitude and longitude to designate position on the globe is attributed to Ptolemy, who probably followed a scheme invented earlier by Hipparchus. Ptolemy was the first to use the expressions "meridians of longitude" and "parallels of latitude." The ancient

Chaldeans had long before divided the circle into 360 degrees, the degrees into 60 minutes, and the minute into 60 seconds, but it is from Ptolemy's adoption of these divisions, stated in Latin, that our words "minutes" and "seconds" come to us. Ptolemy called the 60 subdivisions of the degree the "first small parts," which in Latin is *minutiae primae,* whence our word "minutes." The 60 subdivisions of the minute he called "the second small parts," which in Latin is *minutiae secundae,* whence our word "seconds."

## The celestial sphere

For purposes of astronomical description and navigation it is often convenient to revert to the Ptolemaic concept of a fixed earth about which the heavenly bodies revolve. Such, indeed, is the impression any human being would receive from watching the sky hour after hour, day after day, and night after night. The heavenly bodies seem to be traveling upon the inside surface of an imaginary sphere, the *celestial sphere,* one-half of which we see at any given moment from an apparent vantage point at the center of the sphere. The other half is hidden beneath the horizon at all times, but can be inferred by the observation that sun, moon, and stars disappear below the horizon in the west, only to reappear above the horizon in the east some dozen or so hours later.

On the celestial sphere the sun, stars, and planets seem to be at an equal distance from us. Except for the moon these objects are so distant that the few thousands of miles of separation possible from two viewpoints on the earth's surface would make no perceptible difference in their position. The geometry required is therefore that of a true sphere of infinite radius with the earth occupying only an infinitely tiny center point.

**The celestial coordinates (equatorial system)** The division of the celestial sphere and the location of stars on it are carried out by means of great and small circles and the arcs of such circles, imagined to be drawn upon the celestial sphere in a replica of the geographic grid used on the earth.

First, the *celestial equator* is located as a great circle produced by extending, or *projecting,* the earth's equator outward to the celestial sphere (Figure 1.14). Projections of the earth's axis serve to locate the *celestial poles. Polaris,* the polestar, lies very close to the north celestial pole on the celestial sphere. The position of a star north or south of the celestial equator is measured by its *declination,* which is the arc of an imaginary celestial meridian lying between the star and the celestial equator, just as for the latitude of a place on the earth's surface (Figure 1.15). Declination thus ranges from 0° to 90° north; from 0° to 90° south.

Analogous to the prime meridian as a reference line is an imaginary celestial meridian, better named an *hour circle,* passing through a reference point on the celestial equator known as the *vernal equinox.* East-west position of a star (equivalent to longitude) is measured by *right ascension,* the arc of the celestial equator lying between the vernal equinox and the hour circle of the star (upper sphere in Figure 1.16). Unlike terrestrial longitude, with its 360 degrees (180° east, plus 180° west), right ascension is scaled in time units: hours, minutes, and seconds. Measurement is always eastward from the vernal equinox. There are 24 hours of arc for the entire circumference, 1 hour being equivalent to 15 degrees of arc. Each degree of arc is equivalent to 4 minutes of time. Such a system has obvious disadvantages. Celestial angles are commonly measured with instruments scaled in degrees, minutes, and seconds of arc (not time). More recently, for navigational purposes, right ascension has been replaced by the *sidereal hour angle* (abbreviated to SHA), which is

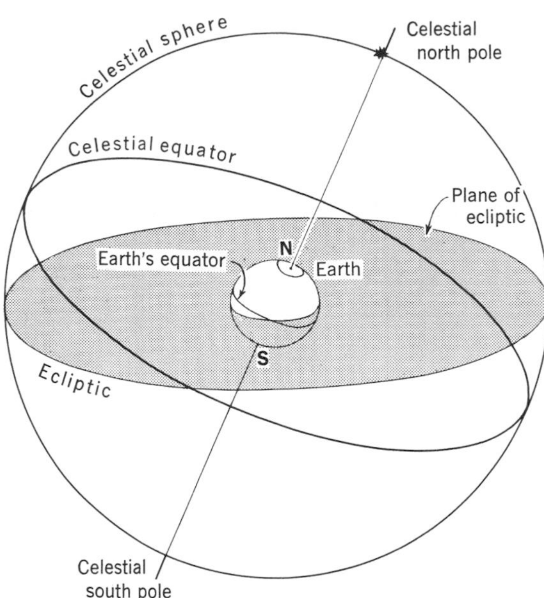


**FIGURE 1.14.** The celestial sphere projects the earth's equator and poles upon the inside of an imaginary spherical surface lying infinitely far away.

**FIGURE 1.15.** Declination on the celestial sphere is analogous to latitude on the earth.

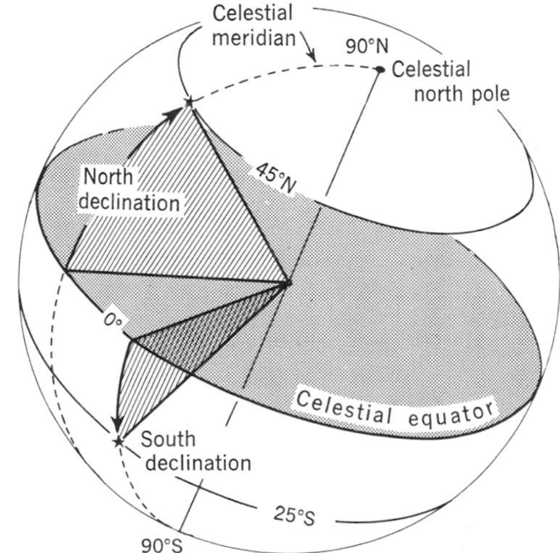

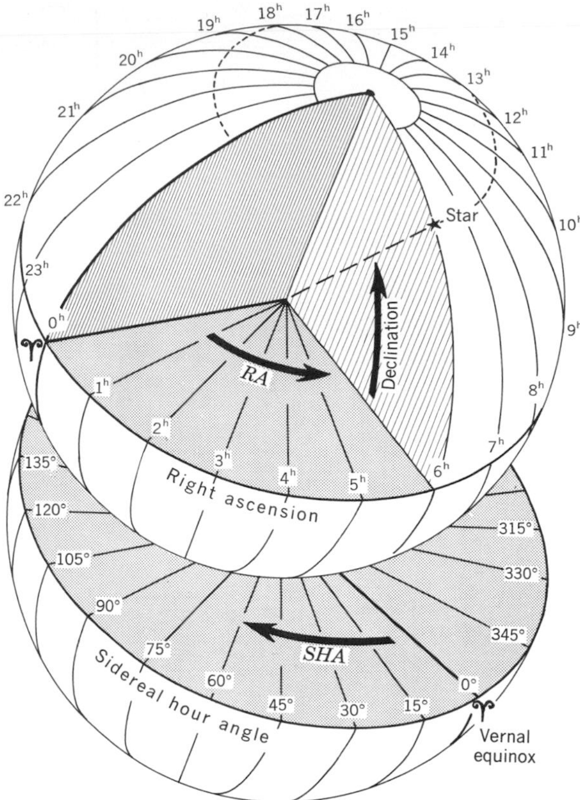


**FIGURE 1.16.** Right ascension of a star is analogous to the east longitude of a point on the earth. An alternative system, by sidereal hour angle, measures the angle in degrees in the westward direction, as in west longitude.

measured from 0° to 360° westward from the vernal equinox (lower portion of Figure 1.16). Thus, a right ascension of $6^h$ would be the same as 270° SHA.

## Celestial globes and maps

Just as the geographic grid and surface features of the earth may be shown on a true-scale earth model (the terrestrial globe), so it is possible to take a sphere and print on it the celestial hour circles of right ascension and the celestial parallels of declination (Figure 1.17). The major stars may then be located on the celestial globe and labeled, just as cities are on the terrestrial globe. It is important to remember that the celestial globe gives us an "outside," or external, view of the celestial relations. In order to see the constellations as they actually appear in the heavens, we should have to split open a transparent celestial sphere and examine the inner, concave surface or build a globe large enough for us to get inside and sit at the central point. (A large planetarium serves the same purpose.) The use of a globe of clear plastic permits us to look across the inside diameter to the other side and thus to see the constellations in their familiar configurations.

Just as there are many advantages in using a flat map of the earth, there are advantages in plotting the stars on a flat chart, termed a *star chart* (Figure 1.18). The star chart shown is based on a simple rectangular grid of equidistantly spaced lines, which greatly distorts both scales and areas, particularly in the higher declinations. The chart should be considered primarily as a graph, although near the celestial equator the shapes of constellations are quite well displayed. Note that east is toward the left on this chart. For a truer picture of constellations near the celestial poles, a type of map grid known as a polar projection should be used (see Appendix I).

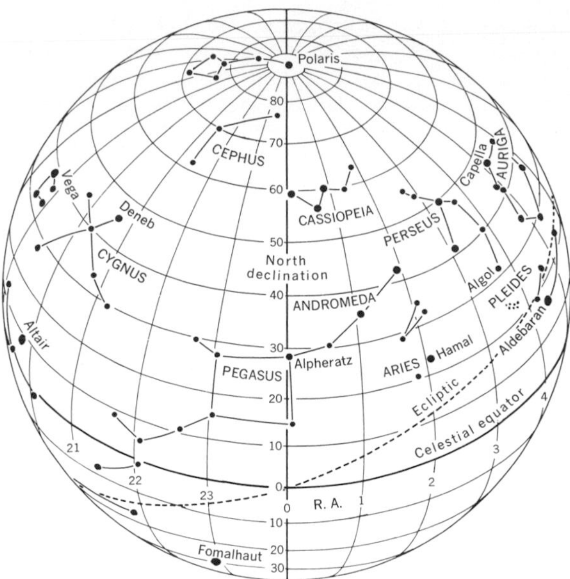


**FIGURE 1.17.** On the celestial globe, constellations are viewed as if from a point outside the celestial sphere. Compare with the star chart, Figure 1.18.

The stars (except for the sun) have fixed positions in the celestial globe or chart; that is, their celestial coordinates are fixed.[6] Of course, as the earth turns, all the heavenly bodies seem to travel constantly from east to west, following the apparent daily rotation of the celestial sphere, but the stars do not move among themselves. On the other hand the sun, moon, and planets change their celestial coordinates slowly from hour to hour and from day to day, seeming to creep gradually from one constellation to another. The nature of these motions will become clearer in the light of explanations in chapters to follow.

## The horizon system of celestial coordinates

Although the celestial sphere turns constantly, we can imagine, projected upon the celestial dome, a system of reference points and circles which are fixed with respect to our observation point on earth (Figure 1.19). The earth seems to be a flat, circular disk, bounded by the horizon. Projected upon the celestial sphere, our

[6] For most purposes the changes in position due to aberration of light and parallax may be disregarded.

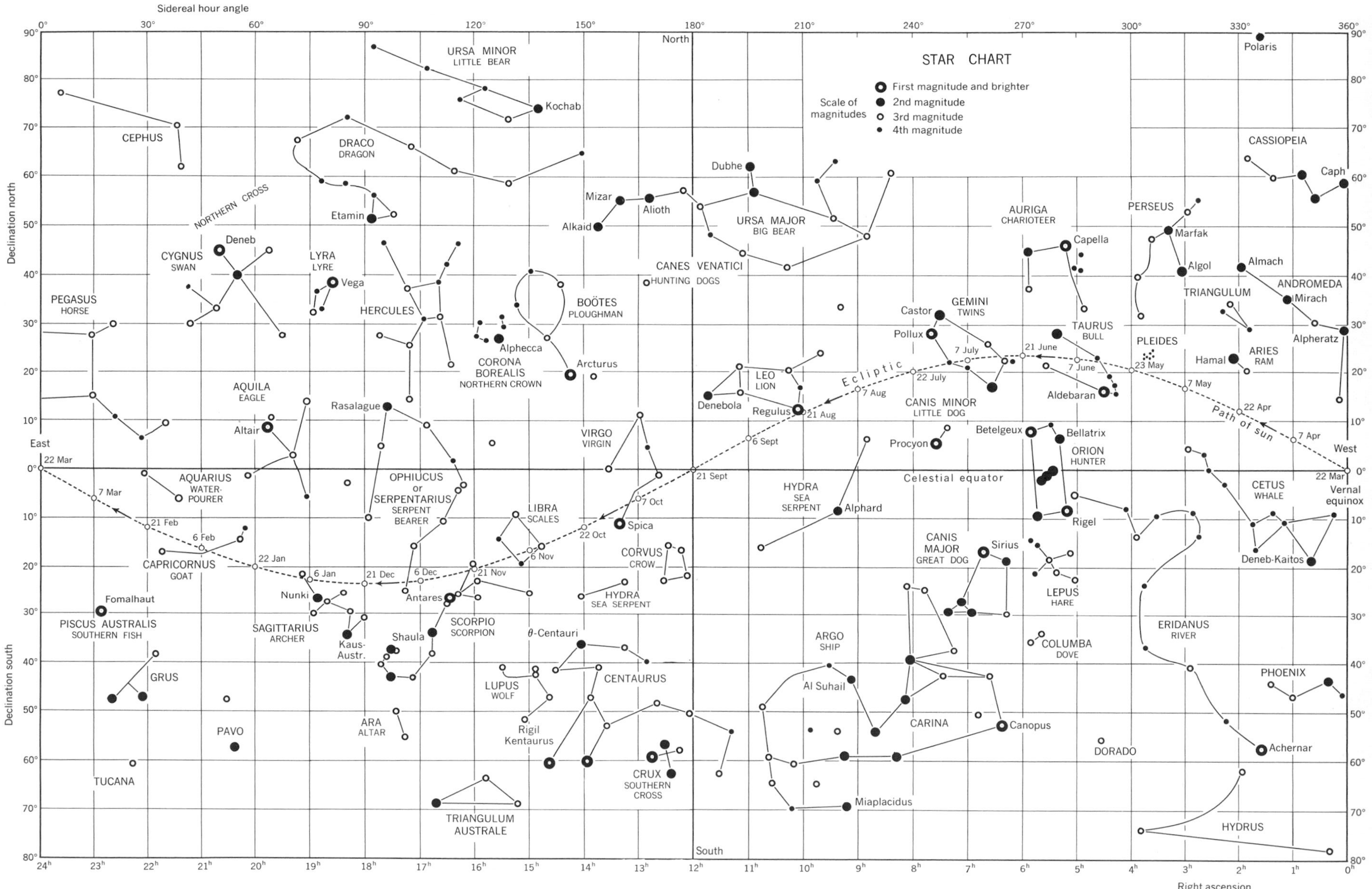


**FIGURE 1.18.** A star chart showing the principal stars and constellations. Dates on the ecliptic give the sun's position at intervals throughout the year. (Data from U.S. Navy Oceanographic Office Chart No. 2100.)

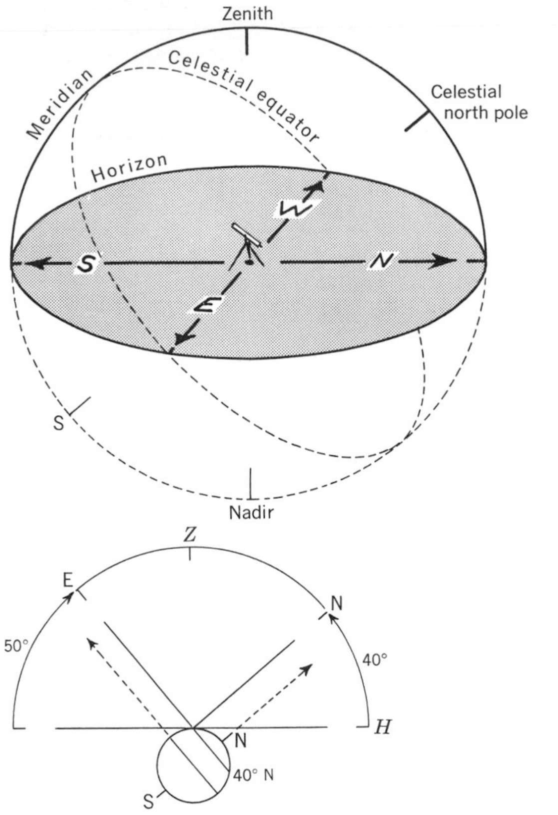

**FIGURE 1.19.** The horizonal system locates celestial bodies on a hemispherical dome fixed with respect to the observer's horizon and zenith.

terrestrial horizon becomes the *celestial horizon,* a fixed great circle dividing the upper, or visible, hemisphere of the celestial sphere from the lower, or nonvisible, hemisphere. Directly above us, at the highest point of the celestial dome, is the *zenith;* directly below us, on the lowest point of the hidden celestial hemisphere, is the *nadir.* Passing directly overhead through the zenith and the celestial north and south poles is a fixed great circle, known simply as the *meridian.* It corresponds to an extension outward of the terrestrial meridian of the point on earth. The meridian intersects the horizon at points whose directions are the true geographic north and south. As the sun, moon, or a given star moves from east to west across the sky, it must cross the meridian. This event is termed the *meridian passage,* or *upper transit,* of the *object.* In the case of the sun the meridian passage is termed *apparent solar noon.*

**Altitude and azimuth** The horizon system of reference points and circles permits us to describe the position of a celestial body at a given instant of time with reference to our position on earth (Figure 1.20). *Altitude* is the angular distance, in degrees, measured upward from the horizon to the object along an imaginary great circle (referred to as a *vertical circle*) that would pass through the zenith point (angle *HCP* in Figure 1.20). Thus the altitude of an object in the sky can range from 0° at the horizon to 90° at zenith. Altitude below the

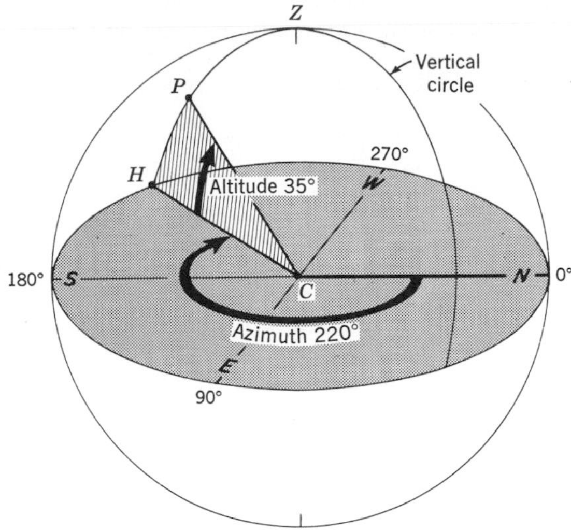


**FIGURE 1.20.** Azimuth and altitude describe the position of a star in terms of the horizon system of coordinates.

horizon can also be stated as a negative angle, although the object cannot be seen.

*Azimuth* is the horizontal direction of a line from the observer to that point where the vertical circle cuts the horizon (angle *NCH* in Figure 1.20). In navigation azimuth is measured with reference to true geographic north, beginning at the north point and going toward the east through a total of 360°. A point lying in the eastern half of the sky would have an azimuth in the range from 0° to 180°; a point in the western half of the sky would fall in the azimuth range 180° to 360°. Any other azimuth system could just as well be used, if desired.

To clarify the distinction between the celestial coordinates—declination and right ascension (or SHA)—and the horizon-system coordinates—altitude and azimuth—the following points may be helpful. The celestial coordinates are permanently located on the celestial sphere, so that the entire system appears to turn from east to west as the earth rotates, but the stars remain fixed in relation to the imaginary gridwork of hour circles and celestial parallels. In contrast to this the altitude and azimuth of a star vary, not only with the latitude of the observer on the earth's surface, but also constantly with time. Therefore a statment of the celestial coordinates of a star holds valid, no matter where or when the star is observed, whereas a statement of the altitude and azimuth of a star is meaningless unless the position of the observer and the exact time of observation are also stated.

## Period of revolution—the year

We do not need to be told that our year is the period of time required for one complete revolution of the earth in its orbit about the sun. On closer examination the definition is not so simple, for the period of revolution is different, depending upon the starting and ending points selected.

What is generally meant by the word *year,* particularly

in so far as our calendar is concerned, is correctly termed the *tropical year,* defined as the time elapsed between two successive crossings by the sun of the celestial equator at the point known as the vernal equinox. The tropical year has a length of 365 days, 5 hours, 48 minutes, and 46 seconds (written $365^d5^h48^m46^s$), or 365.242 days.[7] Because our calendar year is one of exactly 365 days, there is an excess of almost 6 hours, or one quarter of a day, per tropical year. By adding a day (February 29) each leap year, which comes every fourth year, this excess is largely corrected.

This scheme of adding a day every fourth year was decreed by Julius Caesar in 46 B.C., but it made the year about 11 minutes, 14 seconds too long. In 1582, Pope Gregory XIII, on the advice of the astronomer Clavius, instituted the calendar which we now use. According to the Gregorian calendar every year evenly divisible by four is a leap year, except century years, which are only leap years if they are evenly divisible by 400. Thus the year 1900 was not a leap year; the year 2000 will be a leap year. The Gregorian calendar accumulates an error at the rate of less than 1 day in 3000 years.

A second definition of a year is the time elapsed between successive occupations of exactly the same orbital point with reference to a given star. This is the *sidereal year,* with a value of $365^d6^h9^m10^s$ (365.256 days). The adjective "sidereal" simply means "referring to the stars." The sidereal year is thus about $20^m23^s$ (0.0142 day) longer than the tropical year, for reasons discussed in Chapter 2.

We may note a third kind of year, the *anomalistic year,* defined as the time elapsed from one perihelion to the next; it is equal to $365^d6^h13^m53^s$ (365.260 days). The discrepancy between anomalistic and sidereal years is explained in Chapter 2. A fourth year, the *lunar year,* is defined as 12 new moons and is about 11 days shorter than the tropical year. There is still a fifth, the *eclipse year,* which can be defined as the interval between two successive passages of the earth past the line of nodes of the moon's orbit; it has a length of $346^d14^h52^m51^s$ (346.620 days).

[7] All units of days, hours, minutes, and seconds as stated in this chapter are in *mean solar time.*

## References for further study

Wylie, C. C. (1942), *Astronomy, Maps, and Weather,* New York, Harper & Row, 449 pp., chaps. 1, 5.

Hosmer, G. L. (1948), *Practical Astronomy,* 4th ed., New York, Wiley, 355 pp., chaps. 1–5.

Mehlin, T. G. (1959), *Astronomy,* New York, Wiley, 392 pp., chap. 11.

Stumpff, K. (1959), *Planet Earth,* Ann Arbor, Univ. of Michigan Press, 191 pp.

Thiel, R. (trans. R. and C. Winston) (1960), *And There Was Light,* New York, A Mentor Book, MT 290, New Am. Library, 384 pp.

Bartky, W. (1961), *Highlights of Astronomy,* Chicago, Univ. of Chicago Press, 278 pp.

# 2

# The rotating earth

THREE FACTS ABOUT THE earth's motions are of vital consequence in the principles of the earth sciences: first, that the earth turns on an axis, a motion always called *rotation* (to differentiate it from the earth's annual revolution about the sun); second, the *axis of rotation* is inclined at a constant angle with respect to the plane of the earth's orbit, or *plane of the ecliptic;* third, that the orientation of the earth's axis in space with respect to the stars holds nearly constant. A close scrutiny of these facts and their consequences is the aim of this and several succeeding chapters. The indirect consequences of these facts in governing the behavior of the oceans and atmosphere will be seen again and again throughout later chapters.

## Direction of earth rotation

It is essential that the direction of earth rotation be correctly stated and visualized; otherwise many serious errors will result in predicting the effects of rotation. Direction of rotation can be derived in three ways: (1) Imagine that we occupy a vantage point in space such that we can look down upon earth's north pole; the earth will seem to rotate counterclockwise (anticlockwise). (2) Using a globe free to turn on its axis, place a finger on the equator, then push in an eastward direction; the globe will be correctly rotated (Figure 2.1). This method illustrates the commonly used expression "eastward rotation of the earth." (3) We all know that the sun, moon, and stars seem to rise above the eastern horizon, travel westward across the sky, then set in the west. This apparent turning of the celestial sphere was described in

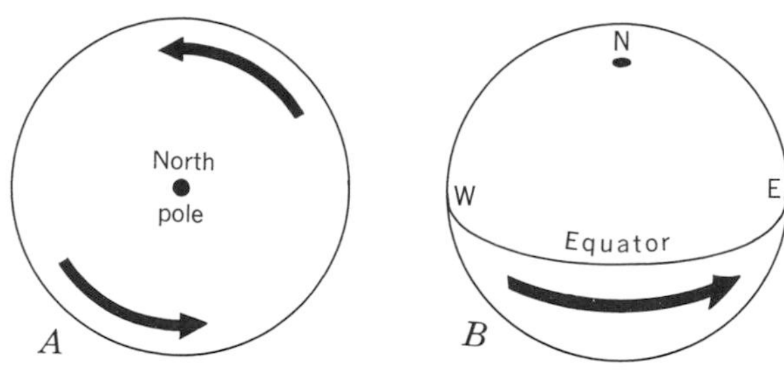


**FIGURE 2.1.** Earth rotation may be described (*A*) as being counterclockwise or (*B*) as being in an eastward direction.

Chapter 1. It follows, then, that the earth must actually be turning in the opposite direction, which is eastward.

Direction of revolution of the earth in its orbit about the sun is similar to that of rotation (Figure 2.2), that is, counterclockwise, if the system is viewed from a point in space looking down upon the earth's north pole. Such motion is referred to by astronomers as *direct motion.* The moon both revolves about the earth and rotates on its own axis in the same counterclockwise direction. A similar direction of motion is found in the other planets and most of their satellites. This fact strongly suggests that the members of the solar system received their motions at the time they and the sun were first formed.

## Inclination of the earth's axis

In the opening lines of this chapter it was stated that the earth's axis of rotation points constantly to the same place among the stars. With respect to the plane of the earth's orbit, correctly termed the plane of the ecliptic, the earth's axis has an inclination from the vertical of 23½° (Figure 2.3), which is to say that the earth's axis at all times makes an angle of 66½° with respect to the plane of the ecliptic. More exactly, these angles are 23°27′ and 66°33′ respectively, but they may conveniently be rounded off to the nearest half-degree.

**FIGURE 2.2.** Moon and earth both rotate and revolve in the same direction.

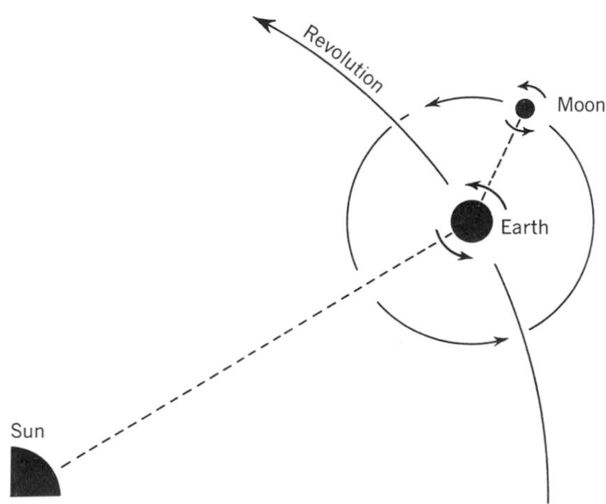


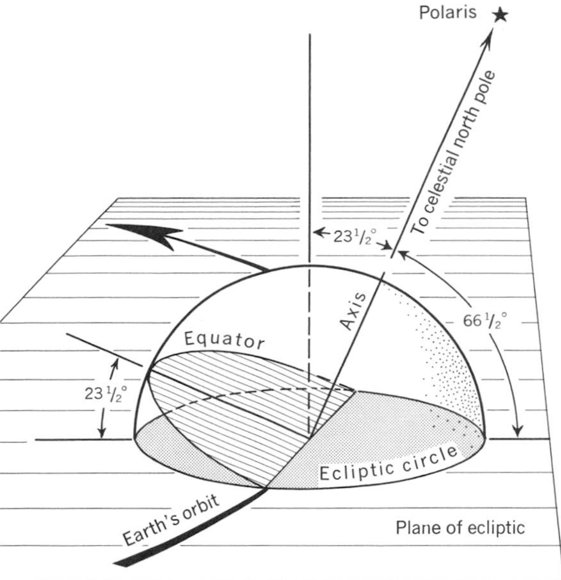


**FIGURE 2.3.** Inclination of the earth's axis.

The earth's axis is almost directly in line with *Polaris,* the polestar, in the constellation of *Ursa Minor.* In the celestial sphere Polaris lies close to the center of apparent rotation of the stars (Figure 2.4), hence it seems to remain almost stationary in the sky throughout the night. Actually, Polaris lies nearly a degree from the true celestial north pole, and careful observation would show that it describes a tiny circle as the earth rotates.

An observer on the earth may be considered to be at the center of the celestial sphere. The plane of the earth's orbit, passing through the observer's position,

**FIGURE 2.4.** Star traces form concentric circles about the celestial north pole when photographed by time exposure of 1 hour. (Yerkes Observatory.)

is thus a plane passing through the center of the celestial sphere; if the plane is extended outward, its intersection with the celestial sphere will be a great circle, which is called the *ecliptic* (Figure 1.14). Since the plane of the earth's orbit, i.e., the plane of the ecliptic, does not change, the great circle of the ecliptic will remain in a fixed or permanent position relative to the celestial sphere and to the stars projected on it. Thus the ecliptic may be accurately represented on celestial globes (Figure 1.17). Because the sun is at one focus of the earth's orbit, it, too, lies in the plane of the ecliptic and appears from the earth to be projected onto the ecliptic. As the earth revolves around the sun once a year, the sun appears to us to travel slowly eastward along the ecliptic, 360° in 365¼ days, or approximately 1 degree each day (Figure 1.18).

Because the earth's axis is tipped 23½° from the perpendicular to the plane of the ecliptic, the plane of the earth's equator must be inclined 23½° to the plane of the ecliptic (Figure 2.3). The plane of the earth's equator, extended outward, intersects the celestial sphere in a great circle, the celestial equator (see Figure 1.14), which will intersect the ecliptic at an angle of 23½° at two opposite points, known as the *equinoxes.* The point at which the sun, as it appears to travel slowly eastward along the ecliptic, crosses from the south to the north side of the celestial equator is called the vernal equinox, or the *first point of Aries,* and serves as the point through which the reference hour circle of $0^h$ is drawn (Figure 1.16). This topic is discussed further in Chapter 3.

## Period of earth rotation: solar and sidereal time

It is common knowledge that the earth rotates on its axis at such a rate as to make one complete turn in a day of 24 hours. In astronomy and the earth sciences two definitions of the day must be considered, as well as two varieties of time. One complete turn of the earth on its axis constitutes the *period of rotation,* but we must define exactly what is meant by a complete turn. What reference point is used?

An absolute framework of reference is provided by the stars. One rotation of 360°, a full circle with respect to the stars, defines the *sidereal day,* which is divided into 24 hours of *sidereal time,* popularly called *star time* (Figure 2.5). We on the earth's surface feel no sensation of the earth turning under us; instead the entire celestial sphere seems to turn around us. Thus the sidereal day is the period of time required for a given star to return to the same position in the sky after one full rotation of the celestial sphere. Suppose that we should aim a telescope exactly upon the celestial meridian, noting the exact time by our watches at which a certain star crosses that meridian. The next meridian passage of that same star a night later will be found to occur about 4 minutes earlier than it did the first night. Our watches follow solar time, the system in daily use throughout the world of civil affairs. According to solar time the sidereal day amounts to about $23^h56^m$.

*Solar time,* defined broadly, is time measured in reference to the sun's position. In Figure 2.5 is shown that a complete turn of the earth with respect to the sun is not the same as a complete turn with respect to the stars. The explanation lies in the fact that the earth is revolving in its orbit. This daily orbital motion is greatly exaggerated in Figure 2.5 to illustrate the principle. On a given day, with the earth located at point *A,* the sun at noon is assumed to be in direct line with a particular star so that the meridian passage of both occurs simultaneously. One sidereal day later, with the earth now at point *B,* the earth has rotated through 360°; therefore the same star is exactly over the meridian, but the sun and star are no longer in line. Instead the earth must turn about 1° more to bring the sun over the meridian. To turn this additional degree requires about 4 minutes of time, making the solar day that much longer than the sidereal day.

The following exact equivalents may be useful for reference:

$24^h$ sidereal time = $23^h56^m4.09^s$ mean solar time
$24^h$ mean solar time = $24^h03^m56.555^s$ sidereal time
one sidereal day = 86,400 sidereal seconds
= 86,164 mean solar seconds
one mean solar day = 86,400 mean solar seconds
= 86,636½ sidereal seconds.

The observed solar day varies in length throughout the year, a fact explained in Chapter 3. Hence a uniform standard of time based on the sun must take the mean

**FIGURE 2.5.** The solar day is about 4 minutes longer than the sidereal day. Angles are greatly exaggerated in this diagram.

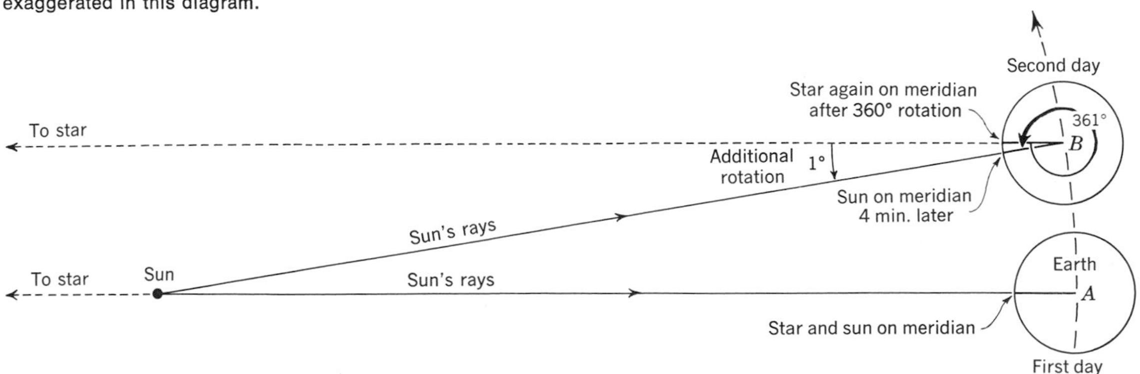

length of a solar day for the entire year, a unit known as the *mean solar day.* Our clocks and watches are regulated to conform to the mean solar day, which is divided into exactly 24 hours of mean solar time.

## Velocity of earth rotation

The speed with which the earth turns on its axis can be described in two ways. *Angular velocity,* or *velocity of rotation,* refers to the rate of turning of the entire sphere in terms of the angle, or arc, turned off in a unit of time (Figure 2.6). Angular velocity, commonly designated by the Greek letter Ω (omega), is expressed in such units as "degrees of arc per second (minute, hour)" or "radians per second" and is the same for all points on the sphere.

To determine the earth's angular velocity, we divide 360° by the period of 24 sidereal hours, obtaining 15° per sidereal hour. Using the number of radians in a full circle ($2\pi$ radians) for a sidereal day of 86,400 sidereal seconds, we find the angular velocity to be 0.00007272 radian per sidereal second. For a sidereal day of 86,164 mean solar seconds (using our customary definition of the second) the angular velocity would be 0.00007292 radian per mean solar second. Angular velocity is a constant value for all points on the earth, provided that the plane of rotation is always taken as the plane of a parallel of latitude (i.e., at right angles to the earth's axis).

Speed of earth rotation may also be stated as the *instantaneous linear velocity* of a point on the earth's surface, which is the velocity of the point in the circular path it follows, stated in such units as miles per hour or meters per second (Figure 2.6).

Because the period and angular velocity of earth rotation are the same everywhere, the linear velocity will vary depending upon the length of the parallel of latitude at which a point is located. From a maximum at the equator, linear velocity diminishes to zero at either pole. To determine instantaneous linear velocity, the length of a parallel of latitude is divided by the number of hours or seconds of mean solar time in the sidereal day. In Table 2.1 is given the instantaneous linear velocity in both miles per hour and meters per second for parallels of latitude at 10-degree intervals from equator to pole, based upon the dimensions of the Clarke ellipsoid of 1866 (see Chapter 10 and Table 10.2).

**FIGURE 2.6.** Angular velocity of the earth's rotation is everywhere constant, whereas linear velocity of a surface point varies with latitude.

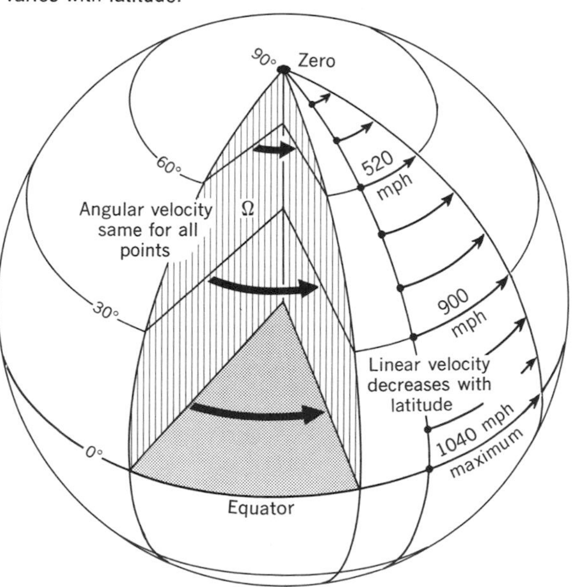


**TABLE 2.1. LINEAR VELOCITY OF ROTATION AT VARIOUS LATITUDES**

| Latitude | Linear Velocity: Miles per hour | Linear Velocity: Meters per second |
|---|---|---|
| 0° | 1,041.41 | 465.06 |
| 10° | 1,024.72 | 458.05 |
| 20° | 978.05 | 437.19 |
| 30° | 901.79 | 403.10 |
| 40° | 798.11 | 356.75 |
| 50° | 670.10 | 299.53 |
| 60° | 521.53 | 233.12 |
| 70° | 356.90 | 159.53 |
| 80° | 181.25 | 81.02 |
| 90° | 0.000 | 0.000 |

## Centripetal force of rotation

One important effect resulting from the earth's rotation is the action of centripetal and centrifugal forces at all parts of the earth, except precisely along the axis itself. Familiar to all who have studied elementary mechanics is the demonstration in which a weight is swung by hand in a horizontal circle (Figure 2.7). Because of inertia the weight tends to follow a straight-line course tangent to the circle at any given instant. Tangential flight is prevented by a *centripetal force* exerted by the

**FIGURE 2.7.** Centripetal force acts upon an object in a circular path of motion.

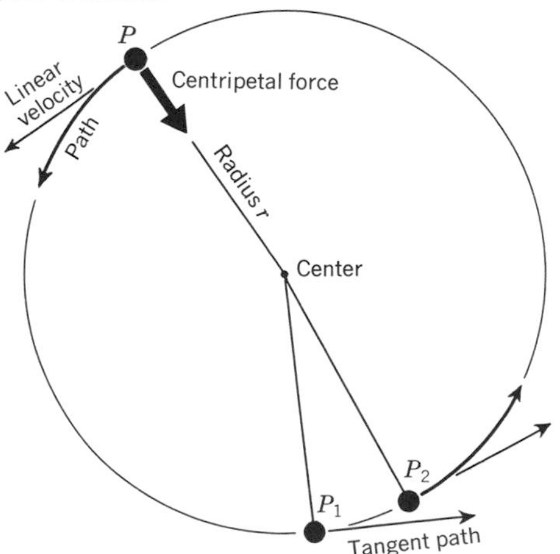

hand as tension acting through the cord. It is this force which changes the direction of the weight from a straight line and causes it to follow a circular path. If at any instant the centripetal force exceeds the strength of the string, causing it to snap, the weight will fly off along the direction of the tangent straight line, indicated in Figure 2.7.

Should a spring balance be inserted into the radial string so as to measure the centripetal force, it would be found to increase as the square of the linear velocity of the weight, but to decrease in direct proportion as the radius of the circle increases. This relation can be expressed by the formula

$$F_c = \frac{MV^2}{R}$$

where $F_c$ is centripetal force,
$V$ is velocity,
and $R$ is radius.

The formula also states that the force increases directly with the mass of the object in motion; however, we shall assume that a constant, or unit, mass is being used.

In the case of the earth a unit of mass at its surface is turning with constant rotational velocity in the path of a parallel of latitude. The radius in the formula is therefore the radius of the parallel; the velocity is the instantaneous linear velocity of the mass in the path of the parallel. The centripetal force, holding the mass to the earth and preventing it from flying off in a tangential path, is a small fraction of the earth's total gravitational attraction for the mass, directed toward the earth's center. A small component of the gravitational force acts as the centipetal force in line with the radius of the parallel of latitude.

Using the data of Tables 2.1 and 10.2, let us compute what fraction of the earth's gravitational force, acting on a unit mass at the earth's equator, will be employed as a centripetal force to keep the unit mass moving in the circular path resulting from its position on a rotating earth. The earth's equatorial radius is about 6,378,200 meters (Figure 2.8). The linear velocity at lat. 0° is about 465 meters per second. Squaring the velocity and dividing by the radius gives us an acceleration of approximately 0.034 meter, or 3.4 centimeters per second per second. The acceleration of gravity at the equator at sea level would be approximately 983 centimeters per second per second if the earth were not rotating; hence at the equator the centripetal force is about 1/289 as great as the gravitational force. This means that an object that now actually weighs 288 grams at the equator would weigh 289 grams if the earth were not rotating.

At progressively higher latitudes the centripetal force is reduced, because the square of the velocity decreases more rapidly than the radius of the parallels. For example, at lat. 30° the centripetal force is about 1/385 of the force of the earth's attraction; at 45° it is 1/578; at 60°, 1/1156.[1] The earth's gravitational attraction as actually measured at a given point on earth

[1] The formula for computing this fraction, assuming a spherical earth, is: Fractional force $= \frac{1}{289} \cos^2$ latitude.

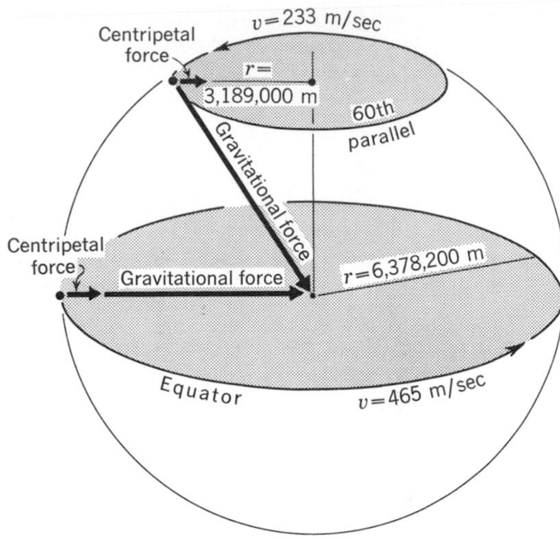


**FIGURE 2.8.** Centripetal force, which decreases as latitude increases, reduces very slightly the weight of an object on the earth's surface.

incorporates the effect of centripetal force and is termed *gravity.* Gravity and the law of gravitation are discussed in Chapter 10. The distinction between "gravitational force of the earth" and "gravity" should be carefully noted.

Centripetal force has an important, though small influence upon the direction taken by a *plumb line.* We are all familiar with the use of a small weight, the *plumb bob,* suspended from a thin cord as a means of establishing the true direction of the vertical, as for example to test the verticality of a brick wall as it is constructed. For uses in astronomy the plumb line should, if the earth were a perfectly uniform sphere, indicate exactly the zenith and nadir in the celestial sphere (Figure 2.9). Of the various reasons why the plumb line actually deviates from the true vertical (see Chapter 10), one that is appropriate to consider here is the effect of earth rotation. If we assume for the moment that the earth is a true sphere, we should find that the plumb line of a nonrotating earth would point exactly to the earth's center (Figure 2.9). Centripetal force directed at right angles to the earth's axis is subtracted from the gravitational attraction and allows the plumb bob to deflect slightly outward, i.e., so that the zenith point is shifted slightly poleward along the meridian of the celestial sphere. Deviation of the plumb bob because of this cause alone is zero at the equator (because there the centripetal force is exactly parallel to gravitational force) and zero at the poles (because there is no centripetal force there). The deviation reaches its greatest value at lat. 45°, where it measures 5′57″, or about one-tenth of a degree.

## Proofs of the earth's rotation

To adherents of the Ptolemaic theory of the universe it seemed reasonable that all heavenly bodies actually revolve about the earth once every 24 hours, because

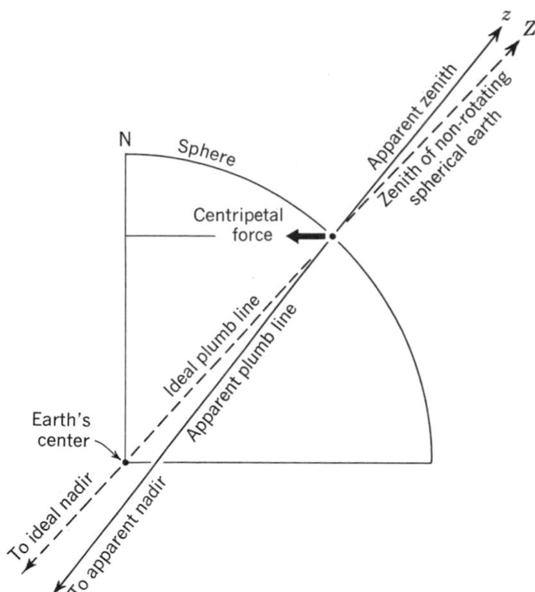


**FIGURE 2.9.** Earth rotation causes a plumb line to be slightly deflected.

the earth seemed to them enormous in comparison with the largest of celestial objects. Moreover, there was no way in which they could even guess at the vastness of outer space and the tremendous masses of the sun and other stars compared with the earth's mass. Using only our eyes and lacking the information gained by the astronomical telescope, we, too, should find it hard to refute the geocentric approach. It is therefore worth while to review several phenomena which require that the earth rotate on its axis.

One proof refers to the principle of shifting of the color spectra of the stars as the observer moves toward or away from the star (Chapter 1). As shown in Figure 2.10, if the earth is rotating there will be a point, *A,* on one side of the earth where an observer is moving rapidly toward a given star, whereas at the same instant the opposite point on the earth (point *B*) is moving away from the same star with equal rapidity. At *A* the star's spectrum will be shifted toward the violet end; at *B* toward the red end. As suggested in the figure,

**FIGURE 2.10.** On a rotating earth the color spectrum of a star is shifted in a series of daily alternations.

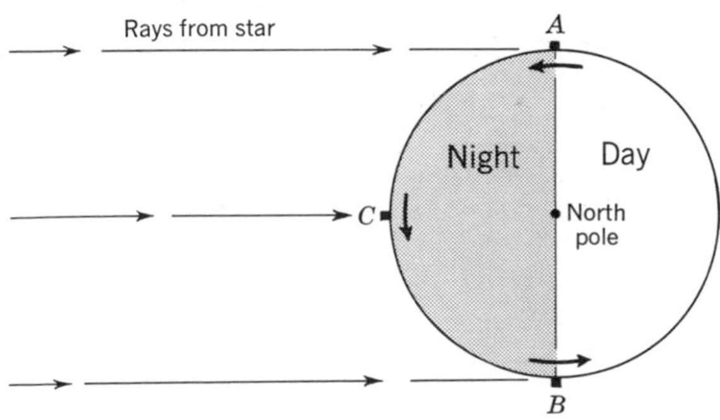


position *A* represents the time of rising of the star in the evening; position *B* its setting in early morning. The fact that observers near *A* and *B* can simultaneously record a spectral displacement of equal magnitude, but in opposite directions, rules out the possibility that the star is the object that is moving, for it could not move in two directions at the same time. Further proofs of earth rotation are considered below.

**Oblateness of the earth** One direct consequence of rotation is that the earth's shape is not that of a true sphere, but instead has been deformed into an *oblate ellipsoid* (also called an *ellipsoid of revolution*). In comparison with a sphere of equal volume, an oblate ellipsoid is a body in which the diameter along the axis of rotation has been shortened and the great circle at right angles to the axis has been enlarged to a greater radius (Figure 2.11). In terms of the earth and its geographic grid, oblateness results in the polar axis being about 27 mi (43 km) shorter than the equatorial diameter (see Chapter 10). The equator and all other parallels remain true circles, whereas the cross section of the earth taken through both poles (a meridional cross section) has the shape of an ellipse whose major axis is the equatorial diameter.

Dimensions of the earth as an oblate ellipsoid and details relating to the discovery and measurement of the amount of oblateness are treated in detail in Chapter 10. Here we are interested in the relation of oblateness to the earth's rotation.

Sir Isaac Newton gave the first theoretical proof of the earth's oblateness, which he showed to be a consequence of the law of gravitation and the laws of motion acting upon a rotating sphere. Imagine that, as shown in Figure 2.11, we could install on the rotating earth a water-filled tube extending from a pole (point *P*) to the earth's center (point *C*) where it would connect with a similar tube extending to the earth's center from a point on the equator (point *Q*). If the earth were a

**FIGURE 2.11.** Fluid in radial tubes, connected to one another at the earth's center, would stand at different heights because of rotation.

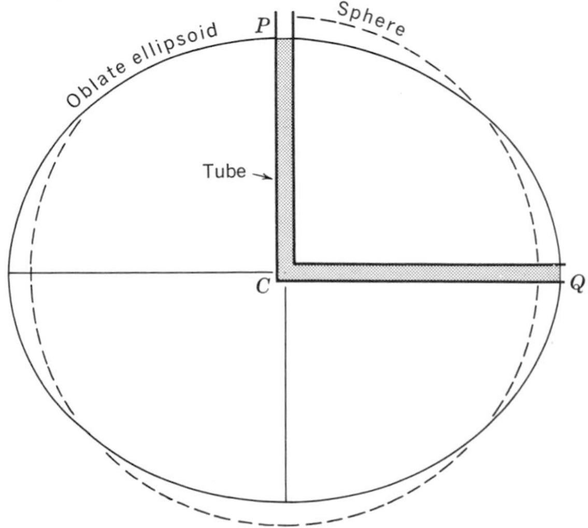

uniform nonrotating sphere, the two columns of water would stand at equal heights (i.e., would have equal lengths), because each column would be acted upon by exactly the same forces and the weight of one column would exactly counterbalance the other. Now imagine that the earth is set in uniform rotation. A centrifugal force, which can be imagined as equal and opposite to the centripetal force and directed radially outward along the line *CQ,* would reduce the weight of the water column in that tube, so that it would exert less pressure at *C* than it would with the earth stationary. Therefore the pressure exerted by the water column *PC,* not affected by centrifugal force, would be the greater. To establish an equilibrium of forces, water would flow from tube *PC* into *CQ,* and the water level in the two tubes would come to rest, that at *Q* standing somewhat farther from the earth's center than that at *P.*

Newton calculated the amount by which column *CQ* would be longer than column *PC* for a body of the earth's mass, dimensions, and rate of rotation. Although not exact, his results agree quite closely with the polar and equatorial radii of the earth as they are now known from geodetic surveys (Chapter 10).

The solid earth itself conforms closely to the expected shape of an oblate ellipsoid produced by rotation, if we disregard the relatively minor irregularities of ocean basins and continents. Although rock at the earth's surface seems to us to be a very strong and brittle substance, not at all resembling a fluid, the behavior of rock deep within the earth, where pressures and temperatures are extremely high, is in many respects like that of a very dense viscous fluid. There is no escape from the conclusion that the solid earth has deformed by internal flowage into an oblate ellipsoid of such dimensions as to be in equilibrium with the forces of gravitation and rotation. As the earth's rotation gradually slows over vast spans of time, we can expect the oblate ellipsoid to become progressively less flattened, approaching more closely the spherical form that a nonrotating earth would have. At present the polar axis is about 1/297 shorter than the equatorial diameter of about 8000 mi (12,700 km); the oblateness is so small that the eye could scarely distinguish the elliptical form of a polar cross section from a true circle.

**Oblateness and the plumb line** We have already seen that the plumb line is deflected slightly by forces of the earth's rotation. To this effect must be added the effect of oblateness upon the plumb line. An object located at the earth's poles, being closer to the earth's center, will be more strongly attracted by the earth's gravitational force than the same object will on the equator, where distance to the center is greater. The effect of oblateness is therefore to reduce the value of gravity measured at the equator by 1/547 of its value as measured at the poles. Adding this fraction to 1/289, the reduction due to rotational force, we have 1/189, which is the combined effect. In practical terms, a man who weighs 188 pounds at the equator would weigh 189 pounds at the North Pole.

The combined effect of rotational force and oblateness upon the plumb bob approximately doubles the deviation due only to rotational force. The maximum total deviation from both causes, at lat. 45°, is 11′31″.

## Eastward deflection of falling bodies

An understanding of the velocity of the earth's rotation enables us to devise an experiment that, if it could be successfully carried out, would prove earth rotation by demonstrating the eastward deflection of falling bodies. Suppose that we drop a heavy ball of dense metal (so as to minimize the effects of air resistance) from a very high tower, labeled point $M_1$ in Figure 2.12. Gravity will act in the vertical direction $M_1P_1$ on a line directed approximately toward the earth's center of gravity. But the ball has a rotational velocity directed eastward along the line $M_1M_2$, giving it an eastward momentum, which it carries when released at $M_1$. Thus, in the time required for the ball to drop through the vertical distance $M_1P_1$, it must travel horizontally a distance equal to $M_1M_2$ (shown greatly exaggerated in the figure), giving the ball a parabolic path and causing it to land at point *Q.* Note, however, that, while the release point at the top of the tower moved from $M_1$ to $M_2$, the plumb point at the base of the tower moved from $P_1$ to $P_2$, a slightly lesser distance than $M_1M_2$, because the ground lies on a circle of lesser radius than the circle followed by the top of the tower. Therefore the ball actually lands a short distance ($P_2Q$) east of the plumb point at the base of the tower. Were the earth not rotating, the ball would follow the path of a plumb line.

The eastward deflection of a falling body was anticipated by Galileo and explained further by Newton. Verification could not be achieved in their day, because

**FIGURE 2.12.** Because of earth rotation a falling body is deflected eastward.

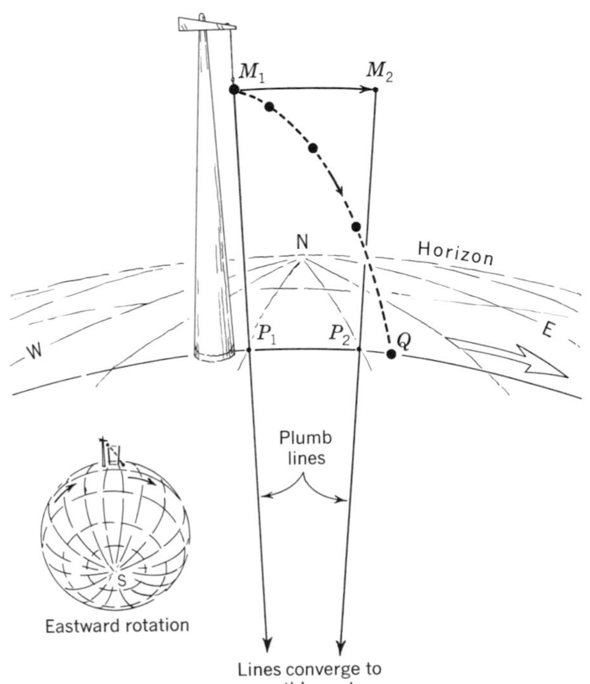

the deflection is so small that high-precision apparatus or a very long fall is needed to measure the deflection; in addition, the effects of air currents may easily overshadow the deflection. At lat. 40° the deflection would amount to 1.2 in. (3 cm) for a fall of 500 ft (150 m). Deflection has actually been confirmed by precision laboratory apparatus which shields the falling weight from all disturbing effects, but a more interesting experiment was attempted in 1909 by F. W. McNair (then President of Michigan College of Mines), using the vertical shaft of the Tamarack Mine at Houghton, Mich. This shaft was then the deepest in the world—4200 ft (1280 m)—and offered an ideal outdoor laboratory in which to test the eastward deflection. Two steel spheres were dropped in succession, but neither one reached the bottom. One was later found lodged in timbers 800 ft (240 m) from the surface. Although the shaft was amply wide to accommodate an anticipated deflection of about 3 ft (1 m), the effects of such disturbing forces as air currents, rotation of the ball, or even magnetic influence of steel structures in the mine shaft seem to have been much greater than the deflection that McNair hoped to demonstrate.

**FIGURE 2.13** This handsome Foucault pendulum knocks over pins in succession to show that its direction of motion is changing (Courtesy of the Franklin Institute, Philadelphia, Pa.)

## The Foucault pendulum

Perhaps the simplest as well as the most impressive demonstration of the earth's rotation is seen in the *Foucault pendulum,* invented by Leon Foucault, a French physicist, and demonstrated by him in Paris in 1851. Today, over a century later, a beautifully designed Foucault pendulum operates continuously in the United Nations Building in New York City, where it serves to symbolize the earth as a unit sphere. Another fine pendulum is shown in Figure 2.13.

Foucault suspected a 62-lb (28-kg) cannon ball from the dome of the Pantheon, using a slender wire about 200 ft (60 m) long (Figure 2.14). As the pendulum swung, a pin projecting from the underside of the ball traced a mark in a circular ridge of sand whose center was directly under the point of suspension of the pendulum. Once set in motion the pendulum was observed to undergo a steady change in direction, the compass direction of motion rotating clockwise at a constant rate of about 11¼° per hour. The basic principle involved in this experiment is that of Newton's first law of motion: Every body remains in a state of rest or of uniform motion in a straight line unless compelled to change that state by an external force acting upon it.

Consider a small area directly under the pendulum at lat. 30° N. (Figure 2.15). The southern edge (in the Northern Hemisphere) is farther from the earth's axis than the northern edge, and therefore the southern edge must be moving faster than the northern edge to complete its rotation about the earth's axis each 24 hours. When an automobile is making a left turn, the wheels on the right side are moving farther and faster than those on the left side, for in addition to its forward motion the automobile is rotating about a vertical axis. If we face east (that is, in the direction of motion of the earth) in the area under the pendulum, the righthand (southern) edge of our small area will be moving faster than the left (northern) edge. Thus in addition to its easterly motion the small area is constantly experiencing a slow, counterclockwise rotation about a vertical axis. But the nature of the suspension of a Foucault pendulum is such that the pendulum is equally free to swing in any direction; it is not constrained to share in the rotation of the earth beneath it. Although in the Northern Hemisphere the surface of the earth is actually rotating in a counterclockwise direction under a pendulum whose plane of swing is not rotating, everything we can see, except the pendulum, shares the rotation of the earth about the vertical axis, so it appears to us as if the plane of swing of the pendulum is rotating in a clockwise direction.

**FIGURE 2.14.** In the Northern Hemisphere the direction of swing of a Foucault pendulum shifts in a clockwise manner. (© 1960, John Wiley & Sons, New York.)

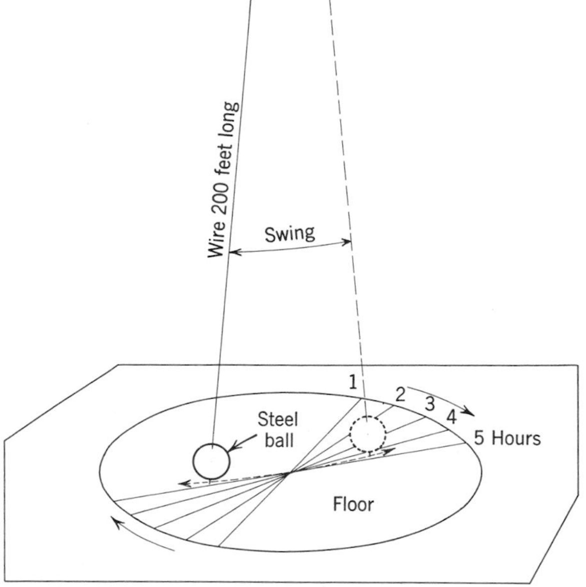

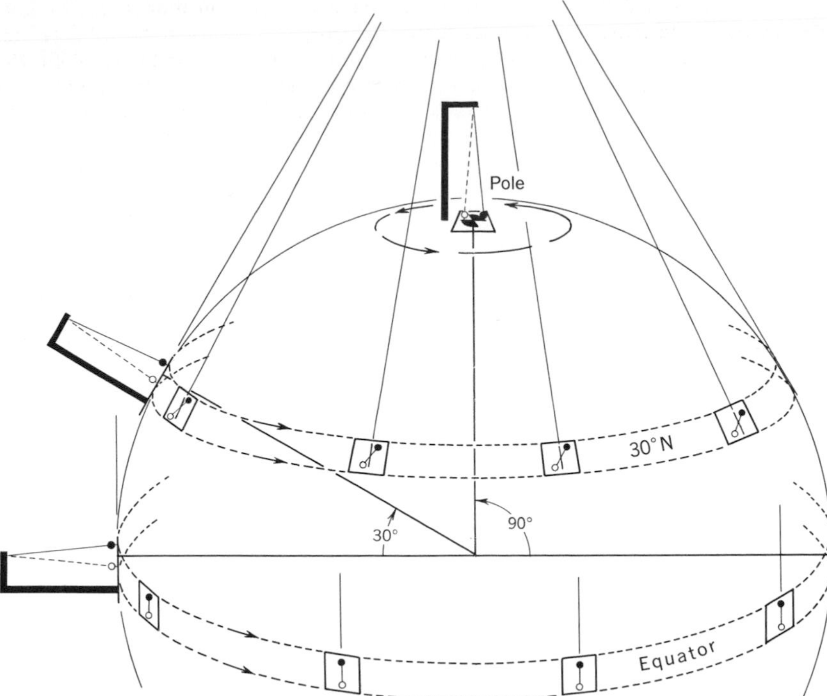


**FIGURE 2.15.** The rate of turning of a Foucault pendulum increases with latitude.

Of further interest is the fact that the rotational velocity of the change in pendulum direction varies with latitude in a systematic way. The rate of turning is easy to determine for either pole (Figure 2.15), where the tangent line in which the pendulum is set moving lies parallel with the plane of the rotating horizon plane. Each sidereal rotation of 24 sidereal hours turns the earth's surface a full 360°, and the tangent line, which is the line scratched by the pendulum in the sand, changes 15° for each hour.

Consider next the case of a Foucault pendulum set in motion on the 30th parallel of latitude (Figure 2.15). As the earth turns, the tangent line describes the surface of a cone whose apex lies on the extension of the earth's axis and whose apical angle is 60° (Figure 2.16*A*). A cone of this kind is described as a *tangent cone* and touches the earth along a parallel of latitude, in this case, the 30th parallel. To determine the actual amount of change of direction the tangent line to a meridian has actually undergone in the plane of the parallel during one earth rotation, we have only to imagine the cone slit from apex to base and unrolled into a flat sheet, a process called *development* (Figure 2.16*A*). In the plane of the developed cone, which shows the actual amount of turning in the plane of the parallel, the change of pendulum direction is only 180°, or ex-

**FIGURE 2.16.** The track of a Foucault pendulum (*A*) on a tangent cone at lat. 30° N. and (*B*) on a tangent cylinder at the equator.

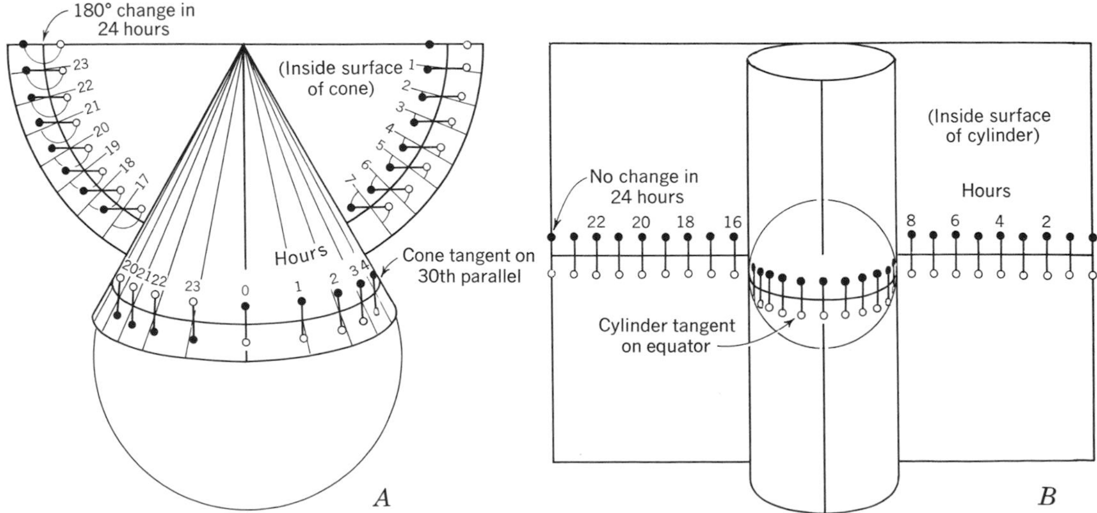

actly half what it is at the poles. Now, the sine of 30° is 0.5, from which we see that the following formula will apply:

$$\text{degrees of pendulum turning per hour} = 15° \times \text{sine latitude.}$$

Table 2.2 gives the hourly pendulum change in degrees and the total time (sidereal) required for 360° of change for 5-degree intervals of latitude.

**TABLE 2.2. RATE OF TURNING OF THE FOUCAULT PENDULUM AT VARIOUS LATITUDES**

| Latitude, degrees | Hourly Change in Pendulum Direction, degrees | Total Time for 360° Change in Direction, hours (sidereal) |
|---|---|---|
| 0 | None | None |
| 5 | 1.31 | 275 |
| 10 | 2.60 | 138 |
| 15 | 3.88 | 93 |
| 20 | 5.13 | 70 |
| 25 | 6.34 | 57 |
| 30 | 7.50 | 48 |
| 35 | 8.60 | 42 |
| 40 | 9.64 | 37 |
| 45 | 10.61 | 34 |
| 50 | 11.49 | 31 |
| 55 | 12.29 | 29 |
| 60 | 12.99 | 28 |
| 65 | 13.59 | 26.5 |
| 70 | 14.10 | 25.6 |
| 75 | 14.49 | 24.9 |
| 80 | 14.77 | 24.5 |
| 85 | 14.94 | 24.1 |
| 90 | 15.00 | 24.0 |

Suppose, next, that we try a similar analysis for a pendulum at the equator. Here the tangent line produces a cylinder as the earth turns (Figure 2.16*B*). When the tangent cylinder is developed, it gives a rectangle on which the traces of successive tangent lines are parallel to one another; hence they have undergone no directional change. Even if we should set the pendulum swinging obliquely with respect to a meridian, it is evident that the angle between this oblique path and the plane of the earth's equator would remain constant. The tangent cylinder can be thought of as a cone so extended in height that its apical angle has been reduced to zero. The sine of 0° is zero; hence the formula yields zero, meaning that there is no change in pendulum direction.

A much smaller, but equally effective version of the pendulum used by Foucault is now made possible by means of an electromagnetic induction system placed beneath the center point over which the pendulum passes. Without imparting any change in direction, the swinging of the pendulum can be maintained indefinitely.

## The Coriolis effect

Perhaps the most remarkable of the persistent physical effects resulting from the earth's rotation is the tendency of all particles of matter in motion on the earth's surface to be deflected toward the right, with respect to their compass direction of motion, in the Northern Hemisphere and toward the left in the Southern Hemisphere. Termed the *Coriolis effect,* after the nineteenth-century French mathematician G. G. Coriolis, who first analyzed it, the phenomenon is not a simple mechanical force, such as gravitation or centripetal force, but rather the apparent, or fictitious, effect of a number of forces that act upon any particle set in motion on the earth's spherical surface.

Without attempting to give a full mathematical explanation, one basic aspect of the deflective effect can be considered in order to gain some understanding of the cause. To begin with, Newton's first law of motion states that, when any particle is set in motion, it will follow a straight line unless compelled to change its path by some external force. In this case the straight-line path is fixed in space with respect to the stars. Now, there is no place on the surface of the turning globe where a horizontal path of travel of finite length can maintain its geographic orientation with respect to the parallels and meridians and at the same time remain fixed in space.

To show why adherence to the first law of motion tends to result in a turning of a moving particle toward the right of its initial path, a large globe and a long piece of string can be used as a demonstration apparatus (Figure 2.17). Attach the string to a point across the room, some 20 or 30 ft (6 to 9 m) away. Holding the string taut, place the free end so as to touch the globe on, say, the 40th parallel of latitude as designated by $P_1$ in Figure 2.17. The string must be exactly tangent to the selected parallel and must lie in the same plane as the parallel. When so fixed, the string represents a true eastward compass direction, which is the desired initial direction of motion, but it is also in the plane of a great circle tangent to the parallel. Mark on the globe a segment of line, designated 1 in the enlarged diagram of Figure 2.17, representing a travel distance of, say, 300 mi (500 km). Next place the end of the string at $P_2$, the end of the first segment, and rotate the globe eastward through 5° of longitude, then add a second line segment in the new compass direction taken by the taut string. Repeat this operation until the globe has rotated through 30°. The six segments of line will represent very crudely the type of curved path taken by the object as it attempts to maintain its original direction in space at the same time that it is following a horizontal path on the earth's surface to which it is held by gravity.

The experiment can be repeated at any northern latitude and with any initial starting direction.[2] It will yield the same result: a travel path curving to the right of the initial direction of motion. In the Southern Hemisphere the direction of initial motion will curve to the left. Along the equator, whether due eastward or due westward, no tendency will be found for the path to

[2] Add rubber bands to the far end of the string so that it will remain taut when shortened. Attach the end of the string to a pencil or chalk and it will be possible to trace a continuously curved path as the globe is steadily turned. Concentrate upon keeping the cord from shifting to left or right of its starting position. Have a second person rotate the globe eastward at a constant rate. Try many starting points and initial directions in both hemispheres.

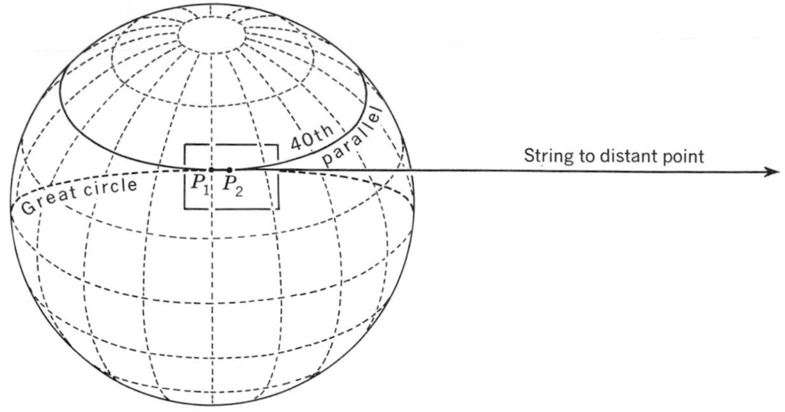


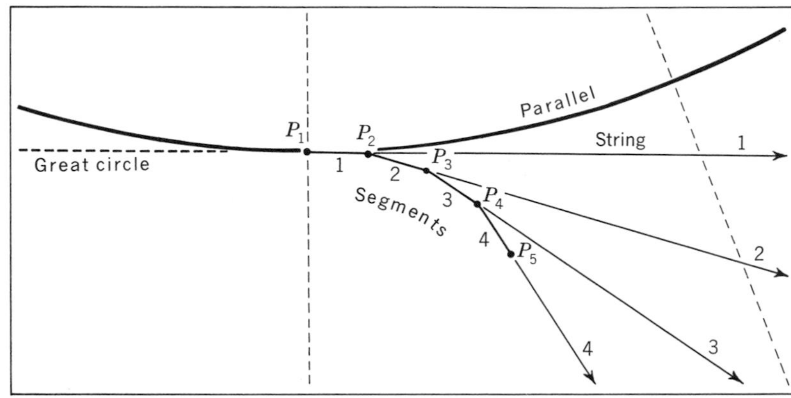


**FIGURE 2.17.** By means of a globe and a long string the principle of eastward deflection of a moving object because of earth rotation can be demonstrated.

curve either left or right. The actual path followed by a moving object at the earth's surface is subjected to normal frictional forces. Only an earth satellite free of the frictional effect of the earth's atmosphere will hold the plane of its path fixed in space as the earth turns beneath it.

Two variables affect the magnitude of the Coriolis effect acting on a given mass: linear velocity and latitude. The effect increases directly with velocity, so that if velocity is doubled, the deflecting effect is doubled. The effect varies in intensity from zero on the equator to a maximum at either pole (Figure 2.18), the relation to latitude being mathematically the same as that for the increase in rate of turning of the Foucault pendulum with latitude; that is, the effect is directly proportional to the sine of the latitude. As explained previously, the north-south horizon line (tangent line) at any parallel between the equator and a pole describes a cone whose apex lies in the line of the earth's axis (Figures 2.15 and 2.16). The effective amount of rotation in this plane is equal to the angle of sector of the developed cone, and this angle varies as the sine of the latitude. A third cause of variation could be a change in angular velocity of rotation, but in the case of the earth this rate is a constant. The following equation expresses the factors controlling the Coriolis effect.[3]

$$\text{Coriolis effect} = V\,2\Omega \sin \phi$$

[3] Coriolis effect is here stated as an acceleration in units of centimeters per second squared.

where $V$ is the linear velocity in centimeters per second, $\Omega$ is the angular velocity of rotation in radians per second, and $\phi$ is the latitude in degrees.

The relation of deflective effect to latitude can be illustrated with the apparatus shown in Figure 2.19. Instead of a globe, a drum combining a cylinder and cone is rotated at uniform rate on a vertical axis. The horizontal circular top, the section of cone, and the cylinder represent, respectively, tangent surfaces at the North Pole, at an intermediate latitude, and at the equator. With the aid of a guide paralleling the drum, a pencil is drawn at uniform speed along the meridian, inscribing an apparent path of motion on a sheet of paper attached to the surface. If the paper were taken off and laid flat, it would be seen that the pencil line is most strongly curved for the polar case, less strongly curved for the intermediate latitude, and a straight line for the equatorial case. The change in angle of trend of the curving lines is proportional to the sine of the latitude (sine of angle between the tangent surface and the earth's axis).

## Illustrations of the Coriolis effect

Later chapters relate how the Coriolis effect modifies winds and ocean currents. These fluids respond readily to the small deflecting force, and the results are of great importance. In firing a long-range projectile, whether it be a large artillery shell or an intercontinental

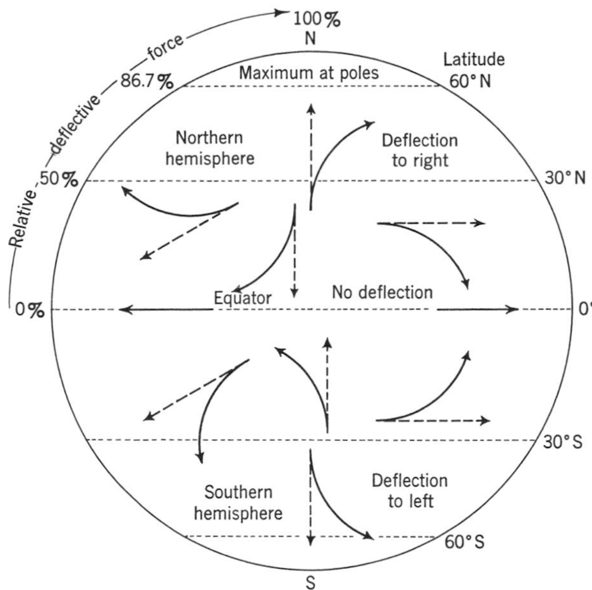


**FIGURE 2.18.** Moving objects tend to be deflected to the right in the Northern Hemisphere and to the left in the Southern Hemisphere. The effect is intensified as latitude increases. (© 1960, John Wiley & Sons, New York.)

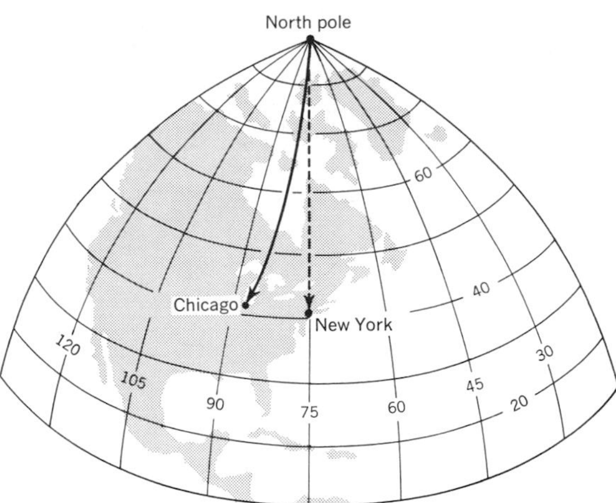


**FIGURE 2.20.** A rocket launched from the North Pole on a course due south along the meridian of New York would veer westward and land near Chicago.

ballistic missile (ICBM), the deflection must be taken into account. It is said that shells of the great World War I German cannon *Big Bertha* were deflected to the right by almost 1 mi (1.6 km) in their 70-mi (113-km) distance of travel. A rocket fired from the North Pole due southward along a meridian of longitude will seem to veer westward at the rate of 15° of longtitude per hour. Thus, if it were aimed down the 74th meridian, the New York area being the target, with an average speed of 3600 mi (5800 km) per hour, the flight would take 56 minutes, and the rocket would actually land near Chicago, which lies about 14° west of New York (Figure 2.20).

**FIGURE 2.19.** A steadily rotating drum could be used to demonstrate the curving path of travel resulting from earth rotation.

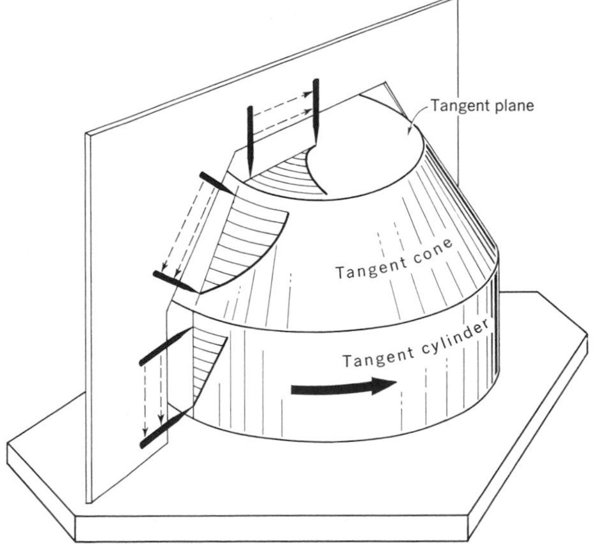


The apparent path of an earth satellite is perhaps the ideal example of deflection produced by the earth's rotation. Suppose that a satellite launched from the North Pole is aimed south along a meridian on a great-circle course. Assume that the satellite travels in a perfectly circular orbit 300 mi (480 km) above the earth at a speed of 18,000 mi (29,000 km) per hour, or about 300 mi (480 km) per minute. Let the earth be considered a perfect, homogeneous sphere. Once the satellite is established in space, its orbit is a true circle with fixed orientation in space, whereas the earth turns beneath it at 15° per sidereal hour. As the satellite travels southward, it seems to veer westward in a curved path such that for every 4 minutes of time it is shifted 1° of longitude westward. Imagine that the satellite in uniform flight has just passed over the North Pole in the direction of the Greenwich meridian. Just 22½ minutes later it will cross the equator at long. 5⁹⁄₁₆° (5.5625°) W. The trajectory of the satellite as plotted on the globe will thus have a westward curvature (to the right in the direction of satellite motion) and will cross the equator obliquely from about NNE to SSW (Figure 2.21). After crossing the equator, the trajectory seems to curve left (concave eastward) even though the westward shift of longitude continues at the constant rate of 1° for 4 minutes of time. The satellite crosses the South Pole along the line of the meridian 11⅛° W. Northward travel on the far side of the globe follows a similar, but reversed path. As the satellite again crosses the North Pole, its bearing is 22½° west of the first crossing. Likewise, each crossing of the equator from north to south will occur at a point 22½° longitude farther west than the previous crossing.

The satellite's orbit is shown on a polar stereographic projection in Figure 2.21, which preserves true angles of intersection of any path with respect to the meridians and parallels. The satellite's terrestrial path shows a curvature to the right in the Northern Hemisphere and to the left in the Southern Hemisphere. It is also obvious

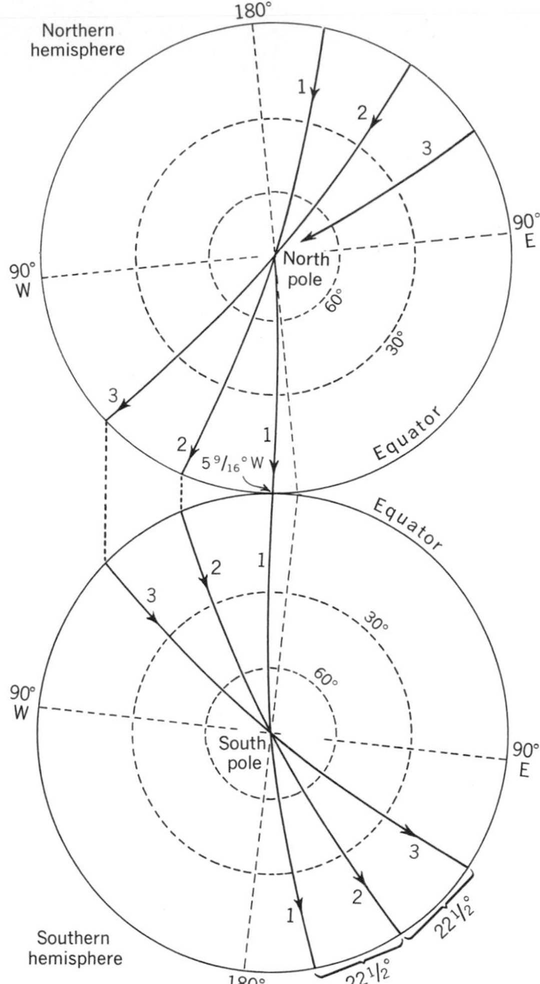


**FIGURE 2.21.** The earth trace of an artificial satellite in polar orbit curves to the right in the Northern Hemisphere and to the left in the Southern Hemisphere. This map combines two polar stereographic projections.

from the sinuous trace of the satellite's path on the globe that the surface velocity (ground speed) of the satellite must be greater than 18,000 mi (29,000 km) per hour, except over the poles.

A fine example of a satellite orbit inclined with respect to the earth's axis is that of Tiros I (1960 Beta 2), launched at 6:40 A.M. EST on April 1, 1960, from Cape Canaveral (now Cape Kennedy), Florida (Figure 2.22). Some 12 minutes after launching, this satellite, which was the first of the TIROS meteorological type, was in a nearly circular orbit, starting at the point labeled *0 minutes* on the map. The first four orbits are shown with marks at positions 5 minutes apart. The direction of launching was to the northeast; the plane of orbit was established on an angle of 48° with the plane of the earth's equator. (Launching in an eastward direction takes advantage of the earth's linear velocity of eastward rotation.)

Circling the earth once each 99 minutes, the satellite had an initial velocity with respect to the earth's surface of about 16,800 mi (27,000 km) per hour and a height of about 433 mi (697 km) above the earth's surface. The elliptical orbit had an eccentricity of only 0.003, which is considered nearly perfect. The earth trace of this satellite is deflected to the right in the Northern Hemisphere and reaches its most northerly point at lat. 48° N., where the path is due east (Figure 2.22). After recurving southeast and crossing the equator, the path enters the Southern Hemisphere, where deflection is to the left of direction of motion. The path reaches its southernmost point at lat. 48° S, where the path is due east, before recurving northeast. Note that successive crossings of the equator from southwest to northeast are separated by 24¾° of longitude, which is the figure obtained by dividing the orbital period of 99 minutes by 4, the number of minutes required for the earth to turn 1°.

## Precession of the earth's axis

The earth's oblateness is responsible for causing other systematic motions of the earth, superimposed on the motions of revolution and rotation thus far described. Consider that the earth's equatorial plane is inclined 23½° with respect to the plane of the ecliptic in which the sun lies at all times. The moon also lies close to the plane of the ecliptic, deviating from it but a few degrees at most (Chapter 8). Both bodies exert a gravitational force upon the earth; that of the moon, although weaker, is the more effective in producing unequal forces within the earth. Because the plane of the earth's equatorial bulge is thus inclined with respect to the sun and moon, these bodies attract the closer part of the equatorial bulge with a force that tends to rotate the equatorial plane into parallelism with the plane of the ecliptic and to tilt the earth's axis into a fully erect position, vertical with respect to the ecliptic (Figure 2.23). Because the earth is rotating, it resists any force tending to change the angle of inclination of its axis, but responds instead by shifting its axis of rotation so as to describe a conical figure in space, a motion termed *precession of the earth's axis.* The direction of precession is reverse, or retrograde, with respect to the direction of rotation. The cone of precession has an apex angle of 47°, twice the angle of inclination of the earth's axis from the vertical.

Precession of the earth's axis is illustrated in principle by the demonstration gyroscope, a heavy wheel on a shaft which can pivot freely, the weight of the rotated rapidly on an axis whose bearings have very small friction (Figure 2.24). When mounted horizontally gyroscope can be exactly counterbalanced by a sliding weight. If the gyroscope is now set in rapid rotation, it will keep a fixed horizontal axis. If we should slide the counterweight farther out on the shaft so as to tend to lower the counterweight and raise the gyroscope, as if on a seesaw, the gyroscope shaft will maintain its horizontal attitude, but will respond instead to the turning force (torque) by rotating the entire assembly in a horizontal circle about the pivot. The principle peculiar to a spinning weight is that the direction of precession is always perpendicular to the direction of application of the external turning force. In the case of the model

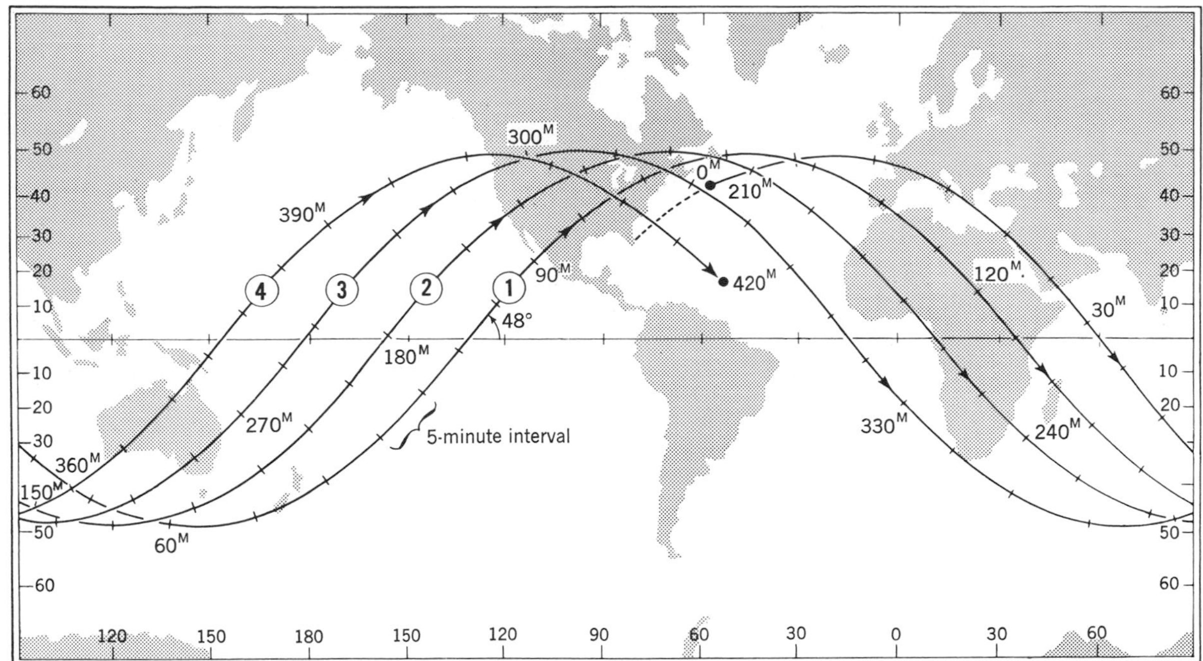


**FIGURE 2.22.** Earth trace of the first four orbits of satellite Tiros I (1960 Beta 2) plotted on the Mercator projection. Marks show the satellite's position at 5-minute intervals; figures show elapsed time at 30-minute intervals. (After *I. G. Y. Bulletin,* No. 35, 1960.)

gyroscope a vertical torque was met by horizontal precession; in the case of the earth a torque tending to turn the earth in the plane in which its axis is tilted produces a precession of the pole in a circle at right angles to that plane.

Precession is extremely slow, judged by time spans of our lives. A complete precessional revolution would take about 25,800 years, so that the annual change in position of the celestial pole is only 50 seconds of arc. Over many centuries, however, the change in celestial pole is easily noticed. Hipparchus, who is credited with discovery of the earth's precession about 120 B.C., became aware of it when he compared his own observations with those of earlier astronomers. Whereas Polaris is now the polestar, Alpha Draconis was the polestar for Egyptian civilizations about 3000 B.C. By A.D. 7500 Alpha Cephus, a rather faint star (third magnitude), will be the polestar. By A.D. 14,000 Vega will be the polestar, although it will never be as close as Polaris now is to the celestial pole (Figure 2.25).

**FIGURE 2.23.** The earth's precession results from tidal attraction applied to the equatorial bulge.

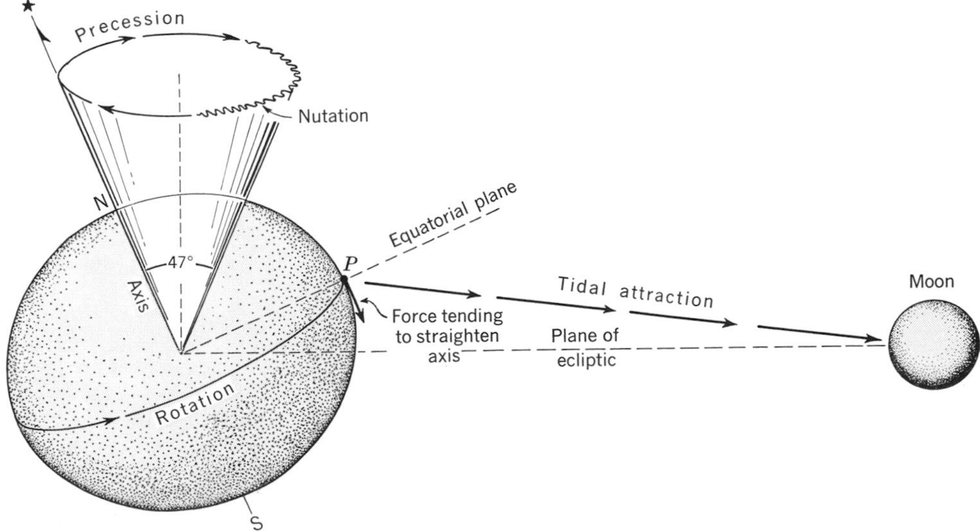

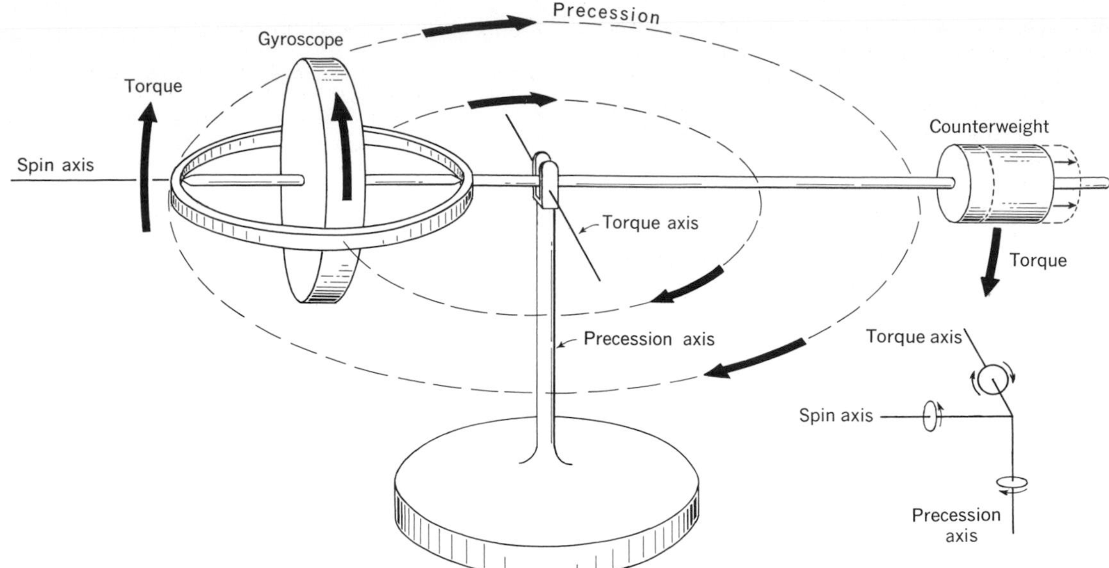


**FIGURE 2.24.** A gyroscope illustrates the principle of precession of the earth's axis of rotation.

Precession has an important effect on the calculation of the length of the tropical year. It was stated in Chapter 1 that the tropical year is reckoned from one vernal equinox to the next, as compared with the sidereal year, which is a revolution of 360° with respect to the stars. Precession causes the vernal equinox to creep gradually westward along the ecliptic, a process called *precession of the equinoxes,* shortening by about 20 minutes the time required for the sun to travel from one vernal equinox to the next. The positions of the points of perihelion and aphelion, when measured with respect to the vernal equinox, will appear to shift by about 50″ per year. Superimposed on this apparent shift is a much smaller actual precession of the major axis of the earth's elliptical orbit.

**FIGURE 2.25.** Position of the celestial pole among the stars during the cycle of precession.

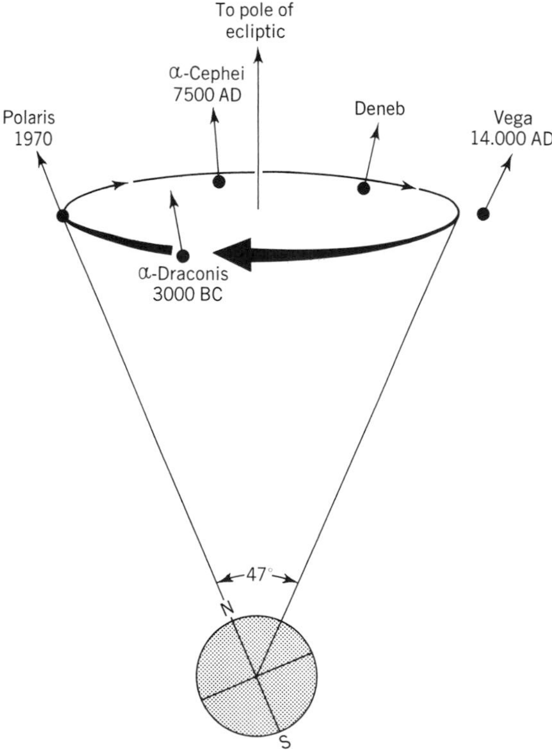


Because of the attraction exerted by other planets, the perihelion and aphelion points would complete a full 360° of precession in the direction of earth's orbital motion in about 108,000 years, which is at a rate of about 12″ annually. We know that the earth covers about 1° of its orbit each sidereal day, so that 12 seconds of arc is equivalent in time to about $4^m40^s$, making the anomalistic year (perihelion to perihelion) that much longer than the sidereal year. With respect to the equinoxes, then, the perihelion point shifts annually by an arc equal to the sum of 50″ and 12″, which is 1′02″ or a total time difference of $25^m07^s$ between the tropical and anomalistic years. At this rate, perihelion will occur on July 1 in about 10,500 years, reversing completely the dates of perihelion and aphelion with respect to the seasons of winter and summer.

**Nutation of the earth's axis** The forces causing precession are not constantly applied. The rate of precession is therefore not constant, but fluctuates slightly, introducing a motion of the polar axis termed *nutation* (from the Latin verb *nutare,* to nod), which may be described as a wavy motion in the precessional orbit. Nutation is illustrated in Figure 2.23, but the waves are enormously exaggerated in terms of the circle of precession.

When either the sun or moon is directly over the earth's equatorial bulge, there is no tendency to straighten up the earth and therefore no force causing precession. Because the sun crosses the celestial equator twice a year and the moon twice a month, we know that twice each year the solar precession will be reduced to zero and 24 or 25 times each year there will be no lunar precession. Furthermore, inclination of the moon's orbit with the plane of the ecliptic results in a 19-year cycle in the moon's effectiveness in producing precession. Thus nutation varies in a complicated way and is applied, for any particular time, as a small correction, never more than a fraction of a second of arc, to the general average value for the precession, which is 50.2″ per year. The astronomer Bradley is credited with the discovery of nutation in connection with his observations of the aberration of starlight.

## References for further study

Moulton, F. R. (1924), *An Introduction to Astronomy,* New York, Macmillan, 577 pp., chap. 3.

Wylie, C. C. (1942), *Astronomy, Maps, and Weather,* New York, Harper & Row, 449 pp., chap. 5.

Hosmer, G. L. (1948), *Practical Astronomy,* 4th ed., New York, Wiley, 355 p., chap. 1.

Mehlin, T. G. (1959), *Astronomy,* New York, Wiley, 392 pp., chaps. 11, 12.

Strong, C. L. (1960), *The Amateur Scientist,* New York, Simon and Schuster, 584 pp., chap. 8.

# 3

# Time[1]

RESEARCH IN THE EARTH SCIENCES today requires the accurate measurement of time and the synchronization of observations on a world-wide basis to an extent never before known. Time is a fundamental dimension of the world of physical phenomena, along with mass, length, and temperature. One cannot express the velocity or acceleration of a particle without stating the changes of distance occurring in given units of time. One cannot express the rhythmic events of the earth sciences—the periods of the tides or an ocean swell, or earth rotation, revolution, and precession—except as the number of events occurring for each unit of time.

Two aspects of time are essential in the earth sciences. First, it is necessary to establish a fundamental unit of time *interval.* Second, it is necessary to distinguish between time in the sense of interval and in the sense of *epoch,* or when an event occurs. The global relations of our standard time systems must be understood, for otherwise it is impossible to correlate physical phenomena observed at many different places on the earth and in space.

## The second of Ephemeris Time

The fundamental unit of time interval recognized internationally, and the same for both metric and English units of measure, is called simply the *second.* However, there are various kinds of seconds, and the one adopted to define the fundamental unit has been changed twice since 1956. At first thought the definition of this unit of time may not seem to present any serious problems. We know that there are, by definition, 3600 seconds in an hour, and

[1] Text and figures relating to time units, time measurement, and earth rotation were prepared with the cooperation of Dr. William Markowitz, Marquette University.

86,400 seconds in a mean solar day. The unit of time, therefore, was primarily defined as 1/86,400 of a mean solar day.

Time can also be defined, not by the rotation of the earth about its axis, but by the orbital motion of the earth or any planet about the sun. This kind of time is called *Ephemeris Time* (ET). Ephemeris Time is also obtained from the orbital motion of the moon about the earth. Astronomers found that the speed of rotation of the earth, and consequently the duration of a mean solar second, was variable with respect to the second of Ephermeris Time, as obtained from either the Earth, Venus, Mercury, or the moon. Ephemeris Time is the time on which dynamical astronomy is based. This means, therefore, that the second of mean solar time is a variable unit. Demands for increased precision made the mean solar second unsatisfactory as the fundamental unit. In 1956, the International Committee of Weights and Measures adopted the following definition of one second of Ephemeris Time (ET): The second is the fraction 1/31,556,925.9747 of the tropical year for $12^h$ Ephemeris Time of January 0, 1900. This fraction is derived from tables of the earth's motion published by Simon Newcomb in 1895.

The time required for the earth to make one orbital revolution about the sun changes slightly, but continuously. This change results from the earth's response to varying gravitational attraction exerted by other planets, a phenomenon known as *perturbation* of the earth's orbit. These effects can be rigorously calculated from the laws of celestial mechanics and the law of gravitation. On the other hand, changes in speed of earth rotation do not affect the orbital motion of the earth about the sun. Hence, Ephermeris Time is independent of variations in speed of earth rotation.

Because the tropical year is changing in length continuously, it was necessary to designate a specific moment in the definition of the ephemeris second. Although the derivation of the second of Ephemeris Time is somewhat involved, astronomers have no difficulty in obtaining this value from astronomical observations of the positions of the sun, moon, or planets with respect to the stars. However, because many observations must be averaged over a long time interval for accuracy, the second of Ephemeris Time cannot be obtained immediately with high precision.

## The second of Atomic Time

The need of a means to obtain immediately a highly precise unit of time interval was met by development of a class of devices collectively designated as *atomic clocks.* In 1955 success was at last achieved in the long search for a device having a constant natural period of oscillation virtually unaffected by outside influences. Atomic clocks use a spectral line in the microwave region of the electromagnetic spectrum produced by a quantum transition of a selected element or molecule. Two elements particularly well suited to this use, because of the sharpness of spectral line they produce, are hydrogen and the alkali metal cesium. Cesium has proved especially desirable because its atom yields a very sharply defined resonance, and its frequency of vibration, about 9200 Megahertz, is easily detected. This element is used in the *cesium-beam atomic clock* (Figure 3.1). Hydrogen is used in a device known as the *hydrogen maser,* which has a higher degree of accuracy than the cesium clock but is more difficult to construct and use.

With the cesium-beam atomic clock the fundamental unit of time interval is reproducible immediately with an accuracy of about 5 parts in $10^{12}$. Relative stability of a single cesium clock is higher, about one part in $10^{12}$. The relative stability of the hydrogen maser is about one part in $10^{13}$.

Construction of the cesium-beam atomic clock in June, 1955, by the National Physical Laboratory, Teddington, England, finally made it possible to obtain immediately a unit of time of very high precision. A joint experiment was carried out with the U.S. Naval Observatory, Washington, D.C., to determine the frequency of cesium in terms of the second of Ephemeris Time. The cesium-beam atomic clock in England was compared with Ephemeris Time obtained from photographic observations of the moon made at Washington. Radio

**FIGURE 3.1.** Master clock installation of the Time Service Division of the U.S. Naval Observatory, Washington, D.C., in the Simon Newcomb Laboratory. (Official U.S. Navy photograph.)

time signals were used to link the two stations. The cesium frequency obtained in the interval 1955 to 1958 was adopted in 1967 to define the present fundamental unit of time as follows: The *second* is 9,192,631,770 cycles of cesium-133 radiation. Hence, the fundamental unit is now based on an atomic quantum transition.

## Epoch and Universal Time

In addition to defining the unit of time interval, we must also define the time scale in the sense of time of day; that is, when an event occurs. Because we live on a rotating earth we require *epoch* based upon that rotation for purposes of navigation, surveying, and satellite tracking. Hence, a dual system is needed for measuring the two aspects of time: *Universal Time* (UT) for epoch and *Atomic Time* (AT) for interval.

Precise time in the sense of epoch is determined by various national observatories. An instrument of very high precision used to determine Universal Time (UT) is the *photographic zenith-tube* (Figure 3.2). This instrument, through which a star is photographed as it crosses the celestial meridian, permits UT to be determined to about 0.005 second in one night.

**FIGURE 3.2.** The photographic zenith tube at the U.S. Naval Observatory is used in a fixed vertical position to observe stars as they cross the meridian and thus to determine mean solar time (Universal Time). (Official U.S. Navy photograph.)

The photographic zenith tube at the U.S. Naval Observatory at Washington, D.C., is compared directly with an atomic clock, by which the difference between Universal Time (UT) and Atomic Time (AT) is obtained. Figure 3.3 is a graph of this difference (UT–AT) plotted continuously from 1955.5 to 1961.0 for Washington and the station at Richmond, Florida. Variations in speed of earth rotation, apparent from variations in this time difference, are discussed in a later paragraph.

The photographic zenith tube observations are also used to determine the slight difference in epochs between UT and radio time signals used for geodetic surveying purposes (Chapter 11). The observer in the field uses a portable transit instrument (see Figure 11.2) to determine his local mean solar time. By comparing this time with that given by time signals, he can determine his longitude difference from Greenwich with high accuracy.

Radio-time signals transmitted by the principal stations about the world are synchronized to within a few thousandths of a second. Atomic clocks are generally used to control the time signals, with very high accuracy. Such time signals are broadcast by the U.S. Navy and the U.S. National Bureau of Standards. Station WWV, located at Fort Collins, Colorado, broadcasts on frequencies of 2.5, 5, 10, 15, 20, and 25 Megahertz; station WWVH, Maui, Hawaii, broadcasts on 2.5, 5, 10, and 15 Megahertz; station NBA of the U.S. Navy in the Canal Zone broadcasts on 24.0 kilohertz.

Thus, in modern research in the earth sciences events can be timed with great precision, not only in terms of short spans of elapsed time from start to stop of some event, but also with respect to a world standard of time, UT, so as to correlate events happening at widely separated points on the globe or in space.

**FIGURE 3.3.** Difference (seconds) between Universal Time (UT) and Atomic Time (AT) from 1955.5 to 1961.0, based on observations made by the U.S. Naval Observatory at Washington, D.C., and Richmond, Florida. Curve 1, difference observed; Curve 2, data smoothed by removing a periodic term. The variations in Curve 1 show the actual changes in speed of rotation. Curve 2 is concave downward until about 1958, showing general deceleration in speed of rotation. After 1958 the curvature is upward, showing an acceleration. (From a figure by William Markowitz, Marquette University.)

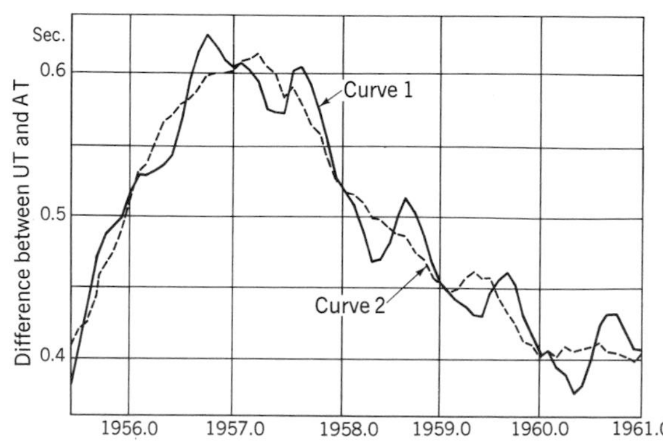

An example of the need for precision timing is the tracking of an earth satellite, carried out by means of tracking cameras which simultaneously photograph the satellite and a clock indicator. (See Figure 10.17.) A satellite in orbit may traverse as much as 5300 seconds of arc, equivalent to 25,000 ft (7.6 km) in distance, for each second of time, so that if it is necessary to locate the satellite to within 2 seconds of arc, or 10 ft (3 m), the time must be fixed to within 1/2500 second. Although it is possible to read time to the nearest 1/10,000 second, actual operating conditions of satellite tracking cameras allow accuracy of time relation to be only about 1/1000 second.

## Changing speed of earth rotation

Evidence that the earth's rotation rate is not constant has accumulated from astronomical observations dating back for centuries. Certain events, such as eclipses and oculations of stars and planets by the moon, can be predicted with great precision in terms of Ephemeris Time.

Assume that an ancient eclipse was observed at sunrise. We could use our modern knowledge of the speed of rotation to compute the longitude at which the eclipse was supposedly seen. However, if the speed of rotation is diminishing, on the average, then the speed was higher in the past and the longitude at which the eclipse was actually observed would be west of the computed longitude. Note that the eclipse still occurred at the same local time, namely sunrise. The analysis of the records of ancient eclipses shows that the speed of rotation is gradually diminishing. The length of the day, in terms of ET, increases about 0.0016 sec per century. The accumulated loss in time of UT with respect to ET is about 3 hours during the last 2000 years.

Changes in speed of rotation have also been derived from a comparison of Universal Time with Ephemeris Time obtained from the orbital motions of the Earth, Venus, and Mercury. The combined evidence is conclusive. Figure 3.4 shows the difference, UT–ET, based on observations of the moon from 1820 to 1950. The speed of earth rotation increased almost steadily from about 1840 to 1880. By then UT had gained 18 seconds on Ephemeris Time. A reversal of trend, setting in about 1895, is clearly evident in Figure 3.4. The earth had lost nearly 30 seconds by 1950 and nearly 40 seconds by 1970. These differences are due to irregular changes in speed of rotation, which are superimposed on a progressive decrease due to tidal friction.

Changes in speed of earth rotation have been revealed in detail since the cesium-beam atomic clock has been in operation. Figure 3.3 shows these changes between 1955.5 and 1961.0. Up to 1957.8 there was a general deceleration, and this was followed by an acceleration. Changes in acceleration, which cannot be predicted, have occurred about every 4 years (to 1970). These cause the irregular changes in speed of rotation. Superimposed upon these changes is an annual rhythm of change in length of day corresponding with the seasons of the year. The speed of rotation is a minimum in April and a maximum about the first of August. The difference in length of days is about 0.0012 second in this annual rhythm. The cause of the annual cycle of changes is meteorological and is explained in Chapter 15 as a result of the seasonal variations in intensity of the prevailing winds in the Northern and Southern Hemispheres.

The changes in acceleration are believed to be due to changes in the magnetic coupling between the earth's mantle and core. (This topic is developed in further detail in Chapter 7, in connection with the dynamo theory of the earth's magnetism.) Material in the liquid iron core, rotating at different rates, may come to the boundary between core and mantle at various time and exert different torques upon the solid earth.

In summary, the changes in speed of rotation are seen to be of three types: (1) a progressive retardation, shown by ancient eclipses and telescopic observations of planets, due to tidal friction; (2) irregular changes in acceleration, due to changes in core-mantle coupling, and (3) annual changes due to winds. It was formerly thought that sudden changes in the length of the day, as much as 0.003 second, occurred. However, observations made since the introduction of the atomic

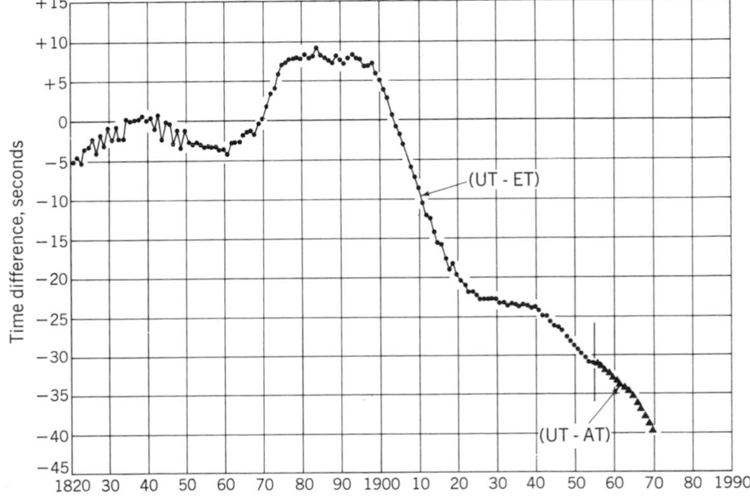


**FIGURE 3.4.** Difference between Universal Time (UT) and Ephemeris Time (ET) in the period 1820.5 to 1954.5, and between UT and Atomic Time (AT) in the period 1955.5 to 1969.5. Notice the very small variations from a smooth curve in the record of (UT–AT) as compared with the earlier record. [Data sources: 1820.5–1950.5, D. Brouwer (1952), *The Astronomical Journal,* vol. 57; 1951.5–1954.5, *American Ephemeris and Nautical Almanac;* 1955.5–1969.5, William Markowitz, Marquette University.]

clock show that such changes do not occur; changes in acceleration occur instead.

## Apparent and mean solar times

In explaining the difference between sidereal and solar days (Chapter 2), it was noted that the solar day changes in length from day to day throughout the year, requiring that an average value for the entire year be computed to serve as the mean solar day, on which our 24-hour mean solar time system is based. If we should determine successive meridian passages of the sun, using the transit and astronomical clock, it would be found that at one time of year the interval would be longer than the 24 hours of the mean solar day; at another time of year the interval would be less. As actually observed, the interval between successive meridian passages of the sun is termed the *apparent solar day.* It ranges from as much as 22 seconds shorter than the mean solar day to as much as 28 seconds longer, and on only four days of the year is it the same length as the mean solar day (Figure 3.5). During the periods of weeks and months in which the apparent solar day is longer than 24 hours the excess accumulates, so that there develops a growing discrepancy between the time at which the sun should, by mean solar time, make its noon meridian passage and the time at which meridian passage actually occurs. The sun will seem to be running *slow* in the same sense that a train is said to be running slow when its arrival at a station is delayed beyond the scheduled time. During two periods a year the sun runs slow, in one of these periods (February) reaching a maximum of 14 minutes; in the other (July) about 7 minutes. During two other periods of the year, when the accumulated effects of a shorter-than-average solar day have become dominant, the sun runs *fast,* arriving over the meridian before noon by mean solar time. Thus in early November the apparent sun attains a maximum of about 16 minutes fast; a second and lesser maximum of about 4 minutes fast is attained in May.

The amount of time by which the actual sun, or *apparent sun,* runs behind or ahead of the imaginary *mean sun* is termed the *equation of time.* In Figure 3.6 is a graph showing how the equation of time varies throughout the year. Figures 3.5 and 3.6 have been placed one above the other so that the effects of changing length of apparent solar day can be seen in the changing equation of time.

Why does the sun run fast or slow in the peculiar way that it does, giving two fast and two slow maxima, but of different amounts? Two effects are combined to produce the curve shown in Figure 3.6.

The first effect is that of varying linear velocity of the earth in its orbit. In conformity with Kepler's second law, the radius vector of a planet's orbit sweeps over equal areas in equal times (Figure 3.7). As explained in Chapter 1, if the radius vector is required to sweep over area *A,* near perihelion, in the same time that it sweeps over area *B,* near aphelion, the earth must have a higher velocity at *A* than at *B.* During one sidereal day the earth near *A* will travel more than 1

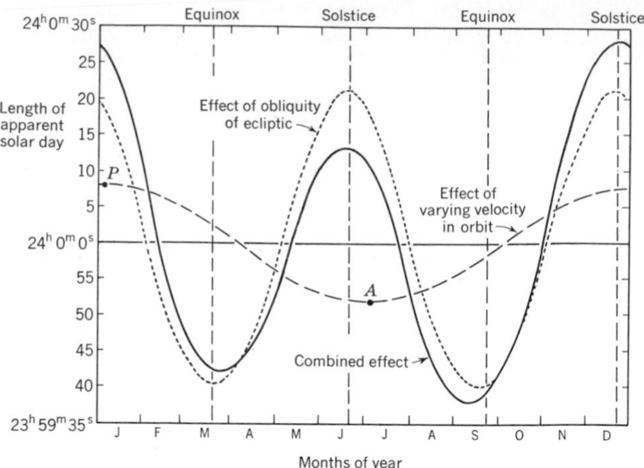


**FIGURE 3.5.** Length of the apparent solar day is determined by two facts: obliquity of the ecliptic and eccentricity of the earth's orbit. [After E. A. Fath (1934), *Elements of Astronomy,* New York, McGraw-Hill.]

degree of arc of its orbit, hence will need to turn more than one additional degree to bring the sun over the meridian. Near *B* the earth will travel less than 1 degree per sidereal day in its orbit, hence will need to turn less than an additional degree to reach solar noon. Therefore in the vicinity of *A,* close to perihelion (January 3), the apparent solar day will be several seconds longer than the mean solar day, whereas in the vicinity of *B,* near aphelion (July 4), the apparent solar day will be several seconds shorter than the mean solar day. A graph of this variation is shown in Figure 3.5 by a dashed line.

To understand the second cause of variation in the equation of time, it wil be necessary first to study the sun's yearly path among the stars.

**FIGURE 3.6.** The equation of time throughout the year. [After E. A. Fath (1934), *Elements of Astronomy,* New York, McGraw-Hill.]

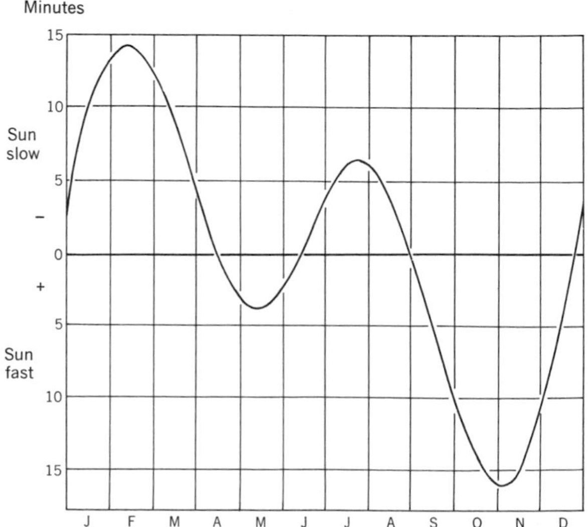

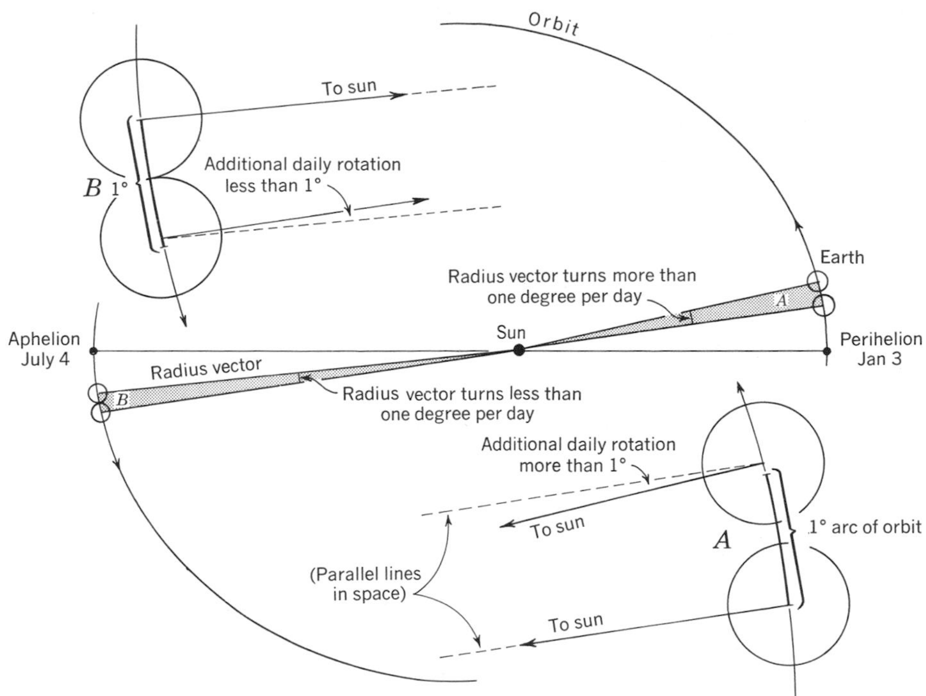


**FIGURE 3.7.** Varying speed of the earth in its elliptical orbit causes small variations in the length of the apparent solar day. For simplicity the orbit is here considered to be divided into a year of 360 days, rather than 365¼ days, so that the mean solar day is represented by an arc of 1 degree of the orbit.

## The sun in the ecliptic

It was explained in Chapter 2 that the plane of earth's orbit, known as the plane of the ecliptic, also contains the sun. When that plane is projected upon the celestial sphere as a celestial great circle, it defines the celestial ecliptic, making an angle of 23½° with respect to the celestial equator, which it intersects at two points, the two equinoxes. The sun is therefore at all times situated at some point on the ecliptic circle. In Figure 3.8 is a simplified star chart, such as that in Figure 1.18, showing on the ecliptic the sun's position throughout the year. For each month there is a particular constellation among whose stars the sun is situated; we cannot see the stars at those times because the blinding light of the sun obscures them.

Each mean solar day the sun shifts its position eastward along the ecliptic by about 1° of celestial longitude, traveling slowly among the various constellations and completing one circuit of the celestial sphere in one tropical year. It has already been noted that the tropical year begins at the instant the sun crosses the

**FIGURE 3.8.** The zodiac, a belt extending 8° on either side of the ecliptic, contains the paths of the moon and planets.

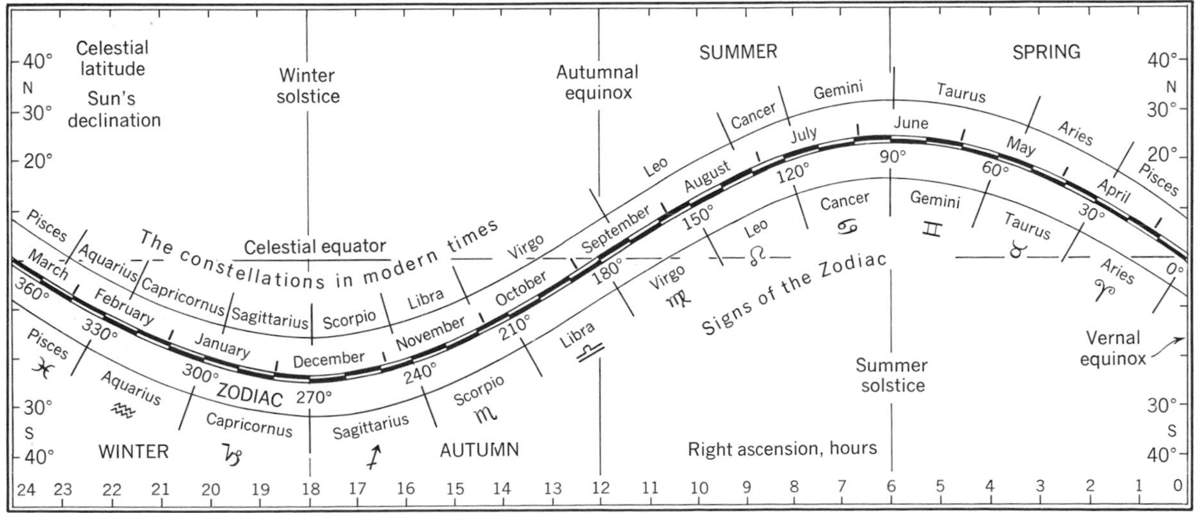

celestial equator from south to north declination, which is at the vernal equinox. The year ends 365.242 mean solar days later, with the attainment of the next vernal equinox.

For those who find it difficult to visualize the annual cycle of the sun among the stars, Figure 3.9 may be helpful. Imagine yourself on the earth at point *A*, representing the date of vernal equinox, on or about March 21. During the day you could look toward the sun in the direction of point $A_1$ and, if the sun's disk could be blotted out and its scattered rays eliminated, you would see that lying near the sun are the stars of the constellation *Pisces.* At night, however, you could look in the opposite direction, toward $A_2$. Precisely at midnight (mean solar time) the hour circle that is 180° of celestial longitude from the vernal equinox would make its meridian passage. That hour circle would lie between the constellations of *Leo* and *Virgo.* Now, as the year progresses, the earth in its orbit travels successively each month from *A* to *B* to *C,* and so forth. At point *B* on April 22 the sun will be in line with point $B_1$ on the celestial ecliptic, which is very close to *Hamal,* a bright star of the constellation *Aries.* Reference to Figure 3.8 will show that the sun on April 22 is on the second hour circle (SHA 330°) and has traveled eastward through 30° of celestial longitude. Six months after vernal equinox, the sun will have arrived at the point of *autumnal equinox,* where the ecliptic recrosses the celestial equator from north to south declination. At that time the sun will have a position between the constellations of Leo and Virgo.

From the star charts (Figures 1.18 and 3.8) it is clear that the sun in its yearly path in the ecliptic ranges in declination from 0° on vernal equinox to a northward maximum of 23½° on June 21, a point termed the *summer solstice;* then it reverses to return to a declination of 0° at autumnal equinox on or about September 23. A maximum southward declination of 23½° is reached on or about December 21, the *winter solstice,* when a reversal again sets in and declination returns to 0° with the next vernal equinox.

**FIGURE 3.9.** This diagram of sun, earth, and ecliptic shows how the counterclockwise motion of the earth in its orbit causes the sun to appear to travel eastward along the ecliptic, passing through the 12 constellations of the zodiac.

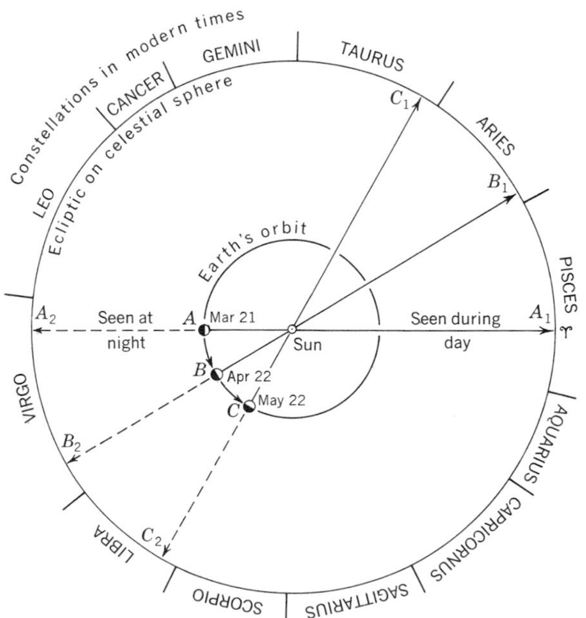


## The zodiac

This is an appropriate place to digress briefly to consider the effect that precession of the equinoxes has had on the place of the sun among the stars. The moon and principal planets are always found within 8° north or south of the celestial ecliptic. This belt of 16° width has, from ancient times, been named the *zodiac* (Figure 3.8). As the sun creeps eastward along the ecliptic, it passes through 12 divisions of the zodiac, each containing 30° of celestial longitude, and each representing a month. The ancients assigned to each division an appropriate name (all but one after people or animals); these we refer to as the *signs of the zodiac.* In Figure 3.8 the 12 signs of the zodiac are shown below the ecliptic with their symbols, whereas the constellations of modern times are shown above the ecliptic. (The actual widths spanned by constellations are not uniform.)

The constellations do not today coincide at all well with the divisions of the zodiac, but are displaced by about one month's time (30°), so that the vernal equinox, which marks the start of Aries in the zodiac (first point in Aries), occurs about one month before the sun actually enters the constellation of Aries. This discrepancy is easily explained by the precession of the equinoxes. Precession of 360° takes 26,000 years; therefore a precession of 30° would take about 2200 years. Whereas about the time of Hipparchus (180–110 B.C.) the signs of the zodiac corresponded closely with the place of the sun among the constellations, a westward shift of the entire ecliptic since then has displaced the stars relative to the zodiac divisions to the positions in which we find them today.

## Apparent sun in the ecliptic

With the foregoing explanation of the ecliptic and its changing declination, it is not difficult to understand the cause of the apparent sun being fast twice a year and slow twice a year for reasons quite apart from varying orbital velocities. The explanation is suggested in Figure 3.10. In *A* we see the ecliptic path near the June solstice. If we assume a circular orbit, so that the sun would move around the ecliptic at a constant rate, it would move 1/365.24 of the circumference each day. For convenience let us call this 1°. Near the solstice, the sun will be as much as 23½° north of the equator, and the hour circles, which may be thought of as being 1° apart at the equator, will have converged so that they are separated by appreciably less than 1° of arc of a great circle. If, then, the sun is moving eastward 1° of arc per day along the ecliptic, which is a great circle, it will cover more than the spacing between the two hour circles, which are a

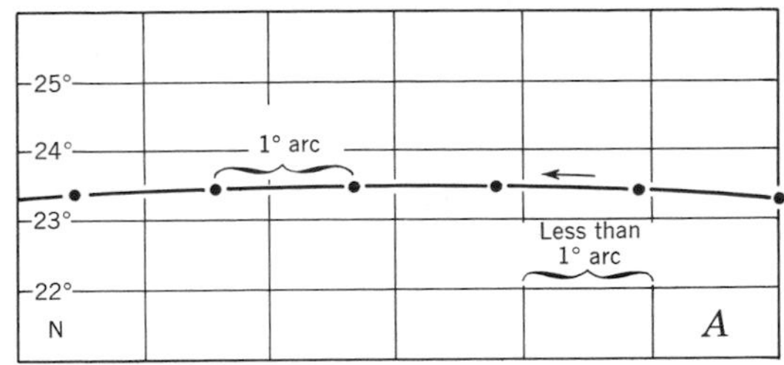


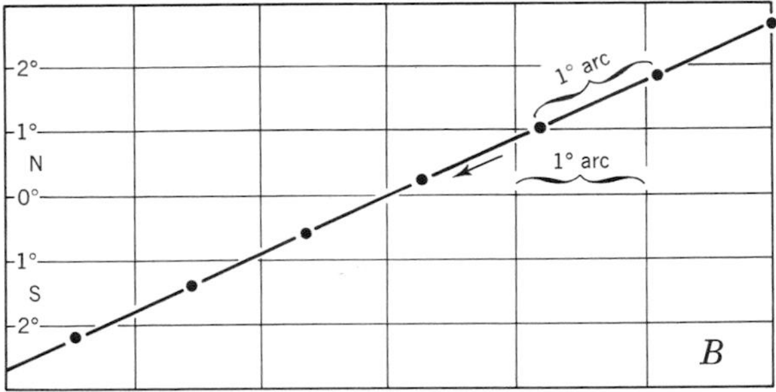


**FIGURE 3.10.** (*A*) Portion of the ecliptic near summer solstice. Daily positions of the sun are marked by dots. (*B*) Portion of the ecliptic near autumnal equinox. (The diagrams are not to correct scale.)

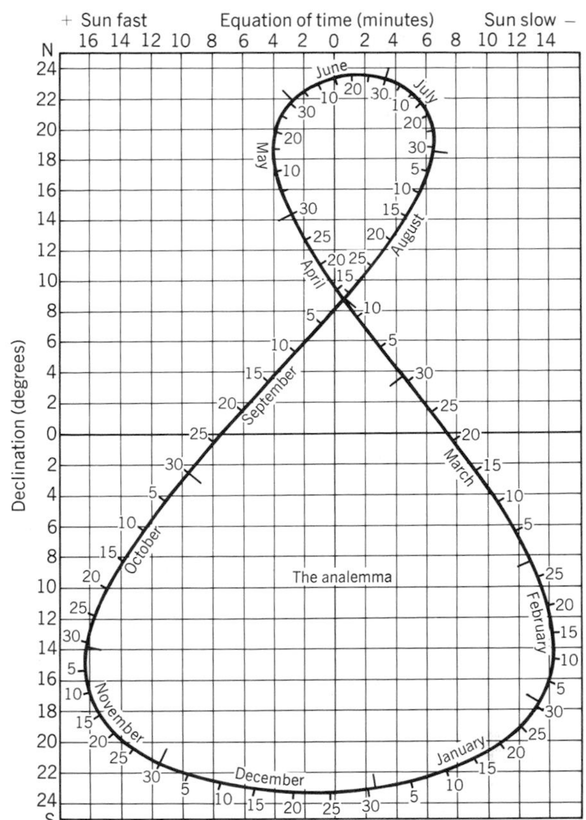


**FIGURE 3.11.** The analemma allows both the sun's declination and the equation of time to be estimated for any date in the year.

degree apart on the equator. Consequently the meridian passage of the sun is delayed slightly, the apparent solar day is longer, and the sun runs slow.

At the time of equinoxes, shown in Figure 3.10*B*, the ecliptic crosses the hour circles at a considerable angle, hence the daily segment of the sun's eastward shift along the ecliptic is shorter than the width of degrees of the hour circles. Here the mean sun will make its meridian passage slightly sooner than the imaginary mean sun, and the sun will therefore run fast. This effect is shown by the dotted line in Figure 3.5, which gives the cycle of variation of length of apparent solar day owing solely to the obliquity of the ecliptic.

To obtain the actual equation of time, the effects of both causes must be superimposed and the algebraic sum cumulated to yield the final graph of Figure 3.6.

## The Analemma

By means of a curiously shaped graph, the *analemma,* it is possible to show simultaneously both the equation of time and the sun's declination for any calendar day of the year (Figure 3.11). Equation of time is scaled to the right (slow) and left (fast) of a vertical center line of zero value; declination is scaled upward (north) and downward (south) from a horizontal line of zero declination. After a desired date has been located on the figure-eight loop, it is a simple matter to read the equation of time to the nearest half-minute and the declination to the nearest half-degree.

A small analemma is often printed on globes, commonly in the eastern Pacific Ocean where little or no land occurs. The line of zero declination lies on the earth's equator, and the declination scale is true in comparison with degrees of latitude on the globe. Usually such analemmas are more decorative than useful because of their small size and the lack of scales.

A rough natural analemma can be plotted in the following way: On the south side of the house, select a window which will receive the noon sun throughout the year. A small area of window pane may be darkened by painting it black or by covering it with an opaque board or fabric. A tiny hole is then made to admit a narrow beam of sunlight, which will cast a spot of light on the floor of the room when the sun is within half an hour or so before and after noon by local time. Daily at noon, as indicated by an accurate clock or radio time signals, the position of the spot of sunlight is marked on the floor and the calendar date noted beside it. When a year has elapsed, the set of points will have described an analemma. That part of the loop having the greatest north declination (June 21) will lie closest to the window. An interesting refinement of this experiment is to use a small mirror glued to the window sill so as to reflect a spot of light upon the ceiling. The analemma can then be plotted on a sheet of cardboard fastened to the ceiling.

The carefully constructed analemma, such as that in Figure 3.11, is reasonably accurate only for every fourth calendar year following the year for which the data were plotted. This is because the normal calendar year of 365 days is about a quarter of a day shorter than the tropical year. Each year for three normal years the entire loop will be shifted in a retrograde manner by a quarter of a day until, on the fourth or leap year, a 29th day is added in February and the loop is restored to the position it held 4 years previously.

The equation of time and declination of sun are also available in published form in various almanacs, including the *Air Almanac,* the *Nautical Almanac,* and the *American Ephemeris and Nautical Almanac. The Observer's Handbook*[2] gives data to the nearest second of time and one-tenth second of arc. A popular and widely available publication, *The Old Farmer's Almanac,*[3] gives the equation of time and sun's declination to the nearest minute for every day of the year.

## Longitude and time

For the study of global time relations it is useful to adopt the Ptolemaic viewpoint and consider that the sun revolves about the earth once every 24 hours of mean solar time. Thus there will be continuously present on the globe a westward-traveling meridian, termed here the *noon meridian of time,* representing the line on which the sun's rays strike the earth most nearly perpendicularly. All earthly points at the moment they are located under the traveling noon meridian will be experiencing the instant of solar noon, or the meridian passage of the sun. This event always occurs simultaneously along a single meridian, regardless of season, and solar noon can always be found on some meridian of the globe. The noon meridian travels westward around the earth at a uniform rate of 1° of longitude for each 4 minutes of time, or 15° of longitude per hour (mean solar time). Thus if the noon meridian is known to reach a given point 5 hours after crossing the meridian of Greenwich, we know that the point lies at long. 75° W.

Imagine now a second meridian of time lying opposite the noon meridian and separated from it by 180° of longitude. The second meridian represents the instant of midnight and may be referred to simply as the *midnight meridian,* or *antimeridian.* The two meridians will, of course, together constitute a great circle passing through the poles. To complete the time reference system, imagine that there are 22 more meridians to occupy the entire globe, spaced 15° of longitude apart (Figure 3.12). These can be called *hour circles,* because they are analogous to the hour circles of the celestial sphere.[4]

This system of 22 hour circles and two meridians travels unceasingly westward at a uniform rate of 15° of longitude per hour around the globe, pivoting on the North and South Poles. Each hour circle can be numbered with the hour of the day which it represents (Figure 3.12).

A simple working model of the hour-circle system can be constructed to use with a small globe. A cardboard girdle is cut to fit around the earth's equator and the hours marked appropriately. Also useful as a global time calculator is the device shown in Figure 3.13. Find a polar map based on an azimuthal projection (see

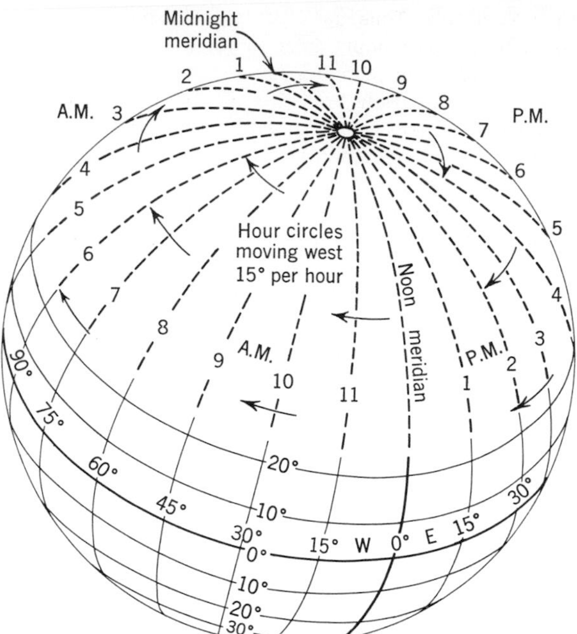


**FIGURE 3.12.** Meridians spaced 15° apart serve as hour circles on a globe. (©1960, John Wiley & Sons, New York.)

Appendix I), paste it on stiff card, and trim it to a circular outline. On a second, larger disk mark the hour circles and the noon and midnight meridians. Attach the map disk to the larger disk with a pin at the North Pole. The map may now be rotated so that any selected meridian coincides with a given hour circle; the hours for all other global meridians are read directly.

From Figure 3.13 we see that when it is noon on the Greenwich meridian (long. 0°), it is 7 A.M. on the 75th meridian west, which is the approximate longitude of

**FIGURE 3.13.** A world map on a polar projection can be adapted into a working model of global time zones. (© 1960, John Wiley & Sons, New York.)

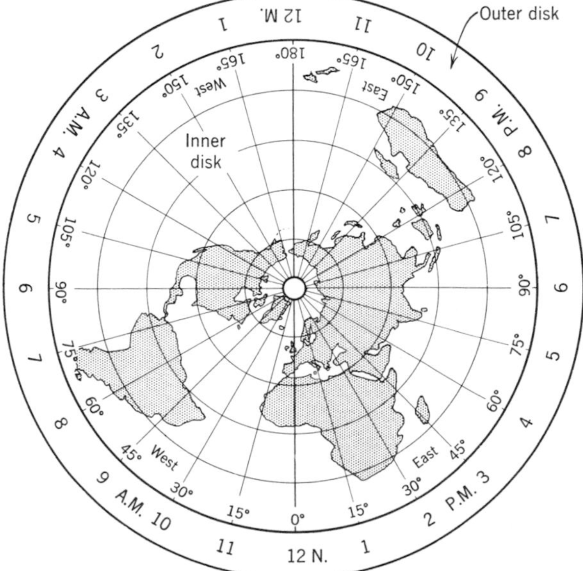


[2] Published annually by The Royal Astronomical Society of Canada, Toronto.
[3] Published annually by Yankee, Inc., Dublin, N.H.
[4] Hour circles of the celestial sphere represent sidereal hours, whereas the terrestrial hour circles imagined here represent hours of mean solar time.

New York City. Thus the rule: places that lie east of you have a later hour, those that lie west of you an earlier hour. We can reason that when the noon meridian is over New York City, the meridian required 5 hours to travel from London to New York, therefore that it is 5 P.M. in London. Similarly, we reason that the noon meridian will require 3 hours more to travel westward to San Francisco (120° W.), hence that it is only 9 A.M. in that city.

**Local mean time** *Local mean time* of a place is the system of mean solar time based upon the meridian of longitude passing through that place. In practice the local time of a city would be reckoned on the basis of the exact longitude of a key point of reference near the center of the city. Such a point might be in a central building, such as the city hall, a historical monument, or a cathedral. The difference in time between this meridian and the Greenwich meridian is calculated, so that the exact time of meridian passage of the mean sun over the local time meridian is known. All clocks of the city are then set to read 12:00 to coincide with the time of local noon.

Local time is precisely the same for all places lying on the same meridian of longitude, regardless of the north-south distance of separation, because meridian passage of the sun takes place simultaneously at all points along a terrestrial meridian. For example, Manchester, New Hampshire, and Valparaiso, Chile, would have almost identical local times because both lie almost on long. 71°30′ W.; yet these cities are separated by 76° of latitude, equivalent to about 5200 mi (8400 km). But the local times of Manchester and Portsmouth, separated in distance by less than 40 mi (64 km), differ by 2⅔ minutes (40′ of longitude).

**Standard time** Before the mid-nineteenth century the use of local time was not a source of trouble in human affairs. The fastest forms of communication were sufficiently slow that the traveler could easily reset his watch to the local time of each town or city he visited. He could gain or lose only a few minutes' time in a day's travel. With the introduction of the telegraph, about 1845, as a means of instantaneous communication between cities, differences in local time were immediately felt.

The problems arising from uses of local time systems are solved by adopting a system of *standard time.* First, a *standard meridian* is selected, usually a multiple of 15°, so as to differ from the time of the Greenwich meridian by multiples of whole hours. Then the local time of the standard meridian is applied to a zone extending on either side of the standard meridian to some convenient boundaries.

Although an ideal system would have zones extending exactly 7½° to either side of the standard meridian, and this practice is followed at sea, the actual boundaries on land are determined by more important economic and political considerations. It is preferable to have the boundary fall along a clearly marked physiographic feature, such as a major drainage divide in mountainous terrain where few people live, or along a state boundary which is clearly posted and already provides governmental separation.

**Daylight saving time and war time** From the standpoint of human activities the standard time system can be improved by a shift in the standard meridian by 15°, or even 30°, to the east so as to delay the occurrence of sunset by 1 or 2 hours and thus provide additional daylight at a time when most persons are awake and active. Particularly in summer, when the span of daylight in the middle latitudes is 14–16 hours, the hour or two of good daylight normally occurring before 6 A.M. (local time), when few persons need it, can well be displaced to the evening, when it is useful to the vast majority and will result in substantial savings in electric power.

The eastward displacement of the standard-time meridian by 15° gives *daylight saving time,* or, as it is termed in England and the European continent, *summer time.* Standard time is advanced by 1 hour throughout the entire year in Great Britain, Ireland, Spain, France, the Netherlands, Belgium, and the U.S.S.R.

**World time zones** The need for a global system of standard time for commercial and scientific purposes led to an international congress, held in Washington, D.C., in 1884, and resulted ultimately in the adoption of a global system of time zones based on standard time meridians spaced at intervals of 15° eastward and westward from the meridian of Greenwich. All times are referred to Greenwich mean time, which is mean solar time (UT) based on the Greenwich meridian. Time zones are designated by the whole number of hours by which the time of the zone differs from Greenwich time. To distinguish whether the time zone lies in the Eastern or Western Hemisphere, the time is described as *fast* for all places having east longitude and *slow* for all places having west longitude. According to this system, Eastern Standard Time of the United States, based on the 75th meridian west, is described as "5 hours slow."

World time zones are shown in Figure 3.14, a map on which standard meridians are indicated by dashed lines, zone boundaries by heavy lines. Numbers give the relation of zone time to Greenwich mean time. Several provincial units and nations find it desirable, because of the distribution of their area, to use a standard meridian which is a multiple of 7½°, giving a standard time which differs by half an hour from standard zones on either side. Thus India uses the time 5½ hours fast; Newfoundland, 3½ hours slow.

For North America, the following standard time zones are currently in use:

| Zone Name | Standard Meridian, W. long. | Hours Slow |
|---|---|---|
| Greenland | 45 | 3 |
| Newfoundland | 52½ | 3½ |
| Atlantic | 60 | 4 |
| Eastern | 75 | 5 |
| Central | 90 | 6 |
| Mountain | 105 | 7 |
| Pacific | 120 | 8 |
| Yukon | 135 | 9 |
| Alaska, Hawaii | 150 | 10 |
| Bering | 165 | 11 |

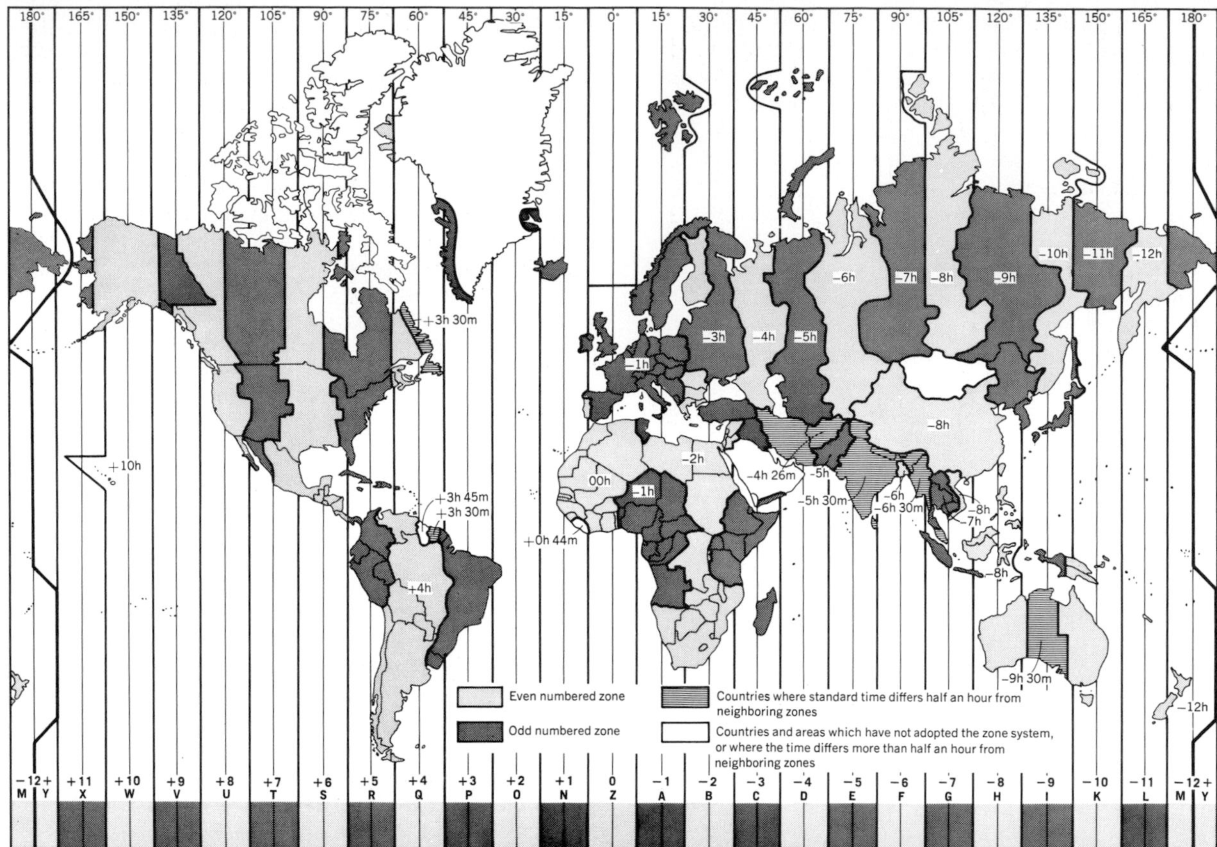


**FIGURE 3.14.** World time zones. (Data from U.S. Navy Oceanographic Office Chart No. 5192.)

A few smaller countries have odd standard times based on local meridians of convenience. Thus in 1970 Liberia operated on a time $44^{m}30^{s}$ fast, Afghanistan on a time $4^{h}26^{m}$ fast. Because changes occur now and then, it is well to consult an authoritative and up-to-date source, such as the *Air Almanac,* for the standard times of various countries.

It is interesting to note that the U.S.S.R. has the greatest number of time zones—eleven in all—and that all are advanced by 1 hour from the meridians on which they are based.

**Expressing time by a standard notation** The layman's practice of dividing the civil day into two 12-hour periods—A.M. (*ante meridian*) and P.M. (*post meridian*)—makes notation difficult and incurs the risk of confusing the A.M. and P.M. The purposes of science, navigation, and military regimen are better served by counting the hours of civil days continuously from 0 to 24. The minutes are added without separation to produce a four-digit number. Thus in the civil day *0930 hours* means 9:30 A.M.; *1409 hours* means 2:09 P.M.; and *2300 hours* means 11:00 P.M. Certain types of clocks and special watches used in astronomy and navigation are made with a 24-hour dial (Figure 3.15).

Although it is a simple matter to apply the four-digit 24-hour system of stating the hours and minutes of the day to any standard time zone of the globe, it has long been a practice of astronomers and earth scientists to use the time of the Greenwich meridian as the standard for recording their data. Thus civil time based on the Greenwich meridian and running on mean solar time is termed Greenwich mean time (GMT). As already explained, the need to take into account the changing period of earth rotation has led to the use of UT, the mean solar time stated in terms of the year to which it applies. In effect, then, UT is identical with GMT except for specification of the year. It is common practice in scientific writing to designate this time standard by simply affixing the letters UT (universal time) to the stated hours.

Research activities of the International Geophysical Year (1957–1958) and in subsequent years have been based on a plan of simultaneous observations of physical phenomena of the upper atmosphere, outer space, or the sun. All such data involving time are stated in GMT or UT. Much of this research goes on in polar regions. Here the meridians of longitude are close together, and it is impractical to maintain reference to standard time zones. Moreover, the long periods of continuous daylight or darkness at the high latitudes offer no sharply defined equivalents of sunrise, noon, and sunset, as we are familiar with in the middle and low latitudes. The use of GMT at high latitudes is therefore

FIGURE 3.15. This chronometer for air navigation use has a 24-hour dial. (Courtesy of the Hamilton Watch Company.)

dictated by the unique characteristics of the polar regions.

**The International Date Line** Using the world time-zone map (Figure 3.14), we can count the time zones in an eastward direction from the Greenwich meridian and shall find that the 180th meridian has the time *12ʰ fast.* A similar count westward around the world would result in the 180th meridian being designated as *12ʰ slow.* Which is the correct result? The answer is obvious when we note that the time differences in the two results total 24 hours, or a full day. When the noon meridian of time coincides with the Greenwich meridian, the midnight meridian will coincide with the 180th meridian. At that precise instant the same calendar day exists on both sides of the 180th meridian. The 24-hour discrepancy represents the difference in time between the beginning and ending of the same calendar day, which at that instant coincides with the 180th meridian. But the midnight meridian is moving steadily westward, toward Asia, and there follows between it and the 180th meridian a widening zone having the succeeding calendar day. The calendar day on the western (Asiatic) side of the 180th meridian is therefore newer than the calendar day lying on the eastern (American) side. If it is Tuesday on the Asiatic side, it is Monday on the American side.

When a traveler crosses the Pacific Ocean, it is necessary that near the 180th meridian the calendar be set ahead or dropped back by one full day. Thus when one is traveling westward (toward Asia), Monday changes to Tuesday, when traveling eastward (toward the Americas) Monday becomes Sunday.

It is interesting that after circumnavigating the globe in a westward direction Magellan's crew arrived in Spain to discover that the date there was September 8, 1522, whereas by their reckoning it was only September 7. They had neglected to skip a day to allow for westward travel across the 180th meridian.

Because of its remarkable properties as the line along which one day disappears and the next emerges, the 180th meridian was named the *International Date Line* at the International Meridian Conference, meeting in Washington, D.C., in 1884. Luckily for mankind, the date line falls in the mid-Pacific where little or no land lies on the meridian, for the Royal Observatory at Greenwich, England, had long been established as the prime meridian for the geographic grid as well as for navigation. In retrospect a prime meridian a few degrees farther east would have been better, allowing the date line to pass through the Bering Strait at long. 169° W. Oslo, Norway (10°41′ E.) would have been an ideal choice, in this respect, to determine the location of the prime meridian. Figure 3.16 shows the deviations of the International Date Line from the 180th meridian, required to run the line between Alaska and Siberia, to include the Aleutian Islands on the American side, and to circumvent certain island groups of the South Pacific.

**Duration of calendar days on the globe** Although the calendar day lasts for 24 hours of mean solar time with respect to any observer remaining fixed at one point on the globe, the total duration of the calendar day on a global basis is twice this long, or 48 hours. The International Date Line may be thought of as a strange kind of slot in the earth's surface, from whence the calendar days mysteriously emerge to spread westward around the globe and into which they mysteriously disappear

FIGURE 3.16. The International Date Line. (Data from U.S. Navy Oceanographic Office Chart No. 5192.)

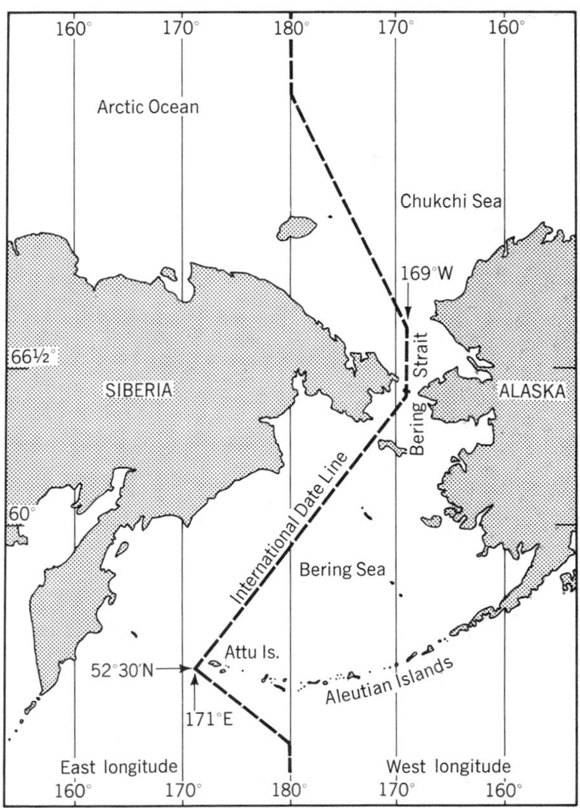

when arrived at from the east. Now, it takes 24 hours for the day to spread over the globe and to envelop it completely. An additional 24 hours is required for the same day to make its disappearance. The total duration of the day must therefore be 48 hours.

An even more curious phenomenon results from the deviations of the date line eastward to pass through the Bering Strait and westward to pass around the Aleutian Islands (Figure 3.16). On the basis of local mean time the new calendar day actually begins in the Bering Strait at long. 169° W., which is 11° east of the 180th meridian and gives the day a head start of $44^m$. Thus, when the midnight meridian reaches the Greenwich meridian, the day has already endured $12^h44^m$. Upon reaching the 180th meridian again, the same calendar day continues across the triangular zone between that meridian and the International Date Line in the region of the westernmost Aleutian Islands, to disappear just west of Attu Island at long. 171°E. The added longitude here is 9°, equivalent to $36^m$ of time added to the day. Altogether, then, the calendar day exists through $49^h20^m$.

As if this strange state of affairs were not enough, it follows from the data above that it is possible for three calendar days to coexist on the globe between 1116 hours and 1236 hours GMT. For example, Tuesday will begin at 1116 hours in the Bering Strait while Monday still covers most of the globe and Sunday is almost gone. But Sunday will not disappear until 1236 hours, so that the coexistence of three days lasts for $1^h20^m$.

## References for further study

Hosmer, G. L. (1948), *Practical Astronomy,* New York, Wiley, 355 pp., chap. 5.

Fairbridge, R. W., ed. (1967), *Encyclopedia of Atmospheric Sciences and Astrogeology,* New York, Reinhold, 1200 pp. (See Chronometry, Time and Astronomic Cycles, Nutation.)

Markowitz, Wm., "Time Measurement," *The Encyclopedia Britannica.* (See latest edition.)

Royal Astronomical Soc. of Canada, *The Observer's Handbook,* Toronto, Canada, issued annually.

U.S. Naval Observatory, *The Air Almanac,* Washington, D.C., U.S. Govt. Printing Office, issued annually.

# Planet Earth in the sun's rays

NO ASTRONOMICAL PHENOMENON is more important to Man than the relation of the earth to the sun's rays. From the sun comes virtually all energy to sustain life processes, to power the circulation of the atmosphere and oceans, and to generate the geologic processes of erosion and transportation which shape the landscape. Variations in the angle at which the sun's rays strike the spherical surface of the earth as it rotates upon its axis and revolves in its orbit result in continually changing imbalances of incoming and outgoing radiant energy. Because of the inclination of the earth's axis, the sun's declination shifts yearly from north to south, bringing the seasons with their different lengths of periods of daylight and darkness.

The general problem of describing the relation of the sun's rays to the earth's surface at various latitudes, hours of the day, and dates of the year is one of solid geometry. Two points of view can be taken: the heliocentric view, in which we imagine ourselves to see the earth from a great distance, as if from outside the solar system; and the geocentric view, in which we, as tiny earth-bound creatures, see the path of the sun in a celestial sphere that arches over our apparently flat earth as a hemispherical dome.

The student of the earth sciences will need to familiarize himself with both viewpoints to be able to visualize on demand the angle of incidence of the sun's rays and the apparent path of the sun in the sky for any latitude and season. In our modern age he may find himself carried within a few hours to a remote and unfamiliar spot on the globe. Can he anticipate the sun's path, the duration of daylight and darkness, the duration of twilight, the compass directions of sunrise and sunset?

## The circle of illumination

At all times the earth's surface lies half in the sun's rays, half in shadow. A great circle,[1] the *circle of illumination,* marks the dividing line between the sunlit hemisphere and the darkened hemisphere (Figure 4.1). From the rule that any two great circles bisect each other, it follows that the circle of illumination and the earth's equator bisect each other. This is an important fact to keep in mind and will be referred to again. It should also be noted that the plane of the circle of illumination, which at all times lies at right angles to the sun's rays, is always perpendicular to the plane of the ecliptic.

Because of the inclination of the earth's axis at an angle of 66½° with respect to the plane of the ecliptic and because of the constancy of the orientation of the axis in space throughout the orbit, the circle of illumination on two dates of the year (the vernal and autumnal equinoxes) passes through the poles, while on two other dates (summer and winter solstices) the circle of illumination is tangent to the parallels of lat. 66½° N. and S. (Figure 4.1). These two parallels are known respectively as the *Arctic Circle* and *Antarctic Circle* (see Figure 4.6). It will be obvious from a study of Figures 4.1, 4.5, and 4.6 that at winter solstice the portion of earth's surface lying within the Arctic Circle remains on the darkened side of the circle of illumination despite the earth's rotation, whereas at summer solstice this same area of the globe is continuously exposed to the rays of the sun. At dates intermediate between equinox and solstice the circle of illumination will be tangent to some parallel of latitude between the Arctic Circle and the North Pole and between the Antarctic Circle and the South Pole.

[1] In this chapter the earth is treated as a true sphere; its oblateness is neglected.

Once the relations of the circle of illumination to the North Pole and the Arctic Circle are visualized at solstice and equinox, most of the details of illumination of the globe will be understandable.

## Solstice and equinox

As explained in Chapter 3, the equinoxes and solstices can be described as points on the ecliptic circle of the celestial sphere occupied by the sun when its declination is either zero (the equinoxes) or at the maximum value of 23½° N. or S. (the solstices). The equinoxes and solstices may also be defined as points in the earth's orbit (Figure 4.2). The major axis of the elliptical orbit defines the points of perihelion and aphelion, with the sun located at one focus. If a straight line is drawn from vernal equinox to autumnal equinox, as in Figure 4.2, the line will pass through the sun. Similarly a line connecting solstices will pass through the sun. Moreover these two straight lines will intersect at right angles.

The critical dates are: vernal equinox, March 20 or 21; summer solstice, June 21 or 22; autumnal equinox, September 22 or 23; winter solstice, December 21 or 22.

**FIGURE 4.1.** Orientation of the earth's axis remains fixed in space as the earth revolves about the sun, producing the seasons.

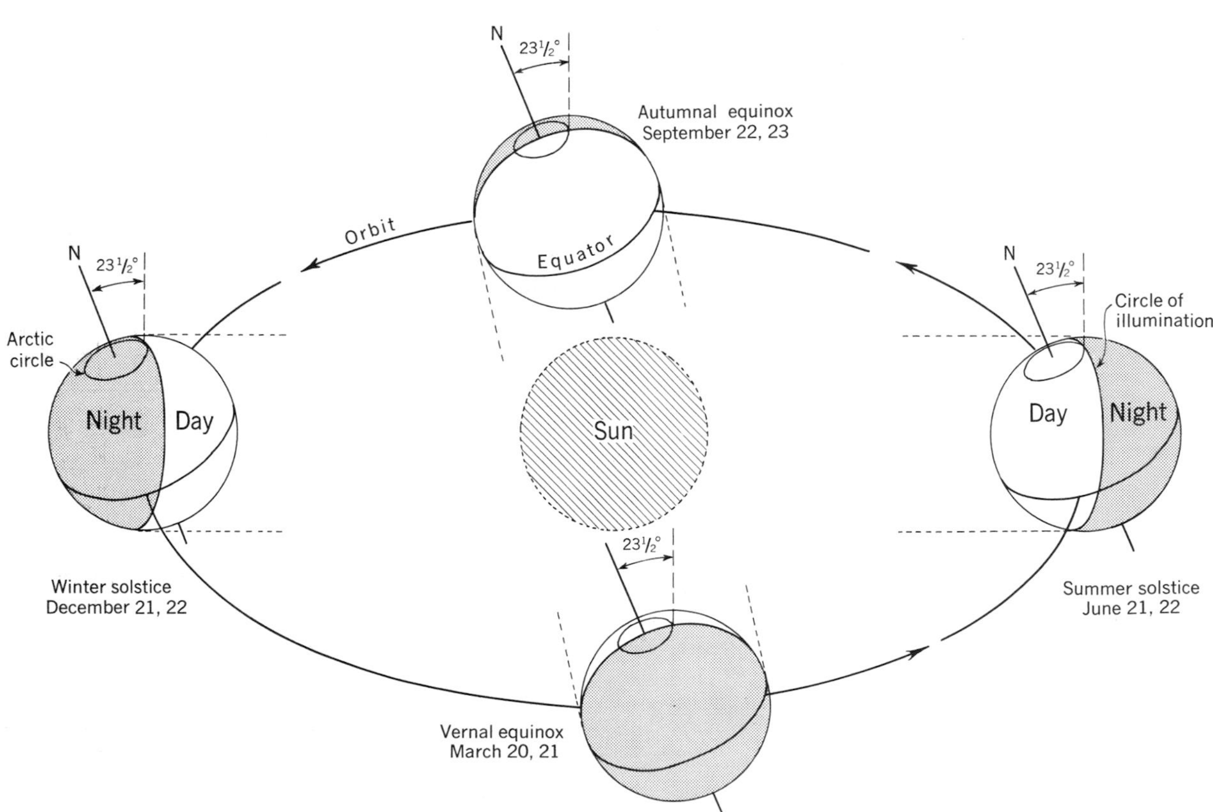

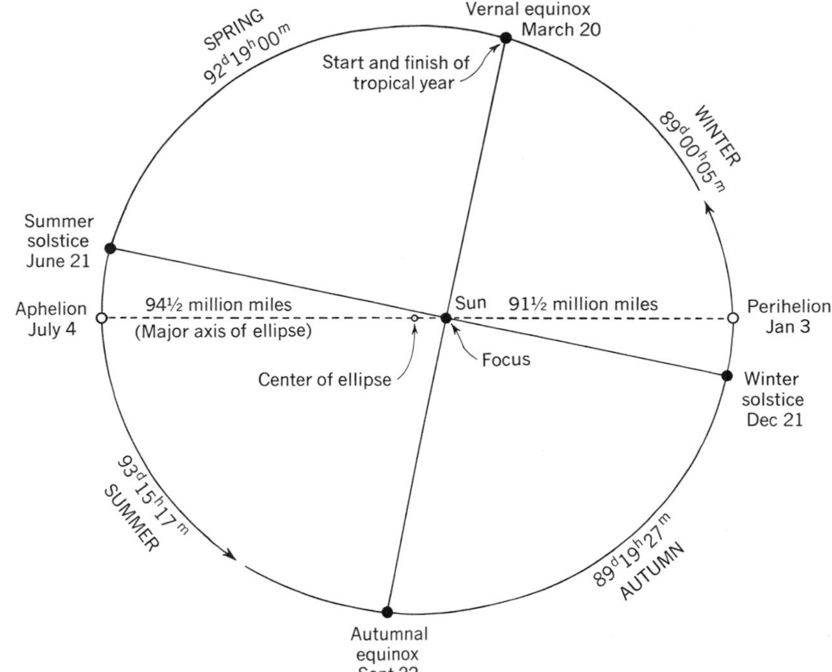


**FIGURE 4.2.** Dates of equinox and solstice; duration of seasons. Figures in this diagram correspond with those of Table 4.1.

The reason for giving alternate calendar dates for each is that the actual instant at which the earth is in a given equinox or solstice point ranges through 2 days because the tropical year is about a quarter of a day longer than a normal calendar year (Chapter 1). Thus vernal equinox occurs $05^h48^m46^s$ later each year for 3 years, bringing it from March 20 into March 21, after which the added day in leap year restores the equinox to March 20. In Table 4.1 are given specific examples

**TABLE 4.1. EQUINOXES AND SOLSTICES, 1960–1961**

| | Date | Hour (EST) | Interval of Elapsed Time |
|---|---|---|---|
| Vernal equinox | Mar. 20, 1960 | 0943 | |
| Summer solstice | Jun. 21, 1960 | 0443 | $92^d19^h00^m$ |
| Autumnal equinox | Sept. 22, 1960 | 2000 | $93^d15^h17^m$ |
| Winter solstice | Mar. 20, 1961 | 1532 | $89^d19^h27^m$ |
| Vernal equinox | Dec. 21, 1960 | 1527 | $89^d00^h05^m$ |
| | Total tropical year | | $365^d05^h49^m$ |

for the tropical year 1960–1961, from which it can be calculated that in 1960, 1961, and 1962 vernal equinox falls on March 20, whereas in 1963 it moves into March 21; leap year 1964 restores it to March 20.

From Table 4.1, we see that the time intervals elapsing between one equinox and the next solstice, etc., are not the same.[2] If the earth's orbit were a perfect circle, the tropical year would be divided into four equal parts, each of about $91^d07^h27^m12\frac{1}{5}^s$. Referring again to Figure 4.2, in which the orbit is shown as an ellipse, it is obvious that the orbit is unequally divided by the line connecting the equinoxes, so that the longer part of the orbit falls in the spring-summer half of the year. Not only does the earth have there a greater length of orbit to negotiate, but it travels more slowly in the region of aphelion than in the region of perihelion. Elapsed times for the four quarters reflect this effect quite nicely. The quarter from winter solstice to vernal equinox is the shortest of all, 89 days, because this quarter contains perihelion and the average orbital velocity of earth is greatest. The longest quarter, over 93½ days, is from summer solstice to autumnal equinox, because this period contains aphelion and hence the lowest average earth velocity.

[2] From one year to the next intervals of elapsed time will differ by several minutes from the 1960–1961 values shown in Table 4.1.

## The equinoxes

Conditions on the dates of equinoxes can be analyzed by means of a meridional cross section of the earth (Figure 4.3). The earth's axis in this diagram appears to have no inclination; this is because the observer is imagined to have his eye in the plane of the equator so that his line of sight is inclined 23½° from the plane of the ecliptic. The sun's rays can be drawn as parallel lines tangent to the poles. The circle of illumination on this date passes through the poles and therefore coincides with the terrestrial meridians as the earth rotates.

Along a meridian coinciding with the illumination circle in one hemisphere, the sunrise is occurring for all points on the meridian; whereas the opposing meridian, 180° distant, is experiencing sunset. Solar noon in Figure 4.3 is occurring along the terrestrial meridian that at any given moment coincides with the right-hand edge of the earth's cross section; midnight

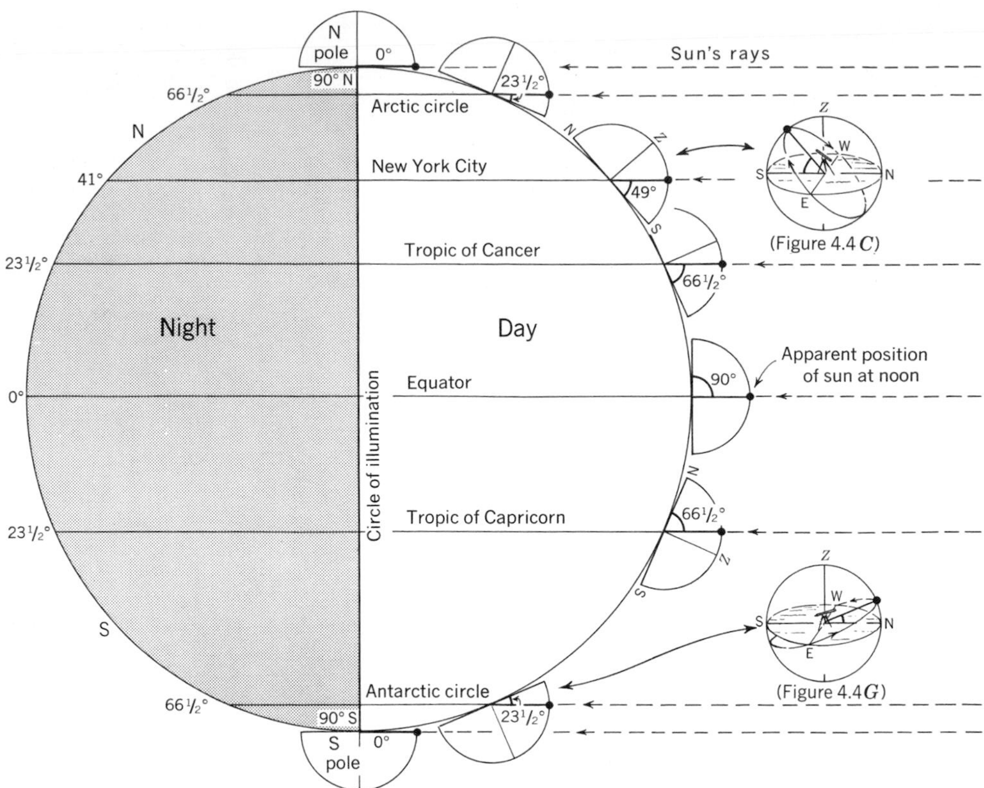


**FIGURE 4.3.** Altitude of the noon sun at equinox.

is represented by the left-hand edge. At each of several latitudes in Figure 4.3 a short segment of straight line has been drawn tangent to the globe to represent the horizon planes of observers at each point. The angle between the sun's rays and the tangent horizon plane is therefore the *altitude of the noon sun,* its angular distance above the horizon measured along the celestial meridian (Chapter 1).

In Figure 4.3 we see that at the equator the sun's noon altitude is 90°, meaning that the noon sun occupies the zenith position. To see how this actually looks to a person at the equator, refer to Figure 4.4*E,* one of a series of perspective drawings showing the horizon circle and celestial meridian according to the horizon system explained in Chapter 1. In each of these drawings the sun's apparent path in the sky is shown for the equinox date by a heavy line labeled "equinox." Note that at the equator the sun at equinox rises exactly in the east, follows a path perpendicular to the horizon plane, reaches zenith at noon, then descends to sunset at a point due west.

Next, consider equinox conditions at the North Pole, lat. 90° N. From Figure 4.3 it is evident that the sun at noon is exactly on the horizon and that it must keep this position throughout the day as the earth rotates. In Figure 4.4*A* we see how this path would appear to an observer at the North Pole. The sun circles the horizon in a clockwise direction, completing one circle of 360° each 24 hours of mean solar time, at the rate of 15° of directional change per hour.

At lat. 41° N., the position of New York City, the altitude of the noon sun at equinox is 49° (Figure 4.3). The sun's apparent path in the sky, shown in Figure 4.4*C,* is in a slanting plane making an angle of 49° with the horizon plane. Note, however, that the sun rises at a point due east and sets at a point due west and that this statement applies at equinox to all other latitudes except the two poles.

From geometrical relations between latitude and the sun's altitude shown in Figure 4.3, the following rule applies to the equinoxes: The altitude of the noon sun on the equinox date is equal to the *colatitude,* equivalent to 90° minus the latitude. For points having the same latitude in the Northern and Southern Hemispheres, the noon altitude is the same, except that it is measured above the south horizon point in the Northern Hemisphere and above the north horizon point in the Southern Hemisphere.

At equinox the circle of illumination exactly divides all parallels of latitude into halves. This means that any point on the rotating earth except the poles will lie for 12 hours on the sunlit side of the globe and for 12 hours on the darkened side, hence that day and night are of equal length—12 hours each—over the entire globe. (For convenience the word "day" is used here to mean the period of time in which the sun is above the horizon.) For all latitudes except the poles, sunrise will occur at 6:00 A.M. (local apparent solar time) and will set at 6:00 P.M.[3] We see now how appropriate is the word equinox,

[3] This statement neglects the effect of atmospheric refraction and such relief features as may increase the height of the horizon.

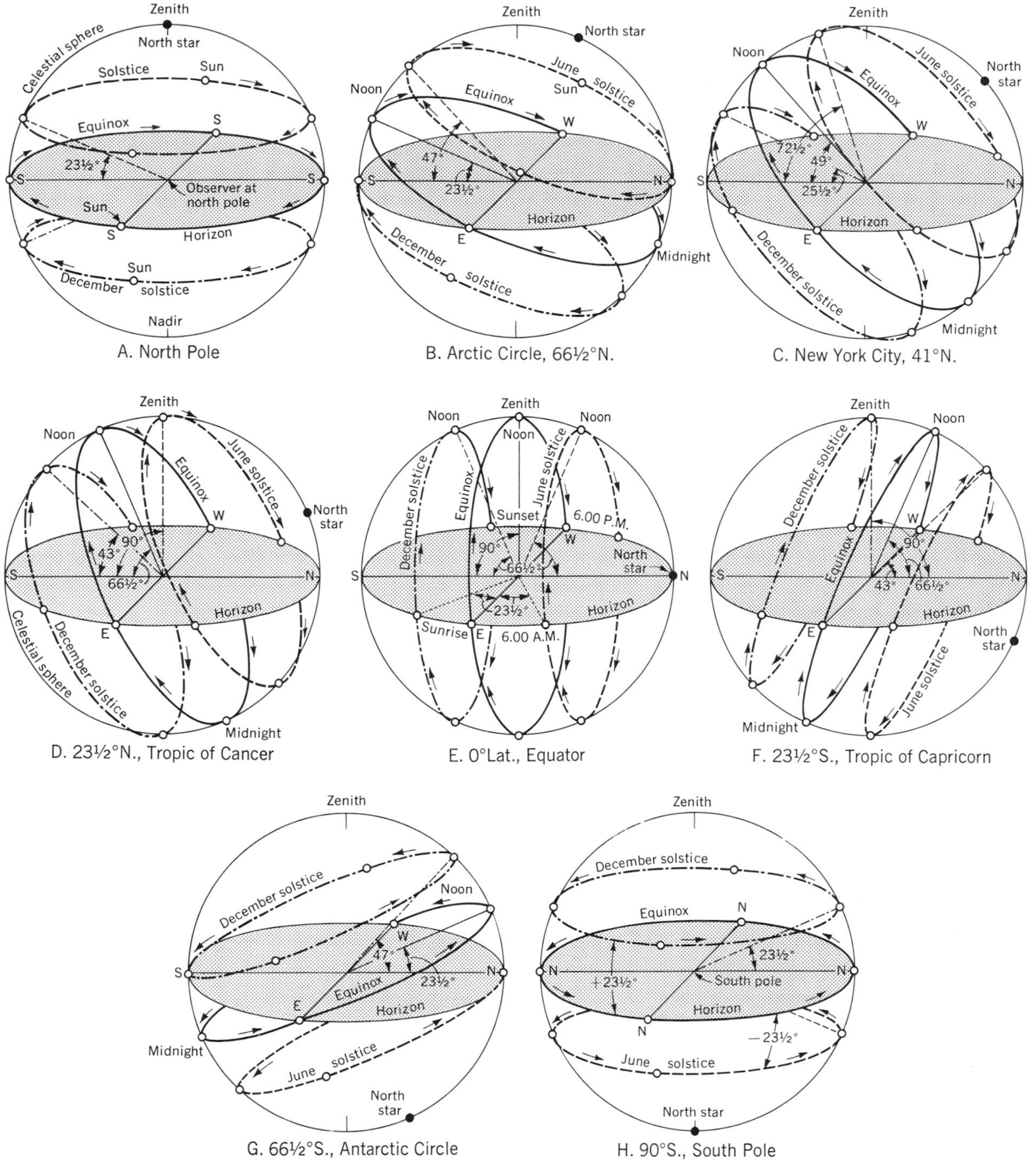

**FIGURE 4.4.** Apparent path of the sun in the sky at the equinoxes and solstices for eight latitudes on the globe.

for it comes from the Latin words *aequus,* equal, and *nox,* night.

## Winter solstice

At winter solstice, December 22 or 23, the north polar end of the earth's axis is inclined the full 23½° away from the sun (Figures 4.5 and 4.6). Our view point in Figure 4.6 is from the plane of the ecliptic opposed to the direction of the earth's orbital motion, with the sun to the right. The circle of illumination is tangent to the Arctic and Antarctic Circles, 66½° N. and S. respectively, but still bisects the equator. For the earth-bound observer, the sun's path in the sky at winter solstice is shown in Figure 4.4 by a series of circular paths labeled "December solstice."

Strikingly different from equinox conditions is the

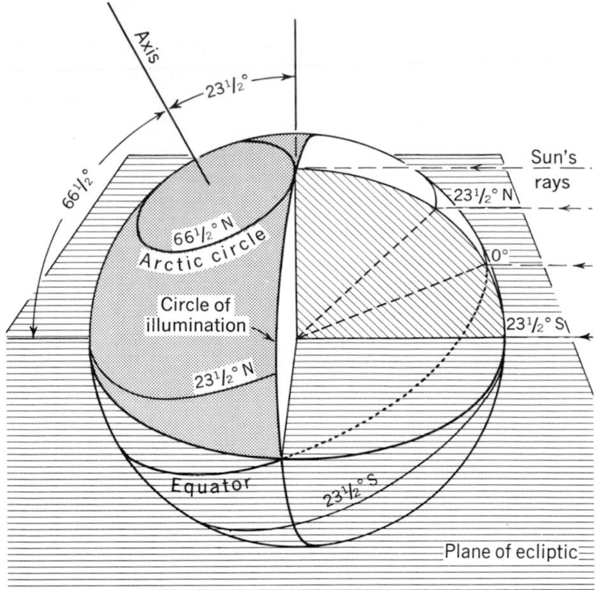


**FIGURE 4.5.** At winter solstice the sun's rays at noon are perpendicular at lat. 23½° S., the Tropic of Capricorn. All the region lying poleward of the Arctic Circle experiences night for the full 24 hours.

manner in which the circle of illumination cuts the parallels of latitude into unequal parts (Figure 4.6). From this inequality it follows that the lengths of day and night will be unequal, except at the equator, and that the disparity increases from the equator poleward until, beyond the Arctic and Antarctic Circles, the day or night will last the full 24 hours. In Figure 4.4 the inequality of day and night is shown in a different way and can be judged by the proportions of the sun's path lying above and below the horizon circle.

Altitude of the noon sun at winter solstice is given in Figure 4.6 for various latitudes. At lat. 23½° S. the sun's noon rays strike the earth perpendicularly, with the sun in the zenith position. Consequently this parallel of latitude has a unique designation: the *Tropic of Capricorn.* The name comes from the constellation of Capricorn, with which in ancient times the sun coincided at the point of its southernmost declination in the ecliptic. Figure 4.4*F* shows the path of the sun at lat. 23½° S. Although the sun's apparent path reaches zenith at noon, the plane of its path is parallel with the plane at equinox, and both paths maintain a constant angle of 66½° with respect to the horizon circle.

Further examination of Figure 4.6 shows that the sun's noon altitude at the equator is 66½°; at lat. 41° N., 25½°; at 66½° N., 0°; at 66½° S., 47°; at the South Pole, 23½°. A study of these numerical relations would reveal that the following rule applies: The sun's noon altitude at a given place is equal to 90° minus the arc of meridian between that place and the parallel equivalent to the sun's declination. The rule applies equally well to any date of the year. We have only to ascertain the declination of the sun from the analemma or from an almanac and the latitude of the place from an atlas or gazetteer.

Of course, if both the sun's declination and the place are in the Northern Hemisphere, the meridian arc

**FIGURE 4.6.** Altitude of the noon sun at winter solstice.

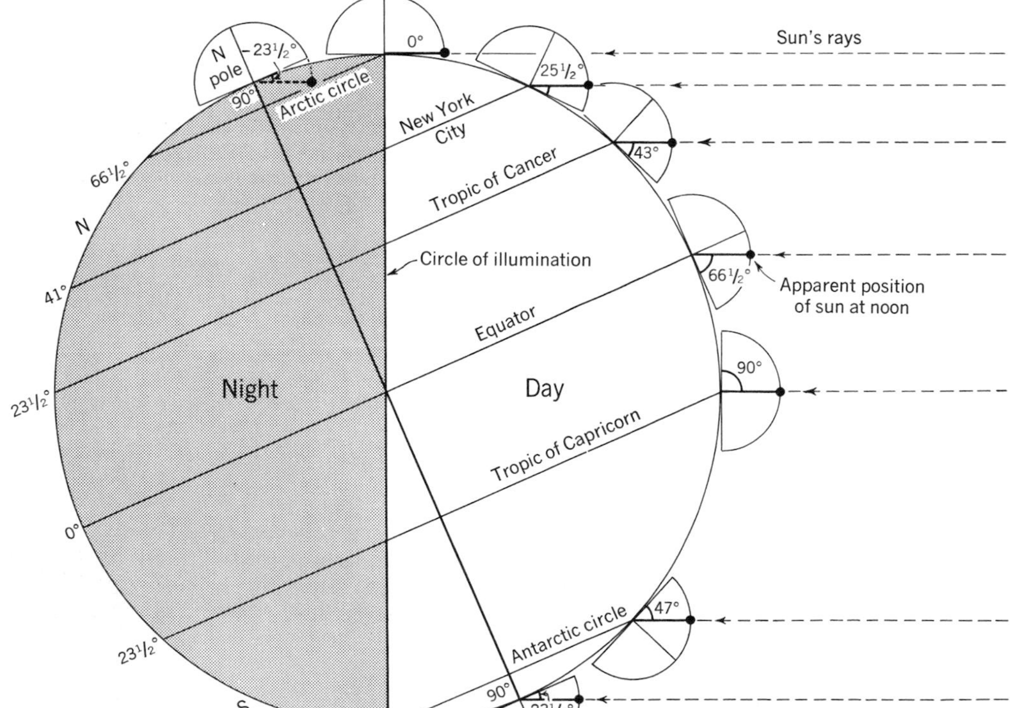

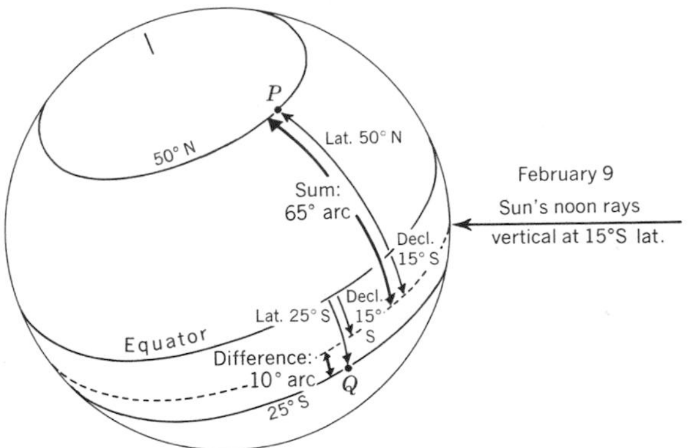


**FIGURE 4.7.** Calculation of sun's noon altitude from latitude and declination.

separating them is the difference in the two values; whereas, if declination is south and the place has a north latitude, the two numbers are added to give the meridian arc. For point *P* in Figure 4.7 the meridian arc is 65°, obtained by adding lat. 50° N. to 15° S. declination; hence the sun's noon altitude at *P* is 25°. For point *Q* at lat. 25° S., the meridian arc will be obtained by subtracting 15° S. declination, giving an arc of 10° and a sun's noon altitude of 80°.

Directions of sunrise and sunset at winter solstice are shown in Figure 4.4. For all latitudes between the Arctic and Antarctic Circles the sun will rise at a point between south and east and will set at a point between south and west. These directions shift southward as lat. 66½° is approached in both hemispheres.

Conditions at the Antarctic Circle on the date of winter solstice are remarkable in that the sun sets and rises simultaneously at the instant of midnight and is visible in the sky throughout the 24 hours (Figure 4.4*G*). At the South Pole on this date the sun's path circles the celestial sphere at a constant altitude of 23½° above the horizon without giving any indication of rising or setting (Figure 4.4*H*). Equally strange is the sun's path at the Arctic Circle (Figure 4.4*B*). Here the sun is below the horizon for the entire 24 hours, except that precisely at noon it reaches the horizon at a point due south; hence it may be said to rise and set at the same instant. As will be explained later, the sun is a disk of light, not a mere pinpoint of light, so that the above statements would need to be slightly modified to include the sun's disk being partially visible even when its center is below the horizon.

## Summer solstice

To study earth–sun relations at summer solstice, June 21 or 22, the same diagram in Figure 4.6 can be used by merely turning it upside down and changing "north" to read "south" and vice versa. The apparent path of the sun in the sky at various latitudes at summer solstice is shown in Figure 4.4 by dashed circles labeled "June solstice." All that has been said concerning winter-solstice conditions will apply if appropriate reversals are made in directions and hemispheres. An additional change will be to substitute *Tropic of Cancer* for Tropic of Capricorn, because at summer solstice the sun's declination is 23½° N. and its noon rays strike the earth perpendicularly on the Tropic of Cancer, lat. 23½° N.

By study of Figure 4.4 it is seen that the sun's noon altitude at summer solstice differs by just 47° from that at winter solstice. The three paths shown in each figure are always in parallel planes forming a constant angle with the horizon plane.

North of the Arctic Circle on the day of the summer solstice the sun remains above the horizon for the entire 24 hours, so that even at midnight it may be well above the horizon (Figure 4.8).

## Intermediate dates

How can the sun's path in the sky and its noon altitude be visualized for dates intermediate between equinox and solstice? This is not a difficult problem if one has in mind the relative rate at which declination changes. From a study of the ecliptic circle (Figure 3.8) or the analemma (Figure 3.11) it is clear that the sun's declina-

**FIGURE 4.8.** The midnight sun seen in late July from Sunrise Point in Smith Sound, near Etah, Greenland, about lat. 78° N. Eight exposures were taken at intervals of 20 minutes, four before and four after midnight. (Courtesy of the American Museum of Natural History.)

tion changes most rapidly near the time of the equinoxes, whereas close to the solstices the rate of change is very small. Our word "solstice" is derived from the Latin *sol,* sun, and *stare,* to stand, implying that the sun seems to stand still before reversing its declination. One month before or after the equinox, the sun is halfway from the equator to one of the Tropics. One month before or after the solstice it is seven-eights of the way from the equator to one of the Tropics. A simple table is useful for rough calculations:

| Declination Change per Month, degrees | Month |
|---|---|
| 11¾ | First month before and after equinox |
| 8½ | Second month before and after equinox |
| 3¼ | Months adjacent to solstices |

Using these figures, or the analemma (Figure 3.11), we can see that during the entire 37-day period from December 4 to January 9 the sun's noon altitude changes by only 1½°, whereas in an equivalent period between September 6 and October 12 the declination change is nearly 14°. This explains why the long nights of winter and the long days of summer seem to persist for so many weeks without noticeable change, whereas during early spring and early fall the lengths of day and night seem to change rapidly.

Changes in declination give the sun's path at the poles the form of a nearly horizontal spiral of very low pitch (Figure 4.9). Although the sun in a single day seems to keep its altitude constant, there is actually a slight increase or decrease in altitude, depending on whether the spiral is ascending or descending. Sunrise at the poles is a very gradual one, the sun gaining altitude by about ⅖° per 24 hours. Since the apparent diameter of the sun is about half a degree, it will take the sun about 30 hours to rise. Once above the horizon, the sun remains there for six months; once it has set below the horizon it remains out of sight for another six months.

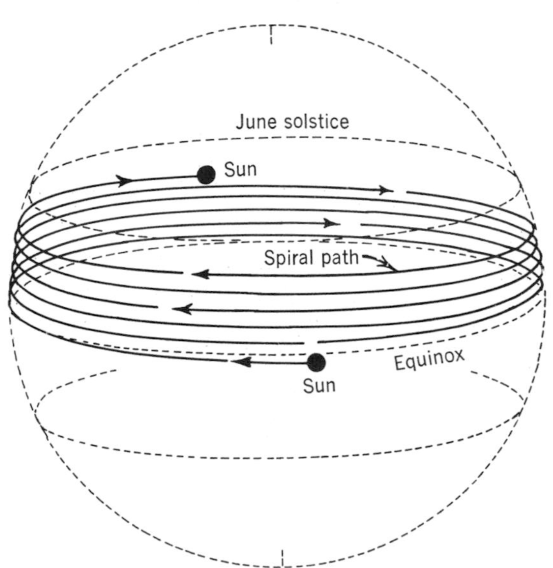


**FIGURE 4.9.** At the North Pole the sun's path throughout the year is a low-pitched spiral in which the sun seems to move parallel with the horizon. (© 1960, John Wiley & Sons, New York.)

## Lengths of day and night

To obtain a rough approximation of the lengths of day and night and the times of sunrise and sunset for any date and any latitude, a small globe marked off in 15-degree meridians can easily be converted into a three-dimensional graph (Figure 4.10).

For winter solstice, adjust a rubber band around the globe so that it forms a great circle tangent to the Arctic Circle at the point where that parallel is intersected by the Greenwich meridian. The rubber band should cross the equator at long. 90° E. and 90° W. and should also be tangent to the Antarctic Circle where that parallel is crossed by the meridian of long. 180°. If we use the principles of hour circles and global time (Figure 3.12), the Greenwich meridian represents noon, and each 15-degree meridian is counted as 1 hour of time, increasing eastward. The daylight period is represented by that part of the globe lying on the Atlantic side of the rubber band; the darkness period by the Pacific side. The rubber band, as the circle of illumination, will mark the point at which a given parallel of latitude experiences sunset (east longitude) and sunrise (west longitude). For any selected latitude it is necessary merely to count the hour circles and fractions thereof from the noon meridian westward to obtain the hour of sunrise or eastward to obtain the hour of sunset.

For summer solstice, rotate the globe so that the

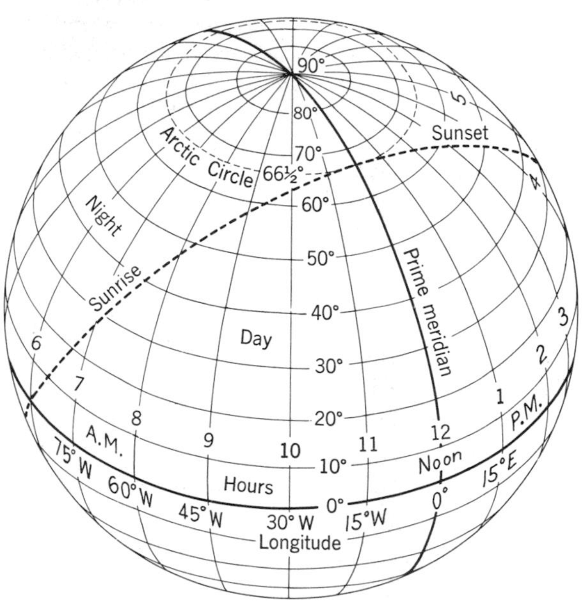


**FIGURE 4.10.** A small globe and a rubber band (dashed line) form a spherical graph from which the time of sunrise and sunset can be estimated for any latitude. (© 1960, John Wiley & Sons, New York.)

180th meridian is before you, representing noon. As before, count the hour circles westward and eastward to the point where the rubber band crosses the parallel in question.

Should it be necessary to determine these facts for some intermediate date, the sun's declination can be determined from the analemma (Figure 3.11) and the rubber band shifted so that it forms a great circle tangent to the parallel whose latitude is the colatitude of the sun's declination. Then proceed as for the solstices. For the equinoxes no graph is necessary.

The global graph is accurate only to the degree that the geographic grid is accurately printed and the rubber band is precisely placed. Results to within a quarter of an hour can be had, but these are in local mean solar time and do not take into account atmospheric refraction or the size of the sun's disk.

More accurate is a sunrise-sunset diagram published by the Oceanographic Office of the U.S. Navy. Figure 4.11 is a simplified and reduced copy of the original diagram, which may be purchased by the general public as Oceanographic Office Publication No. 5175. An interesting feature of this diagram is the incorporation of the equation of time into the graph. Thus the time of sunrise for the equator, which should be 6:00 A.M. local apparent solar time, is shown to be several minutes early or late at various dates, depending on whether the sun is fast or slow.

## Exact times of sunrise and sunset

The discussion thus far of the times of sunrise and sunset and the lengths of days has assumed that the earth has no atmosphere, hence that light rays from the sun undergo no bending, or *refraction,* which in fact they do. It is also assumed that the sun is a true point in space, having no measurable diameter, although in fact the sun appears as a sizable disk if we observe it near sunrise and sunset. Taken into account, both atmospheric refraction and the sun's diameter will affect the time of sunrise and sunset by an amount measurable in minutes.

Should the reader consult his newspaper or an almanac,[4] he will find that on the date of equinox the length of day is perhaps $12^h10^m$ for places such as New York, Chicago, or San Francisco, which lie near lat. 40° N. Why should the length of day at equinox be some 10 minutes longer than the 12 hours it should be for a sphere bisected by the circle of illumination passing through the Poles? By using corrections for refraction and sun's diameter, this discrepancy can be resolved.

Consider refraction first. Light rays entering the earth's atmosphere are bent, or refracted, into a path that is slightly concave earthward, with respect to a straight tangent line (Figure 4.12). This phenomenon enables us to see slightly "down" over the spherical curvature of the earth. In other words the apparent horizon circle is slightly depressed, and we can see a little more than a celestial hemisphere. Lowering of the horizon amounts to about 36 minutes of arc, enabling us to see the sun or other celestial objects when they are actually as much as 36 minutes below the horizon. Consequently the sun is seen earlier at sunrise than it would be if the earth had no atmosphere, and it remains in sight longer at sunset.

Considering the sun as a disk, we find that the average apparent diameter of the sun is equal to about 32 minutes of arc. Astronomical tables usually give the *semidiameter,* which is half the diameter. There is a slight variation with date of year, because of changing distance between earth and sun, so that semidiameter is about 16′18″ at perihelion and about 15′45″ at aphelion.

Now, sunrise is defined strictly as the instant of first

[4] The *World Almanac* and *Old Farmer's Almanac* publish times of sunrise and sunset for every day. The latter publication also gives length of day to the nearest minute.

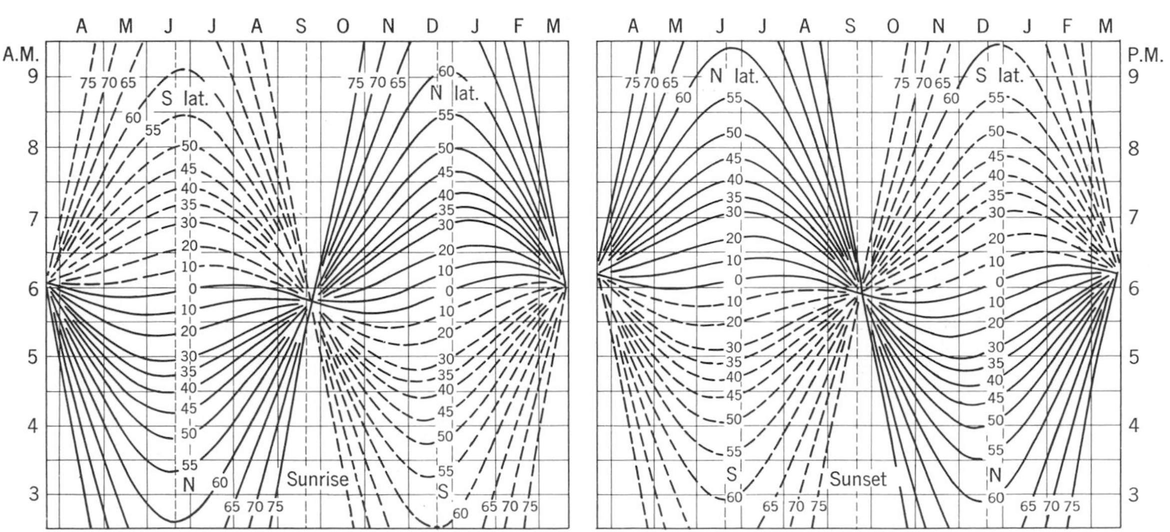


**FIGURE 4.11.** Sunset-sunrise diagram. (Simplified from U.S. Navy Oceanographic Office Publication No. 5175; © 1960, John Wiley & Sons, New York.)

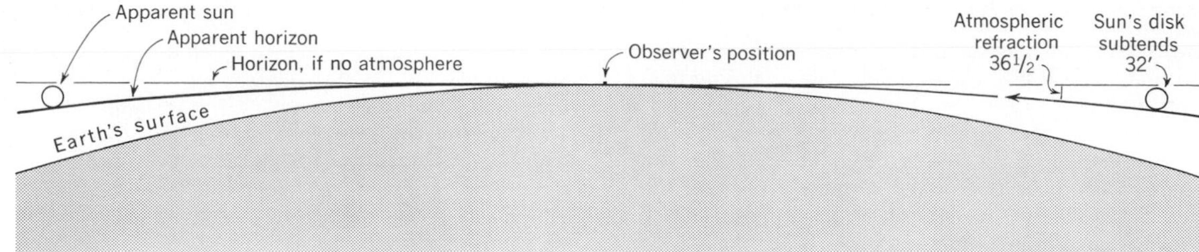


**FIGURE 4.12.** The apparent horizon is extended slightly downward because of atmospheric refraction.

appearance of the *upper limb* (upper rim) of the sun's disk above the sea-level horizon, whereas sunset is the instant of total disappearance of the upper limb below the horizon. Thus defined, sunrise will occur earlier and sunset later than it would if the center of the sun's disk were the point of reference. To this effect we must add the effect of refraction: the sum of 16′ and 36′ is 52′. If the sun's path is in a plane perpendicular to the horizon circle, as at the equator on equinox, 52 minutes of arc is equivalent to about 3½ minutes of time. Doubling this for the combined effect of sunrise and sunset gives 7 minutes of added length of day.

At higher latitudes the sun's path is slanting as it passes below the horizon (Figure 4.13), requiring more time to attain a given angular distance below the horizon. Using a simple right triangle as a model of the two paths, we find that the slanting path for lat. 40° represents the hypotenuse of the triangle and is equivalent to about 68 minutes of arc, or 4½ minutes of time. Doubled to include both sunrise and sunset, the addition to length of day is 9 minutes, which agrees rather well with the stated length of day based on the newspaper or almanac.

At higher latitudes the excess in length of day at equinox increases, because of the lower angle made by the sun's path as it sinks below the horizon. At lat. 72° N. on the date of equinox the length of day as given in the *Air Almanac* is about $12^h21^m$, about 14 minutes longer than the day at the equator, where its length is about $12^h07^m$.

**FIGURE 4.13.** Duration of twilight is lengthened with increasing latitude because of the slanting path of the sun.

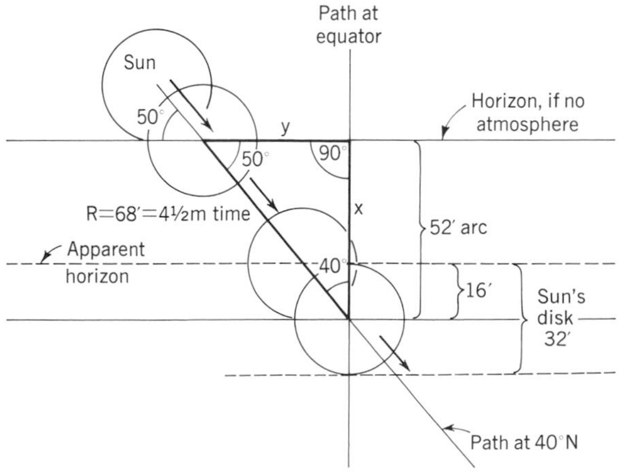


## Sunrise and sunset near winter solstice

Because of the sun's running fast in December, but slow in January, the relations among sunset, sunrise, and length of day are complicated in a way puzzling to the average person, but quite easily explained in terms of the equation of time. In Figure 4.14 is a graph constructed specifically to apply to lat. 40° N. and for local mean solar time; the same effect would apply anywhere at this latitude.

Whereas the shortest day of the year is December 22, this day has neither the latest time of sunrise nor the earliest time of sunset. We note from Figure 4.14 that the earliest sunset occurs about December 8 at this latitude, which is 2 weeks before solstice; the latest sunrise occurs about January 5, which is 2 weeks after solstice. During the 4-week period involved, the equation of time has been changing rapidly from about 10 minutest fast to about 5 minutes slow. Consequently the rate of change in the equation of time exceeds the rate of change of sunset and sunrise times. Between December 8 and 22 the time of sunset would normally shift to an earlier hour as solstice is approached, but the sun in this period is running slower each day by a still greater amount; hence the time of sunset actually becomes later. Similarly from December 22 to January 5 the time of sunrise should come at an earlier hour each day, but, because the sun is becoming slower at a still greater rate, sunrise continues to occur later.

## Almanacs

Authoritative sources of astronomical information required for navigation, and also useful to research workers in the earth sciences, include the *Air Almanac,* the *Nautical Almanac,* and the *American Ephemeris and Nautical Almanac.* All three are published jointly with Great Britain.

The *Air Almanac* is issued through the Nautical Almanac Office of the U.S. Naval Observatory in three volumes yearly: January–April, May–August, and September–December. It may be purchased in the United States through the Superintendent of Documents, but it is also available in a separate printing produced by Her Majesty's Nautical Almanac Office, Royal Greenwich Observatory, England. Included in the *Air Almanac* are the sun's declination, time of sunrise and sunset, duration of civil twilight for a wide range of latitudes, and all information necessary for celestial navigation by means of the sun, moon, planets, and stars.

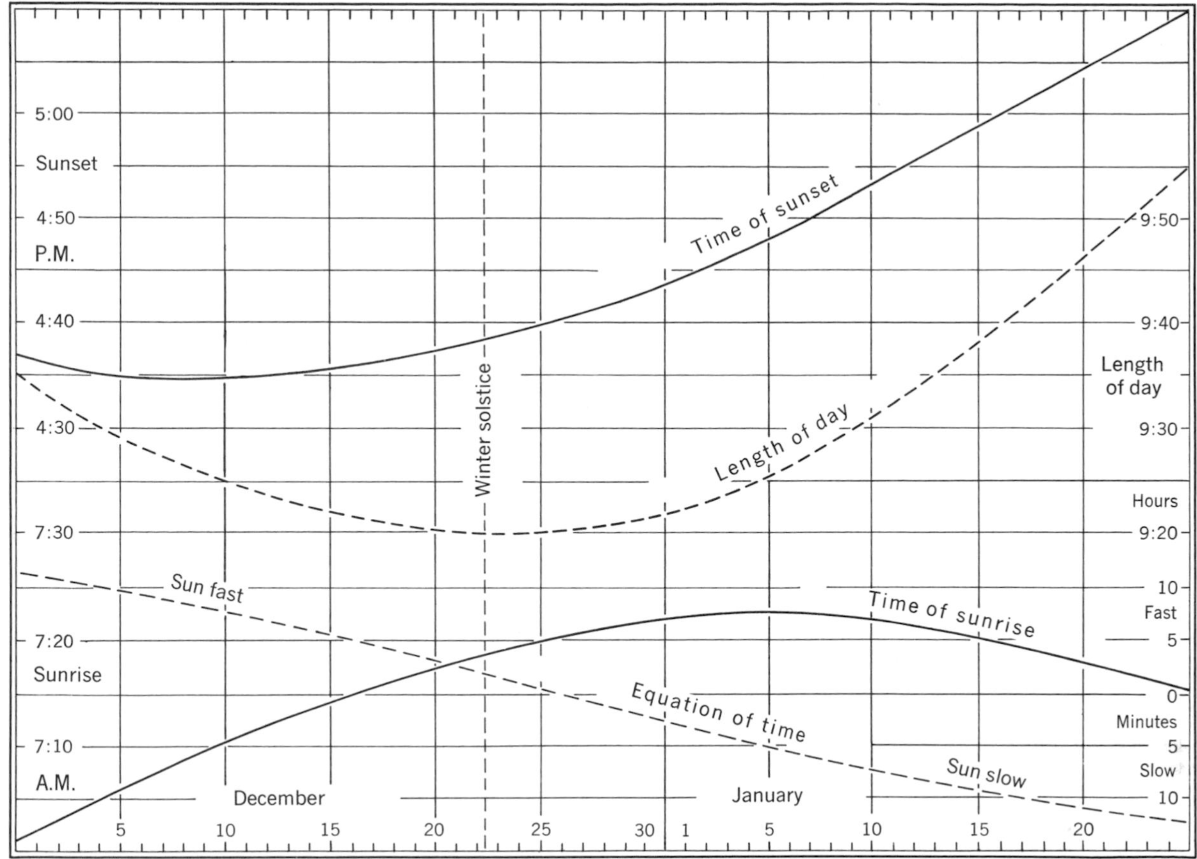


**FIGURE 4.14.** During December and January the times of earliest sunset and latest sunrise are advanced and delayed, respectively, with reference to the solstice date because of rapid changes in the equation of time. Data apply to local mean solar time at the 40th parallel north.

*The Observer's Handbook,* issued annually by the Royal Astronomical Society of Canada, Toronto, gives data on declination of the sun and times of sunrise and sunset.

## Twilight

Thus far the explanation of global illumination has included the assumption that the circle of illumination marks the abrupt change from sunlight to almost total darkness. Not yet taken into consideration is *twilight,* a diffused light persisting after sunset and preceding sunrise. This discussion treats both periods as one phenomenon because they are of equal intensity and similar cause, being only reversed in development. Twilight provides much useful light, especially in the higher latitudes, but in another sense it is detrimental to certain forms of scientific work and navigation because it interferes with observation of stars and space phenomena by obscuring much fainter forms of light.

Twilight is sunlight scattered by contact with atmospheric molecules and reflected by dust and moisture droplets (Chapter 12). After the sun has set, its rays continue to strike the upper layers of the atmosphere, and some of this scattered light reaches the ground (Figure 4.15). As the earth rotates, progressively less of the upper atmosphere is thus illuminated and the light fades, disappearing finally in the western sky.

Duration of twilight depends upon the thickness and composition of the atmosphere and upon the rate at which the sun is sinking below the horizon. If we as-

**FIGURE 4.15.** Twilight results from presence of the earth's atmosphere. (© 1960, John Wiley & Sons, New York.)

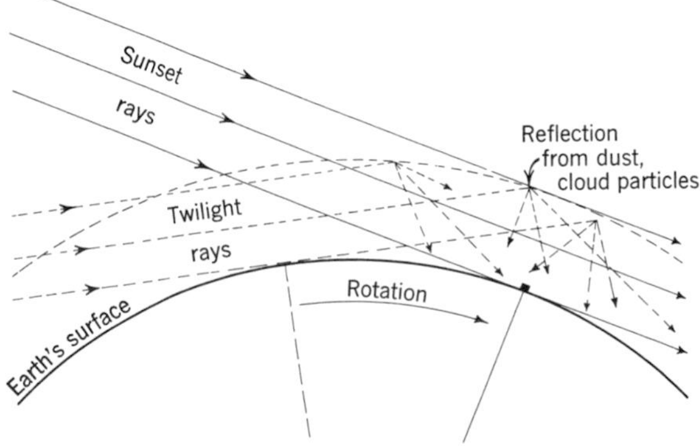

sume uniform atmospheric characteristics, the duration of twilight will depend on the angle of the plane of the sun's path with respect to the horizon plane (Figure 4.4). At the equator twilight should be shortest, at high latitudes it will be much longer, and at the poles it will endure continuously for long spans of time. At the equator the sun's path is perpendicular with respect to the horizon, and the sun will sink at the rate of 15° per hour. At 60° N. the sun's path at equinox makes an angle of about 30° with respect to the horizon and requires about twice as long to reach a given angular point below the horizon as at the equator; hence twilight will last about twice as long.

Twilight is defined in three ways. The longest form is *astronomical twilight,* the period during which any diffuse illumination from the sun can be detected. For practical reasons this form of twilight is considered to persist as long as the sun is between the horizon and a point 18° below the horizon. *Nautical twilight* is defined as enduring while the sun is within 12° of the horizon, a point at which it is light enough to see the outlines of ground objects, but dark enough to see the stars used for navigation. A third form is *civil twilight,* enduring while the sun is between the horizon and a point 6° below the horizon. Civil twilight provides enough illumination for normal outdoor activities to be carried on without the aid of lights. In the middle latitudes near the equinoxes civil twilight lasts about 30 minutes, and this period of time is commonly adopted in legal statutes.

The *Air Almanac* gives duration of civil twilight to the nearest minute for each day of the year for a wide range of latitudes. Tables are also given for the calculation of nautical twilight from civil twilight. An astronomical twilight diagram, published by the Oceanographic Office of the U.S. Navy, is attached to the sunrise-sunset diagram described as the basis for Figure 4.11. A reproduction of the twilight diagram is shown in Figure 4.16. It shows the duration of astronomical twilight for any 5-degree parallel of latitude throughout the year. Note that there is no "zero" line on the graph; instead the central horizontal line on which the initials of the month are marked has a value of 1 hour. The duration of astronomical twilight at the equator is on the order of $1^h10^m$ to $1^h15^m$ throughout the year. With increase in north latitude the length of twilight increases sharply with the onset of summer solstice. Poleward of a critical latitude of about 48°, at June solstice, the sun at no point in its 24-hour circuit reaches a point more than 18° below the horizon, so that astronomical twilight lasts all night.

An extreme duration of twilight is reached at the poles. Here the near-horizontal plane of the sun's apparent path keeps it within 18° of the horizon for a period of 7 weeks after it has set at autumnal equinox and for 7 weeks before it again rises at vernal equinox.

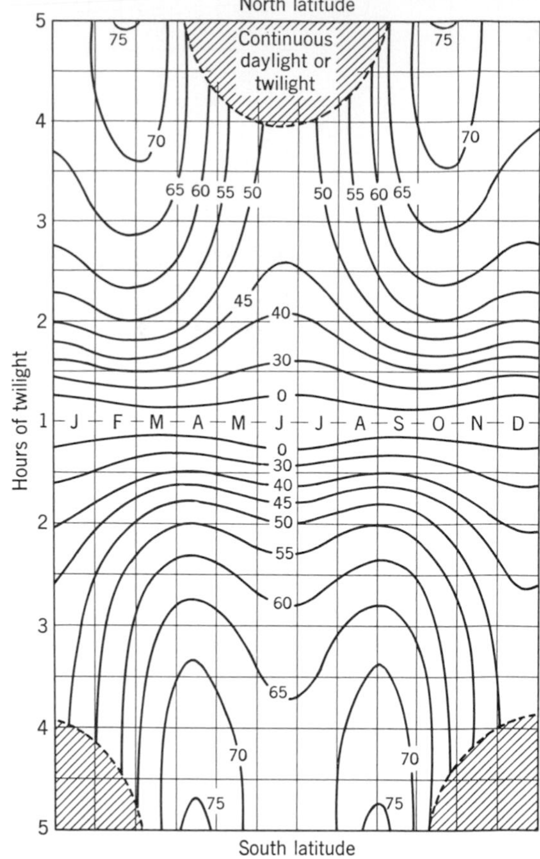


**FIGURE 4.16.** Duration of twilight in hours for every 5 degrees of latitude. (Data from U.S. Navy Oceanographic Office Publication No. 5175; © 1960, John Wiley & Sons, New York.)

## References for further study

Wylie, C. C. (1942), *Astronomy, Maps, and Weather,* New York, Harper & Row, 449 pp., chap. 6.

Mehlin, T. G. (1959), *Astronomy,* New York, Wiley, 391 pp.

Strong, C. L. (1960), *The Amateur Scientist,* New York, Simon and Schuster, 584 pp., chaps. 7, 8.

U.S. Naval Observatory, *The Air Almanac,* Washington, D.C., U.S. Govt. Printing Office, issued annually.

# 5

# The solar family

THE FIRST FOUR CHAPTERS of this book have dealt with planet Earth[1] as a lone spherical object orbiting our Sun and spinning upon an axis, exposing the terrestrial surface to the light rays of the Sun in a rather complex set of daily and seasonal cycles of variation. Perhaps this approach is a natural one in the learning process, because Man's knowledge of the world about him has developed by study of those phenomena closet at hand and most easily observed. The Earth within range of the unaided human senses was Man's first concern and interest; he had to develop the telescope, spectroscope, and radio receiver in order to explore the world of astronomical dimensions. Accordingly, our approach has been at first strongly Earth-oriented. A knowledge of the Earth's motions will be useful now as we turn to examine the other members of the solar family.

How can a study of the members of the solar system be related to the natural science of our Earth? We shall see in a later chapter that all members of the solar system, including the Sun itself, developed at about the same time and were formed from a single collection of matter. While all members of the system have much in common, they also have important individual differences in size and composition, and in the sizes and shapes of their orbital motions with respect to the Sun.

It is by a careful study of both the differences and the similarities of the many objects comprising the whole solar family that a complete hypothesis of origin can be formulated for a particular member of that family, such as our own planet Earth.

This chapter reviews information that is largely astronomical; that is, it deals with the members of the solar system as discrete objects in orbit about the Sun and in some cases in secondary orbits about other bodies. Geological considerations—such as the internal

[1] In Chapters 5 and 6 the names of Earth, Moon, and Sun are capitalized to agree with the planetary names.

composition, surface features, and origins of these objects—require a knowledge of the chemistry of the Earth and solar system. We shall defer these topics until the appropriate background information has been covered. (See Chapter 31.)

## Members of the solar family

The *solar system* consists of the planets and their satellites, asteroids, comets, and meteoroid swarms, all of which move in the gravitational field of the Sun, the preeminent body and center of the entire system.

The term *planet* is limited in common usage to the nine largest bodies revolving about the Sun; they are also often called the *major planets.* In order of distance from the Sun they are: *Mercury, Venus, Earth, Mars, Jupiter, Saturn, Uranus, Neptune,* and *Pluto.* The *asteroids,* sometimes referred to as the *minor planets,* number in the thousands. All have diameters less than 500 mi (800 km), and most are less than a few miles in diameter. Many asteroid orbits are quite eccentric and highly inclined to the plane of the Earth's orbit. In general they are found between the orbits of Mars and Jupiter. A *comet* is a rather large diffuse body of very small mass. Most comets revolve in extremely eccentric orbits, at perihelion passing close to the innermost planets and Sun and at aphelion being in or beyond the region of the outermost planets.

## Inner and outer planets

It has been found convenient to classify the nine major planets into two groups. The *inner planets,* also referred to as the *terrestrial planets,* are those four lying closest to the Sun: Mercury, Venus, Earth, and Mars (Figure 5.1). The four are grouped together because they are relatively small and at the same time have orbits relatively close to one another and to the Sun.

The five *outer planets,* Jupiter, Saturn, Uranus, Neptune, and Pluto, move in orbits of vastly greater diameter than those of the four inner planets and, except for Pluto, are vastly greater in size. It is not feasible to show all nine planetary orbits to the same scale on one drawing, hence the scale of Figure 5.2, in which the orbits of the outer planets are shown, is about one-twentieth that used in Figure 5.1.

In order to convey a stronger impression of the size differences among the planets and Sun, the diameters of these bodies are drawn to a common scale in Figure 5.3, although only a small part of the Sun's disk can be shown.

Table 5.1 gives information in several categories for the nine major planets. It is obvious from the figures giving distance from Sun, diameter, and mass, that the four inner, or terrestrial, planets form a group of quite similar bodies. In the same manner the first four outer planets—Jupiter, Saturn, Uranus, and Neptune—can appropriately be grouped as the *great planets.* In contrast, Pluto has a very much smaller size and, moreover, its orbit is highly eccentric compared with the other planets. Hence Pluto may well be placed in a class by itself.

## The planetary orbits

As explained in Chapter 1, Kepler's first law states that the orbits of the planets are ellipses, with the Sun occupying one focus of each ellipse. The *eccentricity* (degree of flattening) of an orbit is defined as the distance from the center of the ellipse to the occupied focus,

**FIGURE 5.1.** Orbits of the four planets near the sun. The black dots represent perihelion points. [After E. A. Fath (1934), *Elements of Astronomy,* New York, McGraw-Hill.]

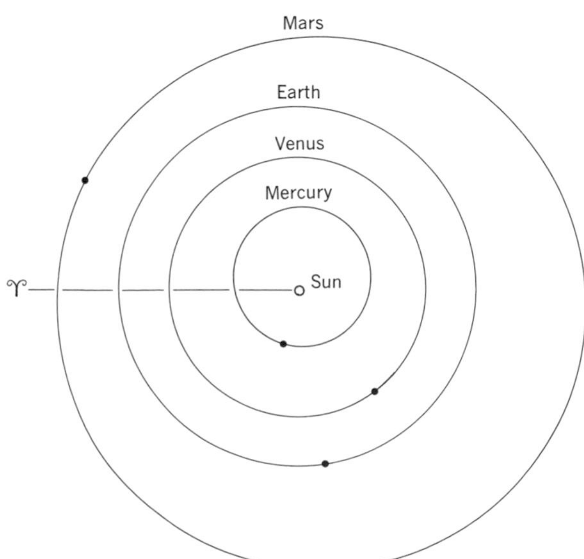


**FIGURE 5.2.** Orbits of the outer planets. The innermost circle represents Mars' orbit, and the dashed circle represents the zone of asteroid orbits. Pluto will not collide with Neptune because Pluto's orbit is inclined more than 17° with respect to the ecliptic.

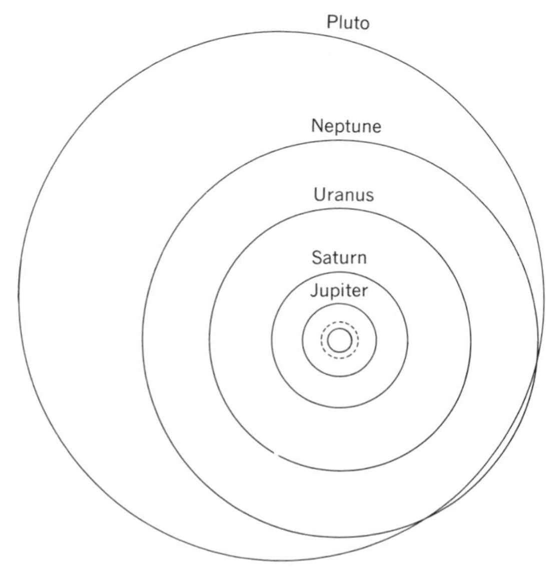

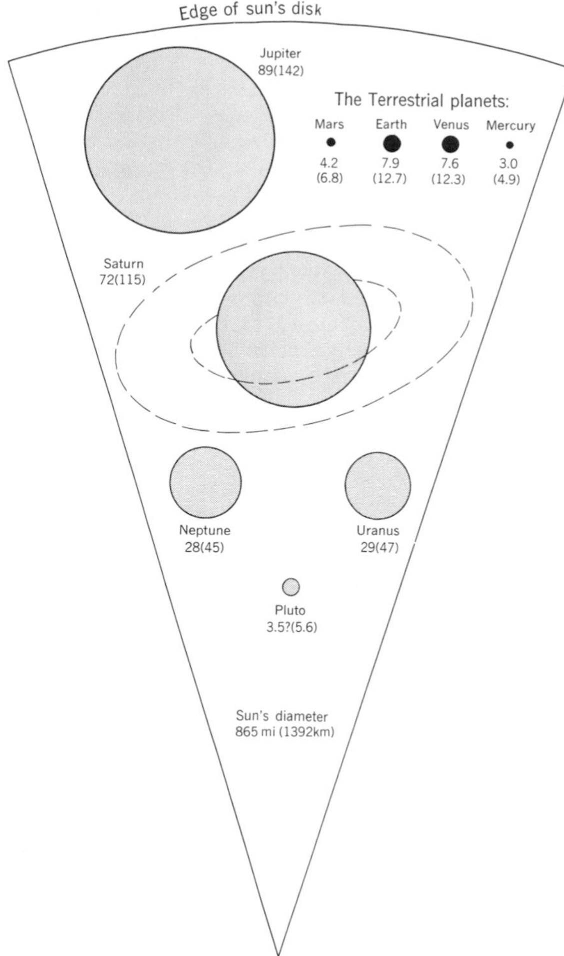


**FIGURE 5.3.** Relative diameters of the Sun and planets. Figures give diameters in thousands of miles, with thousands of kilometers in parentheses. [After C. C. Wylie (1942), *Astronomy, Maps, and Weather,* New York, Harper & Row.]

divided by the length of the semimajor axis. (The semimajor axis is one-half of the long axis of the ellipse.) Eccentricity is very slight for most of the planets (Table 5.1). Of the inner planets, the orbits of Venus and Earth appear almost as concentric circles in Figure 5.1, those of Mercury and Mars are more noticeably elliptical, particularly Mercury, with an orbital eccentricity of over 0.2. The four great planets have uniformly small orbital eccentricities. In contrast, again, Pluto's orbit is highly eccentric (0.247), so that in perihelion Pluto actually lies within the orbit of Neptune. This fact, along with Pluto's relatively small mass, has led to the theory that Pluto was formerly a satellite of Neptune, but escaped into a heliocentric orbit. The orbits of the asteroids have generally higher eccentricities than those of the planets, certain of them exceeding 0.5. All planets revolve about the Sun in the same direction as Earth does.

The planes of the planetary orbits for the most part lie nearly parallel to the plane of Earth's orbit, although there are notable exceptions (Table 5.1). Mercury's orbit is inclined by 7°, that of Pluto by over 17°. Orbits of all the remaining major planets are within 3½° of the ecliptic.

The following description of a scale model of the solar system will help us to appreciate the vastness of interplanetary distances compared with the diameters of the objects themselves:

> . . . consider a model with the Sun represented by a ball 6 inches in diameter, about the size of a grapefruit. On this model the inner planets Mercury, Venus, Earth, and Mars are at the respective distances of 7, 13, 18, and 27 yards, being in themselves not more than the size of a pin's head. The great planets Jupiter, Saturn, Uranus, and Neptune are of the sizes of small peas at about 90, 170, 350, and 540 yards respectively from the Sun. Pluto is a speck of silver about 700 yards away.[2]

Kepler's third law, sometimes referred to as the *harmonic law,* states that for any two planets the squares of the periods of revolution are proportional to the cubes of their mean distances from the Sun. If we let $P_1$ and $P_2$ stand for the periods, in years, of planets *1* and *2* and let $D_1$ and $D_2$ represent their respective orbital distances from the Sun, Kepler's third law can be written

$$\frac{P_1^2}{P_2^2} = \frac{D_1^3}{D_2^3}$$

[2] From F. Hoyle (1955), *Frontiers of Astronomy,* New York, Harper & Row. Quoted by permission.

**TABLE 5.1. THE PRINCIPAL PLANETS**

| | Name | Distance from Sun mi × $10^6$ | Distance from Sun km × $10^6$ | Astronomical units | Eccentricity of Orbit | Inclination to Ecliptic | Period of Revolution, sidereal | Diameter mi × $10^3$ | Diameter km × $10^3$ | Mass, Relative to Earth | Mean Density g/cm³ | Period of Rotation | Number of Moons |
|---|---|---|---|---|---|---|---|---|---|---|---|---|---|
| The Terrestrial Planets | Inner planets | | | | | | Days | | | | | | |
| | Mercury | 36 | 58 | 0.387 | 0.206 | 7°00′ | 88 | 3 | 4.9 | 0.06 | 5.0 | $58^d17^h$ | 0 |
| | Venus | 67 | 108 | 0.723 | 0.007 | 3°24′ | 225 | 7.6 | 12.2 | 0.81 | 5.1 | $243^d$ | 0 |
| | Earth | 93 | 150 | 1.000 | 0.017 | 0°00′ | 365¼ | 7.9 | 12.7 | 1.00 | 5.5 | $23^h56^m$ | 1 |
| | Mars | 142 | 228 | 1.524 | 0.093 | 1°51′ | 687 | 4.2 | 6.7 | 0.11 | 3.9 | $24^h37^m$ | 2 |
| The Great Planets | Outer planets | | | | | | Years | | | | | | |
| | Jupiter | 484 | 779 | 5.20 | 0.048 | 1°18′ | 12 | 89 | 142 | 318 | 1.3 | $9^h50^m$ | 12 |
| | Saturn | 886 | 1430 | 9.55 | 0.056 | 2°30′ | 29½ | 72 | 115 | 95 | 0.7 | $10^h14^m$ | 10 |
| | Uranus | 1780 | 2870 | 19.2 | 0.047 | 0°46′ | 84 | 29 | 47.4 | 15 | 1.7 | $10^h42^m$ | 5 |
| | Neptune | 2790 | 4500 | 30.1 | 0.008 | 1°47′ | 165 | 28 | 44.6 | 17 | 1.6 | $15^h48^m$ | 2 |
| | Pluto | 3670 | 5900 | 39.4 | 0.250 | 17°17′ | 248 | 3.5(?) | 5.6(?) | 0.9 | ? | $6^d$ | 0 |

In order to test this law, we can simplify the calculation by using Earth as one of the two planets, letting the period of earth's revolution be unity and letting the distance of Earth from Sun be defined as one *astronomical unit.*[3]

Kepler's formula then reduces to

$$P = \sqrt{D^3}$$

where $P$ is the planet's period in Earth-years and $D$ is its mean distance from the Sun in astronomical units.

For example, Neptune has a distance, $D$, of 30.1 astronomical units and a period, $P$, of 165 years (Table 5.1). Substituting for $D$ in the simplified equation, we get

$$P = \sqrt{(30.1)^3} = \sqrt{27{,}270.9} = 165 \text{ approx.}$$

The agreement of the calculated period with the observed period is close and would be closer if the exact value of distance had been used.

It should be noted that Kepler's laws apply strictly to the case of a planet completely unaffected by any other gravitational force except that of the Sun. In fact, however, each planet exerts an influence upon all the others, to the extent that the path of a given planet is pulled measurably out of its ideal elliptical orbit by the gravitational attraction of those planets closest to it. The masses of the planets that have no satellites have been calculated from these effects.

## Gravitation and centripetal force

Kepler based his three laws solely upon observations of planetary motion. A valid physical explanation for elliptical orbits and varying speeds was yet to come. Galileo (1564–1642), a contemporary of Kepler, was investigating the principles of the pendulum and the inertia and acceleration of falling bodies. Upon the foundations which Galileo had laid, Sir Isaac Newton developed his laws of gravitation and motion, published in 1687.

The key to planetary motion lies in the *law of gravitation,* which states that any two bodies attract each other with a force that is directly proportional to the product of their masses and inversely proportional to the square of the distance between them. Where $M_1$ and $M_2$ represent the two masses, $R$ the separating distance, and $F_g$ the gravitational force between them:

$$F_g = \frac{G\,M_1M_2}{R^2}$$

The term, $G$, in the above equation is the universal constant of gravitation. (The numerical value of $G$ is given in Chapter 23, but is not of importance in our present discussion.)

Refer back to the discussion of centripetal force of rotation in Chapter 2. Newton's first law of motion states that every body continues in a state of rest or of uniform motion in a straight line unless made to change that state by some external force. As shown in Figure 2.7, the weight swung on a string tends to follow a tangent straight-line path at every instant. However, tangential flight is prevented by a centripetal force, acting as a tension in the radial cord. In the case of a planet, the force of gravitational attraction between planet and Sun is the centripetal force replacing the tension of the string in the example of the weight swung in a circular path. Gravitational force constantly deflects the planet from its straight tangential path.

Let us follow through the verification of Kepler's third law in terms of Newton's law of gravitation for a circular orbit. Centripetal force, $F_c$, is defined as the product of the mass times the square of the velocity divided by the radius, expressed as follows:

$$F_c = \frac{M_1V^2}{R} \tag{1}$$

where $M_1$ is the mass of the planet.

Because the gravitational force plays the role of an equal centripetal force in holding the planet in its circular orbit, we can set the equation for centripetal force equal to that for gravitational force, as follows:

$$\frac{M_1V^2}{R} = \frac{GM_1M_2}{R^2} \tag{2}$$

where $M_2$ is the mass of the sun.

To proceed further, it is necessary to make some substitutions of equivalent terms. Recall that Kepler's law refers to the "periods of revolution" of the planets. Let $T$ stand for period of revolution. When an object moves in a circle, its period $T$ is equal to the circumference of the circle, $2\pi R$, divided by its linear velocity, $V$. Therefore, we write:

$$T = \frac{2\pi R}{V} \tag{3}$$

Solving for $V$ in the above equation, we obtain:

$$V = \frac{2\pi R}{T} \text{ and } V^2 = \frac{4\pi^2 R^2}{T^2} \tag{4}$$

We are now ready to substitute the equivalent term for $V^2$ into the left hand side of the Equation (2), giving the following:

$$\frac{M_1 4\pi^2 R^2}{T^2 R} = \frac{G\,M_1M_2}{R^2} \tag{5}$$

Collecting "$R$'s" and cancelling "$M_1$'s" on both sides, this equation simplifies to:

$$4\pi R^3 = GM_2T^2 \tag{6}$$

For a given planet only $R$ and $T$ are simultaneously variable quantities.

So we see that the cube of the radius is proportional to the square of the period, as stated in Kepler's third law. To obtain this agreement with Kepler's work we have assumed, as he did, that a planet revolves around the center of the Sun, rather than around the common center of gravity of both planet and Sun. (The revolution of two bodies about a common center of gravity is discussed further in Chapter 8.)

[3] The astronomical unit has a value of 92,956,000 mi ($1.496 \times 10^8$ km).

## Bode's law

From the list of planetary distances from Sun, Table 5.1, it is obvious that the planetary orbits are not equidistantly spaced, but increase in such a manner that the radius of each planet's orbit is about 1½ times greater than that of the planet adjacent to it on the inner side. An exact statement of this seemingly consistent progression of distances was formulated by the German astronomer, Johann Bode, in 1772, and now goes by the designation of *Bode's law.*

As shown in Table 5.2, the number 4 is set down as a constant for each planet. To each 4, beginning with the second planet (Venus), is added a number belonging to a doubling progression commencing with 3. (This geometrical progression runs: 3, 6, 12, 24, 48, etc.) Each sum is then divided by 10, giving a series of distances comparable to astronomical units. In comparing the numbers derived by Bode's system with the actual distances, we note that if we include the asteroids as equivalent to a major planet, the agreement is excellent through Uranus, though Uranus had not been discovered in 1772. For Neptune and Pluto, not known in Bode's time, the agreement is poor.

| Planet | Mercury | Venus | Earth | Mars | Asteroids | Jupiter | Saturn | Uranus | Neptune | Pluto |
|---|---|---|---|---|---|---|---|---|---|---|
| Constant | 4 | 4 | 4 | 4 | 4 | 4 | 4 | 4 | 4 | 4 |
| Geometrical progression | 0 | 3 | 6 | 12 | 24 | 48 | 96 | 192 | 384 | 768 |
| Bode number | 0.4 | 0.7 | 1.0 | 1.6 | 2.8 | 5.2 | 10.0 | 19.6 | 38.3 | 77.2 |
| Distances, in A.U. | 0.39 | 0.72 | 1.00 | 1.52 | (2.8) | 5.20 | 9.55 | 19.2 | 30.1 | 39.4 |

Unlike Kepler's laws, which are rational in nature and are explained by application of laws of mechanics, Bode's so-called law is empirical and conforms to no known basic principles of physics. It provides only a convenient statment of planetary distances.

## Angular momentum and elliptical orbits

Any mass in circular motion possesses a property known as *angular momentum.* We can think of the word "momentum" as describing the "quantity of motion". For a body moving in a straight line, momentum is defined as the product of the mass and the velocity ($M \cdot V$). Angular momentum, $L$, which applies to a body traveling in a curved path, is equal to the product of its linear momentum and the radius of the arc in which it is moving:

$$L = M \cdot V \cdot R$$

If the two bodies are moving under their mutual gravitational attraction, they will both orbit around their common center of gravity, or *barycenter,* which is located on a line joining their individual centers of gravity at a distance from each of them which is inversely proportional to their respective masses. If no energy is added to, or taken away from the system, the angular momentum of the system must remain constant, a principle known as the *law of conservation of angular momentum.* Since the Sun is more than a thousand times as massive as the heaviest of the planets (Jupiter), a very close approximation to the actual situation is achieved if we consider the Sun to be stationary and attribute all the motion to the planet. Thus the angular momentum of any planet must remain constant while it orbits the Sun. However, there can be continual changes in both the velocity and radius, provided that one change exactly compensates for the other. Let us apply this principle to the elliptical orbits of the planets.

When a planet approaches perihelion, the radius of curvature of its path is diminishing. In compensation, the linear velocity of the planet is increasing. When the planet approaches aphelion, the radius is lengthening, while the velocity is decreasing. Angular momentum thus is kept constant at all times. Here we have the explanation of Earth's greater orbital speed near perihelion and its slower speed near aphelion, a phenomenon discussed in detail in Chapters 1 and 3.

## Angular momentum of the solar system

A planet possesses angular momentum both because of its revolution about the Sun (heliocentric motion) and its rotation upon an axis. The satellites also possess angular momentum because of corresponding circular motions of revolution and rotation. The Sun, although fixed at the center of the solar system, has angular momentum because of its rotation, a phenomenon discussed in Chapter 6.

The mass and angular momentum of the Sun and of each of the first eight planets are given in Table 5.3 in terms of percentage of the total.[4] At once we see that

**TABLE 5.3. MASS AND ANGULAR MOMENTUM OF SUN AND PLANETS**

| | Mass, percent of total | Angular Momentum, percent of total |
|---|---|---|
| Sun | 99.86590 | 2.7423 |
| Mercury | 0.00001 | 0.0017 |
| Venus | 0.00025 | 0.0576 |
| Earth | 0.00030 | 0.0827 |
| Mars | 0.00003 | 0.0112 |
| Jupiter | 0.09558 | 59.9273 |
| Saturn | 0.02852 | 24.1924 |
| Uranus | 0.00430 | 5.2845 |
| Neptune | 0.00511 | 7.7003 |
| Totals | 100.00000 | 100.0000 |

[4] Inclusion of Pluto would not change this picture greatly. The data of Table 5.3 represent the known facts at a time when they were used to refute the nebular hypothesis of solar system origin, discussed in Chapter 27.

the Sun has almost all of the mass, but only a very small proportion of the total angular momentum. The angular momentum lies largely with the great planets by virtue of their large orbital radii and great linear velocities, combined with their relatively large masses and rapid rotation. Jupiter alone has almost 60 percent of the momentum of the whole system. Even if the planet Pluto, the asteroids, and other minor objects are taken into account, the Sun has 98.85 percent of the total mass, but only about 2 percent of the angular momentum. In Chapter 27 it will be noted that the distribution of angular momentum within the solar system must be explained by any acceptable hypothesis of origin of the solar system.

## Planetary rotation

The periods of rotation of six planets (all but Venus, Mercury, and Pluto) are surprisingly similar, considering the vast differences in diameter and mass. The rotational periods of Earth and Mars differ by less than an hour; those of the four great planets fall between 9 and 16 hours. The period of rotation of Mercury is much longer (59 days); that of Venus is very much longer (243 days). Pluto's rotational period has been established as 6.4 days, but the direction cannot be determined. Except for Uranus, Venus, and possibly Pluto, the directions of rotation of the planets are uniform, that is, they turn counterclockwise when viewed from a point in space above the north polar axis. Such motion is referred to by astronomers as *direct* motion; the reverse is *retrograde* motion.

From the standpoint of the origin of the solar system, the foregoing facts have been considered as being of great importance. Note that with two exceptions the planets all rotate in a uniform direction, all revolve about the Sun in the same direction, all have orbits lying within a few degrees of a common plane. These facts strongly suggest that the members of the solar system had a common mechanism of origin, by which all received the same directions of rotational impulse. Were this not so, we might expect to find the planets revolving in a variety of orbital planes and at least some of them revolving and rotating in opposite directions from others.

## Mercury

Mercury, fourth brightest of the planets, is the closest planet to the Sun, with an orbital radius only two-fifths that of Earth.

The geometrical relationships between Mercury and Sun, from the viewpoint of an observer on Earth, are illustrated in Figure 5.4. For this purpose we consider Earth and Sun to be fixed in space, so that only the relative motion of Mercury in its orbit is shown. Because Mercury orbits the Sun in only 88 days, as compared with 365 for Earth, Mercury makes one complete circuit relative to the line connecting Earth and Sun in a period of 116 days, a value known as the *synodic period.* Mercury is in *inferior conjunction* (*IC*) when located directly in line between Earth and Sun, in *superior conjunction* (*SC*) when directly in line but beyond the Sun.

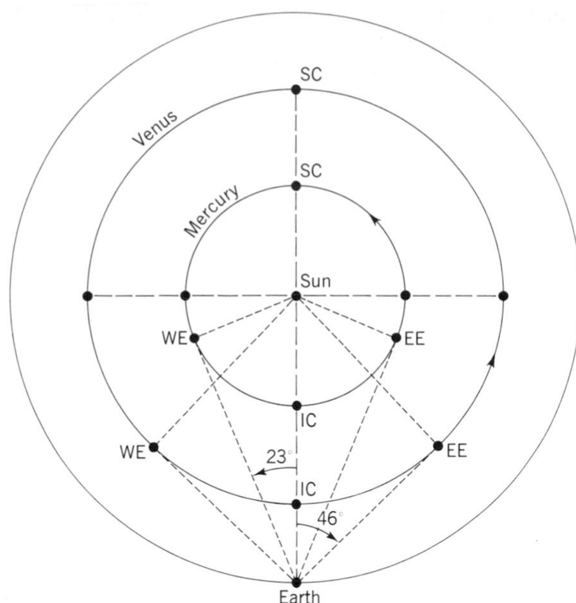


**FIGURE 5.4.** Orbital relationships between Earth and the inferior planets, Venus and Mercury. Angles of elongation shown are for circular orbits of mean radius.

The planetary *elongation* is the angle between a line to the Planet and the Earth–Sun line. Maximum elongation is obtained by drawing lines from the Earth-point in Figure 5.4 tangent to the planetary orbit at points *EE* and *WE.* For Mercury, the maximum elongation ranges from 18° to 28°. This variation occurs because the orbits of Earth and Mercury are elliptical, the eccentricity of Mercury's orbit being especially great. Consequently, there is a variation in the lengths of the legs of the Earth–Sun–Mercury triangle in maximum elongation.

When Mercury occupies the position labeled *EE* in Figure 5.4, it will be situated in the sky in a position to the east of the Sun. Consequently, the planet is visible only in a brief period after sunset when the Sun is well below the horizon but the planet has not yet set. At this time, then, Mercury is an *evening star.* At the elongation point labeled *WE,* Mercury lies west of the Sun and is visible only for a short period preceding sunrise. At this time the planet is a *morning star.*

When the apparent position of Mercury is plotted on the celestial sphere it will be found to shift eastward in celestial longitude (direct motion) for a period of about three months, and then to reverse itself and move westward among the stars (retrograde motion) for only about three weeks. These eastward and westward motions with respect to the Sun are the most rapid of any comparable planetary motions and earned Mercury its name—after the Roman god whose swiftness in change was a distinguishing trait.

In looking over the facts about Mercury in Table 5.1, note that this planet is unusual in having a high orbital inclination from the ecliptic (7°) and a high degree of eccentricity (0.206).

Mercury's rotational period of about 58.7 days has been measured to a high degree of accuracy by radar astronomy. At this rate, Mercury completes three turns on its axis for each two revolutions around the Sun, showing that the planet's rotation has been influenced by the gravity field of the Sun.

Mercury probably has no appreciable atmosphere because its surface gravity is only about three-tenths that of Earth, and the escape velocity is thus only 2.7 mi (4.3 km) per second. On the side of Mercury which happens to be facing the Sun, where intense and prolonged heating prevails, gases would be activiated to high velocities of molecular travel and would readily escape into space. It is estimated that, in perihelion, surface temperatures on Mercury rise to perhaps 790°F (420°C), a value exceeding the melting points of tin and lead. In contrast, temperatures on the shadowed side of Mercury may fall nearly to absolute zero. No other planet has so vast a temperature range on its surface. Although little can be discerned of the surface features of Mercury, it is reasonable to suppose that it resembles our Moon in having an extremely rough terrain of dark color, possibly with numerous craters, and with no evidences of erosion processes. Mercury can be assumed to be completely devoid of any forms of life. The average density of Mercury (5.0), is only a little less than that of Earth, suggesting that, like Earth, Mercury has a core of iron.

## Venus

Venus, the most brilliant object in the sky except for the Sun and Moon, approaches closer to Earth than any other planet; a distance of some 26 million mi ($42 \times 10^6$ km) separates the two bodies at a close conjunction (Figure 5.4). At superior conjunction their distance of separation is about 160 million mi ($260 \times 10^6$ km). As a result of this sixfold difference in separating distances, Venus seems to change greatly in apparent diameter throughout its orbit (Figures 5.5 and 5.6). Moreover, the

**FIGURE 5.5.** The planet Venus photographed at five different phases, showing its true relative sizes at various distances from Earth. Compare with Figure 5.6 to determine position in orbit. Note that in the largest view the atmospheric ring is complete. (Lowell Observatory photograph.)

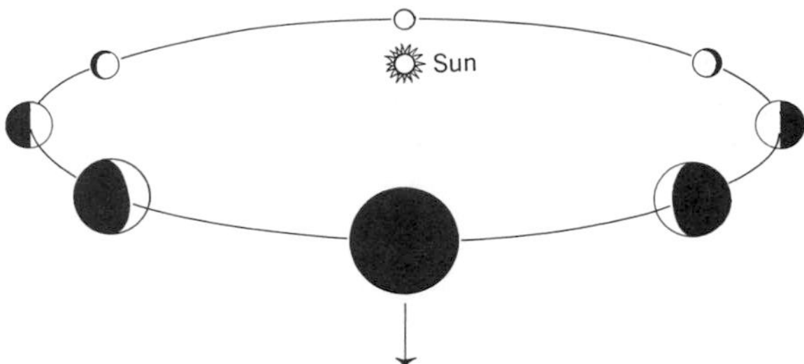


**FIGURE 5.6.** The orbit of Venus is shown here in perspective, as if viewed from a point above the North Pole of Earth. See Figure 5.5 for corresponding photographs. [After F. L. Whipple (1948), *Earth, Moon, and Planets,* 3rd ed., Cambridge, Mass., Harvard Univ. Press, p. 7, Figure 4.]

changing positions of Venus relative to Earth and Sun result in a series of phases of illumination ranging from a full disk to a thin crescent (Figures 5.5 and 5.6). As noted in Chapter 1, observation of these phases showed Galileo that Venus must revolve about the Sun. This discovery gave strong support to the Copernican theory.

As shown in Figure 5.4, the maximum elongation of Venus is much greater than for Mercury, reaching angles of up to 47° twice in its synodic period of 584 days. Because of the large separation in celestial longitude from the Sun in times of maximum elongation, Venus is seen for long periods of time when it is either an evening star or a morning star. At these times, Venus is quite close to the earth and is extremely brilliant. As the angle of elongation decreases, approaching inferior conjunction, the closeness of distance is offset by the reduced percentage of illuminated face seen from Earth. Consequently, the maximum brightness of Venus occurs about 36 days before and after inferior conjunction. Like Mercury, the motion of Venus with respect to the stars is direct during more than half of the synodic period and retrograde during the remainder, but these changes are much slower than in the case of Mercury.

From the standpoint of diameter, mass, density, and length of year, Venus more closely resembles Earth than any other planet does. Moreover, Venus has a dense atmosphere, held by a gravitational force almost as strong as that of Earth. Atmospheric pressure at the surface of Venus is about 100 times as great as on Earth. One proof of the presence of an atmosphere on Venus is that at crescent phase a band of light extends entirely around the full circle, showing that sunlight is refracted around the sphere by a thick layer of gases (Figure 5.5).

Data secured in 1967 by space vehicle *Venera 4* showed that carbon dioxide constitutes from 90 to 95% of Venus' atmosphere. Oxygen has been found in substantial quantities, whereas the presence of water vapor is at most barely detectable. Nitrogen has not been detected. Water was probably present on Venus at an early stage in the planet's history, but hydrogen atoms could not be held to the planet and most escaped into space.

Because of the presence of some kind of fine, suspended particles in its atmosphere—possibly clouds of dust particles or ice crystals—Venus reflects sunlight brilliantly, and little can be seen of its surface. Viewed in ultraviolet light, Venus shows slowly moving dark patches that may be cloud masses. Although water in all forms is believed to be absent from the planet's solid surface, it has been postulated that the patches are clouds of water droplets.

Temperatures on the surface of Venus have been obtained from temperature analysis of radio waves. An average value of 500°C (950°F) was announced in 1968. Despite the almost complete absence of water, a deficiency that would exclude the possibility of life forms such as those found on Earth, Venus has an environment in which humans otherwise might, if located on the dark side and suitably protected from high atmospheric pressure, be able to survive for limited periods.

Until radar was developed, it was virtually impossible to determine Venus' rotation period. Recent studies of reflected radar signals have yielded a period of 243.09 days, which is somewhat longer than the planet's period of revolution of 225 days. Furthermore, Venus' rotation is slowly clockwise, or retrograde, in contrast to the counterclockwise, or direct, rotation of the other planets.

The explanation of Venus' slow clockwise rotation may lie in the effect of tidal forces exerted by Earth. In Chapter 8 it will be explained that the tidal friction resulting from Earth's gravitational attraction has slowed the Moon's rotation to the point that it keeps the same side pointed toward Earth at all times. The tides which the Moon's gravity raises on the Earth have slowed Earth's rotation from a period of considerably less than four hours to its present value of 24 hours. A similar change may have been going on with respect to Venus' rotation.

Venus has no known satellites which might affect its rotation. Its clockwise rotation in a period of 243.1 days with respect to the stars is at such a rate that the same side of Venus faces Earth, on the average, every 145.9 days. The synodic period of Venus (the interval between its closest approaches to the Earth) is 583.9 days which, well within the uncertainties of measurement, is exactly four times the synodic period of rotation of 145.9 days. It thus appears that although Venus is rotating slowly with respect to Earth, each time it passes closest to our planet it presents exactly the same side to us.

The clockwise rotation of Venus was not suspected until the recent radar measurements, and to find a possible explanation it is necessary to go back to our ideas of the early formation of the planets. As explained in Chapter 27, all the planets probably condensed from a vast, thin disk of gas and dust which surrounded the Sun. The particles nearer the Sun would have been moving faster than those farther out, and as condensations into early planets began to occur, those masses would have had a slow clockwise rotation resulting from the initial velocities of the particles. We must then assume that the tidal effects of the Sun on the early planetary condensations stopped this clockwise rotation and caused the entire mass to keep the same side facing the Sun, thus resulting in a very slow counterclockwise rotation relative to space. The conservation of angular momentum as the early planetary masses contracted further would have led to the shorter periods of counterclockwise rotation observed for most of the planets.

The case of Venus seems to be unique. We may postulate that while the tidal forces of the Sun were slowing the clockwise rotation of Venus in its early stage, an extraordinary concentration of mass developed on one side of the planet near its equatorial belt. Eventually the rotation reached a stage at which the mass concentration made exactly four clockwise rotations between two successive nearest approaches of Venus to Earth, at which point Earth's tidal effect on Venus "locked on" to the rotation of Venus and stabilized it at the presently observed value and direction. Artificial satellites sent to orbit around Venus may do much to clarify this picture within the next few years.

## Mars

Passing over the planet Earth, which we have been studying at length in earlier chapters, we come to Mars, the first of the planets to be found in an orbit larger than that of Earth. Such planets are designated as *superior,* in contrast to Mercury and Venus, whose positions are *inferior.* Little more than half as large in diameter as Earth, the mass of Mars is only one-tenth that of Earth and the surface gravity only about one-third. Mars has two satellites—*Deimos,* the outer one, and *Phobos,* the inner one—which differ from our Moon in that they are less than 20 mi (32 km) in diameter and are much closer to the parent planet. Phobos orbits at a height of only 3680 mi (5920 km) above Mars' surface and has a period of only about 7½ hours.

Reddish in hue, Mars has definite surface features, which were recognized and speculated about as early as the mid-seventeenth century (Figure 5.7). Study of these features has enabled astronomers to measure with precision the period of axial rotation of Mars as $24^{h}37^{m}22.7^{s}$, only a little longer than that of Earth. Also, the plane of Mars' equator is inclined about 25° with respect to its orbital plane, a value very close to Earth's inclination of 23½°.

Geometrical relationships of Mars to Earth and Sun are illustrated in Figure 5.8. Again, we assume that Earth and Sun are fixed in space and consider only the relative motion of Mars. The synodic period of Mars is 780 days. When in line with the Sun on the distant side of its orbit, Mars is said to be in *conjunction.* At this time its apparent closeness of position to the Sun, as well as its great distance (235 million mi; $378 \times 10^6$ km), prevent it from being visible. When in *opposition,* opposite from the Sun on the Earth–Sun line, Mars is not only closest (35 million mi; $56 \times 10^6$ km) to Earth, but occupies a position in the celestial sphere opposite to the Sun and is visible during most of the night hours.

Near opposition, Earth, which is moving more rapidly in its orbit than Mars, pulls ahead of Mars for a short period with the result that Mars undergoes a retrograde (westward) shift in position among the stars lasting about two months. During the remainder of the synodic period the shift is direct (eastward). The cycle of retrograde motion is illustrated in Figure 5.9.

All of the superior planets show cycles of retrograde motion when close to opposition. In the cases of the four great planets, the period of retrograde motion ranges from about four months for Jupiter (synodic

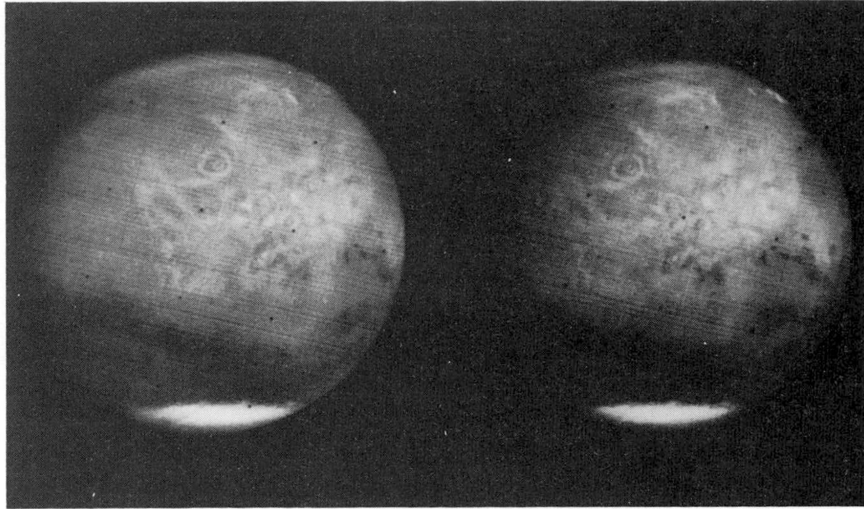

**FIGURE 5.7.** Far-encounter photographs of Mars taken from *Mariner 7* spacecraft at distances between 267,000 and 280,000 mi (430,000 and 450,000 km). The dark spot at upper left is *Nix Olympia.* This photo pair can be viewed stereoscopically for three-dimensional effect. (NASA photograph.)

period 399 days) to just over five months for Neptune (synodic period 367 days). Each of the great planets is thus in retrograde motion for between 31% and 43% of the time. The curious back-looping of the planetary paths among the stars of the zodiac posed a particularly difficult problem for the adherents of the Ptolemaic system of planetary motions (Chapter 1). To explain the retrograde motions it was necessary to consider that a planet moved with uniform motion in a small circle, known as an *epicycle,* the center of which described a larger circular orbit, or *deferent* (Figure 5.10). Although cumbersome, the Ptolemaic geometry, with additional refinements, was capable of describing the observed planetary motions in a satisfactory manner.

Because of the rather high eccentricity of Mars' orbit (0.093) the distance separating Earth and Mars at opposition ranges through a factor of almost two times (Figure 5.11). This separating distance was nearly at the greatest possible value in 1965 and will be nearly at the least possible value in 1988. From the standpoint of the telescopic observation of Mars, as well as the planning of interplanetary travel, this information on distance at opposition is of importance.

As seen from Earth, markings on the surface of Mars consist of dark areas (termed *seas*) and light areas (termed *deserts*) in a permanent pattern. Much speculation arose over the significance of recurrent dark markings, which seemed to form an intersecting network of narrow bands. These were early interpreted as canals, their apparent straightness suggesting that they were artificially produced by Martians, possibly to serve as irrigation canals.

Our knowledge of the surface of Mars has been enormously enhanced by data obtained by *Mariner 6* and *7* spacecraft, which passed close to that planet in 1969 and sent detailed photographs of the Martian surface. (See Figures 31.21 and 31.22.) Extensive cratered areas, resembling the lunar surface, were photographed, along with areas of irregular, ridge-like

**FIGURE 5.8.** Positions of Mars relative to Earth. Sun and Earth are assumed to remain fixed in space while only Mars moves in its orbit.

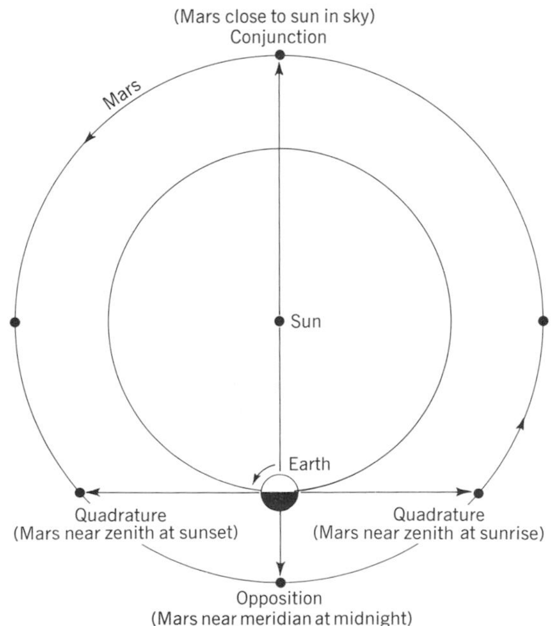


**FIGURE 5.9.** Apparent motion of the planet Mars among stars of the constellation of Taurus. Motion toward the left is direct, and toward the right, retrograde. [After T. G. Mehlin (1959), *Astronomy,* New York, John Wiley & Sons.]

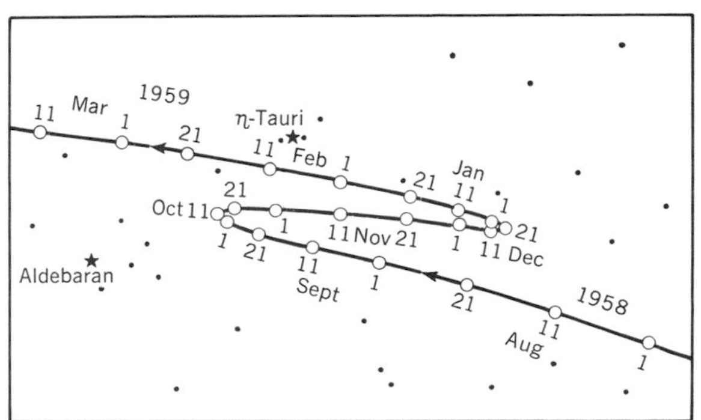

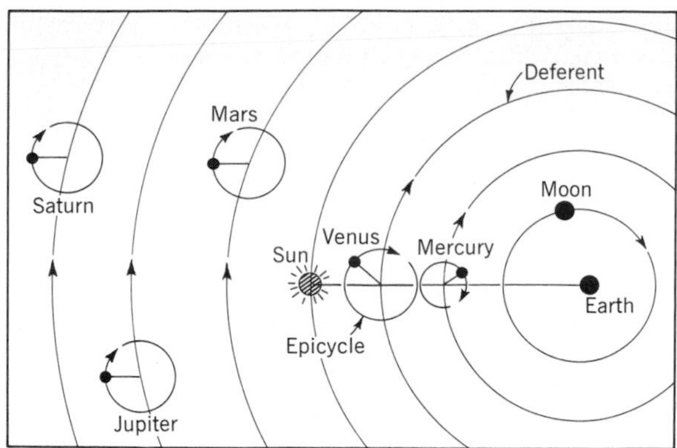


**FIGURE 5.10.** The Ptolemaic system required epicycles superimposed on deferents to explain the retrograde motions of the planets. Notice that the epicycles of Mercury and Venus remain fixed on a line connecting Earth and Sun. (After *Harper Encyclopedia of Science,* J. R. Newman, *Ed.,* vol. 3, New York, Harper & Row.)

relief features and vast featureless expanses. No evidence was obtained to suggest the presence of the supposed canals, or of any forms of life.

Of great interest in the earth sciences is the seasonal growth and disappearance of white *polar caps* on Mars. *Mariner 7* spacecraft photographs provided new and detailed information on this remarkable phenomenon. Like Earth, Mars has a winter season in one hemisphere while it is summer in the opposite hemisphere. The polar cap grows during the autumn season of that hemisphere, spreading equatorward to a maximum in midwinter, then receding with the approach of spring. (Note that the Martian year lasts 687 Earth days, or nearly twice as long as an Earth year.) Until recently it was assumed that the polar caps were a form of snow or frost, possibly similar to the ice crystals in snow or hoar frost on Earth, but carbon dioxide in solid form (dry ice) is now regarded as the most probable substance of the polar caps.

**FIGURE 5.11.** Oppositions of Mars from Earth in the period 1960 to 1990. Relative distance between the two planets can be judged by lengths of the connecting lines. [After F. L. Whipple (1968), *Earth, Moon, and Planets,* 3rd ed., Cambridge, Mass. Harvard Univ. Press.]

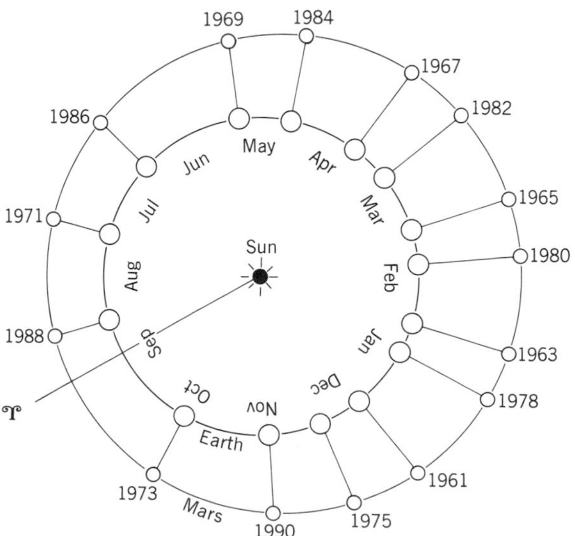


The colors and color changes on Mars are remarkable. The dark areas are of green, blue-green, or gray color, which show a seasonal browning of earth-red colors (brick-red to ochre) and may represent barren areas of weathered rock or soil rich in hydroxides of iron. Note that the average density of Mars is 3.9, a value well below that of Earth. This fact suggests that Mars may have a proportionally smaller core of iron and proportionally greater volume of rock.

The atmosphere of Mars is very thin. Atmospheric pressure at the surface is about one-hundredth that at the Earth's surface. Carbon dioxide is the principal component of the Martian atmosphere. Nitrogen has not been detected, and the amount of free oxygen is very small. Water vapor has been measured in extremely small quantity. Perhaps there was originally much more oxygen, some or most of which may have been taken up by chemical rock weathering. Although there now is little water in any form on Mars, there was probably once much more. Some of the original water may have combined with minerals to be held there permanently. Escape of hydrogen would have been favored by the small gravity of Mars (only one-third that of Earth); the escape velocity is only 3.1 mi (5.1 km) per second.

Surface air temperatures on Mars average much lower than on Earth because of greater distance from the Sun. Data from *Mariner IV* spacecraft gave surface temperature readings at middle latitudes of −171°F (−113°C) for a winter day, −36°F (−38°C) for a summer night. However, in equatorial latitudes under direct rays of the Sun, surface temperatures may rise over 85°F (30°C). Temperature measurements based on the infrared radiation of Mars substantiate these observations and suggest a total daily temperature range of 200F° (112C°) in Mars' equatorial region.

Of all the planets Mars would seem to offer the greatest possibility of harboring life, but the life would have to be adapted to a scanty supply of oxygen and water and to the low density of atmosphere and small gravitational attraction. As far as interplanetary travel is concerned, Mars would perhaps be the most favorable of the planets for human survival, but a visitor from Earth would have to provide his own life-support system.

## The asteroids

As early as the seventeenth century, astronomers had recognized the possibility that there might be a small planet between Mars and Jupiter, but it was not until 1801 that a small planet was observed in this region and named *Ceres.* Shorly thereafter a second object, *Pallas,* was found, followed by *Juno* and *Vesta.* Forty years later a fifth object was found, then many more smaller ones. Now generally called asteroids, these bodies have also been referred to as *planetoids* and as *minor planets.* All follow the planetary laws and are true planets of the Sun in the mechanical sense, if not in size.

Diameters of the four largest asteroids, named above, follow almost in the order of discovery:

| | |
|---|---|
| Ceres | 480 mi (770 km) |
| Pallas | 300 mi (480 km) |
| Vesta | 240 mi (385 km) |
| Juno | 120 mi (190 km) |

Most are very much smaller—a few miles in diameter or less—and show only as points of light rather than as disks. The total number of asteroids runs into the tens of thousands, some 40,000 of which can be detected on photographs. The great majority of asteroids follow orbits between Mars and Jupiter, but some cut inside the orbit of Venus; one is known to sweep outward almost to Saturn's orbit. Their combined mass is perhaps 1/1000 to 1/500 that of Earth.

Of particular interest is *Eros,* an irregularly shaped asteroid about 15 mi (25 km) long. Its orbit has an eccentricity of 0.22, which at times brings it as close as 13½ million mi ($21.7 \times 10^6$ km) to Earth. In January, 1931, Eros came within 16 million mi ($26 \times 10^6$ km) of Earth and provided a useful tool for measuring the distance to the Sun with a new standard of accuracy.

The asteroid *Icarus* came within about 4 million mi ($6.5 \times 10^6$ km) of Earth on June 14, 1968. Observations showed that Icarus is irregular in shape, less than one mi (1.6 km) in width, and may be composed of iron.

Three other small asteroids, *Adonis, Apollo,* and *Hermes,* have eccentric orbits that pass within Earth's orbit (Figure 5.12). In 1937 Hermes came within 0.5 million mi ($0.8 \times 10^6$ km) of Earth, an event that may be considered a "near miss" from a possible major disaster. The smallest asteroids we can observe are about 1 mi (1.6 km) in diameter, but many are probably much smaller than this. It is entirely possible that many of the meteorites (Chapter 31) which strike Earth should be regarded as simply very small asteroids.

## The great planets

Strikingly unlike the terrestrial planets are the four great planets: Jupiter, Saturn, Uranus, and Neptune. Even the smallest of these, Neptune, has almost 4 times the diameter and 15 times the mass of Earth; whereas the giant of the group, Jupiter, has 11 times the diameter and 300 times the mass of Earth. Apart from their size, a second striking difference in these two groups of planets is that of density (Table 5.1). The least dense is Saturn (0.7), about one-eighth the density of Earth and less than three-fourths that of liquid water. The other three have densities of 1.3 to 1.7, values only one-fourth that of Earth.

A third striking difference in the two groups of planets is the extremely low prevailing temperatures on the surfaces of the great planets, ranging from −216°F (−138°C) on Jupiter to −330°F (−201°C) on Neptune. A fourth striking difference is in composition, discussed further in Chapter 26. Whereas the four terrestrial planets are probably all composed of a rock mantle surrounding an iron core and have either no atmosphere or atmospheres of almost insignificant mass, the four great planets have massive atmospheres of methane, ammonia, hydrogen, and water. These volatile substances make up most of the mass of each planet.

Jupiter appears through the telescope as a somewhat flattened disk with dark and light bands extending across the surface in rough parallelism with the planet's equator (Figure 5.13). The bands are made irregular

FIGURE 5.12. Orbits of—the asteroids Apollo, Adonis, and Hermes. [After R. A. Lyttleton (1956), *The Modern Universe,* New York, Harper & Row.]

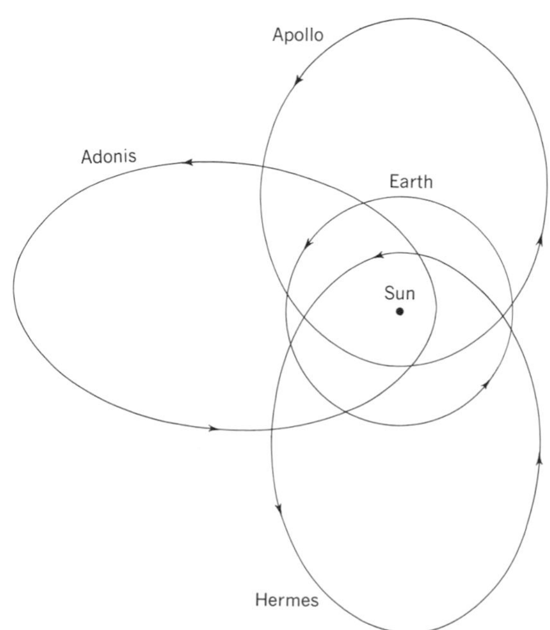


FIGURE 5.13. The planet Jupiter, photographed in blue light with the 200-in. (500-cm) Palomar telescope, shows a large red spot. To the upper right is seen the satellite Ganymede, its shadow visible as a black spot near the planet's upper edge. (The Hale Observatories.)

by cloudlike patches that, if observed over a period of days or weeks, show changing patterns. Apparently the bands are produced by systems of flow in Jupiter's atmosphere analogous to Earth's planetary wind systems. Relatively rapid rotation of Jupiter causes the planet to be appreciably oblate.

Spectroscopic analysis of the light from Jupiter shows that the atmosphere is composed largely of ammonia ($NH_2$) and methane ($CH_4$). The abundance of hydrogen in these gases suggests that the planet as a whole has hydrogen as the predominant constituent. It has been inferred that free hydrogen gas comprises most of the atmosphere beneath the outer gaseous layer of ammonia and methane. All the planet's original oxygen may have been combined with hydrogen to produce water, possibly forming an ice layer beneath the free hydrogen.

Of much interest are Jupiter's 12 moons, four of which are readily visible to the amateur astronomer using only a low-powered telescope. For the student of the earth sciences to be able to see for himself the moons of Jupiter, much as Galileo first saw them in 1610, is too rewarding an opportunity to be missed. From night to night the moons change positions greatly (Figure 5.13). The four large *Galilean satellites,* as they are sometimes called, are *Io, Europa, Ganymede,* and *Callisto,* in order of increasing orbit. Inside the orbit of Io moves another very small satellite. Far beyond the orbit of Callisto are seven more satellites, all extremely small. The faintest ones were discovered only by use of the great telescopes of the Mount Wilson Observatory. It is noteworthy that four of Jupiter's satellites, Nos. 7, 8, 9, and 11, have retrograde orbits; that is, they revolve in the opposite direction from the other moons and hence opposite to the over-all direction of revolution and rotation characteristic of the planets. Three of the four large moons, Io, Europa, and Ganymede, are of such a density as to suggest that they are largely rock masses like our Moon, whereas Callisto has a density of only 0.6 and is presumed to be made of water and ammonia in the frozen state.

Saturn is well known to all through its distinctive *rings,* which are seen as concentric bands of light and dark color lying in a very thin zone in the plane of the planet's equator (Figure 5.14). The rings consist largely of individual fragments of water ice, each revolving about the planet in an orbit as if each were an independent satellite of the planet. The particles may be on the order of size of gravel, or coarse silt; altogether they constitute not more than one-millionth of Saturn's mass. Saturn has ten moons, of which the tenth, *Janus,* was discovered only in 1966. The most remote of the moons is *Phoebe,* revolving in a retrograde orbit of 8 million mi ($13 \times 10^6$ km) radius in a period of 100 days.

Although believed to be generally similar to Jupiter in composition and structure, Saturn's proportion of hydrogen must be larger to yield the low average density of only 0.7.

Uranus and Neptune are nearly twins so far as diameter and mass are concerned. Because of their great distances from Earth these planets are rather difficult to observe and show little or no surface marking. Under spectroscopic analysis both planets show methane to be the dominant atmospheric constituent, whereas ammonia appears only in a trace. The dominance of methane over ammonia is perhaps explained by the ammonia being frozen out of the atmosphere as a result of the very low surface temperature of these planets—under −300°F (−185°C). Lower temperature is a result of their great distances from the Sun. The general composition and structure of these planets are thought to resemble those of Saturn and Jupiter, but the proportion of free hydrogen is much less in Uranus and Neptune.

**FIGURE 5.14.** The planet Saturn and its rings, photographed with the 100-in. (250-cm) Hooker telescope on Mount Wilson. (The Hale Observatories.)

An interesting feature of Uranus' motion is that the axis of rotation is tipped 98° to the perpendicular to its orbit, so that the axis lies almost in the plane of the orbit. This can also be regarded as a retrograde motion with the axis inclined at 82° away from the perpendicular. If so, the moons also revolve in a retrograde manner, with their orbits almost at right angles to the plane of Uranus' orbit. As in the case of the midnight sun observed in arctic and antarctic regions of Earth, at times of solstice on Uranus an observer at the pole would see the Sun move completely around a circle centered at this zenith and having a radius of only 8°.

Uranus has five known satellites. Neptune has two, the larger of which revolves in a retrograde orbit.

## Pluto

As already explained, Pluto is in a class by itself, being on the same order of size as the terrestrial planets, but located in a highly eccentric orbit beyond the great planets. Although its existence was suspected because of irregularities in the orbits of Uranus and Neptune, Pluto was discovered only in 1930 as a very faint object found to have changed position among the stars on successive photographs taken 6 days apart. The mass of Pluto has been calculated, from its distortion of Neptune's orbit, to be 93 percent of Earth's mass, but the planet is too small to permit its diameter to be measured. Consequently Pluto's density cannot be ascertained. Its surface temperature is judged to be not far above absolute zero.

## Meteoroids and meteors

Of great interest to earth scientists are *meteoroids,* those tiny particles of matter traveling at high velocities in space and entering the Earth's outer atmosphere in vast numbers. Meteoroids are of interest not only because they have a place in the solar family, but also because when they enter Earth's atmosphere they become *meteors,* whose luminous trails can be studied to give valuable information about the physical properties and motions of the upper atmosphere (Figure 5.15).

Of still more direct interest in the earth sciences are *meteorites,* which are simply large meteoroids or small asteroids that have managed to reach Earth's surface. These objects are discussed in Chapter 31. The arrival of a meteorite is accompanied by a brilliant flash of light (if bright enough to cast shadows it is called a "fire ball") and some of them produce sounds resembling thunder or gunfire. In contrast, the typical meteoroid, because of its small size and great elevation, yields only a thin trace of light (better known as a "shooting star") and is completely silent. Meteor trails are found in the altitude range of 60–85 mi (97–137 km) above Earth, with paths on the order of 60 mi (97 km) in length. The velocity of meteoroids with respect to Earth is from 8 to 45 mi (13 to 70 km) per second.

It is estimated that most meteoroids have a mass less than ⅓ oz (1 g) and range downward in size to perhaps one-thousandth of that mass. Thousands of millions of such specks of solid matter strike Earth's atmosphere daily. Their presence is a matter of great concern in space travel, for despite their small size the particles have a very high kinetic energy and could readily penetrate space vehicles.

If one watches the sky carefully at a time when a large number of meteoroids are striking Earth and if the meteor trails are sketched on a map of that portion of the sky, it will be found that most of these lines radiate outward from an apparent center point among the stars (Figure 5.16). Meteors forming such a pattern constitute a *meteor shower.* The common point to which their paths point (in reverse) is termed the *radiant,* and for each meteor shower the radiant occupies a fixed place among the stars. Actually, all the meteoroids of a shower are moving in parallel paths, but they seem to diverge because of the effect of perspective.

From a study of meteor trails, individual meteoroid swarms have been identified as groups of particles following highly eccentric orbits about the Sun (Figure 5.17). The swarms are named from the celestial point where the radiant lies. An example is the Leonid swarm, which seems to come from a point in the constellation of Leo. Each year Earth crosses the orbit of the Leonid meteoroid swarm in the period November 14–15. Most of the Leonid meteoroids move in a group

**FIGURE 5.15.** This meteor trail showed a sudden increase in brightness as it traveled toward the lower right. (Yerkes Observatory.)

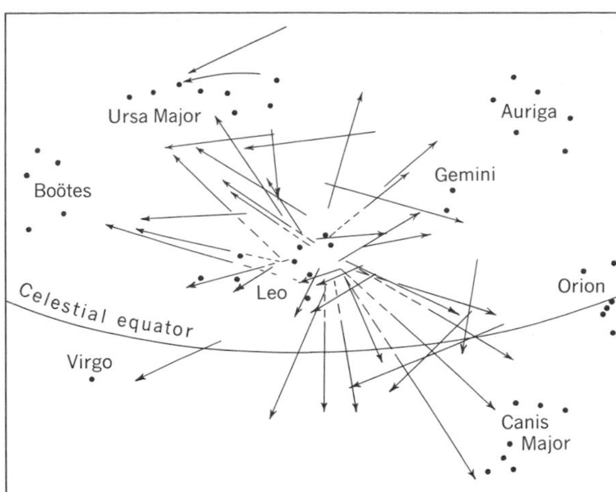


**FIGURE 5.16.** A sky-map plot of meteors observed during one night in mid-November shows that about two-thirds of them seem to radiate from a small area in the constellation of Leo. These are meteors of the Leonid swarm. [After E. A. Fath (1934), *Elements of Astronomy,* New York, McGraw-Hill.]

**FIGURE 5.17.** Orbit of the Leonid meteoroid swarm. The plane of the meteoroid orbit is inclined 17° to the plane of the ecliptic. [After E. A. Fath (1934), *Elements of Astronomy,* New York, McGraw-Hill.]

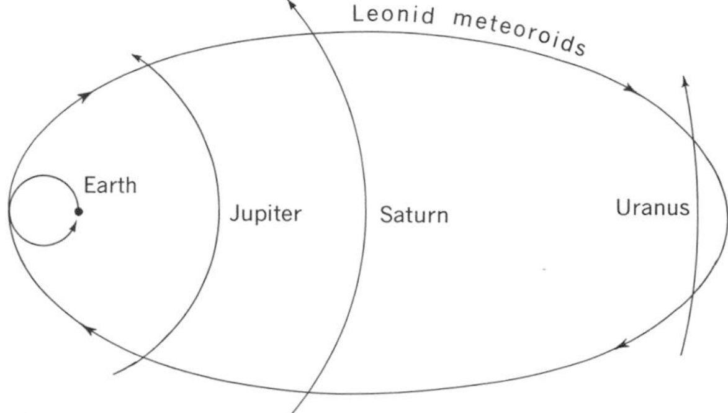

that makes a complete circuit about every 33 years (next appearance in 1999). At least eight other important swarms are known. Some meteoroids will be found scattered around the entire orbit of a swarm, hence at least a few will be seen each time Earth passes through the orbit.

## Comets

Finally, in this brief review of the secondary members of the solar system, we come to the *comets,* to many persons the most bizarre of the astronomical objects. The typical comet consists of a brightly luminous head, termed the *coma,* from which a luminous *tail* streams off in a direction away from the Sun (Figure 5.18). The apparent size of a comet varies greatly, the larger ones having tails 50 million mi ($80 \times 10^6$ km) long that cover many degrees of arc. Within the head of a large comet there is often seen a bright, starlike center, termed the *nucleus.* The material constituting the coma and tail is so diffuse that stars shine through it with undiminished intensity.

Most comets, like meteoroid swarms, follow highly eccentric elliptical orbits around the Sun (Figure 5.19). Because of their high velocity near perihelion, at which time they are visible from Earth, comets are seen for only a very short time in comparison with the total period of their revolution. At aphelion the velocities are greatly diminished, so that a comet spends most of its time among or beyond the outer planets. Most comets have orbital periods of tens of thousands of years. However some, among them Halley's comet, reappear at regular intervals ranging from three years to a few centuries. About 100 such periodic comets are known.

A particular comet group, known as the *Jupiter family* or *Jovian comets,* about 40 in all, have orbits whose most distant points are close to Jupiter's orbit. It is believed that the gravitational attraction of Jupiter entrapped these comets into their relatively small orbits. Their periods range from 3.3 years (Encke's comet) to 8.6 years.

**FIGURE 5.18.** Halley's comet photographed on May 12 and 15, 1910, at Honolulu, Hawaii. The shorter tail (right) covers 30 degrees of arc, the longer tail (left) 40 degrees. (The Hale Observatories.)

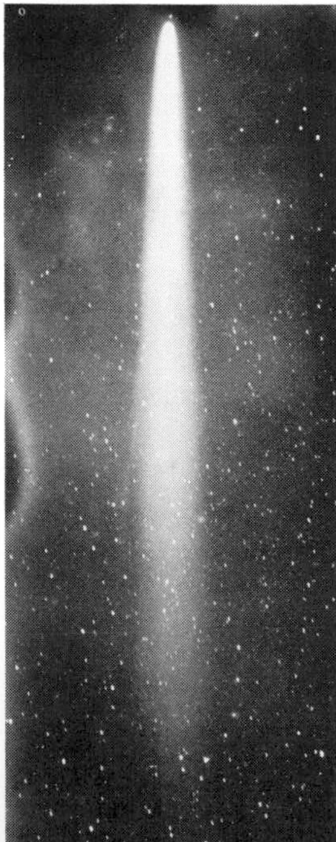

Comets have an extremely low density; the coma and tail consist entirely of fine dust particles or of gaseous matter driven off from the nucleus. The nucleus itself, however, is believed to be an aggregation of small particles of solid matter and frozen gases. Based upon spectroscopic analysis of its composition, this matter is largely methane, ammonia, carbon dioxide, and water.

During close approach to the Sun, some of the gas is vaporized and ionized under the intense heat of the Sun's rays, diffusing outward to form the comet tail, and under pressure of the solar wind (see Chapter 7) the tail is pushed away from the Sun. As a result of passage close to the Sun, a comet may lose part of its mass or be completely disrupted. It is thought that the diffuse dust particles remaining from disintegrated comets may constitute the meteoroid swarms. This possibility is strengthened by noting that the highly eccentric orbits of both meteoroid swarms and comets are much alike. Several cases are known in which the orbit of a meteoroid swarm is identical with the orbit of a previously-known comet.

The source of matter for comets and meteoroids is a topic of speculation. The Dutch astronomer, Jan H. Öort, suggested that the comets originate in a vast cloud, or "reservoir," containing the substance of millions of comets and located between 50,000 and 150,000 astronomical units from the Sun. The matter in such a belt would be at a temperature close to absolute zero and would have been formed early in the history of the solar system (see Chapter 27).

## Inherited energy of masses in motion

The members of the solar family, taken as discrete masses in motion in space, constitute a physical system of inherited kinetic energy. We see now only an apparently unchanging arrangement of bodies in orbital motions about the Sun and about one another. Within the span of human history, these cyclic motions continue with no appreciable change. No phenomena within the experience of Man are so completely reliable, so exact in their schedules, and so beyond the power of Man to alter, as are the apparent motions of the Sun, Moon, planets, and stars. Of all natural phenomena, the mechanical system of large objects in motion in the solar system comes closest to representing an exact equilibrium state without perceptible change.

Yet, on theoretical grounds, we have reason to postulate that this mechanical system is losing energy and must eventually run down. A cause of change lies in the dissipation of energy by tidal flexing of the solid bodies and the motions induced in their oceans and atmospheres (Chapter 9). Kinetic energy of motion is thus transformed into heat, which is disposed of by radiation into outer space. Thus ultimately the system will lose kinetic energy and there will be an increase in the reservoir of entropy. Perhaps these changes are

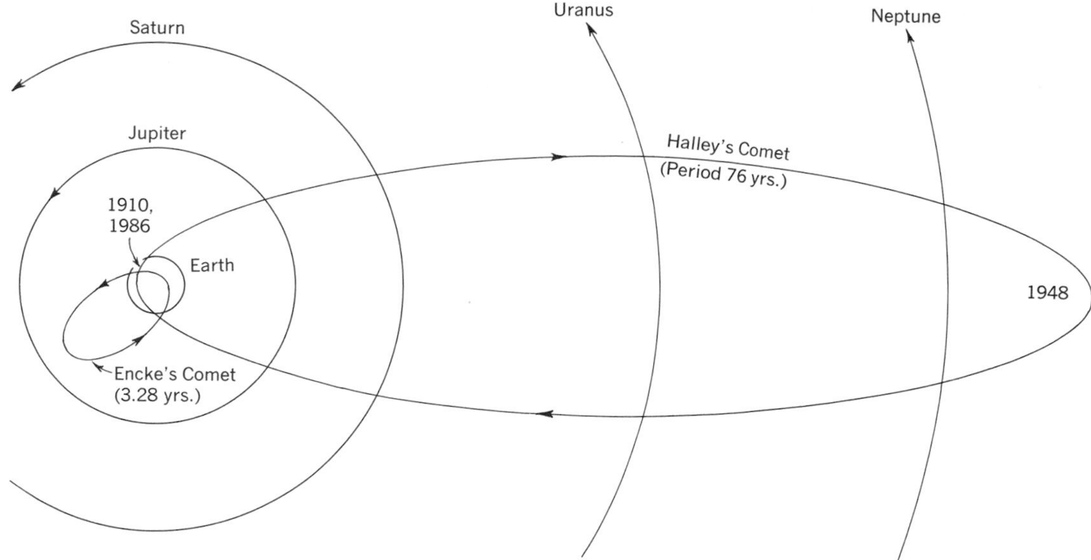


**FIGURE 5.19.** The orbits of Halley's and Encke's comets. The orbital plane of Halley's comet is inclined 18° to the ecliptic, that of Encke's comet 12°. [After R. A. Lyttleton (1956), *The Modern Universe,* New York, Harper & Row.]

so slow that their total effect will be of minor consequence in the span of life available to our Sun, which must ultimately use up its source of energy and cease to shine.

## References for further study

Urey, H. C. (1952), *The Planets; Their Origin and Development,* New Haven, Yale Univ. Press, 245 pp.

Hoyle, F. (1955), *Frontiers of Astronomy,* New York, Harper & Row, 360 pp.

Mehlin, T. G. (1959), *Astronomy,* New York, Wiley, 392 pp.

Fairbridge, R. W., ed. (1967), *Encyclopedia of Atmospheric Sciences and Astrogeology,* New York, Reinhold, 1200 pp. (See Planets, Asteroids, Comets, Meteorites, individual planets by name, Planetary Atmospheres, Kepler's laws.)

Lyttleton, R. A. (1968), *Mysteries of the Solar System,* Oxford, Clarendon Press, 261 pp.

Smart, W. M. (1968), *The Riddle of the Universe,* New York, Wiley, 228 pp., chaps. 1, 2.

Whipple, F. L. (1968), *Earth, Moon, and Planets.* 3rd ed., Cambridge, Mass., Harvard Univ. Press, 297 pp.

# 6

# Our Sun as a star in galaxy and universe

TO UNDERSTAND PLANET EARTH, we must know a great deal about the Sun, for that star, the hub of the solar system, supplies Earth with energy of light and heat, as well as other forms of matter and energy. Earth also receives from all points in space a barrage of energy in the form of light, radio waves, X-ray emissions, and highly energetic nuclear particles. For this reason it is necessary to know something of the stars beyond the Sun and their aggregations—along with diffuse matter in the form of gas and dust—that constitute the galaxies.

Thus astronomy on even the largest scale contributes knowledge of fundamental importance to an understanding of planet Earth. Astronomers and geologists have often worked as partners in developing scientific hypotheses. This cooperation comes about because evidence obtained from matter on Earth can in some instances be applied outward to problems in astronomy. A case in point, discussed in this chapter, concerns the establishment of ages of rocks on Earth. An early calculation of the age of the universe proved incompatible with known ages of rocks, and the astronomical theory was accordingly revised.

The brief and incomplete treatment of so many highly complex and important subjects of astronomy in a single chapter can be justified only if the end result is to place Earth in its proper perspective in the total framework of mass, length, and time of the universe. It is with such an objective in mind that we undertake an examination of the Sun as a star.

## The Sun

The Sun is a huge sphere of incandescent gas more than 100 times the diameter of Earth, with a mass more than 330,000 times that of Earth and a volume 1,300,000 times that of Earth (Table 6.1). The Sun's surface gravity is 34 times as great as that of Earth.

**TABLE 6.1. THE SUN: PHYSICAL DATA**

| | English units | Metric units |
|---|---|---|
| Diameter | $8.65 \times 10^5$ mi | $13.92 \times 10^5$ km |
| Mean distance from Earth | $92.95 \times 10^6$ mi | $149.6 \times 10^6$ km |
| Mass | $2.19 \times 10^{27}$ tons | $1.99 \times 10^{30}$ kg |

Like our Earth the Sun rotates upon an axis, but with an important difference: Whereas Earth is solid and has a uniform rate of rotation at its surface, the Sun is a gaseous body and does not have the same rate of rotation from one part of its surface to another. From a study of the movements of sunspots it is clear that the equatorial region of the Sun rotates with a period of about 27 days, whereas at progressively higher latitudes the rotation is slower. Internal rotation rates may differ greatly from those at the surface.

The visible surface layer of the Sun is termed the *photosphere.* The outer limit of the photosphere constitutes the edge of the Sun's disk as seen in white light. Gases in the photosphere are at a density less than that of Earth's atmosphere at sea level.

Temperature at the base of the photosphere is about 11,000°F (6000°K) but decreases to about 7700°F (4300°K) at the outer photosphere boundary. Light production is about 300,000 candlepower per square inch of surface. Beneath the photosphere, temperatures and pressures increase to enormously high values in the interior, or *nucleus,* where temperatures are between 22 and 32 million degrees F (13 to $18 \times 10^6$ °K).

Above the photosphere lies a low solar atmosphere, the *chromosphere,* a region which includes rosy, spikelike clouds of hydrogen gas termed *solar prominences.* Still farther above the Sun's surface is the *corona,* a region of pearly-gray streamers of light which constitute the Sun's outer atmosphere (Figure 6.1). At times the solar prominences reach far out into the corona as luminous archlike bodies (Figures 6.2 and 6.3) rising to heights of over one million mi ($1.6 \times 10^6$ km) and extending as far as 500,000 mi ($8 \times 10^5$ km) along the Sun's surface. Temperatures increase outward through the chromosphere, rapidly reaching 35,000°F (20,000°K). Temperature increases sharply outward in the corona until values as high as 4 million ($4 \times 10^6$)°F ($2 \times 10^6$ °K) are reached. Thus, surprisingly, the photosphere, or the Sun's surface, is its coolest layer. The intense heating of the corona is an important problem of science.

Although almost all the known elements can be detected by spectroscopic analysis of the Sun's rays, hydrogen is the predominant constituent of the Sun, with helium also abundant. It is estimated that hydrogen constitutes at least 90 percent of the Sun, and hydrogen and helium together total about 98 percent. (Composition of the Sun's atmosphere is given in Table 27.1.)

**FIGURE 6.1.** Photograph of the sun's outer corona taken during a total eclipse. The moon's disk completely covers the sun, permitting this pearly white tenuous outer layer of gases to be seen. (The Hale Observatories.)

## The Sun's interior

The source of the Sun's energy is the conversion of hydrogen into helium within the Sun's interior, a nuclear reaction producing its vast total radiant energy output of about $5 \times 10^{23}$ horsepower ($3.86 \times 10^{33}$ ergs per second).

The process of production of energy within the Sun is that of *nuclear fusion,* in which hydrogen is transformed into helium. In the fusion process, mass is converted into energy. At temperatures over 4 million

**FIGURE 6.2.** This photograph of the entire edge of the sun shows several prominences. (The Hale Observatories.)

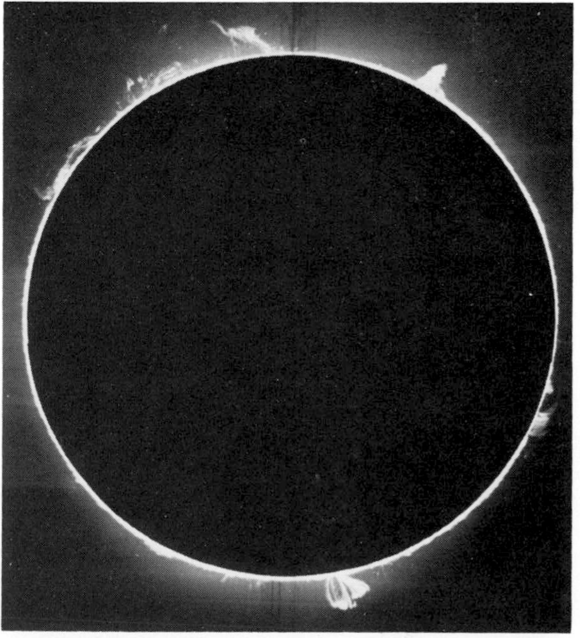

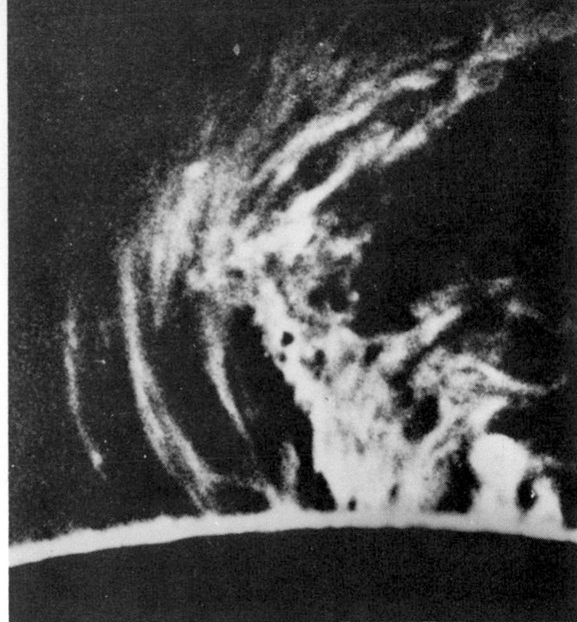

**FIGURE 6.3.** This great solar prominence rose to a height of 140,000 mi (225,000 km). (The Hale Observatories.)

($4 \times 10^6$) °K within the interior of a star, there occur several forms of reactions—involving the elements lithium, beryllium, and boron—in which helium is produced. At internal temperatures exceeding 15 million ($1.5 \times 10^7$) °K yet another series of complex reactions occurs. In these, isotopes of carbon, nitrogen, and oxygen play an essential part in the process of transformation of hydrogen into helium. The mass lost in the fusion process is extremely small (about 0.7%), so that the total mass of the star is scarcely diminished over vast spans of time.[1]

Prior to the knowledge of nuclear reactions, the Sun's energy was attributed entirely to the mechanical process of contraction under its own gravitation. The process, known as *Helmholtz contraction* (also *Kelvin contraction*), depends on the principle that a gas forced to occupy a smaller volume undergoes a rise of temperature. Calculations made over 100 years ago by the physicist, Hermann von Helmholtz (1821–1894), demonstrated that the amount of energy produced by the Sun in one year could be derived through a reduction of about 280 ft (85 m) in its diameter.

Assuming that the Sun was formed from a highly dispersed body of gases, gravitational contraction to its present diameter was calculated to require 50 million years. As will be explained in Chapters 27 and 31, radiometric dating of the age of material in the solar system points to a vastly longer span of time in which the solar system has endured in essentially the complete form we find it today. While the Helmholtz contraction process does not account for the Sun's present production of energy, it remains a valid principle when applied to the early stages of contraction of dispersed matter to produce a star.

Heat produced in the Sun's innermost core region moves outward by a process of radiation through the extremely dense gas of the interior. In a zone nearer the Sun's exterior a process of convection (mixing) is postulated to transport the heat to the surface.

## Sunspots and solar flares

A *sunspot* is a dark spot on the Sun's photosphere and normally consists of a darker central region, the *umbra*, surrounded by a somewhat lighter border, the *penumbra* (Figure 6.4). A single sunspot may be from 500 to 50,000 mi (800 to 80,000 km) across and represents a strong disturbance extending far down into the Sun's interior. The spot has a somewhat lower temperature than the surrounding photosphere. Sunspots form and disappear over a time span of several days to several weeks, during which time they can be seen to move with the Sun's rotation. The frequency of sunspots follows a cycle with an average period of about 11 years. (This subject is discussed further in Chapter 7.)

**FIGURE 6.4.** The whole disk of the sun (above) shows a large sunspot group. Below is an enlargement of the group of spots, showing the umbra and penumbra regions. (The Hale Observatories.)

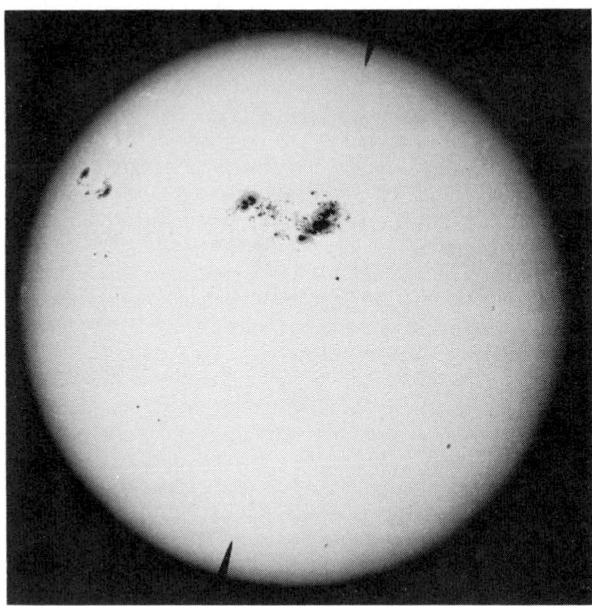

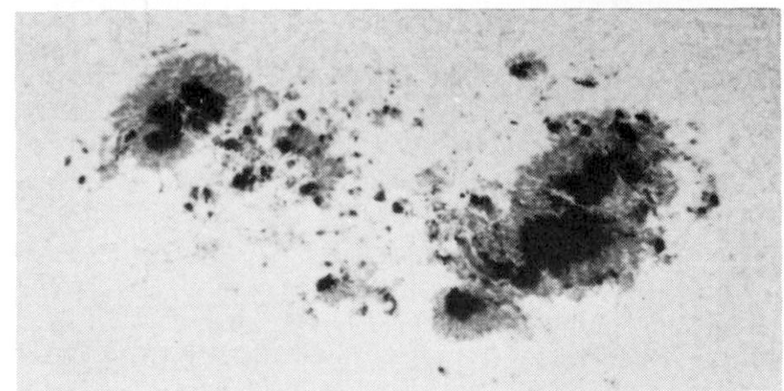

[1] Relationship of energy to mass in a nuclear reaction is given by the Einstein equation $E = MC^2$, where $E$ is energy in ergs, $M$ is mass of matter in grams, and $C$ the velocity of light in centimeters per second. Because $C$ has a value of $3 \times 10^{10}$ cm/sec, the quantity of energy produced by conversion of one gram of matter into energy is truly enormous: $9 \times 10^{20}$ ergs. At its present rate of energy production (about $4 \times 10^{33}$ ergs/sec, or $5 \times 10^{23}$ horsepower), the mass of the Sun will diminish by only one-millionth part of its mass in 15 million ($15 \times 10^6$) years.

It has been found that the sunspots have powerful magnetic fields associated with them—several thousand times as great in intensity as the magnetic field at the Earth's surface. This magnetism takes the form of strong poles associated with the sunspots. Adjacent spots of a pair in the same hemisphere have opposite polarity. The same intense magnetic fields that are associated with (and probably cause) sunspots also produce *solar flares,* which are emissions of ionized hydrogen gas from the vicinity of the sunspots. It is from such flares that X rays are sent out, followed by streams of charged particles—electrons and protons (Chapter 7).

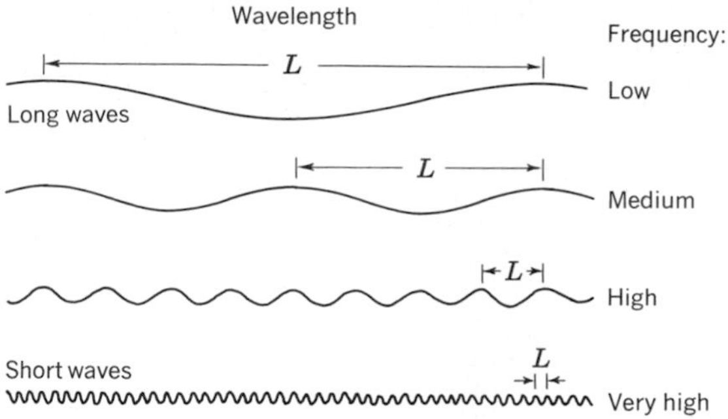


**FIGURE 6.5.** Frequency and wavelength of long and short waves.

## Solar radiation

A star, heated to incandescence at temperatures of many thousands of degrees, radiates energy which travels through space until it falls upon some gaseous, liquid, or solid material which transmits or absorbs the radiation or turns it away by reflection. Described as *electromagnetic radiation,* this radiant energy may be thought of as being in large part a wavelike motion, something like the waves which travel over the surface of a quiet pond from the point where a stone is dropped. Using this illustration for the moment, we can describe the waves in two ways: (1) by the distance separating successive wave crests, or *wavelength,* and (2) by the number of wave crests moving past a fixed point each second of time, or *frequency.* Figure 6.5 illustrates the point that *long waves* have *low frequency* while *short waves* have *high frequency,* provided, of course, that all waves have the same speed of travel. Electromagnetic radiation travels at the constant rate of 186,000 mi (299,800 km) per second ("speed of light"). Solar radiation thus takes about 8⅓ minutes to reach the Earth.

Figure 6.6 illustrates the component parts of the entire electromagnetic spectrum. The horizontal scale is a logarithmic scale (constant ratio scale) such that each division has a value 10 times as great as that next to it on the left. The upper scale gives wavelength in centimeters. English units are not shown, as these are not used in scientific discussions of the electromagnetic spectrum. In treating the visible-light range of wave lengths, a commonly used unit is the *angstrom* (symbol Å). One angstrom unit is equivalent to 0.000,000,01 cm ($10^{-7}$ cm). The expanded scale of colors within the visible light wavelength band is labeled in angstrom units.

At the very short wavelength (very high frequency) end of the spectrum are *gamma rays* and *X rays.* These are high-energy rays capable of deep penetration into opaque substances. Next comes the *ultraviolet* band, followed by the *visible light* band. Composed of still longer wavelengths is the *infrared* band, overlapping the even longer wavelength band of *radio waves,* which continue to lengths of many kilometers.

All parts of the electromagnetic spectrum are radiated into space by the Sun and other stars. Practically all information about the composition and structure of stars is derived from analysis of their spectra.

Electromagnetic radiation is a flow of energy outward into space in all directions from the spherical surface of the Sun. The total energy of radiation is not, however,

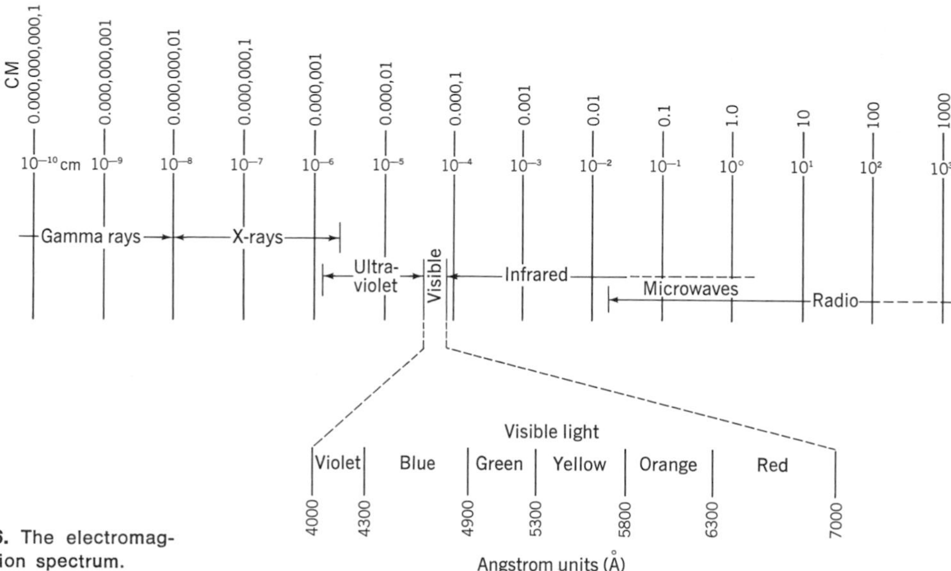


**FIGURE 6.6.** The electromagnetic radiation spectrum.

equally distributed among the various wavelengths. The energy curve of the Sun's radiation is shown in Figure 6.7. Notice that the curve rises from close to zero in the ultraviolet region to a peak value in the blue region of the visible-light band, then declines to very low values in the infrared region. Units of radiation represent the energy emitted per unit of time for a unit of surface area of the Sun's photosphere.

A basic law of physics, Planck's law, relates the intensity of energy radiation at each wavelength to the temperature of the emitting surface. Ideally, this law relates to a surface described as a "perfect radiator" or, more rigorously, a *black body.* A black body not only will absorb all radiation falling upon it, but also will emit radiation in a manner solely dependent upon its temperature. The energy curve of black-body radiation can be calculated for any given temperature. The total energy radiated by each unit of surface per unit of time varies as the fourth power of the absolute temperature (°K). This law is referred to as the *Stefan-Boltzmann law.*

Figure 6.7 shows a number of curves of ideal black-body radiation for various temperatures. Notice that for higher temperatures the peak of the curve rises higher and the total area (total energy) under the curve is also greater. Also, for a higher temperature the peak represents a shorter wavelength and, correspondingly, a higher frequency. The ideal black-body curve that best fits the observed frequency curve of the Sun is that for a temperature of a about 6000°K. Obviously, a star whose temperature is higher than that of the Sun not only will emit a greater total quantity of radiant energy per unit area of its surface, but also will have its peak at a shorter wavelength.

Energy in the Sun's radiation spectrum is apportioned about as follows: ultraviolet wavelengths, 9%; visible light wavelengths, 41%; infrared and longer, 50%.

## Units of interstellar distance

The vastness of interstellar space requires units of length quite different from those applicable to the solar system. Consider that the nearest star to our Sun, *Alpha Centauri,* is about 300,000 times more distant from the Sun than the Sun is from Earth. A convenient unit of interstellar distance is the *light year,* the distance traveled by light in one year's time. Multiplying the speed of light, 186,000 mi per sec, by the number of seconds in the year gives a value of approximately 6 million million miles. A more nearly exact value is $5.880 \times 10^{12}$ mi ($8.898 \times 10^{12}$ km). Alpha Centauri is about 4.3 light years distant from the Sun. Distances to the 15 brightest stars are given in light years in Table 6.2.

**FIGURE 6.7.** Theoretical radiation curves for 5000, 6000, and 7000 °K compared with the observed radiation curve of the sun. [From T. G. Mehlin (1959), *Astronomy,* New York, John Wiley & Sons, Figure 4–8, p. 93.]

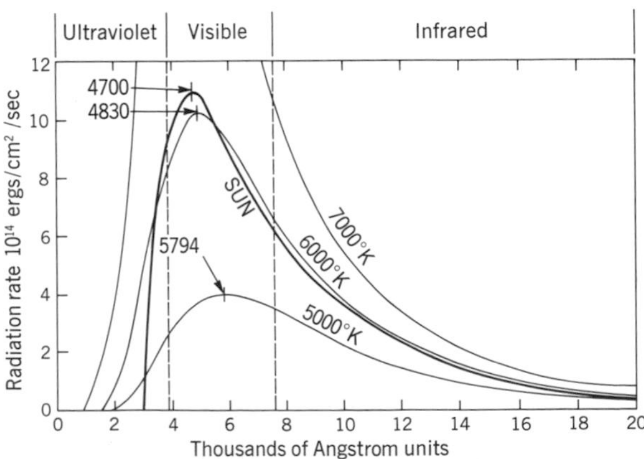


**TABLE 6.2. THE FIFTEEN BRIGHTEST STARS**

| Name | Constellation | Apparent Visual Magnitude | Actual Luminosity (Sun = 1) | Distance (light years) |
|---|---|---|---|---|
| Sirius | Canis Major | −1.44 | 23 | 8.7 |
| Canopus | Carina | −0.72 | 1,500 | 180 |
| Alpha Centauri | Centaur | −0.27 | 1.5 | 4.3 |
| Arcturus | Boötes | —0.05 | 110 | 36 |
| Vega | Lyra | 0.03 | 55 | 26.5 |
| Capella | Auriga | 0.09 | 170 | 47 |
| Rigel | Orion | 0.11 | 40,000 | 800 |
| Procyon | Canis Minor | 0.36 | 7.3 | 11.3 |
| Betelgeuse | Orion | 0.40 | 17,000 | 500 |
| Achernar | Eridanus | 0.49 | 200 | 65 |
| Beta Centauri | Centaur | 0.63 | 5,000 | 300 |
| Altair | Aquila | 0.77 | 11 | 16.5 |
| Aldebaran | Taurus | 0.80 | 100 | 53 |
| Alpha Crucis | Southern Cross | 0.83 | 4,000 | 400 |
| Antares | Scorpius | 0.94 | 5,000 | 400 |

Astronomers also make use of another measure of distance. In Chapter 1 the principle of stellar parallax was explained. A star having a parallax of exactly one second of arc would lie at a distance of about 20 million million ($2 \times 10^{13}$) mi ($3.2 \times 10^{13}$ km) from the Sun. This distance is one *parsec,* a term coined from the words "parallax" and "second." Alpha Centauri lies at a distance of 1.3 parsecs from the Sun. One parsec is equal to 3.26 light years.

## The Sun in our galaxy

In its larger setting, the Sun is but one star among some 100 billion stars grouped into an assemblage termed a *galaxy,* which in turn is but one of a vast number of widely separated galaxies constituting the *universe.*

Our galaxy has the form of a great disk, or wheel, with a marked central thickening at the hub (Figure 6.8). If it could be seen from an outside vantage point, our galaxy would probably be quite similar to the *Whirlpool Nebula* (galaxy *M51*) and to the *Great Spiral galaxy* (*M31*), located in the constellation of *Andromeda* (Figure 6.9).

The Sun occupies a position more than halfway out from the center toward the rim of the galaxy (Figure 6.8). As we look out into the plane of the disk, we see the stars of the galaxy massed in a great band, the *Milky Way,* which completely encircles the sky. For this reason our galaxy is usually designated by the name *Milky Way galaxy.*

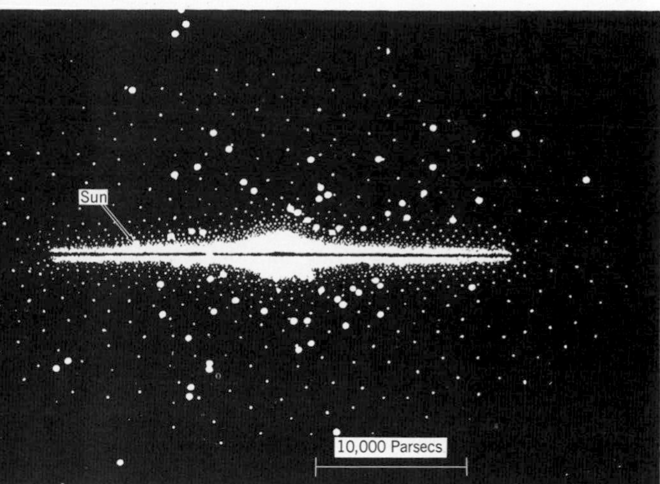


**FIGURE 6.8.** Schematic diagram of the Milky Way galaxy as viewed from a point in the plane of the spiral. Large spots represent star clusters, small spots represent stars. [From O. Struve, *The Universe,* Figure 44, p. 76. © 1962 by the Massachusetts Institute of Technology.]

The Milky Way galaxy rotates about its hub, the center part turning more rapidly than the more distant outer regions. At the position occupied by our Sun, a full cycle of rotation requires about 200 million ($2 \times 10^8$) years. The linear velocity of the solar system in this circuit is about half a million ($0.5 \times 10^6$) mi ($0.8 \times 10^6$ km) per hour.

Thickness of the Milky Way galaxy is from 5000 to 15,000 light years, its diameter about 100,000 light years (Figure 6.8). The galaxy has a system of *spiral arms,* comparable to those in the Andromeda spiral, M 31. Each arm consists of individual aggregations of stars, known as *star clouds,* each having dimensions of 5000 to 20,000 light years. Altogether, about 100 billion ($10^{11}$) stars are contained in the galaxy.

The Milky Way galaxy also contains gas clouds and clouds of cosmic dust. Concentration of these clouds is particularly heavy in the plane of the galactic disk (Figure 6.8). Surrounding the disk is a vast *halo* of widely scattered stars and *globular star clusters* (Figure 6.10).

## Properties of stars

To understand our Sun we must compare it with other stars. In this case the word "star" refers to discrete, gravitationally bound concentrations of matter in our galaxy, as distinct from highly dispersed matter in the form of gas clouds and dust clouds. Measurable properties that distinguish one star from another and enable classification to be made are *mass, size* (volume, radius, or surface area), *density, luminosity,* and *temperature.* Temperature in turn determines the type of radiation emitted by the star and governs the type of spectrum observed.

Mass of a star, which refers to the quantity of matter present, varies over a wide range. Taking the mass of our Sun as unity (1.0), the masses of stars range from as small as about 1/10 that of the Sun to about 20 times greater than the Sun. Stars also have a great range in diameter. For example, a small companion star to *Sirius* has a diameter only 1/30 that of the Sun, whereas the diameter of *Antares* is almost 500 times greater than that of the Sun.

Density of a star refers to the degree of concentration of mass within a given volume of space. Taking as a standard the density of water to be unity (1 gm per cc), the average density of the Sun is about 1.4, or only slightly more than the value for water at the Earth's surface. Stars show a truly enormous range in density, from less than a millionth that of the Sun to more than a hundred million times as great. The companion star to Sirius, referred to above as a very small star, has a mass almost equal to that of the Sun, and consequently a density 35,000 times that of water.

Luminosity of a star is the measure of its total radiant energy output as if measured at the star itself and can be stated in reference to the luminosity of the Sun taken as unity (1.0). The range of luminosity among stars is from as low as one-millionth that of the Sun to as high as half a million times as great. However, for most stars the luminosity ranges between 1/10,000 ($10^{-4}$) and 10,000 ($10^4$) times that of the Sun.

**FIGURE 6.9.** Three spiral galaxies photographed with the 200-in. (500-cm) telescope. Left: The Great Spiral Galaxy, M 31, in the constellation *Andromeda.* Center: Whirlpool Nebula, spiral galaxy M 51. Right: Spiral galaxy NGC 4565, seen edge on. (The Hale Observatories.)

**FIGURE 6.10.** Globular star cluster, M 13, in the constellation of *Hercules.* (The Hale Observatories.)

Star temperature, always given in degrees Kelvin, refers to the surface temperature as calculated in terms of the star's luminosity and diameter. Temperatures range from below 3500° K to 80,000° K. A star's color is closely related to its surface temperature: The hottest stars are blue; those only a little cooler are white; at progressively lower temperatures star color ranges from yellow through orange to red. Table 6.3 gives star color in relation to temperature.

## Stellar distances and brightness

To the observer on Earth the greatest range in brightness of the stars has long been recognized by designations of star *magnitude* for purposes of navigation and general descriptive astronomy. Most persons are familiar with a system used on star charts in which the brightest stars are classed as of the *first magnitude,* those of lesser brightness as *second magnitude,* and so on, down to the sixth magnitude.

When placed on an exact basis, the *apparent visual magnitude* of celestial objects resolves itself into a scale of numbers in which each integer value represents an increase in light intensity by a factor of 2.5 over the next larger integer. Thus a star of magnitude *1.0* is 2.5 times as bright as one of magnitude *2.0,* but 6.25 (2.5 × 2.5) times as bright as one of magnitude *3.0.* The magnitude scale, which is a logarithmic (constant ratio) scale, extends through zero into negative numbers. According to this scale, the Sun's apparent visual magnitude is −26.7, the full Moon, −12.7, and Venus in brightest phase, −4.5.

Table 6.2 gives the apparent visual magnitudes of the 15 brightest stars, together with information on luminosity and distance. Apparent visual magnitude is measured by sensitive photo-electric meters attached to telescopes. Magnitudes as faint as +24 can be measured. It should be obvious that apparent visual magnitude depends upon two factors—luminosity of the star and its distance from Earth. Light emitted from a point source diminishes in intensity inversely as the square of the distance. For two stars of equal distance from Earth, the one with the greater luminosity will appear to be the brighter. There is also the factor that the apparent brightness of a star may be diminished by the presence of a dust cloud in the intervening space (a *nebulosity*).

Table 6.2 lists the luminosities of the 15 brightest stars. Note the very great range in values. *Alpha Centauri* is a star of low luminosity, about equal to the Sun, but appears as an extremely bright star because it is very close to us. *Rigel,* of somewhat fainter apparent magnitude, has a luminosity about 27,000 times greater than that of Alpha Centauri, but is at a comparatively great distance.

To reduce the actual stellar luminosities to a scale that correlates with the scale of apparent magnitudes a system of absolute visual magnitudes is used. The *absolute visual magnitude* of a star is the apparent visual magnitude it would have if it were located at a distance of 10 parsecs from the Sun. In Figure 6.11 absolute visual magnitude is scaled on the left-hand side of the graph in numbers ranging from under −4 to over +16. By reading across to the right-hand side of the graph, a corresponding value of luminosity can be found.

## Star mass and luminosity

It might be reasoned that the larger a star, the greater will be its luminosity, since the area of radiating spheri-

**TABLE 6.3. CHARACTERISTICS OF THE SPECTRAL CLASSES**[1]

| Spectral Class | Typical Stars | Color | Temperature, °K | Characteristics of Lines in Spectrum |
|---|---|---|---|---|
| B | Rigel<br>Spica | Blue-white | 11,000° to 25,000° | Helium and hydrogen strong |
| A | Sirius<br>Vega | White | 7,500° to 11,000° | Lines of hydrogen reach greatest intensity |
| F | Canopus<br>Procyon | Yellow-white | 6,000° to 7,500° | Hydrogen weakening, metals strengthening |
| G | Capella<br>The Sun | Yellow | 5,000° to 6,000° | Metals, particularly calcium, very strong |
| K | Arcturus<br>Aldebaran | Reddish | 3,500° to 5,000° | Maximum metallic lines, molecular bands appear |
| M | Betelgeuse<br>Antares | Red | 2,000° to 3,500° | Many molecular bands, violet spectrum weak |

[1] From T. G. Mehlin (1959), *Astronomy,* New York, Wiley. See p. 50.

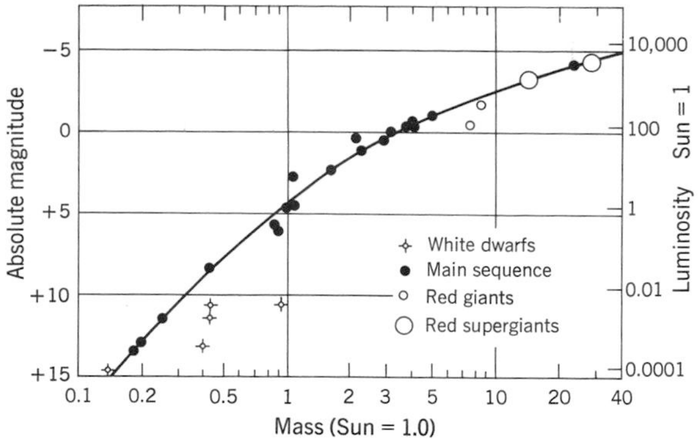


**FIGURE 6.11.** Mass-luminosity diagram. [From T. G. Mehlin (1959, *Astronomy,* New York, John Wiley & Sons, Figure 2-3, p. 45.]

cal surface increases as the square of the diameter, but this reasoning ignores the fact that a hot star may be radiating 10,000 times more strongly per square centimeter of its surface than a cool star. There is a sound scientific reason to associate increased mass with increased luminosity. The more massive the star, the greater will be the gravitational pressure tending to cause contraction, and consequently the higher will be the internal temperature. As internal temperature increases, the rate of production of energy by the nuclear fusion processes also increases. Thus the larger the mass of a star, the greater will be its output of radiant energy.

Figure 6.11 is a graph in which luminosity (also absolute visual magnitude) is plotted against mass for a number of stars whose mass and luminosity have both been independently measured. For the most part, the stars fall on or close to a broadly curved line. At the upper right are enormous stars known as *red supergiants,* below them and to the left are *red giants.* In the middle of the graph are stars of the *main sequence,* ranging from 100 times to about 1/500 the Sun's mass. There is, however, a group of stars known as the *white dwarfs,* whose plotted positions lie far off the typical curve. These are very small stars of extremely high density which produce far less heat from thermonuclear processes than do stars of the main sequence having equivalent masses. Apparently, the white dwarfs have largely exhausted their supplies of hydrogen and have contracted into an abnormally dense state.

The mass–luminosity curve is useful to the astronomer because it enables him to estimate the mass of a star when its luminosity is known, or to estimate the luminosity if only the mass is known.

## Spectral classes of stars

The radiation spectrum produced on the photosphere of a star consists of the full sequence of wavelengths appropriate to the temperature of the radiating surface. However, as this radiation passes through the star's atmosphere (chromosphere) the various elements that comprise the atmospheric gas absorb certain wavelengths. Where absorption occurs, black lines show on the color spectrum. Such lines, first observed in the Sun's spectrum, were known as *Frauenhofer lines.* Each element has its particular set of absorption lines and can be identified with certainty. Moreover, it is possible to determine the physical state of the absorbing element, whether it exists as neutral atoms or in the ionized state. From these observations the temperature of the star's atmosphere can be quite accurately determined. The proportions in which each element is present can also be determined.

The slit spectroscope (described in Chapter 1, see Figure 1.2) attached to a telescope can be focused upon a star and its spectrum photographed and analyzed (Figure 6.12). This procedure has been carried out upon a very large number of stars of our galaxy, with the result that they can be classified according to the *spectral class* to which each belongs. Arranged according to temperature, from hottest to coolest, the six major classes are designated *B, A, F, G, K,* and *M.* Table 6.3 summarizes the characteristics of the six major spectral classes. Figure 6.12 reproduces the actual spectra of six representative stars as photographed by telescope.

In addition to the six main classes, five spectral classes are added to accommodate a few stars which do not fit into the main temperature sequence. At the blue end of the sequence are added classes *W* and *O,* at the red end classes *N, R,* and *S.* Because the spectral classes grade from one to the next, intermediate positions on the scale are designated by numbered subdivisions, of which there are ten within each letter class.

## Spectrum–luminosity relationships

About 1910 two astronomers, Hertzsprung and Russell, working independently, plotted star luminosity against position in the main spectral temperature sequence and found that a distinct and meaningful relationship exists. Figure 6.13 is the *Hertzsprung-Russell diagram* (or simply *H-R diagram*), in which each point represents a star. Luminosity is scaled on the vertical axis (ordinate) and corresponding scales in terms of star mass and absolute visual magnitude are given as well. On the horizontal axis (abscissa) spectral classes are arranged in sequence from highest temperature, on the left, to lowest temperature, on the right.

It is obvious that most of the stars plotted on the H-R diagram lie in a diagonal band commencing with high temperature and great luminosity at the upper left and ending with low temperature and small luminosity at the lower right. This band may be designated as the

**FIGURE 6.12.** Representative spectra of stars of the major spectral classes. Symbols at left designate star and constellation. (Yerkes Observatory photograph, University of Chicago.)

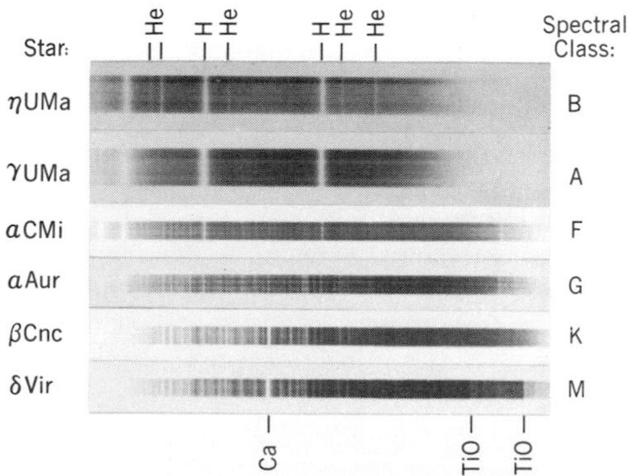

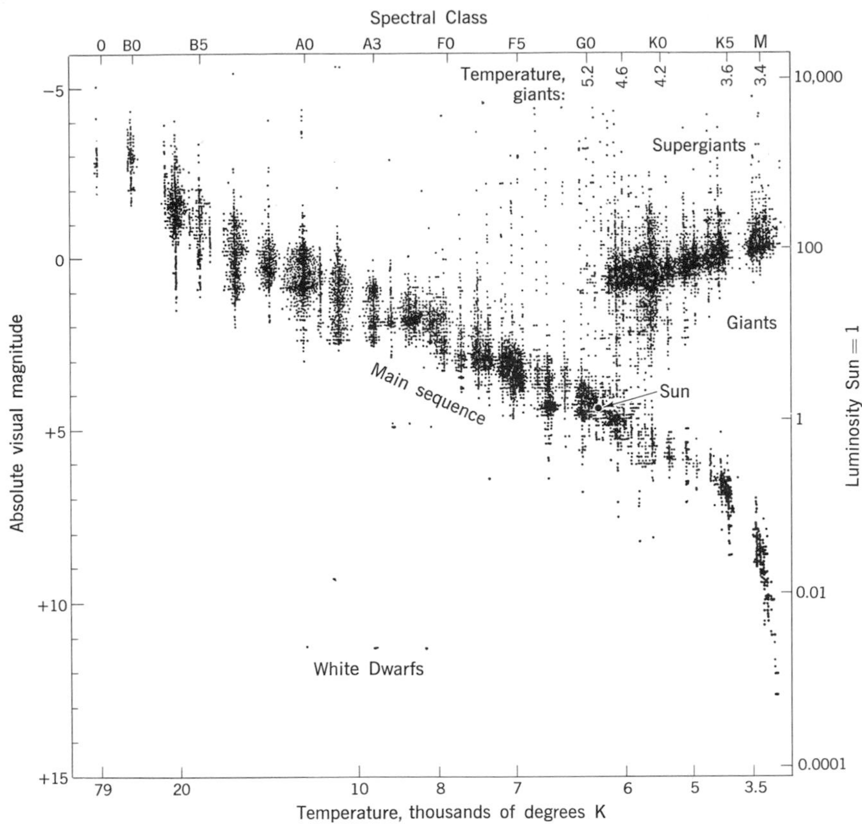


**FIGURE 6.13.** The Hertzsprung-Russell spectrum–luminosity diagram. Each dot represents a star. Altogether a sample of 6700 stars is recorded on the diagram. (Yerkes Observatory photograph, University of Chicago.)

*main sequence.* Our Sun lies about two-thirds of the way down this main sequence. A large isolated cluster of points above and to the right of the main sequence consists of the *supergiants* and *giants.* These are stars of enormous size which have great luminosity despite their cool temperatures. They fall into the spectral classes *K* and *M.* In the lower part of the diagram are a very few stars, the *white dwarfs,* which we have already noted to be very small, but of extremely great density. They are relatively hot stars.

## Stellar evolution

Information about stars that we have reviewed thus far can be organized into a time-sequence pattern describing the life history of a star. Deferring for the moment a consideration of how the universe itself may have originated, we will start with a galaxy already in existence.

Within our Milky Way galaxy there are clouds of cold gas and dust whose temperature is close to absolute zero. Certain of these clouds appear as dark globules on astronomical photographs because the gas effectively absorbs most or all of the starlight that would otherwise pass through from distant stars on the far side. Diameters of the dark globules are on the order of 10,000 to 100,000 astronomical units. (Recall that the solar system has a diameter of about 80 astronomical units at the orbit of Pluto.)

As a working hypothesis, the cloud of cold gas that comprises a dark globule will be taken to represent the initial stage in the life history of a star. Through the gravitational attraction which all particles of the gas cloud exert upon all other particles, the cloud would begin to contract, occupying a smaller volume. Through the Helmholtz principle, already explained, the temperature of the contracting body of gas would increase, and particularly so near the center of the mass, where pressures would be greatest. Eventually, a star would be formed and its interior temperature would attain a value exceeding one million ($10^6$) °K. At this point the first of a series of nuclear reactions would begin to take place, converting matter into energy, and causing the star to begin emitting large amounts of electromagnetic radiation. As contraction continued and interior temperatures rose, other forms of nuclear reactions, which we have previously reviewed, would develop and sustain a high level of energy production. A fully developed star such as our Sun would then exist.

As the Hertzsprung-Russell diagram shows, stars of the main sequence span a very great range in both temperature and mass. Those of small mass can reach only comparatively low temperatures and pressures and therefore produce energy at a relatively slow rate, resulting in stars of faint luminosity. Such small stars will have an extremely long life because the utilization of the hydrogen supply takes place so very slowly. On the other hand, stars at the high-temperature and large-mass end of the sequence are converting their hydrogen supply into energy at an extremely fast rate. Their life expectancies will be short. For example, a star of mass ten times that of the Sun will radiate energy about 10,000 times as rapidly as the Sun. The life of such a large star must therefore be on the order of 1 percent of the life of our Sun, or as short as 100 million years. The small stars will correspondingly have lives vastly longer than the Sun, that is, a duration of as great as thousands of billions of years.

Figure 6.14 is a graph having essentially the same field as the H-R diagram but does not show the plots of the individual stars. The diagonal band shows the position of the main sequence. The chain of arrows represents the evolution of a single star of about the size of the Sun. The path enters from the right and moves horizontally toward the line of the main sequence. This horizontal path is covered comparatively rapidly and represents the stage of contraction of the gas cloud and its rise in temperature. When the star begins to consume its hydrogen by thermonuclear processes it is located on the line of the main sequence. As appreciable amounts of the star's hydrogen are transformed into helium, the star may brighten slightly, probably by less than a magnitude, moving slowly to a position slightly above its original main sequence location.

The next stage in the life history of a star comes when its hydrogen supply is seriously depleted. Nuclear activity ceases first in the central region of the star, which then contracts. Nuclear activity continues in a surrounding zone that gradually moves outward from the center toward the surface. As this happens, the star may expand greatly. Although the luminosity remains high, the surface temperature falls and the star spectrum changes toward the red region. On the H-R diagram (Figure 6.13) this change requires that the plotted position of the star depart from the main sequence and move toward the upper right, occupying a position among the red giants and perhaps reaching the position of the supergiants (Figure 6.13). The final hypothetical stage in the life of the star is suggested in Figure 6.14 by a line that moves downward and to the left, then sharply downward to the region of the white dwarfs. These changes may be quite rapid. The star is now "burned out" and has only a faint luminosity despite its high temperature.

**FIGURE 6.14.** Simplified H-R diagram showing inferred evolution of an average star. [From O. Struve, *The Universe,* Figure 36, p. 55. © 1962 by the Massachusetts Institute of Technology.]

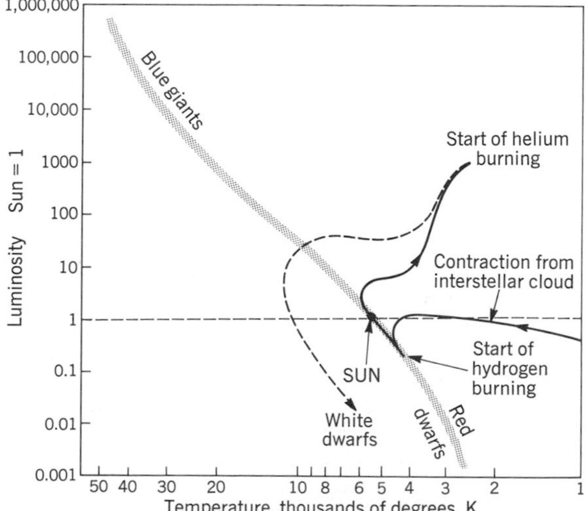


## Binary stars, variable stars, and pulsars

Two stars sufficiently close together may be held within each other's gravitational fields to form a two-body system revolving about a common center of gravity. The mechanics of such a system are essentially similar to that of the Earth-Moon pair and are discussed in Chapters 8 and 9. Such star pairs are known as *binary stars,* and are quite numerous in our galaxy. In some instances both stars of the pair can be observed as separate individuals. In other instances they cannot be optically separated and appear as a single light source that varies regularly in intensity, for there is a sharp drop in brightness as one star of the pair passes behind the other. Still other binary stars systems can be detected only through variations in their spectra.

Quite a different class of stars are those in which the variations in brightness result from actual changes in the intensity of surface radiation of the star and represent changes in the star itself. One class of such stars are the *pulsating variable stars,* which undergo regular pulsations of brightness in cycles that range in length from as short as one hour to as long as several years. Pulsations are known to be associated with rhythmic expansions and contractions of these stars (Figure 6.15). Contraction increases the internal temperature of the star and stimulates more rapid production of thermonuclear energy, while expansion lowers temperature and reduces such activity. Pulsating stars that are very large red giants and supergiants show very long periods of pulsation; those that are relatively hot stars of blue color (*blue giants*) pulsate more rapidly.

The stability of our Sun, with its remarkable constancy of energy output over hundreds of millions of years of time, stands in strong contrast to the behavior of the pulsating variable stars. Life on planet Earth has depended upon the Sun's constancy of energy emission. We might infer that planetary systems belonging to variable stars would not provide stable environments for the evolution of life.

## Novae

On occasion, an extremely faint star bursts into intense brightness, then fades back to its original level. Such stars are known as *novae,* meaning "new," because they had not been observed to exist prior to the episode of brightness. A typical nova increases in bright-

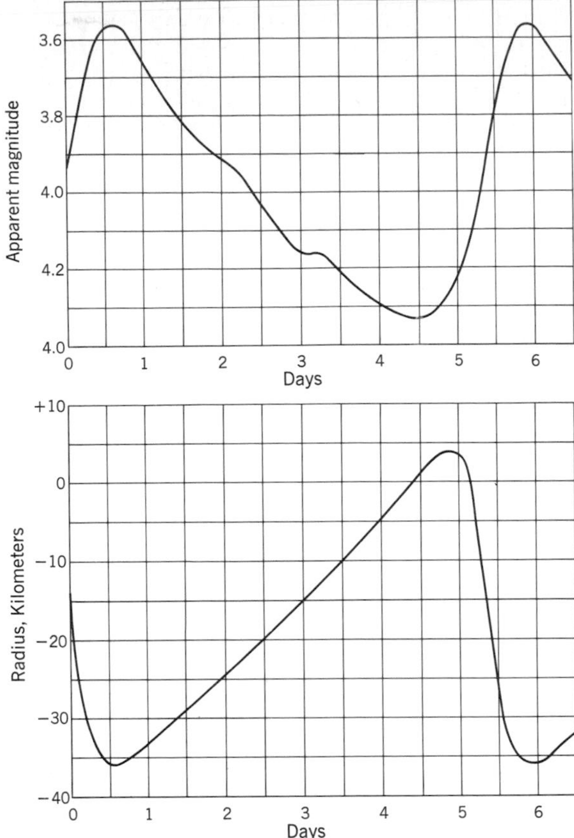


**FIGURE 6.15.** Curves of apparent magnitude and radius for *Delta Cephei* for 6½ days. [From T. G. Mehlin (1959), *Astronomy,* New York, John Wiley & Sons, Figure 6-2, p. 140; based on data of Lick Observatory.]

ness by 10 to 12 magnitudes in a time span of a few hours to a few days. Immediately after the outburst the brightness falls off rapidly for a time and then tends to level off and to diminish gradually over many weeks. Within years the brightness has returned to the original level.

Increase in brightness of the nova is associated with an explosive increase in its size, which may be a diameter increase of from 100 to 200 times. This expansion takes place in the photosphere of the star and is not an explosive enlargement of the entire star interior. The expanded layer of gases gradually dissipates and is lost into space, revealing the main body of the star intact. Novae are interpreted as being stars in the white dwarf stage, near the end of the stellar life cycle. The explosion represents a short period of instability during the final stages of contraction into an extremely dense small star.

A very rare type of nova is one that attains sudden brightness equal to something on the order of a quarter of a billion times the luminosity of the Sun. If it is in our own galaxy its apparent magnitude may exceed that of the brightest planets. Such phenomena are known as *supernovae* and occur within our galaxy with a frequency of about one in several hundred years. Following the outburst, an expanding cloud of gas and dust (an expanding nebula) has been observed surrounding the site of the supernova (Figure 6.16). Like the novae, the supernovae are interpreted as very old white dwarf stars in the last stages of contraction. Unlike the typical nova, however, the outburst of a supernova is believed to be a star-destroying explosion.

**FIGURE 6.16.** The Crab Nebula in the constellation of *Taurus,* photographed in red light. This nebula is the remains of a supernova of A.D. 1054. (The Hale Observatories.)

## Pulsars

Most recently discovered of stars whose brightness varies are the *pulsars.* These stars flash "on" and "off" rapidly, emitting both light waves and radio waves in the same rhythm. Light pulses range in frequency from about one pulse per four seconds in the slowest rhythm to as high as 30 pulses per second. In the case of the high rate of pulsation, the star appears to the eye and on photographs to be continuously bright, but special techniques can reveal the flashing on and off (Figure 6.17). To explain the periodic emission of pulsars it has been suggested that they are extremely small, dense *neutron stars* (dwarfs) rotating rapidly on an axis. The emitting source is situated at one spot on the star and thus gives forth a single turning ray of light or of radio waves, as does a lighthouse or rotating beacon light. The magnetic field of a pulsating neutron star is thought to be enormously strong—some thousand-billion times

**FIGURE 6.17.** Comparison photographs of pulsar NP 0532 in "on" (left) and "off" (right) phases. (Lick Observatory photograph, University of California.)

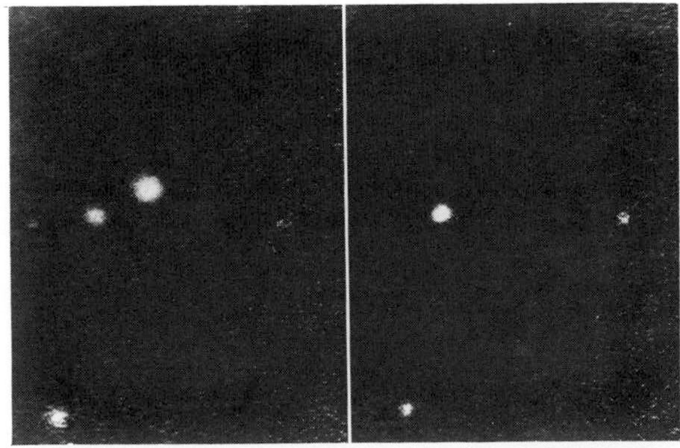

as strong as that of our Sun. A measurable slowing of pulse rate in these stars suggests that energy is being dissipated at a rapid rate.

## Galaxies and the universe

To the most distant limits of telescopic penetration our universe consists of widely spaced galaxies, of which an estimated 10 billion ($10^{10}$) can now be observed, but no outer limit to the universe can be recognized. The total extent of possible observation of light from distant galaxies is estimated to be 10 billion ($10^{10}$) light years. Within this theoretical maximum radius of observation there may be as many as 100 billion ($10^{11}$) galaxies.

Galaxies fall into several classes, according to their shapes. *Spiral galaxies,* such as our Milky Way, are illustrated by the Andromeda spiral, which is the closest galaxy to our own (Figure 6.8). Its distance is about 1.8 billion ($1.8 \times 10^9$) light years and its diameter a bit larger than our Milky Way galaxy. Another class of galaxies are the *barred spirals* in which the two arms uncoil from a central bar (Figure 6.18). Equally important are galaxies of the *elliptical* group (Figure 6.19). These are ellipsoidal or spherical masses having a high degree of symmetry, a form that suggests that they, like the spirals, are rotating. In addition there are galaxies of highly irregular shape, but these are relatively few.

Within the nearer galaxies individual stars and star clusters can be recognized. Clouds of dust and gas that are typical of the spiral galaxies seem to be absent from the elliptical types. Attempts have been made to arrange the several forms of galaxies into an evolutionary series. Edwin P. Hubble, the astronomer who did much of the pioneering work in galactic investigation, suggested a classification which began with the almost spherical elliptical galaxies and then progressed to the more flattened systems, branched into two parallel arms for the spirals and barred spirals, and perhaps ended with the irregular galaxies (Figure 6.20).

**FIGURE 6.18.** Barred spiral galaxy NGC 7741 in the constellation of *Pegasus.*(The Hale Observatories.)

**FIGURE 6.19.** Elliptical galaxy NGC 205 in the constellation of *Andromeda.* (The Hale Observatories.)

When more was known about the galaxies and the ages of the stars in them, Harlow Shapley suggested that the evolutionary sequence might well begin with the irregular galaxies, developing into spiral systems in which the nucleus wound more tightly into the arms with increasing age. Then, as the stars aged and the interstellar clouds of gas and dust were eliminated, the spirals might evolve into elliptical systems of varying degrees of flattening. It is still not understood why some spirals take the normal form and some become barred spirals.

One of the most remarkable phenomena related to the galaxies is that of the shift of their spectra toward the red end. In the spectra of light from the galaxies the extent to which the red shift occurs increases in direct proportion to their radial distance from our point of observation. Widely differing interpretations can be attached to the red shift. One is the possibility that the physical nature of the light itself is altered in proportion to the distance it travels. A second and highly intriguing hypothesis is that the red shift is a true Doppler effect (Chapter 1). If so, all galaxies are in radial motion, receding from our galaxy. Moreover, the speed of recession increases proportionately with increasing distance. The geometry of such apparent radial outward motion can be visualized in terms of a universe that is expanding uniformly in volume. From any single vantage point in this system all other objects will appear to be moving radially outward.

When first discovered by Hubble in the 1920's, the red shift was combined by him with other astronomical measurements to yield the conclusion that radial velocities of the galaxies increase by about 100 mi (160 km) per second for every increase of one million ($10^6$) light years distance.

Hubble's discovery of a law of increase of radial velocity proportionate with distance quickly led to a

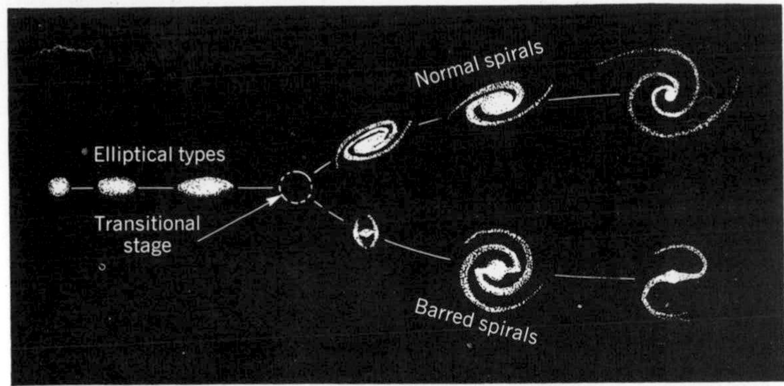


**FIGURE 6.20.** Diagram of sequence of nebular types as arranged by E. Hubble. No nebulae have been recognized in the transitional stage, which is hypothetical. [From E. Hubble (1936), *The Realm of the Nebulae,* New Haven, Yale Univ. Press, p. 45.]

new theory of origin of the universe.[2] Among the first to propose such a cosmological theory was Canon Lemaitre, a Belgian, who referred to the concept as a "fireworks theory." The theory requires an initial point in time at which all matter was concentrated into a small space. From this center it expanded explosively outward in all directions. The elements were created during this explosion and were later formed into the galaxies. Although now commonly referred to as the "big-bang" theory of the universe, the title of *evolutionary theory* is perhaps more fitting.

Using Hubble's first derived estimates of the rate of velocity increase with distance of separation, it could be calculated that all matter of the universe was concentrated into a small space about 2 billion ($2 \times 10^9$) years ago. This point in time was designated the *age of the universe.* As explained in Chapter 27, age determination of meteorites and rocks based upon analysis of radioactive decay of certain elements gives ages much greater than 2 billion years. Ages of meteorites, in particular, are found to be 4½ billion ($4.5 \times 10^9$) years and are the oldest known objects in existence.

In 1952, data obtained from the 200-inch reflector at the Mount Palomar Observatory required Hubble's calculations to be modified to revise the rate of increase in velocity to 40 mi (65 km) per second per million light years and consequently to increase the calculated age of the universe to 5 billion years. This modification placed the evolutionary theory in accord with the established ages of meteorites and rocks. More recently the figures have been revised to increase the age of the universe further, perhaps to as great as 10 billion ($10^{10}$) years.

The evolutionary theory conforms to the principle that the distribution of galaxies is uniform in all directions throughout space. Under this concept, to an observer from any galaxy the average composition of the universe would appear the same. It is interesting to consider that under Hubble's principle the radial velocity of extremely distant galaxies, with respect to our observation point in the solar system, must reach and finally equal the speed of light. This distance would constitute the observable limit of the universe, beyond which we could receive no light or radio waves from the emitting sources.

The hypothesis of a pulsating universe has also been suggested as a modification of the "big-bang" hypothesis. Immediately after the initial explosion all of the matter would be moving outward with high velocities, but the mutual gravitational attraction between all of the parts would tend to slow their outward motion, perhaps finally stopping it and causing the entire system to contract. All of the material would eventually come back to a central point in an implosion that would annihilate all forms of matter—stars, galaxies, and even individual atoms. The result would be another "cosmic bomb" which would explode and start the whole process over again. The interval for one complete cycle has been estimated to be something less than a hundred billion years.

A major rival theory of the universe holds that there was no single point in time at which matter was concentrated in one place. Instead, the production of matter has gone on throughout intergalactic space at a constant rate during all time. Rate of production of matter in the form of hydrogen atoms has been equalled by the rate at which matter is dispersed by the expansion of the universe. This *steady-state* theory of cosmology, proposed in 1948 by the astronomers H. Bondi, T. Gold, and F. Hoyle, has attracted great interest.

The most recent evaluations of information concerning galaxies and other distant objects, based upon such methods as radio astronomy (discussed in the succeeding section), seem to place the evolutionary theory of the universe in a stronger scientific position than the steady-state theory. However, we can anticipate modified and new cosmological theories of the universe to be brought forward from time to time as new information is gained from the development and use of newer tools of astronomy.

## Radio astronomy and quasars

We have noted that a part of the electromagnetic radiation spectrum, that in the long-wave region, consists of *radio waves.* In the range of wavelengths between about 1 cm and about 20 m, radio waves can pass through our atmosphere and be received by *radio telescopes.* These instruments use a huge concave bowl-shaped (parabolic) antenna that can be aimed at a distant emitting source.

Thousands of radio-emitting sources have been discovered and their positions plotted, but only a few can be identified with stellar objects that appear on photographs. Some sources of radio emission lie within our

[2] The science of *cosmology* concerns itself with the nature and origin of the universe.

Milky Way galaxy; others are in distant galaxies, referred to as *radio galaxies.* These radio galaxies, of which about 150 have been identified, are the most powerful of all radio emission sources. What appear to be two galaxies in collision are identified with radio wave emission. Hydrogen gas clouds within our galaxy are also emitting sources. Our Sun shows strong radio wave emission at those times when a solar flare is in progress. A number of stars are known to have flares of similar nature; at such times their brilliance is greatly increased, thus radio emissions received from these stars are believed to be associated with flares.

Among the most important of astronomical discoveries in recent years (since about 1963) has been the finding of extremely small sources of intensely powerful radio emission not related to any surrounding galaxy. Named *quasistellar radio sources,* a term since reduced to *quasars,* these emission sources appear only as pinpoints of light. The distribution of the 100 or so quasars identified is quite uniform with respect to direction from the earth.

A particularly striking feature of quasars is that the lines in their spectra show a very great shift toward the red. Although its use here may be questioned, if the same red shift–distance relationship developed for galaxies is applied to quasars, the extremely large red shift would lead to the conclusion that they are on the order of one to ten billion ($10^9$ to $10^{10}$) light years away, and are thus the most distant known objects in the universe. If so, the luminosities and energy outputs of the quasars are truly enormous. One hypothesis explains the quasars as formed from gas clouds sent outward from the center of an exploding universe at a speed up to 80% that of light.

## Cosmic particles (cosmic rays)

The Earth's atmosphere is continually bombarded with elementary particles traveling at speeds approaching the speed of light and having enormous energy and penetrating power. This form of radiation from outer space, the *cosmic particle* (*cosmic ray*), is an entirely independent phenomenon from the electromagnetic radiation spectrum of a star.

Cosmic particles are *protons,* that is, parts of the atomic nucleus. Approximately 90 percent are hydrogen nuclei, 9 percent are helium nuclei, and 1 percent are heavier nuclei. The energy of cosmic particles is enormous. Measured in units of *electron volts,* the energy of single cosmic particles ranges from one billion electron volts (1 Bev) to 100,000 Bev, but some have energies up to 100 million Bev.

Cosmic particles approach our Earth from all directions. Their space paths seem to be quite at random and they can be visualized as constituting a kind of cosmic "gas" in which particles undergo random collisions and can thus take an infinite variety of paths and a wide range of speeds. Sources of cosmic particles are considered to be varied. They are produced in solar flares, but most come from other sources, believed to be the explosions of supernova and other forms of explosive activity in the central parts of our own and other galaxies. It has been suggested that galaxies which emit

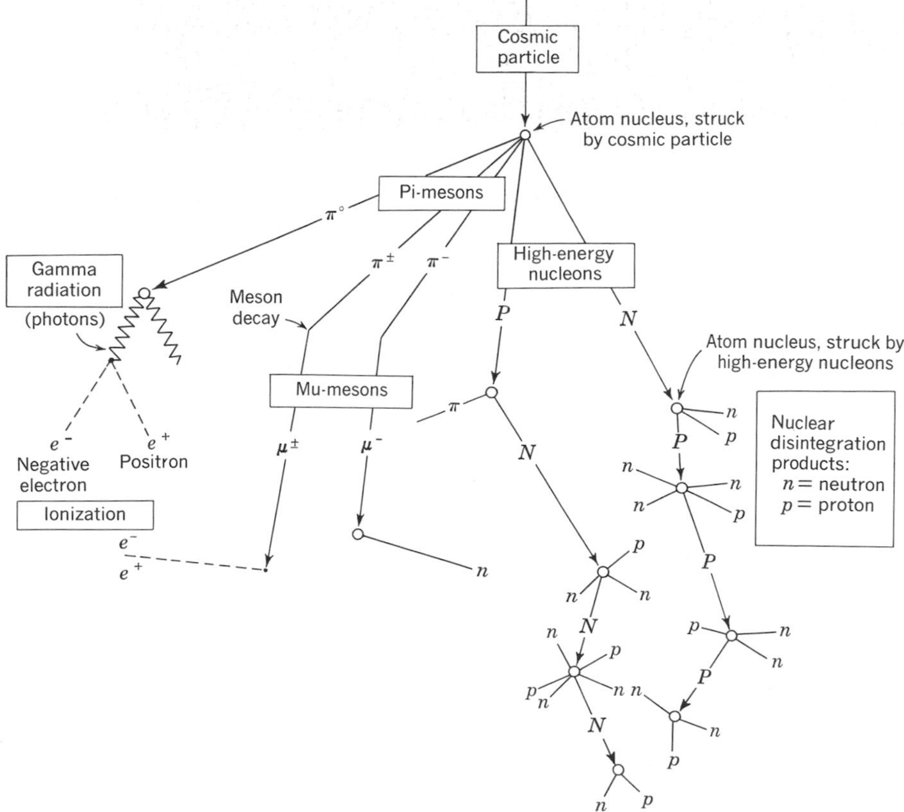


**FIGURE 6.21.** Schematic diagram of a cosmic shower, showing the variety of disintegrations and particles that may result from the impact of a single cosmic particle entering the atmosphere. [After U.S. Air Force, *Handbook of Geophysics* (1960), New York, Macmillan, Figure 18-1.]

radio waves are also sources of important amounts of cosmic radiation.

Cosmic particles are extremely important in the environment of life on the Earth's surface. Certain harmful parts of the solar radiation spectrum—the X rays and gamma rays—are largely stopped by our atmosphere (Chapter 13), but the extremely high energy of cosmic particles enables them to penetrate deep into the lower atmosphere and to reach the Earth's surface. This penetration is accompanied by an elaborate series of secondary nuclear reactions comprising a *shower* of particles and secondary forms of radiation (Figure 6.21). When the high-speed cosmic particle impacts the nucleus of an atom within the atmosphere, there are produced neutrons and protons, mesons, and gamma radiation. The effect of such radiation upon life forms is to induce genetic changes (mutations in genes) which are essential in the process of organic evolution.

## Our Sun in review

Seen in its relative position among the other stars of the Milky Way galaxy, our Sun is a fairly typical star in most respects. It lies somewhat below the midpoint of the main sequence of stars, belonging to the spectral class *G*, which has moderate surface temperatures in terms of the total temperature range. Luminosity and mass are about midway on the constant-ratio (logarithmic) scale of those values. Extreme constancy of energy output over vast spans of geologic time characterizes the Sun, a behavior in strong contrast to the changing energy fluxes of the variable stars and novae.

Our Sun represents one of the basic forms of energy systems, that of conversion of matter to energy in nuclear reactions occurring within a gaseous medium under enormously high pressures and temperatures. The life span of our Sun is neither very short nor very long in comparison with the range found among stars, but it is long enough to assure that our terrestrial environment can continue with little change for a span of time vastly longer than that which has already transpired as geologic time.

In reference to the total size of our Milky Way galaxy, the Sun is no more than an insignificant particle of matter, while in the context of the universe of galaxies, it comes infinitesimally close to being nothing at all. Within the universe there must be a very large number of stars quite similar to our Sun, and many of these must have planets resembling our own. Reason leads us to suppose that spontaneous development of organic life and its evolution to highly complex states must have been replicated a great number of times on unknown planets. But we also realize that the vastness of interstellar and intergallactic space reduces almost to zero the possibilities of identifying and communicating with even the closest of such organic complexes. Despite such odds, the possibility of a discovery that Man on planet Earth is not alone in the universe continues to fire the popular imagination.

## References for further study

Lyttleton, R. A. (1956), *The Modern Universe,* New York, Harper & Row, 207 pp., chaps. 4, 5, 6.

Mehlin, T. G. (1959), *Astronomy,* New York, Wiley, 392 pp.

Bondi, H. (1960), *The Universe at Large,* New York, Doubleday, 154 pp.

Struve, O. (1962), *The Universe,* Cambridge, Mass., M.I.T. Press, 159 pp.

Fairbridge, R. W., ed. (1967), *Encyclopedia of Atmospheric Sciences and Astrogeology,* New York, Reinhold, 1200 pp. See Cosmogeny, Cosmology, Radio astronomy, Red shift, Stars and stellar interiors, Sun.

Smart, W. M. (1968), *The Riddle of the Universe,* New York, Wiley, 228 pp.

# 7

# The earth as a magnet

AWARENESS THAT THE EARTH acts as a great magnet may have been reached during the eleventh century A.D., when mariner's compasses using lodestone were put into use by Arabs and Persians. *Lodestone,* a naturally magnetic variety of the iron mineral *magnetite*[1] ($Fe_3O_4$), could be floated upon a piece of wood or a cork to serve as a magnetic compass (Figure 7.1). Similarly, an iron needle could be magnetized by contact with lodestone and floated on water. That lodestone possessed the property of attracting iron was known to the Greeks as early as the seventh century B.C., for this fact is stated in the writings of Thales (640–546 B.C.).

Use of the magnetic compass in Europe is first mentioned in a Latin treatise written about 1187 A.D. by Alexander Neckham, an English monk. He refers to the magnetization of a needle by contact with lodestone. In the middle of the thirteenth century Petrus Peregrinus, a Frenchman, experimentally investigated the properties of lodestone. He can be credited with the discovery that when a piece of lodestone is broken into many smaller fragments each piece becomes a magnet. Using a small magnetized needle, he was able to demonstrate the magnetic axis within a spherical piece of lodestone, finding that the needle was oriented perpendicular to the surface of the lodestone over the polar position. Peregrinus improved the magnetic compass by replacing the floating lodestone with a magnetized needle pivoting on two bearings and referred to a graduated rim.

By the fourteenth century the mariners' compass was in general use as an essential tool of navigation on British naval vessels and also made possible the great discovery voyages begun in that century by the Portuguese. As the magnetic compass was used in conjunction with celestial navigation methods, it became apparent that the compass did not point exactly

[1] Named for its occurrence in Magnesia, in Asia Minor. See Chapter 22 and Figure 22.7 for a description of lodestone.

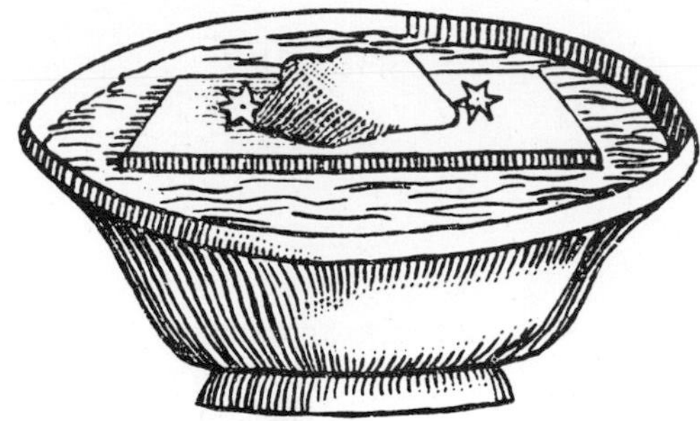

**FIGURE 7.1.** A medieval floating compass. Stars mark the poles of the piece of lodestone. (From Athanasius Kircher, 1643.)

toward true geographic north and that the discrepancy in the two directions changed with positions on the globe. It is said that one reason why the men who sailed with Columbus theatened to mutiny during his historic discovery voyage across the Atlantic in 1492 was that they were disturbed by noting that the compass changed its direction of pointing with respect to geographic north as they proceeded westward.

The first really scientific analysis of the earth's magnetism is contained in a treatise entitled *De Magnete,* published in 1600 by Sir William Gilbert, physician to Queen Elizabeth. In trying to explain why the north-seeking end of a compass needle, if free to rotate on a vertical axis, points downward into the earth's surface in the Northern Hemisphere, but upward in the Southern Hemisphere, Gilbert carried out some of the first truly scientific experiments ever recorded. He made a sphere of lodestone and observed the orientation of a magnetized needle when held at various points with respect to the sphere (Figure 7.2). He was thus able to construct the lines of magnetic force. Gilbert found that the magnetized needle assumed an orientation with respect to the lodestone sphere much like that which the compass needle assumes on the globe, from which he concluded that the earth acts as a great magnet. He supposed that the earth's interior consisted of a magnetic substance, perhaps resembling lodestone.

**FIGURE 7.2.** Gilbert's diagram of his terella with small magnets showing inclination. [From W. Gilbert (1600), *De Magnete.*]

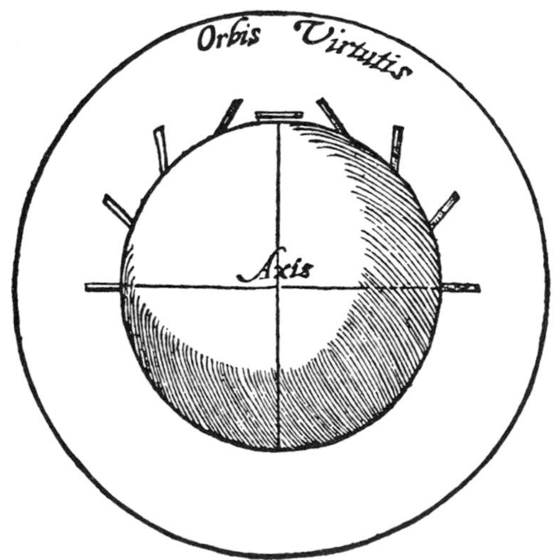


Since Gilbert's time the earth's magnetic field has been mapped in great detail and the scientific specialty of *geomagnetism,* or *terrestrial magnetism,* has become an important part of geophysics.

## The earth as a simple bar magnet

As a simplification, or first approximation, the earth's magnetic field can be described as resembling that of a short bar magnet imagined to lie near the earth's center (Figure 7.3). The long axis of the bar magnet is known as the *earth's magnetic axis* and can be extended to emerge from the earth's surface at points known as the *magnetic poles* and to pass outward indefinitely into space (Figure 7.4). The pole lying in the Northern Hemisphere is named the *north magnetic pole,* that in the Southern Hemisphere, the *south magnetic pole.* The magnetic axis is inclined several degrees with respect to the geographical axis of the earth, so that the north magnetic pole lies about at lat. 70° N., long. 100° W. and the south magnetic pole at lat. 68° S., long. 143° E.

If we locate these two points on a globe, it becomes apparent that they are not antipodal points and that the magnetic axis therefore does not pass through the earth's center, a fact indicated in Figure 7.4. The magnetic axis comes closest to the earth's center at a point lying directly beneath the mid-Pacific. Lying in a plane at right angles to the magnetic axis is the *magnetic equator,* whose plane may be extended outward indefinitely into space.

As is well known, unlike poles of two magnets attract one another, and like poles repel one another. If the earth's magnetic pole lying in the Arctic is to be designated as "north," the end of a compass needle which points toward that pole would be actually the "south" pole of the magnetized needle, whereas by convention we usually speak of it as the "north" pole of the needle. To be strictly correct, that end of the compass which points in the direction of the north magnetic pole should be designated the *north-seeking pole.*

## The magnetic field

For convenience of analysis the magnetic field is imagined to consist of *lines of force,* representing the paths that would be followed by the north-seeking pole of a very tiny magnet free to move in space. The lines of force can be demonstrated by spreading particles of soft iron on a sheet of paper and placing the paper over a bar magnet. The iron filings group themselves into linear masses showing the positions of the lines of force. In Figure 7.3 is a drawing of such an experiment, in which iron filings are used to simulate the earth's magnetic field. Of course, the filings lie in only one plane, whereas the lines of force occupy all three dimensions of space around the magnet. Hence we visualize the earth's magnetic field by imagining the cross section shown in Figures 7.3 and 7.4 to be rotated about the magnetic axis so as to occupy all possible positions.

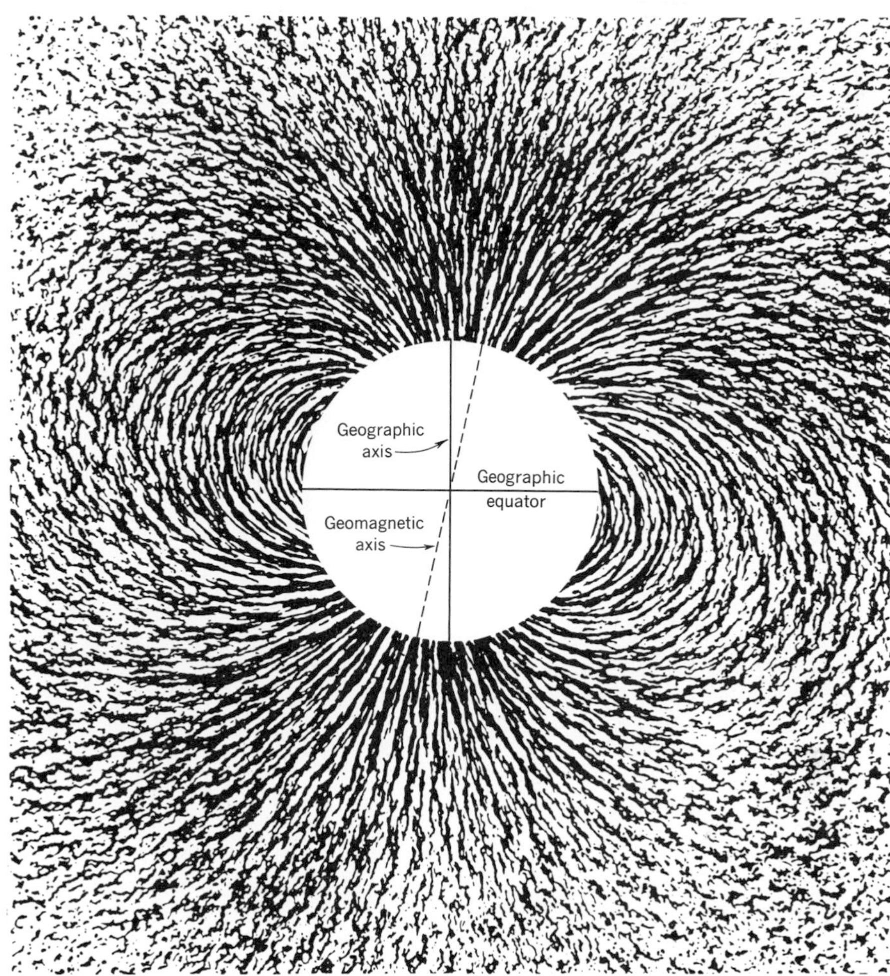


**FIGURE 7.3.** The magnetic field about the earth is illustrated here by the pattern of iron filings around a simple bar magnet. [From J. A. Fleming (1939), *Physics of the Earth,* vol., 8, Washington, D.C., Nat. Acad. Sci., p. 4, Figure 1. Reproduced by permission of the National Academy of Sciences.]

Two aspects of the earth's magnetic field are of interest: (1) the directions of the lines of force, and (2) the magnitude of the forces. In Figure 7.4 the directions of the lines of force, where they intersect the earth's surface, are shown by small arrows. A magnetized needle, perfectly balanced in weight so as to eliminate the effect of gravity, will come to rest with an orientation in space paralleling the line of force at that point. At the magnetic poles the lines of force are perpendicular to the earth's surface; at the magnetic equator they are parallel with the surface. Similar arrows can, of course, be shown at any point in the magnetic field, both within and on the earth and in surrounding space. In three dimensions the force field takes the form of a doughnut-shaped ring surrounding a central region, which can be termed the *magnetic core.*

The magnetic field at the earth's surface is completely described by three quantities, known as the *magnetic elements*—inclination, declination, and intensity. Of these elements, inclination and declination are angular quantities, stated in degrees, whereas intensity is a *vector quantity* (a force) requiring definition in terms of both direction and amount. Figure 7.5 shows the complete set of geometrical relationships among the magnetic elements. Space coordinates of the diagram consist of an *X*-axis directed toward geographic north, a *Y*-axis directed toward geographic east, and a *Z*-axis directed downward to the astronomical nadir. In this diagram, *total intensity* is represented by the arrow *F* and lies parallel to the lines of magnetic force. *Vertical intensity* is shown by the vertical arrow *Z, horizontal intensity* by the horizontal arrow *H.*

The unit of measurement of magnetic field intensity is the *oersted.* A unit magnetic pole in a field of 1 oersted would be subjected to a force of 1 dyne. A *unit magnetic pole* is defined as a pole that repels a like pole 1 centimeter away with a force of 1 dyne. Figure 7.6 is a world map of total magnetic field intensity. Lines on the map are *isodynamic lines,* drawn through points having equal values of intensity. Notice that total intensity reaches its maximum value, over 0.7 oersted, at the south magnetic pole. A second center of maximum value, over 0.6 oersted, lies at the north magnetic pole. Around the magnetic equator is a belt of minimum intensity, dropping to below 0.25 oersted.

For detailed magnetic intensity maps, such as those of the United States issued by the ESSA Coast and Geodetic Survey,[2] magnetic intensity is given in units of *gammas.* One oersted equals 100,000 gammas.

[2] Chart Nos. 3077f, total intensity; 3077h, horizontal intensity; 3077z, vertical intensity.

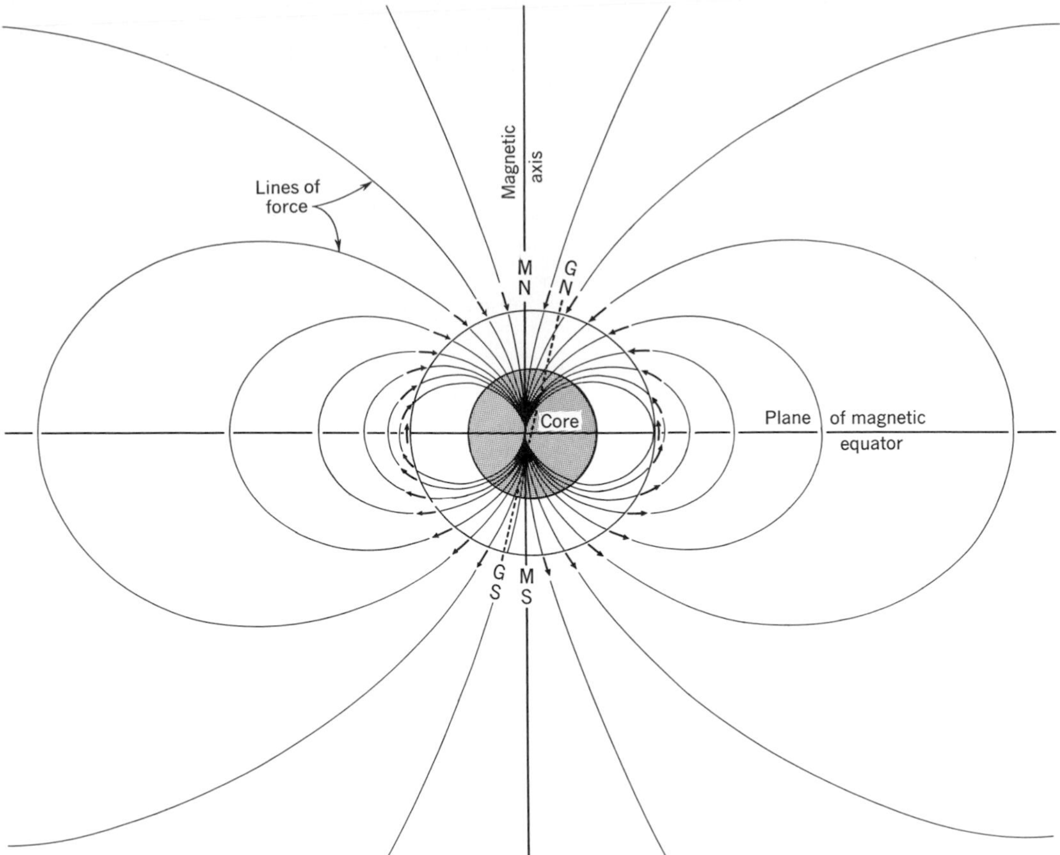


**FIGURE 7.4.** Lines of force in the earth's magnetic field shown in cross section passing through the magnetic axis. Letter *M* designates *magnetic,* and *G, geographic.* Arrows at the surface of the earth show the orientation of a dip needle.

## Magnetic inclination

From Figure 7.4 it is obvious that at the magnetic equator the freely suspended magnetized needle lies parallel with the earth's surface, at the magnetic poles it points vertically down or up, and at intermediate latitudes it has an intermediate angle with respect to the earth's surface. The angle between the force lines and the earth's surface is known as the *magnetic inclination,* or *dip.* In Figure 7.5, inclination is represented by the angle *I.*

Inclination can be measured by means of the *dip needle* (Figure 7.7), a compass needle mounted on delicate horizontal bearings so that it is free to rotate in the vertical plane. The dip needle is perfectly balanced so that it will lie horizontal if not magnetized. The north-seeking end of the dip needle has an earthward component at all places north of the magnetic equator and a skyward component at all places south of the magnetic equator.

Distribution of magnetic inclination can be shown by a map on which are drawn lines of equal inclination, or dip (*isoclinic lines*). In Figures 7.8 and 7.9 are shown isoclinic lines in the vicinity of the north and south magnetic poles.

## Magnetic declination (variation)

Because the magnetic axis is inclined with respect to the earth's rotational (geographic) axis and the magnetic poles do not match the geographic poles, the north-seeking end of the compass needle will normally indicate a direction different from the geographic north of a meridian. The horizontal angle between the geographic meridian and the horizontal component of the lines of magnetic force, shown by the compass needle, is known as the *declination* of the compass and of the magnetic field. (The term *variation of the compass,* or simply *variation,* is used synonymously with declination.)

Declination is stated in degrees east or west of geographic north. In Figure 7.10, for point *A* the compass points several degrees toward the left (west) of the geographic meridian if we imagine ourselves to stand at *A* and face geographic north. At *B* the compass points to the right (east) of true north. At *C* the compass direction coincides with the geographic meridian, which means that there is no declination. At *D* the compass points southward along the meridian, and the declination is 180°.

Because of irregularities in the earth's magnetic field, the compass declination does not conform to the ideal

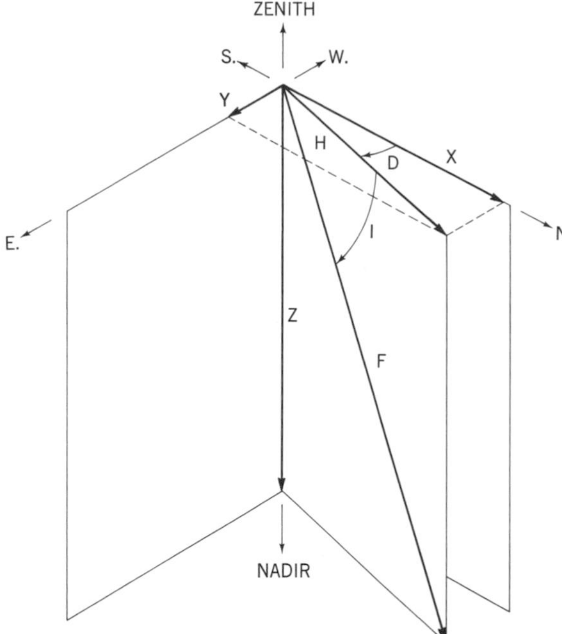


**FIGURE 7.5.** Vectors of the magnetic elements, as if seen from the northeast.

D Declination
I Inclination, or dip
H Horizontal intensity
X North component
Y East component
Z Vertical intensity
F Total intensity

[From ESSA, Coast and Geodetic Survey (1962), *Magnetism of the Earth,* Publ. 40-1, p. 6, Figure 1.)

geometry shown in Figure 7.10. By means of *isogonic lines,* lines drawn through all points having equal declination, the distribution of declination can be shown on a map (Figure 7.11). The line of zero declination, termed the *agonic line,* roughly follows a meridian in the Western Hemisphere, but takes a highly circuitous path in the Eastern Hemisphere. Figure 7.12 is a detailed map for the United States. Note that both maps are based upon conformal map projections which show correctly the angle of intersection of any horizontal line with any meridian or parallel.

The needle of a good magnetic compass is usually equipped with a small sliding weight that can be so adjusted as to compensate for the dip and thus to permit the needle to be in perfect horizontal balance on its jeweled pivot point. No such adjustment is needed at the magnetic equator, where dip is zero. At either magnetic pole there is no horizontal force component at all, so that the needle will swing aimlessly.

Any magnetic compass that is to serve a useful purpose in surveying, map making, or navigation has an adjustable azimuth circle that can be rotated to agree with the declination existing in the region where the compass is being used. With the adjustment correctly made, the sight line formed by the open sights or telescope to which the compass is attached will be a line of true geographic north when the north-seeking end of the needle lies on the zero point of the azimuth scale. In Figure 7.13 is shown a compass dial set for 15° west declination, as would be the value for, say, Boston, Massachusetts. (Refer to Figure 7.12.)

When maps are used in the field, they must be oriented correctly with respect to true north. When orientation is done by means of a magnetic compass, declination must be taken into account. Hence most large-scale topographic maps show on the margin a symbol consisting of two arrows and a numerical statement of the declination in degrees and minutes. The relation of the arrow representing true north to that representing magnetic north tells the user whether the declination is east or west.

As we shall see below, the earth's magnetic field is constantly shifting, therefore the declination of the compass undergoes a small annual change. An isogonic map is prepared for a given calendar year, thus its use in subsequent years may require a correction. For this reason, on many isogonic maps, such as those used in navigation, there will also be drawn lines of equal annual change (Figure 7.12). On large-scale topographic maps the marginal information will usually contain a statement of the annual change, including both the amount and the direction of change and whether it is increasing or decreasing. In the vicinity of New York City, for example, the declination is increasing about 3′ annually. This amount is not large, but over a period of several years it accumulates to a large enough figure to affect the surveying of boundary lines by magnetic compass.

## Measuring the magnetic field

Precise measurements of the direction and intensity of the magnetic field are made continuously at some 90 permanent magnetic observatories distributed widely, but not uniformly, over the earth. In addition many observations are made by field parties to fill in necessary data for areas between permanent stations.

Among the magnetic properties measured are the inclination and declination, the total field intensity, the intensity in the horizontal and vertical directions, and the intensity in the north–south and east–west directions.

In general, an instrument that measures the intensity of the earth's magnetic field is called a *magnetometer.* One basic type is the *oscillation magnetometer,* which uses a bar magnet suspended in a horizontal attitude by a thread or mounted as a dip needle is. The magnet is set in rotary oscillation and the period of oscillation is measured, from which the horizontal or vertical components of field intensity can be calculated. The *deflection magnetometer* has a small fixed magnet mounted near a magnetized compass needle, and the earth's field intensity is compared with the known field of the fixed magnet. A related instrument, using a Helmholtz coil in place of the fixed magnet, is the *sine galvanometer* (Figure 7.14). This instrument has been used in magnetic observatories to measure the horizontal component of the earth's field.

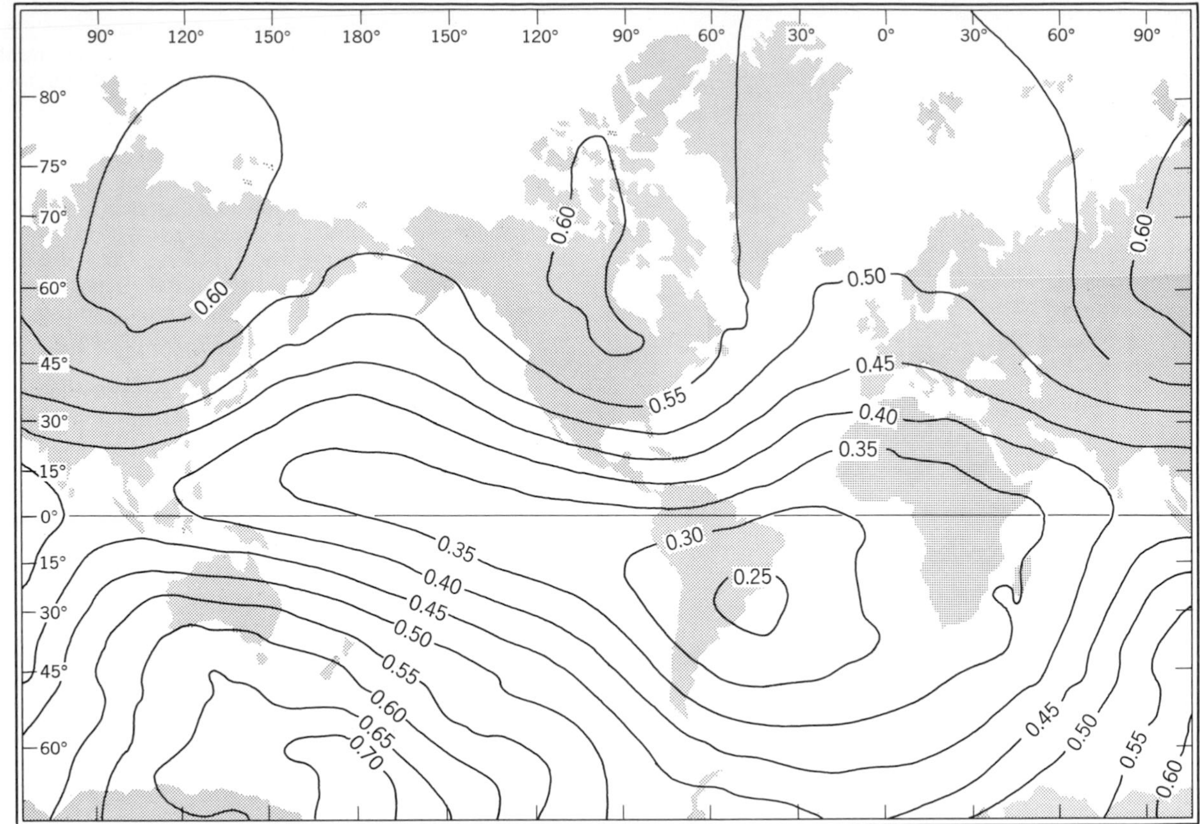


**FIGURE 7.6.** World map of total magnetic intensity for 1955. Values are given in oersteds. (Data from U.S. Navy Oceanographic Office.)

A newer instrument yielding a much higher order of accuracy is the *proton vector magnetometer* (Figure 7.15), which makes use of the principle of precession of spinning protons set in motion by a polarizing magnetic field. A central container of water provides the protons. Output from surrounding sensing coils is fed into automatic data-processing equipment for evaluation.

Portable magnetometers have been developed for out-

**FIGURE 7.7.** This simple dip needle is used by prospectors.

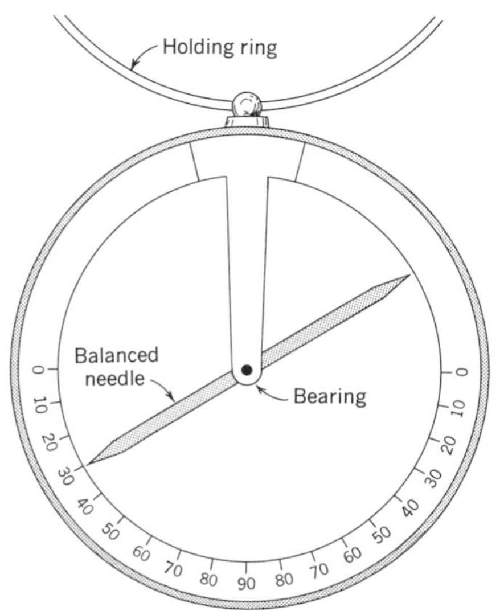


**FIGURE 7.8.** Inclination (dip) of the earth's magnetic field in the arctic region for 1955, shown by isoclinic lines in degrees. (Data from U.S. Navy Oceanographic Office.)

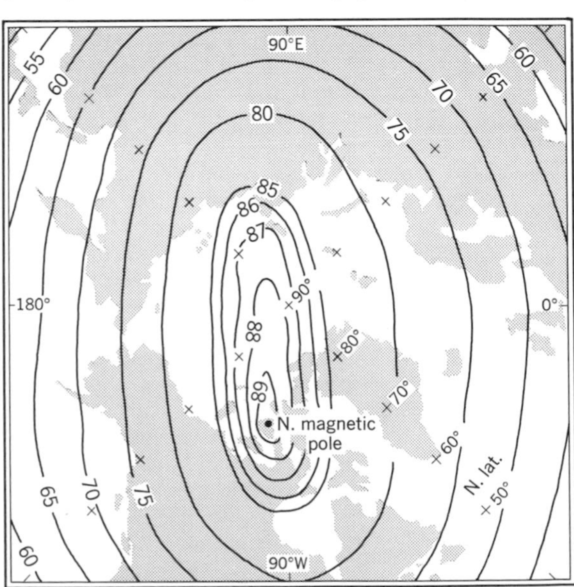

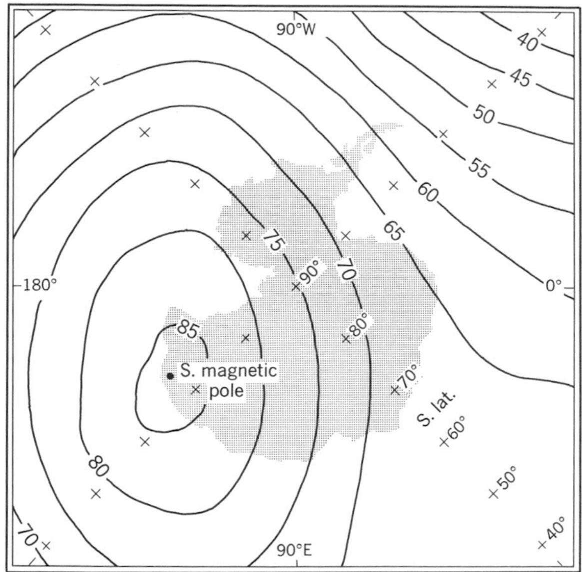


**FIGURE 7.9.** Magnetic inclination (dip) in degrees in the antarctic region. (Data from U.S. Navy Oceanographic Office.)

door use to make detailed maps of the field intensity and thereby to make inferences concerning the presence and outlines of rock bodies beneath the surface. The *airborne magnetometer,* an instrument carried by airplane, is capable of giving a continuous reading of the intensity as it is towed behind the plane along a line of traverse (Figure 7.16). The magnetometer may also

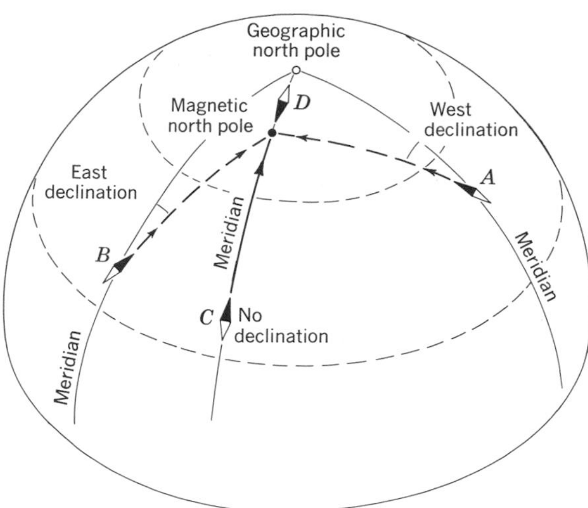


**FIGURE 7.10.** Compass declination depends upon one's position with respect to magnetic and geographic north poles.

**FIGURE 7.11.** World isogonic map. Declination of the compass for 1955 is shown by isogonic lines for every 10 degrees. (Data from U.S. Navy Oceanographic Office.)

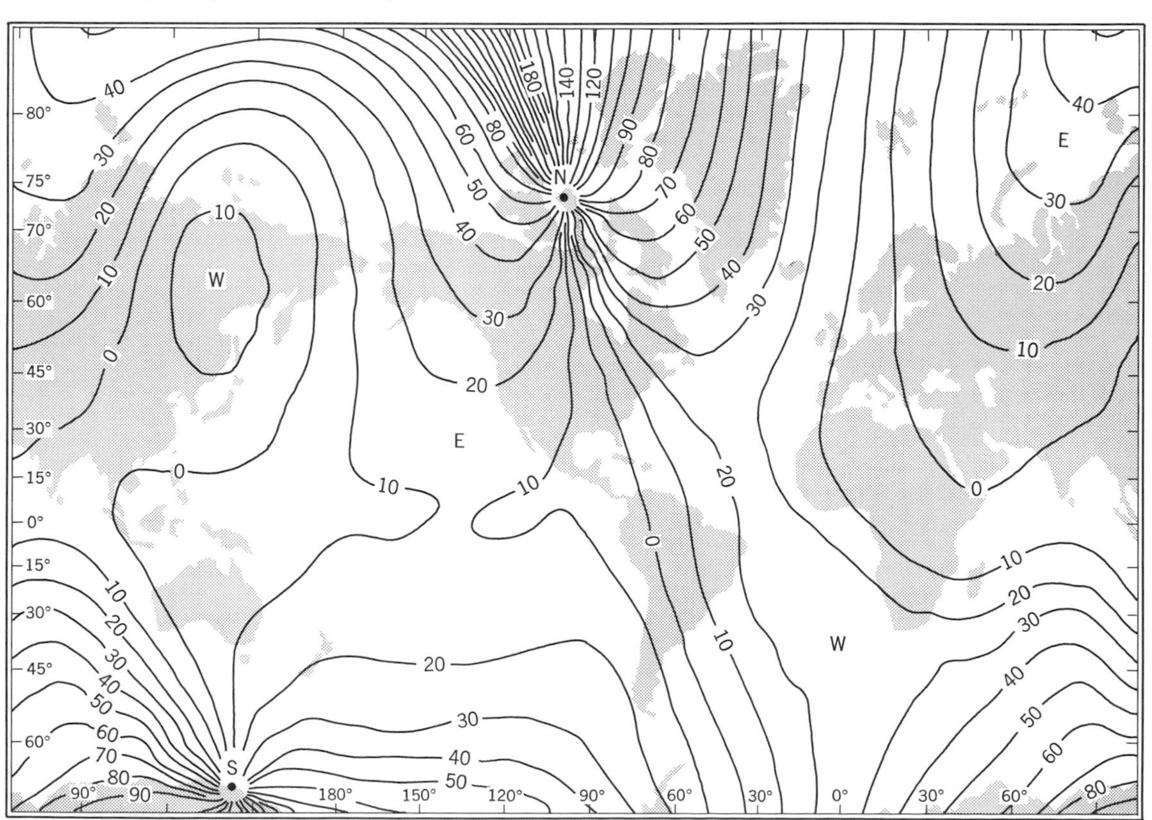

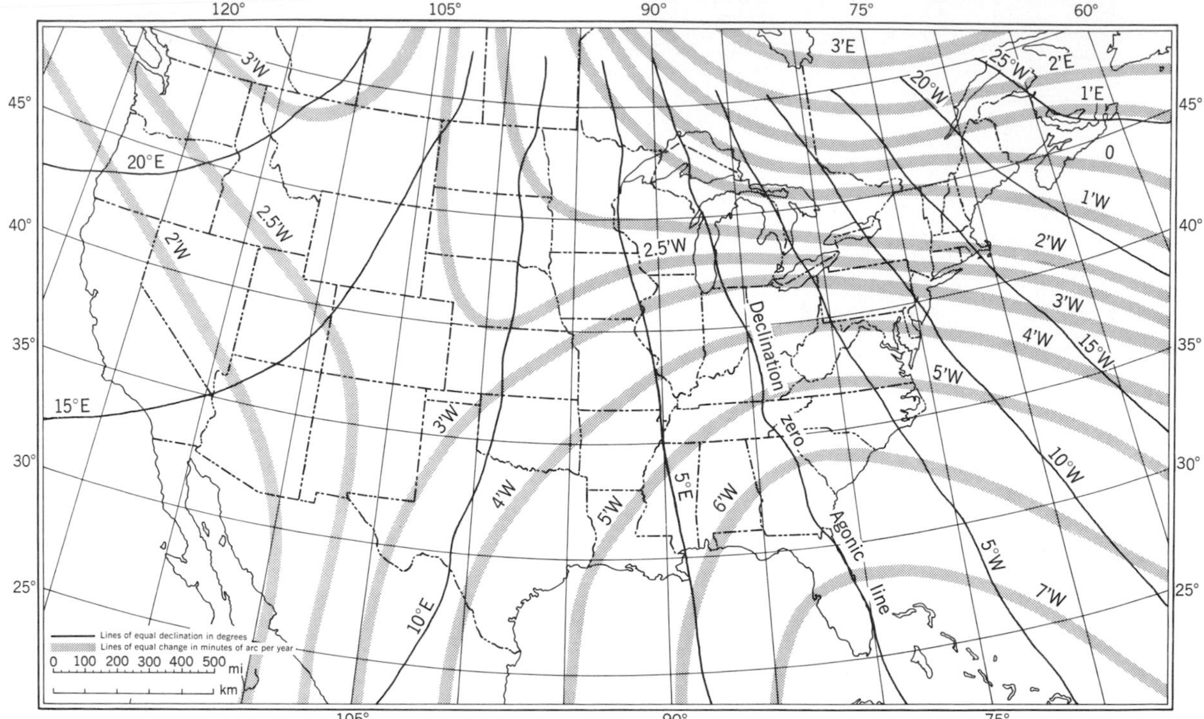


**FIGURE 7.12.** Isogonic map of the United States for 1965. (After ESSA, Coast and Geodetic Survey.)

**FIGURE 7.13.** This explorer's compass has been set for a local declination of 15° west. Conditions are about as shown in Figure 7.10 at point *A*.



be towed behind a ship to yield magnetc data over the ocean basins (Figure 7.17).

## Changes in the magnetic field

Observations from magnetic observatories clearly reveal two major types of changes in intensity and direction of the earth's magnetic field: (1) *long-period changes,* termed *secular* changes, and (2) *short-period changes,* following (a) cyclic or (b) irregular patterns.

Secular changes take the form of a slow drift of the earth's magnetic field, because of which the declination and dip at a given station gradually change. This phenomenon is clearly shown by the records of observatories in London and Paris, including observations begun in the time of William Gilbert. In Figure 7.18 is a graph on which the compass declination is given on the horizontal scale and the dip (inclination) on the vertical axis. When declination and dip are plotted as a single point on the graph and the points for successive dates are connected by a line, it is apparent that from the seventeenth to eighteenth centuries in western Europe declination shifted steadily westward through more than 30° and the dip subsequently began to decrease. By about 1800 the declination change was reversed, although the dip continued to decrease. The data on this graph might suggest that the magnetic pole is slowly precessing with respect to the geographic pole in what may be a cycle of long period. If, however, we examine the same type of record for other locations, the changes follow other periods, and it is not possible to deduce a world-wide cycle. Instead, the secular changes seem to be concentrated in centers of sub-

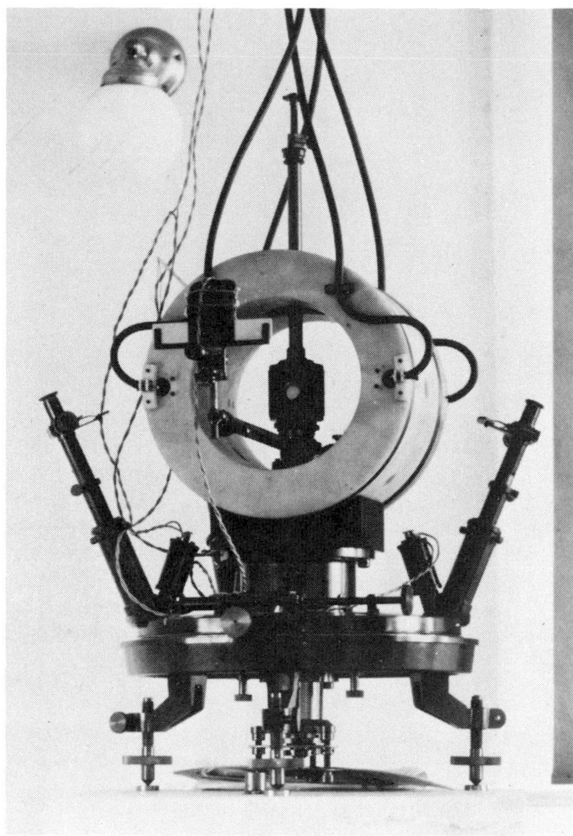

**FIGURE 7.14.** A *sine galvanometer,* one of the older instruments used by the Carnegie Institution's Department of Terrestrial Magnetism to observe minute variations in the horizontal component of the earth's magnetic field. The instrument uses a pair of coils wound on a hollow cylinder of Carrara marble. (Courtesy of the Carnegie Institution of Washington.)

continental size. In some of these centers the change is in one direction, in others it is in the opposite direction, and along other lines the secular changes appear to be zero. These facts lead to the belief that secular magnetic changes are related to internal changes within the earth and that these changes are occurring in definite centers of activity at great depth.

## The dipole field

In analyzing the secular changes of magnetism, it is useful to consider that the total magnetic field consists of two influences, or constituents, each of which can be treated separately. First, there is the main field resulting from the assumption that the earth's interior acts as a simple bar magnet. The ideal symmetrical field resulting from this assumption is called the *dipole field.* It is essentially as shown in Figures 7.3 and 7.4, except that the magnetic axis passes through the earth's center and thus emerges at antipodal points; these points are not the same as the existing north and south magnetic poles, which should be referred to as the *dip poles.* Instead, the poles of the dipole field, best designated as the *geomagnetic poles,* would lie at lat. 79° N., long. 70° W. and lat. 79° S., long. 110° E.

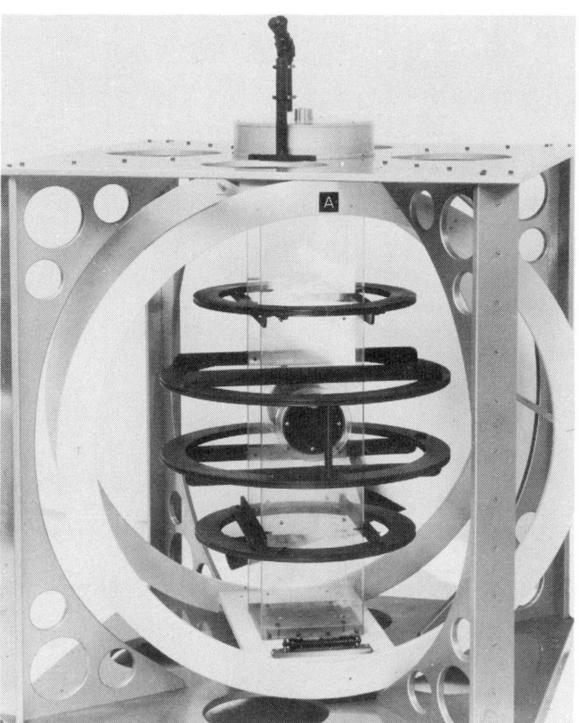


**FIGURE 7.15.** This photograph of the proton vector magnetometer shows coils and sensing head. (ESSA Coast and Geodetic Survey photograph.)

It is therefore possible to have a system of parallels and meridians based upon the dipole axis, the system of latitude and longitude constituting the *geomagnetic coordinates.* In Figure 7.19 is a world map showing the dipolar field by means of arrows representing the north-seeking pole of a compass. If one were to connect these arrows with smooth lines, one would have the meridians of the geomagnetic coordinate system. Notice that the geomagnetic north pole lies close to Thule, Greenland, whereas the dip pole ("magnetic north pole") lies near Prince of Wales Island.

When the dipole field is plotted and the values subtracted from the observed values at all points, there remains the second constituent, a rather irregular magnetic field termed the *residual field,* consisting of centers toward which, or away from which, the compass needle would point if there were no dipole field. The residual field appears to be shifting slowly westward around the earth at a rate such that the pattern would complete a circuit of the earth every 1600 years. Within the residual field, consequently, the patterns are constantly changing as the shift takes place.

## Cause of earth magnetism

It can be shown that about 95 percent of the earth's magnetic field is produced within the earth. Therefore we must look to the earth's interior for a mechanism of earth magnetism capable of explaining not only a simple dipole field, but also a series of constantly changing centers of magnetism engaged in slow westward drift.

**FIGURE 7.16.** Gulf airborne magnetometer in flight. (Courtesy of Aero Service Corporation, Philadelphia, Pa.)

The explanation seems to lie in the properties and internal motions of the earth's core, a spherical body of metallic material—probably of a nickel-iron composition—the outer part of which is liquid in physical state. (The core is described in Chapter 23 and illustrated in Figure 23.23.) The diameter of the core is about 4320 mi (6950 km), or just over half the earth's diameter. The core is surrounded by a mantle consisting of solid rock.

The earth's internal magnetism can be explained by the *dynamo theory,* developed by W. M. Elasser and Sir Edward Bullard in the 1940s and 1950s. According to this theory, through flowage the liquid core turns slowly, with respect to the solid mantle surrounding it, and thus acts as a dynamo generating electric currents that encircle the core and cause it to become an electromagnet (Figure 7.20). The dipole field can be explained by a symmetrical current system following the surface of the core.

The cause of currents within the core has not been established, but several mechanisms have been suggested. One hypothesis attributes currents to the precession of the earth's axis (Chapter 2)—failure of the core to precess as rapidly as the mantle that surrounds it may set up currents in the core. An alternative hypothesis invokes a mechanism based on the outward movement of heat from the core into the mantle, which has been questioned on grounds that very little heat is produced within the earth's core (Chapter 23).

To explain the configuration of the residual field, it is

**FIGURE 7.17.** Aboard the Research Vessel *Vema* a scientist of the Lamont-Doherty Geological Observatory prepares to launch a magnetometer to be towed behind the vessel. (Courtesy of the National Academy of Science, IGY.)

further necessary to suppose that there are large eddy systems, resembling the motions in whirlpools, within the liquid matter of the core. These eddies generate local current systems that set up magnetic centers superimposed upon the dipole field. The continual changing of the convectional pattern as the core rotates within the mantle is believed responsible for the irregular and seemingly unpredictable nature of the secular changes.

That the core moves with respect to the mantle is suggested by the sudden changes in acceleration that have been observed in the earth's rotation (Chapter 3). Such abrupt changes in rotational acceleration suggest that sudden changes occasionally occur in the

**FIGURE 7.18.** Secular changes in compass declination and dip are shown here for Paris and London for more than three centuries of records. [Data from Gaibar-Puertas. After J. A. Jacobs, R. D. Russell, and J. T. Wilson (1959), *Physics and Geology,* New York, McGraw-Hill, p. 122, Figure 6-4.]

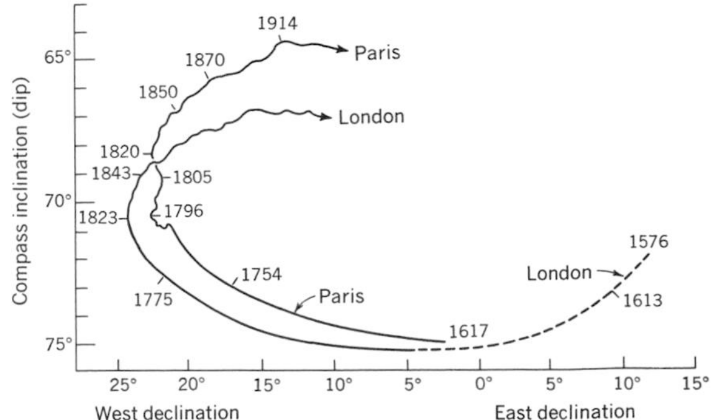

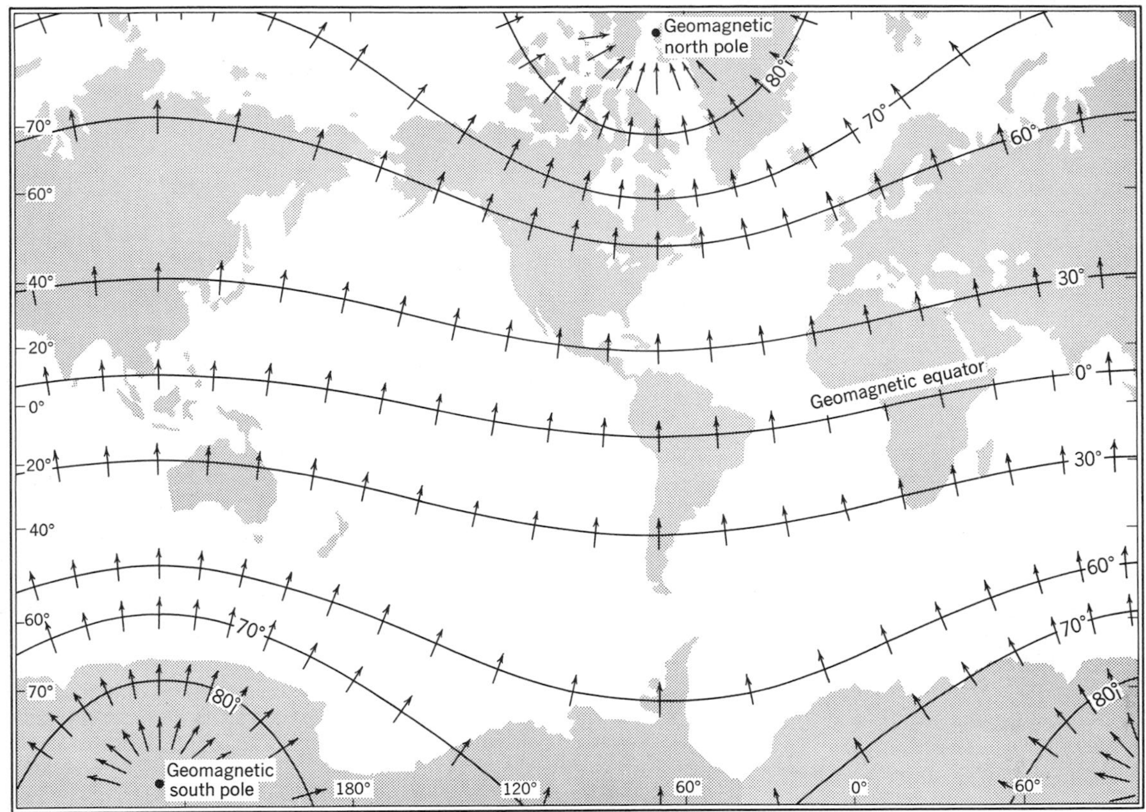


**FIGURE 7.19.** On this map of the earth's dipole magnetic field arrows show the direction indicated by the north-seeking end of a compass. If connected by smooth lines, the arrows would produce geomagnetic meridians. The curved lines running generally across the map from left to right are geomagnetic parallels. [Data from E. H. Vestine. After *Handbook of Geophysics* (1960), New York, Macmillan.]

**FIGURE 7.20.** Schematic representation of electric currents on the earth's core believed capable of producing the earth's dipole magnetic field. [After S. K. Runcorn (1955), *Scientific American,* vol. 193 no. 3, p. 158.]

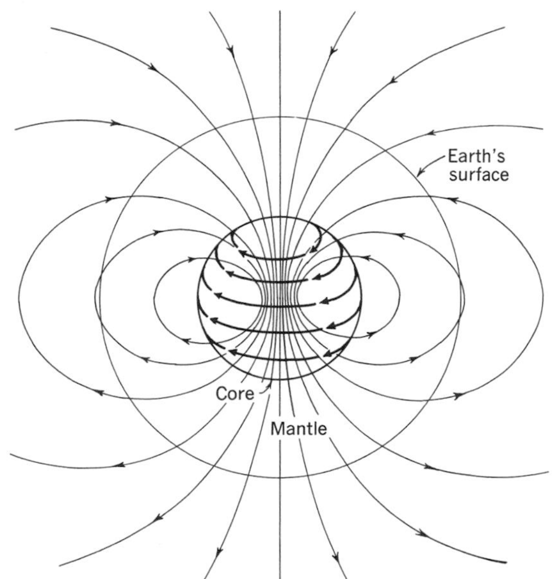


relative speeds of rotation of mantle and core. If angular momentum is to be conserved, the rotational velocity of the mantle must increase to offset a decrease in rotational velocity of the core, and vice versa.

There is good reason to suppose that the core is rotating slightly less rapidly than the mantle surrounding it, so that by comparison the core may be described as shifting westward, carrying the features of the magnetic field with it. Occasional sudden shifts in rotational rate occur when the core and mantle undergo a sudden slippage with respect to one another, but otherwise the relative motion is the slow, continuous flowage of a highly viscous fluid.

## Rhythmic magnetic fluctuations and the ionosphere

The sensitive magnets of the magnetic observatories record rhythmic fluctuations of magnetic intensity and direction. These fall into daily and annual solar cycles and lunar cycles. The solar cycles are well marked and show that the intensity of solar radiation has a strong connection with the magnetic field. Changes in magnetic intensity of a few tens of gammas and in declination of a few minutes of arc follow a rhythmic daily pattern.

The rhythmic variations in magnetic field associated

with daily and annual solar and lunar cycles are produced by changes in the electric currents in the upper atmosphere. To understand these phenomena we need to examine the effects of the solar electromagnetic radiation as it passes through the earth's atmosphere.

Molecules and atoms of nitrogen and oxygen of the upper atmosphere absorb the highly energetic gamma rays, X rays, and ultraviolet rays of the solar spectrum. In so doing, each affected molecule or atom loses an electron, becoming a positively charged molecule or atom known as an ion. The process, known as *ionization,* begins at an altitude around 600 mi (1000 km) and is effective down to about 30 mi (50 km). Because the atmosphere becomes increasingly rarefied upward, while the intensity of short-wave radiation dies out earthward, there is a region from about 50 to 250 mi (80 to 400 km) above the earth where the concentration of positive ions and negative electrons is most dense; this region is known as the *ionosphere.*

Electrons ejected from molecules of oxygen and nitrogen during the ionization process are free to travel as an electric current. Thus we can think of the ionosphere as an electrically conducting layer. The earth itself is an electrical conductor, but the intervening atmospheric layer from the ground to the 50-mi (80-km) level is a poor conductor and can be imagined as an insulator. In a way, then, the earth and ionosphere are like the two wire conductors of an electric cable with protective insulation between.

Because the formation of ions in the ionosphere requires solar radiation, we should expect the greatest density of ions to be on the illuminated side of the earth and the least on the dark side. Figure 7.21 shows diagrammatically the way in which the ions form into a number of dense layers on the sunlit hemisphere. In hours of darkness the ionized molecules recapture the free electrons; thus ionization rapidly disappears and only one or two thin layers remain on the darkened hemisphere.

The ionosphere is extremely important in radio-wave transmission. Figure 7.22 shows how the paths of radio waves sent out from a transmitter on the earth are reflected back to earth by the ionosphere. Before the nature of the ionosphere was understood, two early radio experimenters independently discovered the radio-wave reflection principle. The name *Kennelly-Heaviside layer,* named in their honor, was first applied to the lower part of the ionosphere, about at the 50- to 60-mi (80- to 97-km) level, where the principal reflection takes place. As shown in Figure 7.22, the reflection of radio waves makes possible long-distance radio-signal transmission. Extremely long radio waves, with lengths over 1000 ft (300 m), travel by reflection with very little loss and are used in the transatlantic radiotelephone transmission. Reflection becomes poorer as the radio wavelength shortens, until reflection is no longer possible. In Figure 7.22 is shown the *skip zone,* in which radio waves cannot be received from a transmitter because the receiver is too close to receive reflected waves, yet too distant to receive the ground waves, which die out rapidly. The skip distance becomes greater as the wavelengths become shorter.

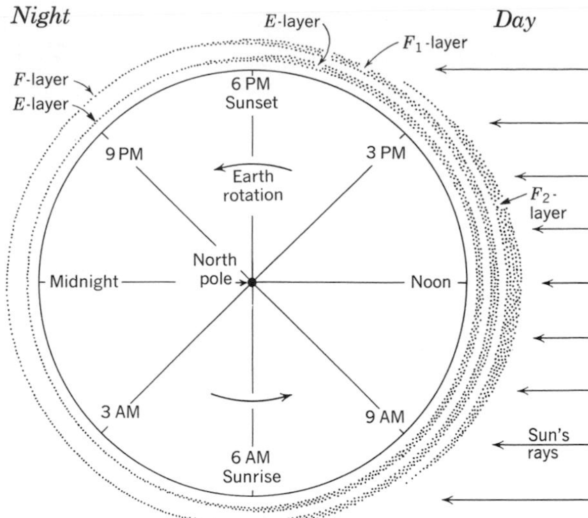


**FIGURE 7.21.** A schematic representation of the ionospheric layers under the sun's rays and in hours of darkness. [After B. F. Howell, Jr., (1959), *Introduction to Geophysics,* New York, McGraw-Hill, p. 351.]

Radio-wave reflection may occur from any one of five ion layers that may be present in daytime. They are given the designations *D, E,* $F_1$, $F_2$, and *G* from base to top (Figure 7.21). Much amateur short-wave communication uses the reflection on the *E*-layer. During the day all but one or two of the layers on the opposite side of the globe disappear, and radio transmission becomes poor. This explains a fact known to amateur *D-X* (long-distance reception) radio fans, that the night hours bring in distant stations from far across the globe.

The movement of electrons within the ionospheric layer takes the form of electric *dynamo currents,* measured in thousands of amperes, which flow in vast horizontal circular patterns, one in the Northern Hemisphere and one in the Southern Hemisphere (Figure 7.23). Each current system acts as a dynamo, setting up a magnetic field which is superimposed on the earth's

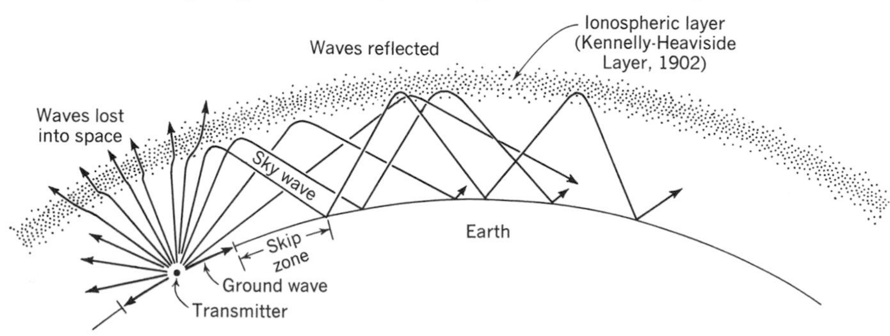


**FIGURE 7.22.** Reflection of radio waves from the ionosphere. [After J. C. Johnson, *Physical Meteorology,* p. 321, Figure 10.1. © 1954 by the Massachusetts Institute of Technology.]

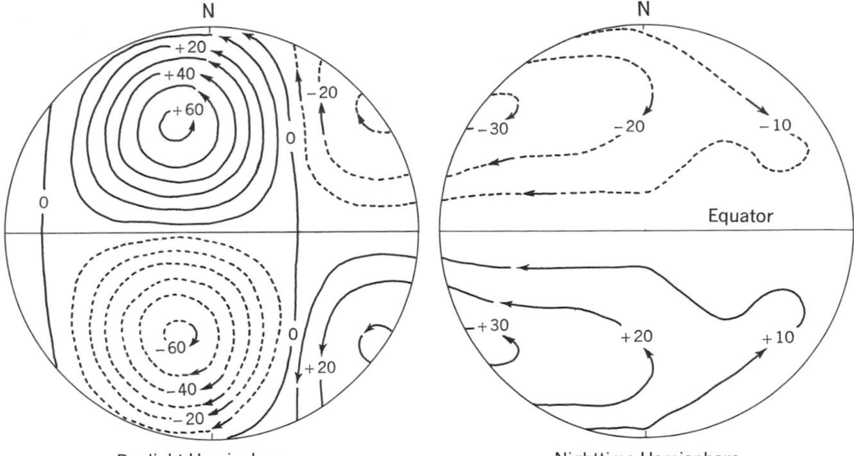


**FIGURE 7.23.** Schematic representation of dynamo electric currents in the ionosphere during equinox conditions. Figures give electric current in thousands of amperes. [After S. Chapman and J. Bartels (1951), *Geomagnetism*, London, Oxford Univ. Press.]

main internal field. Because ionization of the upper atmosphere depends upon the direct action of sunlight, the dynamo currents are intensively developed on the illuminated side of the globe. Therefore, as the earth rotates, a diurnal rhythm of magnetic variation is felt.

Using the concept of hour circles of time moving westward around the earth (Chapter 3), one can imagine that the two sets of currents, one in the Northern Hemisphere and one in the Southern Hemisphere, move westward around the earth at a rate of 15° per hour. At an observatory in the middle latitudes of the Northern Hemisphere the approach of the current system over the locality is accompanied by an increasing south-flowing current, which deflects the compass needle eastward (Figure 7.24). After the center of the system has passed, the current is flowing northward, deflecting the compass needle westward until its original position is restored. The daily cycle of compass declination will, of course, be different at different latitudes (Figure 7.25), being in general opposite in phase in the Southern and Northern Hemispheres.

Because intensity and duration of sunlight vary rhythmically with the seasons, following the changes in sun's declination from 23½° N. at summer solstice to 23½° S. at winter solstice (Chapter 4), we should expect to observe corresponding seasonal changes in magnetic declination, inclination, and intensity. The three sets of triple curves in Figure 7.26 illustrate these seasonal rhythms very nicely—daily ranges are greatest in summer, least in winter.

The ionosphere responds to the tide-raising forces of both sun and moon by undergoing a rhythmic movement much like the ideal equilibrium tide (Chapter 9). Because the sun's rays cause ionization and heating of the atmosphere, it is difficult to separate the sun's radiational effect from its tidal effect, both being part of the same diurnal cycle. The moon, however, has no ionizing or heating effect on the atmosphere through its reflected rays, hence the effects of atmospheric tides alone are seen in the lunar cycles of magnetic variations. These tidal effects are, on the average, less than one-tenth the magnitude of the solar effects, but a study

**FIGURE 7.24.** The daily cycle of change in magnetic declination for a typical middle-latitude station reflects changes in direction and strength of the dynamo current passing overhead. Compare with Figure 7.23.

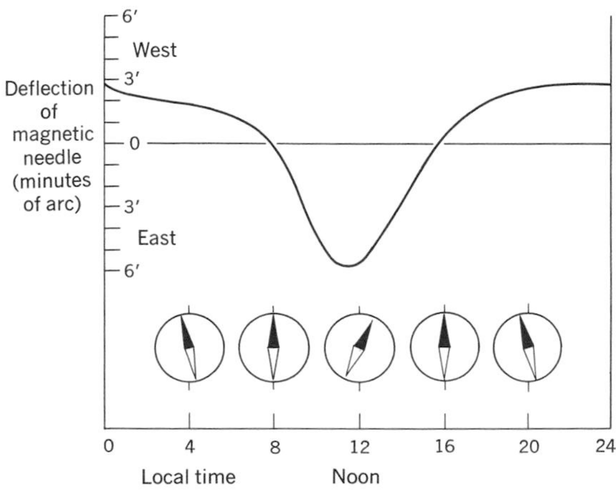


**FIGURE 7.25.** Average hourly values of declination throughout the month of June, 1951, at Cheltenham, Maryland, and Sitka, Alaska. Notice that the cycles are in opposite phase. [After E. J. Chernosky (1960), *Handbook of Geophysics*, New York, Macmillan, Figure 10-4.]

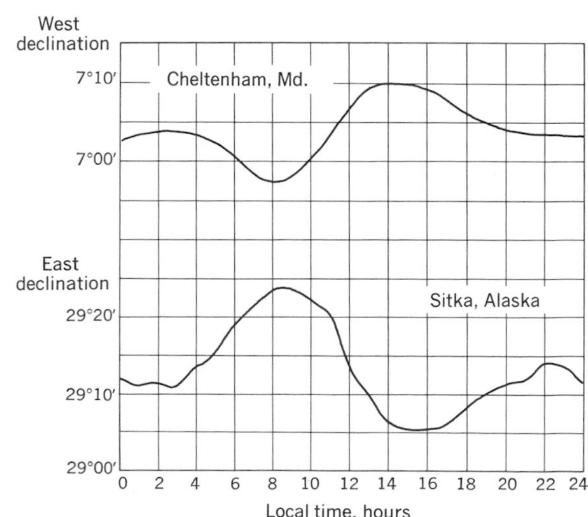

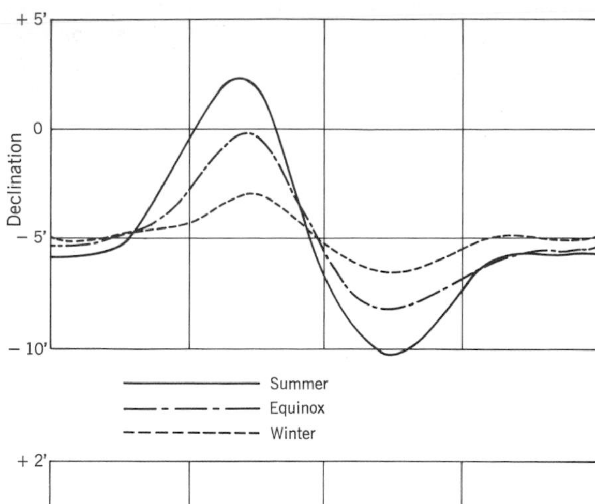


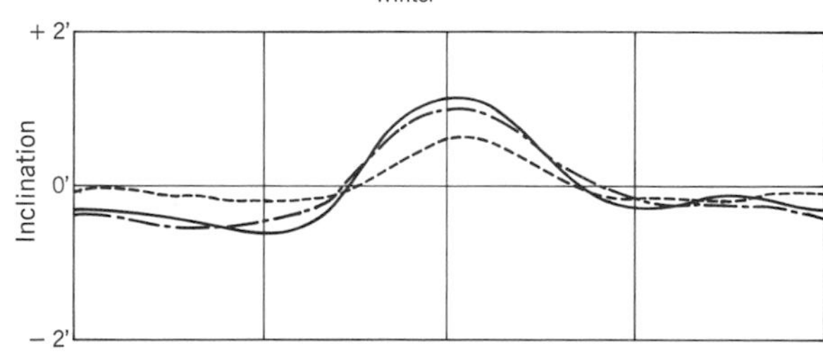


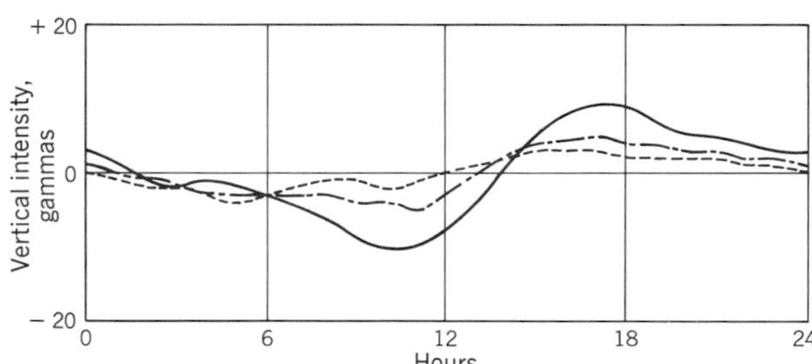


**FIGURE 7.26.** Average daily curves of declination, inclination, and vertical intensity for summer, equinoxes, and winter at Sitka, Alaska, 57° N. [Data from ESSA, Coast and Geodetic Survey (1962), *Magnetism of the Earth,* Publ. 40-1, pp. 24–25, Figures 9, 10, 11.]

of magnetic declination and intensity records will reveal a semi-daily lunar cycle. Declination in this semidaily cycle may vary through an amplitude of from 1/10 to 1 minute of arc. The semimonthly tidal cycle, analogous to the spring and neap tides of the oceans, is clearly seen in Figure 7.27, where the daily noon peak of

**FIGURE 7.28.** Air photograph of the Fredericksburg Geomagnetic Center at Fredericksburg, Virginia. Buildings on the loop at right house magnetographs and other instruments. (ESSA Coast and Geodetic Survey photograph.)

intensity changes by approximately 45 gammas in about 7 days.

## Magnetic storms and solar flares

Magnetic fluctuations are monitored continuously at magnetic observatories, such as that located at Fredericksburg, Virginia, operated by the ESSA Coast and Geodetic Survey (Figure 7.28). Figure 7.29 shows a typical assemblage of observatory instruments, constituting a *magnetograph.* These use extremely sensitive magnets suspended or balanced in such a way as to respond to very rapid, slight changes in direction and intensity of the magnetic field. The magnetograph simultaneously records fluctuations in declination, horizontal intensity, and vertical intensity. The resulting record comprises a *magnetogram,* an example of which is shown in Figure 7.30. Normally, fluctuations on the magnetogram are small, when conditions are referred to as being magnetically *quiet;* occasionally, however, there occur rapid, irregular fluctuations in the magnetic field in bursts of several hours or days each. Such fluctuations, which are concurrent at all observing stations, are referred to as *magnetic storms.* A graph of a

**FIGURE 7.27.** This graph shows typical daily fluctuations of intensity of the earth's magnetic field as observed at Huancayo, Peru, throughout part of the month. The effects of the moon's changing phases are superimposed on the daily solar cycle. [After S. Chapman and J. Bartels (1951), *Geomagnetism*, London, Oxford Univ. Press.]

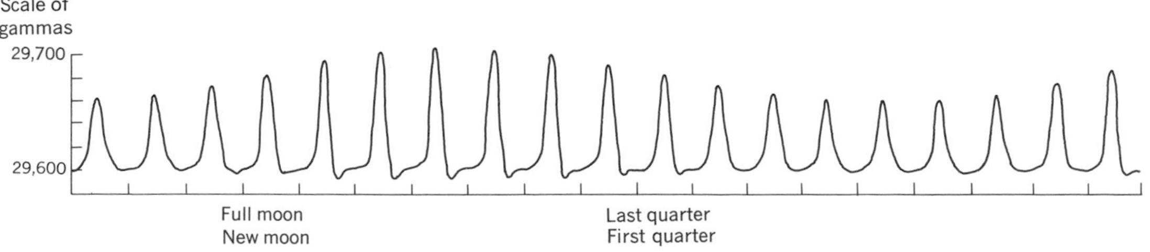

**FIGURE 7.29.** A typical magnetograph assembly at the Fredericksburg Geomagnetic Center. Instrument at right measures the *Z* element; that in center, the *D* element; that at left, the *H* element. (Refer to Figure 7.5.) Recorder is at far left. (ESSA Coast and Geodetic Survey photograph.)

magnetic storm is given in Figure 7.30, showing the fluctuations in the horizontal and vertical components of magnetic field intensity and in declination.

The first phase of a severe magnetic storm is felt by all stations within a minute of the same instant of time. This phase consists of a rapid increase in the horizontal component of magnetic field intensity by an amount of 50–100 gammas within a few minutes. There follows a second phase in which the horizontal intensity drops within a few hours to 100 gammas or more below the normal value, but with many irregularities and alternations (Figure 7.30). The gradual return to normal field strength may require several days.

During severe magnetic storms, which average usually less than one per year, field intensities may vary by as much as 5% of the normal field at high latitudes and as much as 2% at low latitudes. Small storms occur with a frequency of several times per month. One well-known effect of a severe magnetic storm is the disruption of radio communication, particularly the long-distance travel of short radio waves over expanses which are in daylight.

Magnetic storms are clearly the direct result of streams of elementary particles being discharged by the sun during a solar flare and reaching the earth usually within 13–26 hours. The sighting of the solar flare is, however, marked at the same instant at all observatories by a sudden movement of the magnetic needles, a phenomenon known as a *crochet* (from the kink made on the magnetogram). A crochet can be seen in the record of Figure 7.30 at about 08:00 hrs. The sudden commencement of activity occurred 10 hours later. Clearly both the light rays from the flare and the impulse responsible for the crochet travel together, whereas the stream of particles travels more slowly as an ion gas cloud. This observation suggests that ultraviolet rays of the light spectrum are suddenly increased in intensity when the solar flare occurs and that this increase in turn causes a sudden increase in the ring currents of the ionosphere, producing the crochet.

The stream of charged particles—termed *plasma*—from a solar flare consists of electrons and protons, derived from hydrogen atoms emitted by the solar flare, which travel earthward at a speed of 1000–2000 mi (1600–3200 km) per second. As the ion cloud of a solar flare approaches the earth, the electrons are trapped by the earth's magnetic field and are guided earthward along the lines of force, which they follow in general, but with curiously corkscrew paths in detail (see Figure 7.34). The arrival of electrons in the outer magnetic field temporarily intensifies the lines of magnetic force and increases the intensity of the ring currents, in turn bringing about the magnetic fluctuations which we call a magnetic storm.

The magnetic storm of February 10–11, 1958, whose record is shown in Figure 7.31, is considered an extreme one, with one peak value during the first hour estimated to be 500 gammas, about 1/100 of the total field intensity. The first sudden rise in magnetic intensity occurred at 0127 UT on February 11, which was 28 hours after a solar flare that occurred at 2108 UT on February 9. In Figure 7.32 is shown the second phase of

**FIGURE 7.30.** Magnetogram for a magnetically disturbed day, 12 September 1957, recorded at Tucson, Arizona. Refer to Figure 7.5 for explanation of elements *H, Z* and *D*. [From ESSA, Coast and Geodetic Survey (1962), *Magnetism of the Earth,* Publ. 40-1, p. 26, Figure 14.]

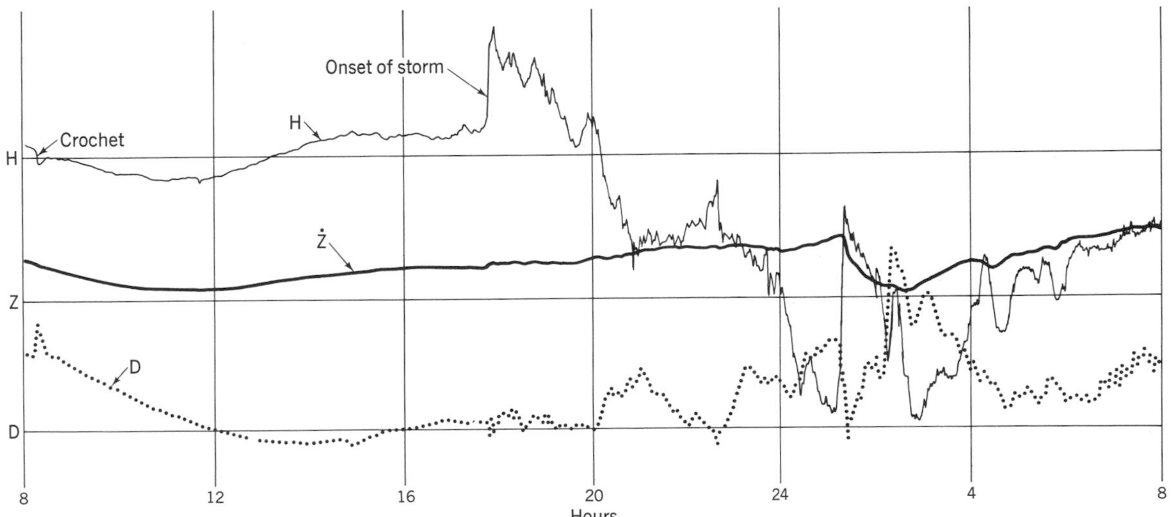

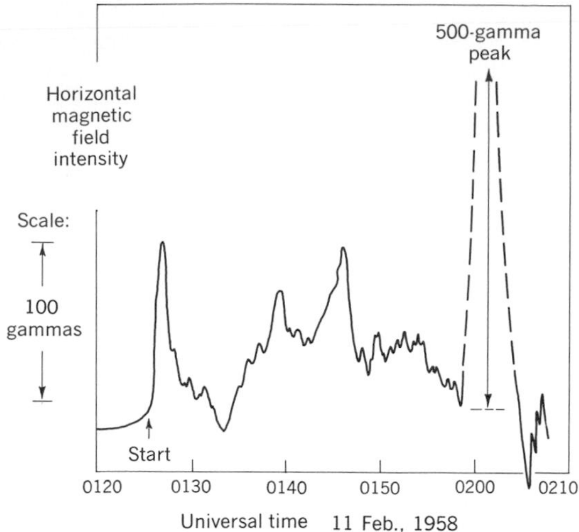


**FIGURE 7.31.** A great magnetic storm on 10 and 11 February, 1958, caused these strong and rapid fluctuations in the intensity of the earth's magnetic field, as recorded at the Fredericksburg Geomagnetic Center. The first phase of the storm is shown here. (After *IGY Bulletin,* No. 18, 1958.)

the magnetic storm, extending through 1000 UT of the same day, but on a different time scale. Above the magnetogram is a graph of the X-ray intensity received by a balloon launched at 0445 UT of the same day, which recorded data at about 100,000 ft (30 km). Two strong depressions (called *bays*) of the magnetogram show that severe ionization of the upper atmosphere occurred at the same time as bursts of X rays, which arrived along with the solar ion cloud. It may be of further interest to note that this magnetic storm set up, by induction, electric currents within the earth's surface. These were felt as voltage-changes of 1000–2500 volts in the transatlantic cables and seemed to be correlated with the peaks of magnetic intensity.

Magnetic-storm activity is conspicuously increased at times when sunspots are most numerous. This is because solar-flare activity is closely associated with the occurrence of sunspots, hence the bursts of solar ion clouds sent earthward can be expected to be more frequent in periods when sunspots are more numerous. It has long been known that the frequency of sunspots varies according to an 11-year cycle, commonly referred to as the *sunspot cycle.* In Figure 7.33 the cycle is clearly shown, the annual number of sunspots being plotted for successive calendar years. Above the sunspot graph is a graph showing the frequency of magnetic storms. The two are strikingly in phase, despite minor irregularities of both graphs. Solar flares occur in much greater numbers than sunspots. As many as 2000 to 4000 flares occur per year during times of maximum sunspot activity. Flares are thus about 20 times more frequent events than sunspots, but their duration is correspondingly shorter. A single sunspot group in the course of its duration will produce as many as 40 flares.

## The aurora and night airglow

One of nature's great spectacles is the *aurora borealis,* or *northern lights,* of the northern latitudes, and its Southern Hemisphere counterpart, the *aurora australis.* The aurora borealis, seen at night in the northern sky, takes the form of light bands, rays, or draperies, continually shifting in pattern and intensity (Figure 7.34). This light emanates from the ionosphere in a region 50–175 mi (80–280 km) above the earth, with the tops occasionally at 500–600 mi (800–950 km), and is apparently given off by atoms of gas which have been excited by solar radiation. In a general way this light is emitted by the gases in the ionosphere in much the same way that fluorescent minerals, paints, or chalks give off a soft glow when ultraviolet light (so-called black light) is cast on them. The auroral light, however, continues during the hours of darkness, after the solar radiation is gone, with maximum intensity 1–2 hours before midnight, hence it is not produced by direct ultraviolet rays.

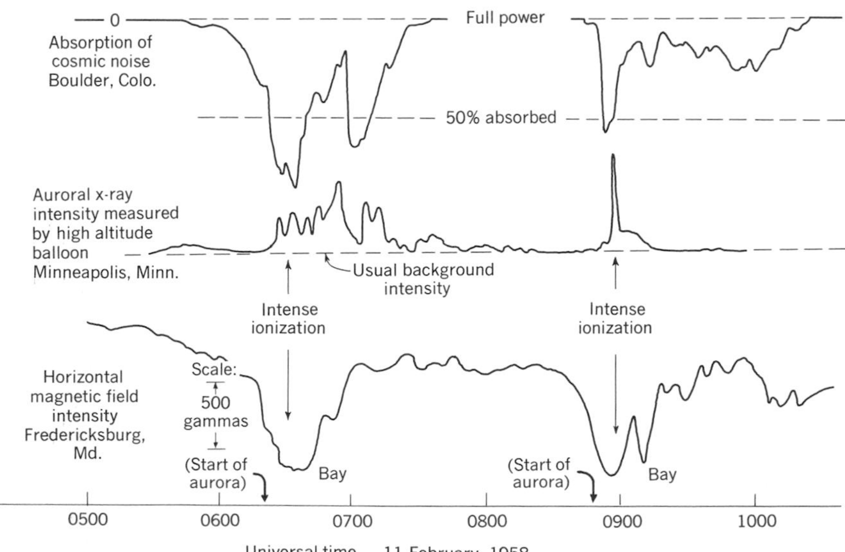


**FIGURE 7.32.** Second phase of the magnetic storm whose beginning is shown in Figure 7.31. The uppermost graph shows the degree of absorption of cosmic noise recorded at the earth's surface. The middle graph shows the intensity of X rays recorded by instruments carried by a balloon into the upper atmosphere. Periods of intense ionization occurred at 0630 and 0900 UT. Note that the scale of the magnetogram is different from that of Figure 7.31. (After IGY Bulletin, No. 18, 1958.)

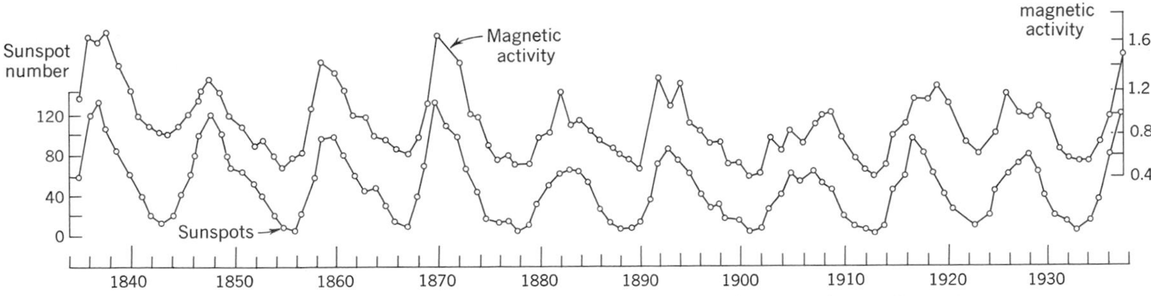


**FIGURE 7.33.** A remarkably close correspondence exists between cycles of change in number of sunspots and in the intensity of magnetic disturbances. [After S. Chapman and J. Bartels (1951), *Geomagnetism*, London, Oxford Univ. Press.]

Most commonly the aurora is greenish, a color produced by the excitation of atomic oxygen. Very rarely, red and violet colors are produced, the latter by excitation of molecular nitrogen.

Displays of the aurora are closely correlated in time with magnetic storms and in geographic location with the earth's magnetic field. Zones of maximum occurrence of auroras consist of two rings, or circles, one surrounding each of the geomagnetic poles (Figure 7.35) at a distance of 22½ degrees of arc, or about 1550 mi (2500 km) radius. These circles mark two terrestrial zones where lines of magnetic force enter the earth in the Northern and Southern Hemispheres with an inclination of about 70° to 80°. Bursts of electrons and protons from solar flares, as they reach the earth's magnetic field, become trapped between lines of force of the magnetic field as illustrated in Figure 7.36. These particles travel in corkscrew paths, passing alternately from one conjugate point to the other. As the electrons and protons impinge upon the atmosphere in the ionospheric layer, they excite the molecules of oxygen and nitrogen, causing them to emit light, which appears to observers on earth as the aurora.

Occurrence of the aurora in close correlation with a magnetic storm is illustrated by the data for February 10–11, 1958, in Figure 7.32. Considered one of the most spectacular auroral occurrences in several years, it was reportedly seen as far south as Cuba. Where observed and recorded by sky cameras at Minneapolis, Minnesota, Fargo, North Dakota, and the Yerkes Observatory at Williams Bay, Wisconsin, the aurora began at 0620 UT and again at 0848 UT, which coincided closely in time with the occurrence of magnetic bays and X-ray bursts shown in Figure 7.32.

As is the case for magnetic storms, auroral displays follow in frequency and intensity the 11-year sunspot cycle illustrated in Figure 7.33. They are also most frequent at equinoxes and have a 27-day period.

**FIGURE 7.34.** These three photographs of the aurora borealis, taken during the winter night in Alaska, suggest the varied forms of auroral displays. (Courtesy of The American Museum—Hayden Planetarium.)

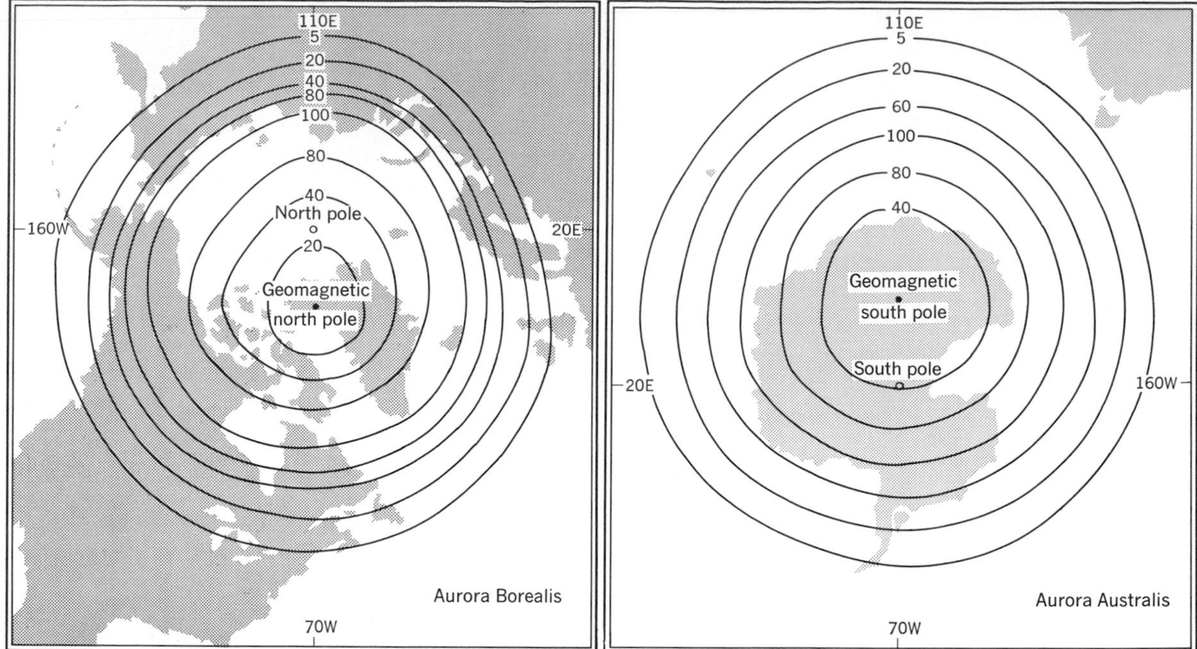


**FIGURE 7.35.** The relative frequency of days having occurrences of the aurora is shown by nearly circular lines centered on the north and south geomagnetic poles. (After *Handbook of Geophysics,* 1960, New York, Macmillan, pp. 15–24, 15-25.)

Closely related to the auroras, and probably of the same origin, is a very faint light glow, or luminescence, about 1/10,000 the brightness of the aurora, coming from the upper atmosphere at heights of 45–185 mi (70–300 km). It does not exhibit structure (arcs), but covers the entire sky at all latitudes. This phenomenon, called the *night airglow,* is also believed to come from oxygen and nitrogen molecules which have been excited by solar radiation, but it shows no marked correlation with sunspot activity or magnetic fluctuations.

## The Van Allen radiation belts

One of the most remarkable scientific discoveries of recent times relating to the earth's magnetic field in space was the encounter, in 1958, of U.S. earth satellites *Explorer I* and *Explorer III* with a large region around the earth containing a very high intensity of charged particles—protons and electrons—trapped in the geomagnetic field. Geiger counters carried by these satellites relayed to earth the intensity of radiation encountered in their highly elliptical orbits (see orbit data in Table 8.1), which extended out as far as 1750 mi (2800 km) from the earth. Similar apparatus carried by lunar probes *Pioneer III* and *Pioneer IV* showed that a still larger zone of intense radiation exists beyond the first.

In Figure 7.37 is a graphic representation of the radiation belts as seen in meridional cross section in comparison with the earth (left). The geomagnetic axis and equator form the vertical and horizontal lines of reference; distance from earth is scaled in units equal to the radius of the earth. The numbers 10, 100, 1000, and 10,000 on the diagram are lines of equal radiation intensity. The path of Pioneer III is shown on the outbound and inbound trips through the radiation belts.

The two belts of maximum radiation intensity shown in Figure 7.37 were named the *Van Allen radiation belts,* after the physicist who described them in 1959 through analysis of Geiger-counter data provided by the satellites. Visualized in three dimensions, the two belts would form two doughnutlike rings paralleling the plane of the geomagnetic equator.

**FIGURE 7.36.** The sinuous line shows the typical path of a particle tapped within the lines of force of the earth's outer magnetic field. [After R. Jastrow (1959), *Jour. Geophys.* Research, vol. 64, p. 1794, Figure 4.]

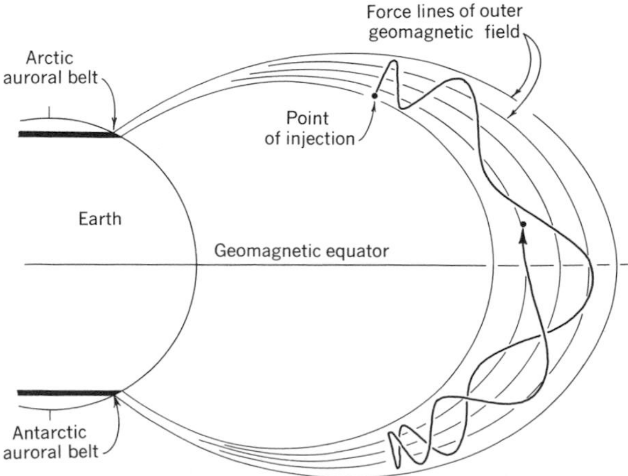

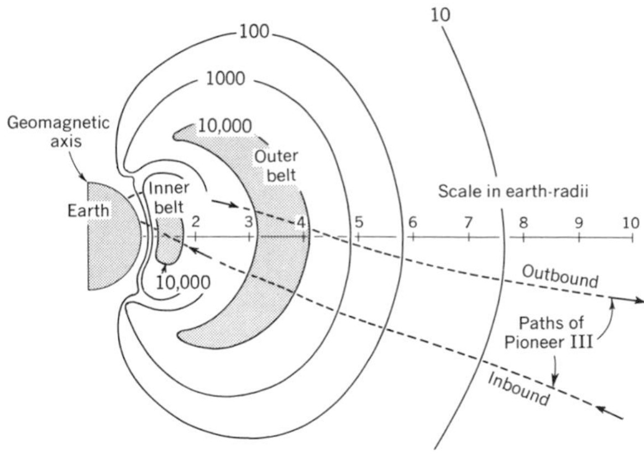


**FIGURE 7.37.** A schematic cross section of the Van Allen radiation belts, as deduced from geiger-counter data supplied by satellites Explorer IV and Pioneer III. Each contour line of equal radiation intensity has a value 10 times that of the next lower line. [After J. A. Van Allen (1959), *Jour. Geophys. Research,* vol. 64, p. 1684.]

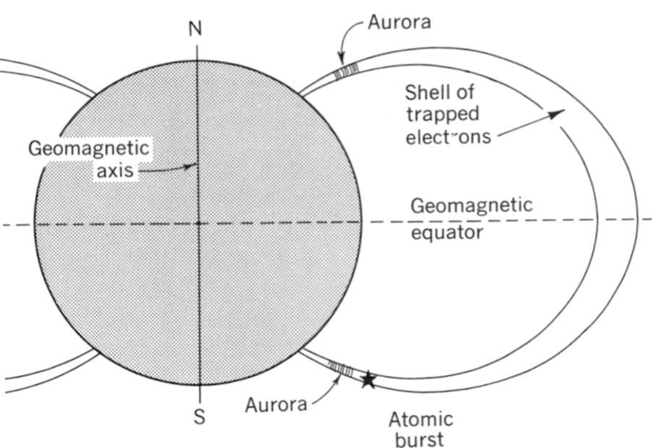


**FIGURE 7.38.** In the Argus experiment an atomic-bomb burst in the upper atmosphere created a shell of trapped electrons and caused auroras to appear. [After A. M. Peterson (1959), *Jour. Geophys. Research,* vol. 64, p. 933.]

## The Argus experiment

To test the trapping of electrons in the magnetic field surrounding the earth, a global experiment was carried out in 1958 by scientists working under the direction of the U.S. Atomic Energy Commission. The purpose of the *Argus experiment,* as it was known, was to explode an atomic bomb far above the earth's atmosphere and thereby to release a great quantity of electrons into the earth's magnetic field. Small atomic bombs, three in all, were exploded on August 27 and 30 and September 30, at latitudes ranging from 38° to 50° S., in the South Atlantic. From the point of explosion, electrons traveled in a great arch in space, reaching out to approximately 4000 mi (6400 km) and returning near to the earth at a latitude in the Northern Hemisphere approximately equivalent to the latitude of release in the Southern Hemisphere. Reports from instruments carried by U.S. satellite *Explorer IV,* which passed in and out of the electron belt several times, showed that the electrons quickly spread completely around the earth into a shell-like form (Figure 7.38). Electrons traveled in north-south paths in the shell, reflecting from the points closest to the earth at the latitudes where the magnetic lines of force enter the earth. By good fortune the electron shell was located between the inner and outer Van Allen radiation belts and hence was not affected by them.

The explosion was accompanied by an auroral glow extending upward and downward along the magnetic line passing through the point of the bomb burst. Simultaneously another auroral glow was seen in the North Atlantic at the point where the same magnetic force line returns to the earth. These man-made auroras represented the points of reflection of electrons. The natural auroras are found farther poleward, over zones where the magnetic force lines enter the earth at about 70° geomagnetic latitude. The force lines for this latitude extend some 10 earth radii beyond the earth in the plane of the geomagnetic equator.

## Whistlers

Yet another atmospheric phenomenon related to the earth's magnetic field is the *whistler,* a long descending wail heard on the loudspeaker of a radio receiver. Whistlers consist of natural radio waves of audio frequency, which can be received on an antenna, amplified, and converted into sound. Although discovered as early as 1886 and for many years a puzzling problem, whistlers have now been explained as originating in lightning flashes. We are all familiar with the static noises heard on the AM radio receiver when a thunderstorm is in the vicinity. The lightning stroke sends out a radio-frequency discharge consisting of noise—a wide range of frequencies combined—and these impulses travel with the speed of light. Therefore the lightning flash, if not too distant, is followed without perceptible delay by a static noise sent in a path relatively close to the earth's surface. If the lightning flash is not more than 500 mi (800 km) distance from the receiver, there will follow after the static noise at least one whistler and perhaps as many as five or six in succession, each being fainter and more drawn out than the previous one.

The radio-frequency waves emanating from the lightning flash travel outward from the earth, following the lines of the magnetic field in space until the corresponding terrestrial point (*conjugate point*) is reached, then are reflected back along the same path to return to the starting point (Figure 7.39). As the radio waves travel, the originally sharp impulse is spread out in time, or dispersed, because the shorter wavelengths travel faster than the longer ones, and when the reflected wave train is received it has been transformed into a long, drawn-out signal.

The arrival time of a whistler and the time intervals between successive whistlers can be calculated from a knowledge of the length of the travel path. For a whistler produced by a flash in the vicinity of the receiver, the length of travel is twice the distance along the magnetic force lines to the conjugate point, hence successive whistlers arrive at intervals of time following the ratio 2:4:6:8, etc., where one unit is the time required for travel from source to the conjugate

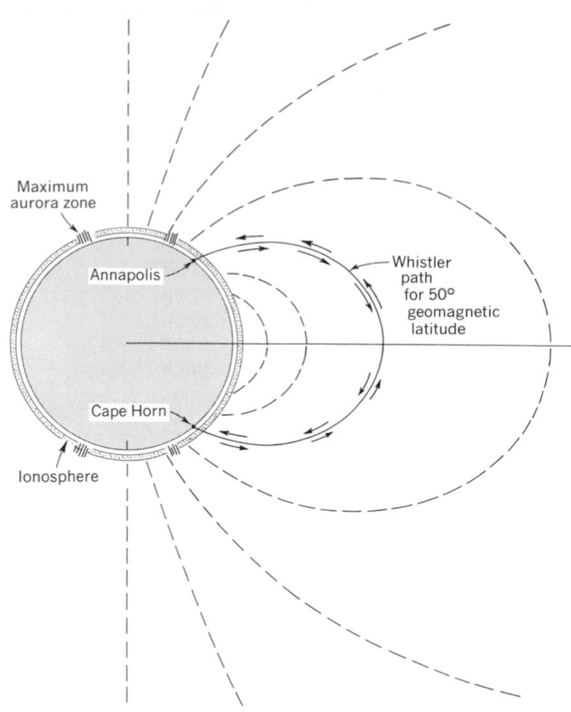


**FIGURE 7.39.** The whistler path between Annapolis, Maryland, and Cape Horn follows lines of force for a geomagnetic latitude of about 50°. Lines of force are indicated for each 10 degrees of geomagnetic latitude. (After *IGY Bulletin,* No. 6, 1957.)

point. If the whistle originates at the conjugate point, the first arrival occurs in one unit of travel time, and the successive arrivals follow at intervals of two units, in the ratio 1:3:5:7:9, etc.

Whistlers are not observed at very high latitudes because the travel paths along the lines of the magnetic field would be too great, nor do they occur near the geomagnetic equator because here the paths are too short (Figure 7.39). Travel time of whistlers between New Zealand and Alaska, for example, is about 1–3 seconds, depending upon the frequency of the waves.

The investigation of whistlers is included within a group of atmospheric phenomena termed *sferics,* a contraction of the word atmospherics, which refers to the radio waves produced by electrical discharges in the atmosphere. Study of sferics includes the detection and location of lightning strokes by electronic means.

## The magnetosphere and solar wind

Further satellite probes quickly led to new information about the extent and form of the earth's magnetic field and the region of entrapped energetic particles. The effective limit of the external magnetic field lies perhaps 40,000 to 80,000 mi (64,000 to 130,000 km) from the earth. All of the region within this limit is referred to as the *magnetosphere.* In terms of earth-radii, marked off on the equatorial scale in Figure 7.37, the magnetosphere extends out to 10 to 20 earth-radii, which is many times farther out than the outer Van Allen radiation belt.

The simplest geometrical model for the shape of the magnetosphere would be a doughnut-shaped ring surrounding the earth. Such a form was initially inferred from the configuration of the Van Allen radiation belts. The plane of the ring would lie in the plane of the magnetic equator, while the earth would occupy the opening in the center of the doughnut.

As information sent to earth by orbiting satellites and space probes accumulated, it became apparent that a symmetrical shape for the magnetosphere does not exist. The reason for such lack of symmetry lies in the influence of continuous emission of charged particles from the sun, a phenomenon to which we next turn our attention.

Bursts of solar plasma from flares are intermittent phenomena. In addition to the flare emissions there exists a steady flow of plasma outward from the sun. This phenomenon is known as the *solar wind* and can be regarded as an extension of the sun's outer corona. Unlike electromagnetic radiation, which travels at the speed of light in essentially straight-line radial paths from the sun, the slower plasma appears to follow curved paths.

We have noted in Chapter 6 that the sun rotates on its axis. From observations of sunspot motions it is known that the period of rotation is about 24½ days at the sun's equator and about 32 days at latitude 60°, the average value being 27.4 days.

Rotation of the sun affects the outward paths of flow of the solar plasma and the lines of magnetic force that the flow generates. Imagine that you are watering the lawn with a garden hose. Suppose that you stand in one spot on the lawn, turning at a uniform rate toward your left (anticlockwise). The water drops of the spray will appear to follow curved paths as they travel outward. These paths take the mathematical form of the Archimedes spiral. (Actually, a particular drop follows a straight radial path, but those drops preceding and following it occupy different radii.) Similarly, the solar plasma in both solar wind and solar flares seems to travel outward from the sun in spiral paths. Lines of force of the sun's magnetic field also take this form (Figure 7.40). The force lines intersect the earth's orbit at an angle different from a radial line to the sun. This angle, which is about 45°, has been appropriately dubbed the *garden hose angle* by space physicists. The strength of the interplanetary magnetic field at the earth's orbit is about $5 \times 10^{-5}$ oersteds. The plasma of the solar wind here has a density of about 5 protons per cubic centimeter.

Outward flow of the solar wind continues far beyond the earth's orbit. It has been estimated that outward flow continues to a distance of about 50 astronomical units from the sun. At this distance the *intergalactic magnetic field,* with an intensity of about $5 \times 10^{-6}$ oersteds, is encountered.

Under pressure of the solar wind, the lines of force of the earth's magnetic field are strongly distorted. Between the plasma of the solar wind, with its force lines radiating spirally from the sun, and the earth's magnetic field there exists a sharply-defined boundary known as the *magnetopause.* Under pressure of the

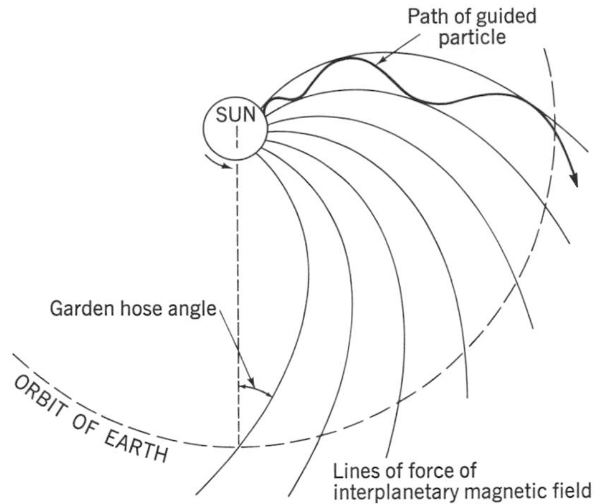


**FIGURE 7.40.** Magnetic field of the sun, showing the garden-hose effect caused by the sun's rotation. [Based on a drawing by K. G. McCracken (1967), in *Encyclopedia of Atmospheric Sciences and Astrogeology,* R. W. Fairbridge, Ed., New York, Reinhold, p. 489, Figure 1.]

solar wind the magnetopause is pressed close to the earth at the subsolar point (Figure 7.41). Here the distance to the magnetopause is on the order of 10 earth radii (about 40,000 mi, or 64,000 km). Lines of force in this region are crowded together and the magnetic field is intensified. On the opposite side of the earth, in a line pointing away from the sun, the magnetopause is drawn far out from the earth and the force lines are greatly attenuated. The extent of this magnetic "tail" is not known, but the entire shape of the magnetosphere has been described as resembling a comet. Length of the magnetic tail has been estimated to be at least four million ($4 \times 10^6$) mi ($6 \times 10^6$ km) and is possible vastly longer.

In advance of the magnetopause, on the side close to the sun there is developed a curved *shock front* on the magnetosphere. Here the smooth flow of the solar plasma is disrupted and the flow lines become irregular as they diverge and pass around the magnetosphere.

Lacking an atmosphere, the moon's surface is subject to direct impact of gas ions of the solar wind, as well as to the intensified particle flux from solar flares. To measure this effect astronauts of the Apollo 10 mission in 1969 placed a sheet of aluminum foil in an orientation such as to receive the impact of the solar wind for a period of 77 minutes. Analysis made later showed that the foil had trapped ions of helium-4 at the rate of about 5 to 7 million atoms per square centimeter per second. Thus a calculation of the solar wind flux could be made without the disrupting presence of a magnetic field. (The moon has no appreciable external magnetic field.)

Analysis of lunar dust collected on the Apollo 11 mission showed a great enrichment with the noble gases (helium, neon, argon, krypton, and xenon), most of which are thought to have been derived from the solar wind. Analysis of lunar rock materials has led to the conclusion that the average flux of protons from solar flares has not changed significantly in the past 10 million years.

It is interesting to consider whether other planets of the solar system have magnetic fields resembling the earth. Thus far, instruments on the Mariner space vehicles have detected no magnetic field or indication of a magnetosphere on Mars. Similar space probe data show that a magnetosphere seems to be missing from Venus as well. Both planets have atmospheres that show ionization, e.g., they have ionospheres. There is some suggestion that the ionosphere surrounding Venus acts to deflect the solar wind, causing it to diverge around the planet. The boundary between Venus' ionosphere and the solar wind has been named the *ionopause.* Venus' period of rotation is very long (243 days) compared with that of Earth (24 hours) and Mars (24½ hours). If a planetary magnetic field results from dynamo action between a liquid iron core and a surrounding solid rock mantle, the slow speed of rotation of Venus could explain the lack of a magnetic field. The same argument cannot be applied to Mars. However, Mars is a much smaller planet than either Earth or Venus and we might propose the hypothesis that a liquid iron core does not exist in Mars. Mercury, a still smaller planet

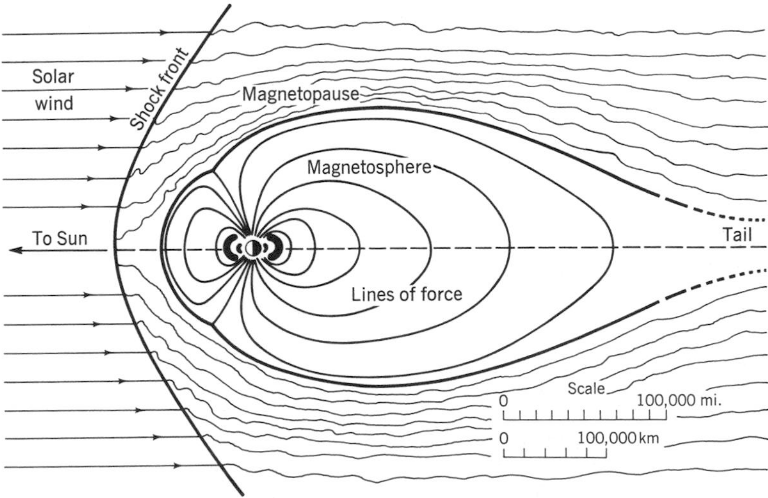


**FIGURE 7.41.** Cross section of magnetosphere, showing magnetopause and shock front. [Based on data of C. O. Hines, *Science* (1963), and B. J. O'Brien, *Science* (1965); © 1969, John Wiley & Sons, New York.]

and possessed of a slow rotation, would seem to be even less likely to have a magnetic field and a magnetosphere.

Study of radio waves emanating from Jupiter has revealed that this giant planet has a magnetosphere very much larger than that of Earth. As in the case of Earth, the Jovian magnetic polar axis is inclined about 10° with respect to the axis of rotation. However, the magnetic dipole center lies about 7/10 of the radial distance south of the planetary center (Figure 7.42).

Belts of trapped energetic particles within the Jovian magnetosphere resemble the earth's Van Allen radiation belts. It is now generally thought that the bulk of the interior of Jupiter consists of hydrogen in a very dense liquid or metallic state. There may exist a mantle region of liquid hydrogen comparable to the earth's rocky mantle, and a core region of hydrogen in the metallic state (see Chapter 5). If so, a dynamo mechanism may result from convection within the liquid hydrogen mantle, explaining the off-center location of the dipole.

## Cosmic rays and the earth's magnetic field

Some cosmic rays are generated in solar flares (Chapter 6). These highly energetic particles, largely protons of hydrogen and helium, are believed to be channeled in paths between the spiral lines of force of the sun's magnetic field, as shown in Figure 7.40. The incoming cosmic particles are guided by the lines of force of the geomagnetic field and tend to be concentrated in higher latitudes. Thus if a Geiger counter operating at high altitudes (near the top of the atmosphere) is taken from low to high geomagnetic latitudes, the intensity of cosmic radiation strongly increases.

Cosmic particles penetrate the magnetosphere more deeply than the relatively weak ions of the solar plasma. As the cosmic particles cause disintegration of atoms in the outer atmosphere of the earth secondary radiation products are produced (see Figure 6.21). These secondary particles become entrapped in the inner Van Allen radiation belt.

Surprisingly, the intensity of cosmic radiation decreases when the intensity of solar radiation from flares increases, suggesting that the solar particles serve as a screen to absorb cosmic particles at distances far beyond their normal depths of penetration into the atmosphere. This effect is illustrated in Figure 7.32.

**FIGURE 7.42.** Magnetosphere of the planet Jupiter. [After NASA (1967), *Handbook of the Physical Properties of the Planet Jupiter,* Washington, D.C., p. 48, Figure 8-1.]

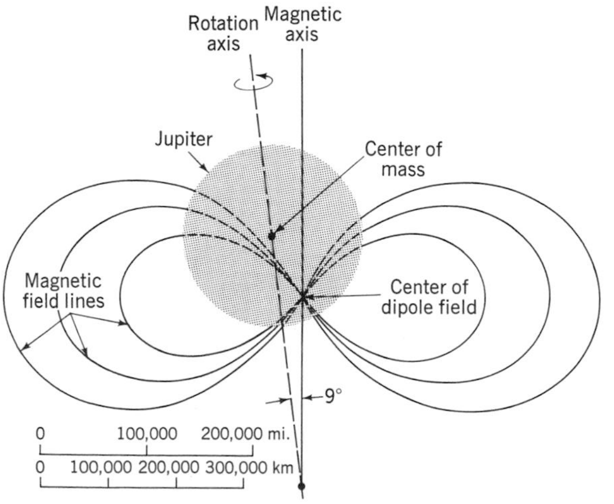


## Electromagnetic systems in review

In this chapter we have examined a physical system in which a flow of matter and energy from the sun interacts with the external magnetic field of the earth. The earth's magnetism itself constitutes an independent physical system, possibly produced by earth rotation acting upon a liquid iron core. Therefore, two quite unlike physical systems engage in interaction in the magnetosphere. The sun's spectrum of electromagnetic radiation is an entirely different and indepedent form of energy transmission from sun to earth and, moreover, does not include the transmission of matter. Whereas the electromagnetic radiation flux is remarkably constant, the emanation of charged particles from the sun takes place in irregular bursts of matter from sunspot flares superimposed upon the steady flow of plasma from the sun's corona.

Yet, we have found that there is a linkage between the solar radiation system and the earth's magnetic field. This linkage comes about as solar radiation ionizes layers in the upper atmosphere, creating fluxes of electrons, and these in turn cause rhythmic daily and seasonal variations in the intensity and direction of the magnetic field at the earth's surface.

On the basis of information presently available, planet Earth seems to be unique among the inner planets in possessing a strongly developed magnetic field and an enveloping magnetosphere. Thus we add yet another dimension of contrast between the environment of Earth and that of its close neighbors in space.

## References for further study

Chapman, S. (1951), *The Earth's Magnetism,* 2nd ed., London, Methuen, and New York, Wiley, 127 pp.

Fraser, R. (1957), *Once Around the Sun,* New York, Macmillan, 160 pp., chaps. 1, 5.

Howell, B. F., Jr. (1959), *Introduction to Geophysics,* New York, McGraw-Hill, 399 pp., chap. 22.

Jacobs, J. A., R. D. Russell, and J. T. Wilson (1959), *Physics and Geology,* New York, McGraw-Hill, 424 pp., chap. 6.

Parasnis, D. S. (1961), *Magnetism; from Lodestone to Polar Wandering,* New York, Harper & Row, 128 pp.

Nelson, J. H., L. Hurwitz, and D. G. Knapp (1962), *Magnetism of the Earth,* ESSA Coast and Geodetic Survey, Publ. 40-1, U.S. Government Printing Office, Washington, 79 pp.

Jacobs, J. A. (1963), *The Earth's Core and Geomagnetism,* Oxford, Pergamon, New York, Macmillan, 137 pp.

Bates, D. R. (1964), *The Planet Earth,* Oxford, Pergamon, 370 pp., chaps. 6, 12, 13, 14, 17.

# The moon and man-made satellites

STUDENTS OF THE earth sciences have joined the astronomers in an intense investigation of the moon, extending to that satellite body certain of the same fields of scientific inquiry carried out upon the earth. Like the earth, the moon is a cold spherical body whose surface layer consists, in part at least, of rocks similar to those found on earth. Lunar relief features are intriguing for their resemblance in form to a few rare topographic forms found on earth, although the differences in relief patterns are far more striking than the similarities. Closeness to earth and absence of an atmosphere allow us to photograph and map the moon's surface from various distances by telescope and from lunar orbiting satellites with a degree of clarity far exceeding that possible for any other celestial body. Direct observation of lunar topography and the sampling of lunar surface materials by use of manned space vehicles is being rapidly exploited. New knowledge of the moon is being used to make new inferences or confirm old hypotheses concerning origin and early history of both earth and moon.

Gravitational attraction between earth and moon and between earth and sun subjects the earth to unequal forces which tend to deform our rotating globe in a never-ending sequence of rhyhmic motions—the tides. Not only are the ocean waters strongly affected, producing obvious oceanic tides, but even the atmosphere and solid earth show detectable responses. Tidal forces must be taken into account in several branches of the earth sciences quite apart from the principal object of tidal study, which is the periodic rise and fall of the ocean level and its accompanying ebb and flood currents.

Although a tiny object in comparison with the sun, the moon, by its very closeness to the earth, causes the dominant tide-raising force and dictates the tidal rhythms. For this reason a study of tides is more meaningful if the moon and its motions are first thoroughly understood.

As the earth's single natural satellite, the moon illustrates basic principles of mechanics that must be applied in the successful launching of artificial earth satellites. We therefore take the opportunity to consider in this chapter how a variety of space orbits can be achieved.

## The moon as a satellite

As the earth's single, large, natural satellite, the moon has a mass about one eighty-first that of the earth and a diameter of 2160 mi (3476 km), about one-fourth that of the earth. The moon revolves about the earth in an elliptical orbit for which the mean distance between the earth's center and the moon's center is 238,859 mi ($3.844 \times 10^5$ km) (Figure 8.1). As already noted (Chapter 2), the direction of revolution can be described as counterclockwise if we imagine ourselves to be viewing the earth and moon from a point in space above the earth's north pole. This direction of revolution is the same as that of the earth's revolution and rotation (Figure 2.2). The plane of the moon's orbit is within a few degrees of parallelism with the plane of the ecliptic.

The form of the moon's orbit is that of an ellipse with an eccentricity of about 1/18, or 0.055. By comparison, the earth's orbit about the sun has an eccentricity of only 1/60, or 0.017 (see Table 5.1). The moon is said to be in *perigee* when it occupies the point in its orbit closest to earth and in *apogee* when at the point most distant.[1]

Distance from the earth's center to the moon's center is about 221,500 mi ($3.564 \times 10^5$ km) in perigee and about 252,700 mi ($4.067 \times 10^5$ km) in apogee (Figure 8.1). As already explained in terms of Kepler's second law (Chapter 1), the moon's linear velocity in orbit is greatest at perigee and least at apogee.

[1] From the Greek words *peri*, near; *ge*, earth; *apo*, from. The points of nearest and farthest distance in the orbits of man-made satellites are now also described as perigee and apogee.

**FIGURE 8.1.** Dimensions of the moon's orbit.

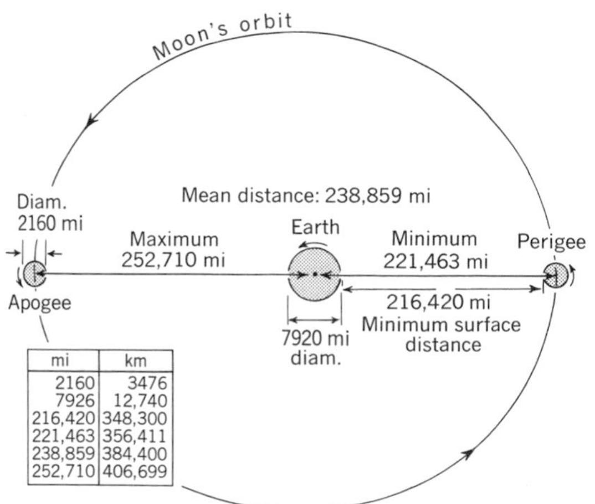


| mi | km |
|---|---|
| 2160 | 3476 |
| 7926 | 12,740 |
| 216,420 | 348,300 |
| 221,463 | 356,411 |
| 238,859 | 384,400 |
| 252,710 | 406,699 |

## Center of earth-moon revolution

Newton's law of gravitation states that any two bodies attract each other with a force proportional to the product of their masses and inversely proportional to the square of the distance between them. We are so accustomed to thinking in terms of *gravity*, which is the force by which small objects are attracted by the earth, that we neglect the force by which the small object attracts the earth. In the case of the moon and earth both masses are relatively large, and it is not correct to say that the moon revolves about the earth's center. Actually both earth and moon revolve about a *common center of gravity*, or *barycenter*, located at a point on the line connecting the centers of mass of the two bodies. This point lies about 2886 mi (4645 km) from the earth's center and is thus almost three-fourths of the distance from the earth's center to its surface (Figure 8.2).

We have noted that the moon's mass is about one eighty-first that of the earth. This ratio can be computed from the dimensions of the earth's and moon's orbits of revolution about their common center of gravity. For purposes of calculation, assume that the earth revolves in a small orbit of 2900 miles radius about the common center of gravity, whereas the moon's orbit about this center averages 236,000 miles radius. Dividing the latter figure by 2900 gives roughly the ratio of 1/81.

Because of the revolution of the earth and moon about their common center of gravity, the earth's orbit about the sun is not a true ellipse but a type of wobbling

**FIGURE 8.2.** Earth and moon revolve about a common center of gravity.

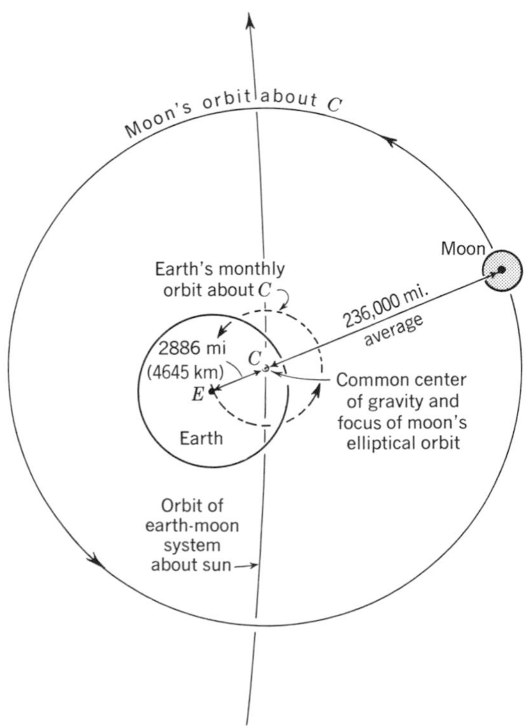

path which at times brings the earth ahead of the position it would occupy if there were no moon; at other times it is behind that position. Therefore the sun's apparent eastward progress along the ecliptic is not uniform and does not strictly agree with Kepler's law of areas. The difference in position of the sun in the ecliptic with respect to its position in an ideal uniform motion is about 6 seconds of arc. It is this observed discrepancy that permits the position of the common center of gravity of the earth and moon to be calculated.

Strictly speaking, then, the "earth's orbit" of which we speak in Chapter 1 is the orbit of the common center of gravity of the earth and moon. Perhaps we should instead speak of the "orbit of the earth-moon pair," for this is the orbit which conforms with Kepler's planetary laws.

## Moon's orbit with respect to the sun

While the moon is revolving about the earth, both bodies are moving rapidly in orbit about the sun. (For the moment, neglect the small motion of earth about the common center of gravity.) Consequently the moon's path with respect to the earth's orbit is a sinuous one, with changing linear velocity (Fig. 8.3). When the moon crosses the earth's orbit, its velocity in that orbit will be the same as the earth's velocity. When the moon is between earth and sun (position labeled "new moon"), its own earth-orbital motion opposes the forward motion of the earth, so that the moon's linear velocity in solar orbit is reduced and it drops behind the earth. When the moon lies on the opposite side of the earth from the sun (position labeled "full moon"), its own earth-orbital velocity is added to the solar-orbital velocity, and the moon moves rapidly ahead of the earth.

Despite the repeated crossing and recrossing of the earth's orbit by the moon to bring it to positions as far as 250,000 mi ($4 \times 10^5$ km) from the orbit, the sinuousity of the moon's path is actually very small when shown on a true scale diagram. Actually the path is always concave toward the sun, as shown in the upper part of Figure 8.3. Whereas parts of the moon's path shown in the lower part of Figure 8.3 are drawn as concave away from the sun, this condition never really exists; it appears on the lower diagram only because of great exaggeration.

## Period of moon's revolution—the month

Should the moon be observed among the stars at the same hour on two successive nights, it will be found to have shifted about 13 degrees eastward in the celestial sphere. This shift is in the same direction as the 1-degree daily eastward shift of the sun in the ecliptic and occurs for much the same reason. After the lapse of one mean solar day of 24 hours, the moon, revolving in the same direction as the earth's rotation, has moved 13.2° eastward in celestial longitude, while the sun has moved 1° eastward. For the moon to reach again the celestial longitude of a given star will require as many days as 360° divided by 13.2°, which is 27.3 days, a period of time designated the *sidereal month.* The exact mean value of the sidereal month is $27^{d}07^{h}43^{m}11.5^{s}$, or 27.32166 days.

With reference to the sun the moon is shifting its celestial longitude eastward by only 12.2° per mean solar day. (Here the sun's daily change of 1° is subtracted from the moon's daily change of 13.2°.) Thus, if we should record the exact time when the moon and sun are on the same celestial meridian, then wait until the moon again reaches the meridian occupied by the sun, it will be found that this interval is the same as 360° divided by 12.2° or 29.5 days, which is the *synodic month.* We are all familiar with the word "synod," referring to a meeting of churches or church officials. In this case the word refers to the meeting of the sun and moon on the same meridian, a condition also termed *conjunction* in astronomical language. The exact value for the mean length of the synodic month is $29^{d}12^{h}44^{m}2.8^{s}$, or 29.53059 days, but the actual length of a given synodic month may be quite different, the total range of variation in observed length being about 13 hours.

The synodic month is of particular interest here because it is the period to which the phases of the moon and the rise and fall of the ocean tides are adjusted.

## Inclination of the moon's orbit

The plane of the moon's orbit forms an angle of 5°09′ with the plane of the ecliptic (Figure 8.4). This means that twice each month the moon in its orbit passes through the plane of the ecliptic. The point of such passage, where the moon moves from south of the ecliptic to north, is termed the *ascending node;* where it passes from north to south, the *descending node.* The interval of time required for the moon to travel from one ascending node to the next ascending node is the *tropical month* of 27.32 days; it is analogous with the tropical year of the sun.

Although the moon's path in the sky seems to be quite like that taken by the sun, the two paths normally are somewhat different. Even when the sun and moon are moving across the sky on nearly the same meridian (new moon), the moon may have a declination as much as 5°09′ greater or less than the sun's declination.

Turning to the star chart on which the sun's ecliptic circle is plotted (Figure 8.5), we see that the moon's position through a tropical month forms a similar type of wavelike curve with two "equinoxes" and two "solstices" (using an analogy with the sun), except that the elapsed time is only 27.32 days, instead of 365¼ days which the sun requires. This diagram shows us that the moon will experience a full cycle of declinational change each 27.32 days, in contrast to the yearly cycle of declinational change which the sun experiences.

Because of the gravitational attraction of the moon by the sun, the nodes of the moon's orbit shift slowly, or *regress,* westward with reference to celestial coordinates. The rate of regression is such that a complete turn of 360° of the line connecting the nodes takes 18.6 years.

In the upper ecliptic chart (Figure 8.5*A*) the ascending node of the moon's orbit happens to coincide with the vernal equinox, an event to be expected every 18.6

years. Under such conditions the moon's maximum declination south and north (points *WS* and *SS*) is 5°09′ greater than 23½°. Adding these two figures (and using the exact sun's solstice declination of 23°27′), we obtain 28°36′ as the moon's maximum declination north or south, occurring at the point when the moon is on the celestial meridians *WS* and *SS*. When located at points *VE* and *AE* (vernal and autumnal equinoxes), the moon will have zero declination and will be on the celestial equator.

The moon's total declination range can be equal to two times 28°36′, or just over 57°, whereas that of the sun is only 47°.

In the lower ecliptic chart (Figure 8.5*B*) some 9.3 years after the date represented in *A*, the regression of the nodes has brought the ascending node to coincide with the autumnal equinox at point *AE*. According to this relation the moon's maximum possible declination is 5°09′ less than 23°27′, or 18°18′, at the points *SS* and *WS*. It is just such a condition that is illustrated in Figure 8.4.

Of course, the nodes may cross the ecliptic at any two points besides the equinoxes. Then the difference in maximum declinations of moon and sun will fall between zero and 5°09′, the exact amount depending upon where the nodes happen to be situated on the ecliptic.

## Conjunction, opposition, quadrature, and syzygy

A knowledge of the simple geometrical relations of the earth, moon, and sun is of primary importance for understanding the phases of the moon and the tidal variations produced by sun and moon upon the earth (Figure 8.6). Assume for the moment that the moon's orbit lies in the plane of the ecliptic, and consider only the alignment of the three bodies in a single plane.

When all three bodies lie along a single straight line, with moon and sun on the same side of the earth, the moon and sun are said to be in *conjunction;* if aligned with the earth located between them, the moon and sun are in *opposition.* Because both of these conditions are identical in so far as their tide-producing effects

**FIGURE 8.4.** The plane of the moon's orbit is inclined with respect to the plane of the ecliptic. Conditions shown are for winter solstice with nodes located about on the earth's orbit.

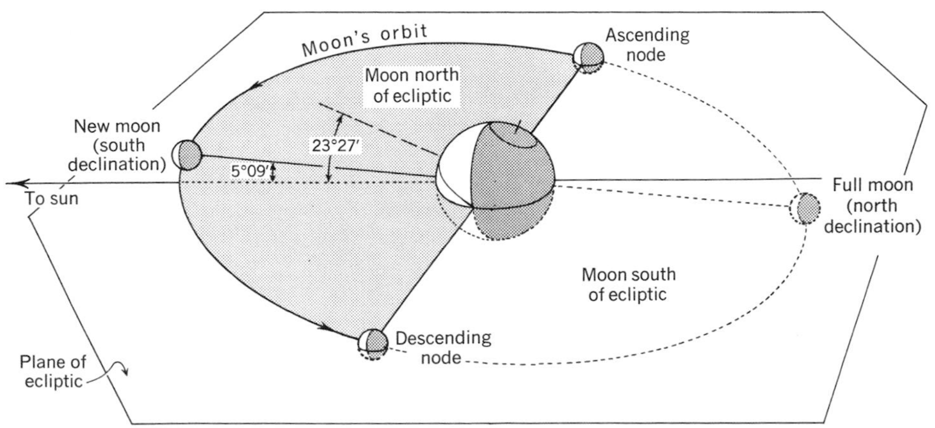

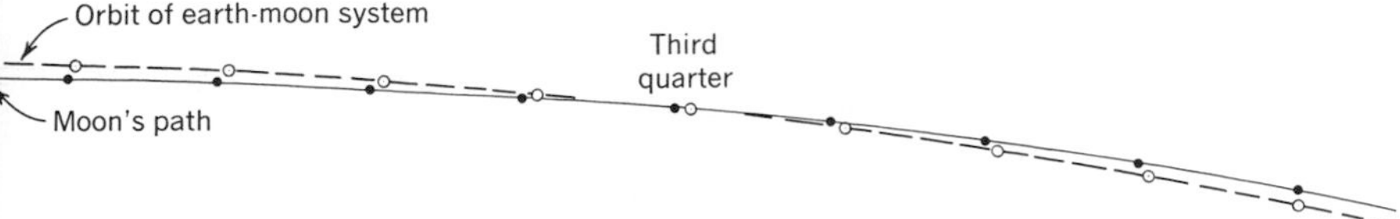


**FIGURE 8.3.** The upper part of this diagram shows portions of the orbits of moon and earth-moon system plotted to true scale. Note that the moon's orbit is everywhere concave toward the sun (disregarding small imperfections in the drawing of the line). Below is a greatly exaggerated diagram to show the moon orbit in a synodic month.

are concerned, they are given the common name of *syzygy,* which can be applied to either position singly, or to both collectively, for which the plural, *syzygies,* is used.

A contrasting relation, termed *quadrature,* exists when the line from earth to moon makes a right angle with respect to the line from earth to sun (Figure 8.6). In each synodic month the moon will be found twice in syzygy, twice in quadrature.

## Lunar eclipse

As shown in Figure 8.6, when the sun and moon are in opposition the moon may cross the earth's shadow, which is relatively large in proportion to the moon's diameter, giving an eclipse of the moon, or *lunar eclipse.* If the earth's shadow merely passes across one edge of the moon's disk without entirely enveloping it, a *partial eclipse* is said to occur, whereas if the earth's shadow completely covers the moon, as shown in Figure 8.7, a *total eclipse* results.

In a lunar eclipse two shadow zones are encountered (Figure 8.8). Because of the sun's relatively large size there is formed an inner cone of complete shadow, the *umbra,* surrounded by a zone of partial shadow, the *penumbra.* As the moon enters the penumbra, it goes gradually from full illumination into a region of increasingly dim light; then it crosses an abrupt boundary into the nearly total darkness of the umbra. Diameter of the earth's umbra is about 5700 mi (9200 km), where it is crossed by the moon, or about three times the moon's diameter. In a total eclipse the moon lies entirely within the umbra for almost 2 hours; the total elapsed time from its first contact with the umbra to the time it is entirely free of the umbra may last about 3¾ hours.

If the moon's orbit lay exactly in the plane of the ecliptic, a total lunar eclipse would result once each synodic month at the time of opposition (full moon). As we know, the moon's orbital plane is inclined by about 5° from the ecliptic, so that a large share of the times that the moon is in opposition it will pass above or below the earth's shadow. Only when the full moon occurs near one of the two nodes of its orbit is there a chance of a lunar eclipse. Therefore opposition must occur near a node to produce an eclipse. A line connecting the nodes will twice yearly coincide with the line between earth and sun. This gives two periods per year within which an eclipse might occur, but unless the moon happens to be at opposition within those periods the eclipse will not occur.

For example, in 1968 two total eclipses of the moon took place: the first was on April 12, with the moon reaching the center of umbra at 11:47 P.M. EST; the second was on October 6, with the moon at its midpoint of eclipse at 6:42 A.M. EST. Note that these eclipses were separated by 176 days, which is very close to the length in days of six average synodic months of 29½ days. These were the two dates in 1968 when opposition occurred near the moon's nodes.

**FIGURE 8.5.** Celestial chart of the region near the ecliptic, showing (*A*) ascending node at vernal equinox and (*B*) ascending node at autumnal equinox. See Figure 3.8 for details of the ecliptic. [After R. F. Moulton (1924), *Introduction to Astronomy,* New York, Macmillan.]

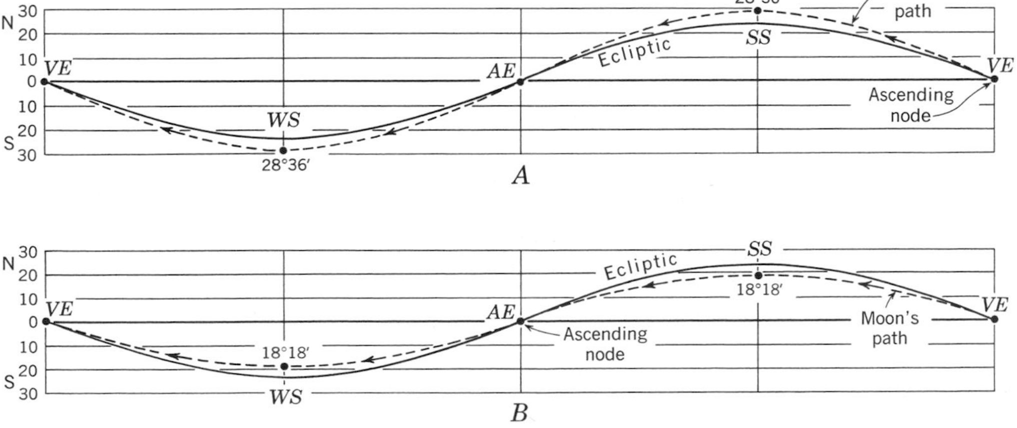

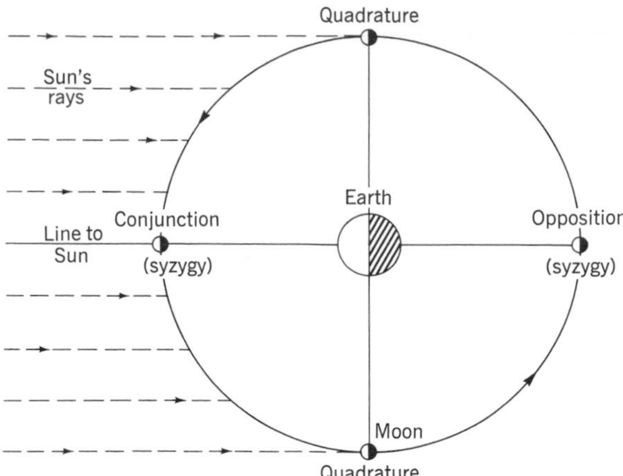


**FIGURE 8.6.** Relative position of moon, earth, and sun determine the moon's phases.

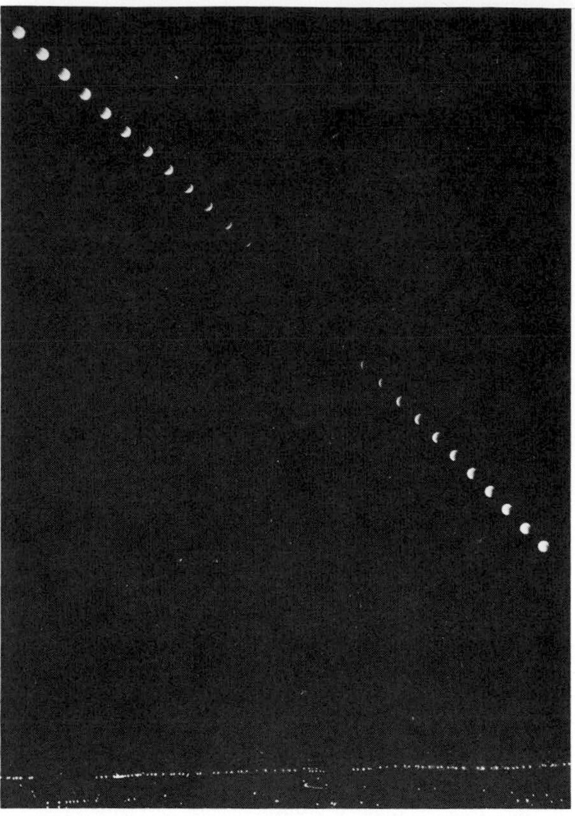

**FIGURE 8.7.** An eclipse of the moon, recorded by multiple exposures at equal time intervals. The photograph has, however, been condensed in the region of totality. (Courtesy of The American Museum—Hayden Planetarium.)

## Solar eclipse

An eclipse of the sun, or *solar eclipse,* occurs when the moon is in conjunction with the sun and casts its shadow upon the earth (Figures 8.6 and 8.9). For persons in the shadow zone on earth the moon's disk seems to pass across the sun's disk, partially or totally obscuring the sun. We have seen in Chapter 4 that the sun's disk subtends an arc of about 32′. The moon's disk subtends an arc of about 31′, although the figure varies somewhat with perigee and apogee as well as with location of the observation point. Thus, by remarkable good fortune, as far as the astronomer and earth scientist are concerned, the moon's disk in certain eclipses appears slightly larger than that of the sun, permitting studies of the sun's peripheral region, or *corona,* to be viewed and photographed at total eclipse (Figure 6.1).

The moon's core of total shadow forms only a very narrow track across the earth—up to 168 mi (270 km) wide—hence a total eclipse is rarely seen by an individual unless he makes a special effort to travel to the predicted track. The shadow of totality travels across the earth's surface at some 1000–4000 mi (1600-6400 km) per hour, and the total phase lasts, at most, only 7½ minutes. The region of partial eclipse, in contrast, is a very broad zone, up to several thousand miles wide.

As with the lunar eclipse, a solar eclipse requires that the sun be aligned near one of the nodes of the moon's orbit. This normally limits the occurrence of solar eclipses to two periods per year. In many eclipses the zone of totality completely misses the earth, there being only a partial eclipse visible at high latitudes. For example, in 1968 there were two solar eclipses. The first, a partial eclipse visible only in Antarctica and the South Pacific, occurred on March 28. The second, a total eclipse with path of totality in Siberia, occurred on September 22. Note that the elapsed time between these two eclipses was 177 days, or the equivalent of 6 synodic months of 29½ days. Furthermore these dates are both

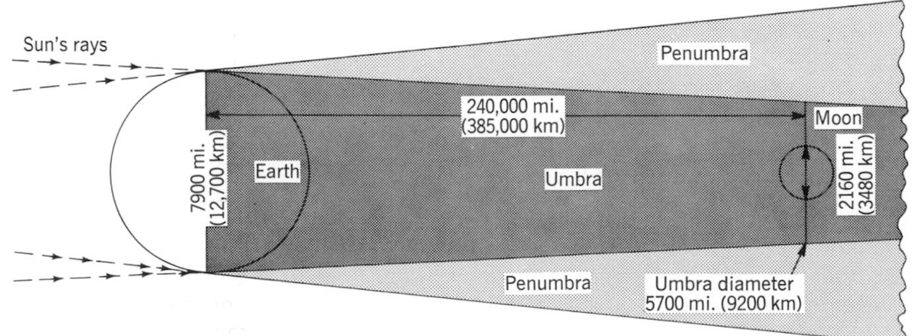


**FIGURE 8.8.** Diagram of lunar eclipse. Scale of diameters of earth, moon, and umbra is about ten times the scale of separating distance. Point of the umbra cone lies 860,000 mi (1,380,000 km) from the earth's center.

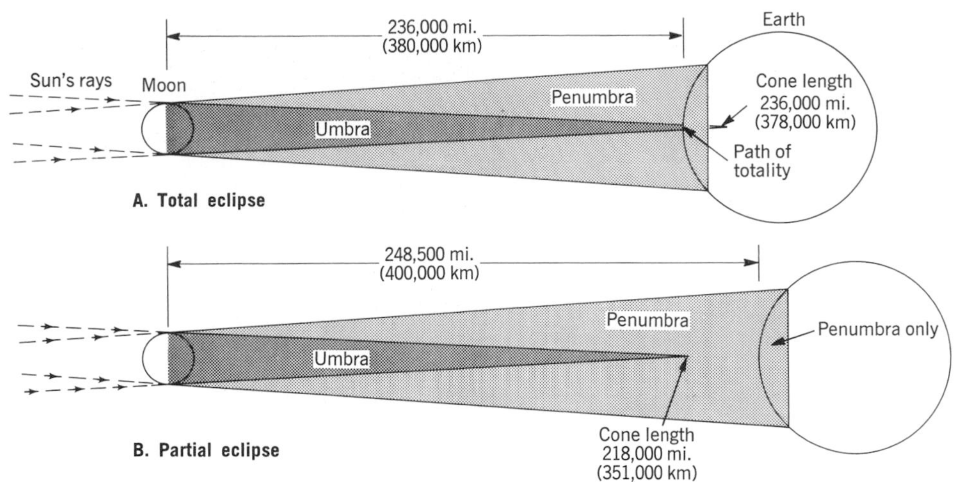


**FIGURE 8.9.** Diagrams of solar eclipses. *A.* Long umbra cone and minimum separating distance allow a total eclipse to occur. *B.* Short umbra cone and maximum separating distance allow partial eclipse only. [Based on data of T. G. Mehlin (1959), *Astronomy,* New York, John Wiley & Sons, pp. 317–322.]

14–15 days (which represents half a synodic month) later than the dates of lunar eclipses of 1968, previously mentioned. This is the time required for the moon to cover half its orbit and to go from one node to the other.

## Phases of the moon

The series of changes in appearance of the moon throughout the synodic month are termed the *phases of the moon* (Figure 8.10). Moonlight consists of sunlight falling upon the moon's surface and reflecting to earth. The moon is at all times divided by a great circle of illumination into a sunlit hemisphere and a shadowed hemisphere. The phases of the moon are simply the varying proportions of the sunlit and shadowed halves that we see from the earth.

The phase of *new moon* begins the synodic month (Figure 8.10). At this point the moon is in conjunction with the sun, and both occupy the same celestial meridian. Obviously the sunlit half of the moon is opposite to the half we can see from the earth, hence the moon's disk is completely dark (except for a faint glow of light reflected upon it from the earth). Actually we cannot see the new moon for another reason—it lies so close to the sun that the sun's blinding rays obscure it. If we were able to see both the moon and sun on the day of new moon, they would seem to rise together in the east and move westward across the sky together, except that the moon would travel more slowly, and on the second day it would be 12.2° of celestial longitude eastward of the sun.

As the moon travels the first quadrant of its orbit, it can be described as having a *crescent* configuration. When one-eighth of the orbit is completed, in 3¾ days, the moon appears in the sky as a slender crescent whose points are directed away from the sun. An angular distance of about 45° then separates moon and sun, so that both are visible throughout much of the day. The sun will, however, set first, and the crescent new moon is most beautifully displayed low in the western sky during the twilight of early evening.

When quadrature is reached, about 7½ days after the new moon, the moon is in the phase of *first quarter,* appearing as a half-disk of light. At this point the moon is trailing the sun by about 90° in the sky, hence it will rise about at noon, make its meridian passage about at sunset, and set about midnight (assuming equinox conditions).

While in the second quadrant of its orbit the moon presents a *gibbous* configuration. The word gibbous, meaning rounded or bulging, is an appropriate description of the moon in this period because at an age of around 11 days it is about three-quarters illuminated.

The mid-point in the synodic month is reached at 14¾ days; the moon is now in opposition and in the phase of *full moon,* and we can see the whole of the illuminated hemisphere. Because the moon and sun are at opposite points in the celestial sphere at full moon, we can expect the moon to make its meridian passage close to midnight. If the date is near equinox, we can expect the full moon to rise as the sun is setting, and vice versa.

At this point it is possible to explain a popular expression, that the winter full moon "rides high," meaning that its path in the sky maintains a high altitude and therefore gives a more brilliant light. In Figure 8.4 are shown the conditions at this time of year, near winter solstice. Whereas the sun has its most southerly declination at this time, the full moon has its greatest northerly declination, because the noon sun and midnight moon occupy diametrically opposed points in the celestial sphere. In contrast, at summer solstice the full moon will have a south declination and will take a path low in the sky.

During the balance of the synodic month the moon's phases again assume, in reverse order and in reverse (mirror-image) shape, the phases of the first half. A second period of gibbous configuration is followed by

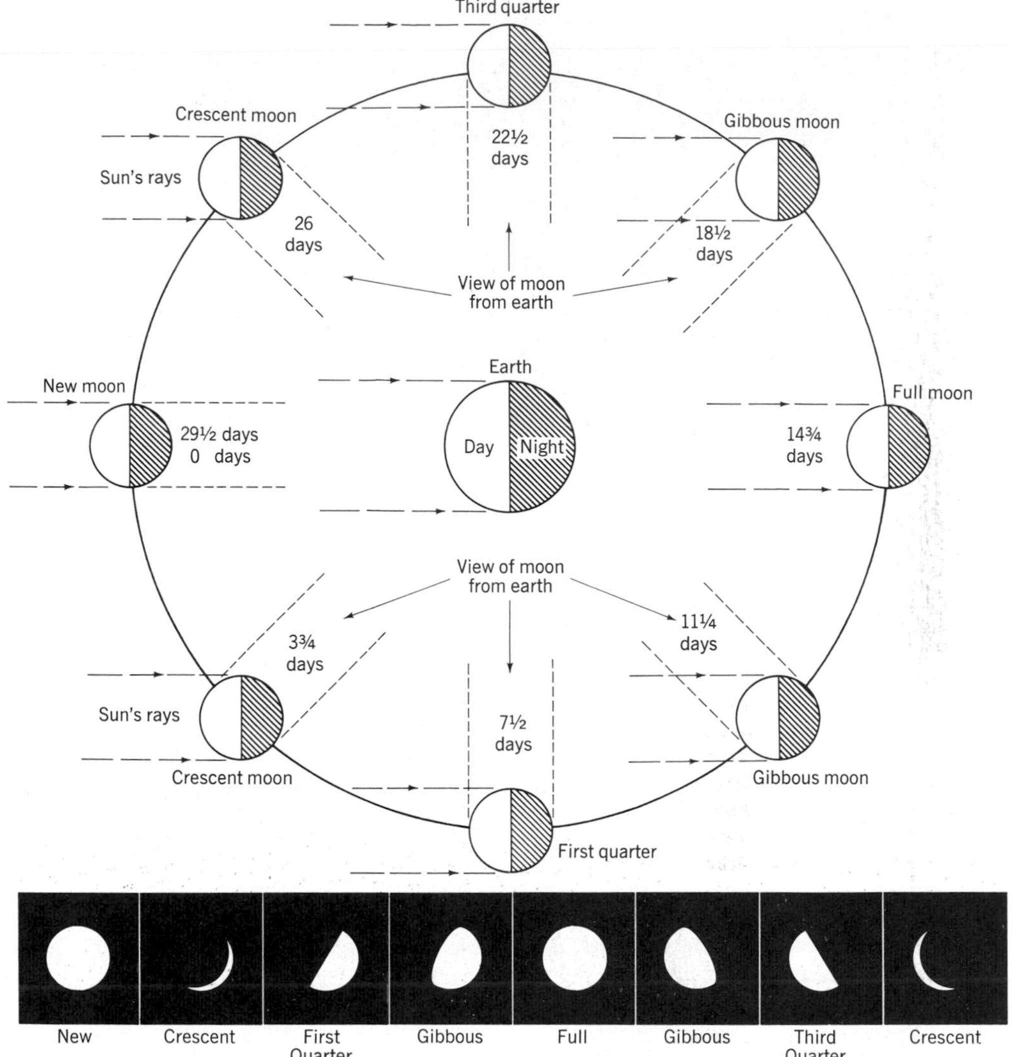


**FIGURE 8.10.** The moon's phases throughout the synodic month. Diagrams below show outline of moon as seen in southern half of sky. (© 1960, John Wiley & Sons, New York.)

the phase of *third quarter,* at 22½ days, when the moon is again in quadrature. The moon now trails the sun by 270° and therefore seems rather to be 90° ahead of the sun in the sky. Thus a third-quarter moon will be near the meridian when the sun is rising and will set about at solar noon. In its final quadrant the crescent configuration again occurs. At an age of 26 days the moon is moving across the sky about 45° ahead of the sun; hence it will shine brilliantly in the predawn hours and will be visible in the sky much of the day. Finally, after a lapse of 29½ days, the synodic month ends with the moon again in the new phase and the moon and sun in conjunction.

In Figure 8.11 the moon is shown as it appears in photographs in crescent, first-quarter, gibbous, and full positions. Whereas the circular outline of the moon is a very sharp line, the circle of illumination, or *terminator,* along which the sun's rays graze the moon's surface, is made irregular by the shadows and illuminated crests of mountainous relief features.

## Rotation of the moon

A careful comparison of telescopic photographs taken of the moon at many different times of the month and over many years would show that only 59 percent of the moon's surface can be seen; the other 41 percent is never subject to direct view from earth.

It would be infinitely improbable that by mere chance the moon's sidereal day should exactly equal its sidereal month. Obviously there is a mechanical cause, and it is found in the effect of tidal friction, which has gradually slowed the moon's rotation to the degree that it keeps the same point on its surface directly on the line between earth and moon. In such a position the moon is no longer subject to the repeated flexing by tidal forces that affect a rotating body.

Why, if the moon's period of rotation and revolution are identical, can we see more than 50 percent of its surface? The various circumstances permitting us to see an additional 9 percent are termed *librations* by the

*A.* Crescent moon, age 3 days.

*B.* Age 5 days.

*C.* Near first quarter, age 8 days.

*D.* Full moon, age 14 days.

**FIGURE 8.11.** Photographs of the moon at progressively greater ages, taken with the Hooker 100-inch telescope of Mount Wilson Observatory. (The Hale Observatories.)

astronomer. First, the plane of the moon's orbit is inclined 5°9′ to the ecliptic, and in addition the moon's equator is inclined 1°32′ to the ecliptic. It is therefore possible for the moon's equator to have an inclination of 6°41′ with respect to the plane of its orbit. This enables us to see at times as far as 6°41′ of latitude beyond each of the moon's poles, constituting the libration in latitude.

A second libration, that of longitude, results from the moon's changing velocity from perigee to apogee and back. After completing one quarter of its orbit—that after perigee—the moon has not rotated through an angle proportionate to its distance of travel in orbit, hence a zone of longitude is exposed along the edge toward perigee. Similarly, in the orbital quarter after apogee the rotation is somewhat excessive, and an additional zone of longitude is exposed along the opposite edge of the moon.

Still another type of libration results from the fact that the moon is not viewed from the earth's center, but from widely separated surface points. When the moon is on the horizon, about one additional degree of the moon's longitude can be seen along one edge beyond that which is visible to an observer under the meridian of the moon. This libration is possible because of the relatively large diameter of the earth in proportion to the moon's distance.

## Moonlight

The moon, like the earth, receives its surface heat and light almost exclusively by intercepting radiant energy from the intensely hot surface of the sun (Chapter 13). Because the moon and earth are, on the average, at the same distance from the sun, the quantity of energy reaching a small unit area of the moon's surface will not differ greatly from that reaching a similar area at the outer limits of the earth's atmosphere.

The intensity of moonlight depends upon the phase of the moon, the relative efficiency of the moon's surface as a reflector, and the distance between moon and earth. If the moon were a perfect reflector of the visible rays, it would when full provide about 1/100,000 the amount of light we receive from the sun. Actually the proportion reflected is much less, so that at full moon the intensity of moonlight is only about 1/500,000 that of sunlight. Altogether the radiant energy that the earth receives from the moon cannot be more than 1/2,500,000 that which the earth receives from the sun. In other words, the earth receives from the sun in 13 seconds as much radiant energy as it receives from the moon in an entire year.

## Man-made earth satellites

The possibility of placing in orbit about the earth an object whose orbital radius and velocity are precisely adjusted to enable the object to circle the earth indefinitely, as does our natural satellite the moon, was clearly forecast by Sir Isaac Newton and has continued to intrigue the minds of men for many generations. The basic mechanical requirements of an artificial earth satellite could be estimated by anyone familiar with Newton's laws of gravitation and motion as applied to the moon's orbit.

Centripetal force of a body in circular motion has been discussed in Chapters 2 and 5. For a planet the centripetal force is equal to the attraction of the sun for the planet. In the case of the moon the centripetal force is the gravitational attraction of the earth for the moon.

In following a circular path, the planet or satellite constantly deviates in course from a straight line tangent to the circle. Because the direction of motion is constantly changing, the velocity with respect to a straight line in space is also constantly changing. Now, a changing velocity is termed an *acceleration,* hence we say that an object following a circular path with a uniform rate of turning is subjected to a constant *centripetal acceleration,* which simply means that the acceleration is in the direction toward the center of the circle.

Centripetal acceleration, $A$, depends upon two variable factors—the instantaneous linear velocity, $V$, and the radius of the circle, $R$, as expressed by the following equation:

$$A = \frac{V^2}{R}$$

This equation tells us that the centripetal acceleration varies as the square of the linear velocity and inversely as the radius of the circular path. To compute approximately the centripetal acceleration of the moon, we can assume that the moon has a perfectly circular orbit 239,000 miles in radius and 1,502,000 miles in circumference, which it travels in 655 hours, for an average linear velocity of about 2290 miles per hour. Using the above equation, we obtain

$$A = \frac{(2290)^2}{239{,}000} = \frac{5{,}244{,}100}{239{,}000}$$
$$= 22 \text{ mi/hr}^2 \text{ approx.}$$
$$= 0.0089 \text{ ft/sec}^2 \text{ approx.}$$

The increase in the velocity of a freely falling body is known as the *acceleration of gravity,* $g$, and is usually stated in units of feet, or meters, per second per second. As we have seen above, the acceleration due to the earth's gravity at the average distance of the moon is $g = 0.0089$ ft/sec$^2$ (0.27 cm/sec$^2$).

If an object were released from a point in space on the moon's orbit (but not traveling in that orbit), it would begin to fall toward the earth, drawn by the earth's gravitational field. The formula for computing the distance, $D$, which a body will fall in $T$ seconds if it has an acceleration of $g$ feet per second per second is

$$D = \tfrac{1}{2} g T^2$$

If we substitute the value of 0.0089 ft/sec$^2$ for $g$ and 1, 2, and 3 seconds for $T$, we find that at the end of the first second of fall the object will have fallen a distance of about 0.0044 ft (0.135 cm) toward the earth; at the end of the second second, a distance of 0.018 ft (0.54 cm); at the end of the third second, a distance of 0.04 ft (1.2 cm), and so on. These distances are the exact amounts that the moon must be deflected from a straight line in 1, 2, and 3 seconds if it is to maintain its orbit around the earth. In other words, the earth's gravitational attraction for the moon produces exactly the centripetal acceleration required to maintain the moon in its orbit. Under these conditions, if no other forces such as frictional resistance come into play, the moon must forever continue to circle the earth as its satellite.

## Conic sections and satellite orbits

Returning to the subject of orbits of the planets, asteroids, meteoroids, and comets about the sun (Chapters 1 and 5), we can now make certain generalizations about the space orbit of any object of very small mass moving in the gravity field of an object of much larger mass. The same principles apply to objects orbiting the sun (heliocentric orbits) as to objects (satellites, both natural and man-made) orbiting the planets.

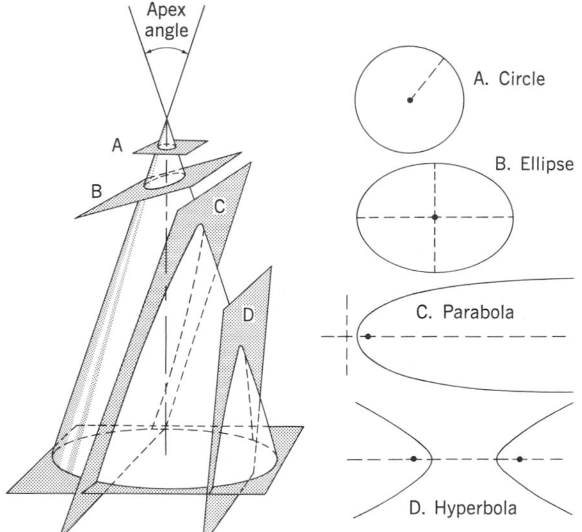


**FIGURE 8.12.** The conic sections. [After T. G. Mehlin (1959), *Astronomy,* New York, John Wiley & Sons, p. 383, Figure A-IV.]

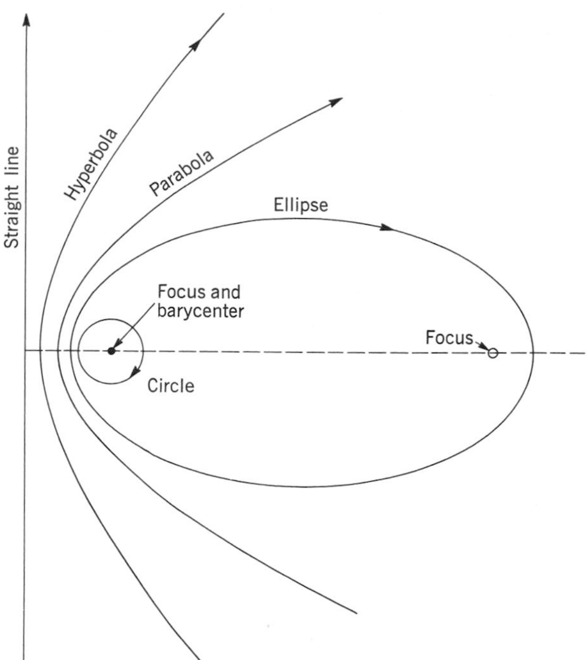


**FIGURE 8.13.** Schematic diagram of space paths about a common center of gravity.

An object traveling in space under the gravitational influence of another body follows one of several related curves of a family known as the *conic sections.* These are illustrated in Figure 8.12 by a three-dimensional drawing of a right circular cone cut by planes having various orientations with respect to the axis of the cone. The four kinds of curves thus produced are shown beside the cone. A plane cutting the cone at right angles to its axis produces a true circle (A); a plane cutting fully across the cone obliquely to the axis produces an ellipse (B). A third case is the parabola (C), produced by a plane parallel with the side slope of the cone, which makes the angle between plane and cone axis equal to one-half the apex angle of the cone. Where the plane forms an angle with the cone axis that is less than half of the apex angle, a hyperbola results (D). These four varieties of curves form a sequence starting with the circle and progressing through ellipses of increasing eccentricity until the parabola is attained. When the parabola is passed, hyperbolas of increasingly more open curvature are produced. The end of the sequence is a straight line.

The various conic sections are shown in Figure 8.13 as space paths nested about a common point, representing the center of gravity with respect to which an object is traveling. For the elliptical path, there are two foci, one of which is occupied by the center of gravity. The straight line represents a case in which the gravitational attraction is reduced to zero and the space path is completely unaffected. Both the parabola and hyperbola are open curves, with extensions toward infinity in either direction. They would represent objects that approach the gravitational field of the central mass from a great distance in outer space, are turned by the attractive force, but then leave the force field and travel indefinitely away into outer space.

Orbiting planets and satellites follow either the circle or the ellipse, but in fact the perfect circle is only approached in nature rather than achieved. To be strict in concept, it should be kept in mind that the occupied focus of the ellipse will be the common center of gravity, or barycenter, between the two bodies, each of which revolves about the other. We are simply neglecting the motions of the main body, which may be very large and move in a very small orbit about the barycenter.

It has been noted in Chapter 5 that certain comets and meteoroid swarms travel in extremely elongate elliptical orbits. Only a small portion of a comet's orbit can be observed during the short time that it makes its close approach to the sun. While it is very difficult to distinguish parabolic, hyperbolic, and ellipsoid orbits, none of the approaching comet orbits has been identified as truly hyperbolic. Consequently it is concluded that all known comets are truly members of the solar system and follow elliptical paths whose extremely great elongation takes them far out beyond the orbit of Pluto in aphelion (Chapter 5).

## Launching a satellite into orbit

The problem of successfully launching an artificial satellite into orbit about the earth can now be approached as a problem of calculating the correct combinations of velocity and radius of orbit to produce a value of centripetal acceleration exactly matching the earth's acceleration of gravity. We might begin by calculating the velocity needed to orbit a satellite close to sea level, using a value of 32 ft/sec$^2$ (980 cm/sec$^2$) as the acceleration of gravity, but because of the frictional effect of the earth's atmosphere we should only be wasting our time. Instead, it is practical to consider a height of, say, 300 mi (480 km) above sea level for the satellite's orbit, because here the drag of the atmosphere on the satellite can be dismissed as unimportant for at least several months of orbiting.

Taking the earth's radius to average 3950 mi (6360 km), we add 300 mi (483 km) to obtain an orbital radius, *R*, of 4250 mi (6843 km). At an elevation of 300 miles the acceleration of gravity is reduced to about 27.5 ft/sec² (838 cm/sec²), which is equal to about 0.0052 mi/sec². Using now the equation $A = V^2/R$ and knowing that A must be set equal to g, we have

$$A = g = \frac{V^2}{R}$$

We know *g* and *R*, but not *V;* therefore we write

$$V^2 = gR \qquad \text{or} \qquad V = \sqrt{gR}$$

Substituting our values of *g* and *R*, we obtain

$$V = \sqrt{0.0052 \cdot 4250} = \sqrt{22.10} = 4.70 \text{ mi/sec.}$$

The equivalent of 4.70 miles per second is just under 17,000 miles per hour, which is the answer we seek. If we can raise a satellite up to an elevation of 300 mi (480 km) and propel it horizontally to reach a velocity of 17,000 mi (27,000 km) per hour, the earth's gravitational attraction will provide exactly the required centripetal acceleration, and the satellite will orbit the earth successfully (Figure 8.14). This critical velocity is described as the *circular velocity,* since it produces a circular orbit.

Should the velocity be less than 17,000 miles per hour, the satellite will be drawn earthward and will eventually be slowed by atmospheric drag, causing it to hit the earth or be burned up in frictional heat. Should the velocity be greater than 17,000 miles per hour, the satellite will be carried to greater height above the earth, will reach a position of apogee on the opposite side of the earth, and will go into an elliptical orbit in which perigee is near the initial starting point. Such a satellite is said to possess *elliptical velocity.* If the velocity equals or exceeds 24,000 mi (39,000 km) per hour, the escape velocity for the earth's gravitational field, the satellite will travel farther and farther away from the earth, never to return. At the escape velocity the satellite orbit is a parabola; and the satellite is said to possess *parabolic velocity.* If the satellite is impelled at even higher speed its space path with be a hyperbola, and it has *hyperbolic velocity.* As velocity is increased to approach an infinitely large value, the space path approaches the straight line. Thus in theory the entire family of conic sections is encompassed.

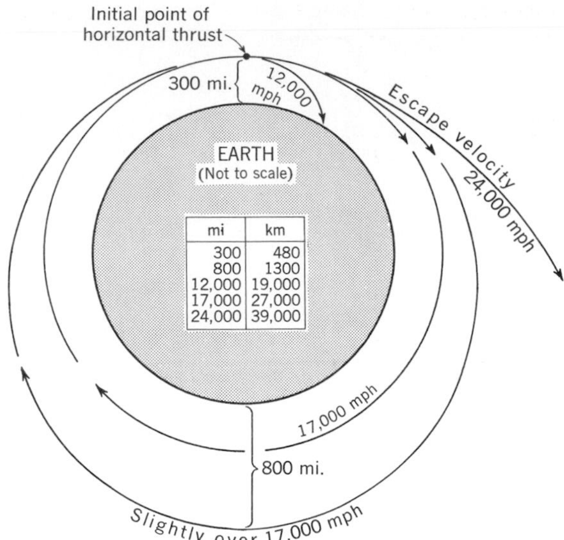


| mi | km |
|---|---|
| 300 | 480 |
| 800 | 1300 |
| 12,000 | 19,000 |
| 17,000 | 27,000 |
| 24,000 | 39,000 |

**FIGURE 8.14.** Four possible trajectories of an artificial earth satellite placed in orbit at a height of 300 miles. The earth, 8000 miles in diameter, is obviously not drawn to scale. [After R. A. Lyttleton (1956), *The Modern Universe,* New York, Harper & Row.]

Launching of the satellite is achieved by a multistage rocket (Figure 8.15). For example, the first two stages may lift the rocket higher and increase its velocity, at the same time gradually changing the trajectory from a vertical one at take-off to a horizontal one at the desired orbital height. Then a final-stage rocket impels the satellite horizontally to reach the exact velocity required, at which point the satellite may be separated from its rocket.

**FIGURE 8.15.** Launching trajectory of an earth satellite using a three-stage rocket to achieve an orbit at about 300 miles height. [After R. Fraser (1957), *Once Around the Sun,* New York, Macmillan.]

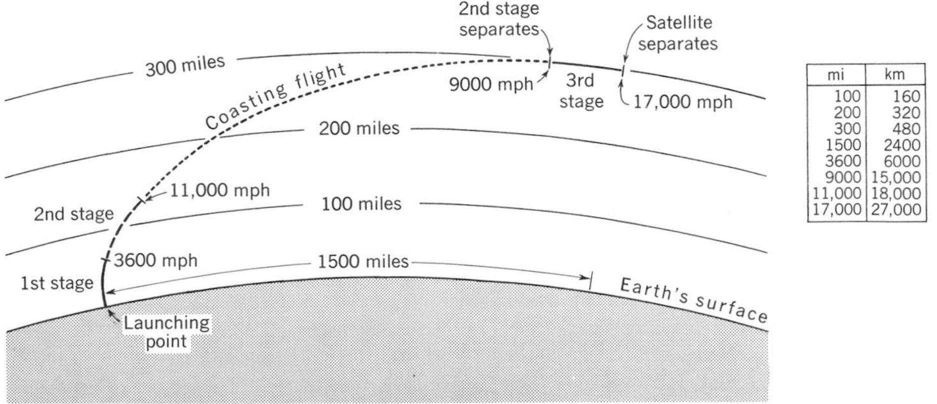


| mi | km |
|---|---|
| 100 | 160 |
| 200 | 320 |
| 300 | 480 |
| 1500 | 2400 |
| 3600 | 6000 |
| 9000 | 15,000 |
| 11,000 | 18,000 |
| 17,000 | 27,000 |

**TABLE 8.1. EARLY EARTH SATELLITES OF HISTORICAL INTEREST**

| Name of Satellite | Initial Perigee, miles | Initial Apogee, miles | Period | Inclination to Equator, degrees | Eccentricity | Launching Date | Date of Fall | Life, or Estimated Life |
|---|---|---|---|---|---|---|---|---|
| Sputnik I | 142 | 588 | $1^h36^m$ | 65 | 0.05 | Oct. 4, 1957 | Jan. 4, 1958 | 92 days |
| Sputnik II | 140 | 1,038 | $1^h44^m$ | 65 | 0.08 | Nov. 3, 1957 | Apr. 14, 1958 | 162 days |
| Explorer I | 224 | 1,573 | $1^h55^m$ | 33 | 0.14 | Jan. 31, 1958 | Apr., 1970 | 12 yr |
| Vanguard I | 409 | 2,453 | $1^h48^m$ | — | 0.19 | Mar. 17, 1958 | — | 200–1000 yr |
| Explorer III | 121 | 1,746 | $1^h56^m$ | 33 | 0.17 | Mar. 26, 1958 | Jun. 28, 1958 | — |
| Discoverer I | 176 | 519 | $1^h36^m$ | 87 | 0.03 | Feb. 28, 1959 | Early Mar. 1959 | — |
| Explorer VI | 156 | 26,357 | $12^h30^m$ | 47 | 0.76 | Aug. 7, 1959 | ? | 2 yr |
| Tiros I | 429 | 467 | $1^h39^m$ | 48 | 0.003 | Apr. 1, 1960 | — | 50–100 yr |
| Echo I | 945 | 1,049 | $1^h58^m$ | 47 | 0.01 | Aug. 12, 1960 | — | Indefinite |

Source: Based on data furnished by National Aeronautics and Space Administration.

## Orbits of earth satellites

Obviously a satellite orbit that is highly elliptical, with perigee at relatively low height—less than 150 mi (240 km)—will have a short life because the atmospheric drag at perigee will slow the satellite and cause its orbit to shrink. Thus the first two successful earth satellites, *Sputnik I* and *Sputnik II,* launched by the U.S.S.R., had heights of only 140 mi (225 km) at perigee and lasted only a few months (Table 8.1). *Discoverer I,* whose height at perigee was only 176 mi (283 km) lasted only a few days. *Explorer I,* although in a highly elliptical orbit, had a perigee height of 224 mi (360 km), hence a life of several years. *Vanguard I,* also in a highly elliptical orbit, has a perigee height of over 400 mi (640 km) and will therefore orbit for hundreds of years. Of those satellites listed in Table 8.1, *Explorer VI* had the most extreme ellipticity of orbit, apogee being over 26,000 mi (42,000 km).

An exceptionally fine example of a nearly circular orbit is that of *Tiros I,* a meteorological observation satellite launched by the United States on April 1, 1960. The terrestrial path of this orbit is described in Chapter 2 as an example of the deflective effect of the earth's rotation. At a height of about 429 miles in perigee and 467 miles at apogee, the orbit of Tiros I is close to perfection. The height of 460 mi (740 km) was intended, but the burn-out velocity of the third-stage rocket was 16,812 mi (27,056 km) per hour, which was slightly more than had been intended.

A fine example of a satellite at a level of 1000 mi (1600 km) above the earth is *Echo I,* an aluminized plastic balloon 100 ft (30 m) in diameter, used to reflect high-frequency radio waves for long-distance communication. At a height of 1000 mi the acceleration of gravity is reduced to about 20.5 ft/sec$^2$ (625 cm/sec$^2$), only two-thirds that of $g$ at sea level. Using a radius of 4950 mi (7980 km) and solving for the velocity by use of the equation $V = \sqrt{gR}$, we obtain a speed of about 4.4 mi (7.1 km) per second, which is about 15,800 mi (25,400 km) per hour. The velocity of Echo I was approximately 16,000 mi per hour at perigee (945 mi) and 15,600 mi per hour at apogee (1049 mi), which agrees closely with our estimate of 15,800 mi per hour for a circular orbit at 1000 mi. The length of an orbit at 1000 mi height is just over 31,000 mi, which we divide by 15,800 to obtain a period very close to 2 hours for one circuit of the earth, whereas Echo I had a period of $1^h58^m$.

The examples cited above for orbits at approximately 300, 450, and 1000 mi show linear velocities that are less as the orbit is higher. After noting this fact, one might be led quickly to an interesting possibility. Suppose that the orbital radius is increased to the point that the period of satellite rotation exactly balances that of the earth's period of 360-degree rotation (sidereal day of $23^h56^m4.09^s$). Then the satellite, if launched in the plane of the earth's equator and in the direction of earth rotation (eastward), will remain constantly fixed over a point on the earth. The radius of such an orbit will be about 26,300 mi (42,300 km), giving the satellite a height of about 22,300 mi (35,900 km) above the earth. Here the acceleration of gravity is reduced to only 0.75 ft/sec$^2$ (23 cm/sec$^2$). The satellite velocity will be about 2 mi (3.2 km) per second, or 7000 mi (11,300 km) per hour.

Satellites occupying a fixed position relative to a point on the equator are referred to as *geosynchronous satellites.* They are particularly valuable for intercontinental radio and television communication, since they can be permanently positioned midway between two continents. Another application of geosynchronous satellites is in meteorological observation. Figure 8.16 shows pictures of the earth taken at various times of the day from a meteorological satellite (Applications Technology Satellite) positioned at an altitude of 22,300 mi (42,300 km) above the mouth of the Amazon River. Such sequences of photographs show the development and change of cloud patterns in storms and other weather phenomena.

Another interesting possibility is that of a polar orbit at just the right altitude required to produce an orbital period such that the hourly rate of westward shift of longitude of the earth-track, where it crosses the equator, is exactly the same as the hourly rate of westward shift of the noon meridian, namely 15 degrees per mean solar hour. Such an orbit would be described as *sun-synchronous,* because the plane of the satellite orbit maintains a fixed angle with respect to the sun's rays.

For a truly polar orbit crossing the equator at right angles, as illustrated in Figure 2.21, the orbit plane will remain fixed in space with respect to the stars. On the other hand, the sun changes it position with respect to the stars by about one degree per day, as explained in

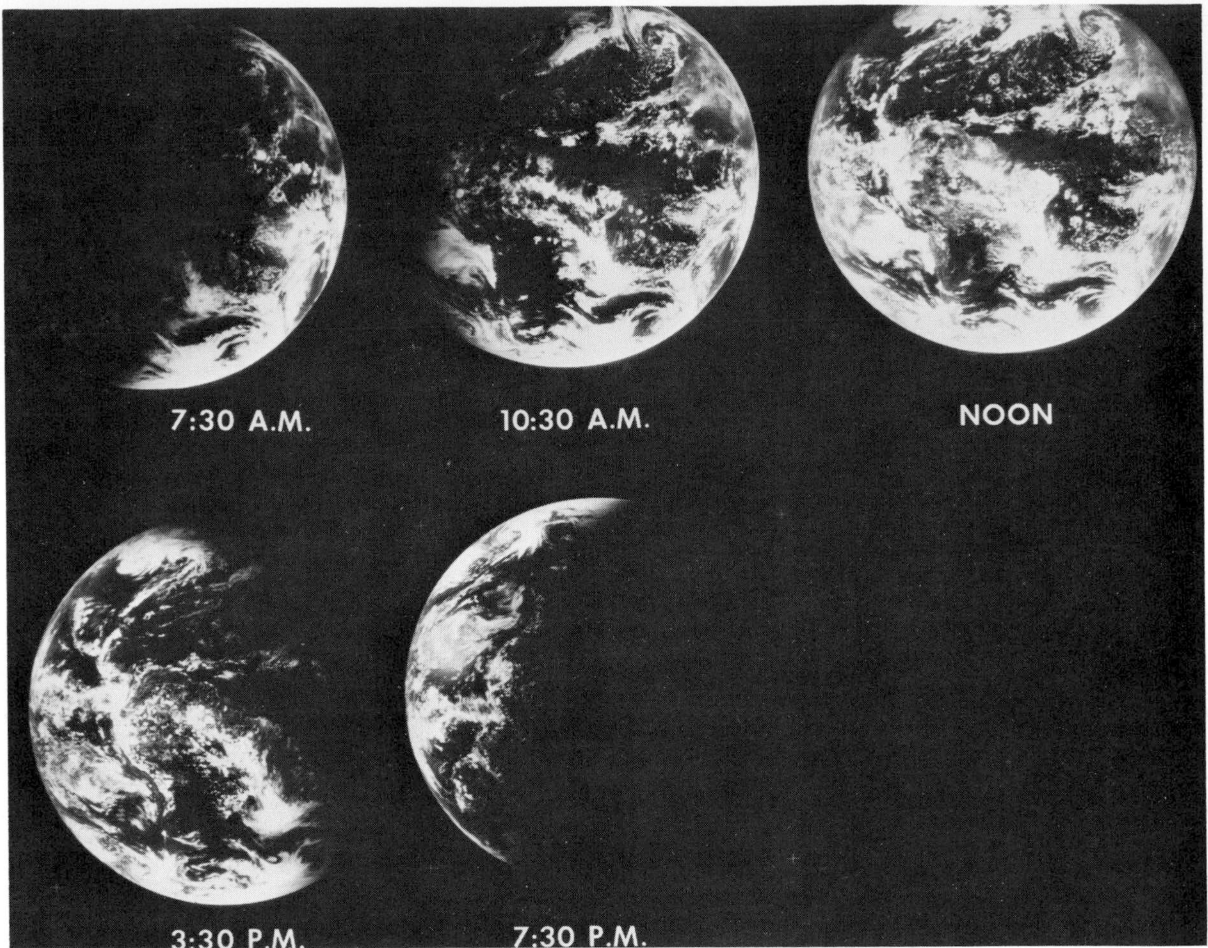


**FIGURE 8.16.** Changing phases of earth illumination are shown in these photographs taken from an Applications Technology Satellite occupying a fixed earth position over the equator. (NASA photograph.)

Chapter 3 (see Figure 3.7). Consequently a truly polar orbit could not remain parallel with the sun's rays.

To obtain a truly sun-synchronous satellite orbit requires that we make use of an effect of the earth's oblateness upon the space-orientation of the orbit. As explained in Chapter 10, the effect of the earth's equatorial bulge is to exert a torque upon the satellite orbit each time the equator is obliquely crossed. The principle is that of precession of a gyroscope when a torque is applied, as explained in Chapter 2 in the discussion of the earth's precession (see Figure 2.24).

For a satellite crossing the equator with an easterly component of motion (direct orbit), as in the case of Tiros I pictured in Figure 2.22, the effect of the torque is to increase slightly the rate of westward shift of the earth-track (see Figure 10.16). To attain a sun-synchronous orbit, it is necessary to achieve a decrease in the rate of westward shift of the earth-track by about one degree per day. This adjustment can be made by placing the satellite in a retrograde orbit, that is, an orbit in which the earth-track has a westward component of motion as it moves across the equator. An angle of 80° between retrograde orbit and the plane of the earth's equator produces the correct amount of retrograde shift, keeping the satellite orbit at a constant angle with respect to the sun's rays. Figure 8.17 shows the earth-track of such an orbit. Notice that the earth-track is tangent to the 80th parallels of latitude north and south. An orbit of 114-minute period, with an altitude of about 900 mi (1450 km) and an inclination of 80°, will shift westward with respect to the earth about 28½° per orbit, which is at the rate of almost exactly 4 minutes per degree, or 15 degrees per hour. As shown in Figure 8.17, in the two-month interval from March 1 to May 1 the orbit has retrogressed eastward through about 60 degrees with respect to space coordinates. A complete 360-degree cycle of retrogression would be required to occur in each tropical year of 365¼ days in order that the satellite remain sun-synchronous.

The sun-synchronous orbit is ideally suited for use by satellites of the Tiros Operational Satellite (TOS) series. These vehicles send to earth pictures of the earth's cloud cover as well as various other kinds of information. Initiated in 1966, the TOS program makes

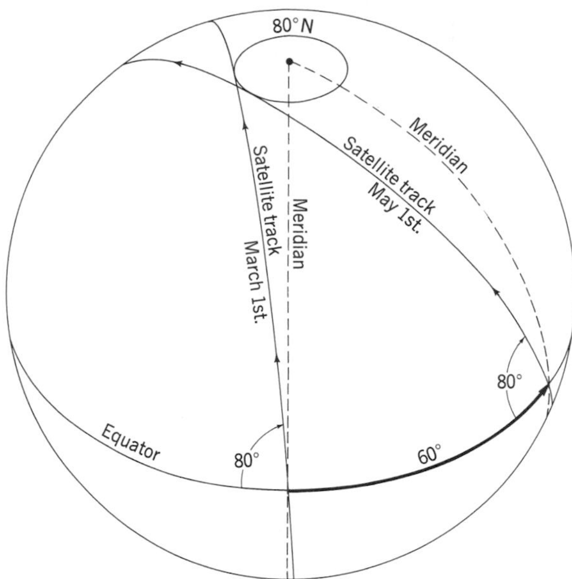


**FIGURE 8.17.** The earth-track of a sun-synchronous satellite in retrograde orbit crosses the equator at an angle of 80° and is tangent to the parallel of latitude at 80°.

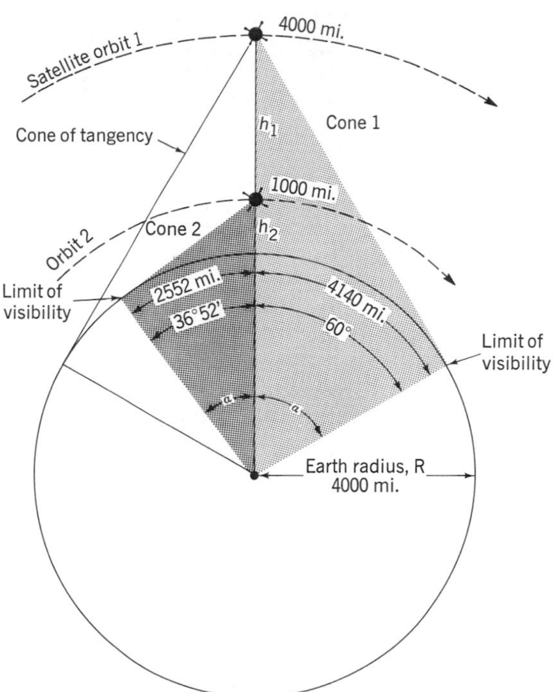


**FIGURE 8.18.** Limit of earth visibility from an orbiting satellite (© 1969, John Wiley & Sons, New York.)

use of two satellites, each performing a separate function, making daylight equatorial crossing at 9 A.M. and 3 P.M. of the local time of the longitude where the earth-track crosses the equator.

## Radius of visibility from a satellite

Radius of visibility, and hence also the radius of direct-line radio wave transmission from orbiting earth satellites, obviously must increase as the altitude of the satellite above the earth's surface increases. The *limit of visibility* can be shown as a small circle on the spherical earth beneath, and is referred to as the *horizon circle* (Figure 8.18). If the earth had no atmosphere, the horizon circle would actually represent the earth's horizon as seen by an astronaut in the orbiting spacecraft. The sight lines to the horizon from a single point above the earth form a cone, which is tangent to the globe along the horizon circle. Figure 8.18 shows the zone of visibility for two satellite orbits, one at a height of 1000 mi (1600 km), the other at a height of 4000 mi (6400 km). Radii of the horizon circles are given in miles and in degrees of arc. The formula that relates limit of visibility to altitude is as follows:

$$\text{cosine } \alpha = \frac{R}{R+h}$$

where $\alpha$ is angular distance in degrees of arc,

$R$ is earth radius (approx. 4000 mi),
and $h$ is altitude above surface, in the same distance units as for $R$.

The radius of visibility in angular units will approach 90°, or a complete hemisphere, only as the altitude approaches infinity, therefore a complete hemisphere cannot be seen from a single point.

## Lunar probes and man-made planets

A further step in carrying man-made devices into space is to shoot a rocket toward the moon so that it will come into control of the moon's gravitational field and will either strike the moon, pass close to the moon and return toward earth, or pass close to the moon and enter an orbit about the sun. Any rocket launching designed to permit a space vehicle to escape from the earth's gravitational field, which requires an initial velocity exceeding about 24,300 mi (39,100 km) per hour, is referred to as a *space probe*. If the object is to pass close to the moon, it may be referred to more specifically as a *lunar probe*. If the objective is to strike the moon, the launching has been called a *moon shot* and the vehicle a *moon rocket*.

The first space vehicle to achieve any of these goals, *Lunik I*, was launched by the U.S.S.R. on January 2, 1959, and passed within 4000 mi (6400 km) of the moon. It continued to travel beyond the moon to enter into a heliocentric orbit with a period of about 15 months, becoming the first artificial planet. The second artificial planet, *Pioneer IV*, was launched by the United States on March 3, 1959; it passed within 37,500 mi (60,000 km) of the moon and went into a heliocentric orbit.

On September 12, 1959, the U.S.S.R. successfully launched *Lunik II*, a rocket which struck the moon at 5:02 P.M. EST on September 13, 1959, the first man-made object to be landed on the moon. *Lunik III,* a Soviet rocket launched on October 4, 1959, carried out for the first time a lunar probe in which the vehicle became a satellite of the earth-moon system, an object termed a *cislunar satellite.* About 3 days after launching, Lunik III passed the moon, then 3 days later, at a distance of about 292,000 mi (470,000 km) from the earth, it swung about the apogee point of a highly elliptical orbit. The space vehicle then returned to its perigee point about 29,500 mi (47,500 km) from the earth on October 18. The total length of orbit of Lunik III was about 625,000 mi (1,000,000 km) and required about 15 days to complete.

A U.S. space probe, *Pioneer V,* illustrates the heliocentric orbit of an artificial planet. This space vehicle, weighing about 96 pounds, was launched on March 11, 1960, by a three-stage rocket. It achieved a velocity of 24,869 miles per hour at burn-out of the third rocket stage, which is about 575 miles per hour faster than the minimum escape velocity. The initial orbit is shown in Figure 8.19. Pioneer V has an orbital period, or "year," of 311 days, compared with 365 days for earth and 225 days for Venus, a planet whose orbit is closely approached by Pioneer V. The mean velocity of Pioneer V is less than that of the earth (67,000 miles per hour), but greater than that of Venus (78,000 miles per hour), and its perihelion is at 74.9 million miles from the sun (this is about 8 million miles outside the orbit of Venus). Aphelion, occurring close to the earth's orbit, lies at about 93 million miles from the sun. The possibility that Pioneer V will reenter the earth's atmosphere and be consumed is very remote, however, and may not happen for another 100,000 years.

**FIGURE 8.19.** During its first year, 1960, space probe Pioneer V traveled in this orbit between Earth and Venus. Distances between earth and Pioneer V are given in millions of miles. (After *I.G.Y. Bulletin,* No. 34, April, 1960.)

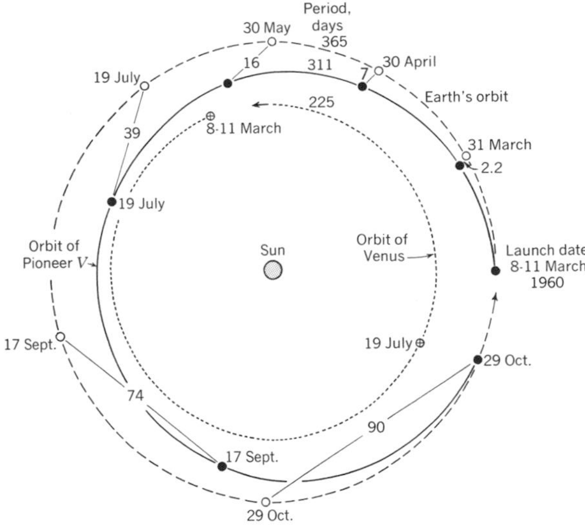


The capability to send space craft to the moon, to orbit the moon, to land upon the moon, and to return to earth, depends upon the application of rocket power to increase or decrease at will the orbital velocity of the vehicle. This ultimate capability was achieved by Apollo 10 and 11 missions in 1969. It is beyond the scope of this chapter to enter into details of the orbital modifications made by self-powered spacecraft in achieving man's goal of landing men on the moon and returning them to earth with samples of the lunar surface. Such details belong in the field of space technology and are elaborations upon the simple principles of orbital mechanics we have covered in this chapter.

A span of 270 years separates the publication of Sir Isaac Newton's diagram of artificial satellite orbits from the time of realization of his concept to yield a working tool of science. The various pioneering earth satellites and space probes of the earliest period of space exploration (1957–1960), which have been used in this discussion, are even now objects of largely historical interest. However, they illustrate well the basic principles of attaining the desired space paths from among the available range of conic sections.

## References for further study

Lyttleton, R. L. (1956), *The Modern Universe,* New York, Harper & Row, 207 pp., "The Moon," pp. 55–78.

Mehlin, T. G. (1959), *Astronomy,* New York, Wiley, 392 pp., chap. 12.

Gamow, G. (1962), *Gravity,* Garden City, N.Y., Doubleday, 157 pp.

Glasstone, S. (1965), *Sourcebook on the Space Sciences,* New York, Van Nostrand, 937 pp.

National Aeronautics and Space Administration (1966), *Significant Achievements in Satellite Meteorology 1958–1964,* Sci. and Tech. Info. Div., NASA, Washington, D.C., U.S. Govt. Printing Office, 141 pp.

Whipple, F. L. (1968), *Earth, Moon, and Planets,* 3rd ed., Cambridge, Mass., Harvard Univ. Press, 297 pp., chaps. 2, 7.

# 9

# The tide

THE PERIODIC RISE and fall of the ocean level, termed simply the *tide,* was long suspected by ancient peoples to be in some way related to the celestial bodies. Aristotle in 350 B.C. noted that the tide was synchronized with the moon, but the Greeks generally were little concerned with tides because the Mediterranean Sea has very small tidal fluctuations. Those few who sailed along the shores of the Atlantic were well aware of tides of great range. Pytheas of Massilia, who lived in the fourth century B.C., was familiar with tides in the region of the British Isles and the North Sea and is said to be the first to have actually measured the rise and fall of the tide. The Roman historian Pliny the Elder (A.D. 23–79) described the variations in tidal range accompanying the moon's phases and changes in declination, but it was not until Sir Isaac Newton published the consequences of his law of gravitation in his *Principia* (1687) that the basic mechanics of tidal behavior could be understood.

## The tide-producing forces

We have learned in the preceding chapter that the earth and moon form a single system revolving about a common center of gravity. Centrifugal forces within this revolving system exactly balance the forces of gravitational attraction between the two bodies, and the system as a whole is in perfect equilibrium, but these statements assume that the centrifugal and attractive forces act only at two reference points: the centers of gravity of the earth and moon. Actually, at points other than the earth's center the opposed forces are unbalanced.

For a particle of matter at the earth's center, point *C* in Figure 9.1*A*, centrifugal force caused by the earth's revolving about the earth-moon system's common center of gravity

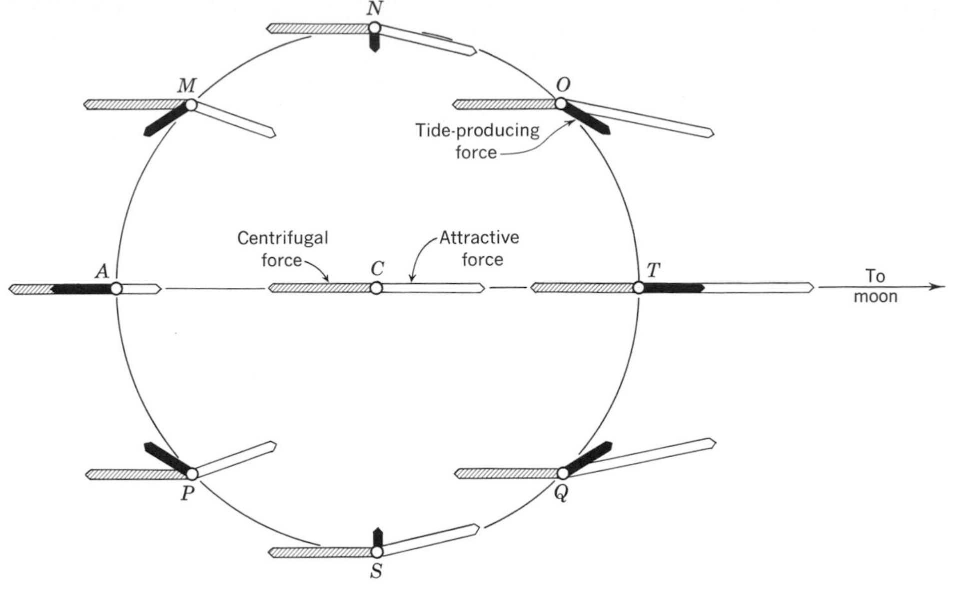


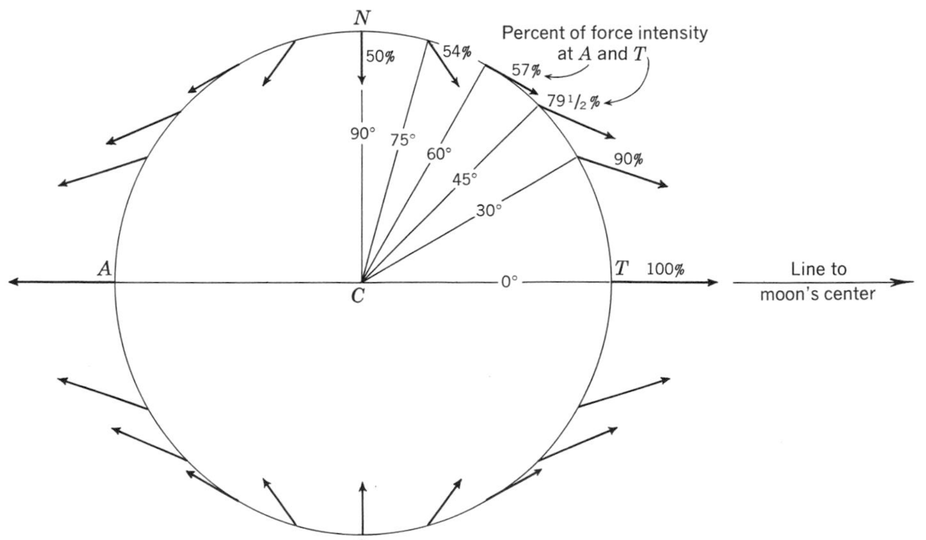


**FIGURE 9.1.** The tide-producing force is produced by combined action of centrifugal force and the moon's gravitational attraction. (*B*) Direction and intensity of the tide-producing force varies with position on the globe. [After G. H. Darwin (1898), *The Tides,* Boston, Houghton Mifflin; and A. Defant (1961), *Physical Oceanography,* vol. II, New York, Pergamon.]

is exactly equal and opposite to the gravitational force exerted by the moon along the line between earth's center and moon's center. If we select a unit of mass, say that amount of matter which would weigh 1 kilogram at sea level, it can be computed that the moon's gravitational attraction acting upon that mass at the earth's center produces a force of 3.38 milligrams. The centrifugal force is the same, and, because the forces are opposed, there is no tendency for the mass to move with respect to the system as a whole.

Consider next the conditions at point *T,* which is also on the connectng line between earth and moon, but lies on the earth's surface. Here the moon's gravitational attraction, amounting to 3.49 milligrams, is greater than that at *C* because *T* lies closer to the moon, whereas the centrifugal force applied to the kilogram of mass remains constant at 3.38 milligrams. There is thus set up a force difference of 0.11 milligram acting upon the kilogram of mass at *T,* tending to move the mass in the direction of the moon. At point *A* the moon's gravitational attraction of 3.27 milligrams is less than that at *C,* whereas centrifugal force is constant at 3.38 milligrams. Here the force difference of 0.11 milligram is directed away from the earth's center.

At this point in the analysis of the tide-producing forces, the question may arise: How can it be shown that centrifugal force acts upon every unit of mass in the earth with equal intensity and in the same direction? Constancy of centrifugal force may at first thought seem impossible, because we know that the distances from various points within the earth to the common center of gravity of the earth-moon system differ greatly, hence the radii of the circular paths of these points differ greatly and, consequently, there must be different

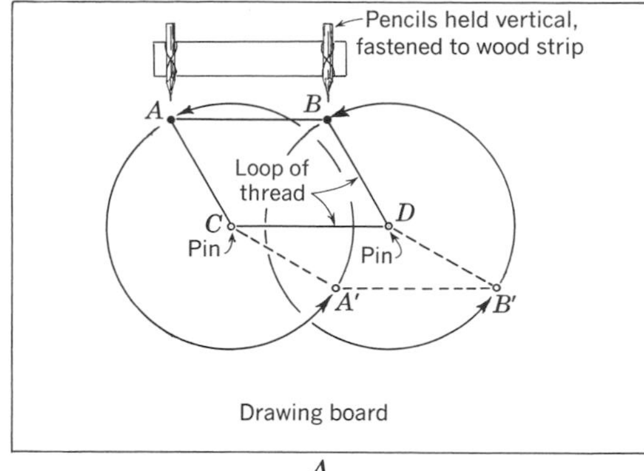


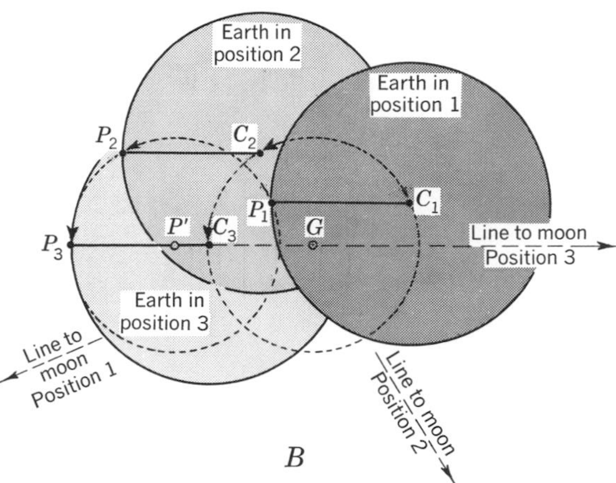


**FIGURE 9.2.** (*A*) Revolution of a body without rotation can be demonstrated with this simple device. (*B*) The earth can be imagined to revolve about the earth-moon center of gravity without rotation occurring. [After G. H. Darwin (1898), *The Tides,* Boston, Houghton Mifflin.]

intensities of centrifugal force. Such a mistaken concept arises when the earth's rotation on its axis is imagined to be involved in the analysis; actually we must deliberately remove, or annul, the rotational motion and consider only revolution.

To understand what is meant by revolution of a body without rotation, perform the experiment shown in Figure 9.2*A*. Two pins or thumbtacks are set in place near the center of a drawing board covered with a sheet of paper. Next two pencils are fastened to a strip of wood or stiff cardboard so that their points are spaced exactly the same distance apart as the two pins are. A loop of thread or thin string is then stretched into a parallelogram, passing around the pencil points (*A* and *B*) and the pins (*C* and *D*). The pencils, held vertical, are moved anticlockwise, with thread kept taut and the wood strip held at all times parallel with the edge of the drawing board. The pencils will describe circles of equal and parallel radii, the line *AB,* connecting the points, maintains its fixed orientation in space and is not rotated. Obviously centrifugal force of equal masses at *A* and *B* will maintain the same magnitude and direction of application.

In Figure 9.2*B* this principle is applied to the earth in revolution about the common center of gravity, *G,* of the earth-moon system. Assuming the earth not to rotate on its axis, we find that the earth's center, *C,* or any point elsewhere, such as point *P,* describes a circle of equal radius in equal time. Hence centrifugal force is the same for unit masses at all points throughout the earth when we are referring only to the revolution of the earth-moon system. Of course, as explained in Chapter 2, earth rotation occurs and a centrifugal (centripetal) force is thereby set up, but that rotation is not mechanically related to the tide-producing forces with which we are concerned here.

Returning to Figure 9.1*A,* we note that at points *M, N, O, P, S,* and *Q* the gravitational attraction of the moon is exerted in a direction toward the moon's center, whereas the centrifugal force is everywhere exerted in a direction parallel with the line *AT.* The tide-producing forces are directed at various angles with respect to the earth's surface, depending on the relative direction and magnitude of the gravitational and centrifugal forces at a particular point. Thus at *N* the tide-producing force is directed toward the earth's center and is about half as great as the force at *T.* At *M, O, P,* and *Q* the force is directed at some intermediate angle. In Figure 9.1*B* is shown the completed set of tide-generating forces for various latitudes.

Because the gravitational attraction between two bodies decreases as the square of the distance separating them, the moon's attractive force for a mass at *T* is 3.4 percent greater than it is for the same mass at *C,* whereas it is 3.3 percent less at *A* than at *C.* Therefore the tide-producing forces on the side of the earth away from the moon are slightly less than at corresponding points on the side toward the moon.

The true magnitude of the tide-producing forces can be appreciated if we compare the tidal force of 0.11 milligram at point *T* with the force of the earth's gravity of 1 kilogram (1,000,000 milligrams) on the same mass. The ratio comes out to one part in 9 million. At the points *T* and *A* the tide-producing force is directed vertically upward and tends to reduce by one nine-millionth part the weight of any object at that location. The 300,000-ton deadweight of a huge modern oil tanker is about 67 pounds less when the moon is in the zenith than when the vessel is located at a point where the tide-producing force parallels the earth's surface.

If the earth's sphere were to respond to the tide-producing forces by deforming freely, there would be produced a prolate ellipsoid with the long axis lying along *AT.* This figure would have a circular cross section in any plane passing through the body at right angles to *AT,* whereas any plane passing through the body parallel with *AT* would yield an elliptical cross section. An equilibrium shape would be reached when the inequalities of the earth's own gravitational attraction, resulting from development of the prolate form, exactly counterbalanced the tide-producing forces at all points.

## Tractive forces on the earth's surface

To understand the development of ocean tides, we must resolve the tide-producing forces into a set of forces acting horizontally at all points over the earth's surface, for it is the horizontal forces, or *tractive forces,* which cause the water to move. If we take the tide-raising forces shown in Figure 9.1*B* and reduce each force arrow to a component tangent to the earth's surface, as indicated in Figure 9.3*A*, it is apparent that there is no tractive force at *A*, *T*, *N*, and *S*, whereas midway between these points the tide-producing force is nearly tangent to the earth's surface and hence is largely tractive in effect.[1]

The next step is to construct the tractive forces for the entire globe as a spherical surface. When this is done (Figure 9.3*B*), it is apparent that the sublunar points *A* and *T* are centers of zero tractive force toward which the force arrows converge. Maximum tractive force lies in two small circles, one at 45° of arc from the point *A* and the other at 135°. In a great circle passing through *N* and *S*, the plane of which is perpendicular to the line *AT*, tractive force is again zero. Surface water of the oceans will tend to respond to the tractive forces; this must lead toward an accumulation, or a heaping up, of water at the sublunar centers *A* and *T*, with an attendant rise in sea level. On the other hand, a withdrawal of water will tend to take place along the great circle zone through *N* and *S*, where the sea level must fall.

[1] It is desirable here to avoid speaking of the line *AT* as the earth's equatorial diameter or referring to points *N* and *S* as the earth's poles, because the moon's changing declination causes the force system to shift through a considerable angle with reference to the geographic grid, thus moving points *N* and *S* away from geographic north and south.

## Tides on a rotating earth

If the earth were not rotating on its axis, the heaping up of water at the two tidal centers, *A* and *T* (Figure 9.3*B*), and the lowering of sea level along the great-circle zone would quickly reach a state of equilibrium, becoming permanently fixed in geographic coordinates. We should then have no tidal fluctuations due to the moon's attraction. But the earth rotates, causing the two tidal centers to move westward around the earth, and the tractive forces are constantly changing in direction and magnitude. Our next problem is, therefore, to consider how the tractive forces change at various points on the globe. It will be assumed for simplicity that the points *N* and *S* are the earth's north and south poles, respectively, and that the points *A* and *T* sweep around the earth's equator (Figure 9.4).

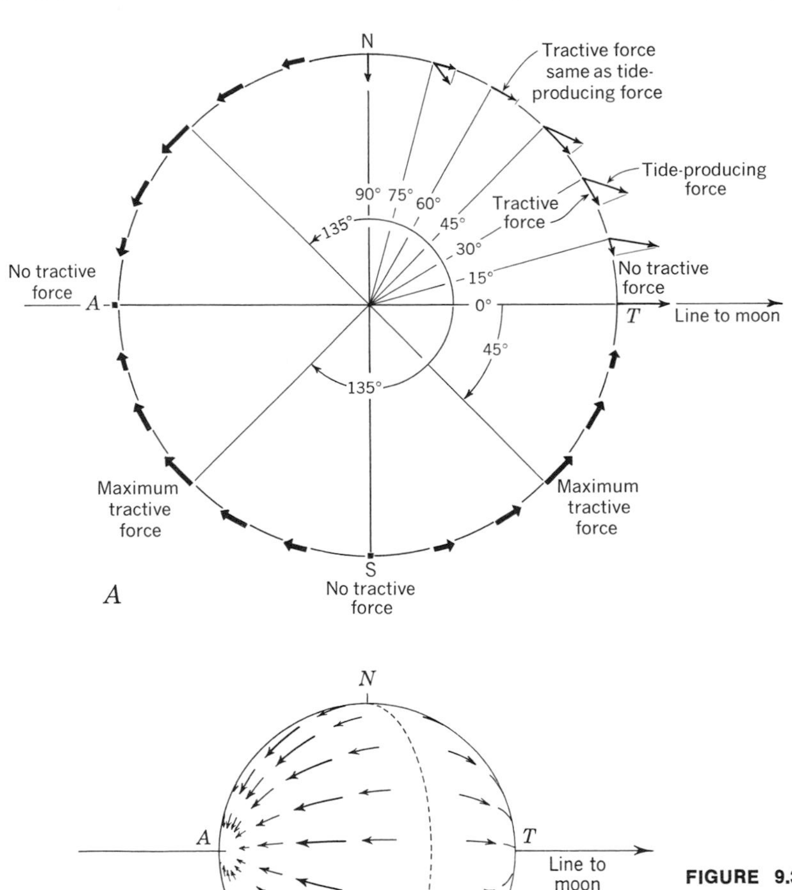


**FIGURE 9.3.** *(A)* Tide-producing force can be resolved into tractive force, acting parallel to the earth's surface. *(B)* Seen in three dimensions, the tractive forces converge to two tidal centers. [*(B)* © 1960, John Wiley & Sons, New York.]

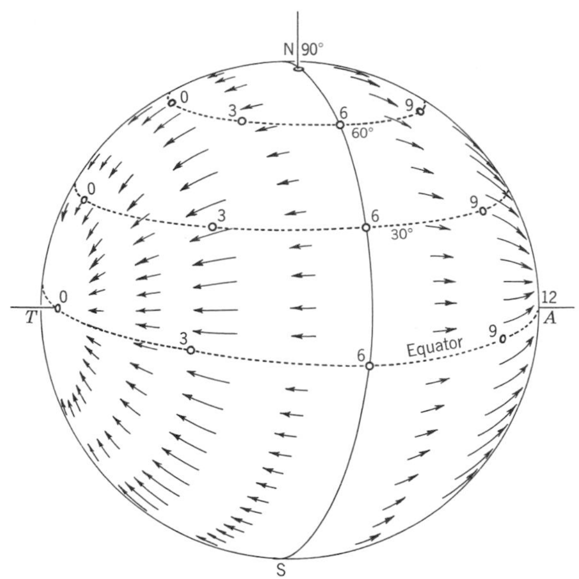


**FIGURE 9.4.** Tractive forces at a fixed point on earth change in direction and intensity as the earth rotates on its axis. Figures give lunar hours. [After G. H. Darwin (1898), *The Tides,* Boston, Houghton Mifflin.]

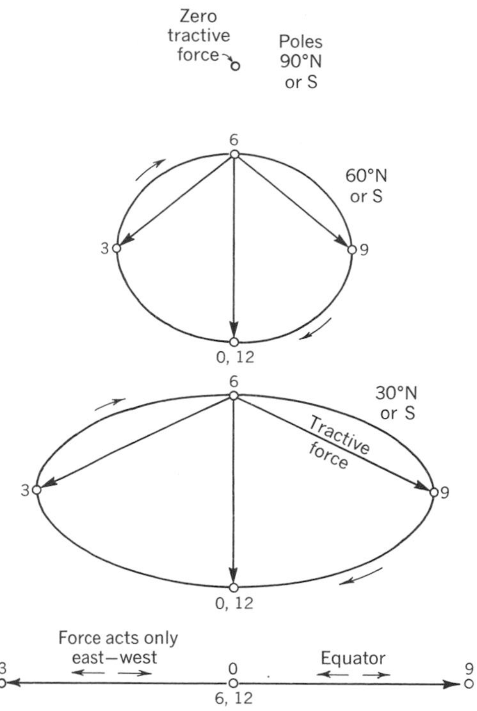


**FIGURE 9.5.** The magnitude and direction of the tractive force for various latitudes. Numbers give lunar hours. Force arrows are drawn from a reference point at 6 lunar hours to points on an ellipse. [After A. Defant (1958), *Ebb and Flow,* Ann Arbor, Univ. of Michigan Press.]

Suppose that we design a remarkably sensitive plumb bob whose most minute deflections—angles as small as 0.001″—can be measured, with all disturbing effects eliminated. Were it not for tidal forces, such a plumb bob would tend to hang at rest at right angles to the sea level surface, in equilibrium with gravity, but because of the tides it will be pulled first in one direction then in another by the tidal tractive force. Should we be successful in observing the cyclic motion of the plumb bob, we would find that its period is one-half of the moon's day of $24^{h}50^{m}$ (time elapsed between successive meridian passages), or $12^{h}24^{m}$, which may be called the *semidaily interval* (semidiurnal interval). For our present purposes it would be simpler to let the moon's day, or *lunar day,* consist of 24 equal *lunar hours,* thus the semidaily interval will consist of 12 lunar hours.[2]

In Figure 9.5 are shown the theoretical paths of a plumb bob at various latitudes throughout a semidaily cycle of 12 lunar hours. Zero hour is the time of the moon's meridian passage. At the equator the plumb bob will sweep west to a maximum at $3^{Lh}$, reverse and sweep east to another maximum at $9^{Lh}$, then reverse again to regain the starting point at $12^{Lh}$. Obviously the tractive forces at the equator have no north-south component, as shown in Figure 9.4. At the North Pole, 90° N., the plumb bob will remain fixed, for this point lies on the great circle of zero tractive force throughout the entire lunar day. At intermediate latitudes the plumb bob will describe a horizontal ellipse, becoming more flattened equatorward, but becoming more circular and shrinking in size poleward.

Although the tidal forces were long understood as a consequence of tidal theory, it was only in recent decades that sufficiently sensitive plumb bobs were invented to enable the tractive tidal force to be measured. A cleverly devised horizontal pendulum, vastly more sensitive than a simple plumb bob, is installed in a deep cave or mine shaft where temperatures are nearly constant and most mechanical disturbances can be eliminated. Deflection of the pendulum is greatly magnified by reflecting a light ray from a mirror attached to the pendulum. With such an apparatus the elliptical path of the ideal plumb bob has been plotted and found to agree in form with the theoretical values, except that the magnitude of the observed deflection is less by about one-third (Figure 9.6). This discrepancy is explained by the motion of the earth's crust itself because of the tidal forces, a subject discussed later in this chapter.

## The semidaily tide curve

If two centers of tidal heaping travel continually around the earth, separated by zones of sinking water level, we should expect the ocean level at the shores to rise and fall accordingly. In Figure 9.7 is a tide graph, or *tide curve,* showing changing water level as observed in Boston Harbor throughout a 24-hour period. The simplest way to get such information is to record the water level, at hourly or half-hourly intervals, with reference to a long board scaled off into feet, a *tide staff,* at-

[2] Whenever lunar time is given in this chapter, the word "lunar" is used, or the symbol "Lh" (lunar hour) used instead of "h."

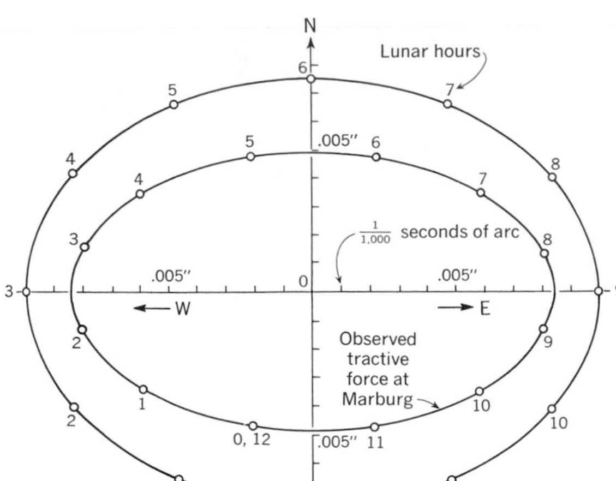


**FIGURE 9.6.** Changes in direction and magnitude of the tractive force of the semidaily lunar tidal constituent. Time in lunar hours. [Data from Schaffernicht. After A. Defant (1958), *Ebb and Flow,* Ann Arbor, Univ. of Michigan Press.]

tached vertically to a pier or sea wall. Because of the confusing effects of waves a far superior method is to measure the changing water level in a stilling well, which is simply a water-filled shaft connected to the open sea by a pipe of large diameter. The water level in the well quietly rises and falls with the tide and can be precisely read on a scaled board or continuously measured by an automatically recording tide gauge activated by a float which turns a drum.

The tide at Boston Harbor, shown in Figure 9.7, reached its highest level, or *high water,* at about 1:00 A.M.; a second high water came at about 1:30 P.M., the time difference being about 12½ hours. Ideally this

**FIGURE 9.7.** A graph of the rise and fall of tide at Boston Harbor for a 24-hour period. Dots show water level at half-hour intervals. [Data by H. A. Marmer; © 1965, John Wiley & Sons, New York.]

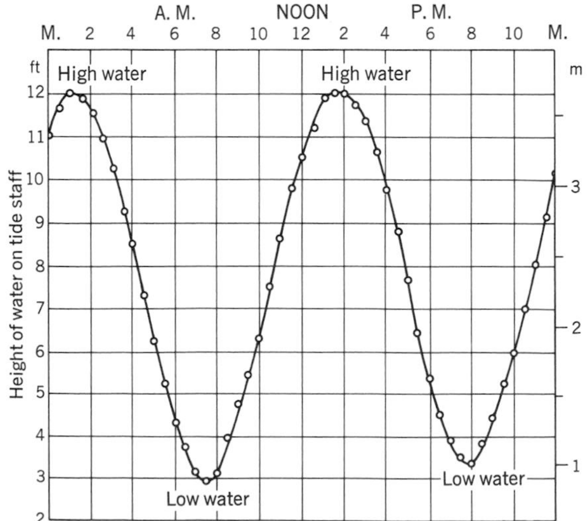


semidaily period should be $12^h25^m$ ($12.42^h$). The tide reached its lowest level, termed *low water,* at 7:15 A.M., which was 6¼ hours after high water. Ideally this interval should be $6^h12^m$ ($6.21^h$). The difference between height of high water and that of low water is termed the *range of tide.* In this example the range was about 9 ft (2.7 m), but the low waters were not quite the same height. Continued observations of tide in Boston Harbor would show that the tide has an average range of about 10 ft (3 m), but on occasion is as great as 14 ft (4.3 m) or as small as 7 ft (2.1 m).

The small open dots plotted on the tide curve of Figure 9.7 show the tide height at half-hourly intervals. From their spacing it is obvious that the water level does not change at a constant rate, but instead changes most rapidly in the mid-tide zone, between high and low water; here the rate of change exceeds 2 ft (0.6 m) per hour. In contrast, in the hour preceding or following high or low water the change of level is only about 0.6 ft (0.18 m).

## Lunitidal interval

One might suppose from the tidal principles thus far mentioned that the time of high water in Boston Harbor would coincide with the moon's meridian passage, or 12 lunar hours thereafter, because the two tidal bulges should have their centers always on the line connecting earth and moon. It may be puzzling to learn that high water at Boston Harbor occurs 11 hours after the moon's meridian passage, whereas for New York Harbor (Ft. Hamilton tide gauge) the lag is 7¾ hours. The time interval elapsing between the moon's meridian passage and the occurrence of high water is termed the *lunitidal interval,* or *establishment of the port.* Except for minor variations the interval remains fixed for a given coastal point, but it differs widely from one coastal point to another. (Check this by comparing times of high water in Figure 9.11.) More will be said of this lag in arrival of the tidal crest in the discussion of tidal theory.

## Diurnal inequality of the tide

Because, as explained in Chapter 8, the moon undergoes its full range in declination throughout a tropical month of 27.32 days, there will be only two times during the month when the sublunar points (points *A* and *T* in Figure 9.3) lie on the equator. At two other times, analogous to the summer and winter solstices of the sun, the moon reaches its maximum declination north and south, causing one sublunar point to sweep westward around the earth over the region of the Tropic of Cancer and the opposite sublunar point to sweep over the region of the Tropic of Capricorn (Figure 9.8). For a point in the middle latitudes of either hemisphere the result will be an increased range of tide corresponding with the passage of the nearer sublunar point and a decreased tidal range with passage of the more distant point. The tide curve for this part of the tropical month shows that either successive high waters are of different height or

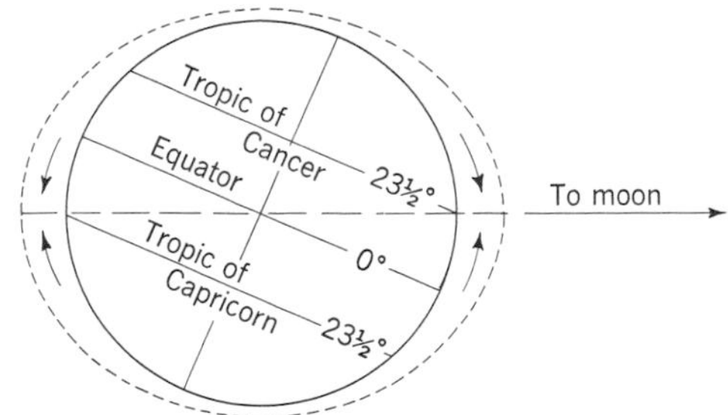


**FIGURE 9.8.** When the moon's declination is at its greatest, the sublunar points are shifted to positions well north and south of the equator. (© 1960, John Wiley & Sons, New York.)

successive low waters are of different height, or both are of different height (Figure 9.9). This type of tide curve is said to exhibit *diurnal inequality,* and the tides occurring at this time are termed *tropic tides* because then the moon's declination is in the latitude of the Tropic of Cancer or of Capricorn. When the moon is close to the celestial equator, with sublunar points both traveling close to the earth's equator, the diurnal inequality disappears, and the tides are termed *equatorial tides* (Figure 9.9).

Figure 9.10 is a photograph of a sandy beach on which there are two lines of stranded flotsam, each line representing the upper limit of swash at high tide. Because of diurnal inequality in successive high waters, the second high water did not reach as high a point on the beach as the first.

Several good examples of diurnal inequality are shown in a set of typical tide curves for representative United States ports on the Atlantic and Gulf Coasts (Figure 9.11). The moon's greatest south declination was on the ninth day, its greatest north declination on the twenty-third day, and on the sixteenth day it was over the equator. Note how the inequality disappears, or largely disappears, during the equatorial-tide regime. An especially striking case is Key West.

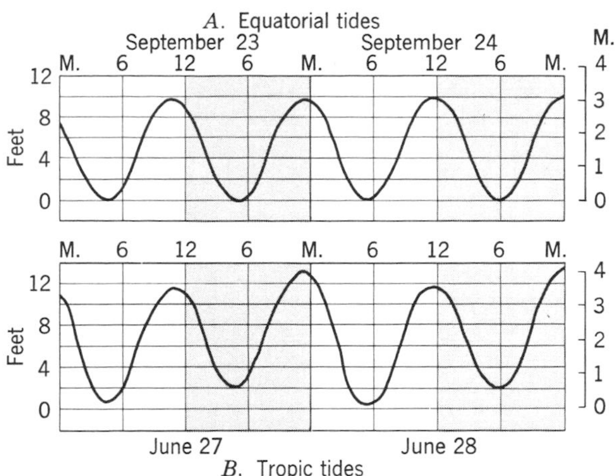


**FIGURE 9.9.** Equatorial and tropic tides observed at Portland, Maine. (Data by Rude; © 1969, John Wiley & Sons New York.)

## Spring and neap tides

The sun's role as a tide-raising agent must next be considered. Exactly as in the case of the moon, the sun tends to draw the ocean waters into two opposed tidal centers; these centers would, on the average, sweep westward around the globe once every 12 hours of mean solar time (although actually they are synchronized with the apparent sun). Although enormously greater in mass than the moon, the sun is so distant that its tide-producing force[3] is only five-elevenths as great as that of the moon. Even though the lunar tide-raising force governs the period of high and low waters, the sun's tide-raising force causes important modifications in the tide curve.

Because of the earth's daily rotation, the sun's tide-

[3] Not to be confused with the sun's gravitational attraction for a unit of the earth's mass—a vastly greater attraction than the corresponding attraction exerted by the moon upon the same mass.

**FIGURE 9.10.** The upper limit of swash at high water reached different levels on this beach at Sandy Hook, New Jersey, because of the diurnal inequality of high waters. High water, marked by the pole at *A,* was about a foot higher than the succeeding high water, marked by the pole at *B.* (Photograph by A. N. Strahler.)

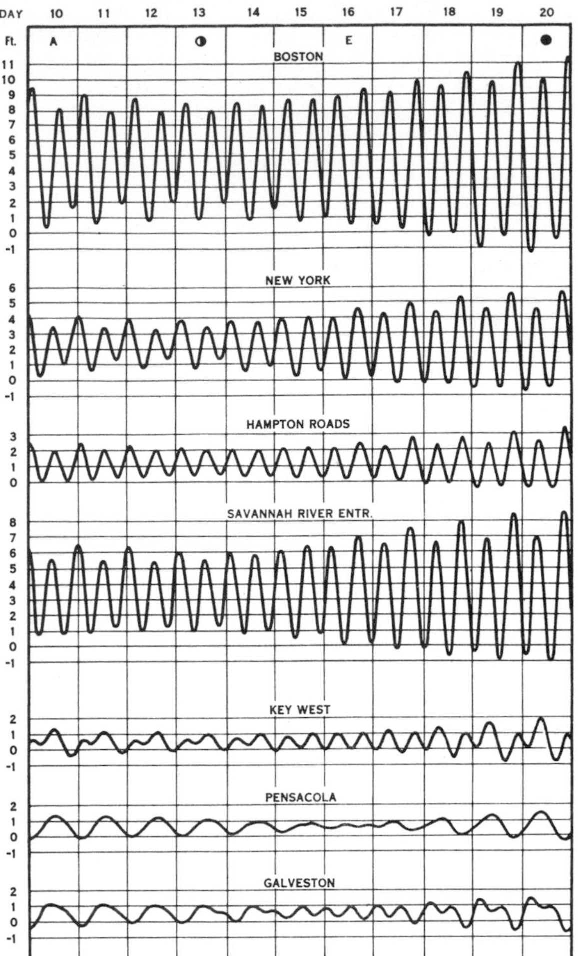


**FIGURE 9.11.** Typical tide curves for ports of the United States Atlantic and Gulf coasts. The letter "A" indicates date on which moon had its greatest declination, and the letter "E" the date on which moon's declination was zero. (From *Tide Tables,* 1961, ESSA Coast and Geodetic Survey.)

raising force increases and decreases in a cycle whose period is 12 hours, as compared with the semidaily lunar period of 12.42 hours. There are two times in the synodic month when the two semidaily cycles are in phase; these are, of course, at syzygies (conjunction and opposition). At two other times in the synodic month the semidaily lunar and solar semidaily cycles will be in opposite phase, specifically at the two points of quadrature. Therefore at syzygies the tide-raising forces of moon and sun are added together to produce tides of unusually large range, termed *spring tides,* whereas at quadrature the sun's tide-raising force acts at right angles to that of the moon, resulting in tides of unusually small range, termed *neap tides* (Figure 9.12). Spring tides occur when the moon is new and full, neap tides when the moon is in first quarter and third quarter. In general, spring tides are 20 percent greater in range than average, neap tides are 20 percent smaller in range. The tide curves of Figure 9.11 show clearly the differing ranges of spring and neap tides.

## Effect of the sun's declination

As explained in Chapter 4, the sun's declination ranges from 23½° N. at summer solstice to 23½° S. at winter solstice, and is zero at equinoxes. If the sun were the sole tide-producing body, the closer tidal bulge would sweep westward around the Tropic of Cancer at summer solstice while the farther tidal bulge would sweep over the Tropic of Capricorn. At equinox both bulges would follow the equator. Thus inequality of successive high waters and of successive low waters would characterize the solstice seasons. This form of diurnal inequality operates on a cycle whose period is 12 mean solar hours.

The moon, of course, governs the timing of the tidal cycle, so that diurnal inequality due to the moon's range of declination dominates the pattern of tropic tides and equatorial tides. Diurnal inequality due to the sun's declination modifies the curve appreciably, but these effects are not easily discernible by examination of a set of tide curves, such as those shown in Figure 9.11.

## Priming and lagging of the tide

When the moon and sun are within a few degrees of conjunction, the tidal center is shifted from a point directly beneath the moon to a point nearer the line to the sun (Figure 9.13). As the old crescent moon approaches the sun's meridian, the tidal center, *T,* shifts slightly eastward, so that high water reaches the observer after the moon has crossed the meridian; here the tide is said to *lag.* As the moon enters the new crescent phase, the tidal crest, *T,* drops back (westward) so that the high water arrives in advance of the moon's meridian passage; here the tide is said to *prime.*

The same lagging and priming will also occur as the moon enters and leaves opposition (full moon).

## Perigean and apogean tides

Yet another lunar tidal cycle to be anticipated is that resulting from the elliptical form of the moon's orbit, which brings important differences in the moon's distance and hence in its tide-producing forces. When in perigee the moon's tide-producing force is increased by some 15–20 percent over the average; when in apogee it is reduced by about 20 percent.

The moon's period for travel from perigee to perigee is termed the *anomalistic month,* with a length of 27.5 days. (It is slightly longer than the sidereal month.) Because of the difference between the anomalistic period and the synodic period of 29.53 days, the relations between the perigean-apogean tides and the spring-neap tides change constantly. When perigee coincides with syzygies the tide range is abnormally great, whereas when apogee coincides with quadrature the tide range is abnormally small. In the example shown in Figure 9.12, perigee coincided with full moon on the sixteenth

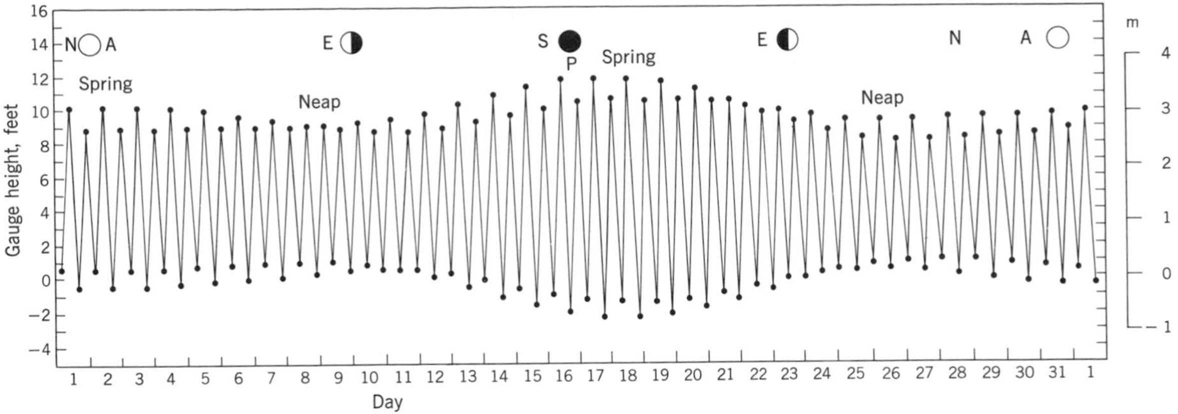


FIGURE 9.12. One month's tide record for Boston Harbor shows spring and neap tides and the effects of apogee (*A*) and perigee (*P*) upon tide range. Diurnal inequality appears with north lunar declination (*N*) and south declination (*S*) but largely disappears when declination is zero (*E*). (Data from *Tide Tables,* 1961, ESSA Coast and Geodetic Survey.)

day, causing an unusually great range in the spring tides. Apogee coincided with new moon on the second day, with the result that the spring tides were of reduced range.

Now, we could also introduce the anomalistic year of the earth's revolution from perihelion to perihelion as a weak tidal cycle of long period, although the effects of difference in distance between perihelion and aphelion are relatively small. Of special interest in the earth sciences is a rare event, occurring approximately every 1600 years, when perigee coincides with syzygy as well as with perihelion, the moon's nodes are in the line connecting the earth with the moon, and the declination between the moon and sun is zero. These conditions, which give the greatest possible tide-raising force, have the following schedule of occurrence: 3500 B.C., 1900 B.C., 250 B.C., A.D. 1433, A.D. 3300.

FIGURE 9.13. The tide lags behind the moon as the synodic month draws to a close, but precedes the moon just after new moon. [After R. C. H. Russell and D. H. Macmillan (1954), *Waves and Tides,* London, Hutchinson's.]

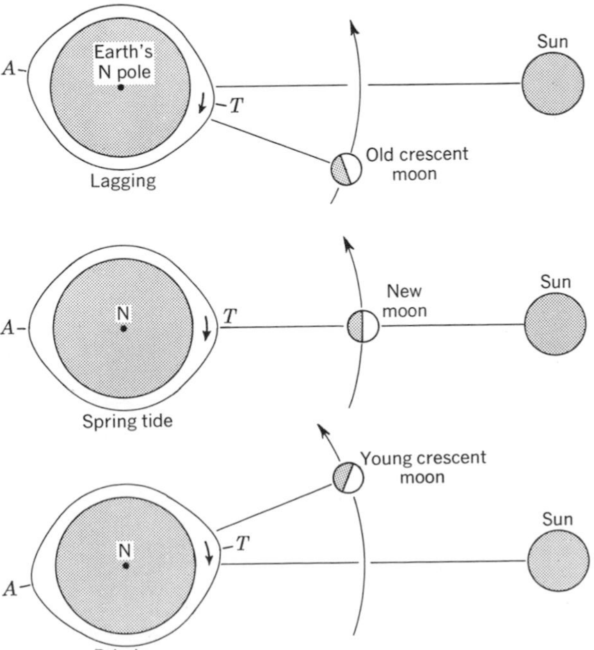


## Harmonic analysis of tide curves

We have referred to several astronomical cycles which influence the form of the tide curve by simultaneously imposing rhythmic variations in the tide-raising forces of moon and sun. Each cycle of influence presents by itself a simple wave-like pattern of changes that closely approximates the ideal mathematical form of the *sine wave.* An example is shown in Figure 9.14. The sine wave describes a rhythm of change known in science as *simple harmonic oscillation.* Many phenomena of the physical world exhibit simple harmonic oscillation. Examples are the vibration of a stretched string, the swing of a pendulum, and the bobbing up and down of a weight on a coil spring. In Figure 9.14 the sine wave is used to depict the increase and decrease in magnitude of a specified physical quantity (vertical axis) with the passage of time (left to right on the horizontal axis).

The *period* of a sine wave is equal to the elapsed time for passage of one wavelength. (See period of ocean waves, Chapter 17.) In Figure 9.14 the wave period is 12 lunar hours, which is the same as the lunar semidaily tide cycle. The *amplitude* of the sine wave is the height of the wave crest above the midline (zero height), or the depth of the wave trough below that line. As applied to an ideal symmetrical tide curve, amplitude is exactly half the tide range.

A third parameter necessary to describe a particular sine curve is the *phase,* or elapsed time between a selected reference point on the wave form and some arbitrary zero reference point in time. In the example in Figure 9.14, the phase is defined as the elapsed time

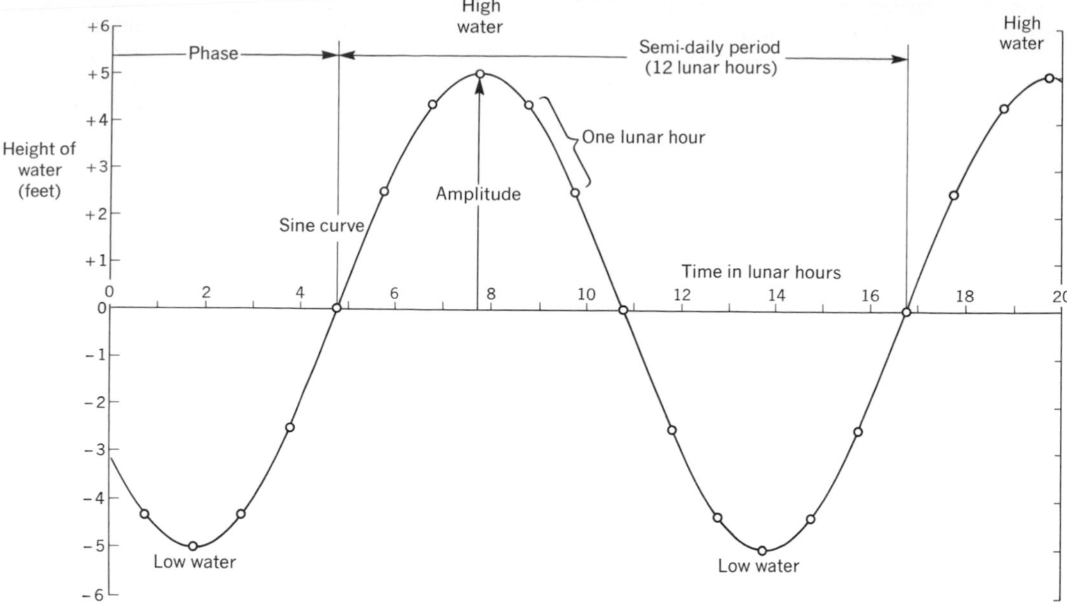


**FIGURE 9.14.** This graph of simple harmonic oscillation illustrates the features of an idealized semidaily tidal cycle.

between the zero time reference and the point at which the rising curve crosses the zero height line. As the phase increases, the entire curve is translated toward the right. Maximum phase value possible is equal to one wavelength, at which limit it drops back to zero.

Referring back to the semidaily tide curve shown in Figure 9.7, note the similarity between this observed tide curve and the pure sine wave. We can fit a sine curve to the tide curve by determining the period, amplitude, and phase of the tide curve and calculating a sine curve having the identical three values. The sine curve now becomes the mathematical model appropriate to the observed tide curve. Whereas we can assume that the period of the sine wave will be exactly equal to 12 lunar hours (12.42 mean solar hours), the values for amplitude and phase must be based upon direct observations made by tide gauge at the port for which the curve is desired.

The daily tidal cycle of 24 lunar hours, resulting from the moon's declination, can also be described as a sine wave of pure form. Here the wave period is assumed to be exactly 24 lunar hours. Figure 9.15*A* shows sine waves representing the semidaily and daily tide curves in the same phase. Amplitude is the same for both curves, which cross the line of zero amplitude at the same points in time. We next combine these two curves by summing their amplitudes. Where the curve is below the zero line the amplitude has a negative sign. Algebraic sums of the amplitudes produce a third curve known as the *resultant curve*. Here we have a mathematical model for a tropical form of the semidaily tide curve. Successive high waters are of unequal height, and successive low waters are of unequal height.

In Figure 9.15*B* two sine waves are again drawn to represent semidaily and daily tide curves. However, in this instance the two curves differ in phase by three lunar hours, and the amplitude of the daily curve is twice that of the semidaily curve. The resultant curve is now dominated by the daily cycle. Note that a daily period alternates with a semidaily period.

In Figure 9.15*C* both curves are again in the same

**FIGURE 9.15.** Combinations of daily and semidaily tide curves in different phases and amplitudes yield different resultant tide curves. [After G. T. Rude, (1931), *Physics of the Earth,* vol. 2, Washington, D.C., Nat. Acad. Sciences.]

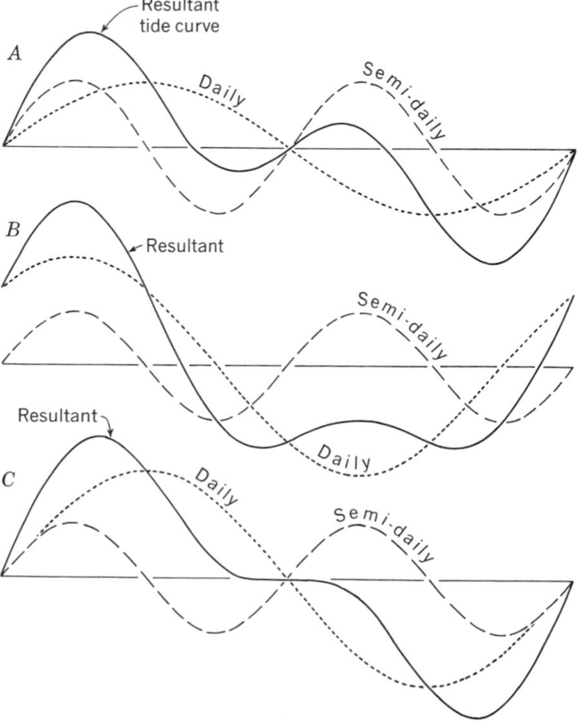

phase. As in the preceding example, amplitude of the daily curve is twice that of the semidaily curve. The resultant curve is remarkable in that the height remains constant at zero amplitude for a period of several hours.

What the mathematician has done in the examples given above is to combine two sine waves, a procedure that may be termed *harmonic synthesis.* In like manner he can combine three, four, or more sine waves and can choose from an infinite range of periods, amplitudes, and phase differences. Reversing this procedure, the mathematician can take any complex, sinuous wave and reduce it to a number of simple sine waves. This process of dissection is known as *harmonic analysis.* Tide curves are especially amenable to harmonic analysis and therein lies the basis for predicting future tide curves on the basis of observations taken from past curves.

Each periodic phenomenon that is involved in changes in the magnitude and timing of lunar and solar tide-raising forces can be treated as a sine wave and is termed a *harmonic constituent* of the tide curve. Each constituent can be imagined as generated by a separate and hypothetical satellite body orbiting, in a special path and with the given period, an earth fixed in space. Table 9.1 lists the eight most important harmonic

**TABLE 9.1. IMPORTANT HARMONIC CONSTITUENTS OF THE TIDE CURVE**[a]

| | Period, mean solar hours | Theoretical Amplitude, percent |
|---|---|---|
| Semidaily cycles | | |
| Main lunar semidaily constituent due to earth rotation | 12.42 | 100.0 |
| Main solar semidaily constituent due to earth rotation | 12.00 | 46.6 |
| Semidaily constituent due to monthly variation in moon's distance (apogee versus perigee) | 12.66 | 19.1 |
| Solar-lunar constituent due to changes in declination of sun and moon | 11.97 | 12.7 |
| Daily cycle | | |
| Solar-lunar constituent due to moon's declination | 23.93 | 58.4 |
| Main lunar constituent due to moon's declination | 25.82 | 41.5 |
| Main solar constituent due to sun's declination | 24.07 | 19.3 |
| Long-period cycles | | |
| Moon's fortnightly constituent due to lunar phases (syzygies, quadratures) | 327.86 (13.66 days) | 17.2 |

[a] Data from A. Defant (1958) and D. H. Macmillan (1966).

constituents and refers to the astronomical phenomenon to which each is related. Theoretical amplitudes given in the table are compared with the main lunar semidaily constituent (100 percent) and are calculated from astronomical data. These amplitudes do not apply directly to the tide curve of a given place. As noted above, actual amplitudes and phases of constituents can only be determined by tide gauge records for the place in question.

Figure 9.16 shows four examples of tide curves observed on particular days at four different ports. They illustrate the differing degrees of significance of semidaily and daily harmonic constitutents in creating curves characteristic of certain coastal locations at certain times. As will be explained in later paragraphs, the local pecularities of a tide curve are dictated by the configuration and geographical location of the local water body. Curve *A* is almost a pure semidaily curve of the equatorial type with no appreciable daily constituent. Curve *D* is dominated by the daily constituent, and hence shows only one high and one low water per lunar day. Curves *B* and *C* are known as mixed types, because both daily and semidaily constituents are important. Curve *C* is a particularly interesting mixed type in which the daily constituent has twice the amplitude of the semidaily. (Harmonic synthesis is shown in Figure 9.15.) The resulting curve contains a period of sev-

**FIGURE 9.16.** These tide curves illustrate semidaily, daily, and mixed types. (Data by G. T. Rude and H. A. Marmer.)

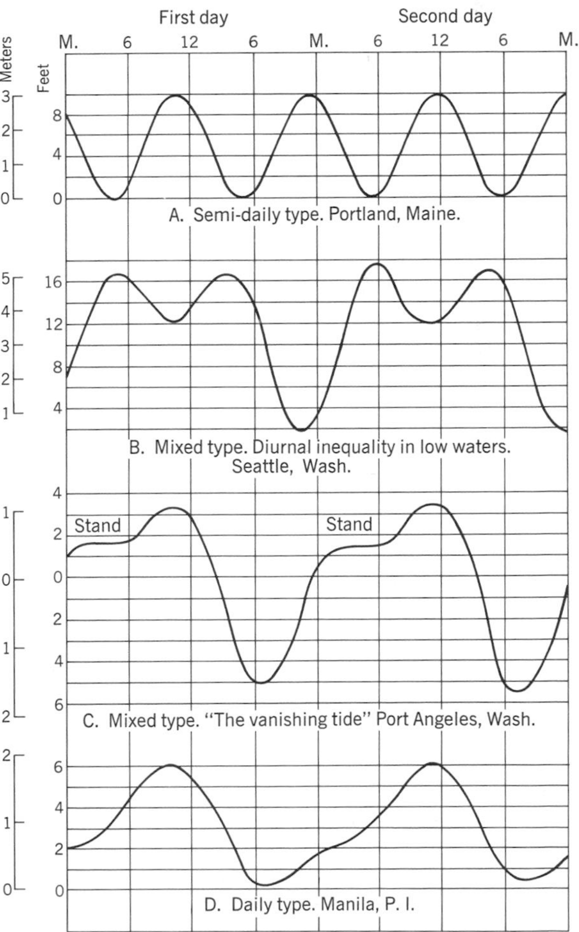

eral hours when the sea level takes a *stand,* i.e., does not change. The result is a curve form known as the *vanishing tide.*

## Tide prediction by harmonic analysis

Elaborate machines have been perfected that take into account the periods of all the important constituents. Using values for amplitudes and phases read from the observed tide curves the machine produces a composite tidal curve that predicts the tide at a given coastal point with great accuracy for long periods in advance. The first machine of this type was invented by Lord Kelvin in 1872. By 1919 a machine was able to handle 20 constituents and to supply the figures for one year's tide tables for a port in less than 2 days. A large modern tide-predicting machine handles as many as 62 constituents.

The electronic computer has now superseded the mechanical tide predicting machine. Since 1966 the ESSA Coast and Geodetic Survey has used the computer to generate the data for the tide tables that it publishes yearly. These tables, which may be bought from the U.S. Government Printing Office, are in four volumes and cover the ports of the world. The heights of high and low waters for every day of the year are given for a large number of reference stations. For intermediate coastal points corrections are furnished which can be added to or subtracted from the data of a reference station.

## Development of tidal theory

When Sir Isaac Newton developed his theory of tides, he assumed, for purposes of speculation, that the earth was covered by an ocean of uniform depth and that the flow of water to two centers of tidal rise would quickly bring about an equilibrium form of the sea surface in which pressure differences would exactly balance the tractive forces. As the earth rotated, this ideal *equilibrium tide* would sweep westward as a great tidal wave whose wavelength would be half of the earth's circumference and whose height would be equal to the difference in sea level between that at the tidal centers and that at the great circle of lowered level. The various tidal constituents could then be introduced to vary the basic semidaily harmonic oscillation. Newton's *equilibrium theory,* which we have used thus far in this chapter, is valid as a fundamental explanation of the tide, but it is obviously not the full explanation. The existence of the lunitidal interval is not explained by the equilibrium theory, which requires that alternate high waters coincide exactly with the moon's meridian passages.

The cause of the lunitidal interval, or lag in the arrival of tides, lies in the inability of the oceans to respond instantly and completely to the rapidly moving system of tractive forces. Newton was well aware of this discrepancy between theory and fact, but he was not successful in making the necessary corrections.

The French astronomer and mathematician Laplace next carried forward tidal analysis with his *dynamical theory* of tides, in which it was reasoned that the tide-producing forces would set up waves within the ocean basins, but that the wave properties themselves would be influenced by the form and dimensions of the ocean basins, the deflective effect of the earth's rotation (Coriolis effect), and frictional forces: Friction would act to retard the flow of water, and the Coriolis effect would turn the direction of flow.

According to Laplace's theory, it is first imagined that there exists along the earth's equator a continuous channel of uniform depth and width encircling the globe. If the water in this channel could respond to the tide-producing forces in the manner postulated by Newton's equilibrium theory, there would be set up a tidal wave of 12,000 mi (19,300 km) length with a speed of about 950 mi (1530 km) per hour. On the other hand, if the water in this channel were disturbed by some violent shock so as to generate a great sea wave, that wave would travel along the equatorial channel at a velocity proportional to the square root of the water depth (see "Seismic sea waves," Chapter 23). For a sea wave to travel at the same speed as the equilibrium tidal wave, the water depth would need to be almost 14 mi (22.5 km). In a channel of that depth the natural wave period of the channel would match that of the tidal wave, and the two waves would be in resonance, resulting in the growth of gigantic tidal waves. On the other hand, if the water depth of the channel were more or less than 14 miles, an interference of the two waves would result.

It can be shown that if the water depth were greater than 14 miles, high water should always coincide with the moon's meridian passage, or 12 lunar hours thereafter, with a lunitidal interval of zero or 12 lunar hours, in accordance with the equilibrium theory. If, however, water depth were less than 14 miles, the theoretical wave and the natural sea wave would be in opposite phase, so that the resulting tidal wave would have its trough coincide with moon's meridian passage; the lunitidal interval would be either 6 or 18 lunar hours. Tides of the first type (in water depth greater than 14 miles) are designated as *direct,* those of the second type (in water depth less than 14 miles) as *indirect.* Because the oceans are everywhere far less than 14 miles deep, we should expect indirect tides in the equatorial region.

At higher latitudes, because of the reduced length of parallels, the velocity of the equilibrium tidal wave would be less. At lat. 60° it would be half that at the equator, or about 475 mi (764 km) per hour. Here our theoretical channel would need to be only 3½ mi (5.6 km) deep for a natural sea wave to be in resonance with the tidal wave. If some reasonable figure, such as 4 mi (6.4 km), is taken as the depth of an ideal ocean divided into many parallel channels, Laplace's dynamical theory would lead us to the conclusion that in the low latitudes all tides would be indirect, whereas in the high latitudes all would be direct, and that at some critical latitude resonance would generate enormous tides. If, however, the separating walls of the channels were removed, longitudinal flow would occur, and it would be expected that in the zone between direct and indirect tides the tide would disappear.

## Standing waves in closed basins

Laplace's dynamical theory, to apply to the oceans of the earth, would need to be modified by imagining that the latitudinal channels are cut into segments, representing the compartmentation of the oceans between the continents. This modification would produce water bodies essentially resembling those in rectangular troughs. When such a water body is subjected to a disturbance, the water moves back and forth, heaping up first in one end of the trough then in the other, in what is known as a *standing oscillation,* or *standing wave.* That shown in Figure 9.17*A* is termed a *mononodal wave* because there is one axis, or *node,* where the water level is fixed and with respect to which the water on either side rises and falls. A *binodal wave* is illustrated in Figure 9.17*B*.

The period of a standing oscillation depends upon the length and depth of the water body.[4] The tide-producing forces acting upon an imaginary ocean channel closed at the ends would set up standing oscillations whose period would be that of the equilibrium tide, but whose amplitude and phase would depend upon the natural period of the water body. It can be shown that if the natural period of the water body is much shorter than the lunar period, the phase of standing wave will match that of the equilibrium tides, whereas if the natural period is much longer the two oscillations will be out of phase, so that alternate low waters will coincide with the moon's meridian passage. When the natural period is nearly the same as the lunar-tide period the tides are strengthened by resonance and will be much higher.

We have now considered an ideal mechanism that comes close to matching the conditions of nature—namely, an assemblage of closed basins whose dimensions will largely determine the range and phase of the tide.

[4] The formula $T = \frac{2L}{\sqrt{gH}}$ applies, where $T$ is the period in seconds, $L$ the length in meters, $H$ the depth in meters, and $g$ the acceleration of gravity in meters per second squared. Units of feet and seconds may also be used in this formula.

**FIGURE 9.17.** (*A*) A mononodal standing wave. (*B*) A binodal standing wave.

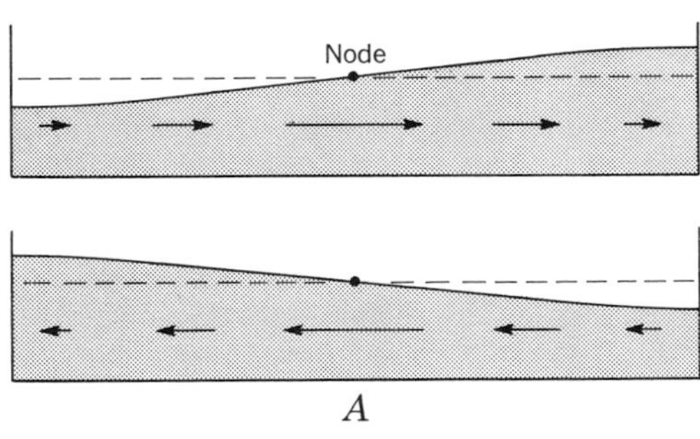


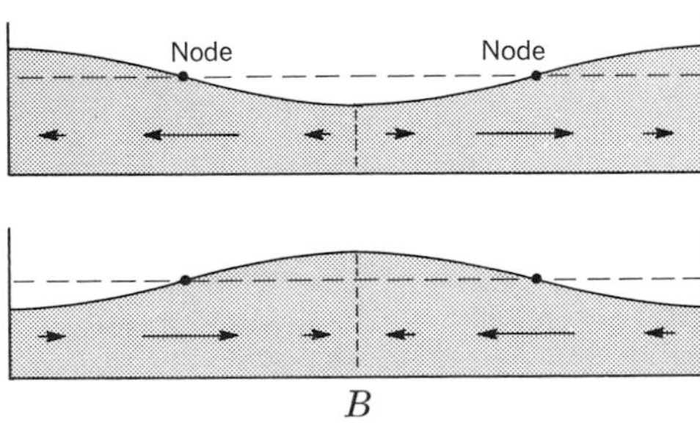


## Seiches

The phenomenon of the standing oscillation is well illustrated in certain lakes that are sensitive to the disturbing effects of sudden barometric pressure changes and violent storms. Lake Geneva in Switzerland is particularly susceptible and has experienced oscillations of water level amounting to as much as 5 ft (1.5 m). Because an occurrence of such oscillations is locally referred to as a *seiche,* this word has been adopted as the scientific term for all such phenomena. In Lake Geneva, seiches may be mononodal with a period of about $1^{h}14^{m}$ or binodal with a period of $35\frac{1}{2}^{m}$.

A particularly fine example of a mononodal seiche is that shown in Figure 9.18, which is a graph analogous to a tide curve, for oscillations in water level at the two ends of Lake Vättern in Sweden. This long narrow lake, occupying a glacial trough, is ideally formed for the development of a standing oscillation; its mononodal period is just under 3 hours. Note that the high and low waters are in opposite phase at the two ends of the lake.

Tides in a large bay or small sea connected to the open sea, such as the Adriatic Sea or the North Sea, will operate in certain respects as seiches in a lake, in that they may have independent oscillations determined by the depth and length of the basin. In addition, the ocean tide acts at the open end of the basin to force a sympathetic lunar-tidal oscillation. If the dimensions of the basin are such that the natural period of oscillation is close to that of the lunar tides, the basin will

**FIGURE 9.18.** Graph of a seiche in Lake Vättern, Sweden, showing rise and fall of level occurring in opposite phase at opposite ends of the lake. [After A. Defant (1958), *Ebb and Flow,* Ann Arbor, Univ. of Michigan Press.]

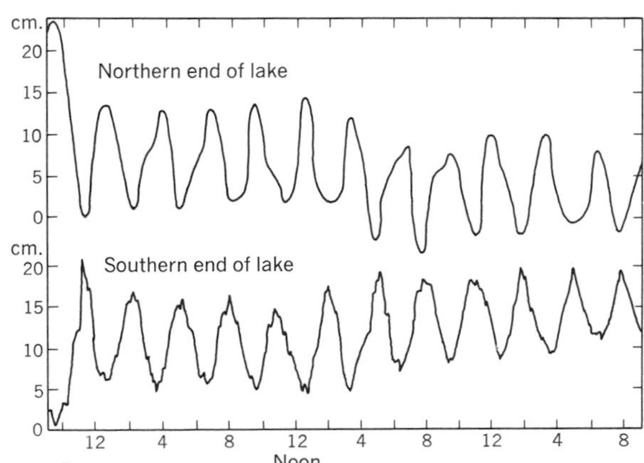

have strong tides in phase with those of the open ocean. If, however, the dimensions are not so scaled, the basin will be dominated by independent tides having the characteristic period of the basin.

One good example of a long narrow water body whose natural period of oscillation is about 12½ hours and hence closely matches the semidaily tide period is Long Island Sound. About 90 mi (145 km) long and averaging 65 ft (20 m) in depth, this water body has a tide range of about 2.5 ft (0.75 m) at the eastern end, or mouth, but the range increases to 7.5 ft (2.3 m) at the western end, or head.

Perhaps the most spectacular example of the tide is seen in the Bay of Fundy, Nova Scotia, where the tide range increases from about 10 ft (3 m) at the mouth of the bay as much as 50 ft (15 m) at the head (Figure 9.19). Here, too, the natural period of oscillation of the water body is about 12½ hours, causing a strong resonant oscillation. Another factor, the narrowing of the cross-sectional area of the bay toward its head, is held responsible for further increasing the tide range, because the energy of the tide is concentrated into a much smaller volume of water.

## Tides of seas and oceans

Thus far the discussion has centered on lakes, bays, or seas of long narrow shape. In a broad basin the deflective effect of the earth's rotation plays an important part, turning the water motion to the right (Northern Hemisphere) and causing a *transverse* wave motion. Here the tidal wave rotates counterclockwise about a central point, known as the *amphidromic point,* where there is no tidal movement (Figure 9.20). If we should draw lines through all points which experience high water at the same hour, known as *cotidal lines,* they will be found to radiate from the amphidromic point to the shores of the sea. From the amphidromic point outward the range of tide increases, hence it is possible to draw a second set of lines, called *corange lines,* representing points having the same tide range. These lines will have a concentric arrangement, crossing the cotidal lines as an approximately orthogonal system.

**FIGURE 9.19.** Low tide along the shores of the Bay of Fundy. These fishermen are removing shad caught in nets that at high tide are completely covered by water. (National Film Board, Ottawa, Canada.)

The North Sea, shown in Figure 9.20, has one amphidromic point lying close to the Norwegian coast and another point lying west of Denmark. A third amphidromic point lies at the northern entrance to the English Channel, between the Netherlands and the Suffolk coast of England. We see from this map that high water occurs first at the northern tip of Scotland, then proceeds southward, arriving at the Dover Straits some 12–14 hours later.

Tides of the great open oceans are not well understood, despite our wealth of knowledge of the tides at coastal points surrounding the oceans. Over the ocean deeps an accurate record of the rise and fall of tides is difficult to obtain, hence the location of amphidromic points and cotidal lines cannot be made with assurance. It is postulated that for the semidaily tide an amphidromic point lies in the North Atlantic, whereas in the South Atlantic the tidal wave originating in the Southern Ocean travels northward, so that the cotidal lines are drawn across the ocean from west to east (Figure 9.21*A*). The daily tide constituent, on the other hand, has amphidromic points in both South and North Atlantic Oceans (Figure 9.21*B*).

## River tides

The lower parts of many of the world's rivers experience tidal fluctuations and are described as *tidal rivers.* Examples are particularly numerous in the middle and higher latitudes where the coastal regions have recently subsided and where the rising of sea level following the disappearance of the ice sheets of the last glaciation (Wisconsinan stage) has caused the lower parts of the rivers and their valley areas to be inundated by sea water. Such elongate bays, often branching landward into many parts, are actually arms of the sea, or *estuaries.* There is no clear distinction between a tidal river and an estuary.

The progress of the tide into an estuary or tidal river is governed by the laws of very low progressive oscillatory waves in very shallow water, so that the speed of the wave depends upon the water depth; thus

$$C = 3.36\sqrt{D}$$

where $C$ is the wave speed in knots and $D$ is the water depth in feet. In metric units the formula is

$$C = 3.13\sqrt{D}$$

where $C$ is wave speed in meters per second, $D$ is depth in meters. For an estuary of 50-foot depth, the wave velocity would be about 25 knots, and a point located 25 nautical miles (29 statute miles) up river would experience high water 1 hour later.

Because of the control of wave velocity by water

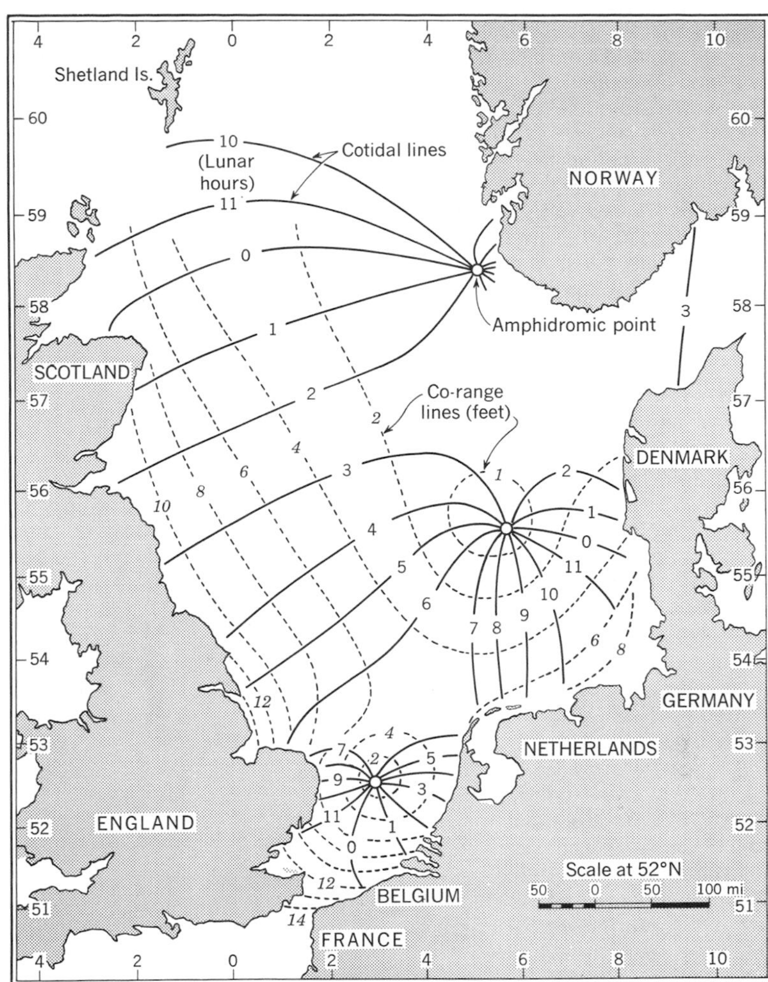


**FIGURE 9.20.** A cotidal map of the North Sea. [After A. T. Doodson and H. D. Warburg (1941), *Admiralty Manual of Tides,* Admiralty Chart No. 301, London, Her Majesty's Stationery Office.]

depth, the wave crest (high water) travels more rapidly than the wave trough (low water), hence the tide curve becomes quite asymmetrical (Figure 9.22). The elapsed time between one low water and the next high water is shortened, so that the wave crest tends to catch up with the wave trough preceding it.

Usually the range of tide decreases with distance upriver because of the frictional losses of energy along the channel bed. For example, the Hudson River has a tide range averaging 4.4 ft (1.3 m) at New York Harbor, but the range decreases to 3.0 ft (0.9 m) at Troy, which is situated at the head of the tidal portion, 131 mi (211 km) upriver.

## Tidal bores

The steepening of the incoming tidal wave in some tidal rivers becomes so strongly developed that a turbulent wall of water, termed a *tidal bore,* moves upriver with the rising tide. This effect usually occurs at the point where the gradient of the river bed suddenly steepens and there is a narrowing of the cross section. Among the rivers whose tidal portions characteristically develop bores are the Amazon, Colorado, Yangtze, Fuch'un (Tsientang), Hooghly, Severn, Trent, Elbe, and Weser. The bore of the Amazon, referred to locally as the *pororoca,* reaches a height of 16 ft (26 m) and resembles a great rapid; it moves upstream at a speed of 12 knots (22 km per hr). Another spectacular bore occurs in the Peticodiac River, at the head of the Bay of Fundy, a locality well known for its vast tide range (Figure 9.23).

## Alternating tidal currents

The rise and fall of the tide are accompanied by horizontal water motions, termed *tidal currents,* which cause convergence of the water toward the crest of the tidal wave and a divergence and sinking of the water level at the wave trough. A current that flows in one direction for 6¼ hours, then reverses its flow to the opposite direction for another 6¼ hours, is described as *alternating.* Flow of this type is found in estuaries and tidal rivers where the incoming current, or *flood current,* accompanies the rising water level. An outgoing current, the *ebb current,* accompanies the falling water level.

Alternating flood and ebb currents in the lower reaches of a tidal river are illustrated by the graph of current and tide at the entrance to New York Harbor (Figure 9.24). Note that the flood current reaches its highest velocity about at high water, but continues to

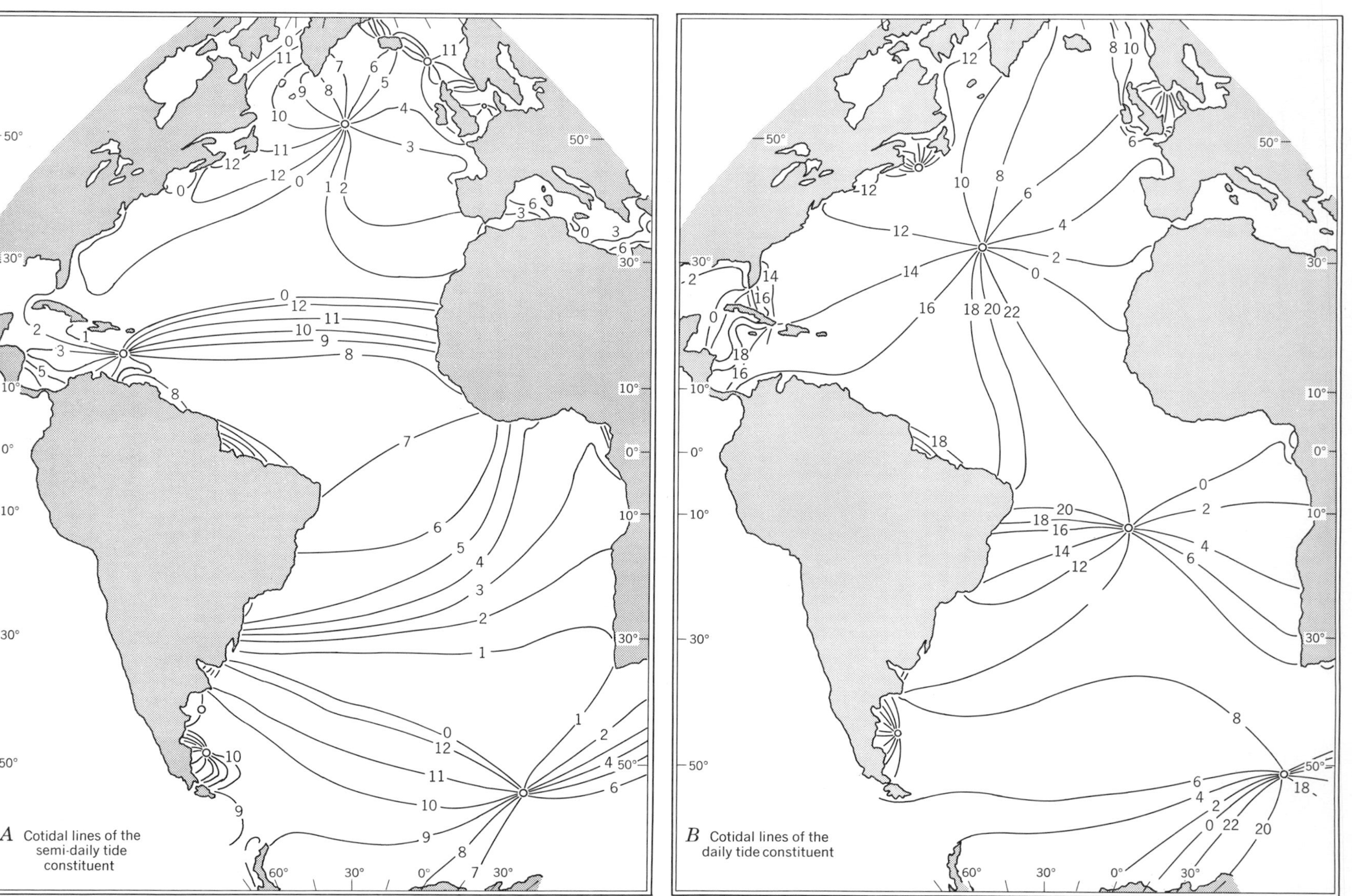


**FIGURE 9.21.** Cotidal maps of the Atlantic Ocean. Figures give lunar hours based on the moon's meridian passage at Greenwich. [Data by G. Dietrich, 1944. Map modified and simplified after A. Defant (1961), *Physical Oceanography*, vol. II, New York, Pergamon.]

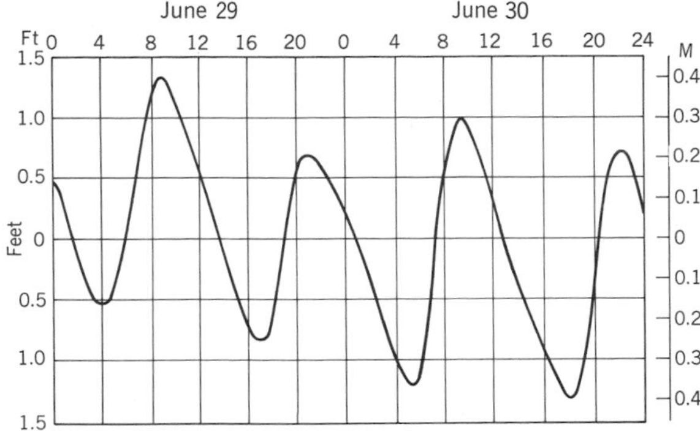


**FIGURE 9.22.** This tide curve for the Hudson estuary near Albany, New York, illustrates a typical river tide. (Data by H. A. Marmer; © 1969, John Wiley & Sons, New York.)

flow upriver as the tide falls. When the tide level has dropped to its mid-point, the current has stopped entirely, a moment known as *slack water.* Then the current reverses to become an ebb flow, which in turn reaches its greatest velocity about the time of low water. The two curves are, in this case, approximately in phase. Farther upriver these phase relations change, so that at the head of the tidal river high water coincides with slack water.

One point concerning river tides is particularly noteworthy: The ebb current is considerably stronger than the flood current, a result of the contributions of fresh-water discharge by the watershed draining into the head of the tidal river. The ebb current must carry more water to the sea than is returned by the flood current. Should a float be observed during successive tidal cycles, it will be found to travel farther seaward on the ebb current that it is carried upriver by the flood. Large coastal cities depend upon this seaward flow to carry away sewage.

## Rotatory tidal currents

Over the open water of a shallow sea, tidal currents are commonly *rotatory,* with the current changing direction in a clockwise manner, shifting through 180° of azimuth in 6¼ hours and returning to the original direction after a semidaily period of 12½ hours (Figure 9.25). Rotatory currents can be observed from a moored vessel, such as a lightship, from which a current meter is suspended or from which a series of floats is sent out at intervals.

Figure 9.25*A* shows the currents observed during a 12-hour period at the Nantucket Shoals Lightship. From many such measurements it is found that the average pattern of the rotatory current here approximates a simple ellipse, shown in Figure 9.25*B.* The times at which high and low water occur at Boston Harbor, a convenient tidal reference point, are shown on the ellipse.

Rotatory currents also show the effects of the various tidal constituents which influence the cycle of rise and fall of tide level. Figure 9.26 illustrates rotatory currents at the Swiftsure Bank Lightship near the Strait of Juan de Fuca. When the moon's declination is zero and equatorial tides dominate, ellipses of tidal currents for two successive semidaily periods are closely matched. When the moon's declination is large and

**FIGURE 9.23.** Tidal bore of the Petitcodiac River, Moncton, New Brunswick. (National Film Board, Ottawa, Canada.)

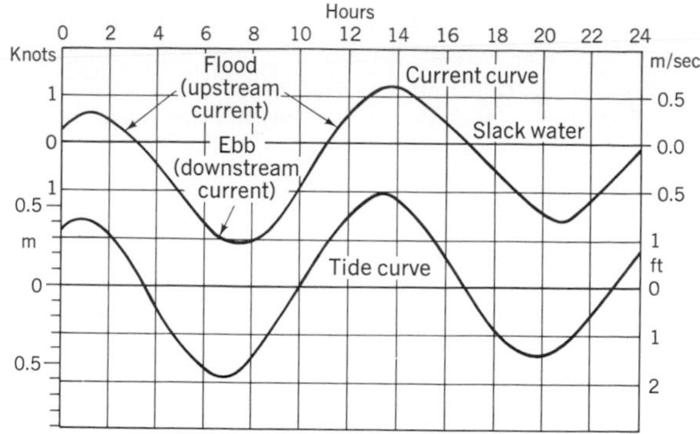


FIGURE 9.24. At the entrance to New York Harbor, ebb and flood currents are in phase with the tide curve. (Data by H. A. Marmer; © 1969, John Wiley & Sons, New York.)

tropic ties dominate, one ellipse is larger than the next, a form of diurnal inequality.

## Hydraulic currents

Locally, strong tidal currents are produced at constrictions in the mouths of bays or in the narrow straits between two seas by the differences in water level set up by the rising and falling tide. Such flows are described as *hydraulic currents* because they result from the difference in level of the sea surface and the resulting gradient of the water surface. Hydraulic currents, often reaching several knots velocity, maintain narrow tidal channels free of accumulating sediment because of the intensity of scour of the rapidly flowing water. Good examples are found in The Race, at the eastern end of Long Island, and The Hell Gate, where Long Island Sound is joined to the East River.

## Earth tides

Of considerable interest in the earth sciences are the responses of the solid earth to the tide-producing forces. Such *earth tides* are detected by use of the most sensitive pendulum-type instruments. We have seen that the observed pull of the tide on a plumb bob is actually somewhat less than that which would be expected from a computation of the forces (Figure 9.6); this discrepancy may be explained by postulating that the earth's crust is responding to the tidal forces and is itself rising and falling. Somewhat similar measurements with extremely delicate instruments (gravimeters), which record minute variations in the force of gravity by the degree of stretching of a spring (see Chapter 10), have been made of the vertical component of the tide-producing forces. Here, again, the observed spring movement is about two-thirds that to be expected, because the earth's crust itself rises and falls with the tide, changing the force of gravity and thus reducing the motion of the spring.

Investigations reported in 1970 showed that in middle latitudes, at times of high earth tide, a surface point on the crust is about 1 ft (30 cm) more distant from the earth's center than at low earth tide. Another crustal movement that must be distinguished from the solid earth tide in coastal zones is that caused by the

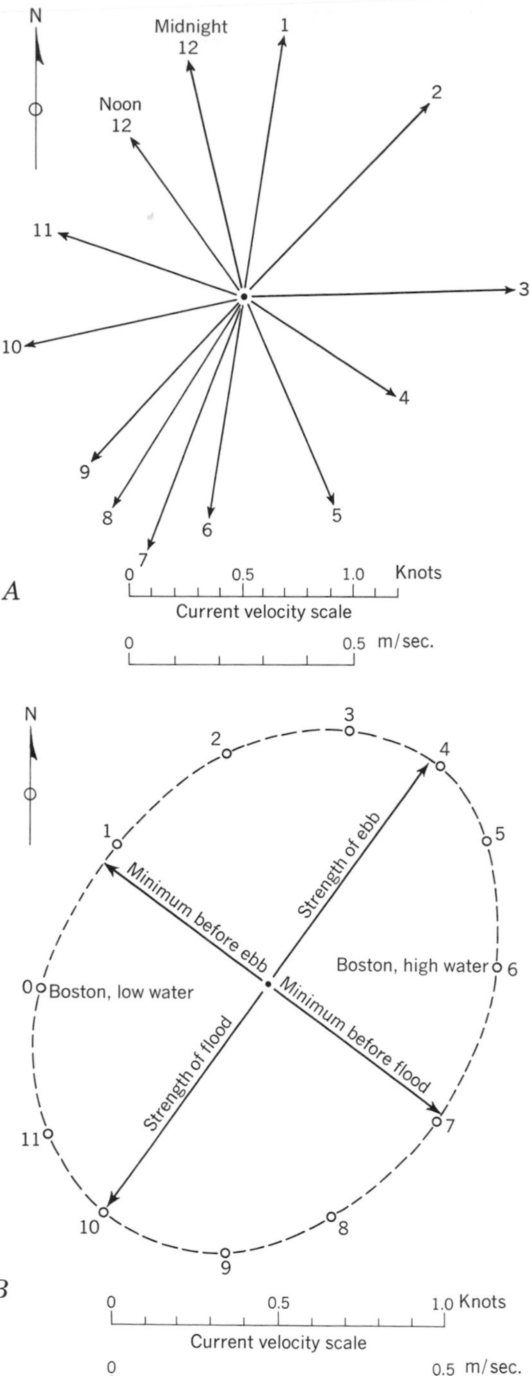


FIGURE 9.25. (*A*) Rotatory tidal currents observed at the Nantucket Shoals Lightship through a 12-hour period. An arrow shows the current speed and direction for each hour. (*B*) Vectors of average tidal currents at the Nantucket Shoals Lightship form an elliptical figure. [After H. A. Marmer (1932), *Physics of the Earth,* vol. 5, Washington, D.C., Nat. Res. Council.]

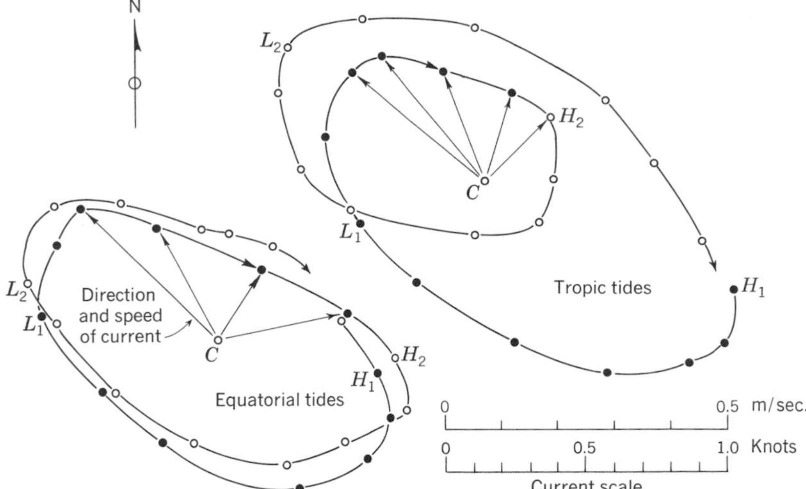


**FIGURE 9.26.** Semidaily rotatory tidal current at the Swiftsure Bank Lightship, strait of Juan de Fuca, reflects the moon's changing declination by changes in the elliptical figure formed by the current vectors. [After H. A. Marmer (1932), *Physics of the Earth,* vol. 5, Washington, D.C., Nat. Res. Council.]

changing load of sea water as ocean tides rise and fall. Along the Atlantic coast of North America the ocean tide lags about 8 hours behind the solid earth tide, so that a deficiency of water mass occurs at high earth tide. The result is to increase the crustal rise by about 0.5 in (1.3 cm). Along the Pacific coast ocean and earth tides are about in phase, with the result that the load of ocean water is increased at high earth tide and the crustal rise is reduced by about 0.5 in (1.3 cm).

## Atmospheric tides

The atmosphere is subjected to the same set of tide-raising forces as are the oceans and solid earth. However, atmospheric responses are exceedingly small because of the small mass of the atmosphere. The masses of equal volumes of air and water are related by a ratio of about 1:1000, hence the gravitational attractions of moon and sun are correspondingly smaller.

If tides affect the atmosphere, we should expect to observe them through minute cyclic variations in the barometric pressure (Chapter 15). In middle and high latitudes the changes of barometric pressure as a result of temperature changes and weather disturbances are so large as to conceal any very small semidaily fluctuations, but in the equatorial latitudes, where these disturbing effects are often very small, a regular daily cycle of pressure change has been observed. Throughout the tropics this pressure cycle characteristically has a range of about 2 mm of mercury and reaches its maximum value about 2 hours before noon and 2 hours before midnight, which means that the cycle conforms to the semidaily solar period, not to the semidaily lunar period. The explanation seems to lie in the theory that the natural period of oscillation of the earth's atmosphere is close to the semidaily solar period, which means that the sun's tide-raising force sets up resonant oscillations. The lunar period is evidently not close enough to the natural atmospheric period to cause comparable tides, but a very faint semidaily lunar cycle of pressure fluctuations has been detected with a range of perhaps one-fourth to one-twentieth that of the solar atmospheric tide. The tide-producing forces of both the moon and sun also affect the ionospheric layer of the earth's upper atmosphere (Chapter 7), causing a corresponding fluctuation in the intensity of the earth's magnetic field. These fluctuations can be shown through minute cyclic changes in magnetic declination at the earth's surface. (See Figure 7.27.)

## Slowing of earth rotation by tidal friction

Continual flexing of the solid earth by tidal forces and ceaseless horizontal water motions in tidal currents are met by frictional resistance. Work is done in overcoming this resistance. The continuous work done by tides upon the whole earth is estimated to be on the order of two billion horsepower. The action is that of a brake upon the earth's rotation. (The evidence for and amount of slowing of earth rotation are discussed in Chapter 3.)

Slowing of the earth's rotation by tidal friction has the effect of changing the angular momentum of the moon. Recall that the total angular momentum of the earth-moon system must remain constant, therefore the slowing of earth rotation must be accompanied by an increase in angular momentum of the moon. This increase takes the form of an increase in the moon's distance from earth, along with a decrease in the moon's linear velocity. It is estimated that with each revolution about the earth, distance to the moon is increased by about ⅓ in. (0.8 cm).

Sir George Darwin, son of Sir Charles Darwin and an authority on tides, was intrigued by the implications of the change in the moon's angular momentum and distance. Looking back into farthest reaches of geologic time, Darwin reasoned that the moon must have been very close to the earth, and may have been at that time a single body.[5] He therefore proposed a theory of origin of the moon in which a large chunk of the earth was torn out to become the moon. Darwin reasoned that if the rate of rotation at this early time in earth history was as rapid once in three hours, the centrifugal

[5] Such a single body might be called an "earthoon" or a "moorth" depending upon which word strikes one's fancy.

forces acting upon the earth would exceed the gravitational forces that hold it together, and that a violent rupture would occur, much as when a flywheel reaches the limit of its cohesive strength and ruptures. Pieces of the earth would have been hurled far from the earth's surface and would have later become consolidated into a single object, the moon. This and other hypotheses of the moon's origin are discussed further in Chapter 31.

Looking far into the future, George Gamow, a physicist-astronomer of great distinction, has written[6]

> A few more words may be said about the future of the moon as it can be calculated on the basis of celestial mechanics. As a result of gradual recession, the moon eventually will get so far from the earth that it will become rather useless as a substitute for lanterns at night. In the meantime solar tides gradually will slow down the rotation of the earth (provided the oceans do not freeze up), and there will come the time when *the length of a day will be greater than the length of a month.* The friction of lunar tides will then tend to accelerate the rotation of the earth, and, by the law of conservation of angular momentum, the moon will begin to return to the earth until at last it will come as close to the earth as it was at birth. At this point, the earth's gravity forces will probably tear up the moon into a billion pieces, forming a ring similar to that of Saturn. But the dates of these events, as given by celestial mechanics, are so far off that the sun probably will have run out of its nuclear fuel and the entire planetary system will be submerged in darkness.

[6] George Gamow, *Gravity,* 1962, Anchor Books, Doubleday & Company, Garden City, N. Y., p. 91. Reprinted by permission of the publisher.

## References for further study

Darwin, G. H. (1898), *The Tides and Kindred Phenomena in the Solar System,* Boston and New York, Houghton Mifflin, 278 pp. Reprinted (1962), San Francisco and London, Freeman.

Doodson, A. T., and H. D. Warburg (1941), *Admiralty Manual of Tides,* London, Her Majesty's Stationery Office, 270 pp.

Defant, A. (1958), *Ebb and Flow,* Ann Arbor, Univ. of Mich. Press, 121 pp.

Defant, A. (1961), *Physical Oceanography,* vol. 2, New York, Pergamon, 598 pp.

Macmillan, D. H. (1966), *Tides,* New York, American Elsevier, 240 pp.

Clancy, E. P. (1968), *The Tides, Pulse of the Earth,* Garden City, N.Y., Doubleday, 228 pp.

U.S. Coast and Geodetic Survey, *Tide Tables,* Washington, D.C., U.S. Government Printing Office, published annually in four volumes.

# 10

# The earth's figure and gravity

THAT THE EARTH resembles a sphere in form is a fact we have all accepted, with little thought to the difficulties that beset the scholar of ancient times called upon to prove the spherical form with only a limited range of travel and only the simplest of instruments available. By noting that after the sun has set below the horizon its rays still shine on high clouds and mountain summits above him, he could infer that the earth's surface is convex upward. With a telescope at his disposal the seventeenth-century scholar might have noted that a ship sailing away from him seemed to sink beneath the horizon, as if the sea surface were curved convexly upward and the degree of sinking increased regularly with distance, but this observation would not be a satisfying proof of the earth being an entire sphere. Perhaps he would have pondered the fact that in all lunar eclipses, when the earth's shadow falls on the moon, the edge of the earth's shadow appears through the telescope to be an arc of a circle. From this it might be reasoned that the object casting the shadow is a sphere, for otherwise its shadow would not be circular in a wide variety of positions.

As one accustomed to measuring the vertical angle between a heavenly body and the earth's horizon (altitude of an object in the sky), the astronomer of ancient civilizations might have noted that the polestar of his time, which would hold a fixed angle of altitude at a given place, would increase this angle by 1 degree of arc for every 70 mi (110 km) or so of travel northward on a meridian. With the correct assumptions about relations of the earth to the stars generally, he could reason that the earth's surface is spherically curved if this change in angle should prove constant on all meridians on which it is measured. Because he was without the ability to travel freely over the globe, he could not have carried out such a proof.

With the advent of circumnavigation of the earth by Magellan's crew in 1522 there could be no doubt left in the mind of the average person that the earth was a solid, probably rotund object, but the fact of circumnavigation alone could equally well be accomplished on a earth of strongly ellipsoidal form, or even of some quite lopsided shape. With the prospect of being able to navigate freely over the earth's oceans, a simple but powerful tool—the spring balance—could be brought into play. If Newton's theory of gravitation (about 1680) had been available, an expedition might have been equipped to weigh a given mass of metal with a sensitive spring balance at many points at sea level over the earth's surface. If the weight proved always the same, it could have been assumed that all observation points are approximately equidistant from the common center of gravity and therefore that the earth has a roughly spherical surface. In those times a pendulum clock, using basically the same principle of a constant force of gravity to keep constant time, would have provided a far more sensitive instrument.

As the precision of measurement of the earth's form improved, it became evident that the spherical form, although proved beyond doubt as an approximate description of the earth, was not accurate enough and needed to be modified. Thus the earth science of *geodesy* (from Greek words meaning "to divide the earth") evolved throughout the eighteenth and nineteenth centuries with increasingly precise findings for the best possible description of the earth's form. The *geodesist,* as the earth scientist who pursues geodesy is named, considers his field to be part of the broader field of geophysics. In this chapter some of the elementary concepts of geodesy and the earth's gravity are treated, along with the problem of division of the earth's surface for purposes of describing position and direction.

## Eratosthenes' measurement of the earth

Among the scholars of ancient Greece, Pythagoras (about 540 B.C.) and contemporaries of Aristotle (384–322 B.C.) believed the earth to be spherical and had speculated, quite erroneously, on its dimensions. The first scientifically sound approximation of the earth's circumference based on direct measurement was made by Eratosthenes, librarian at Alexandria, about 200 B.C. At Syene, Egypt, a place on the upper Nile River near the Tropic of Cancer (lat. 23½° N.), at the time of summer solstice (June 21) it could be observed that the sun's noon rays were nearly perpendicular to the earth's surface and shone upon the floor of a deep vertical well (Figure 10.1).

On the same solstice date at Alexandria, located approximately on the same meridian as Syene, the sun's noon rays were observed to make an angle of one-fiftieth of a circle (7°12′) with respect to the perpendicular. Assuming the sun's rays to be parallel, it is evident that the earth's surface between Syene and Alexandria must be curved in an arc of 7°12′. It remained only to establish the north-south distance between the two places, a value then estimated as 5000 stadia. Multiplying by 50, Eratosthenes obtained 250,000 stadia as the earth's circumference. If the stadium is taken to be equivalent to 185 meters, his figure becomes 46,250 km, or about 26,660 mi, a figure surprisingly close to the true value of about 25,000 mi (40,000 km).

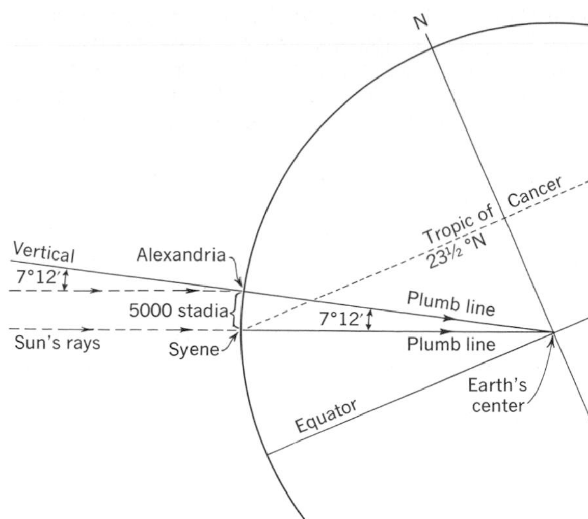


**FIGURE 10.1.** Eratosthenes' method of estimating the earth's circumference.

Doubt exists that the distance between Syene and Alexandria was actually measured on the ground, and we are also uncertain of the actual equivalent of the stadium as a unit of length measure. Nevertheless, Eratosthenes' method was sound in principle and has since been applied with great precision of measurement to determine the earth's form and dimensions. His principle was used by Arabs of the ninth century, who actually measured with cords the ground distance necessary to result in a change of 1 degree in the altitude of a star. Whether their results were more accurate we shall never know, because their units of length are not known in modern terms, but it is suspected that their results were considerably more accurate than those of Eratosthenes, who may have relied on travelers' estimates for the distance from Syene to Alexandria.

Eight centuries of scientific stagnation then elapsed, with no better estimates of the earth's dimensions until in 1615–1617 a professor of mathematics at the University of Leyden, Willebrord Snell, carefully surveyed by triangulation an area of level ground and calculated that a degree of latitude was equivalent to 66.73 mi (107.4 km). This was later corrected to 69.07 mi (111.1 km), a figure close to the true value for his latitude. From that date on, developments in knowledge of the earth's shape and relation to the solar system came rapidly.

## The earth as an oblate ellipsoid

Suspicion that the earth was appreciably different in form from a true sphere seems to have been strongly aroused by a remarkable fact observed by a French astronomer, Jean Richer. In 1671 he was sent by Louis XIV to the island of Cayenne off the coast of French Guiana at lat. 5° N. to make certain astronomical observations. He took with him, among other instruments, a highly accurate clock whose pendulum was of just the length required to beat seconds in Paris. Soon after his arrival in Cayenne Richer noticed that his clock was losing about 2½ minutes per day, a very great error for a precision clock, and he was forced to shorten the pendulum by nearly a quarter of an inch to regulate the clock so that it would keep time with respect to the stars.

When these facts were later reported by Richer to his scientific colleagues in Europe much discussion was aroused, but the correct explanation came 15 years later when Newton, applying his laws of gravitation and motion, published the statement that the earth's form should be that of an *oblate ellipsoid,* a geometrical form differing from a sphere in being somewhat flattened at the poles and bulging outward around the equator (Figure 10.3). This form would, Newton inferred, result from the response of an otherwise spherical earth to the centrifugal force of rotation, tending to redistribute the earth's mass outward from its axis of rotation and deforming it into a figure in equilibrium with the opposed forces of gravity and rotation. (Newton's analysis is discussed in Chapter 2 and illustrated in Figure 2.11.) Richer's observation that the force of gravity is less at the equator than in the high latitudes could be fully explained by an ellipsoidal earth form in which surface points at the equator are situated farther from the earth's center of gravity than points in high latitudes.

The oblate ellipsoid, an ellipse of revolution about its minor axis, has the form of an ellipse when cut through the plane of the poles (that is, in meridional cross section). The equatorial diameter forms the major axis of the ellipse, and the line of poles forms the minor axis (Figure 10.4). In equatorial cross section an oblate ellipsoid is a true circle, but the diameter of this circle is greater than the length of the polar axis.

Although the oblate ellipsoidal form of the earth was advocated by Newton on rational grounds and was seemingly well supported by Richer's observations, disagreement among prominent astronomers concerning the earth's form persisted through the remainder of the seventeenth century and well into the early eighteenth century.

Meanwhile another French astronomer, Jean Picard, had continued the measurement of meridian arcs begun by Snell in Holland; by 1671 he had carefully surveyed by triangulation with a telescope the length of a little over 1 degree of arc of a meridian and recalculated the earth's circumference. Picard's geodetic surveying was continued early in the eighteenth century by Giovanni Cassini, astronomer in charge of the Paris Observatory, who with the aid of his son measured an additional meridian arc and found a poleward decrease in length of a degree. This led to the conclusion that the earth was actually a *prolate ellipsoid,* that is, a sphere deformed by a stretching of its polar axis and contraction around the equator (resembling a U.S. football). It is little wonder that, with groups of distinguished scholars supporting opposed theories of earth form, a major scientific controversy arose, with the "earth-flatteners" opposed to the "earth-elongators."

To settle the controversy—oblate ellipsoid versus prolate ellipsoid—the Royal Academy of Sciences of Paris sponsored two scientific expeditions whose plan, even in this day of global and space explorations, is exciting for its boldness of concept. One party was sent to the Arctic Circle in Lapland, where in 1736–1737 a meridian arc of 0°57′ was precisely measured at lat. 66° N. and found to be longer than an equivalent length of arc as previously measured by Picard near Paris. As shown in Figure 10.2 by a greatly exaggerated flattening of the ellipse, the nearer the poles, the longer the arc required to represent a given angle, say 5°, because it must be fitted by a circle of larger radius. The Lapland expedition, which included the celebrated Swedish astronomer Celsius, therefore brought back results in agreement with the hypothesis of an oblate ellipsoidal earth.

In the meantime a second expedition, which had set out for Peru in 1735, began their survey in 1736 near Quito, a city almost on the equator.[1] They completed the measurement of more than 3° of meridian arc in 1743 and found the length per degree of arc to be appreciably shorter than that in France and still less than that in Lapland. The success of this experiment evidently attracted the interest of Voltaire, who is said to have quipped that the outcome "flattened the poles and the Cassinis." Another arc was measured in South Africa in 1752, still another by Mason and Dixon in 1768 on the north-south boundary between Maryland and Delaware. Geodetic work then increased rapidly in accuracy and scope.

How is the ground distance actually measured in such geodetic surveys as those described above? The long spans of distance—69 mi (111 km) for each degree of arc—are actually measured by the procedure of triangulation surveying (described in Chapter 11), in which the dimensions of horizontal triangles surveyed by telescopic instruments are calculated by trigonometric means. Only a short ground line (the base line) is actually measured by a measuring tape or chain at the start of the survey.

[1] Now in Ecuador, Quito was then included in the Spanish colony of Peru.

**FIGURE 10.2.** Circles fitted to the earth's curvature at equator and poles.

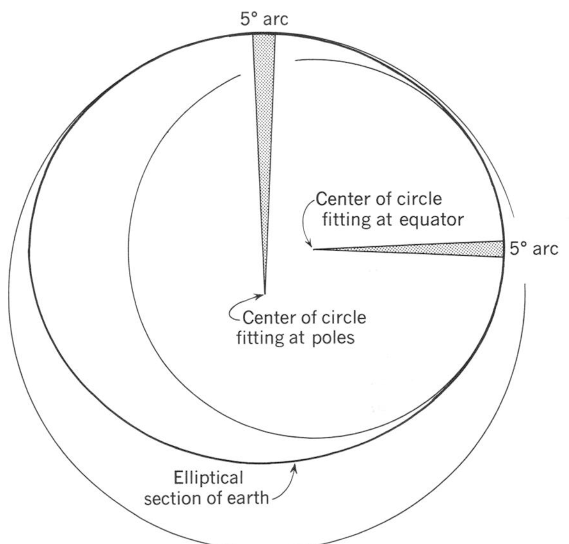

## Earth ellipsoids

We have now established that an oblate ellipsoid is a much better description of the earth's figure than is a sphere, although for many general purposes the spherical model is quite adequate. What are the actual dimensions of the *earth ellipsoid,* the idealized geometrical model selected to approximate the earth's true form? Being a simple model and an idealized concept, the earth ellipsoid has been assigned dimensions based upon the best geodetic information for the lengths of meridian arcs in various parts of the earth. Unfortunately, these measurements, precise as they may be, do not agree from one region to another for the earth's curvature at a given latitude. Consequently several geodesists calculated what they believe to be the best earth ellipsoid. Selection of an ellipsoid for a particular area was made at a given time, in hopes that the ellipsoid dimensions would correspond to the geodetic data of that part of the world.

Earth ellipsoids are described in terms of the lengths of the *semimajor axis* (equatorial radius) and either the *semiminor axis* (one-half the polar axis) or the ratio of their difference to the semimajor axis, a constant known as the *flattening* (Figure 10.3). Flattening is quoted as a decimal number part or in fractional form. Table 10.1 gives the dimensions, in international meters, of eight ellipsoids that have been or presently are in wide use.

When a nation, or group of nations, establishes a system of military maps covering a large area, it is necessary to establish a *geodetic datum,* that is, to select a particular ellipsoid as the reference figure, and identify a certain point with specific coordinates as the *origin* (see Chapter 11). Dimensions of the selected ellipsoid permit calculation of the exact lengths of degrees of latitude and longitude. Figure 10.5 is a world map showing how the earth has been zoned by the Western powers into regions, each of which uses a selected ellipsoid as the datum for their military maps. Dimensions of these ellipsoids are given in Table 10.1.

Oldest of the ellipsoids described in Table 10.1 is the *Everest ellipsoid,* calculated in 1830 by the geodesist Sir George Everest, first head of the Topographical Survey of India and the man after whom the world's highest mountain was named. Everest's ellipsoid was used in mapping of a large part of southeast Asia (Figure 10.5) but turned out to be a very poor fit. His ellipsoid shows the least amount of flattening as well as the shortest semimajor axis. The *Bessel ellipsoid* was calcuated in 1841 by a Prussian astronomer of that name. Its use was largely limited to military mapping in eastern Asia and the East Indies.

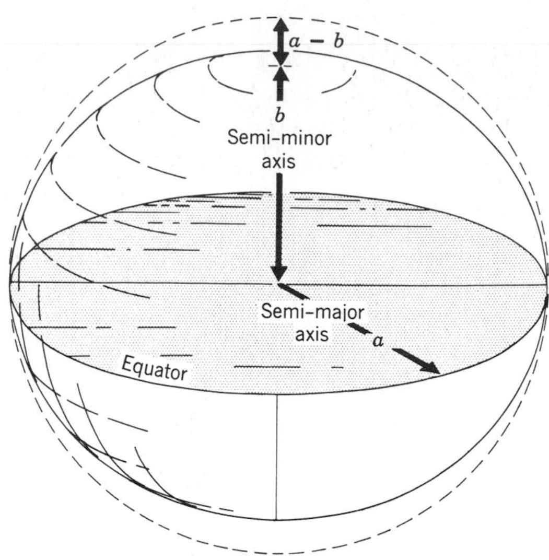


**FIGURE 10.3.** Semimajor and semiminor axes of the earth ellipsoid. (© 1960, John Wiley & Sons, New York.)

Two ellipsoids in Table 10.1 bear the name of General A. R. Clarke, head of the English Ordnance Survey. The *Clarke ellipsoid of 1866* was adopted for the geodetic datum of North America and the Philippines (Chapter 11). General Clarke recalculated the ellipsoid dimensions in 1880, and these were adopted for mapping of the southern half of the African continent (Figure 10.5).

The *International ellipsoid* was computed by J. F. Hayford of the U.S. Coast and Geodetic Survey in 1909 and was adopted in 1924 by the International Union of Geodesy and Geophysics (IUGG) as a world standard. Many world areas not assigned to the Everest, Bessel, and Clarke ellipsoids have used the International ellipsoid as the datum for mapping (Figure 10.5). The *Krasovskiy ellipsoid* of 1942 is used by the U.S.S.R. and its satellite nations.

Major advances in calculation of the earth ellipsoid were made possible by the advent of orbiting earth satellites. (The principle is explained in later pages of this

**TABLE 10.1. DIMENSIONS OF SELECTED ELLIPSOIDS**

| Ellipsoid | Semimajor Axis[1] *a* | Semiminor Axis[1] *b* | Flattening *f* | Fractional equivalent |
|---|---|---|---|---|
| Everest, 1830 | 6,377,276 | 6,356,075 | 0.003,324 | 1/300.8 |
| Bessel, 1841 | 6,377,397 | 6,356,079 | 0.003,343 | 1/299.15 |
| Clarke, 1866 | 6,378,206 | 6,356,584 | 0.003,390 | 1/294.98 |
| Clarke, 1880 | 6,378,301 | 6,356,584 | 0.003,408 | 1/293.47 |
| International (Hayford, 1909) | 6,378,388 | 6,356,912 | 0.003,367 | 1/297.00 |
| Krasovskiy, 1942 | 6,378,245 | 6,356,863 | 0.003,352 | 1/298.3 |
| Astrogeodetic, or Mercury Datum (Fischer, 1960) | 6,378,160 | 6,356,778 | 0.003,352 | 1/298.3 |
| Geodetic Reference System (IUGG, 1967) | 6,378,160 | 6,356,775 | 0.003,353 | 1/298.25 |

[1] Measurements in international meters.

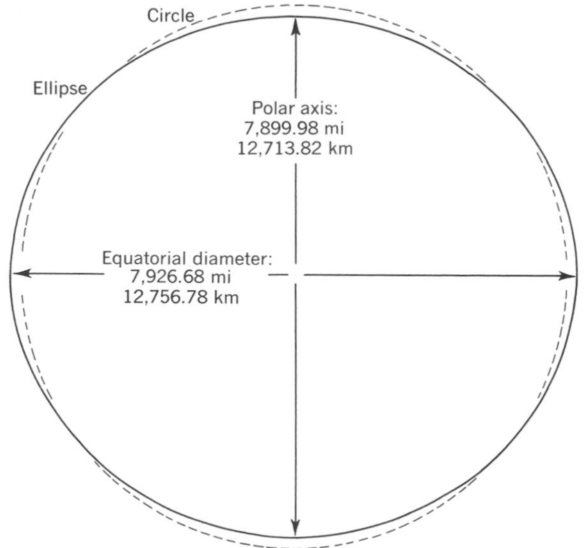


**FIGURE 10.4.** Dimensions of the International ellipsoid of reference.

chapter.) Using earth-satellite data combined with all available geodetic data, a new ellipsoid was calculated by Irene Fischer of the U.S. Army Topographic Command (at that time called the U.S. Army Map Service) and first designated in 1960 as the *Astrogeodetic ellipsoid.* It was adopted for use by the Manned Space Flight Programs of NASA under the name of the *Mercury Datum.* The Fischer ellipsoid of 1960 uses a flattening of 1/298.3 and a semimajor axis of 6,378,160 meters. A revision by Mrs. Fischer in 1968 to include all currently available data has been designated as the *Modification of the Mercury Datum* (abbreviated as *MMD 68*). This modified ellipsoid uses the same flattening as in the 1960 Fischer ellipsoid, but the semimajor axis is shorter by some 10 meters.

The International ellipsoid was replaced as a world standard in 1967, by action of the International Union of Geodesy and Geophysics, in favor of an ellipsoid designated as the *Geodetic Reference ellipsoid, 1967.* The semimajor axis of this ellipsoid is the same as the Fischer ellipsoid of 1960, but the reciprocal of the flattening is referred to more decimals: 1/298.25. These same dimensions had been adopted in 1964 by the International Astronomical Union.

## Lengths of degrees of latitude

On a perfect sphere, parallels of latitude spaced, say, 1 degree apart would be separated by exactly the same ground distance (1/360 of the earth's circumference) regardless of position on the globe. On an oblate ellipsoid, with its varying degree of meridian curvature

**FIGURE 10.5.** For purposes of military mapping the earth is zoned into regions, each assigned a particular ellipsoid of reference. (Based on data of Department of the Army, TM 5–241; © 1960, John Wiley & Sons, New York.)

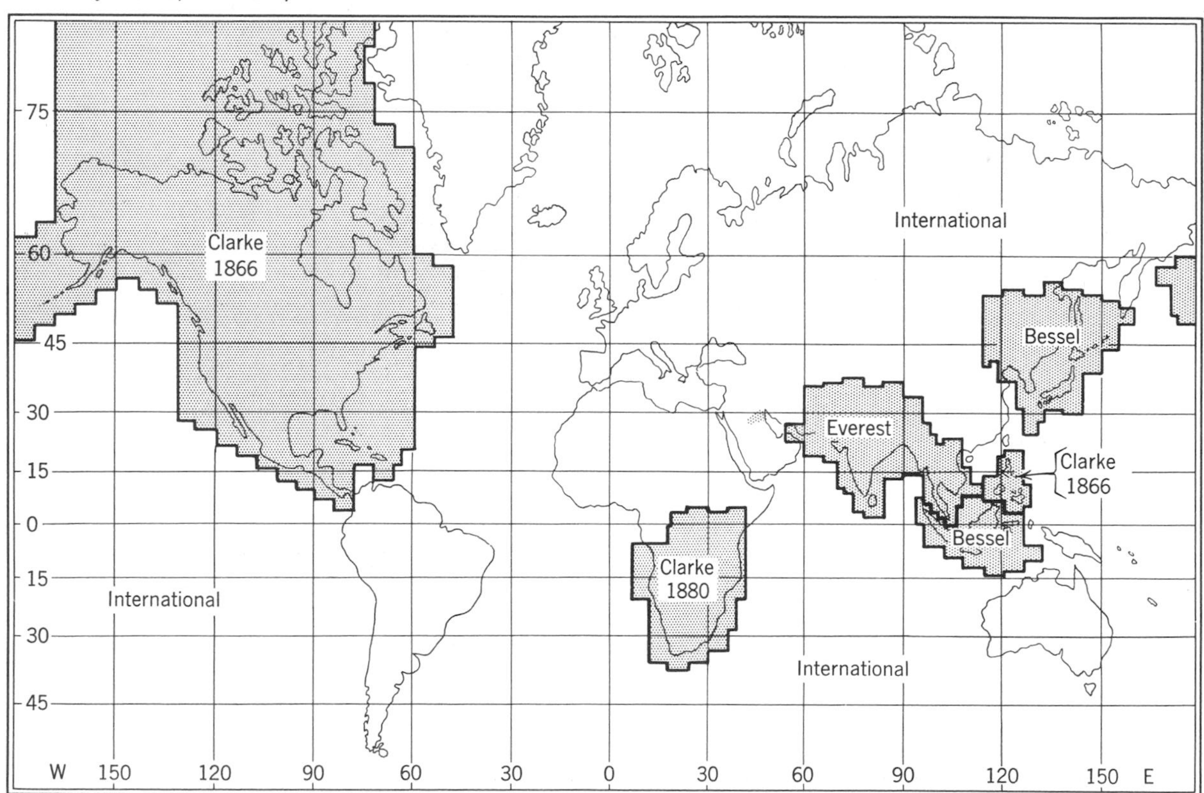

from equator to pole, the length of 1 degree of latitude (a 1-degree arc of a meridian) increases systematically from equator to pole, for reasons already explained (Figure 10.2). The length of 1 degree of arc of the equator (a degree of longitude) would, on the other hand, be the same at all points around the earth, but this constant would differ slightly from the length of 1 degree of meridian arc (latitude) at the equator. Taking the data of the Clarke ellipsoid of 1866 for a standard, we compute the length of 1 degree of longitude on the equator by dividing the equatorial circumference by 360°; thus

$$1° \text{ of longitude} = \frac{24{,}901.92 \text{ statute miles}}{360°}$$

$$= 69.172 \text{ statute miles.}$$

In metric units,

$$= \frac{40{,}075.90 \text{ km}}{360°}$$

$$= 111.322 \text{ km.}$$

Dividing the last numbers by 60, we obtain the length of 1 minute of longitude as 1.15 statute mi (1.85 km), which is very close to the length of 1 nautical mile. A 1-second arc of longitude would thus be 0.019 statute mi., or about 100 ft (30.6 m).

Because the meridians converge poleward, the length of a degree of longitude will diminish poleward with increasing latitude, as the figures in Table 10.2 indicate, until the value of zero is reached at either pole. From the table it is seen that the length of a degree of longitude is reduced to very nearly one-half its equatorial value at the 60th parallel.[2]

**TABLE 10.2. LENGTHS OF DEGREES OF LATITUDE AND LONGITUDE**

| | Length of 1° of Latitude | | Length of 1° of Longitude | |
|---|---|---|---|---|
| Latitude, degrees | statute miles | kilometers | statute miles | kilometers |
| 0 | 68.704 | 110.569 | 69.172 | 111.322 |
| 5 | 68.710 | 110.578 | 68.911 | 110.902 |
| 10 | 68.725 | 110.603 | 68.129 | 109.643 |
| 15 | 68.751 | 110.644 | 66.830 | 107.553 |
| 20 | 68.786 | 110.701 | 65.026 | 104.650 |
| 25 | 68.829 | 110.770 | 62.729 | 100.953 |
| 30 | 68.879 | 110.850 | 59.956 | 96.490 |
| 35 | 68.935 | 110.941 | 56.725 | 91.290 |
| 40 | 68.993 | 111.034 | 53.063 | 85.397 |
| 45 | 69.054 | 111.132 | 48.995 | 78.850 |
| 50 | 69.115 | 111.230 | 44.552 | 71.700 |
| 55 | 69.175 | 111.327 | 39.766 | 63.997 |
| 60 | 69.230 | 111.415 | 34.674 | 55.803 |
| 65 | 69.281 | 111.497 | 29.315 | 47.178 |
| 70 | 69.324 | 111.567 | 23.729 | 38.188 |
| 75 | 69.360 | 111.625 | 17.960 | 28.904 |
| 80 | 69.386 | 111.666 | 12.051 | 19.394 |
| 85 | 69.402 | 111.692 | 6.049 | 9.735 |
| 90 | 69.407 | 111.700 | 0.000 | 0.000 |

Source: From S. S. Gannett, "Geographic Tables and Formulas," *U.S. Geological Survey Bulletin* 650, 1916, pp. 36–37. Based on Clarke ellipsoid of 1866.

Lengths of degrees of latitude (1-degree arcs of a meridian) on the Clarke ellipsoid of 1866 are also given in Table 10.2. At the equator

$$1° \text{ of latitude} = 68.704 \text{ mi } (110.569 \text{ km}).$$

At lat. 89° to 90° N. or S.

$$1° \text{ of latitude} = 69.407 \text{ mi } (111.700 \text{ km}).$$

The difference between these two figures is about 0.7 mi (1.1 km), a large quantity to be reckoned with when precision is required in map making or when one's exact position must be located on the globe for navigation.

## Statute mile, nautical mile, and meter

For the purposes of marine and air navigation, as well as for many aspects of the earth sciences, the *nautical mile* is used as the unit of length or distance. Velocity of travel of aircraft and the speed of the upper-air currents are now given in terms of the *knot*, which is the mariner's traditional measure of speed, defined as 1 nautical mile per hour. For purposes of modern science, which demands extreme precision in its standards of measurement, the nautical mile can no longer be defined simply as the length of 1 minute of arc of the earth's equator, or some similar definition, because such a definition depends upon the ellipsoid dimensions selected.

In 1954 the U.S. Department of Defense adopted the *international nautical mile*, exactly equal to 1852 *international meters*,[3] or 6076.103333 . . . feet (the digit 3 repeats indefinitely). If the latter number is divided by 5280 (number of feet per statute mile), we obtain the equivalent:

$$1 \text{ international nautical mile} = 1.150777 \text{ statute miles.}$$

For the student of the earth sciences most rough calculations can be made using the value 1.15 statute mi (1.85 km) equals 1 nautical mile, or 1 statute mile equals 0.87 nautical mile.

Is there a particular latitude on the earth ellipsoid where 1 nautical mile is exactly equal to 1 minute of arc of a meridian? To answer this query, multiply the length of a nautical mile by 60, to obtain the length of a degree of arc:

$$1.150777 \times 60 = 69.04663 \text{ statute miles per degree.}$$

Next turn to Table 10.2 and examine the second column of figures. On the Clarke ellipsoid of 1866 the value for lat. 45°, 69.054, comes close to the calculated value,

[2] For a truly spherical earth the length of a unit of longitude would vary as the cosine of the latitude. The cosine formula may be used for rough approximations.

[3] The international meter is the absolute standard of length. Until 1960 the standard meter was represented by the distance between two microscopically thin lines engraved near the ends of a bar of platinum-iridium alloy carefully protected in a vault in Paris. To increase the standard of accuracy and to ensure absolute permanence, an international agreement was reached in 1960 to redefine the international meter as 1,650,763.73 wavelengths of the orange-red light given off by electrically excited krypton-86 gas at —210°C.

and from this observation we might conclude that the nautical mile is approximately equal to the length of a minute of latitude at the 45th parallels. Trying another approach, we can add the entire second column of figures in Table 10.2 and divide the sum by 19 to obtain the mean length of a degree, which comes out to 69.055. On an ellipsoid this average should agree with the value for lat. 45°, and it nearly does. Therefore we may say that the international nautical mile closely approximates the 1/5400 part of the length of a meridian between the equator and a pole.

## Gravity and the earth's figure

In the opening paragraphs of this chapter it was stated that the force of gravity, as measured by a pendulum clock, is roughly constant the world over and that this observation is proof of the earth's generally spherical form. If a sufficiently precise series of observations is made with a highly refined pendulum clock (such as Richer's clock), the differences in force of gravity reveal that the earth is an oblate ellipsoid, but that there are important, though minor, departures from the ellipsoidal form. The study of the earth's gravity is a major branch within the field of geophysics and has been intensively pursued by geophysicists the world over for many decades. *Gravimetry,* the precision measurement of the force of gravity, thus complements the precision triangulation surveys carried out by the geodesist in his attempts to measure the earth's curvature by surveying instruments.

Underlying all gravity studies is Newton's law of gravitation: Two bodies attract one another with a force directly proportional to the product of their masses and inversely proportional to the square of the distance between them. In the case of a pendulum or spring balance, variations in the earth's gravitational force per unit mass, or *gravity,* may vary because of differences in mass (quantity of matter) in the earth's crust directly below or beside the instrument, differences in distance to the earth's center of gravity, or differences in the centrifugal force of the earth's rotation. The last effect can be quite precisely calculated for any given latitude and is already included in the stated standard value of gravity.

Gravity is stated, not in terms of force (which depends upon the mass of the object being attracted by the earth), but in terms of *acceleration of gravity, g,* which is obtained by dividing the force of gravity by the mass upon which it acts. Acceleration of gravity, in terms of distance per unit time per unit time, describes the rate at which an object of any mass would increase its rate of fall at the earth's surface if dropped in a vacuum chamber where no air resistance would act upon it. From repeated experiments it can be shown that the acceleration of gravity is approximately 32 feet per second per second (about 980 centimeters per second per second).[4] The problem in establishing an absolutely precise standard value for the acceleration of gravity is to agree upon a point on the earth where precise experiments yield a refined value that can be accepted for the calibration of instruments and the computation of data the world over.

[4] Also given as 32 ft/sec$^2$ (about 980 cm/sec$^2$).

A world standard station for all gravity measurements was set up at Potsdam, Germany. There the value of 981.274 centimeters per second per second was determined for the acceleration of gravity by absolute pendulum methods.[5] The unit of gravity, known as the *gal* (named for Galileo), is equal to 1 cm/sec$^2$. Because gravity differences over the earth's surface are comparatively minute, the thousandth part of a gal, termed the *milligal,* is used as the unit for stating differences in gravity measurements. Observations on the absolute determination of gravity have been completed at Washington, D.C., and Teddington, England. At these and several other stations the acceleration of gravity is painstakingly measured by absolute pendulum methods. The resulting values are, however, slightly different from that obtained at Potsdam. For example, at Washington gravity is determined to be 980.083 cm/sec$^2$. Besides the standard stations there are hundreds of base stations where gravity is carefully computed for comparison with the Potsdam standard. A goal of geophysicists is to dot the entire globe with gravity stations so that the entire gravity field of the earth can be analyzed and the actual figure of the earth precisely determined.

## Measurement of gravity

Gravity may be measured with either the pendulum apparatus or the gravimeter. The pendulum apparatus is used at standard stations for absolute gravity measurements. Pendulums may also be used to make relative gravity measurements, that is, to observe differences in gravity from one point to another. In its simplest form a pendulum apparatus would be a single pendulum so constructed that its length remains constant. The period of the pendulum, that is, the number of swings per unit of time, depends only on its length and the acceleration of gravity. Therefore, if the length is held constant, differences in period from one place to another reflect differences in gravity. The reliability of a pendulum is particularly great because of its constant length.

Actually one pendulum is not enough in the gravity apparatus, because its motion disturbs the housing from which it is hung. To cancel out the effects of such disturbances, two pendulums may be swung simultaneously in opposite phase from one instrument housing. In Figure 10.6 is shown a modern apparatus consisting of two quartz pendulums hung on precise knife edges. Still another type was invented and used by the Dutch geophysicist F. A. Vening Meinesz. It consists of three pendulums so arranged that two of them would largely cancel out the disturbing effects of motions of the submarine which he used as his platform for taking gravity measurements at sea.

The *gravimeter* uses the spring balance as its basic mechanism (Figure 10.7). A weight is hung from a coiled spring, whose change in length is proportional to the change in acceleration of gravity. Slight changes in

[5] A more recent recomputation of Potsdam data gives 981.2663, but the older value has served as a standard for several decades.

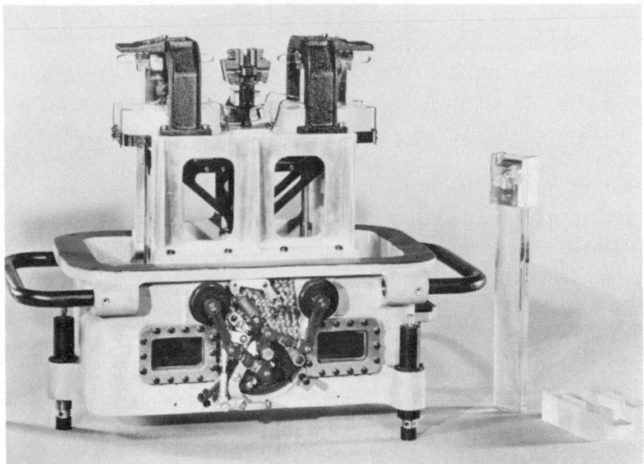

**FIGURE 10.6.** The Gulf gravity pendulum is shown here with top case removed. At right is a quartz pendulum and the Pyrex flat on which it rests. (Courtesy of Gulf Research & Development Company.)

spring length are amplified by a combination of mechanical, optical, and electrical means. The gravimeter must be calibrated against a series of base stations so that the differences in spring length can be interpreted as gravity values. An extremely sensitive spring gravimeter is illustrated in Figure 10.8.

## Correcting gravity readings

Suppose that we have calibrated a portable gravimeter at a series of base stations and have taken the instrument to a distant field location, perhaps in a mountainous region, where we have set it up and taken a reading of gravity. For what reasons might this gravity reading differ from that of the base station?

**FIGURE 10.7.** Simplified schematic diagram of a spring gravimeter. [After B. F. Howell, Jr. (1959), *Introduction to Geophysics,* New York, McGraw-Hill, p. 212, Figure 14.3.]

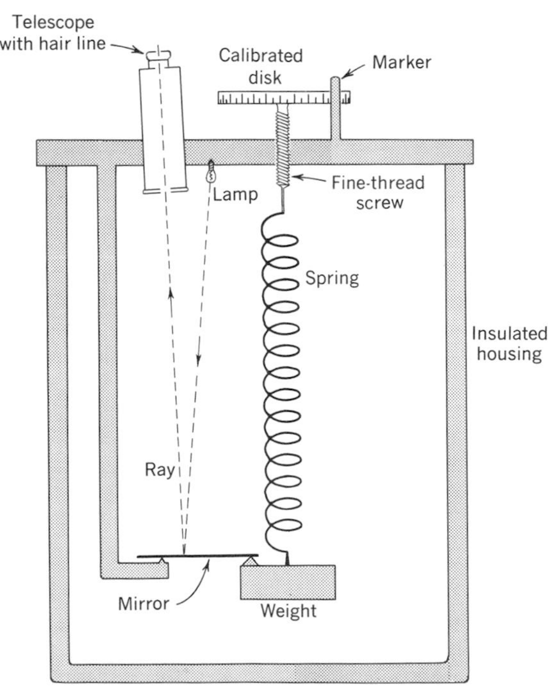


Suppose first that the earth were of perfectly spherical outline and that the various types of materials composing it were formed into concentric, uniformly thick, spherical shells, arranged in order of decreasing density from the center outward. Under such conditions, gravity would be the same at all surface points, provided only that we take into account the effect of centrifugal force of the earth's rotation varying with latitude. The question is then: In what ways can the conditions at our surface point of observation differ from such an ideal situation?

First, the earth approximates an oblate ellipsoid. Not only does this shape require a correction for the centrifugal-force distribution on the ellipsoid, but the greater mass lying nearer the equator must be taken into account. By use of the *international gravity formula of 1930* the expected normal gravity can be computed for any latitude. A value of 978.049 gals is assumed for the equator. The formula applies to the International ellipsoid (Hayford, 1909), for which the flattening ratio is exactly 1/297. Figure 10.9 shows diagrammatically how gravity increases poleward from the equator, taking only the earth's ellipsoidal shape and rotation into account. From this formula it follows that, where a gravity determination is being made at sea, an error in ship's position of 1 mile either north or south of the true location would result in an error of about 1 milligal in the corrected gravity reading. Until precise positioning methods based upon earth satellites became available, accurate positioning of a gravity station at sea was a problem considerably more difficult to solve than for fixed land stations on a well-surveyed continent.

Second, if our gravimeter has been taken to a higher elevation above sea level than that of the base station, it will register a lower value of gravity simply because it is farther from the earth's center. The correction of elevation, known as the *free-air correction,* can be obtained by solving a simple formula. As a rough approximation we can say that the value of gravity decreases about 1 milligal for 10 feet of ascent or about 1 milligal per 3 meters (Figure 10.10).

A third correction to be made on our gravity reading is required by the earth's gross surface configuration. Where a high mountain or high plateau exists, a large mass of rock lies above sea level. This mass exerts a gravitational pull of its own. Therefore gravity at the imaginary ellipsoid surface will be somewhat less on high continental masses than it would be on a plain, all other conditions being the same.

The correction for effects of masses lying above the ellipsoid surface or for deficiencies of mass below that level is termed the *Bouguer correction,* after Pierre Bouguer, a leader of the early eighteenth century geodetic expedition to Peru. The Bouguer correction for mass distribution with respect to the ellipsoid surface is made with the assumption that the rock material has uniform density throughout, and hence that one need calculate only the volume of material between the earth's solid surface and the ellipsoid of reference.

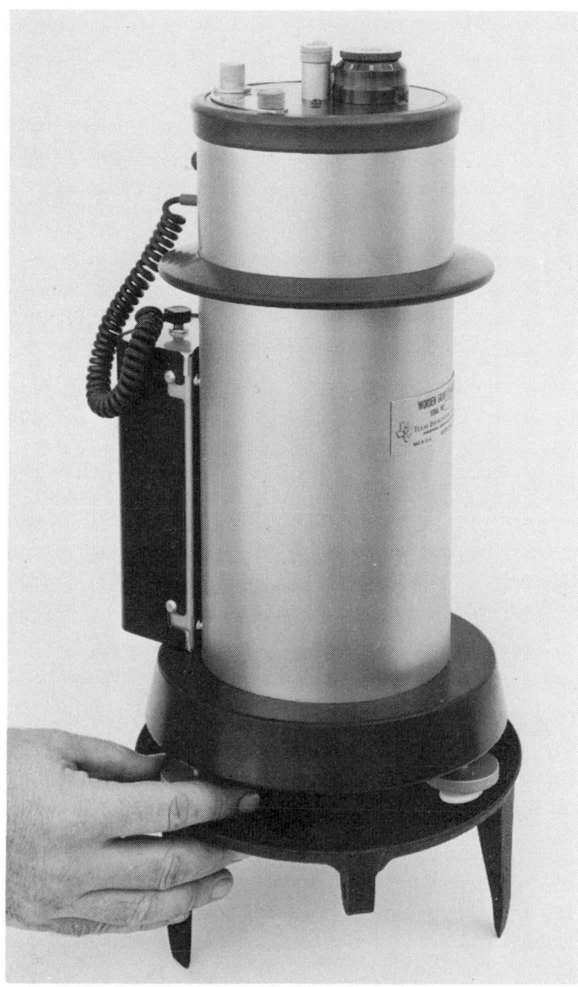

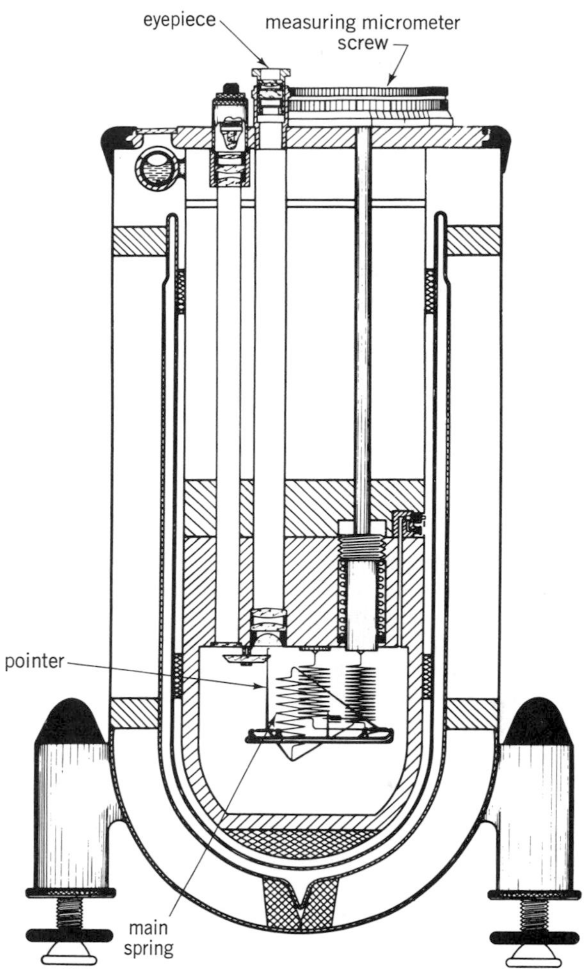


**FIGURE 10.8.** External view of the WORDEN gravimeter (left) and cross-sectional drawing of internal details (right). (Courtesy of Texas Instruments Incorporated.)

This assumption requires modification in view of geologic facts.

After applying the three classes of corrections thus far noted, plus a correction for the varying tidal pull of earth and sun, we may find that the observed value of gravity does not agree with the standard (Potsdam) value. A difference between observed and predicted gravity values is, in general, termed a *gravity anomaly.* When such an anomaly is found, a cause other than those already taken into account must be sought to explain the discrepancy.

The cause of such an anomaly, termed a *Bouguer anomaly,* lies in the different density of the great rock masses lying side by side in the earth's crust or mantle. In other words, the crustal or mantle rock under the station is actually denser or less dense than the average. In Chapter 25, dealing with the earth's crust, the meaning of such anomalies is discussed, with theories of crustal structure and crustal deformation that seem to explain the anomalies. Our concern in this chapter is with the earth's form, and it is to this subject that we now return.

## The geoid

If it were possible to crisscross all continents with a gridwork of sea-level canals, or better still, of sea-level tunnels, and somehow to do away with the fluctuations in sea level due to tides and winds, the sea water would everywhere come to rest to define a surface known as the *geoid.* In comparison with the ellipsoid of reference, which is a mathematically perfect but idealized surface of reference, the geoid would show broad undulations. In some places the geoid passes below the ellipsoid, elsewhere it rises above, but for the most part it is separated by not more than a few tens of feet at most from the best-fitting ellipsoid (Figure 10.11).

The reason for undulations existing in the geoid surface, as well as for its nonsymmetrical pattern over the globe, has already been explained in the discussion of the Bouguer correction of gravity readings and is illustrated in Figure 10.12. The reduced pull of gravity where excess crustal mass lies above the ellipsoid level causes a rise in the geoid surface, whereas over the

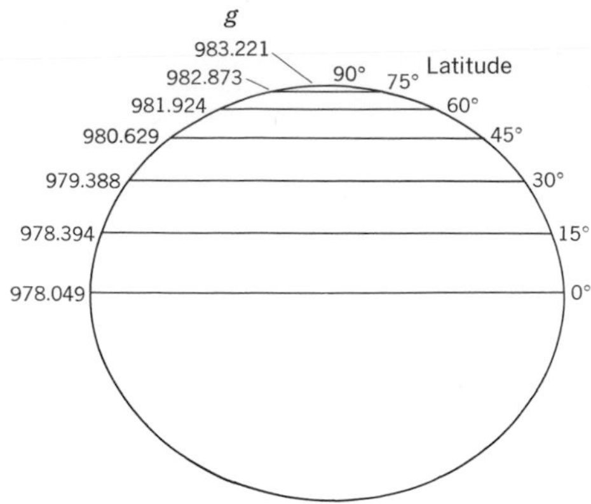


**FIGURE 10.9.** Values of normal sea-level gravity for a rotating oblate ellipsoidal earth of flattening 1/297.

oceans, where mass is displaced downward, the geoid surface is depressed below the ellipsoid. As explained in Chapter 25, not all mountain masses show a reduced gravity in proportion to the volume of rock present, and one could not predict the position of the geoid merely by looking at a relief map of the globe.

An important principle in geodesy concerns the effect of the geoid surface upon the attitude assumed by a plumb bob at rest at a given place on the earth's surface. If the earth were a true ellipsoid with uniformly distributed mass and a perfectly smooth surface configuration, the plumb bob, from which the astronomer and surveyor can tell the direction of the vertical,[6] would everywhere hang perpendicular (normal) to the ellipsoid surface (Figure 10.13). However, a plumb bob actually hangs perpendicular to the geoid surface, as shown in Figure 10.12, hence it will not be indicating the true perpendicular to the ellipsoid where the geoid is sloping with respect to the ellipsoid.

The irregularly undulating form of the geoid causes errors in calculating the earth's radius. As shown in Figure 10.11, plumb lines from points *A* and *B* would intersect at point *C*, giving a calculated earth radius longer than the true value. Plumb lines from *D* and *E* would intersect at point *F*, giving too small a value for the earth's radius.

[6] Surveying instruments, such as the transit, level, and theodolite, use a level bubble to determine the horizontal and vertical. Exactly the same problem applies to the level bubble as to the plumb bob, because both respond to the direction of pull of gravity at a given place. Similarly, the problem applies to a sextant used with reference to the sea surface.

**FIGURE 10.10.** Values of gravity with increasing elevation above the earth, based on sea-level value at equator.

| Elevation (ft) | Elevation (m) | g cm/sec$^2$ |
|---|---|---|
| 20,000 | 6100 | 976.169 |
| 15,000 | 4600 | 976.639 |
| 10,000 | 3000 | 977.108 |
| 5,000 | 1500 | 977.579 |
| Sea level 0 | 0 | 978.049 |

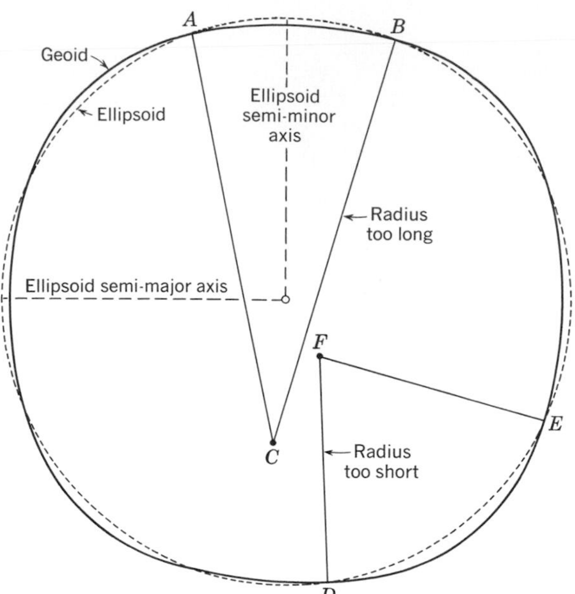


**FIGURE 10.11.** The irregular shape of the geoid can cause errors in calculating the earth's radius. [After W. A. Heiskanen and F. A. Vening Meinesz (1958), *The Earth and Its Gravity Field,* New York, McGraw-Hill, p. 239, Figure 8–9.]

Deflections of the plumb bob corresponding to undulations in the geoid surface give rise to difficulties in determining latitude. The astronomer, using the stars as measuring points, can compute the latitude of his position on earth by measuring the angles between stars and the vertical as indicated by a plumb line. Such a determination of latitude is called *astronomical latitude.* Whatever deflections happen to be affecting the plumb line become included as errors in the astronomical

**FIGURE 10.12.** Diagrammatic and highly exaggerated cross section showing the relation between ellipsoid and geoid under continents and over ocean basins. [After W. A. Heiskanen and F. A. Vening Meinesz (1958), *The Earth and Its Gravity Field,* New York, McGraw-Hill, p. 237, Figure 8–5.]

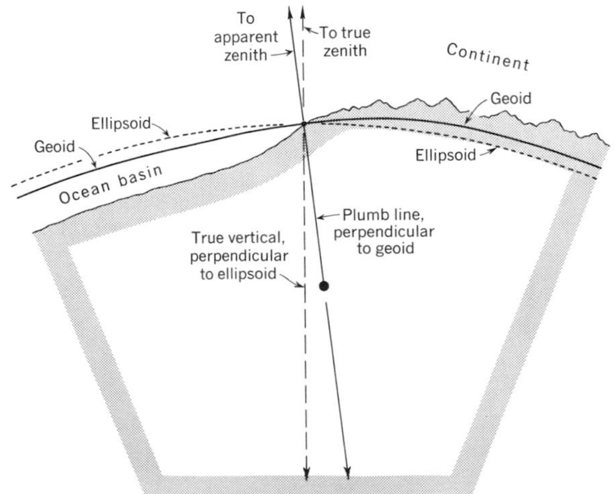

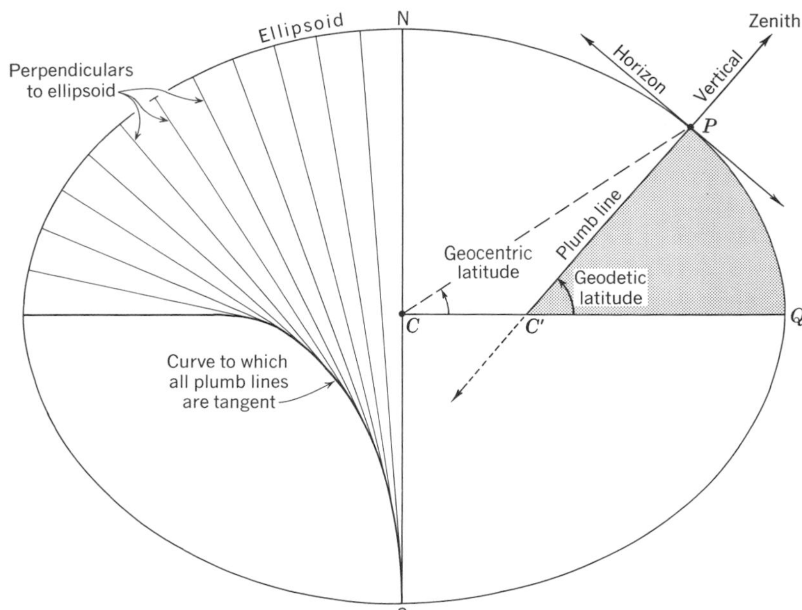


**FIGURE 10.13.** Plumb lines extended from the surface of the ellipsoid define geodetic latitude.

latitude. If the astronomical latitude is corrected for deviations of the plumb line so as to determine the vertical with respect to an ellipsoid, the corrected value becomes the *geodetic latitude,* which is equivalent to a meridian arc of the ellipsoid between the point and the ellipsoid's equator (arc *PQ* in Figure 10.13). Note that geodetic latitude is not the same as *geocentric latitude,* which is the angle between a line to the earth's center and the plane of the earth's equator (Figure 10.13). Geocentric and geodetic latitudes could be identical only on a truly spherical earth.

## Geoidal maps and profiles

An isopleth map (Appendix I) can be made to show the configuration of the geoid. Such a *geoidal map* of the world is shown in Figure 10.14. The isopleths are contour lines of the geoid at equal height in meters above or below the imaginary surface of the Modified Mercury Datum (MMD-68).

Notice that the geoid has negative values over much of North America. A prominent negative center, or depression, lies over Hudson Bay, and a well-defined doming over southern Alaska. The Pacific coastal belt of the United States shows a distinct depression. Figure 10.15 is a profile of the geoid drawn from north to south from North America, through Central and South America. This *geoidal profile* shows the vertical differences between geoid and ellipsoid, using a greatly exaggerated vertical scale. The profile is drawn with respect to the MMD-68 ellipsoid, which has a flattening of 1/298.3 (see Table 10.1).

The newly-adopted world datum, the Geodetic Reference ellipsoid of 1967, will replace the previously used North American datum (Clarke ellipsoid of 1866) and the European datum (International ellipsoid of 1909) with a single ellipsoid of reference. Figure 10.14 is therefore a partial map of the new world datum. Geoidal contours are lacking over vast areas of the continents, but bands of contours carry the surface entirely across Asia and South America.

## World-wide gravity research

The vital scientific importance of accurately determining the geoid for the entire globe is obvious when we consider that all determinations of vertical and horizontal lines (except in certain highly specialized determinations of latitude by astronomical methods) depend upon application of a precise correction to compensate for the effects of the geoid's irregularities. Moreover, all elevations with respect to mean sea level are actually based on the geoid surface. This is why the determination of gravity at many stations over the globe must be carried forward as rapidly as possible.

The theory that gravity measurements would permit the geoid to be calculated was suggested in the mid-nineteenth century by Sir George Stokes, an English physicist. In 1928 Dr. Vening Meinesz, mentioned earlier in this chapter as the inventor of the Vening Meinesz gravity pendulum, developed formulas necessary for calculation of the geoid from gravity data. Still more recently (1957), a new instrument, the *Graf sea gravimeter,* was found suitable for use on surface vessels at sea.

Great emphasis was placed upon increasing our fund of gravity data during the International Geophysical Year (1957–1958). Gravity stations were arranged along four meridional arcs: Alaska to Chile, Greenland to Argentina, Norway to South Africa, and Japan to Antarctica. By means of compound quartz pendulums, such as those shown in Figure 10.6, new standards for accuracy of gravity determinations were set up for use in an international gravity control system. Gravimeters were taken over the thick ice of Antarctica to assist in estimating ice thickness. Even floating ice masses, such as ice islands and ice floes (Chapter 17), were used as

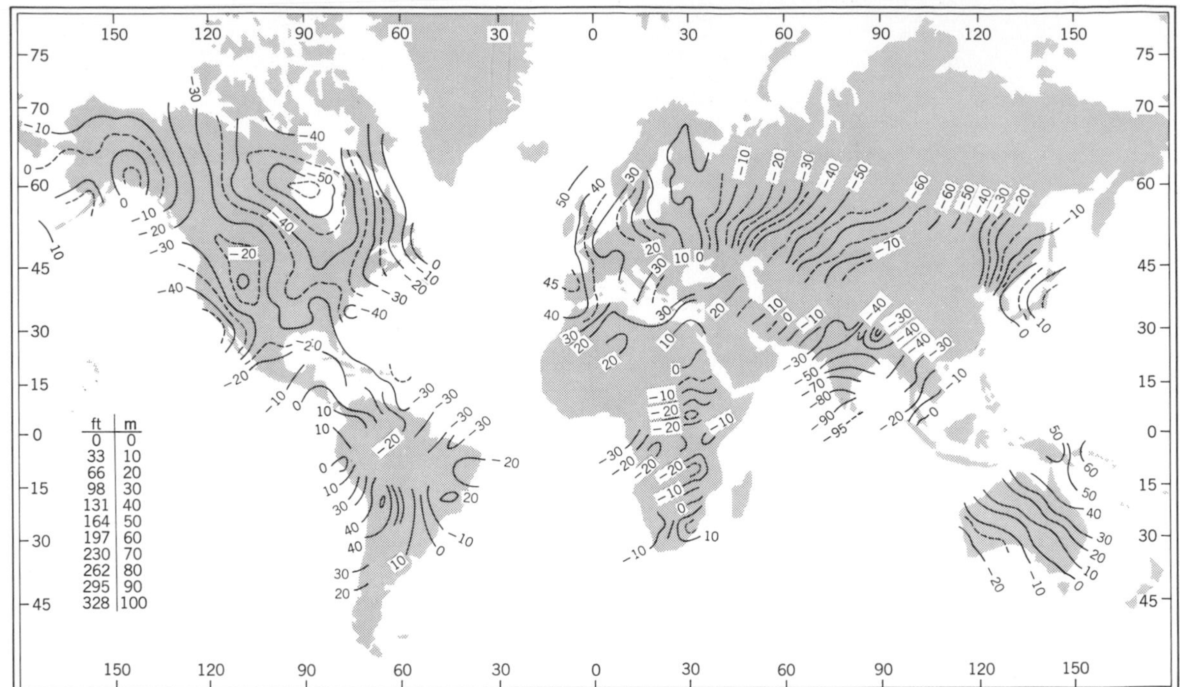


**FIGURE 10.14.** World geoidal map. Geoid contours in meters are drawn with respect to the Modified Mercury Datum (MMD 68). (After I. Fischer and others, Army Map Service, *Bulletin Géodésique,* No. 88, pp. 220–221, Figure 7a.)

platforms for gravity measurements over the Arctic Ocean basin.

A special project of the IGY gravity program was the detection and analysis of earth tides, which cause rhythmic fluctuations in the value of gravity. For this study gravimeters sensitive to gravity changes of one part per billion were used at 13 locations.

## Earth satellites and the earth's figure

Earth satellites provide a new means of detecting variations in gravity and hence in estimating the earth's oblateness and the shape of the geoid. The effect of the earth's oblateness upon a satellite (whose orbit is an ellipse with the earth's center of gravity occuping one focus) is to cause a progressive shifting of the satellite's orbit. The equatorial bulge exerts a torque on the satellite orbit, turning its plane in space, causing it to shift westward, and increasing the amount of the westward longitude displacement that the satellite normally experiences because of earth rotation each time it crosses the equator (Figure 10.16).

From the orbital shifts of U.S. satellites *Explorer I* and *Vanguard I* it was calculated that the earth's oblateness is about 1/298.4, as compared with 1/297 for the International ellipsoid. Further satellite observations quickly led to more accurate values of oblateness.

**FIGURE 10.15.** Geoidal profile from Hudson's Bay region southward through central America and along the western side of South America. (Same data source as Figure 10.14.)

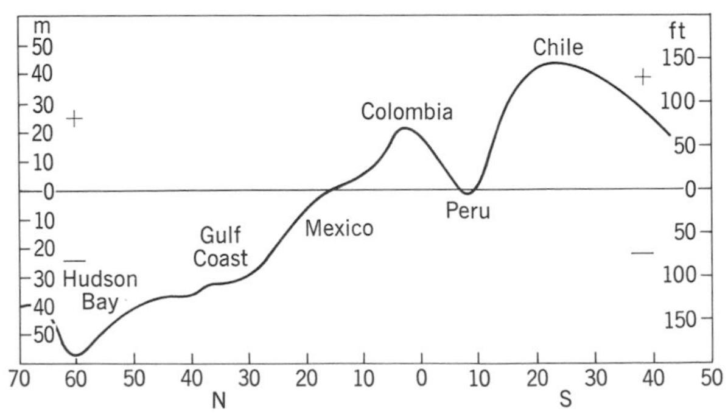


**FIGURE 10.16.** Westward orbital shift of an eastward-moving earth satellite because of the earth's equatorial bulge.

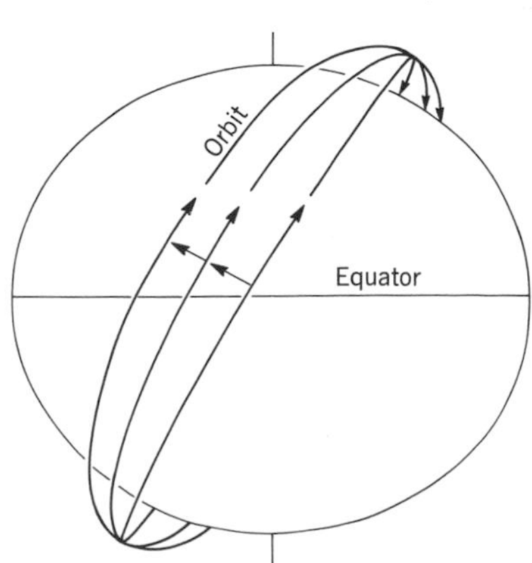

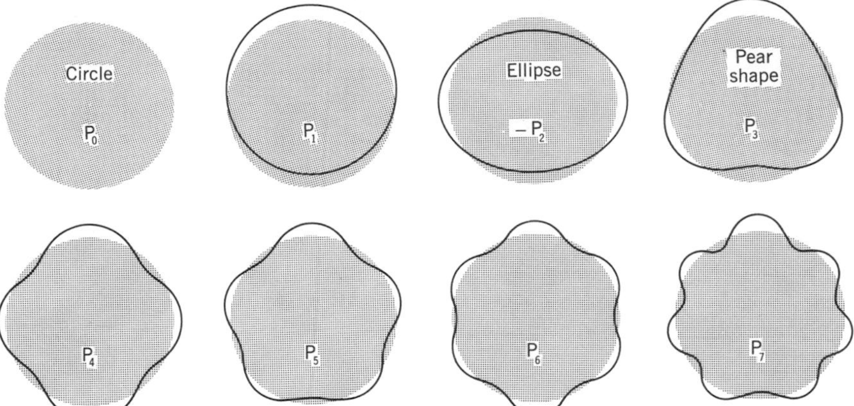


**FIGURE 10.17.** Outlines of the first through seventh harmonics. [After F. L. Whipple (1968), *Earth, Moon, and Planets,* 3rd ed., Cambridge, Mass., Harvard Univ. Press, p. 65, Figure 48.]

These were used, with other data, to establish values for the Astrogeodetic ellipsoid (Fischer, 1960) with a flattening of 1/298.3 (see Table 10.1). Since about 1964 the value of 1/298.25 ± .01 has been accepted as a refinement.

If the earth were of perfect ellipsoidal form and of uniform density throughout, the westward shift of a satellite orbit in space would take place in a perfectly uniform manner. Because the true figure of the earth is, instead, a geoid whose undulating surface reflects inequalities in the distribution of mass within the solid earth, it would be anticipated that the position and velocity of all components of motion of an orbiting satellite must vary about the uniform westward shift depending upon gravitational disturbances along the satellite's orbit. Information on the external gravity field is also gained from observing changes in altitude of the perigee point of the orbit as it shifts from one hemisphere to another. Here, then, is a method whereby the form of the geoid can be estimated from its effect on a satellite orbit quite independently of gravity measurements taken at the earth's surface. Moreover, the satellite method gives world-wide coverage, in contrast with the more fragmentary coverage seen in world maps based only on surface measurements.

Geodetic satellites provide data for two quite different purposes. One is the exact determination of geographical position of points on the earth's surface, a subject treated in Chapter 11 under the heading "Satellite geodesy." Satellites suited to such work are usually of the large balloon type, whose reflected light is photographed against a background of stars (see Figure 11.17). For purposes of measuring the earth's gravity field, much denser satellites—such as *Anna, Geos,* and *Transit*—are used because they are much less subject to disturbances from air drag and other causes than are the large balloon satellites. Orbits of these gravity-measurement satellites are determined with great precision through both optical and radio-tracking methods.

Consider, first, a schematic outline of the geoid as seen in a meridional (north-south) profile. This analysis assumes that any cross section of the geoid taken at right angles to the earth's axis is a true circle. We temporarily ignore all east-west undulations of the geoid for purposes of simplification.

Determination of the geoidal profile by satellite data makes use of the mathematical method of harmonic analysis, somewhat analogous to the harmonic analysis of tide curves (Chapter 9). Recall that in explaining a complex tide curve it is dissected into sine curves of various periods and amplitudes. These are superimposed in a particular combination of phases to produce a close approximation of the actual tide curve. Similarly, the profile of the geoid can be fitted by combining a series of mathematical equations which begins with a simple form and progresses to more elaborate forms. The *second harmonic* describes an ellipse, and is therefore a description of the earth ellipsoid (Figure 10.17).

The *third harmonic* describes a cross section which resembles a pear in outline. In three dimensions, the third harmonic produces a pear-shaped solid when fitted to the earth by placing one corner at the earth's North Pole and the opposing flattened portion over the

**FIGURE 10.18.** Average meridional geoidal profile based upon harmonics through the twenty-first. [After D. King-Hele (1967), *Scientific American,* vol. 217, p. 71.]

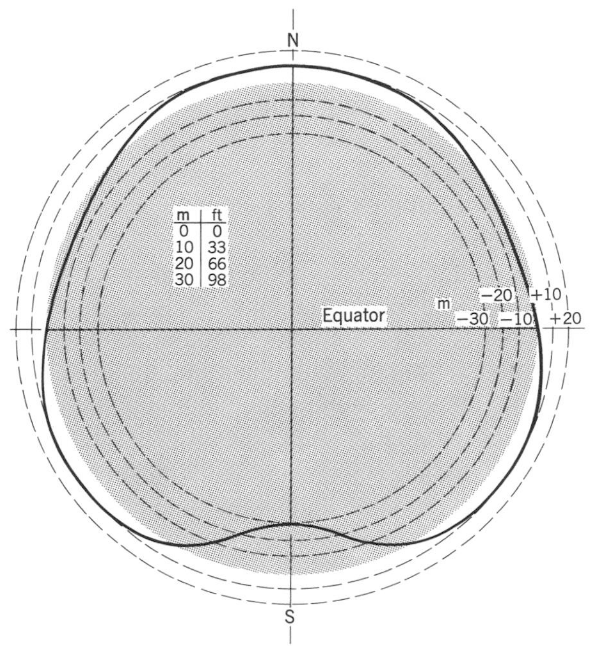

South Pole. In this orientation a bulge surrounds the earth in the Southern Hemisphere. The pear-shaped undulations of the third harmonic surface are extremely small values superimposed upon the ellipsoid of reference, or second harmonic. Whereas the ellipse has a polar diameter about 27 mi (43 km) shorter than the equatorial diameter, the bulges of the "pear" of the third harmonic figure rise above the ellipsoid by distances on the order of only 20 to 50 ft (6 to 15 m). Such distances are about on the same order of magnitude as the departures of the geoid from the ellipsoidal datum as shown on the world geoidal map, Figure 10.14. The third harmonic figure is thus just one of about 100 harmonic components of the geoid determined from satellite data and is the fifth largest.

The *fourth harmonic* produces a figure with four rounded corners (Figure 10.17); the *fifth harmonic* describes a figure with five undulations, and so forth. As each harmonic is added, the geoidal form is slightly modified. By proper selection of the numerical constants for each harmonic, as derived from satellite data, a synthetic geoidal profile can be produced that approximates the geoidal profile of the earth.

Figure 10.18 shows the meridional profile of the geoid generated by the use of harmonics. The reference circle labeled as zero represents the ellipsoid of reference. The flattening is so slight (1/298.25) that the ellipse has actually been drawn as a circle. Additional concentric circles represent intervals of 10 m (33 ft) of elevation above and below the ellipsoid. Obviously, the elevation scale is enormously exaggerated and the illustration should be treated as a circular graph. The heavy line represents the geoidal profile, so adjusted that it has zero elevation at the earth's equator. The pear-shape shows up well as a bulge about 10 m (33 ft) high centered over the North Pole and a bulge of about equal height surrounding the Southern Hemisphere in middle latitudes. Over the South Pole is a flattened area falling to about 30 m (100 ft) below the ellipsoid. Although this area appears as a concavity on the exaggerated diagram, the geoidal surface is everywhere outwardly convex. Surrounding the Northern Hemisphere at low latitude is a flattened belt passing below the reference surface.

We turn next to longitudinal differences in configuration of the geoidal surface as revealed by variations in

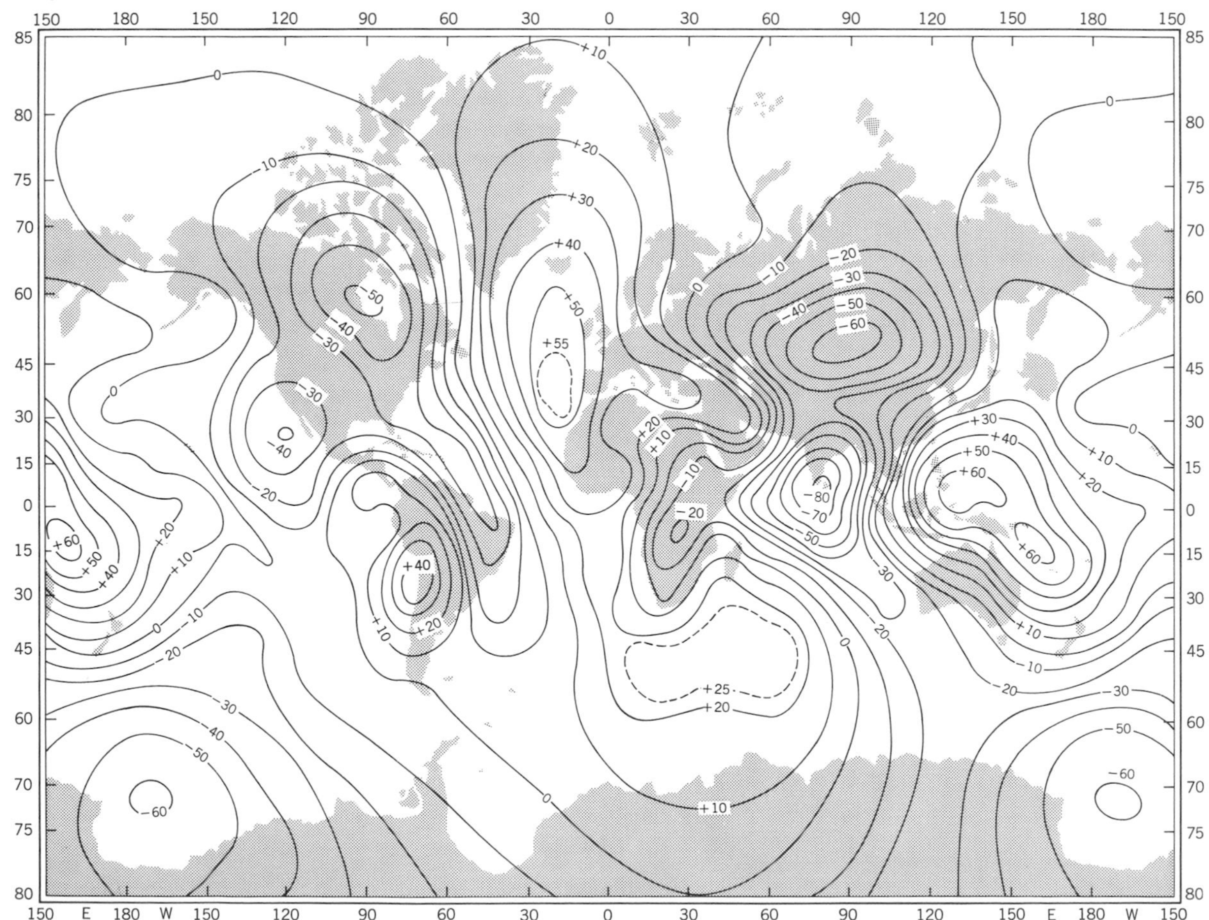


**FIGURE 10.19.** World map of geoidal heights based upon a combination of satellite data and terrestrial gravimetry. The reference ellipsoid used here is the Modified Mercury Datum, Fischer, 1968. [After I. Fischer, U.S. Army Topographic Command (1969), Washington, D.C., Pan Am. Inst. of Geog. and Hist.]

the orbit of a satellite. As explained in Chapter 2, the earth's rotation causes the earth-track of a satellite to drift westward around the earth's surface. With each pass over a given parallel of latitude, the satellite is affected by a different value of gravity because of undulations in the geoid. Using methods of extreme precision of timing and astronomical positioning or the Doppler effect, very slight variations in satellite velocity and position can be detected as the earth longitude of its orbit is changed. Combining satellite data with gravity measurements made at the earth's surface, a world geoid map such as that shown in Figure 10.19 can be constructed. This map, which uses harmonics through the thirteenth, is more generalized than the world geoidal map based only on surface gravity measurements (Figure 10.14).

The generalized geoid of Figure 10.19 has four major positive centers in which the geoid rises above the ellipsoid, and four negative centers in which it falls below the ellipsoid. Positive centers lie over the eastern North Atlantic, New Guinea, western South America, and the Southern Ocean between Africa and Antarctica. The vertical departure from the ellipsoid is particularly large in the European and New Guinean centers: 55 to 60 m (180 to 200 ft). Negative centers lie over the Indian Ocean, North America, the antarctic region, and central Asia. The Indian Ocean center is particularly low (−80 m, −260 ft). We should be aware that a number of such geoidal maps, differing in details, have been published, but reasonably good agreement in the locations and magnitudes of the positive and negative centers has been found since 1965. Hence the centers described above are now generally accepted as real phenomena.

For scientists who investigate solid-earth structure, the large-scale undulations of the geoid depicted in Figure 10.19 arouse great interest. These undulations represent areas of excess mass or of mass deficiency deep within the earth's mantle. The problem is to explain how such mass differences have originated and how they are maintained. (The structure of the earth's interior is discussed in Chapter 23.) Thus we see that determination of the geoid is not only extremely important for all kinds of astronomical observations that use the plumb line as a reference, but also for geological interpretations concerning the structure of the earth and the processes that operate within it.

## References for further study

Heiskanen, W. A., and F. A. Vening Meinesz (1958), *The Earth and Its Gravity Field,* New York, McGraw-Hill, 470 pp.

Howell, B. F., Jr. (1959), *Introduction to Geophysics,* New York, McGraw-Hill, 399 pp., chaps. 12, 14.

Jacobs, J. A., R. D. Russell, and J. T. Wilson (1959), *Physics and Geology,* New York, McGraw-Hill, 424 pp., chap. 4.

Dobrin, M. B. (1960), *Introduction to Geophysical Prospecting,* New York, McGraw-Hill, 446 pp., chaps. 8, 9, 10, 11.

Garland, G. D. (1965), *The Earth's Shape and Gravity,* Oxford, Pergamon, 183 pp., chaps. 1–4.

# 11

# Position, elevation, and direction on the earth's surface

IN MANY BRANCHES of the earth sciences it is essential that the location of points on the earth's surface be determined with great accuracy so that the distribution of various physical properties can be described. In this chapter we consider first *horizontal control,* that is, the determination of the relations among points on the earth's surface as to distances and directions of separation, measured on the surface of some ideal earth figure. As explained in Chapter 10 this ideal figure is an ellipsoid of revolution, obtained by rotating an ellipse about its minor axis.

Second, we consider *vertical control,* the determination of the vertical distances separating points by reference to some ideal surface of reference, such as sea level or the geoid. The establishment of both horizontal and vertical control on a continental and world-wide basis is a major concern of geodesy, a branch of the earth sciences which, as we have already seen, also includes the determination of the earth's figure.

The data of the earth sciences frequently take the form of lines on the earth's surface. A line may represent the path of travel of particles in a fluid, such as winds or ocean currents; it may represent a force acting in a particular direction; it may represent the discontinuity between two substances of unlike properties, such as a weather front separating unlike air masses or the line of contact between two rock bodies of contrasting types. In general the term *azimuth* refers to the orientation of a horizontal line, or the horizontal projection of a sloping line, upon the earth's surface or, more specifically, upon the ideal surface of an ellipsoid.

## Relative and absolute location

If someone drives a stake into the ground and asks us to describe its location in precise terms, we can answer in two ways. First, the direction and distance between the point in question and one or more other selected points of reference nearby can be measured, constituting the *relative* location of the point. All systems of instrumental surveying on the ground involve determinations of relative location that may be carried out without reference to any world-wide system of location. Second, where a single point on the earth's surface has been chosen as the one point with respect to which all other points are described, the position of the stake in question can be described according to a system of *absolute* location. We have already seen that the intersection of the equator and the meridian passing through the Royal Observatory of Greenwich, England, has been accepted almost universally as the single point of absolute location and that the prime meridian of Greenwich and the equator fix the entire geographic grid of meridians and parallels lying upon an imaginary ellipsoid of reference whose dimensions have been agreed upon.

To the geodesist the precise determination of latitude and longitude of a point is referred to simply as the determination of *geographic position.* Two methods of determining geographic position are *astronomical* and *geodetic.* In the first of these methods an approximate determination of absolute location is made by means of the stars. In the second, direct ground surveys are made, using an arbitrary reference point (which can be given absolute location by some system of datum fixing) with respect to which the relative locations of other points are given.

## Astronomical determination of geographic position

The determination of the latitude and longitude of a point makes use of *geodetic astronomy,* a specialized form of astronomy carrying to a high degree of precision essentially the same kinds of celestial observations used by marine and air navigators to determine their geographic positions.

Astronomical determination of latitude makes use of the principle that the arc of celestial meridian lying between the zenith point of a place and the celestial equator is equal to the terrestrial latitude of the point of observation (Figure 11.1), or, in other words, latitude equals declination plus zenith distance (zenith distances of stars north of the zenith and declinations of stars south of the equator are considered negative). Now, if we can observe a star, *R,* at the instant of its crossing the meridian and if we measure the arc *RZ* between the star and the zenith (the same as angle *RPZ*) and add to this arc the declination of the star (arc *QR*), we shall know the whole arc *QZ,* which is equal to the latitude of point *P* on the earth. The declinations of the principal stars are, of course, accurately known, and the data are available in tables, such as those found in the various almanacs. If the star lies north of the zenith, as for example point *T* in Figure 11.1, the arc *ZT* is subtracted from the star's declination. If the star lies south of the celestial equator, as at point *U,* the star's declination is subtracted from the arc *UZ.*

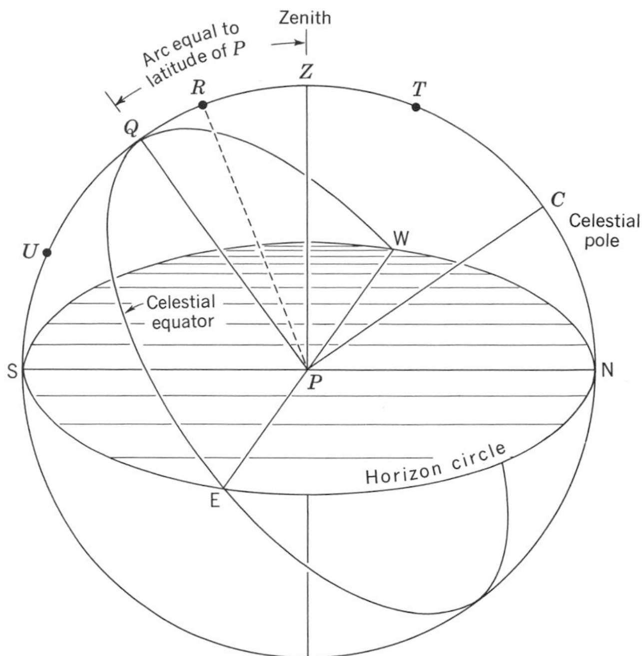


**FIGURE 11.1.** Astronomical latitude is obtained from measurements of the positions of stars as they cross the meridian.

The problems involved in accurate determination of astronomical latitude are largely instrumental. One of the simpler, older instruments is the ***zenith telescope.*** This is simply a telescope fitted with a delicate level bubble and a filar micrometer[1] for measuring the difference in zenith distances of a north and a south star having nearly the same zenith distance. From this measurement the latitude can be computed. A portable instrument used for the same observations and also for the determination of longitude is the *broken-telescope transit* (Figure 11.2).

We have already become familiar in Chapter 10 with a theoretical problem arising from the use of the level bubble or plumb bob as a means of determining the zenith, namely, that these devices tell us the horizontal and vertical with respect to the geoid surface so as to yield what is termed the *astronomical latitude.* The true geographic latitude, which is also termed the *geodetic latitude,* must contain a correction for the deflection of the plumb line resulting from the geoid surface's being irregularly warped and not coinciding with the ellipsoid surface.

Astronomical determination of longitude has been largely explained in Chapter 3, in the discussion of timing the earth's rotation. Using the transit instrument or meridian circle and a chronograph, we can determine the exact instant of a star's meridian passage. To determine the longitude of the observing station, we need determine only the Greenwich time of the transit of the

[1] A filar micrometer is a device for precision measurement of extremely small angles; it has a fine wire stretched across the field of view of a movable eyepiece.

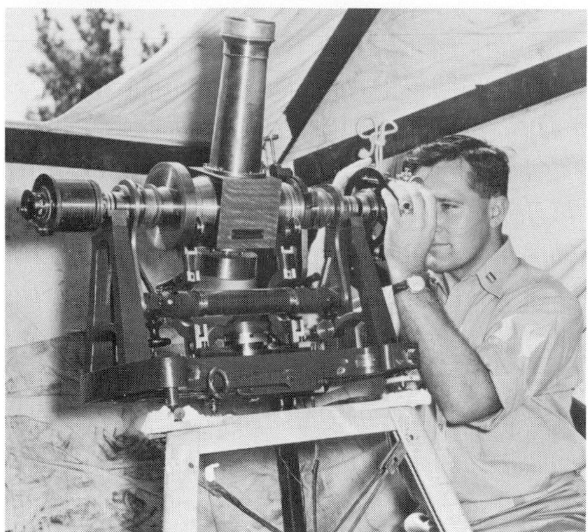

**FIGURE 11.2.** The broken-telescope transit in use at a field location to determine longitude. (ESSA Coast and Geodetic Survey photograph.)

star over the local meridian. The difference in time between the star's meridian passage at our observing station and its meridian passage at Greenwich is converted into the difference in longitude of the two stations by using the knowledge that the earth rotates at a rate of 15° for each hour of sidereal time.

In practice, radio time signals are used, following mean solar time, which is easily converted to determine longitude differences. For example, the time signals of station WWV, Beltsville, Maryland, will supply the exact time as determined by clocks at the U.S. Naval Observatory in Washington, D.C. The chronograph of the field station will automatically record these signals on the same sheet of paper on which the meridian passage of the star is recorded. It is then a simple matter to calculate the longitude difference between the field station and the standard time meridian to which the time signals apply.

By means of the most refined equipment the astronomical latitude and longitude of a point can be determined to within an error of about 20 to 30 ft (6 to 10 m). Just how close to the true geodetic latitude and longitude the results will fall depends upon the accuracy of the correction made for the inclination of the geoid surface with respect to the ellipsoid. Because the plumb line may, in certain places, be deflected as much as 1 minute of arc from the true vertical and because 1 minute of arc represents about a nautical mile (1.15 statute mi, 1.84 km), it is obvious that the local deviations of the plumb line are a possible source of vastly greater errors in position than those arising from instrumental errors.

An interesting example of the errors of geographic location due to failure to correct for the deflection of the plumb line is seen in certain of our state boundaries surveyed by means of uncorrected astronomical determinations of latitude and longitude. These surveys were carried out at an early date and attempted to locate the state boundary along a certain geodetic parallel or meridian, as specified by law. Because of unknown deflections of the plumb line, errors of position as much as 0.5 mi (0.8 km) from the correct location on the ellipsoid of reference resulted. Because the deflections would vary from place to place, the surveyed boundary also deviated back and forth to give a zigzag line. Once marked by surveyor's monuments, the boundary line is fixed for all time, but, when plotted correctly on a map, it clearly shows the errors with respect to the meridian or parallel it was intended to follow. Some boundaries are defined as astronomic meridians or parallels. In these cases it is correct to indicate the boundary by a smooth line.

## Wobble of the poles

A precise study of latitude and longitude reveals a very slight shifting, termed the *wobble,* of the position of the earth's axis. This motion is not a change in the orientation of the earth's axis in space, as are precession and nutation (Chapter 2), but rather represents a movement in the orientation of the earth itself so that the axis of rotation pierces the surface at different places. The rotational north and south poles are therefore not fixed on the earth's surface, but move continuously. The astronomically determined latitude and longitude change correspondingly.

The latitude of a place determined by a single observation of a single star is usually accurate only within 0.1 second of arc. However, by observing several stars at each station and combining the observations of up to 39 stations, astronomers are able to locate the position of the rotational pole with reasonable confidence. The mean position of the rotation pole is available from 1900, as determined by the International Latitude Service. This organization is now called the International Polar Motion Service. Since 1957 a second organization, the Bureau International de l'Heure (International Time Service) has been making independent pole position determinations.

Analysis of the pole position data reveals that the path of the rotation pole on the surface of the earth is irregular, but roughly circular, with an approximate diameter of not more than 0.6–0.7 second of arc, which corresponds to a distance of 60 to 70 ft (18 to 21 m) (Figure 11.3). Thus the wandering of the rotation pole is confined to an area of about the size of the infield of a baseball diamond. The polar path takes a counterclockwise direction, but the rate of movement in the path is not uniform.

The wobble has an annual component and the Chandler component. The annual wobble has been attributed to seasonal changes in the distribution of masses in the atmosphere. The Chandler wobble has a period of 14 months. If the earth were a rigid body the period of the wobble would be 10 months. The lengthening of the wobble by four months is due to elastic yielding of the earth. Geophysicists have good reason to believe that the Chandler wobble is subject to damping (to being suppressed) and would cease if it is not regularly or sporadically excited. The nature of the mechanism that can produce the Chandler wobble has been the subject of much discussion and speculation by those who study earth rotation.

In 1968 two geophysicists, L. Mansinha and D. E. Smylie, announced that a linkage has been found between major earthquakes and abrupt changes in the

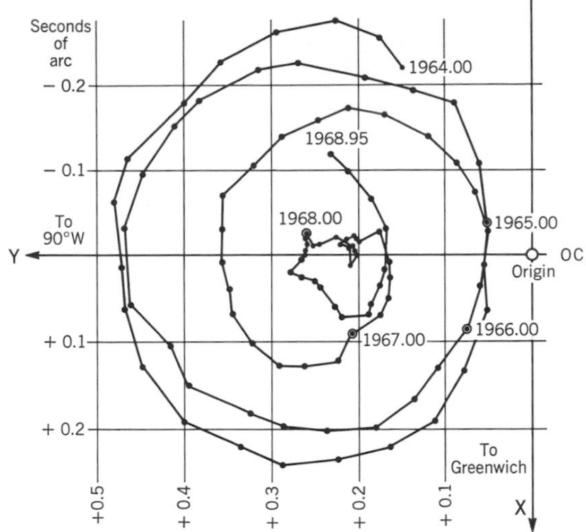


**FIGURE 11.3.** Wobble of the pole is shown by this plot of pole positions at 1/20-year intervals. The point labeled *origin* is an arbitrary zero point for the field of rectangular coordinates (Conventional International Origin). Each 1/10 second of arc is equal to a distance of about 10 ft. (3 m). (Data from *1968 Annual Report,* Bureau International de l'Heure.)

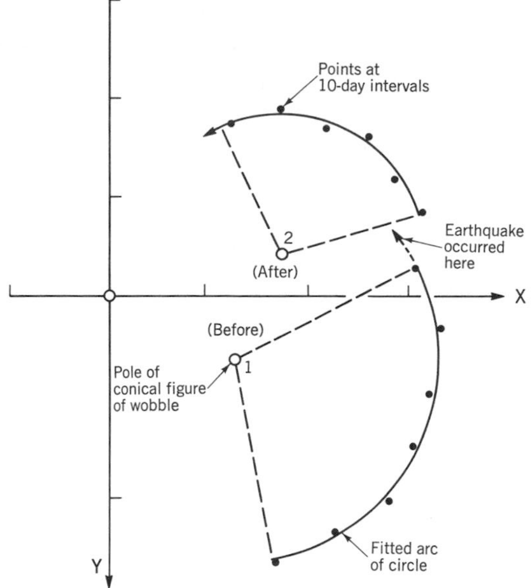


**FIGURE 11.4.** According to one hypothesis, the pole path shifts abruptly to a new arc following a large earthquake. [After L. Mansinha and D. E. Smylie (1968), *Science,* vol. 161 p. 1129.]

position of the rotation axis. They proposed that large earthquakes provide the mechanism for sustaining the Chandler motion. As explained in Chapter 22, earthquakes are generated by sudden displacements of large masses of the earth's outer zone. Displacements of mass due to earthquakes are now thought to extend over distances of thousands of miles and thus constitute major redistributions of mass over the earth.

Careful analysis of the plotted pole positions show that there are abrupt changes in the curvature of the lines fitted to the points (Figure 11.4). The data are first adjusted to remove the annual component, leaving only the Chandler component. An arc of the circle is then fitted to a portion of the curve; each arc has a center representing an axis about which Chandler wobble is occurring. Abupt change to an arc of different radius and center has been found to coincide in time with the occurrence of a major earthquake. Of 22 major earthquakes occurring in the period 1957 to 1968, an abrupt change in the wobble axis coincided with the time of occurrence of 15 quakes, while a definite effect was noted for the remaining 7. This evidence is considered as strong support for earthquakes as a primary cause of Chandler motion.

It should be pointed out that certain astronomers familiar with problems of earth rotation and polar wobble do not interpret the data as correlating with earthquakes. Perhaps the data of future years will provide the basis for a decision as to whether a cause-and-effect relationship actually exists between pole path changes and earthquakes.

## Geodetic determination of geographic position

Geodetic methods for determining geographic position consist of direct surveys on the ground, beginning at a starting point whose geodetic latitude and longitude are known, or assumed. The starting point may serve as one end of a *base line,* which is simply the straight line connecting the starting point with a second point (Figure 11.5). Length of base line is measured directly on the ground with great precison. The azimuth of the base line or some other line must be measured with respect to the north-south line of a meridian. The ends of the base line subsequently serve as two apices of a triangle, the third apex of which is an unknown point. All three angles of the triangle are measured. Distances from each end of the base line to the third point are calculated by trigonometry.

The general procedure whereby systems of horizontal triangles are surveyed and the distances of their legs calculated on the basis of a single direct base-line measurement is known as *triangulation.* A major benefit of triangulation is that the differences in longitude and latitude between the original station and any other station on the triangulation system can be determined

**FIGURE 11.5.** Principle of a triangulation survey. (© 1960, John Wiley & Sons, New York.)

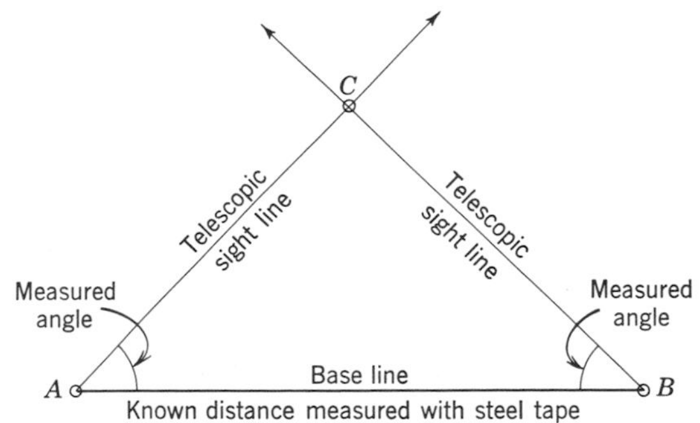

without being seriously affected by the deflections of the plumb line owing to irregularities of the geoid. Consequently the magnitude of the deflections of the vertical can be ascertained by triangulation, and the form of the geoid can thereby be mapped. From the scientific standpoint the determination of oblateness of the earth (Chapter 10) and the deflections of the plumb line from the vertical are perhaps the most important purposes of geodetic surveys.

Equally important, but in an applied sense, is the use of triangulation in locating with great precision the key points needed in many forms of mapping and surveying operations. Any surveying party, beginning the work of mapping in a new area, uses the established triangulation stations as the basis for surveying less accurate systems of triangulation adequate for locating the features of the terrain.

**FIGURE 11.6.** Base-line measurement along a railroad track. The nearer of the two kneeling men is matching the zero mark of the tape to a mark on the rail. (ESSA Coast and Geodetic Survey photograph.)

## Base lines

Measurement of the base line is a key operation in setting up any triangulation system, for upon the accuracy of the determination of the length of the base line depend all subsequent calculations of distances. From the earliest development of triangulation surveys until near the close of the nineteenth century, base lines were measured by means of a set of *bars,* which were simply metal rods, perhaps 5 m (16 ft) each in length, which were laid end to end successively along the base line. To overcome the serious problem of change of length of bar resulting from temperature change, bars were devised that consisted of two strips of unlike metals fastened together at one end. Such bars acted as bimetallic thermometers and enabled their temperatures to be calculated precisely and hence their true length to be ascertained. Although the bars were extremely accurate, their use was very slow and gave way early in the twentieth century to the use of long wires or tapes made of *invar,* an alloy of nickel and steel which has an extremely small proportion of length change accompanying a temperature change.

In establishing a base line, a site is selected which will give several miles of clear ground, as nearly level as possible, such as a railroad line or highway right of way. First, a series of stakes is laid out at 50-m (164-ft) intervals along the survey line and a strip of soft metal, such as copper, fastened to the top of each stake so that precise marks can be made on the stake. An intermediate support is usually used at the mid-point between the stakes supporting the ends of the tape. This support is held on line and on grade with the ends of the tape. The invar tape is then stretched to span the distance between stakes, and the position of the end of the tape is marked on the metal strip of the forward stake. The tape is then moved forward to the next stake and a new mark made. The tape must be stretched with exactly the right tension, as determined by a spring balance (Figure 11.6), and the temperature of the tape taken at two points by attached thermometers so that length corrections can be made. If the ends of the tape are not at exactly the same elevation, a correction for slope is made on the basis of previous determinations of the elevation differences. According to the practice of the U.S. Coast and Geodetic Survey, three tapes are used in base-line measurement in such a way that their measurements can be compared and any errors due to changes in tape length can be caught. The tapes are checked for accuracy both before and after use in the laboratories of the U.S. National Bureau of Standards.

When invar tapes are used in the manner described above, the length of a base line several miles long can be measured with a probable error of about one part in 2 million. The actual error is always less than one part in 300,000, which means that a line 5 miles long will be measured with certainty to within 1 inch of its true length and probably to within ⅙ inch. Such precision of base-line measurement is referred to as being of the *first order.*

With unlimited time and the finest equipment much higher accuracy can be obtained with invar tapes. An example is the measurement of distance between Mount Wilson and San Antonio Peak, California, carried out in 1924 by the U.S. Coast and Geodetic Survey in order that Professor A. A. Michelson could conduct his experiments to determine the velocity of light. The base line for this survey was located near Pasadena. Eight tapes were used, and each section of the base line was measured four times; the probable error was estimated to be one part in 11,600,000. The base line of just over 40 km (25 mi) was thus measured to within 3.45 mm (about ⅛ in.).

## Electronic distance-measuring devices

Within the past two decades the measurement of base lines has been revolutionized by the perfection of entirely different principles of distance measurement, included under the general category of electronic distance-measuring devices. These devices are based upon the transmission of either high-frequency radio waves or light waves along a straight-line path between a transmitting-receiving instrument located at one end of the line and a reflector at the other.

Distance measurement by use of light rays was invented in 1923 by a Finnish physicist and put into practice by the Finnish Geodetic Institute. The instrument uses the principle of the interference of light. During the 1950s, base lines had been measured in several countries by the light-interference method, with accuracies ranging from one part in 9 million to as high as one part in 20 million.

Another device using light rays for precision distance measurement is the *Geodimeter,*[2] which measures the time required for light to travel to a reflecting target and to return to a receiver (Figure 11.7). The light is modulated in intensity by an electronic system and is reflected back to a light-sensitive tube, where it sets up an electric current. The device is normally used at night and is effective with first-order accuracy up to distances of 3 to 25 mi (5 to 40 km), depending upon conditions of atmospheric visibility. The Geodimeter has been used by the U.S. Coast and Geodetic Survey for measuring first-order base lines during the last several years, and by 1960 that organization had used the instrument in the measurement of 84 geodetic lines.

A precision instrument for distance measurement by means of radio waves was introduced in 1957 under the name of *Microdistancer* equipment, used in connection with the *Tellurometer*[3] system of distance measurement. A radio transmitter sends a beam of radio waves of a wave length of about 10 cm (4 in.) to a receiver, from which the waves are retransmitted back to the original transmitting point. The Tellurometer system can be used in daylight and offers certain advantages for ease of field use where large areas must be covered with minimum expenditures of effort. The ultimate precision of the Geodimeter system of distance measurement over that of the Tellurometer system is, roughly, by a factor of 3.

Also of interest in geodetic surveying are *Hiran* (High Precision Shoran) and its predecessor, *Shoran* (Short Range Navigation), which are distance-measuring systems using radar techniques developed in the years following World War II. These systems have three components: a moving station (which may be carried in a plane, ship, or truck) and two fixed but portable ground stations. The moving unit includes a radio transmitter, a receiver, and a device to determine the time of travel of a radio pulse from transmitter to ground station and a response from the ground station. Use of two ground stations permits the distance between them to be computed. Although not giving the same accuracy as the Geodimeter and Tellurometer systems in first-order base-line measurement, the Hiran equipment is capable of a high degree of precision in the measurement of very long lines—about 75 to 500 mi (120 to 800 km)—in connection with trilateration. An interesting use of Hiran in geodetic work was to measure the distance from the island of Crete to North Africa in order to complete the meridian arc from Finland to South Africa. Although meridian arcs had been completed in Europe and Africa, it remained for Hiran to span the Mediterranean Sea.

Yet another principle—that of the laser beam—has been adapted to the problem of base-line measurement. In the late 1960s a helium-neon laser was developed for use in a distance measuring instrument named the *Geodolite,*[4] which can operate in daylight at distances up to 40 mi (65 km) with an accuracy of one part in one million. The laser beam emitted by the instrument is directed by telescope to a reflecting target and returns through a receiving telescope. Distance is calculated by comparing the phase of the modulated outgoing beam with that of the returning beam. Accuracy of distance measurement with the Geodolite is limited by the accuracy of measurement of wavelength of the orange spectral line of krypton-86, which is on the order of one part in one million.

[2] Product of the Geodimeter Co., Division of Berg, Hedstrom & Co. Inc., New York, N.Y.
[3] Product of Tellurometer Limited, Cape Town, South Africa.

**FIGURE 11.7.** Distance measurements being made at night with the Geodimeter. (ESSA Coast and Geodetic Survey photograph.)

## Triangulation

Triangulation requires the measurement of horizontal angles by means of a *theodolite,* a telescopic instrument that can be rotated on a horizontal base so as to be sighted first upon one point and then upon another. The horizontal arc is read on a finely graduated scale by means of small microscopes (Figure 11.8). Each angle is read many times and the average computed.

The theodolite is placed precisely over a *triangulation station,* a point marked in a bronze disk set for

[4] Product of Spectra-Physics Corporation, Mountainview, California.

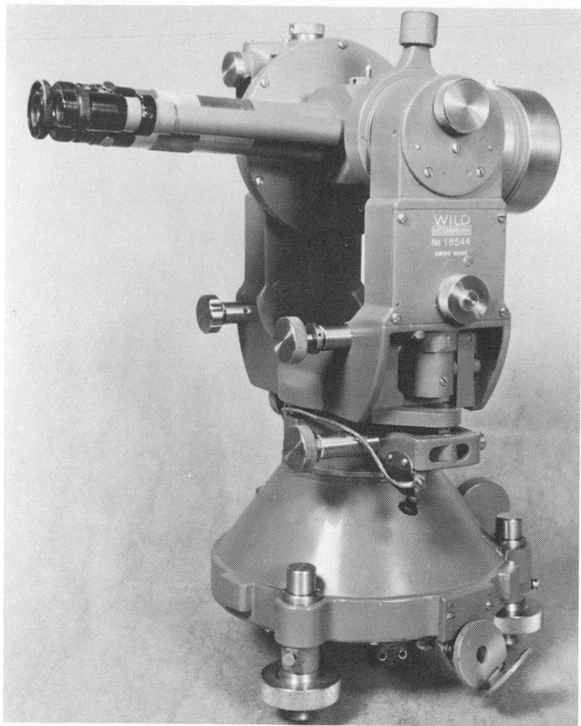


**FIGURE 11.8.** The Wild theodolite is used in triangulation surveys for precision measurements of horizontal arcs. (ESSA Coast and Geodetic Survey photograph.)

permanence in bedrock or on a concrete post deeply embedded in the ground (Figure 11.9). Where the terrain is rugged, triangulation stations are located on prominent peaks or ridge crests, to provide a clear view to other stations many miles away. In flat country a *triangulation tower* is used (Figure 11.10). It actually consists of two separate towers, an inner one on which the theodolite is mounted, and an outer one supporting the observing platform.

In triangulation observations the theodolite is sighted upon a light mounted over the distant station. Sightings are usually made at night; this procedure enables distances up to several tens of miles to be used and takes advantage of the fact that at night the air is less affected by turbulent motions that make accurate pointings on daytime signals either difficult or impossible.

**FIGURE 11.9.** A metal triangulation marker of the type used today. (ESSA Coast and Geodetic Survey photograph.)

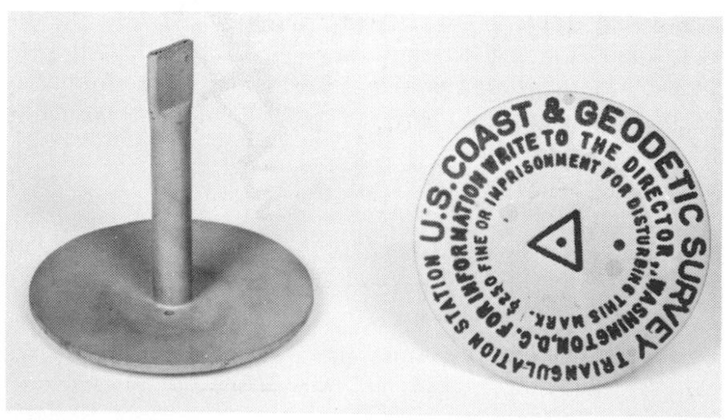

**FIGURE 11.10.** This steel triangulation tower is 90 ft (27 m) high. (ESSA Coast and Geodetic Survey photograph.)

In triangulation of first-order accuracy the sum of the three angles of a surveyed triangle must approach the ideal value of 180° plus the spherical excess to within 1 second of arc.

Triangulation may proceed from the base line by the formation of a *quadrilateral* (Figure 11.11), using two points, *C* and *D*, which lie along a line roughly parallel with the base line, *AB*. The quadrilateral thus consists of four triangles, each of which can be separately described. The opposite side of the quadrilateral, line *CD*, can now be used as a computed base line for erecting a second quadrilateral, to which a third can be added, and so forth. The result is a zone, or band, of triangulation stations directed cross country, and the bands in turn intersect to form a network (Figure 11.12).

Systems of quadrilaterals are particularly useful in large continental areas, such as the United States, and

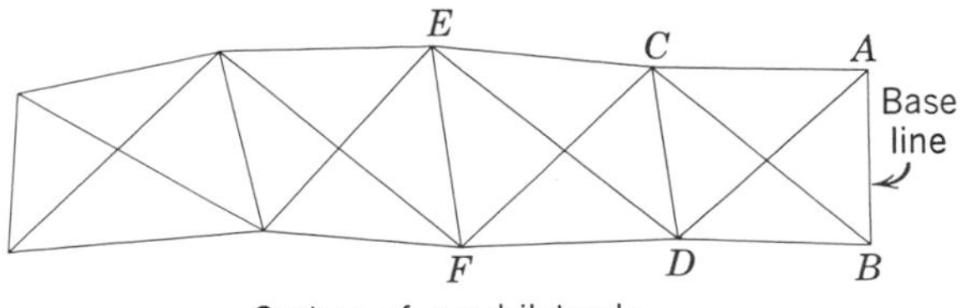


**FIGURE 11.11.** A system of quadrilaterals is built from a measured base line, *AB*. (© 1960, John Wiley & Sons, New York.)

are usually run along east-west and north-south lines to form a great gridwork of meridian and parallel arcs (Figure 11.13). In the western United States, which has a particularly striking pattern of 16 original triangulation loops, the *closing errors* were in all cases less than one part in 150,000. In the outermost circuit or perimeter of the 16 loops, a total distance of 5300 mi (8500 km), the error of closing was only 33 ft (10 m), or one part in 848,000.

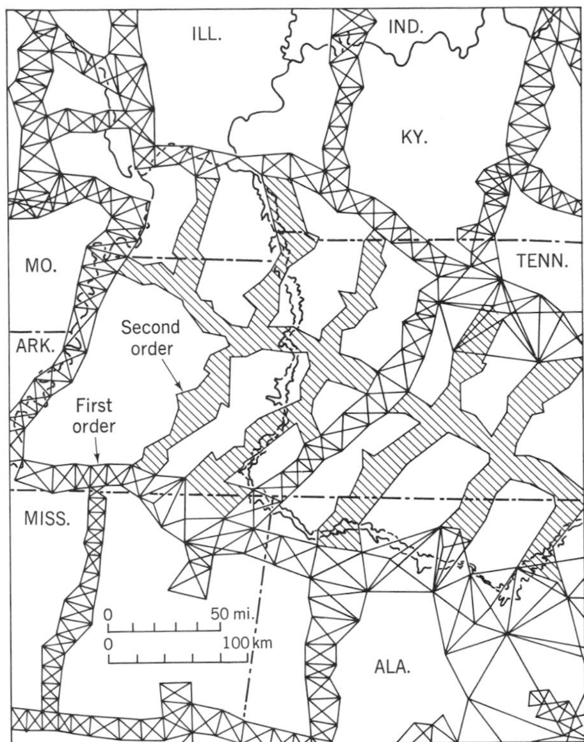


**FIGURE 11.12.** A triangulation network of quadrilaterals in the Tennessee Valley region. (Data from Tennessee Valley Authority; © 1960, John Wiley & Sons, New York.)

## Bearings and azimuths

The plotting of directions on a map and the statement of the direction of a line as observed in field investigations are frequently required in the earth sciences. Almost invariably, direction is stated in terms of the angle, in degrees, between the given line and a north-south line. This may be done by two systems of notations: (1) *compass quadrant bearings* and (2) *azimuths, or full-circle bearings.*

In many forms of mapping and land surveys, as well as geologic mapping, the compass quadrant system is used. Here the circle is divided into four quadrants of 90° each. The direction of any line is measured with respect to either north or south, whichever forms the smaller (acute) angle. For example, in Figure 11.14*A* the arrow pointing roughly northeast has a bearing of N. 49° E. that pointing about west-southwest has a bearing of S. 70° W. This system is not well suited to the needs of science because a given numeral between 0° and 90° is repeated for four different directions; moreover, the combination of letters and numerals is inconvenient and the addition and subtraction of bearings is confusing.

The azimuth system,[5] used generally in the sciences

[5] In navigation the word "bearing" is synonymous with "azimuth." The student should ascertain for himself which system is intended and should not rely upon the usages given here.

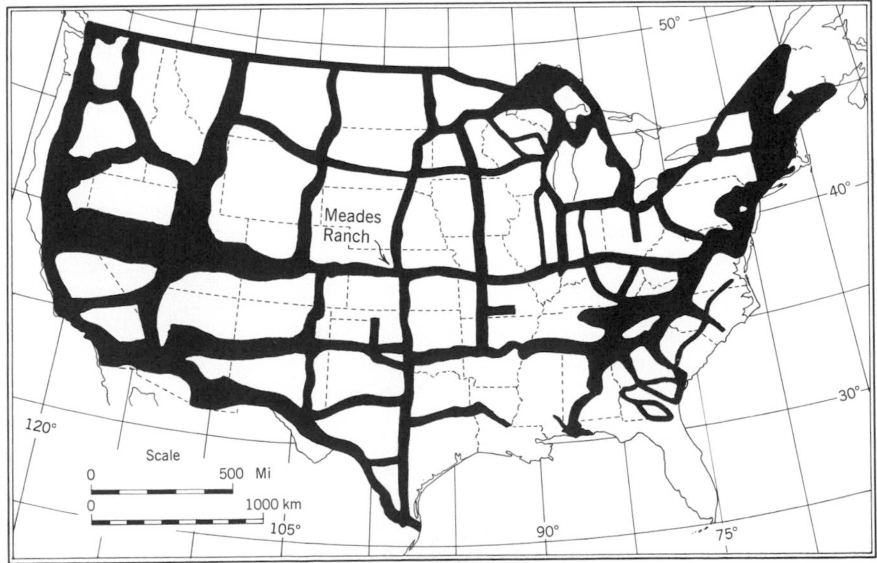


**FIGURE 11.13.** The black bands on this map show the extent of first-order triangulation in the United States in 1929, shortly after the North American datum of 1927 had been established. (Data by C. V. Hodgson, National Research Council, 1931; © 1960, John Wiley & Sons, New York.)

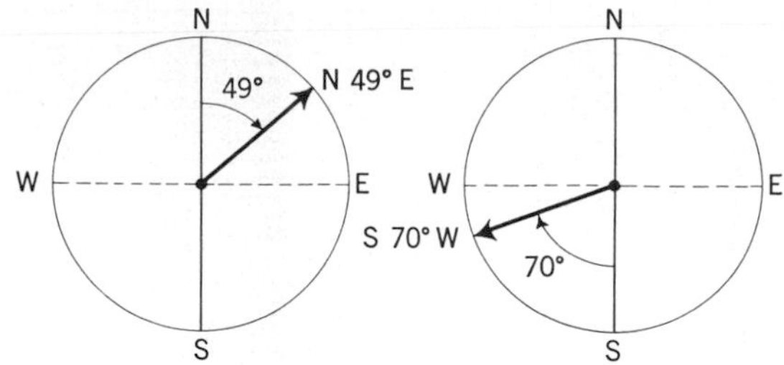


*A.* Compass quadrant bearings

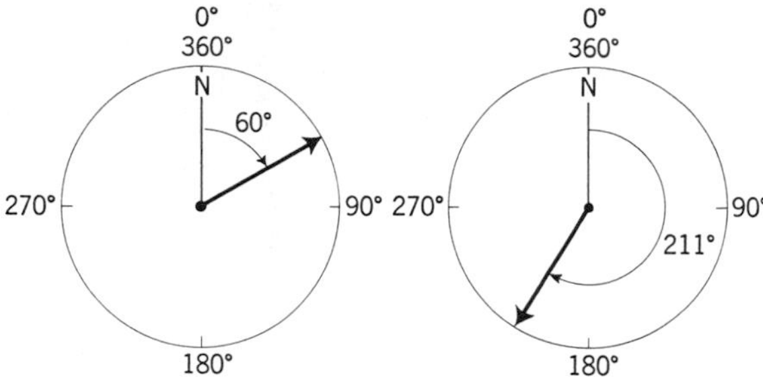


*B.* Azimuths

**FIGURE 11.14.** Either bearings or azimuths may be used to designate directions. (© 1960, John Wiley & Sons, New York.)

as well as for navigation and military purposes, numbers the degrees clockwise from 0° at the north point through a full circle of 360° (Figure 11.14*B*). Here no letters are needed and no numbers are repeated, and the addition and subtraction of azimuths are relatively simple. In the United States geodetic azimuths are reckoned from the south instead of from the north—i.e., 0° is to the south, 90° to the west, 180° to the north, and 270° to the east.

Although *geographic north,* the direction followed by a geographic meridian on the ellipsoid of reference, normally provides the reference line for measurement of bearings and azimuths, any other convenient or useful reference line, such as *grid north* (the meridional lines of a rectangular map grid) or *magnetic north* (the direction in which a magnetic compass points), may be used.

The azimuth of a line on a map should not be measured directly by means of a protractor laid upon the line at the intersection of a meridian unless the map is based upon a map projection of the *conformal* type. Examples are the *stereographic* and *Mercator* projections, described in Appendix I. Even then, in cases of small-scale maps or very long lines, this method is not accurate, since the geodetic line projects as a curve in most cases. These projections should be used wherever the shapes and orientations of lines and shapes or areal bodies must be truthfully shown. The equatorial Mercator projection, in particular, has the unique property that any straight line, regardless of its orientation on the map, represents a line of constant geographic azimuth (rhumb line) on the earth's surface.

It is important in triangulation surveys that the geodetic azimuth of the base line and of a number of triangle legs at intervals throughout the network be ascertained with great precision, both to give correct orientation of the network at the outset and to ensure that the arc of triangulation does not curve to the right or left as it is carried across country.

Determination of azimuth, of a type known as a *Laplace azimuth,* is done astronomically at a given triangulation station by measuring the horizontal angle between the north star, Polaris, and the triangulation station lying at the other end of the base line or triangle leg. Corrections must, of course, be made for the position of Polaris with respect to the true celestial north pole and for the deflection of the vertical. Laplace azimuths are determined at intervals of about six to eight quadrilaterals along the arc of triangulation. In the United States the average spacing is about 150 mi (240 km).

## Adjustment of triangulation

Triangulation arcs, such as those shown in Figure 11.13, were begun at coastal points, where precise determinations of geodetic latitude and longitude provided the initial data for computing the latitudes and longitudes of all other triangulation stations. When the mapping of any vast continental area, such as the United States, is in its early stages, there will inevitably exist for some time many detached triangulation systems, each based on one or more stations at which astronomical latitudes and longitudes have been determined. When several such systems join it becomes necessary to eliminate gaps, overlaps, or offsets existing between each two separate systems. Eventually all such discrepancies are eliminated by choosing a single point in the country as the initial reference point, or *datum*, and referring all other stations to that point.

The datum for the United States is based on a triangulation station named *Meades Ranch,* located in central Kansas. This point was selected because it lies near the geographic center of the 48 contiguous United States and is common to two great arcs of triangulation extending across the nation—one along the 39th parallel of latitude, the other along the 98th meridian (Figure 11.13). For the Meades Ranch triangulation station a latitude and longitude were computed in such a way as to minimize the differences between the astronomical latitudes and longitudes and the triangulation latitudes and longitudes. This computed value turned out to be very close to the value obtained by basing the position on the datum used in New England. The latter value was adopted, thereby saving the labor of recomputing, or *adjusting,* all triangulation data for the northeastern part of the United States.

After the standard datum had been adopted for the United States, the triangulation system was connected with the systems in Canada and Mexico. Those countries then adopted the datum based on the single initial point, Meades Ranch, so that the geographic positions of all three countries are based on a common datum, known as the North American datum of 1927, which is referred to the Clarke ellipsoid of 1866 (see Chapter 10).

All horizontal distances determined by base-line measurement and by triangulation must be reduced to

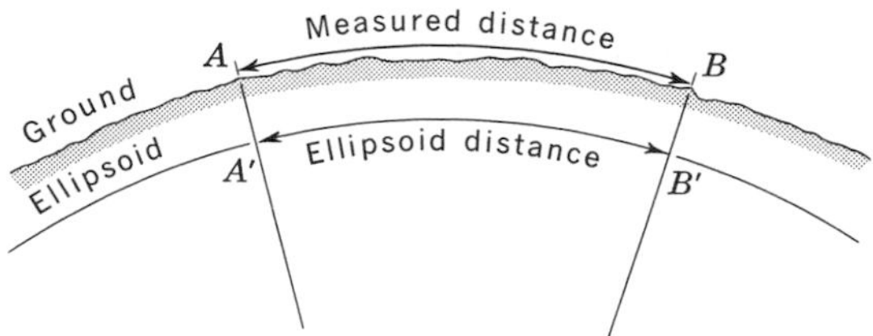


**FIGURE 11.15.** Measured distances must be reduced to distances on the ellipsoid of reference.

distances along the surface of the ellipsoid of reference. As shown in Figure 11.15, the measured distance between *A* and *B* will be greater than the equivalent distance *A'B'* between verticals along the surface of the ellipsoid. The appropriate correction is commonly referred to as "reduction to sea level," but strictly speaking the sea-level surface is that of the geoid, and it may lie well above or below the ellipsoid of reference. It is therefore important that a well-fitting ellipsoid be selected, a matter discussed in Chapter 10. In the case of the North American datum of 1927 the use of the Clarke ellipsoid of 1866 as the reference ellipsoid results in differences of only a few meters between geoid and ellipsoid over much of the central and eastern United States, so that reduction to sea level is close to being correct. The discrepancy between geoid and ellipsoid is, however, serious in the far western part of the United States and in Canada and Alaska.

## Triangulation by orbiting satellite[6]

Orbiting satellites, such as the pioneering balloon-type satellites Echo 1 and Echo 2, offer an opportunity to perform geodetic triangulation in three-dimensional space over much longer distances and more accurately than the traditional methods of geodetic surveying. Such satellites are designated "passive" because, like the earth's moon, they merely reflect the Sun's light. A fixed camera photographs the passage of the satellite against the star background, which accurately determines the instantaneous direction of the satellite at any instant of the passage, using precision time measurement. Two such directions, at the same instant, from two cameras photographing the same event from two different station locations on the earth, fix a plane containing the two stations for each corresponding satellite image and the intersection of these planes yields the direction of the line in space joining the two stations. Proceeding in this manner from station to station, the geometric shape of a network of triangles, the lengths of whose sides are on the order of the satellite height, can be established. The scale of this network is fixed by measuring the length of at least one of the legs. The accuracy obtainable at present, in a net covering the entire globe, is 1 part in a million.

The U.S. National Geodetic Satellite Program of worldwide triangulation is supported by cooperative

[6] Assistance in preparing this section on triangulation by orbiting satellite was given by Dr. Hellmut H. Schmid, Director, Geodetic Research and Development Laboratory, Coast and Geodetic Survey, ESSA.

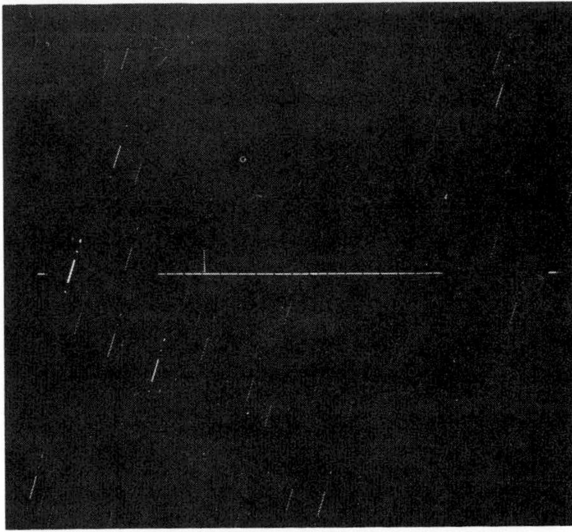

**FIGURE 11.16.** This photographic trace of geodetic satellite *Pageos I* shows as a horizontal line against a background of stars, which, like the satellite, move during the exposure period. The short light dash at left is a one-second exposure. After a lapse of 14 seconds, a 32-second exposure leaves a continuous trail of dashes. The 14-second lapse and a final one-second exposure complete the observation. (Smithsonian Astrophysical Observatory photograph.)

work of the Coast and Geodetic Survey, ESSA (Department of Commerce), and the Corps of Engineers (Department of Defense). Orbiting satellites have been launched by NASA to meet the surveying requirements. In 1966 a specialized geodetic satellite, *Pageos I,* was launched into a polar orbit approximately 2600 mi (4200 km) in height. Its shiny aluminum surface reflects sunlight brilliantly and is readily photographed (Figure 11.16). The earth track of this satellite, in shifting westward around the globe, allows triangulation to be done from all groups of observing stations.

Figure 11.17 illustrates the concept of the world net of triangles set up for satellite triangulation. In addition, a denser continental net, composed of smaller triangles, covers North America. The program is international in scope and involves teams from several countries. Figure 11.18 shows the status of satellite surveying operations as of May 1968. Triangles span all of the earth's land masses. For the first time, triangulation has been completed between stations in North America, Europe, and Greenland. Positions of isolated islands of the vast oceans have now been determined with precision.

## Determination of elevations

An accurate knowledge of *elevation,* the vertical distance of a point above or below a datum of reference, such as sea level or the geoid, is essential in many branches of the earth sciences. To prepare topographic maps of the earth's surface, elevations must be known at closely spaced points over the ground. We must know elevation to correct the value of gravity and to

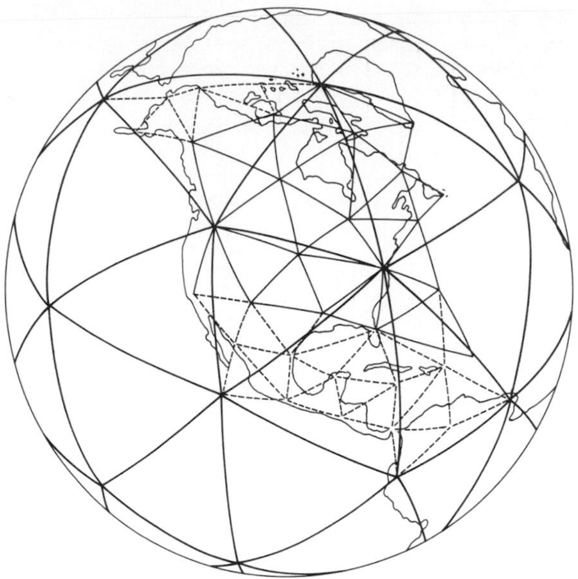


**FIGURE 11.17.** World satellite triangulation net (large triangles) and North American densification net (small triangles). Dotted lines show planned future work. (Courtesy of H. H. Schmid, ESSA Coast and Geodetic Survey.)

correct a barometer so as to give standard-pressure readings. Gradients upon which water flows, above or below the ground, can be determined only when elevations are known.

The instrument used for determining differences in elevation from one ground point to another is known as the *spirit level,* or simply the *level.* It consists of a telescope upon whose axis a sensitive level bubble (spirit level) is attached. The bubble is simply a small air-filled cavity in the fluid sealed inside a slightly curved tube. The tube is mounted with the bend convex upward (Figure 11.19). Under the influence of gravity the center of the bubble comes to rest at the highest point possible in the tube, thereby carrying out essentially the same function as a plumb bob does in indicating the vertical direction. If the radius of curvature of the tube is made very large, the bubble with be extremely sensitive to minor amounts of tilting. The operator simply adjusts the tilt of the telescope tube with a micrometer screw until the bubble is exactly centered with respect to marks on the glass tube. If the instrument is in perfect adjustment, the sight line will then be a true horizontal line, tangent to the surface of the geoid at that place. A newer instrument, the *automatic level,* does not contain a spirit bubble but sets up its own horizontal line of sight through a freely swinging compensator after it is brought to rest by centering a circular bubble.

To measure the difference in elevation between two points, *A* and *B* (Figure 11.20), the level instrument is set up midway between them and the telescope tube carefully leveled. A scaled rod, called the *level rod,* is held vertically on point *A.* The instrument man sights the rod and reads the height at which a cross hair in the telescope field falls upon the graduations of the rod. This height, $h_1$, is added to the elevation of *A* (if such information is known) or simply recorded as the height of instrument above *A.* The telescope is then swung about and sighted upon the same level rod (or a second rod), which has now been moved to *B.* Again the rod reading, $h_2$, is taken, but this time it is subtracted from the height of the instrument, giving the height difference between *A* and *B.* The above procedure is known as *differential leveling.*

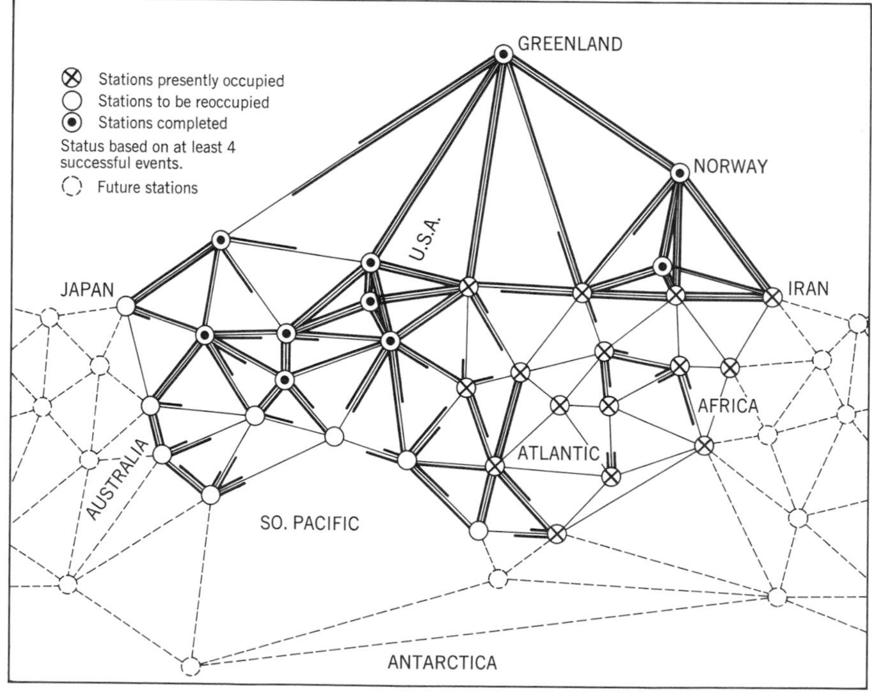


**FIGURE 11.18.** Status of field operations as of May 1968 in worldwide satellite triangulation. Lengths of heavy bars are proportional to numbers of successful missions. One complete bar represents four or more missions. (Courtesy of H. H. Schmid, ESSA Coast and Geodetic Survey.)

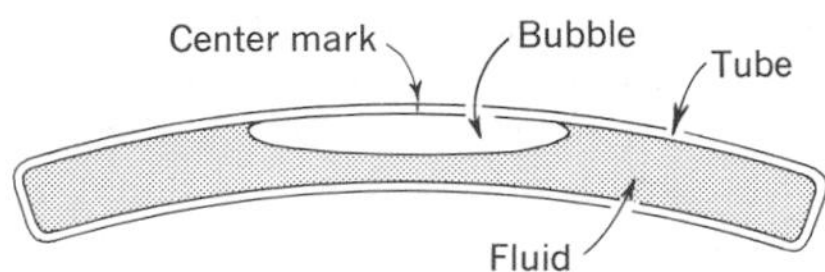


**FIGURE 11.19.** A level bubble.

It is rare that any level instrument gives a true horizontal sight line when the level bubble is centered, hence the sight line actually slants up (as in Figure 11.20) or down to some small degree. By equalizing the distances of the two sight lines, this error is canceled and the effects of curvature and refraction will substantially balance. Normally, for general leveling purposes the line of traverse is divided into convenient units of length marked by stakes, termed *turning points,* on which the rod is placed. The instrument and rod thus advance alternately, leapfrogging along the line of survey.

Leveling normally requires a starting point in the form of a *bench mark* whose elevation has been previously determined with respect to a sea-level datum. Like the triangulation monument the bench mark consists of a bronze disk firmly embedded in bedrock, in the masonry of a substantial building, or on a massive concrete post set flush with the ground. Particularly to be avoided in placing the bench mark are soils or structures liable to undergo settlement or heaving through changes in load or moisture content.

Leveling is classified as of first-order, second-order, or third-order accuracy according to certain specifications for the maximum allowable discrepany in results obtained by running the line first forward to the objective point then backward to the starting point. To qualify as first-order leveling, for a section of 1 to 2 miles length the discrepancy, $D$, in feet, should not exceed a value calculated by the formula:

$$D = 0.017\sqrt{M}$$

where $M$ is the distance in miles separating the ends of the line. For a line 1 mi long the maximum discrepancy would be 0.017 ft, or about 1/5 in.; for a line 2 mi long it is 0.024 ft, or just over 1/4 in. (In metric equivalents the discrepancy for 1 km is 5.2 mm; for 2 km, 7.3 mm.) Second-order leveling has less stringent requirements and may be used to provide lines of bench marks in areas between first-order lines. Third-order leveling is still less demanding and is used to satisfy the needs of certain mapping and engineering activities. The automatic level is not usually used where first-order accuracy is required, but it will give good second- and third-order results.

## The fundamental level net

A task of the U.S. Coast and Geodetic Survey and a number of cooperating agencies has been the surveying of a national network of first-order level lines with the intention that, when the survey is completed, no point in the contiguous 48 states will lie more than 50 mi (80 km) from a first-order bench mark. Most level lines of this net have followed railroad lines and highways. Bench marks are placed about 1 mi (1.6 km) apart in locations where they can be conveniently reached by surveyors and engineers.

The datum, or level of reference (zero elevation), for the fundamental level net was first defined as the mean sea level at a point on the coast which marked the beginning of a first-order level line. When lines of the fundamental level net were joined, there were found to be discrepancies resulting partially from the fact that mean sea level is not the same for the various coastal points. All lines of the fundamental level net were therefore adjusted to agree with a single datum, referred to as the *sea-level datum of 1929.*

Accuracy of the fundamental level net far exceeds that implied by the minimum standards of first-order leveling stated above. In any level circuit of 100 miles length the error of vertical closure is on the order of only 3/4 in. (13 mm in 100 km). Thus, if a level circuit of this length were actually carried out, the final figure of elevation of the starting bench mark would agree with the starting figure by 3/4 in., on the average. One

**FIGURE 11.20.** Principle of differential leveling.

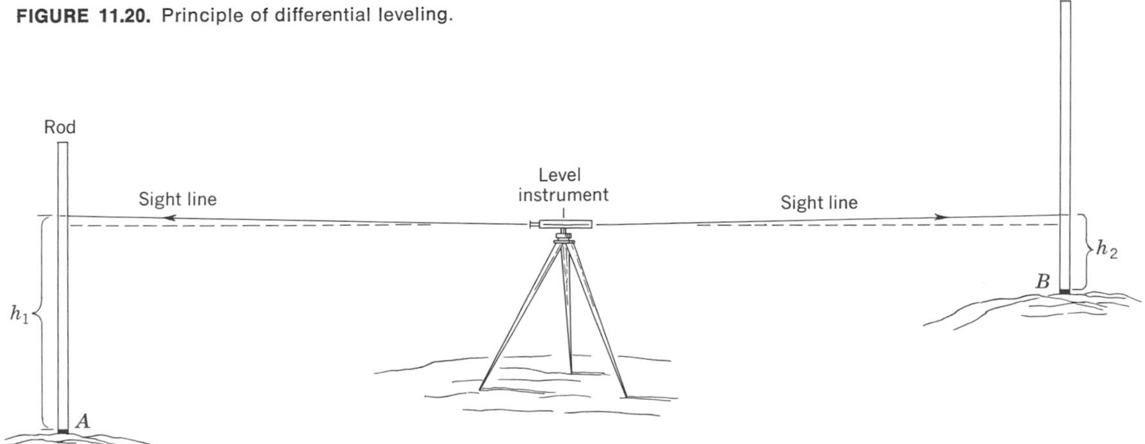

circuit of 575 mi (925 km) circumference in New England has a closing error of only 0.0663 ft (0.02 m), which is at the average rate of only 0.00011 ft per mi (0.02 mm per km) of circuit!

## Mean sea level

If the sea were to come completely to rest, free of the disturbing forces of tides, ocean currents, changing water temperatures, winds, changing atmospheric pressures, and the influxes of fresh water from the lands, the still-water level at any point on the coast would represent the geoid surface, which we have seen is a surface with respect to which the forces of gravity and earth rotation are in perfect balance—therefore, an *equipotential surface.* We could then run a level line from the sea-level datum at any coastal point to meet the level line from any other coastal point and would find perfect agreement in the elevations, subject only to errors in leveling. This agreement would result because the process of spirit leveling makes use of the geoid as its surface of reference, the level bubble being always at rest with respect to the direction of gravity wherever the instrument is set up. Where the geoid rises with respect to the ellipsoid, the level line rises accordingly; where the geoid slopes downward, the level line slopes down accordingly.

Because the sea surface will never come to rest, the geodesist can never have use of a still-water level datum, termed the *geodetic sea level,* representing the equipotential surface of the geoid. Instead he must use an average value of the sea level, termed *mean sea level,* based upon the records of tide gauges operating for long periods at certain coastal points. The individual figures, or variates, from which the mean value is computed are the hourly heights of water level. If we take the 24 hourly readings of a given day, sum them, and divide by 24, the mean sea level of that day is obtained. Followed from day to day, this mean value might show a range of 1 to 2 ft (0.3 to 0.6 m) within a single calendar month, largely through local meteorological causes. Even the monthly averages would show almost as great a range in value throughout a given calendar year.

If, however, the monthly averages of sea level are taken over a period of many years, the yearly range is greatly reduced. Several examples are shown in Figure 11.21. Clearly there are annual cycles of rising and falling mean sea level. These cycles are believed to reflect the combined effects of seasonal changes in atmospheric pressure and winds, ocean currents, and water temperatures acting in a complex relation that raises or lowers slightly the entire sea level at the margins of the ocean basins. Where a tide gauge is located on or close to the shores of a tidal river or estuary, there is the added seasonal range due to changing quantities of runoff from streams draining into the tidal waters.

Averaging of sea level for the period of the entire year largely removes the effects of seasonal variations in level, but, even so, the yearly averages at a given

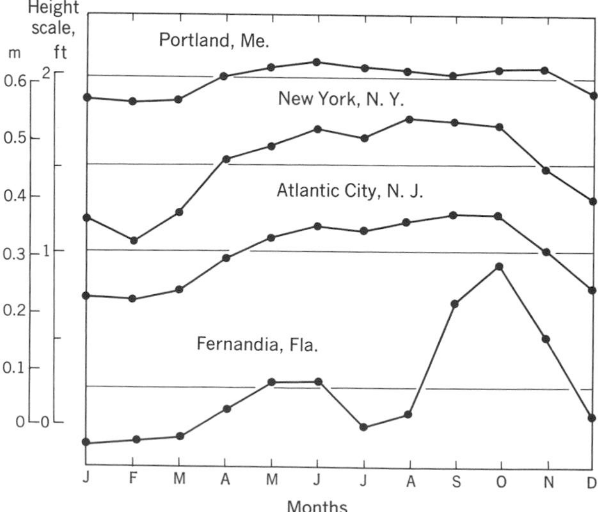


**FIGURE 11.21.** The annual cycle of change of sea level at selected Atlantic Coast ports. Each dot represents the average sea level for the month, based upon a long period of record. The horizontal line represents mean sea level for the port. [After H. A. Marmer (1931), *Physics of the Earth,* vol. 2, Washington, D.C., National Academy of Sciences.]

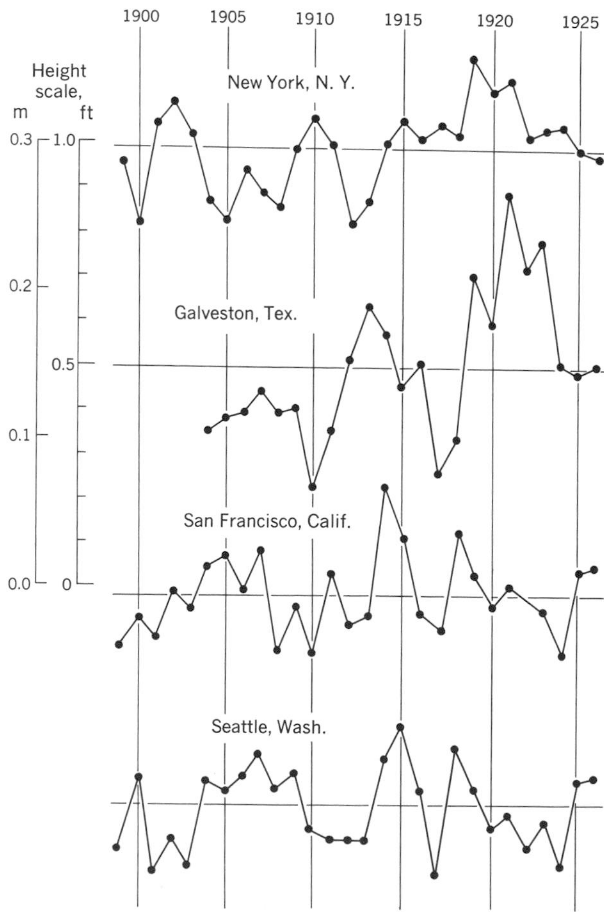


**FIGURE 11.22.** Sea level for successive years at various ports. Each dot represents the average sea level for a particular year. The horizontal line represents mean sea level for the port. [After H. A. Marmer (1931), *Physics of the Earth,* vol. 2, Washington, D.C., National Academy of Sciences.)

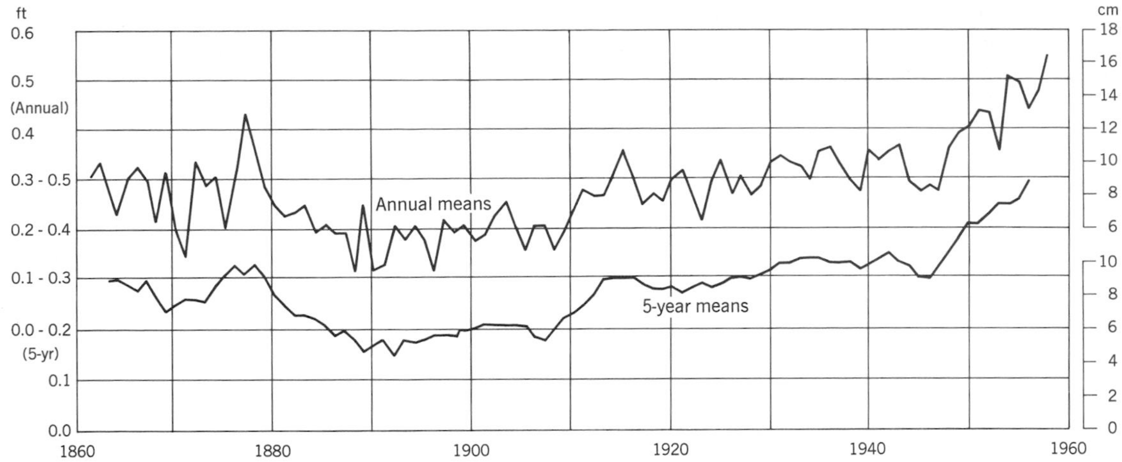


**FIGURE 11.23.** Worldwide fluctuations in sea level for almost a century are shown by the upper graph of mean annual values. The lower graph shows a smoothed curve using running five-year means. [Data from R. W. Fairbridge and O. A. Krebs, Jr. (1962), *Geophysical Journal,* vol. 6, pp. 532–545.]

station show seemingly irregular fluctuations, ranging through perhaps half a foot. Examples of such yearly averages for a series of years are shown in Figure 11.22. The causes of such yearly variations are not definitely known, but are assumed to represent the differences from one year to the next in the total effect of meteorological and oceanographic processes.

How, then, is some figure of mean sea level arrived at for geodetic use in leveling from a coastal point? The only practical course is to use the yearly sea level averaged over a long period of years. Generally this period is at least 19 years, so as to span a full cycle of regression of the moon's nodes (Chapter 8) and hence to include all the tidal constituents.

It has already been noted that two or more level lines, each run from a different coastal point and each one using the mean sea level of the starting point as its datum, may not agree in elevation at the common bench mark where the lines come together. This shows that mean sea level is not the same as the ideal geodetic sea level. Instead the mean sea level is on the average permanently higher or lower at one coastal point than at another, a condition to be expected in view of the location of a given coastal point with respect to prevailing systems of meteorological and oceanographic elements. In 1929 a least-squares adjustment was made of all first-order leveling in the United States and Canada, in which mean sea level was held at zero at 26 tide stations located along the Atlantic and Pacific Oceans and the Gulf of Mexico. Holding local mean-sea-level values along all coasts caused slight distortions in the level net. The elevations resulting from this adjustment are referred to as being based on the sea-level datum of 1929. Some foreign countries have used a single mean-sea-level determination as a basis for elevations.

## Rise of mean sea level

From the analysis of long-term tide gauge records it has become apparent that a gradual rise in mean sea level with respect to geodetic reference marks has been taking place over the past half century or so. This trend was first recognized in 1941 and is now clearly evident in the data of all four great oceans. Figure 11.23 shows world annual mean sea levels in the century 1860–1960. Reversal of what appears to have been a slight downtrend occurred about in the last decade of the nineteenth century and the annual values have since shown an average upward trend of about 0.05 in. (1.2 mm) per year. Minor cycles of rise and fall are superimposed on the upward trend.

Rise of mean sea level can be attributed to a number of possible causes, including release of water by melting of glacial ice, a warming of ocean water (causing an increase in water volume), and crustal changes, reducing the capacity of the ocean basins. The question of cause will be taken up again in Chapter 40, in connection with the water balance of the Antarctic icecap.

## References for further study


National Research Council (1931), *The Figure of the Earth,* vol. 2, *Physics of the Earth,* National Research Council Bull. 78, Washington, D.C., National Academy of Sciences, 286 pp. chaps. 12, 14, 15.

Hosmer, G. L. (1948), *Practical Astronomy,* 4th ed., revised by J. M. Robbins, New York, Wiley, 355 pp., chaps. 11,12.

Fairbridge, R. W., ed. (1966), *The Encyclopedia of Oceanography,* New York, Reinhold, 1021 pp. See Mean sea level, Mean sea level changes.

# TWO

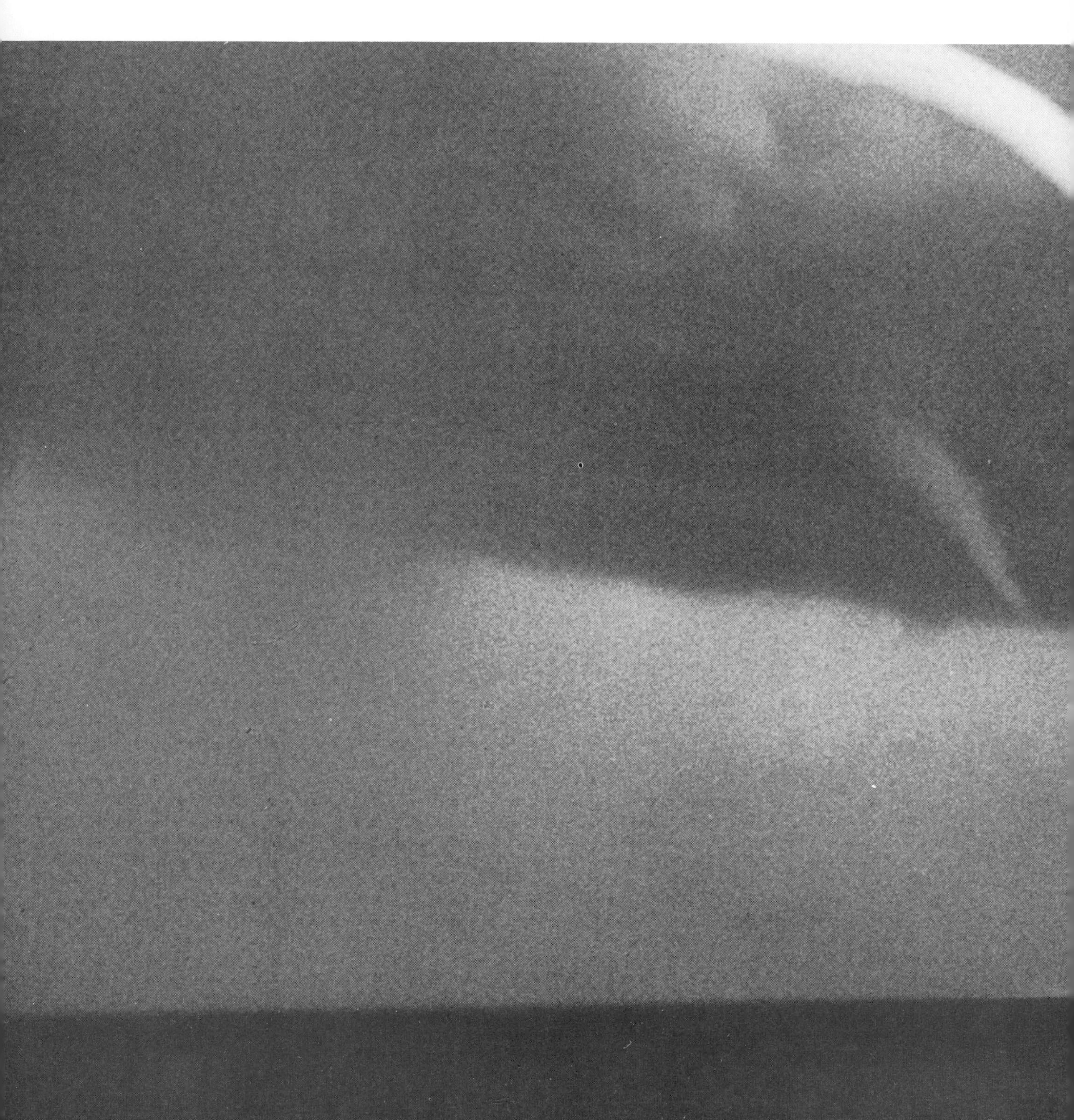

# The atmosphere and oceans

*Waterspouts off the Bahamas. ESSA, courtesy Environmental Science Services Administration.*

# 12

# The atmosphere and oceans

WITH REFERENCE TO the kinds of substances of which the earth is composed, it is often said that three great earth realms are the lithosphere, the hydrosphere, and the atmosphere. The lithosphere, or solid realm, which is treated in Part Three of this book, consists principally of mineral matter having the properties of an elastic solid—that is, of rock materials which strongly resist flowage. The hydrosphere, or water realm, includes all liquid or frozen water standing in bodies such as the oceans and lakes, flowing over or under the ground in streams or glaciers, or being held almost motionless in the soil and rock. The atmosphere, or gaseous realm, is the enveloping layer of gases in which are suspended countless minute solid and liquid particles.

The atmosphere and oceans are treated together in this part of the book because both are strictly classed as *fluids,* substances that flow easily when subjected to unbalanced forces and that seek to come to rest in the lowest possible places under the influence of gravity, with the denser fluids eventually resting below the less dense fluids. Fluids are subdivided into *liquids* and *gases.* As a liquid the water of the oceans, lakes, and rivers is able to flow freely, but it cannot be appreciably compressed into a smaller volume. A liquid poured into a container will come to rest with a free horizontal surface and will not expand to fill the entire container. The atmosphere, on the other hand, behaves as a true gas in that it not only flows freely, but also is easily compressed into a smaller volume when pressure is applied. Gas will also expand rapidly by diffusion to occupy any given small container uniformly. Thus the oceans and atmosphere have certain flowage properties in common as well as certain distinct differences in the way in which they occupy space.

Both the atmosphere and the oceans, as vast fluid layers in ceaseless motion, have a common role in the physical processes of planet Earth. This role is to transfer heat, received by electromagnetic radiation from the sun, from one part of the globe to another. Inequalities in the heating of the atmosphere and oceans are basically responsible for generating and sustaining enormous flow systems which serve to regulate the earth's heat budget. So far as we know, no other planet has both a dense atmosphere and extensive oceans of liquid matter. Thus planet Earth possesses a unique combination of surface fluids, which together have provided a favorable environment for the development of life, sustained with remarkable constancy for hundreds of millions of years.

## Composition of the atmosphere

The earth's atmosphere consists of a mixture of various gases surrounding the earth to a height of many miles. Held to the earth by gravitational attraction, this spherical shell of gases is densest at sea level and thins rapidy upward. Although 97% of the mass of the atmosphere lies within 18 mi (29 km) of the earth's surface, the upper limit of the atmosphere cannot be drawn sharply because the density of gas molecules grades imperceptibly into the near-emptiness of interplanetary space. A working figure of 6000 mi (10,000 km) for the thickness of the atmospheric shell can be useful. Note that this thickness approaches the diameter of the solid earth itself. The science of *meteorology* deals with the physics of the lower 60 mi (100 km) of the atmosphere, while the science of *aeronomy* deals with the overlying portion. From the earth's surface upward to an altitude of about 60 to 75 mi (100 to 120 km) the chemical composition of the atmosphere is highly uniform throughout, in terms of the proportions of its component gases. The name *homosphere* has been applied to this lower uniform layer, in contrast to the overlying *heterosphere*, which is nonuniform in an arrangement of spherical shells (see Figure 12.2).

The homosphere consists of (1) a mixture of gases referred to collectively as the *pure dry air,* (2) water vapor, and (3) dust particles. The first two components are true gases composed of discrete molecules, whereas dust consists of solid particles much larger than molecules, but still so tiny as to mix freely with the gases and to stay aloft almost indefinitely. Clouds and fog, which are composed of tiny water droplets or ice crystals, are also present much of the time in the lower atmosphere the world over.

Consider first the individual gases of pure dry air. One group, making up almost the entire volume, is unvarying in proportions over the entire globe and from the ground surface to a height of 50 mi (80 km). In Figure 12.1 these gases are listed and their proportions given. The largest part by far is *nitrogen,* about 78 percent, or more than three-fourths, of the pure dry air by volume. Nitrogen can be thought of as an inactive gas, or space filler, for the most part, although it is extracted from the air by certain bacteria which form nitrogen compounds vital to plant life. *Oxygen,* the second largest component, makes up about 21 percent, or one-fifth, of the air by volume. Oxygen is chemically very active, combining readily with rock-forming minerals in rock decay, with metals in rusting, with fuels in burning, and with food to provide heat and energy in animals. Despite its chemical activity the quantity of oxygen in the air remains constant from year to year because the amount used is exactly balanced by oxygen given back to the atmosphere by plants. Both nitrogen and oxygen exist in the *molecular state,* in which each molecule consists of two atoms and is neutral in charge.

Because nitrogen and oxygen together make up about 99 percent of the air, the nine other gases listed in Figure 12.1 are measured in very small parts. Of the remaining 1 percent the gas *argon* takes more than

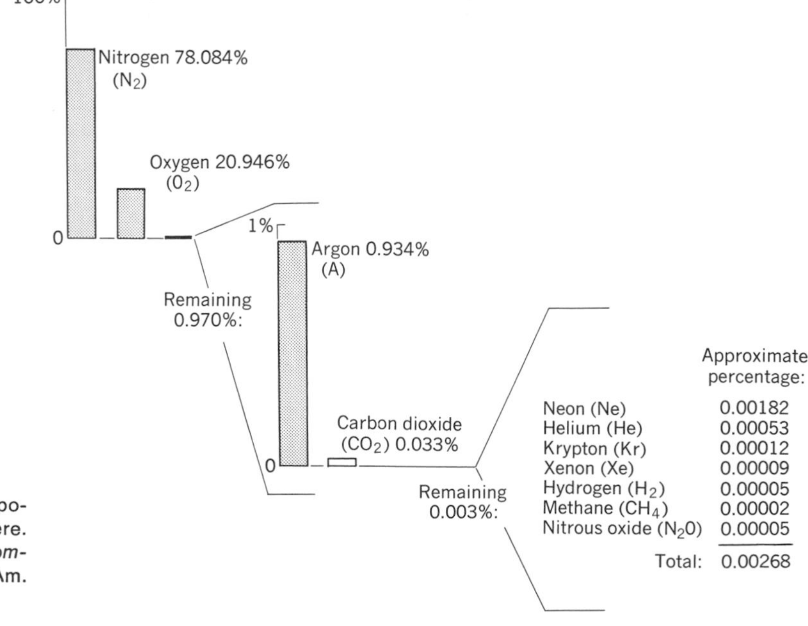


**FIGURE 12.1** The nonvarying components of the earth's lower atmosphere. [Data from E. Glueckauf (1951), *Compendium of Meteorology,* Boston, Am. Meteorological Soc., p. 6, Table V.]

nine-tenths of one percent. Argon and its less abundant relatives *neon, helium, krypton,* and *xenon* are known as *inert gases,* meaning that they do not combine chemically with other elements of the atmosphere, oceans, or earth. These gases exist in the *atomic state,* that is, as single atoms of an element.

*Carbon dioxide,* although forming only 33/1000 of one percent of the air, is an extremely important chemical compound, both in climate control and in sustaining life on earth. Climatically, carbon dioxide is important as an absorber of heat and as an insulating blanket, helping to regulate air temperatures near the earth's surface. Biologically, carbon dioxide is essential for the growth of plant life.

Since man has begun to burn prodigious quantities of wood, coal, and oil, much more carbon dioxide is being released into the atmosphere now than half a century ago. Since 1900 the amount of carbon dioxide has increased more than 10 percent and is believed to be rising steadily. Although commonly listed as one of the unvarying constituents, carbon dioxide actually varies in concentration in the horizontal direction over the earth, in some places being added to, in other places being taken from the atmosphere. For example, over the water of the Arctic Ocean the carbon dioxide content is only about one-half the average value because of absorption by the cold ocean water.

To complete the list of nonvariable gases, minute quantities of *hydrogen, methane,* and *nitrous oxide* have been measured. Besides these unvarying constituents there are several gases whose proportion differs greatly from place to place. Most important in the science of the atmosphere is *ozone,* an uncommon molecular form of oxygen found only in traces in the lower air, but in higher concentrations in the upper atmosphere. Then there are important amounts of *sulfur dioxide, nitrogen dioxide,* and *ammonia* introduced into the lower air layers over large cities by fuel combustion and industrial processes.

The second major component of the homosphere is *water vapor,* the gaseous state of water in which individual water molecules ($H_2O$) have the same freedom of movement as molecules of nitrogen or oxygen gas, therefore the water molecules diffuse, or mix completely with the air. Water vapor is not visible to the eye and should not be confused with fog and clouds, which are composed of liquid or solid particles.

The amount of water vapor present in the air varies greatly from time to time and place to place throughout the earth's atmosphere. In very warm humid air of equatorial regions the weight of water vapor in a given volume of space can be one twenty-fifth as great as the weight of the air with which it is mixed, whereas in very cold and dry arctic regions the proportion is sometimes as little as one part water vapor to 10,000 parts air. Water vapor supplies the water for all clouds and rain, and during condensation it releases latent heat which supplies the energy for storms. More will be said of this essential atmospheric ingredient in the discussion of moisture and precipitation (Chapter 18).

Dust in the lower atmosphere consists of particles so tiny that, for example, 250,000 of them placed side by side would be needed to make a line 1 inch long. Most atmospheric dust comes from the earth's surface. Smoke from grass and forest fires is an important source. Winds blowing over dry land surfaces of deserts raise mineral particles thousands of feet into the air. Volcanoes in eruption contribute dust clouds whose travel in world-wide atmospheric circulation can be easily followed. Especially important in the formation of clouds and precipitation are tiny salt crystals left by the evaporation of spray droplets swept up in turbulent winds blowing over crests of breaking waves. Dust is also added by meteoroids that vaporize upon entering the upper atmosphere, creating countless solid particles.

Whereas the gases of pure dry air are of uniform proportions throughout the homosphere, despite its rapidly decreasing density upwards, the additional components (water vapor and suspended solid and liquid particles) are by no means uniformly distributed either horizontally or vertically. Because both water vapor and atmospheric solids originate mainly from the earth's surface and depend upon air motions to be lifted vertically, these components tend to be most heavily concentrated in the lowermost air layers and to diminish to nearly zero values at the top of the homosphere.

## The heterosphere

The heterosphere, encountered about 55 mi (90 km) above the earth's surface, consists of four gaseous layers, each of distinctive composition (Figure 12.2).

**FIGURE 12.2.** Homosphere and heterosphere. (Based on data of R. Jastrow, NASA, and M. Nicolet.)

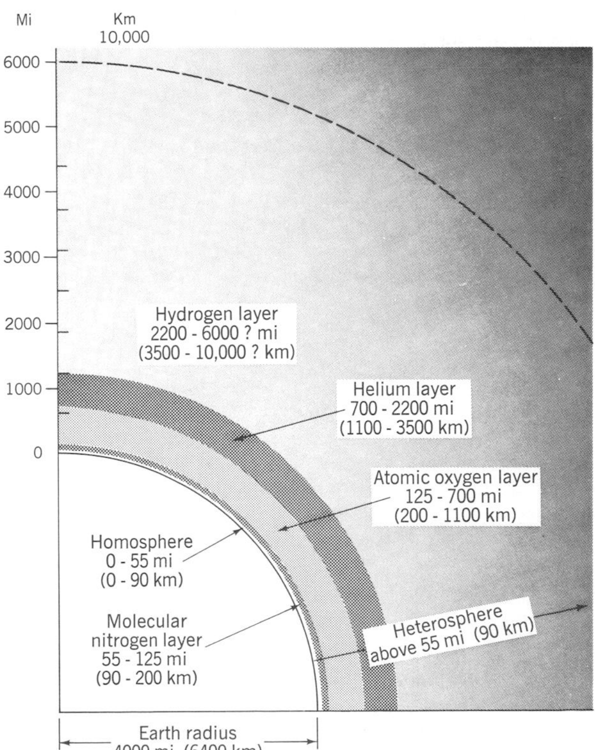

Lowermost is the *molecular nitrogen layer,* consisting dominantly of molecules of nitrogen ($N_2$) and extending upward to about 125 mi (200 km). Above this height lies the *atomic oxygen layer,* consisting dominantly of oxygen atoms (O). Between about 700 and 2200 mi (1100 and 3500 km) lies the *helium layer,* composed dominantly of helium atoms (He). Above this region lies the *atomic hydrogen layer,* consisting of hydrogen atoms (H). No definite outer limit can be set to the hydrogen layer. A height of 6000 mi (10,000 km) may perhaps be taken as an arbitrary limit, for here the density of the hydrogen atoms is approximately the same as that found throughout interplanetary space. However, hydrogen atoms rotating about the earth, and hence belonging to the earth's atmosphere, may exist as far out as 22,000 mi (35,000 km).

It should be noted that the four layers described above have transitional boundary zones, rather than sharply defined surfaces of separation. The arrangement of predominant gases is in order of their weights: molecular nitrogen, the heaviest, is lowest; atomic hydrogen, the lightest, is outermost. It should further be kept in mind that at the extremely high altitudes of the heterosphere the density of the gas molecules and atoms is extremely low. For example, at 60 mi (96 km), close to the base of the heterosphere, the atmosphere has a density of only about one millionth that at sea level.

Some confusion may arise as to the physical distinction between the gases of the heterosphere and the charged particles of the magnetosphere, described in Chapter 7. Whereas most of the magnetosphere lies far out beyond the limits of the heterosphere (see Figure 7.41), the inner Van Allen radiation belt of entrapped energetic particles is in the same height range as the hydrogen layer of the heterosphere. The important distinction lies in the physics of two fundamentally different systems. The heterosphere consists of atoms and molecules which are neutral in charge and which turn with the earth's rotation, being gravitationally bound to the earth, as is any terrestrial particle. In contrast, the particles of the magnetosphere are ions, bearing electrical charges and moving at high speeds in paths not related to the earth's gravitational field. The charged particles are, instead, controlled by the lines of force of the magnetic field, as explained in Chapter 7.

## Structure of the atmosphere

Let us pursue further the important concept that the atmosphere consists of zones, or layers, arranged like spherical shells according to altitude above the earth's surface. Homosphere and heterosphere comprise the first order of subdivision into layers, and these in turn are subject to further subdivisions. For the most part the layers are not at all sharply defined, and their limits are arbitrarily established. Because various different physical and chemical properties are arranged in altitude zones, the system of layering and the names applied to the layers depend upon the class of properties selected.

One basis for describing the structure of the atmosphere as it changes upward with increasing altitude is according to density and pressure of the air. As we shall see, these properties change very smoothly, without distinct breaks to use for distinguishing layers. Another basis for subdividing the atmosphere into layers is according to temperatures encountered with increasing altitude. Because rather rapid temperature changes are encountered at various levels, this property has provided the basis for one of the principal schemes of naming the atmospheric layers. Yet another, and very useful, system of atmospheric layers is based upon the chemical and electrical properties of the atmosphere. For example, we find one layer, roughly between 12 and 80 mi (20 and 130 km), in which chemical reactions are induced by solar radiation. Above this is a zone in which solar radiation produces electrical phenomena. Chemical distinctions among layers of the heterosphere have been described in an earlier paragraph. Still higher we find a zone in which molecules of the atmosphere can escape into outer space. In the ensuing pages these altitude zones, or shells, of the earth's atmosphere are individually named and described.

## Density and pressure of the atmosphere

The force of gravity draws all matter earthward, even the air, which we think of as having almost no substance or weight. Molecules of the atmospheric gases are attracted earthward and tend to crowd together progressively more densely from the outer limits of the atmosphere to sea level, because any one layer of the atmosphere is being compressed by the weight of the layers above it. Any surface exposed to the atmosphere is thus under a force represented by the weight of the gases lying above the surface. This force, when measured for a standard unit of area, such as the square inch or square centimeter, is known as *atmospheric pressure* and is the same on an exposed surface, no matter whether the surface is turned up, down, or in any other attitude with respect to the ground.

*Density* of the atmosphere could be stated by the number of molecules of gas occupying a given volume of space, but, because the air consists of a variety of gases in different proportions, it is simpler to define air density as the total mass of the air in a given volume of space. Mass of air is given in grams, volume in cubic meters. Figure 12.3, which shows many physical properties of the atmosphere, includes a graph of air density from the ground level upward. Density at sea level is 1200 grams of air per cubic meter, or about 2¾ pounds in a little over a cubic yard of space. At 3½ mi (5½ km) the density has fallen to less than half the sea-level value; at 12 mi (19 km) it is only one-thirteenth the sea-level value.

Density in the upper atmosphere from 40 to 90 mi (65 to 145 km) above the earth can be measured by study of the brightness and change of speed of meteors and by the drag on earth satellites. Despite the extreme rareness of the air at this high level there is enough frictional resistance to cause a meteor to heat to incandescence and vaporize completely. It is estimated that at a height of about 105 mi (170 km) the air density is only one-millionth of a gram per cubic meter. Whereas at sea level a gas molecule travels on the average about

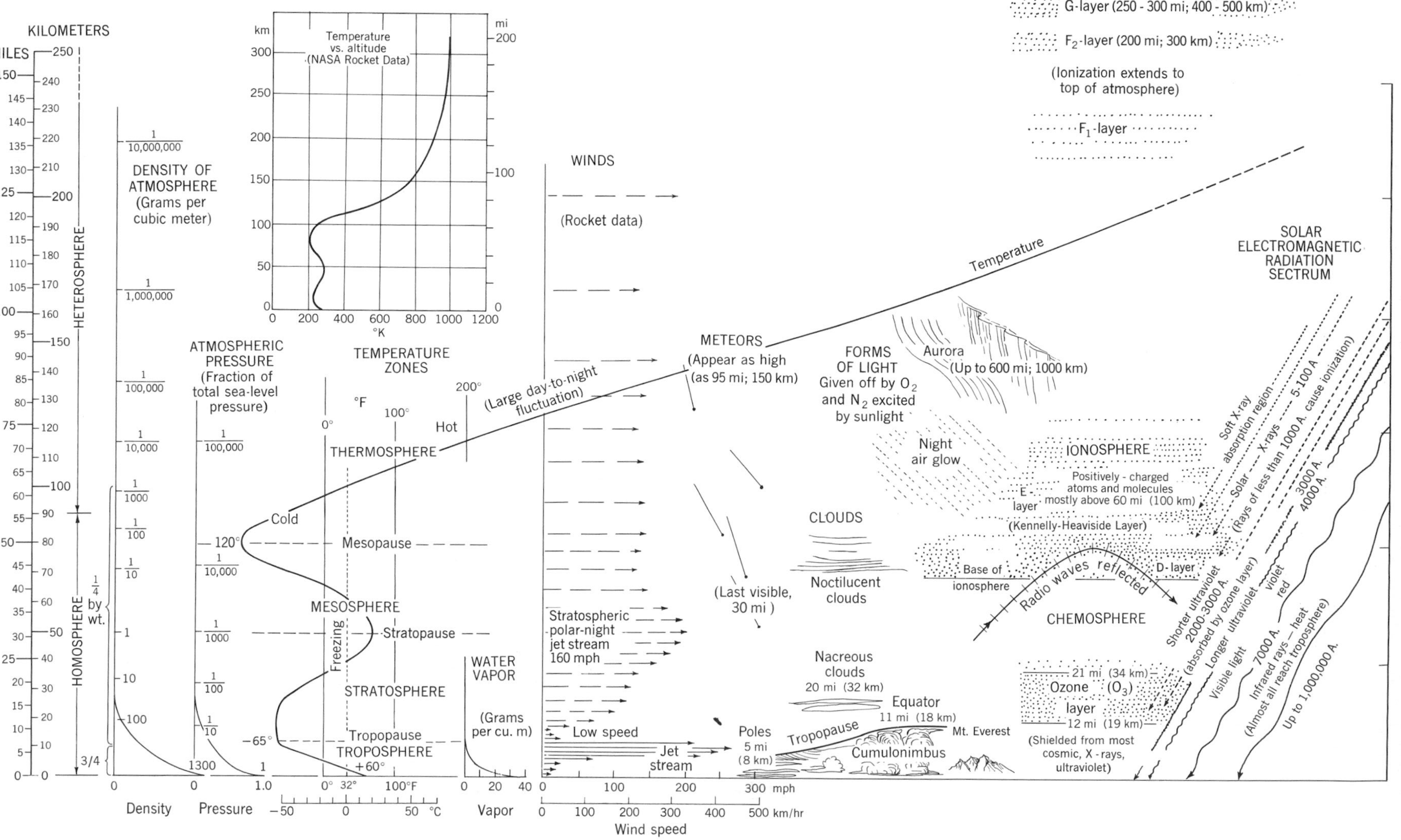


**FIGURE 12.3.** Physical properties of the atmosphere.

0.00001 in. ($2.5 \times 10^{-5}$ cm) before striking another molecule, at 60 mi (100 km) height a molecule averages about half an inch (1 cm) of travel path between collisions, and at 250 mi (400 km), about 300 ft (90 m). Eventually, at about 21,000 mi (34,000 km) from earth, we reach a region in which gas molecules traveling at high speed may escape into outer space, never to return. This region of molecular escape has been named the *exosphere;* it lies far beyond the 6000-mi (10,000-km) arbitrary limit given for the heterosphere.

In summary, about three-fourths of the earth's air is contained in the lowermost 6 to 7 mi (10 km) of the atmosphere, compressed by the weight of the overlying air in such a way that the density is greatest at sea level and decreases very rapidly upward.

*Air pressure,* or *atmospheric pressure,* one of the physical properties of weather measured routinely at all observing stations, is an essential part of all weather description and forecasts. Atmospheric pressure has an average value at sea level of 14.7 pounds per square inch (about 1 kg per sq cm). The pressure graph in Figure 12.3 shows how rapidly air pressure decreases with increase in elevation above sea level. Taking the sea-level pressure as 100 percent, we see that air pressure has fallen to 10 percent at 11 mi (18 km) and to a mere 1 percent at 20 mi (32 km). Thus 99 percent of the mass of the atmosphere lies below an elevation of 20 miles. At 70 mi (112 km) air pressure is only 1/100,000 of the sea-level value. As a general rule, pressure decreases by one-half for each 3½ mi (5½ km) of ascent into the lower atmosphere.

Air pressure can be demonstrated and measured by a very simple device, the *mercurial barometer* (Figure 12.4*B*). The demonstration is often called Torricelli's experiment, after the man who first performed it in 1643. A glass tube of very narrow bore and about 36 in. (90 cm) in length is sealed at one end, filled with mercury, and inserted open end down into a dish of mercury. Instead of pouring out of the tube, the mercury column stands at rest with a height of about 30 in. (76 cm), a vacuum occuping the section of empty tube above it. We may imagine that the mercury column in the tube represents the balancing weight on the scales in Figure 12.4*A*. In other words, a square column of mercury 1 inch thick and 30 inches high actually weighs as much as the entire column of atmosphere 1 inch square in cross section extending from the solid earth to interplanetary space. The exact average height of the mercury column at sea level is 29.92 inches, which is taken as the standard sea-level pressure of the atmosphere. In metric units the established value is 76 centimeters, or 760 millimeters.

The mercurial barometer, although serving as the standard instrument for measurement of barometric pressure, is replaced by the *aneroid barometer* where portability and resistance to rough handling are essential requirements. The principle of the aneroid instrument is illustrated in Figure 12.5; the instrument itself is shown in Figure 12.6. A flexible metal diaphragm, covering a sealed and partly evacuated metal chamber, moves in response to pressure changes. The movement of the diaphragm is greatly magnified by a mechanical system, and the pressure is read directly from the position of a pointer on a calibrated dial.

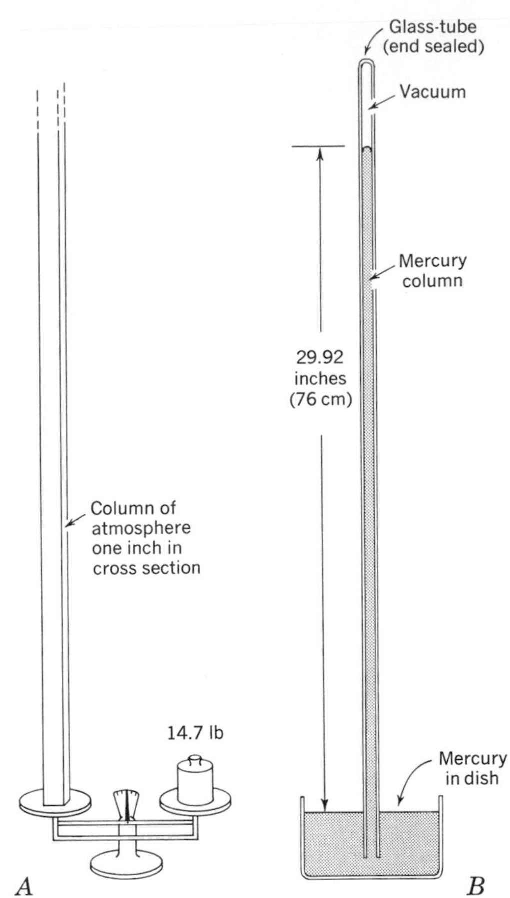


**FIGURE 12.4.** (*A*) Atmospheric pressure as the weight of a unit column of air. (*B*) Principle of the mercurial barometer.

In modern weather science air pressure is stated in somewhat different units, those of force per unit area; this system has the advantage of being independent of the density of any fluid. The unit is the *millibar,* 1013.2 millibars being equal to 29.92 in. (76 cm) of mercury. The

**FIGURE 12.5.** Mechanism of the aneroid barometer. (© 1960, John Wiley & Sons, New York.)

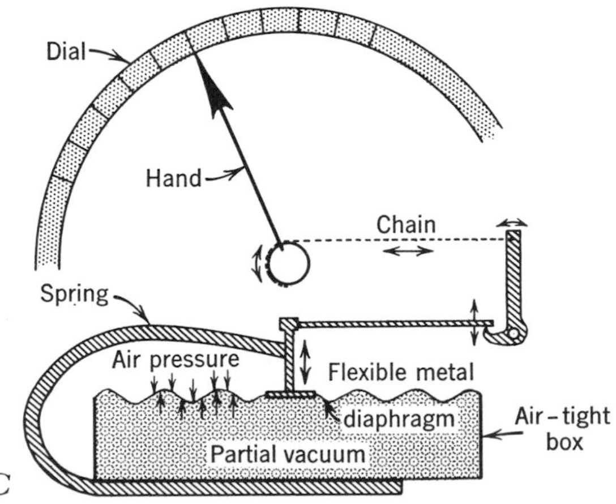

**FIGURE 12.6.** An aneroid barometer. (Taylor Instrument Company, Rochester, New York, Manufacturer. Photograph by courtesy of Science Associates, Inc.)

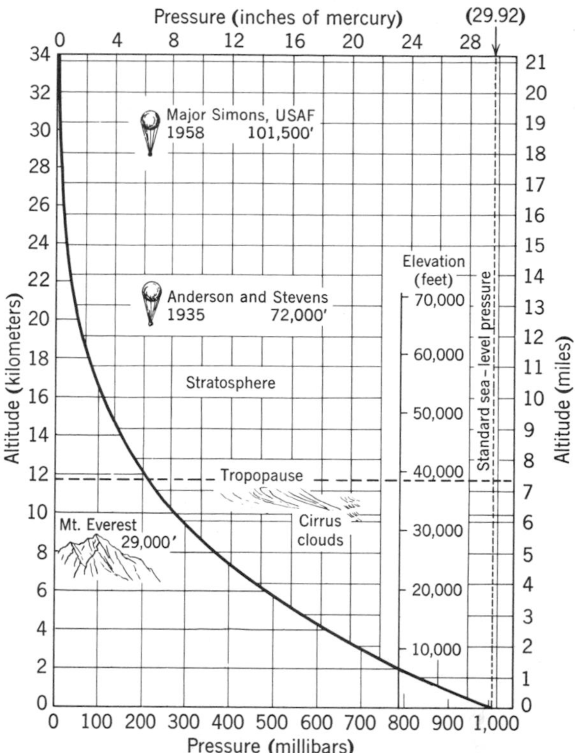


**FIGURE 12.7.** A smooth curve represents the decrease of atmospheric pressure with increasing elevation. No perceptible break occurs at the tropopause. (© 1960, John Wiley & Sons, New York.)

millibar is one-thousandth of a *bar,* which is defined by physicists as a force of one million dynes per square centimeter of surface. The dyne in turn is defined as the force necessary to give a mass of 1 gram an acceleration of 1 centimeter per second per second. Because all three systems of stating pressure—inches, millimeters, and millibars—are used today in weather reports and maps, it is useful to know all three.

In Figure 12.7 is a detailed graph of air pressure in the lower part of the atmosphere, where most of Man's activities, including airplane flights, take place. Pressure is given in inches of mercury at the top and in millibars at the bottom. At sea level the pressure is 29.92 inches (1013.2 millibars); it decreases about 1 inch in the first 1000 feet of ascent, but this rate steadily becomes less at higher altitudes. A fairly accurate formula is that pressure decreases by about one-thirtieth of itself for each 950 feet of rise. The graph shows us that at 3½ mi (5½ km) elevation the pressure is half the sea-level value.

On the earth's highest point, Mt. Everest in the Himalaya, the pressure at 29,000 ft (8.8 km) is one-third that at sea level, and the mercury column stands only 10 in. (25 cm) high. Although mountain climbers who have spent weeks acclimating themselves to the rarefied air can survive at this altitude, a flier needs oxygen to stay alive at this elevation. The 40,000-foot level (about 8 mi, 13 km) is approximately the highest level at which a pilot can survive while breathing oxygen but without being enclosed in a pressurized cabin or pressure suit, for here the pressure is a mere 6 in. (15 cm) of mercury. Above this level a man's lungs could not absorb enough pure oxygen to stay alive because there would be insufficient pressure to force the gas into his lung tissues. Still worse difficulties would arise at the 60,000-ft (18-km) level, because here the human blood boils at its normal body temperature of 98.6°F (37°C).

The limit of sustained, level jet plane flight is somewhere in the range of 80,000–90,000 feet (15–17 mi, 24–27 km). Here the pressure is less than 1 in. (2.5 cm) of mercury. Air density above this level is so low that oxygen cannot be provided for fuel combustion and the lift force on the wings is too weak to keep the plane climbing at the available speed.

Free balloons filled with helium gas have carried men still higher (Figure 12.7). Army captains Orvil A. Anderson and Albert W. Stevens reached 72,000 ft (22 km) in 1935, a record which held for over 20 years. By 1958 an Air Force officer, Major David G. Simons, had reached approximately 102,000 ft (31 km) in a pressurized container attached to a helium balloon (Figure 12.8). In 1961 Commander Malcolm D. Ross, USNR, reached 113,740 ft (34.7 km), for a new record in a manned balloon.

Man has, of course, ascended much higher into the atmosphere by means of rocket-powered aircraft and multi-stage rockets. Unlike jet engines, rockets carry their own oxygen for combustion and are not, therefore, hindered by lack of oxygen or reduced air pressure. In addition, rocket craft profit from the greatly reduced friction of the rarefied air. Multistage rockets now

**FIGURE 12.8.** A stratosphere balloon is prepared for launching in an iron mining pit at Crosby, Minnesota, on August 20, 1957. In the sealed gondola of this craft Major David G. Simons, U.S.A.F., reached an altitude of approximately 102,000 ft (31 km), at that time a new altitude record for a manned balloon ascent. (U.S. Air Force photo.)

readily place manned and unmanned space vehicles into earth, earth-moon, and solar orbits (Chapter 8). Thus man is able to probe the entire atmosphere and to measure its physical and chemical properties by means of automatic recording instruments which transmit their information to ground observers by radio from rockets and orbiting satellites. As we shall see, an enormous increase in knowledge of the upper atmosphere has occurred in recent years and has produced a new branch of the earth sciences.

## Measurement of atmospheric temperature

Air temperature is a measure of heat energy present in the air. This energy exists in the form of the high-speed motion of the gas molecules, which is greater with increased temperature. We cannot measure molecular activity directly, but only indirectly through its effect in changing the volume or electrical property of a sensing element exposed to the air.

The common *liquid-in-glass thermometer* serves well for most weather observations at stations near the ground and takes advantage of the principle that the expansion of fluid in the thermometer bulb is directly proportional to the temperature (Figure 12.9). By using a tube of extremely narrow but uniform diameter, small changes in temperature are detected by the relatively large changes in length of the liquid column. Mercury or alcohol is used in these thermometers.

Another principle is demonstrated by the *compound-metal (bimetallic) thermometer,* in which strips of two different metals (brass and iron) are bonded together into a single strip. Because one metal has a different coefficient of expansion than the other, the strip bends as the temperature rises and, in so doing, moves a pointer on a calibrated dial. A third type of thermometer uses the *Bourdon tube,* a hollow curved metal tube filled with liquid. When heated, the liquid expands, straightening the tube and thereby moving an indicator hand.

Still a fourth principle is used in the *electrical-resistance thermometer,* which consists of a thin platinum wire encased in a porcelain tube. The resistance of the wire to passage of an electric current increases with temperature, which can be measured with sensitive electrical meters. A fifth principle is utilized by the *thermocouple,* which uses two wires or strips of unlike metals joined together in a loop, or circuit, and connected to a sensitive volt-meter; difference in temperature between hot and cold junctions of the two metals sets up a weak electric current, whose strength varies with the temperature difference. The same principle is used in the pyrheliometer, described in Chapter 13, for the measurement of solar radiation.

Although the liquid-in-glass thermometer is the standard instrument for observing air temperature near the ground, it is fragile and cannot record temperatures automatically, but must be read by an observer. The metallic and electrical types not only are compact and sturdy, but will operate automatic recording devices as well. Therefore they are used in places where a continuous record is to be made and where the instruments are inaccessible or out of sight, as on sounding balloons sent up through the atmosphere, below ground for soil-temperature studies, or under water.

Temperature scales commonly used in weather science are the *Fahrenheit* and *Centigrade* scales (Figure 12.10). On the Fahrenheit scale (designated as °F), the freezing temperature of water is 32° F and the boiling point of water is 212° F. The Fahrenheit scale is not only in general use in the United States in everyday life, but also in the reports of surface weather conditions issued by the U.S. Weather Bureau. The Centigrade, or Celsius, scale (designated °C) takes 0° C for the freezing point and 100° C for the boiling point of water. The Centigrade scale is used for upper-air weather observa-

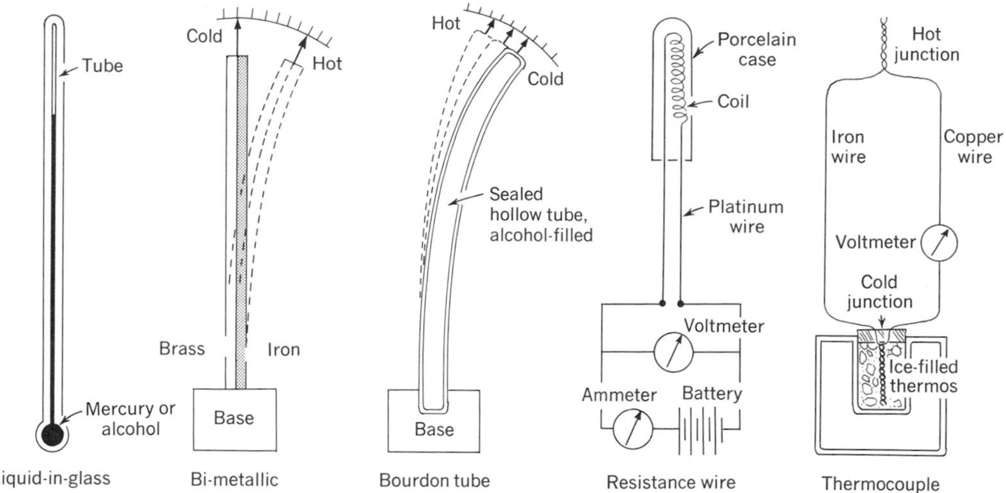


**FIGURE 12.9.** Principles used in five types of temperature-sensing devices.

tions in the United States. It is also used in Great Britain, Europe, and in various branches of science. Fahrenheit temperatures may be converted to Centigrade, and vice versa, by use of the graphic scale or formulas in Figure 12.10 and Appendix III. (The use of F° or C° following a number indicates a temperature range rather than a specific temperature, i.e., 6 F° is read as "six Fahrenheit degrees," not as "six degrees Fahenheit.")

In stating temperatures in the upper atmosphere and for any mathematical scientific research, the *absolute Centigrade scale* (or *Kelvin scale*) is used. This scale has the same degree units as the ordinary Centigrade scale, but has the zero point at −273° C, a value known as *absolute zero,* or 0° K.

## Vertical distribution of air temperature

Figure 12.3 includes a graph of temperature from ground level to more than 100 mi (160 km) height. Starting at the ground, let us examine the great range of temperatures one would encounter in a vertical ascent. Most of us know from experience that, as we climb a mountain or rise in an airplane, the temperature falls steadily. This rate of temperature drop, averaging about 3½ F° for each 1000 feet (6.4 C° per km), is called the *average temperature lapse rate.* This almost-constant decrease in air temperature is shown in the lower part of Figure 12.11. The air continues to become cooler with increasing height up to about 6 to 8 mi (10 to 13 km) in the middle latitudes and thus drops to −70° to −75° F (−57° to −60° C) at that level. Above this height the temperature remains almost constant with increasing altitude, as shown on the graph in Figure 12.11 by a bend in the temperature line and its nearly vertical attitude above the bend.

The term *troposphere* is applied to the lowermost layer of the atmosphere through which the temperature decrease averages 3½ F° per 1000 ft (6.4 C° per km). The term *stratosphere* is applied to the layer above, in which the temperature is nearly constant. The boundary between the two layers is called the *tropopause.*

The tropopause is encountered much higher in the equatorial belt of the globe than in the middle latitudes and is much lower over the polar regions. Altitude and temperature values are given in Figure 12.12. Seasonal changes occur in both altitude and temperature of the tropopause, as shown by representative values for July and January, Figure 12.12.

The troposphere contains almost all the water vapor of the atmosphere, as the graph in Figure 12.3 shows, and therefore contains nearly all clouds, precipitation, and storms. Today, jet aircraft can maintain flight in the stratosphere and thus avoid many weather hazards. Within the troposphere turbulent motions carry moisture and dust to much higher levels over equatorial regions than over polar regions. The thickness of the troposphere thus seems to be determined by the height to which atmospheric mixing is sustained.

Upward through the stratosphere, temperatures rise gradually up to a level of about 30 mi (50 km), where the *stratopause* is encountered, marked by a temperature

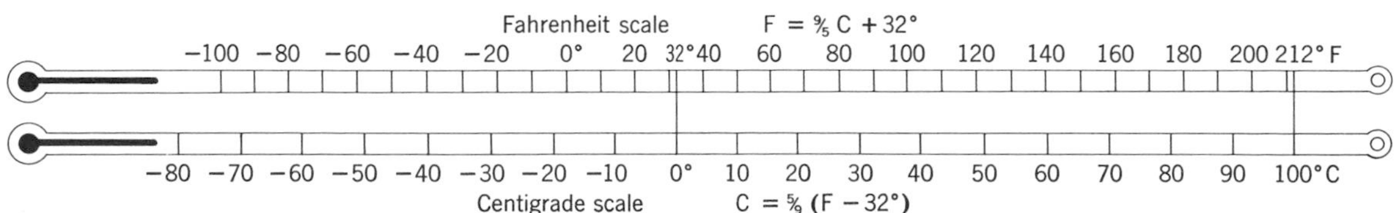


**FIGURE 12.10.** Comparison of Fahrenheit and Centigrade scales. (© 1960, John Wiley & Sons, New York.)

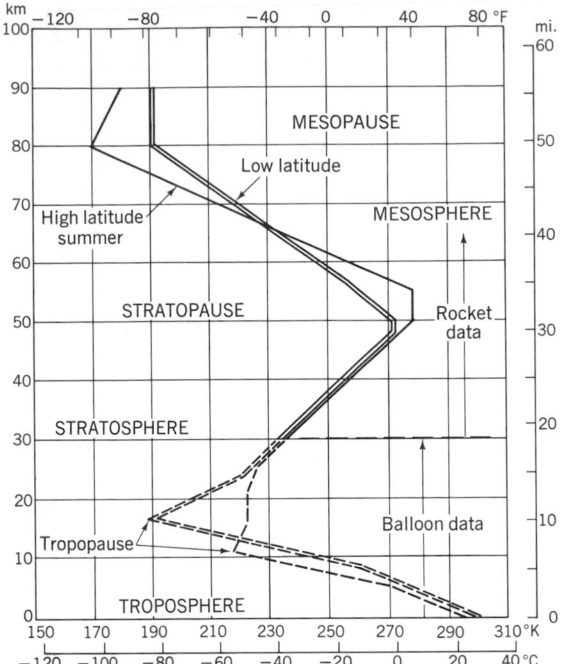


**FIGURE 12.11.** Temperature profiles based on rocket soundings for low latitudes and high-latitude summer. [After N.A.S.A. (1966), Publication NASA-SP-96, p. 124, Fig. 77.]

maximum of about 32° F (0° C) but with a range of 36 F° (20 C°) more or less than that value. (Cause of heating at this level is explained in a later paragraph.)

Above the stratopause lies a zone of diminishing temperature, the *mesosphere,* clearly shown in the example in Figure 12.11. At the *mesopause,* about 52 mi (85 km), temperatures reach a minimum value, averaging about −120° F (−83° C). However, the minimum value can be as much as 45 F° (25 C°) greater or less than the average value.

Above the mesopause lies the *thermosphere,* a zone of rapid temperature increase to extremely high values of over 1300° F (700° C) at an altitude of 125 mi (200

**FIGURE 12.12.** Average elevation and temperature of the tropopause shown schematically for July (left) and January (right). [Data from *Handbook of Geophysics* (1960), New York, Macmillan.]

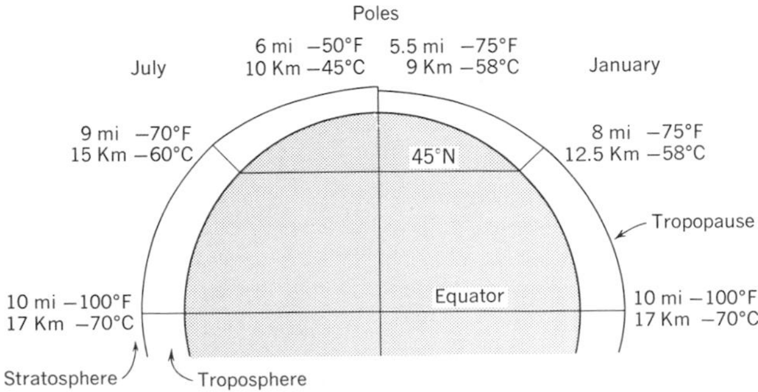


km). Above this altitude the rate of temperature increase falls off, and there is only a slight increase of temperature in the next 100 mi (160 km). This region of approximately constant temperature is designated the *isothermal region.* Because the scale of Figure 12.3 does not permit the high temperatures and high altitudes of the thermosphere and isothermal region to be shown, these are shown in a separate inset graph with different altitude and temperature scales.

It is important to know that temperatures in the thermosphere fluctuate widely with time of day and also show marked changes with latitude and season. The thermosphere lies in the heterosphere, above 55 mi (90 km), and is a region of extremely rarefied atmosphere. This is also a region in which the ionospheric layers are found, with vast swarms of electrons in motion (Chapter 7). Consequently, the meaning of the word "temperature" in the thermosphere is quite unrelated to concepts of temperature which we as humans base upon our sensory experience in the lower atmosphere. High temperatures within the thermosphere are attributed to the absorption of solar X rays, gamma rays, and ultraviolet rays by atoms of nitrogen and oxygen (Chapter 7).

Temperatures in the upper atmosphere are measured by several methods. Up to perhaps 20 mi (32 km) thermometers are carried by balloons, and the data are sent back by radio. Between 20 and 35 mi (32 and 56 km) temperatures can be computed from the behavior of sound waves sent out from a ground explosion and reflected back to earth.

Particularly designed to reveal temperatures and winds in the stratosphere and mesosphere at levels from 20 to 50 mi (32 to 80 km) is the *rocket-grenade* method, in which a rocket carries aloft and ejects 18 or 20 high-explosive grenades. The positions in time and space of each explosion are determined electronically and a set of microphones on the ground receives the sound waves. By suitable mathematical calculations it is possible to determine direction and speed of the wind in each layer. The speed of sound waves can then be computed, permitting temperatures to be determined as well, since speed of sound waves is mathematically related to temperature. The graphs of temperature and altitude shown in Figure 12.11 are based upon rocket-grenade and balloon data.

Temperatures within the thermosphere can be obtained directly from instruments mounted in rocket probes and earth satellites and indirectly from analysis of the light emitted from the aurora and from radio-wave behavior in the ionosphere.

## The ozone layer

The effects of solar radiation upon the atmosphere are of profound importance. Energy of the sun's electromagnetic radiation spectrum acts upon various levels of the atmosphere to produce the layered arrangements of thermal, electrical, and chemical properties that have been described on preceding pages. In Chapter 7 the action of solar radiation in ionizing gas molecules was discussed. The ionospheric layers, with their great surges of electric ring currents, were conveniently analyzed in connection with the magnetic field of the earth because of the close physical relationship between the ionospheric currents and the external magnetic field. Figure 12.3 shows the position of the ionosphere in relation to other upper atmospheric phenomena, such as the thermal zones. A review of the discussion of the ionosphere given in Chapter 7 will be appropriate here.

Let us continue to trace the effects of solar radiation as it penetrates deeper into the earth's atmosphere. Below the ionosphere, the base of which can be placed at about the 50 mi (80 km) level, lies the *chemosphere.* This shell is identified with respect to important chemical effects produced by solar radiation. Whereas solar X rays and the shorter ultraviolet rays (under 1000 angstroms) are almost completely absorbed within the ionospheric region, the ultraviolet rays in the 1000 to 2000 angstrom range of wavelengths pass readily into lower levels of the atmosphere. In a region known as the *ozone layer,* largerly concentrated in the altitude range of 12 to 21 mi (20 to 35 km), the absorption of the longer ultraviolet rays produces an important chemical effect upon the atmospheric oxygen. This effect is felt to a lesser degree at altitudes as low as 6 mi (10 km) and as high as 35 mi (55 km).

The ozone layer contains a concentration of the gas ozone, a form of oxygen in which the molecule consists of three oxygen atoms ($O_3$) instead of the usual molecule of two atoms ($O_2$). In this layer of the atmosphere ultraviolet rays act upon oxygen molecules, causing them to split into single atoms. When a single oxygen atom collides with an ordinary two-atom oxygen molecule, an ozone molecule is formed. The process is reversible, so that ozone eventually breaks down and re-forms into ordinary oxygen molecules.

The ozone layer shows seasonal changes in altitude and degree of concentration, as illustrated by the altitude–concentration graph of Figure 12.13. In general the layer is lowest in winter and highest in summer. It has also been found that the center of concentration of the ozone layer varies in height with latitude, being much higher in the low latitudes than in the high latitudes (Figure 12.14).

Ozone would be a deadly poison to life if present in large concentrations, but fortunately it is almost completely absent in the troposphere. At the same time the ozone layer is essential to all life on earth, because it fully absorbs the shorter ultraviolet rays that would otherwise destroy all exposed bacteria and severely burn animal tissues. The ozone layer also absorbs much of the longer ultraviolet radiation and some of the visible and infrared wave lengths as well. This absorption heats the ozone layer, causing the temperature maximum of the stratopause, reached at about 30 mi (50 km). It is interesting to note that if all atmospheric ozone were brought down to sea level, at these pressures it would form a layer only 0.1 in. (0.25 cm) thick.

**FIGURE 12.13.** This graph of the concentration of ozone in the atmosphere above Flagstaff, Arizona, shows that seasonal changes occur in the level of greatest concentration. [After *Handbook of Geophysics* (1960), New York, Macmillan, p. 8-5.]

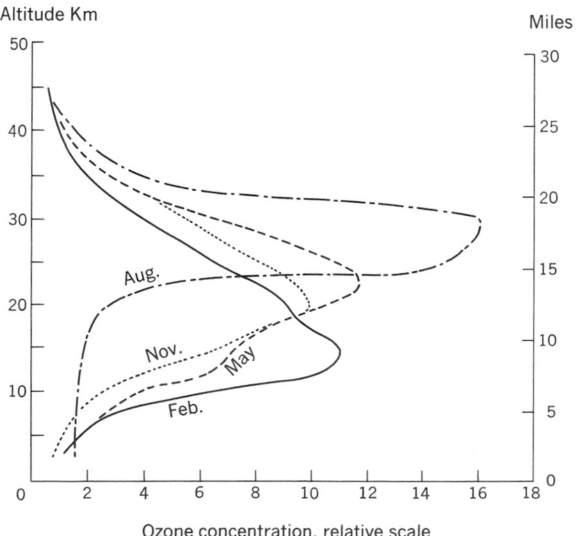


## The oceans

The first part of this chapter has described the earth's atmosphere as an arrangement of gaseous shells defined in terms of physical and chemical properties. In later chapters we shall return to a detailed examination of the lowermost layer, the troposphere, and the complex processes that operate within it. Throughout the second part of the present chapter we shall turn, instead, to the oceans of the globe, for an overview of the nature of this great liquid layer which underlies the atmosphere.

The oceans of the globe are studied in the science of *oceanography.* In this book our concern is with various phases of physical, geological, and chemical oceanography, rather than with biological oceanography, which treats the living organisms of the sea. Certain aspects of geological oceanography—the size, depth, distribution, and bottom topography of the principal

**FIGURE 12.14.** When the average elevation of greatest concentration of ozone is plotted against latitude, there results a marked decrease in level as latitude increases. [After *Handbook of Geophysics* (1960), New York, Macmillan, p. 8-6.]

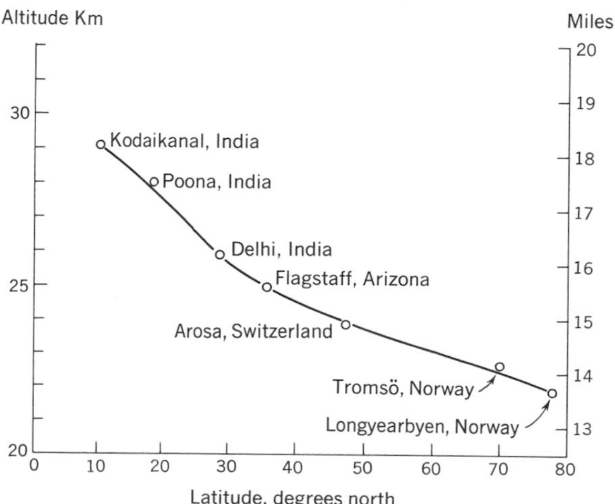

ocean basins—are discussed in Chapter 24 in a study of the earth's major crustal features. In the present chapter we are concerned mainly with the physical and chemical properties of the ocean waters.

Consider some comparative statistical data, using the term *world ocean* to designate the combined oceans of the earth. The world ocean occupies about 71% of the earth's surface and has a mean depth of about 3800 m (12,500 ft), including shallow seas as well as the main basins. The round figure of 4000 m (13,000 ft) applies quite well to the average depth of the main portions of the Atlantic, Pacific, and Indian oceans. Volume of the world ocean is estimated as about 1.4 billion cubic kilometers ($1.37 \times 10^9$ cu km), which is equivalent to about 317 million cubic miles and constitutes 97.2% of the world's free water. Most of the remaining 2.8% is locked up in icecaps.

Comparing masses of atmosphere and world ocean with the total earth mass (including atmosphere and oceans) the following estimates apply:

| | |
|---|---|
| Atmosphere | $0.0052 \times 10^{21}$ kg |
| World ocean | $1.43 \times 10^{21}$ kg |
| Entire earth | $5{,}983 \times 10^{21}$ kg |

On a fractional basis, these figures show that the world ocean has a mass about 1/4000 that of the entire earth, while the atmosphere has a mass about 1/275 that of the world ocean.

In what basic ways does the water of the ocean behave similarly to the air of the atmosphere? In what ways is their behavior different? How is their behavior linked together? In the introduction to this chapter it was noted that both air and water are fluids in the strict sense of the word: both tend to come to rest in a state of fluid (hydrostatic) equilibrium; both respond freely to unequal forces by flowage.

One important difference is that the atmosphere, being gaseous, has no distinct upper boundary; instead, the gas molecules become less closely spaced until for all practical purposes the atmosphere ceases to exist and interplanetary space sets in. In contrast the fluid of the oceans has a clearly defined upper surface where the water is in relatively sharp contact with the air.

Our primary concern is with the lower boundary of the atmosphere and the upper boundary of the oceans. The study of the lower boundary of the atmosphere is essential to an understanding of the earth's atmospheric circulation and storms, whereas it is the upper boundary of the oceans that is the most vital region they possess in terms of the intake and outgo of energy and matter. The direct absorption and radiation of heat occurs through this upper ocean boundary; the loss of moisture (and of latent heat) by evaporation and the gain by precipitation take place here; the dragging force of the wind to produce waves and surface currents is exerted upon this surface.

A basic difference is also seen in the configuration of the ocean basins, for which the continental margins act as side walls to restrict the motion of the ocean water. On the other hand, the atmosphere, although somewhat inhibited at lower levels by terrain features, has no such compartmentation by high physical barriers and is free to circulate on a global scale.

Another difference in behavior of atmosphere and oceans is attributable to the great differences between the densities and viscosities[1] of the two fluids. Air, a substance of low density and viscosity, moves so freely under applied stresses that it quickly attains high velocities; it also quickly comes to rest. This means that the mechanical property of acceleration (rate of change of velocity) is important in explaining the dynamics of air motions. In contrast, ocean water, with its much greater density and viscosity, is comparatively sluggish in motion, changing velocity only very slowly and to a much lesser degree than air. Acceleration is therefore not so important a factor in the dynamics of the ocean.

Perhaps the most striking physical difference between the atmosphere and oceans is in the changes that occur when the confining pressure is changed. The atmosphere, a gas, expands readily when pressure is reduced (as in the case of rising air) and contracts when pressure is increased (as in the case of descending air). Such volume changes are accompanied by large changes in temperature, a phenomenon of fundamental importance in atmospheric processes (Chapter 18). The water of the oceans, in contrast, is nearly incompressible for all practical purposes and experiences only very slight temperature changes, even when it is raised or lowered through many thousands of feet of vertical distance to the accompaniment of enormous pressure changes.

Behavior of the atmosphere and oceans is vitally linked through their contact at the ocean surface. We shall see in Chapter 19 how the earth's air masses are modified by contact with the ocean surface. In Chapter 16 we shall see how the properties of sea water are modified and the ocean currents set in motion by contact with the atmosphere and by exchange of energy through the atmospheric layer.

## Composition of sea water

Sea water is *brine,* a solution of salts. Origin of the salt constituents of the oceans is discussed in Chapter 22. Certain of the elements in sea water have probably come from deep within the earth's interior throughout geologic time by a process known as *outgassing.* Another group of elements has been derived from the lands, through processes of rock weathering. While streams can bring these elements in solution to the oceans, evaporation of sea water cannot remove them through the atmosphere.[2] However, the various elements of sea water can enter the solid state as sedimentary deposits on the ocean floors, and can thus be removed from sea water. It is believed that the rate at which the various elements are added to the oceans is closely balanced by the rate of removal through precipitation as sediment, and that the composition of sea water has held quite constant for much of the geologic time in which complex life forms have existed.

One way of describing the chemical composition of

[1] Viscosity refers to the degree to which a fluid resists flowage. For example, in comparing lubricating oils one that behaves sluggishly has high viscosity, whereas one that flows readily has low viscosity.

[2] Sea salts may, however, be lifted into the atmosphere as minute crystals carried by water droplets released from wave crests. Much of the chlorine in rain and stream water is believed to originate in this way.

sea water is to list the ingredients that one would need to add to pure water to make an artificial brine closely resembling natural sea water. Table 12.1 lists the five

**TABLE 12.1. PRINCIPAL CONSTITUENTS OF SEA WATER**

| Name of Salt | Chemical Formula | Grams of Salt per 1000 Grams of Water |
|---|---|---|
| Sodium chloride | NaCl | 23 |
| Magnesium chloride | $MgCl_2$ | 5 |
| Sodium sulfate | $Na_2SO_4$ | 4 |
| Calcium chloride | $CaCl_2$ | 1 |
| Potassium chloride | KCl | 0.7 |
| With other minor ingredients to total | | 34.5 |

most important constituents.

Notice that in these five salts the first element is always a metal: sodium (Na), magnesium (Mg), calcium (Ca), or potassium (K). Reference to Chapter 20, on the composition of igneous rocks, will show that these elements are common in the feldspars and dark minerals making up the bulk of igneous rocks. Notice also that in four of the five salts chlorine (Cl) constitutes the second element. Chemical analysis of sea water shows that chlorine makes up 55 percent of the total weight of all matter dissolved in sea water; sodium is next with 31 percent. In sodium sulfate ($Na_2SO_4$) the combination of the elements sulfur (S) and oxygen (O) in the ratio of one atom to four is called the *sulfate radical* ($SO_4$); this radical ranks third in total weight, with about 8 percent. Magnesium, potassium, and calcium are next, in that order, with about 6 percent for the three combined. Less abundant but important elements are bromine, carbon, strontium, boron, silicon, and fluorine. A complete list of elements known to be present in sea water would include at least half of all the naturally occurring elements. In addition to salts, sea water contains dissolved gases of the atmosphere, principally nitrogen, oxygen, argon, and carbon dioxide.

## Temperature structure of the oceans

Just as the meteorologist recognizes a set of atmospheric properties (temperature, pressure, humidity), the oceanographer lists certain physical properties of sea water which are essential in describing the state of the ocean water. These physical properties are temperature, salinity, and pressure. It will be necessary to examine each in turn and to take note of the special units of measurement applied to them.

Within the troposphere, air temperatures are typically highest at sea level, diminishing upward to very cold values at a rather uniform temperature lapse rate. Water temperatures within the oceans attain their warmest values at the sea surface, since it is here that solar radiation is received. In contrast to the uniform thermal gradient in the lower atmosphere, temperature of the ocean body does not change uniformly with depth.

As a general statement, the temperature structure of the oceans over middle and low latitudes can be described as a *three-layer system* (Figures 12.15 and 12.16). There the surface water is subjected to intense solar radiation—year around in low latitudes and in summer in middle latitudes. The heated water takes the form of an upper layer of quite uniform temperature, a result of mixing within the layer. This warm layer may attain a thickness of 1600 ft (500 m) and a temperature of 70° to 80° F (20° to 25° C) or higher in equatorial latitudes.

Immediately below the warm layer, water temperatures drop sharply downward. This layer of rapid tem-

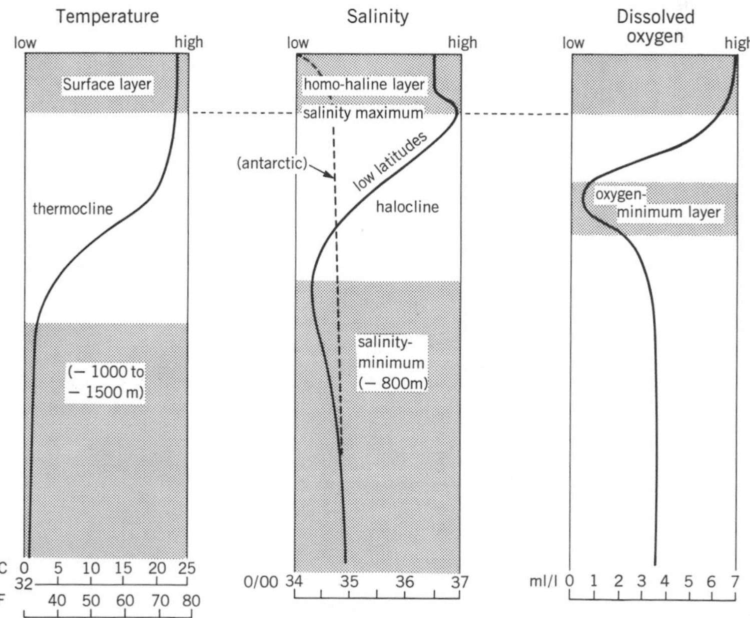


**FIGURE 12.15.** Typical changes in temperature, salinity, and dissolved oxygen are shown diagrammatrically for oceans in low and middle latitudes. [After W. E. Yasso (1965), *Oceanography*, New York, Holt, Rinehart and Winston, Figure 2-4; modified by data of A. Defant (1961), *Physical Oceanography*, New York, Pergamon, vol. 1, chap. 4.]

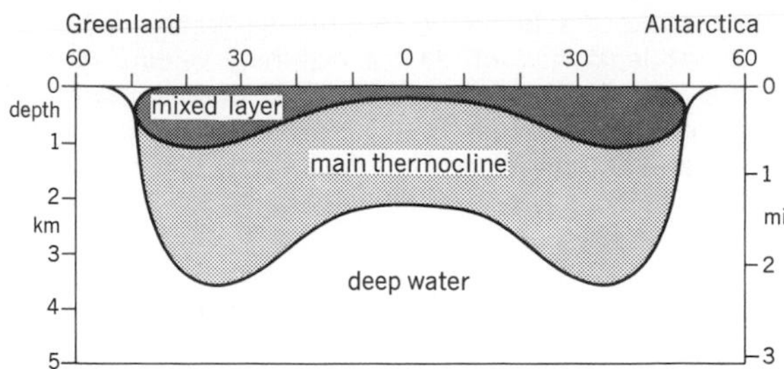


**FIGURE 12.16.** Schematic diagram of the oceans as a three-layered system. [After J. Williams, *Oceanography*, Copyright © 1962, Boston, Little, Brown, p. 94, Figure 7–4.]

perature change, which may be 1600 to 3300 ft (500 to 1000 m) thick, is known as the *thermocline* (explained in Chapter 14). In low latitudes, temperatures decline gradually from about 40° F (5° C) immediately below the thermocline to about 34° F (1° C) close to the bottom at depths of around 13,000 ft (4000 m). In arctic and antarctic latitudes, surface water temperatures are close to 32° F (0° C) and hence the temperature changes with increasing depth are very slight. (The subject of ocean water temperatures and their variations with latitude, season, and depth are discussed in greater detail in Chapters 14 and 16.)

In comparing and contrasting the temperature structure of the oceans with that of the atmosphere it may be pointed out that temperature differences within the atmospheric layers are very much larger than within the oceans and involve vastly greater vertical dimensions. Furthermore, the temperature structure of the atmosphere is highly uniform for all latitudes, the differences between poles and equator being only moderately expressed in the differences in height and temperature of the tropopause (Figure 12.12). In contrast, the oceans show a great difference in temperature structure as one progresses from equatorial to arctic latitudes (Figure 12.16). Greater uniformity of atmospheric temperature is to be expected because of the great freedom of the air to move globally without restraints.

In contrasting atmosphere and oceans, it should be emphasized that the entire atmosphere is penetrated by solar radiation, and hence receives an input of energy at all levels as well as from the earth's surface. In contrast, the ocean receives its heat only at the upper surface. Depth of penetration of solar radiation in the oceans is very small, and warm water tends to remain on top. Consequently the vast bulk of the ocean waters lies cold and dark upon a solid floor through which only a very small flow of heat takes place from within the earth. Actually, this flow of terrestrial heat, while of great geological importance, is insignificant in influencing the temperature of the ocean body.

## Salinity of ocean waters

Although the proportions in which the various chemical elements are present in relation to one another in sea water are remarkably constant throughout all oceans, the *salinity* of the water, which is the total weight of dissolved solids to weight of water, is a variable quantity, differing in value from place to place over the oceans and at various depths. Salinity is measured from water samples taken at any desired depth by a ***water bottle,*** shown in Figure 12.17.

Salinity is commonly expressed as the ratio of solids to water. Thus the total value given in Table 12.1 is 34.5 grams of salt per 1000 grams of water, which is the same as a salinity of 3.45%. Because the percentage is small, salinity is usually stated in parts per thousand, with a special symbol: ‰. Thus the figure 34.5 ‰ is read "3.45 parts per thousand" and is the same proportion as 3.45%.

The problem in actually determining the salinity of sea water is that the laboratory process of distilling off the water to leave the salts behind results in certain chemical changes. For this reason salinity is defined as the amount of solid matter per unit of mass of sea water

**FIGURE 12.17.** This water bottle takes a sample of 1½ qts (2 liters) of sea water at any desired depth. The valves are operated by a small weight, or messenger, which slides down the supporting wire and activates the mechanism. (Courtesy of the G. M. Manufacturing Co., New York.)

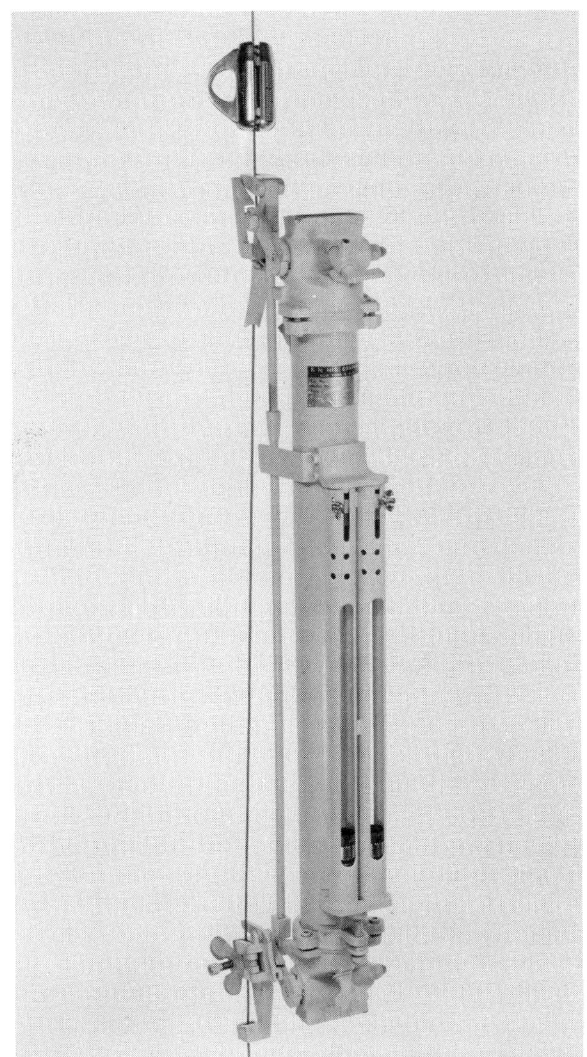

when all the carbonate has been converted to the oxide form, when bromine and iodine have been replaced by chlorine, and when all included organic matter has been oxidized. Direct measurement of salinity is never carried out because salinity can be accurately estimated by much simpler procedures. One can determine the concentration of the chlorides alone (so-called *chlorinity* of the water) and, by multiplying by a constant, obtain the salinity. Salinity can also be accurately estimated from measurements of water density and temperature or electric conductivity, or even by determining the degree to which it bends light rays (its *refractive index*).

In the oceans generally, salinity ranges between 33 and 37 ‰, depending upon the geographic location. In certain bays or arms of the sea largely shut off from the open ocean and located in tropical deserts, salinity is abnormally high. An example is the Red Sea, with salinity of 40 ‰ or more. Near the mouths of large rivers salinity may be low because of mixing with fresh river water.

If one were to make a general statement about the relationship of salinity to depth, it would be that a three-layer system closely analogous with the three-layer temperature system is typical in low and middle latitudes (Figure 12.15). A shallow surface layer of uniformly high salinity (35.0 to 36.5 ‰) corresponds with the uniformly warm layer. Below this layer is a zone of rapid decrease in salinity, the *halocline,* which corresponds with the thermocline. Below the halocline differences in salinity are very small and salinity lies in the range of 34.6 to 34.9 ‰ for most of the ocean body.

It is interesting to include an observation concerning the vertical distribution of dissolved oxygen in the ocean in connection with the changes in temperature and salinity. Although the distribution of oxygen is not well known for the entire world ocean, certain generalizations can be made. An oxygen-rich surface layer is characteristic of the oceans generally, because atmospheric oxygen is dissolved in the sea water to the saturation point and phytoplankton (oxygen-releasing plants) live in surface layers. It is also known that for the vast bulk of water at great depth the oxygen content is about on the order of half the surface value. This reduction is attributed to the consumption of oxygen through biological activity. Over large areas a very strongly defined layer of minimum oxygen content is found immediately below the oxygen-rich surface layer (Figure 12.15). Here, at depths on the order of 1600 to 3300 ft (500 to 1000 m), the oxygen content falls to values less than one-tenth of the surface-layer value.

## Density of sea water

Density of sea water is defined as the mass of a unit volume of water. One cubic centimeter of pure fresh water at 39° F (4° C), which is the temperature of greatest density of pure water, has a mass of 1 gram and therefore has a density of 1.00 g/cc.[3] This density is equivalent to a weight of 62.4 pounds for 1 cubic foot of water.

Sea water, because of the presence of dissolved solids, is slightly denser than pure fresh water. Compared with a density of 1.000 g/cc for pure fresh water, sea water has a density of about 1.026–1.028 g/cc. Both temperature and salinity affect the density. Sea water becomes increasingly dense as it becomes colder until the freezing point is reached, at about 28° F (−2° C). This is an important principle because it means that sea water cooled near the surface will tend to sink, displacing water of less density. Density also becomes greater as salinity increases, so that where surface evaporation is great the water near the surface may become slightly denser than that below it, and it therefore then sinks to a lower level. Because temperature is the stronger of the two controls of density, the densest sea water is formed in the cold arctic and polar seas. This very cold water sinks to the bottom and tends to remain close to the floor of the deep ocean basins.

Just as in the atmosphere, where air of lesser density tends to rise while that of greater density tends to sink, so in the oceans water of a greater density than that adjacent to it at the same depth will tend to sink, while water of lesser density than that adjacent to it will tend to rise. This is a fundamental cause of vertical movements, or convection, in both atmosphere and oceans.

## Pressures within the oceans

The principle of *hydrostatic pressure,* or confining pressure in a fluid, applies within the oceans. In descending into the ocean, the pressure which the water exerts equally in all directions upon any exposed surface increases in direct proportion to the depth. Taking the atmospheric pressure at sea level to be 1 *bar,* or 14.7 pounds per square inch (2117 pounds per square foot, about 1 kg per sq cm), we can estimate the confining pressure at any depth in the ocean. In absolute units of *pounds per square foot* we have only to multiply the weight of a cubic foot of water, which is 62.4 pounds, by the depth in feet and add this product to the sea-level pressure of about 2000 pounds (1 ton) per square foot. Thus at a depth of 1000 feet the pressure would be 62,400 + 2000 = 64,400 pounds per square foot. Ocean depths of 20,000 feet are not uncommon. Here the confining pressure would be 1,250,000 pounds per square foot!

In metric units, the pressure increase will be about one gram per square centimeter for each centimeter of depth, and will amount to 1 kg in 10 m, or 100 kg per km. Thus a water layer 10 m thick produces a confining pressure about equal to atmospheric pressure at sea level (1 bar).

Oceanographers, by agreement, state ocean pressure after atmospheric pressure is subtracted. Thus by definition the pressure has a value of zero at the sea surface. Also, a specialized unit of pressure is used. Just as in meteorology, where the millibar is the standard unit, oceanography uses as its unit of pressure the *decibar,* defined as 100,000 dynes per square centimeter. One scientific advantage of using this unit, apart from its conformity to the metric system, is that the water pressure in decibars is approximately equal to the water depth in meters.

While, in contrast to the gases of the atmosphere,

[3] Precisely, the temperature of maximum density of pure water is 3.98° C, and its density at that temperature is 0.999973 g/cc.

ocean water can be loosely described as "incompressible," such is not strictly the case. All liquids and crystalline solids contract somewhat in volume under an increase in confining pressure, even though the amount may be scarcely measurable. Under enormous confining pressures near the bottom of the deep ocean basins the density of sea water is measurably increased by the pressure. Consider, for example, a small mass of surface water with a salinity of 35 ‰ at 0° C and a density of 1.028. If forced to descend to a depth of 4000 m (13,000 ft) this same water would increase in density to a value over 1.048. Thus we see that three variable quantities determine the density of sea water: temperature, salinity, and pressure.

As pressure upon a given mass of sea water is increased, there is an automatic rise of temperature, just as in the case of a gas undergoing compression. Conversely, a decrease in pressure is associated with an automatic decrease in temperature. These temperature changes, which occur without any gain (or loss) of heat energy from outside sources, are described as *adiabatic* temperature changes. Because of increase in pressure alone, the mass of water cited in the sample above, when lowered to a depth of 4000 m (13,000 ft) would experience a temperature increase of about 0.5 C° (0.9 F°). Although given little attention in ocean processes, adiabatic temperature changes are of paramount importance in the atmosphere. Pressure changes resulting from rising and sinking of large bodies of air are associated with very large changes in temperature. The importance of the adiabatic process in the atmosphere is stressed in Chapter 18.

## Static and dynamic concepts

The description of the atmosphere and ocean waters completed gives a largely static concept of these vast fluid layers. It will be necessary to replace this static concept with a dynamic one. Fluids move readily, and the state of motion is the rule in nature, while equilibrium at rest is the exception. Fluids in motion transfer heat energy, and we shall be interested in the importance of these motions in maintaining the thermal environment of our planet Earth.

Moreover, the ocean waters and the atmosphere exchange both matter and energy through their common surface of contact. Matter, in the form of water, passes from the ocean surface to the atmosphere and back again. In these exchanges of matter, water changes its physical state and takes up or releases heat energy. Flow of the atmosphere over the sea surface transfers energy to the ocean by a mechanical process and sets the waters in motion. Ceaseless fluxes of matter and energy are therefore the principal concern of the remaining chapters of this second part of the book.

## References for further study

Johnson, J. C. (1954), *Physical Meteorology,* New York, Technology Press of M.I.T. and Wiley, 393 pp.

Byers, H. R. (1959), *General Meteorology,* New York, McGraw-Hill, 540 pp., chaps. 1, 2, 3.

Massey, H. S. W., and R. L. F. Boyd (1959), *The Upper Atmosphere,* New York, Philosophical Library, 333 pp.

Pickard, G. L. (1963), *Descriptive Physical Oceanography,* New York, Pergamon, 200 pp., chaps. 2, 3, 4.

Bates, D. R. (1964), *The Planet Earth,* New York, Pergamon, 370 pp., chaps. 5, 7.

Yasso, W. E. (1965), *Oceanography,* New York, Holt, Rinehart and Winston, 176 pp., chap. 1.

# 13

# The earth's radiation balance

LIFE PROCESSES ON EARTH, and almost all exchanges of matter and energy at the interface between our atmosphere and the ocean and land surfaces, are powered by radiant energy received from the sun. All circulation systems within the atmosphere and oceans are sustained by solar energy. Global movements of water in the vapor state and as liquid water or ice depend upon solar energy. To understand the processes of our dynamic planetary surface environment we must examine a great natural system: the flow of energy from sun to earth and from earth to outer space. This energy system operates largely through the mechanism of electromagnetic radiation, but it also involves energy storage and transfer as heat within gaseous, liquid, and solid substances of the atmosphere, hydrosphere, and lithosphere.

Some basic principles of electromagnetic radiation were explained in Chapter 6. The sun, as a star with incredibly high internal temperatures that it generates by thermonuclear processes, radiates energy not only with high total intensity but with particular concentration in the shorter wave lengths. The earth, in contrast, has no comparable heat-producing mechanism. (Heat produced internally is negligible, so far as surface temperatures are concerned.) Consequently, the earth takes a secondary role in the radiation system—it gains heat by interception of solar radiation and loses heat by radiation into outer space.

We, as humans, are acutely aware of the operation of the sun-earth-space radiation system through our extreme sensitivity to temperature of the air that surrounds us. We readily sense a gain or loss of heat by direct radiation and conduction. The cyclic nature of temperature changes is familiar to all. There is a daily rhythm of rise and fall of air and ground temperatures as well as a seasonal rhythm. There are also systematic average changes in air temperature from equatorial to polar latitudes as well as from oceanic to continental surfaces. It follows that the lower atmosphere and the surfaces of the lands and oceans must be receiving and giving up heat energy in daily and seasonal cycles. There must also be great differences in the quantities of heat received and given up at low latitudes as compared to high latitudes.

Despite the existence of thermal cycles and latitudinal contrasts in temperature, the geologic record indicates that the global thermal environment through at least a billion years of time has not drifted so far toward either increasing heat or decreasing heat as to render the earth's surface too hot or too cold to support life.

As solar energy is intercepted by our spherical planet the level of heat energy present tends to be raised. At the same time our planet radiates energy into outer space, a process that tends to diminish the planetary level of heat. Incoming and outgoing processes are simultaneously in action. Over long spans of time an average planetary surface temperature is sustained. For a planet close to the sun (Mercury) the average surface temperature will be high, for a distant planet (Uranus or Neptune) it will be very low. Fortunately, the earth's orbital radius is such that the average planetary temperature is favorable to life processes; the extremes of heat and cold are neither sufficiently large nor sufficiently persistent to destroy life.

These considerations lead to the concept of a global *heat budget,* analogous in many respects to the money budget of a complex institution such as a large corporation or a government. A first requirement of a balanced heat budget is that over a long period of time the average level of heat energy remain constant. All departures from the average, whether in cycles of short period or long period, are balanced out by equal and opposite departures. Furthermore, because equatorial regions receive much more energy than is lost directly into space and polar regions lose much more energy than is received, there must be included in the system mechanisms of heat transfer adequate to export heat from a region of excess and to import heat into a region of deficiency. On our planet, motions of the atmosphere and oceans act as heat transfer mechanisms. Thus a study of the earth's heat budget will not be complete until the patterns of global air and water circulation are described and explained (Chapters 15 through 19).

Storage of heat energy in the latent form is an important part of the earth's heat budget. Changes of state between gaseous, liquid, and solid phases are accompanied by the taking up of heat energy or the release of heat energy. Thus water, as it changes from vapor state in the atmosphere to liquid and solid states in the oceans and upon the lands (or reverses the process), liberates or absorbs large quantities of heat. Consequently a study of the earth's heat budget will also not be complete until the processes of change of state of water in the atmosphere are examined in Chapters 18 and 19.

Upon further reflection, it becomes apparent that the movement of water through atmosphere, oceans, and upon the lands comprises a system of equal importance to the flow of heat and that the activities of these two systems are closely intermeshed. The concept of a *water budget* with a *water balance* can be developed and takes its place beside the heat budget (Chapters 33 and 34). The heat budget can be thought of as dealing with energy, the water budget with matter. Together these two great systems form one grand planetary flow system of matter and energy that permits us to relate and explain many environmental phenomena within a single unified frame of reference.

A system approach to the earth's heat budget logically begins with an examination of radiative transfer of energy from sun to earth, and from earth to space. Incoming radiation is traced as it penetrates the atmosphere and is partially absorbed and transformed. The mechanism of radiant energy output of the earth as a low-temperature body is then examined. This aspect of the total heat budget is referred to as the *radiation budget.* In the chapter which follows, the temperature aspect of the heat budget is developed, including the heating and cooling of the lower atmosphere and the surface layers of the continents and oceans.

## Solar and terrestrial radiation compared

Figure 13.1 shows the electromagnetic emission spectra of the sun and the earth. (Refer to Chapter 6 and Figures 6.6 and 6.7 for the background of this discussion.) The wavelength scale on the horizontal axis of Figure 13.1 (as in Figure 6.6) is a constant-ratio (logarithmic) scale, but spans only the range from ultraviolet through infrared wavelengths. (In this chapter the *micron* is used; it is equal to 0.0001 cm.) The smoothly-arched curve at the left is the radiation curve of a black body at 6000° K, representing the idealized sun. The smooth symmetrical curve at the right is the radiation curve of a black body at 300° K (27° C, 80° F), representing the idealized earth.

The standard unit of radiation is the *langley,* equal to one gram calorie[1] of heat received (or emitted) by one square centimeter of surface (about 1/16 square inch). Units used on the vertical scale of Figure 13.1 are langleys per minute for each subdivision of the spectrum having a width of one micron (0.0001 cm). The idealized sun at 6000° K radiates about 100,000 langleys per minute (ly/min). Less than 0.0025 percent of this quantity, or 2.3 ly/min, is intercepted by the earth. Actually, the solar radiation at the outer limit of the atmosphere, on a surface held perpendicular to the sun's rays, is approximately 2.0 ly/min, a value known as the *solar constant.* The actual solar radiation curve is shown as a highly irregular line below the smooth curve.

For many years, scientists of the Smithsonian Institution of Washington have evaluated the solar constant from measurements made at the earth's surface. Since the advent of orbiting satellites, carrying instruments to measure solar radiation continuously over long periods of time, the solar constant has been more precisely determined—the value of 1.95 ly/min at a height of 53

[1] The gram calorie, the standard unit for expressing amount of heat, is that quantity of heat needed to raise the temperature of one gram of water through 1C° at 15° C. It takes 252 calories to equal 1 British thermal unit (BTU).

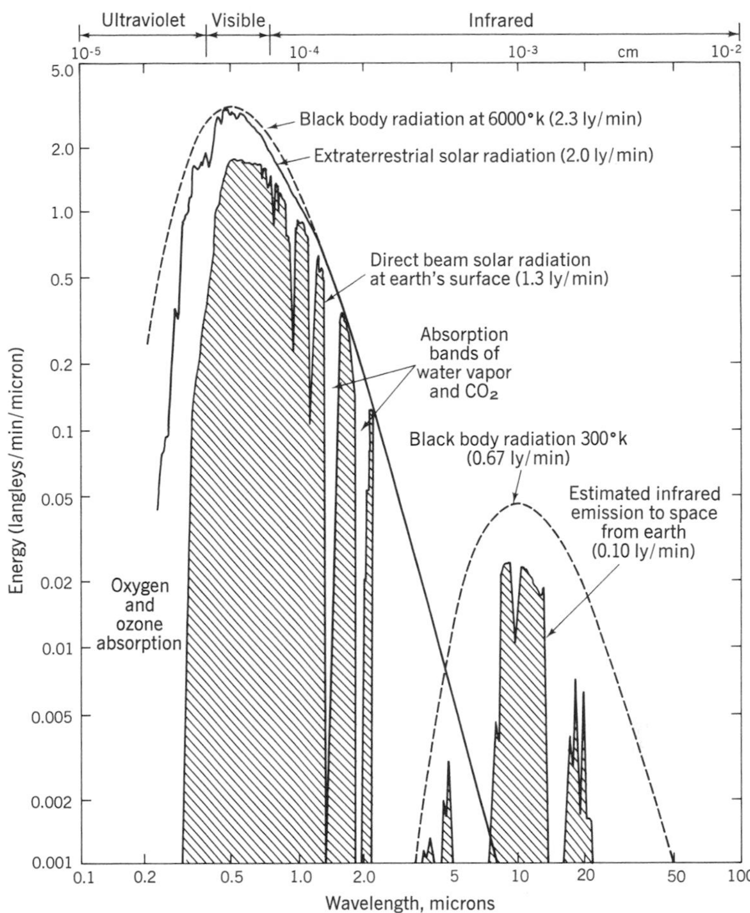


**FIGURE 13.1.** Spectrum of incoming and outgoing radiation from sun and earth. Logarithmic scales are used for both energy and wavelength. [From W. D. Sellers (1965), *Physical Climatology,* Chicago, Univ. of Chicago Press, p. 20, Figure 6.]

mi (85 km) was announced in 1968. From surface observations it was known that the solar constant actually fluctuates slightly, being increased or decreased by as much as 1.5 percent, because of variations in the ultraviolet output of the sun.

Notice in Figure 13.1 that the smooth curve at the right, representing the radiation of a black body at 300° K, differs from the solar radiation curve in two respects. First, the emission is entirely within the infrared portion of the spectrum and is not visible. The peak occurs at about 10 microns (0.001 cm). Second, the black body radiation at 300° K is only 0.67 ly/min, or about one-third the value of the solar constant. The actual curve of outgoing terrestrial radiation lost to space shows sharp peaks and conspicuous gaps. It lies below the smoothly arched curve and totals only 0.1 ly/min. This quantity is only 1/20 as large as the solar constant.

The question will immediately arise: How can a radiation balance be achieved if incoming radiation is so much greater than outgoing radiation? We might anticipate two possible answers: (a) A substantial part of incoming radiation is reflected back into space and is ineffective in causing heating of the earth, and (b) a part of the incoming energy is absorbed by the atmosphere and radiated back into space without affecting the earth's surface. Both mechanisms will be examined in paragraphs to follow.

## Solar radiation over a spherical earth

Because the earth is a sphere (disregarding oblateness), only one point on earth presents a surface at right angles to the sun's rays. This *subsolar point* coincides with the occurrence of solar noon at a latitude equal to the sun's declination; at this instant the sun is in the zenith position for an observer at the subsolar point. In all directions away from the subsolar point the earth's curvature causes the receiving surface to be turned away from the sun at an increasing angle with respect to the rays, until, at the circle of illumination, a horizontal surface parallels the rays. The hemisphere lying beyond this great circle is, of course, in darkness.

We shall now make use of the information covered in Chapter 4 about illumination of the globe as controlled by latitude and the seasons. Whereas the earlier discussion related to light and darkness, the present discussion substitutes energy of the entire electromagnetic radiation spectrum.

Assuming for the moment that the earth possesses a geometrically perfect spherical surface, but has no atmosphere, the total quantity of solar energy received by one square centimeter of horizontal surface in one day will depend upon two factors: (a) the angle at which the sun's rays strike the earth, and (b) the length of time of exposure to rays. These factors are varied by latitude and by the seasonal changes in the path of the sun in the sky.

If the earth's axis were perpendicular to the plane of the ecliptic (e.g., if there were no axial tilt) the conditions of equinox would prevail throughout the entire year. Equinox conditions at noon are shown in Figure 13.2. Radiation at the equator is 100%, with a value of 2.0 ly/min. At 30° N. and S. the percentage is reduced to 86.6%, or 1.73 ly/min; at 60° N. and S. values are zero.[2] These facts lead to the general statement that the earth will receive its greatest total solar radiation at the equator and the least at the poles.

For an entire day at equinox, the input of solar radiation will need to be totaled for each minute that the sun is above the horizon. The changing angle, from zero at sunrise to a maximum value at noon, then back to zero at sunset, will need to be determined for each minute of the 24-hour day. When this calculation is made, the daily radiation totals are roughly as follows:

| Latitude | ly/day |
|---|---|
| 0 | 890 |
| 10 | 880 |
| 20 | 840 |
| 30 | 770 |
| 40 | 680 |
| 50 | 570 |
| 60 | 445 |
| 70 | 305 |
| 80 | 155 |
| 90 | 0 |

(Referring to Figure 13.4, these values can be read along the dashed vertical line for either the vernal equinox or autumnal equinox.)

Because of the earth's annual cycle of declination from 23½° N. to 23½° S. from solstice to solstice, the incoming radiation at a given parallel of latitude will change through an annual cycle. The resulting curves

[2] The equation is $Q = 2.0 \cos \phi$, where $Q$ is radiation in ly/min and $\phi$ is latitude in degrees.

**FIGURE 13.2.** Radiation intensity and latitude.

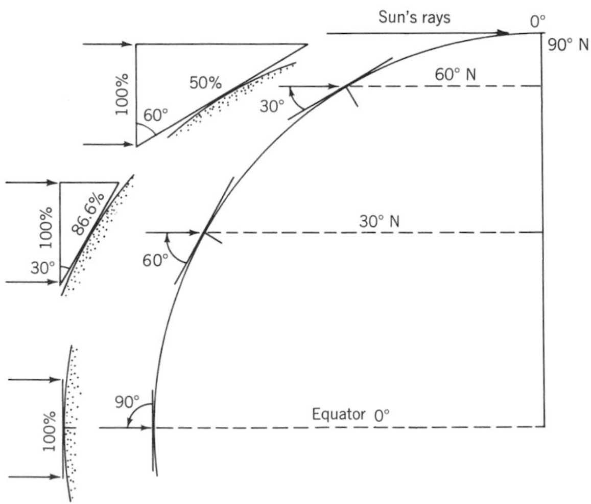


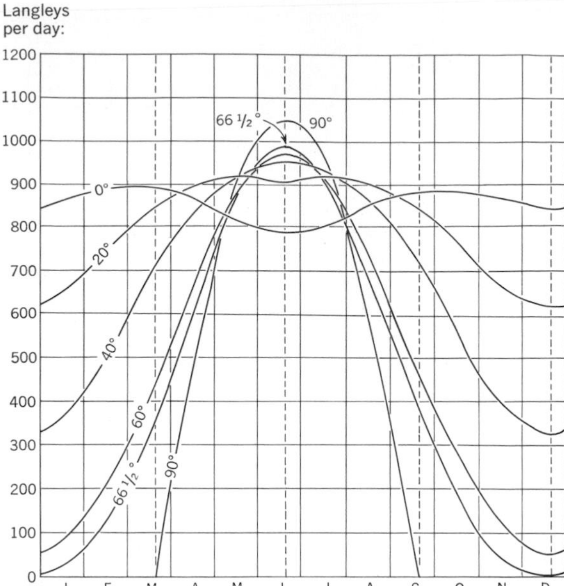


**FIGURE 13.3.** Annual cycle of variation in daily quantities of solar radiation at selected latitudes in the Northern Hemisphere. (Data from Smithsonian Institution, Washington, D.C.)

are shown for various north latitudes in Figure 13.3. Notice that the equator has a cycle with two maxima and two minima, because the sun passes overhead twice per year; nevertheless, radiation is very strong throughout the entire year. At 20° N. latitude the double maxima persist, but with only a slight dip at summer solstice. At all latitudes between 23½° and 66½° the radiation curve shows one maximum and one minimum, the amplitude increasing with higher latitude. Poleward of 66½° a part of the year has no incoming radiation. At the poles, this period of zero value is 6 months long and spans the entire period between equinoxes.

A careful study of the curves drawn in Figure 13.3 will reveal that they are not symmetrical with respect to the equinoxes and solstices. A factor that must be taken into account is the varying distance between earth and sun because of the elliptical form of the earth's orbit (Chapter 1). Radiation will be slightly less at aphelion (July 4) than at perihelion (January 3). Take, for example, the peak radiation at the poles, occurring at solstice. The north pole peak value is about 1050 ly/day, whereas the south pole reaches a peak value of 1185 ly/day. This difference is explained by the earth being closer to the sun around the time of December solstice, but farther from the sun around the June solstice. Notice that at the equator only about 780 ly/day are received at June solstice, as compared with 840 ly/day at December solstice.

Figure 13.4 is a graph showing incoming solar radiation throughout the year. The curved lines are isopleths of daily total radiation (ly/day). A careful comparison of the right and left halves of this graph will reveal differences that can be attributed to the varying earth–sun distances from perihelion to aphelion.

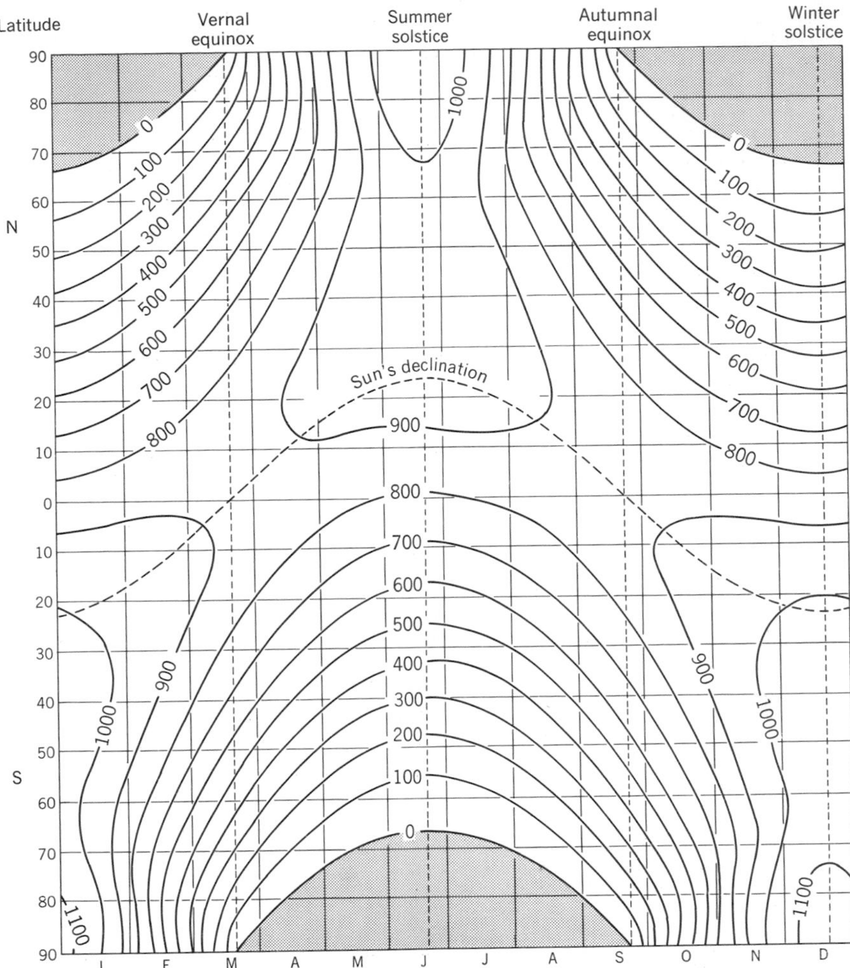


**FIGURE 13.4.** Solar radiation in langleys per day received on a horizontal surface outside the earth's atmosphere throughout the year at any latitude. Values are based on a solar constant of 1.94 ly/min. [After S. Fritz (1951), *Compendium of Meteorology,* Boston, Amer. Meteorological Soc., p. 19, Figure 3.]

## Radiation losses in the atmosphere

As solar radiation penetrates the earth's atmosphere, a series of selective depletions and diversions of energy take place. These are summarized in Table 13.1. The unit used in this table is the *kilolangley,* equal to one thousand langleys. At an altitude of 95 mi (150 km) the radiation spectrum possesses almost 100% of its original energy, but after penetration to an altitude of 55 mi (88 km) absorption of X rays is almost complete and some of the ultraviolet radiation has been absorbed as well. As noted in Chapter 12, the ionosphere is developed in this region of the atmosphere by the effect of the highly energetic X rays, gamma rays, and ultraviolet rays upon molecules and atoms of nitrogen and oxygen.

As solar radiation penetrates into deeper and denser atmospheric layers gas molecules cause the visible light rays to be turned aside in all possible directions, a process known as *Rayleigh scattering* (Figure 13.5). Where dust particles are encountered in the troposphere, further scattering occurs. The total process may be described as *diffuse reflection.* That the clear sky is blue in color is explained by Rayleigh scattering of the shorter visible wavelengths. These predominantly blue light waves reach our eye indirectly from all parts of the sky. The red wavelengths and infrared rays are less subject to scattering and largely continue in a straight-line path toward earth. The setting sun appears red because a part of the red rays escape deflection from the direct line of sight.

As a result of all forms of short-wave scattering, some solar energy is returned to space and forever lost, while at the same time some scattered short-wave energy is also directed earthward. The latter is referred to as *diffuse sky radiation,* or *down scatter.*

Absorption is another form of energy loss that takes place as solar radiation penetrates the atmosphere. Both carbon dioxide ($CO_2$) and water vapor are capable of directly absorbing infrared radiation. An additional but minor form of energy absorption is that which occurs in the ozone layer (see Chapter 12) as oxygen molecules are broken into atoms and re-formed into ozone molecules. Absorption results in a rise of sensible temperature of the air. Thus some direct heating of the lower atmosphere takes place during incoming solar radiation. Although carbon dioxide is a constant quantity in the air (0.033 percent by volume), the water vapor content of air varies greatly from place to place, being as low as

**TABLE 13.1. THE GLOBAL RADIATION BUDGET***

| INCOMING SOLAR RADIATION (Short-wave) | Kilolangleys per year | | Percent | |
|---|---|---|---|---|
| Total at top of atmosphere | | 263 | | 100 |
| Reflection from clouds to space | 56 | | 21 | |
| Diffuse reflection to space (Rayleigh scatter, dust) | 14 | | 5 | |
| Direct reflection from earth's surface | 14 | | 6 | |
| Total reflection loss to space by earth-atmosphere system (Earth's albedo) | 8 | 84 | | 32 |
| Absorbed by clouds | 8 | | 3 | |
| Absorbed by molecules, dust, water vapor, $CO_2$ | 40 | | 15 | |
| Absorbed by earth's surface | 131 | | 50 | |
| Total absorbed by earth-atmosphere system | | 179 | | 68 |
| Sum of absorption and reflection | | 263 | | 100 |
| OUTGOING RADIATION (Long-wave) | | | | |
| Infrared radiation from earth's surface | 258 | | 98 | |
| Lost to space | 21 | | 8 | |
| Absorbed by atmosphere | 237 | | 90 | |
| Infrared radiation emitted by atmosphere | 361 | | 137 | |
| Lost to space | 158 | | 60 | |
| Absorbed by earth's surface as counter-radiation | 203 | | 77 | |
| Effective (net) outgoing radiation from earth's surface | | 55 | | 21 |
| Effective (net) outgoing radiation from atmosphere | | 124 | | 47 |
| Effective (net) outgoing radiation from earth-atmosphere system | | 179 | | 68 |

* Data from W. D. Sellers (1965), *Physical Climatology,* Chicago, Univ. of Chicago Press, Tables 6 and 9.

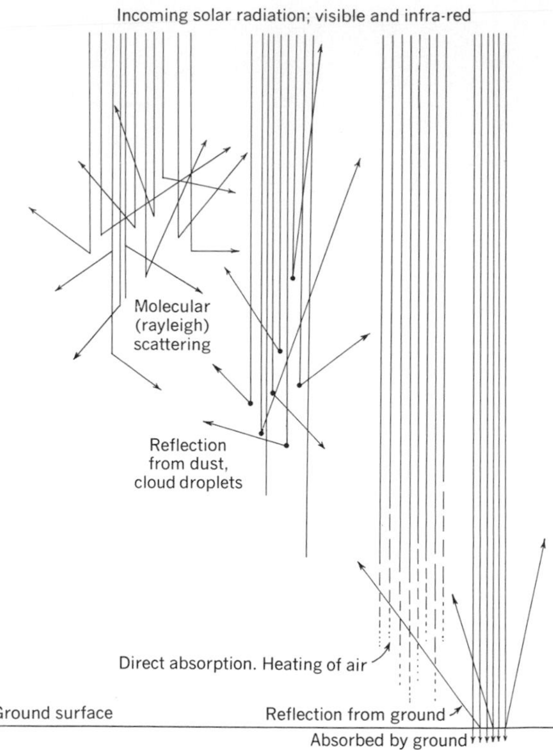


**FIGURE 13.5.** Schematic diagram of scattering, reflection, and absorption of solar radiation entering the atmosphere.

0.01 percent by weight under arctic winter conditions to as high as 1.8 percent by weight in humid equatorial regions. Absorption of infrared radiation correspondingly varies from one global environment to another.

All forms of direct energy absorption listed above—namely X ray, gamma ray, and ultraviolet absorption in the ionosphere and ozone layer, combined with direct long-wave absorption by carbon dioxide, water vapor, and other gas molecules and dust particles—are estimated to total as little as 10% for conditions of clear, dry air, to as high as 30% when a cloud cover exists. A world average figure is about 18% (Table 13.1).

Figure 13.6 shows in a highly diagrammatic way the range of values of the various forms of reflection and absorption that may occur. When skies are clear, reflection and absorption combined may total about 20%, leaving as much as 80% to reach the ground.

Yet another form of energy loss must be brought into the picture. The upper surfaces of clouds are extremely good reflectors of short-wave radiation. Air travelers are well aware of how painfully brilliant the sunlit upper surface of a cloud deck can be when seen from above. Cloud reflection can account for a direct turning back into space of from 30–60% of total incoming radiation (Figure 13.6). Thus we see that under conditions of a heavy cloud layer, the combined reflection and absorption from clouds alone can account for a loss of 35 to 90% of the incoming radiation and allow 45 to 0% to reach the ground. A world average value of 21% for cloud reflection, based on about 50% cloud coverage, is listed in Table 13.1.

The surfaces of the land and ocean reflect some short-wave radiation directly back into the atmosphere. This quantity, which is very small, averages about 6% on a global basis. This reflection combined with cloud reflection and diffuse reflection give a total global reflective loss of about 32% in Table 13.1.

## The earth's albedo

The percentage of radiant energy reflected back by a surface is termed the *albedo.* This is an important property of the earth's surface because it determines the relative rate of heating of the surface when exposed to solar radiation. Albedo of a water surface is very low (2%) for nearly vertical rays, but high for low-angle rays. For oceans generally, albedos range from 6 to 10%. Albedo is extremely high for snow or ice (45–95%). For fields, forests, and bare ground the albedos are of intermediate value, ranging from as low as 5% to as high as 30%. Albedo of cloud layers is high, up to 90%.

In calculating the earth's radiation balance, it is extremely important to determine albedos over large regions, and ultimately to estimate the earth's total

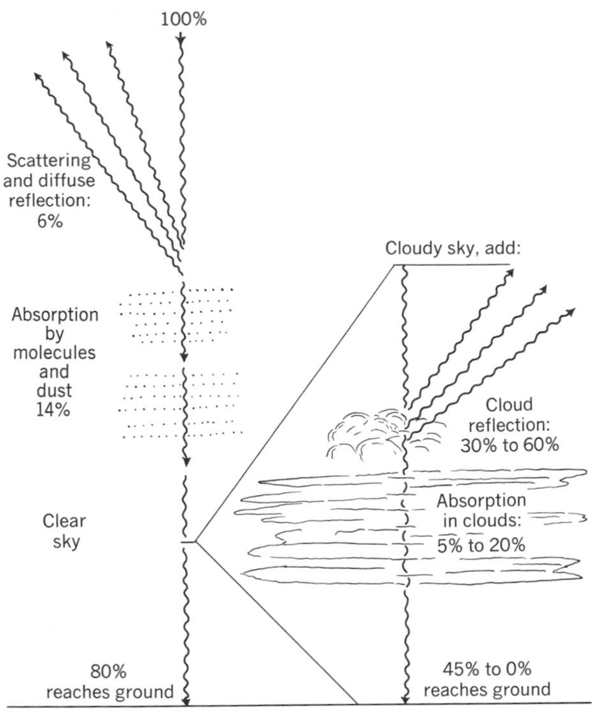


**FIGURE 13.6.** Schematic diagram of losses of incoming radiation on clear and cloudy days.

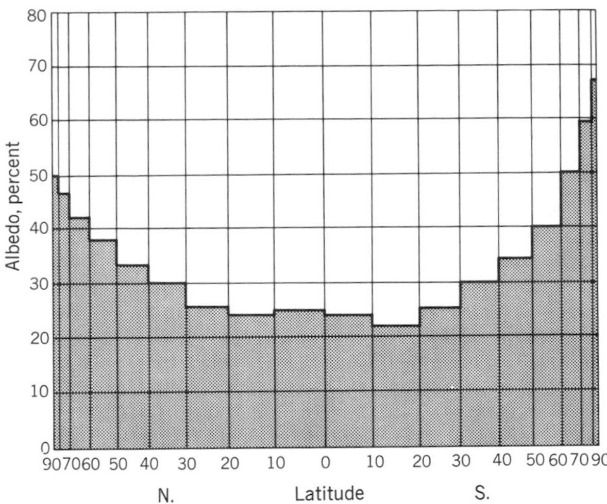


**FIGURE 13.7.** Meridional profile of earth's mean albedo based on satellite data. Latitude is scaled proportionate to sine of latitude, and graph areas are in true proportion to earth's surface areas between successive ten-degree parallels of latitude. [Data from T. H. Vonder Haar and V. E. Suomi (1969), *Science,* vol. 163, p. 667, Figure 1.]

average albedo year in and year out. Table 13.2 gives approximate average ground-surface values for latitude belts of the North American continent. Notice that whereas summer albedos are small and show very little difference with latitude, winter albedos are large, because of snow cover, and show a strong latitudinal range.

We turn next to consider the albedo of unit portions of the earth as measured from beyond the outer limits of the atmosphere. Meteorological satellites, continually orbiting the earth and providing long-term data, have made a major contribution to the global assessment of the radiation budget. Figure 13.7 shows the average albedo profile from pole to pole as measured from outer space. Figure 13.8 shows the global distribution of mean annual albedo. Both illustrations are based on data of orbiting satellites of the *Tiros* type and represent many months of observations. It is interesting to notice that albedos range from high values (50 to 60) near the poles to low values (20 to 30) in tropical and equatorial latitudes. The hemispheres are quite similar in this respect, despite the great preponderance of land areas in the Northern Hemisphere. Similarity of hemispheres suggests that albedo depends more upon cloud cover than upon the albedos of the land and sea surfaces. To understand the distribution of centers of high and low albedo shown on the world map (Figure 13.8) requires a very thorough knowledge of world weather and climate and is too complex a problem for discussion here. Notice, however, that albedo is uniformly distributed around the Southern Hemisphere, over the vast Southern Ocean and the pole-centered continent of Antarctica, whereas the pattern is very irregular where oceans and continents alternate around the earth's circumference.

**TABLE 13.2. AVERAGE ALBEDOS OVER THE NORTH AMERICAN CONTINENT***

| Latitude Zone (°N.) | Prevailing Surface Type | Albedo: Winter (average snow cover) | Albedo: Summer |
|---|---|---|---|
| 65–70 | Tundra (treeless surface) | 83 | 16 |
| 55–65 | Tundra and conifer forest | 60–67 | 16 |
| 45–55 | Forest and grassland | 46–50 | 15 |
| 35–45 | Shrubland (West)<br>Cropland (Midwest)<br>Woodland (East) | 29–39 | 16 |
| 25–35 | Desert and shrubland (West)<br>Cropland and woodland (East) | 18–19 | 17–18 |
| 20–25 | Highlands, desert, rain forest | 16 | 16 |
| | Continental mean | 43 | 16 |

* Greatly simplified after Kung, Bryson, and Lenschow (1964), *Monthly Weather Review,* vol. 92.

Recently published estimates of the earth's albedo, based on satellite measurements, give values between 29 and 34. These are average annual values for the earth as a planet. Table 13.1 uses the value of 32, which falls within the range obtained by satellite observation. Consider other planetary albedos for comparison:

| | |
|---|---|
| Mercury | 6 |
| Venus | 76 |
| Earth | 29–34 |
| (Moon) | (7) |
| Mars | 16 |
| Jupiter | 73 |
| Saturn | 76 |
| Uranus | 93 |
| Neptune | 94 |
| Pluto | 14 |

Earth's albedo is intermediate between the low values of the moon and inner planets with little or no atmos-

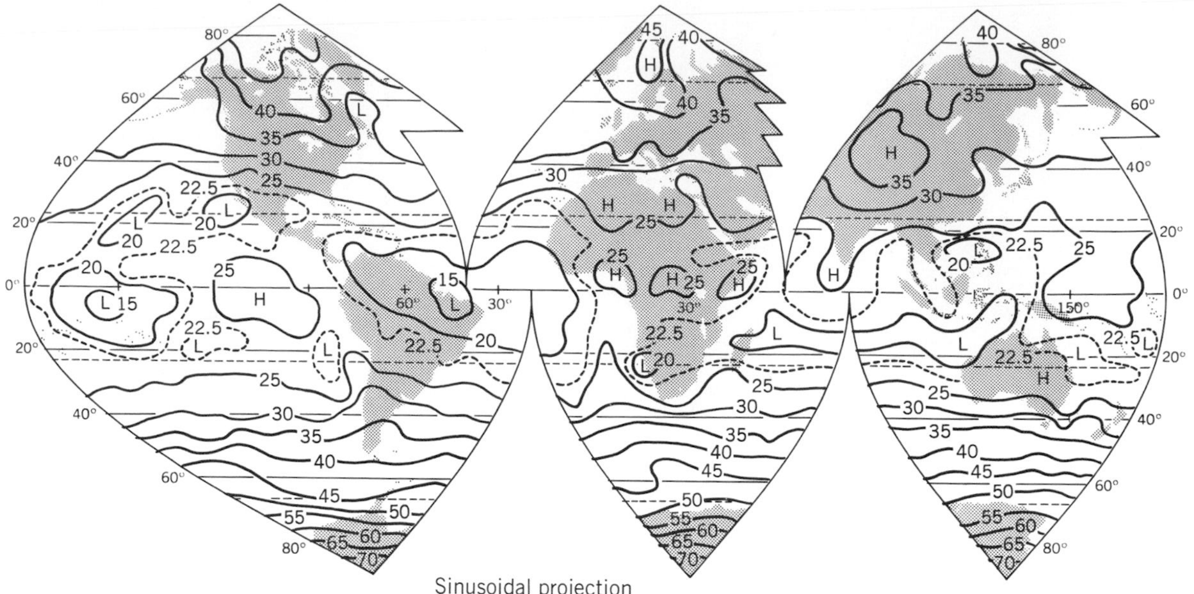


**FIGURE 13.8.** World map of mean planetary albedo compiled from satellite data. Values are in percent. For explanation of sinusoidal map projection refer to Appendix I. [Data from T. H. Vonder Haar and V. E. Suomi (1969), *Science,* vol. 163, p. 668, Figure 2a.]

phere (Mercury and Mars), and the high values of those planets with dense atmospheres (Venus and the great planets). Again, we find planet Earth to have another unique environmental property as compared with the other planets.

## World distribution of incoming radiation

Solar radiation actually absorbed by the earth's surface varies greatly not only from pole to pole, but also from land areas to ocean areas within the same latitude zone. Figure 13.9 is a profile from pole to pole, showing the mean annual radiation received at the earth's surface (lower line) as compared with radiation entering at the top of the atmosphere (upper line). The shaded area between the curves represents the total loss of energy by the various forms of reflection and absorption discussed in earlier paragraphs, excluding reflection from the surface.

Figure 13.10 shows mean annual global distribution of radiation received at the surface. Centers of high values (over 180 kly/yr) lie over continents in tropical latitudes (about on the Tropics of Cancer and Capricorn); these are the great tropical deserts of the world. There are secondary centers of concentration over equatorial oceans. Many factors of weather and climate enter into the pattern of the distribution of absorbed solar radiation.

## Long-wave radiation

The surfaces of the continents and oceans, possessing heat derived originally from absorption of the sun's rays, continually radiate this energy back into the atmosphere, a process known as *ground radiation* or *terrestrial radiation.* This infrared radiation occurs at wavelengths longer than 3 or 4 microns and is referred to here as *long-wave* radiation (Figure 13.1). The atmosphere also radiates long-wave energy both toward the earth and outward into space, where it is lost. It is essential to understand that long-wave radiation is quite different from reflection, in which the rays are turned back directly without being absorbed. Long-wave radiation from both ground and atmosphere continues during the night, when no solar radiation is being received.

**FIGURE 13.9.** Meridional profiles of mean annual values of entering solar radiation at top of atmosphere and radiation absorbed by earth's surface. Area between the two curves represents energy loss in atmosphere. [Data from W. D. Sellers (1965), *Physical Climatology,* Chicago, Univ. of Chicago Press, p. 22, Figure 7.]

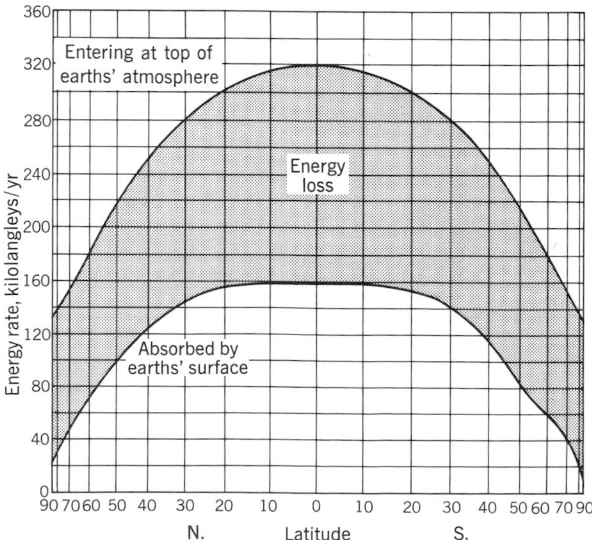

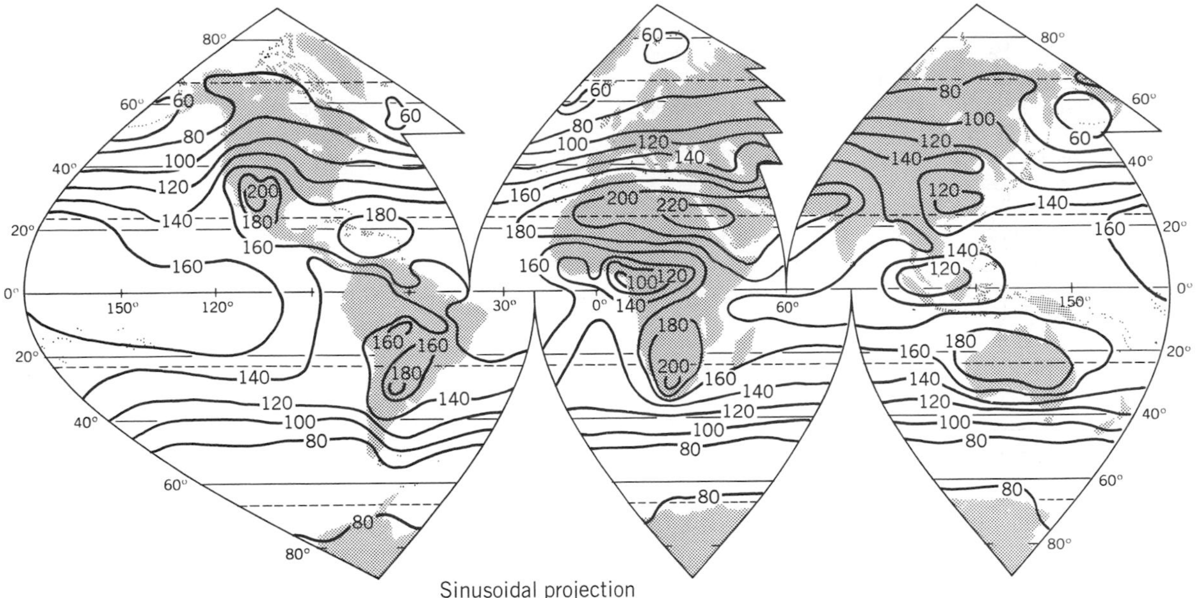


**FIGURE 13.10.** World map of mean annual solar radiation received at the earth's surface. Units are kilolangleys per year. [Based on data of M. I. Budyko (1963), *Atlas Teplovogo Balansa,* Moscow, U.S.S.R., Gidrometeorologischeskoe Izdatel'stvo.]

Energy radiated from the ground is easily absorbed by the atmosphere because it consists largely of very long wavelengths (4 to 50 microns), in contrast to the visible light rays (0.4 to 0.7 microns) and shorter infrared rays (0.7 to 3.0 microns) which make up almost all of the entering solar radiation (Figure 13.1). Absorption of long-wave radiation by water vapor and carbon dioxide takes place largely in wavelengths from 5 to 8 microns and 12 to 20 microns. However, radiation in the range of wavelengths between 8 and 11 microns passes freely through the earth's atmosphere and into outer space (see Figure 13.1). About 8% (21 kly/yr) of the long-wave radiation directed outward leaves the atmosphere in this manner (Table 13.1).

Thus the atmosphere receives much of its heat by an indirect process in which the incoming energy in short-wave form is permitted to pass through, but that in long-wave form is not readily permitted to escape. For this reason the lower atmosphere with its water vapor and carbon dioxide acts as a warm blanket which returns heat to the earth and helps to keep surface temperatures from dropping excessively during the night or in winter at middle and high latitudes. Somewhat the same principle is employed in greenhouses and in homes using the solar-heating method. Here the glass permits entry of short-wave energy. Accumulated heat cannot escape by mixing with cooler air outside. The expression *greenhouse effect* has been used by meteorologists to describe this atmospheric heating principle.

A perfect radiator, or black body, emits infrared radiation according to the Stefan-Boltzman law, under which the energy emitted is proportional to the fourth power of the absolute temperature. Most surfaces, however, are not perfect radiators. Instead, the emission of energy takes place at less than the black body rate. Such an imperfect radiating surface can be described as a *gray body.* The proportion of emission of a gray body, as compared to the black body, is known as the *infrared emissivity.* It ranges numerically from close to zero, for no emission, to unity (100 percent) for the black body case. Highly polished silver has an infrared emissivity of only about 2 percent, an example of extremely low emissivity. Most natural terrestrial surfaces have an emissivity that is in the range of from 85 to 99 percent. A few representative values are as follows:

| | Emissivity | Albedo |
|---|---|---|
| water | 92–96 | 6–10 |
| snow | 82–99 | 75–95 |
| dry sand | 89–90 | 35–45 |
| plowed dry ground | 90 | 5–15 |
| pine forest | 90 | 5–15 |
| alfalfa | 95 | 15–25 |

We can conclude that most natural surfaces are highly efficient emitters of infrared radiation. Most bare ground and vegetated surfaces have low albedos and consequently absorb incoming short-wave radiation readily. We should expect that such surfaces will heat readily to high temperatures and will therefore be strong infrared radiators.

## Terrestrial radiation and the radiation budget

Returning to consideration of the earth's total radiation budget, it is a requirement of a radiation balance that just as much energy, on the average over long periods of time, is sent out from the entire planet earth into space as is received from the sun. It can also be inferred that the earth's total surface (including both land and water surfaces) on the yearly average must return to the atmosphere exactly as much energy as it receives, otherwise the surface temperature would rise or sink.

The lower part of Table 13.1 gives a summary of outgoing radiation. Certain of the large radiation quantities listed here may prove confusing. Notice that infrared radiation from the earth's surface is 258 kilolangleys per year (kly/yr), whereas the total absorption of solar radiation by the earth's surface (upper part of table) is only 131 kly/yr. The explanation lies in the exchange of energy between atmosphere and the earth's surface. Radiation returned to earth is designated *counter-radiation.* To obtain the effective (or net) value of the outgoing radiation from the surface (55 kly/yr), we must subtract the amount absorbed by the earth's surface as counter-radiation (203 kly/yr), from the total infrared radiation from the earth's surface (258 kly/yr). The summed values of effective outgoing radiation from earth's surface and atmosphere total 179 kly/yr, which equals the total absorbed by the earth-atmosphere system. It should be kept in mind that the figures in Table 13.1 are estimates and are subject to revision as more data are obtained.

Two lines of figures in Table 13.1, when compared, appear to constitute a discrepancy in the radiation budget. Notice that whereas the earth's surface absorbs 131 kly annually, the effective outgoing radiation from this same surface is given as only 55 kly annually. Accepting the data as valid, we must look for an explanation, which lies in the fact that the earth's surface gives back heat energy to the atmosphere not only by long-wave ground radiation, but also by two other heat transfer mechanisms. The first of these is by *latent heat* associated with evaporation and subsequent condensation of water. As water evaporates from free water surfaces and moist soil, heat energy is absorbed and enters into a latent (stored) form in water vapor. This water vapor diffuses and mixes with the lower atmosphere, carrying the latent heat with it. Condensation in clouds and precipitation in the form of rain and snow releases the latent heat into sensible heat form, raising the temperature of the atmosphere. (This process is treated in further detail in Chapter 18.)

The second additional mechanism for transfer of heat energy from ground to atmosphere is by direct conduction. Heat is transferred directly from land or sea surfaces to the air in contact with it. Turbulent air motions accompanying winds mix the heated air with higher layers. Of course, when the ground is colder than the air above it, conduction acts in reverse and the ground receives heat from the air.

Orbiting earth satellites have provided global information on the average outgoing long-wave radiation from the earth as a planet. Sensing instruments, directed earthward, can measure the long-wave radiation emanating from the earth-track below the satellite. The albedo of the earth below is measured at the same

**FIGURE 13.11.** Meridional profile of mean long-wave radiation from the earth, as determined from satellite data. [Data from T. H. Vonder Haar and V. E. Suomi (1969), *Science,* vol. 163, p. 667, Figure 1.]

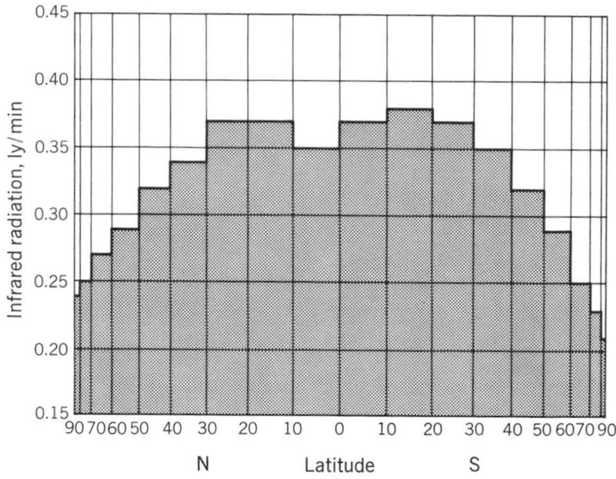


**FIGURE 13.12.** World map of mean outgoing infrared radiation, based on satellite data. Values are in langleys per minute. [Data from T. H. Vonder Haar and V. E. Suomi (1969), *Science,* vol. 163, p. 668, Figure 2b.]

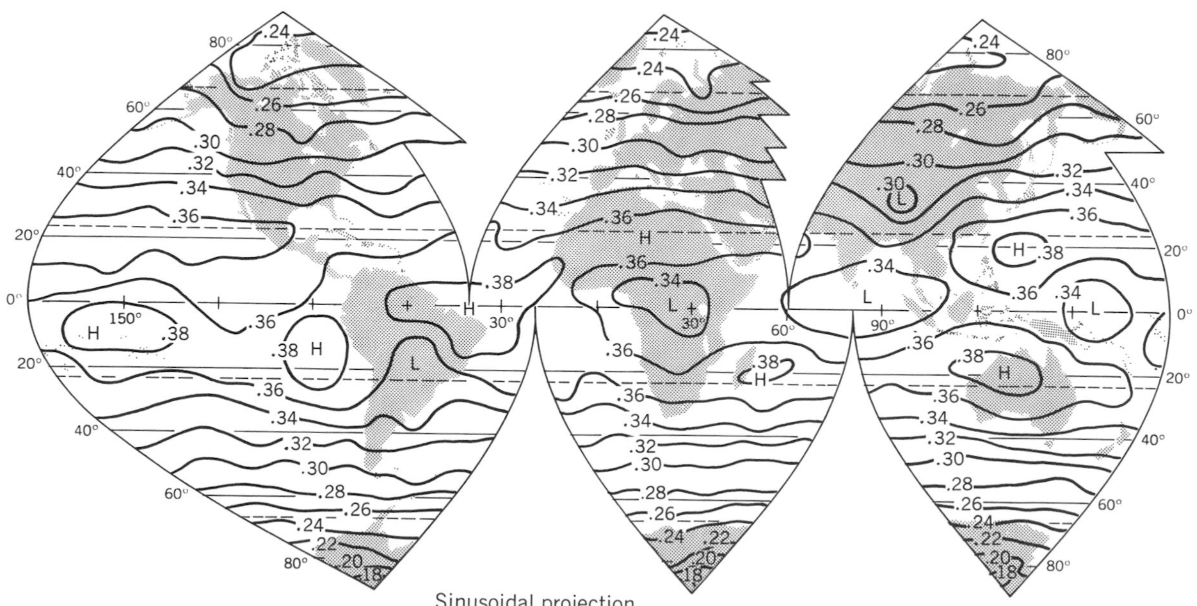

time through other instruments, also directed downward, but sensitive to reflected short-wave radiation (see Figures 13.7 and 13.8).

Figure 13.11 is a profile of average outgoing infrared radiation from pole to pole. Figure 13.12 is a world map of this same radiation. The average value of the profile is about the same as shown in Table 13.1, namely 179 kly/yr. Notice the double maxima in the profile, about over latitudes 15–20° N. and S., and a small dip over equatorial latitudes. On the world map, centers of somewhat lower radiation lie along much of the equator, where cloud cover is concentrated and water vapor content is high. Irregular belts of higher values on either side lie largely over dry or desert areas. Here there is little cloud cover to reflect back and absorb outgoing radiation and the air contains relatively less water vapor to absorb the radiation.

Subtracting the outgoing radiation value of 55 kly/yr from the incoming value of 131 kly/yr leaves a difference of 76 kly/yr that must be otherwise transferred to the atmosphere. About two-thirds of this quantity moves by upward latent heat transfer, and about one-third by conduction and mixing.

## Measurement of radiation at the ground surface

Measurements of the incoming short-wave radiation are made continuously at a network of observing stations on the ground. Various types of instruments are available and perform a variety of functions. The *pyrheliometer* is a standard instrument for precision measurements; it is designed to measure the incoming radiation in a narrow beam directed at right angles to the receiving surface of the instrument.

An instrument used more widely is the *pyranometer,* which measures all short-wave radiation emanating within the 180-degree arc of the sky dome. It therefore senses both the direct solar beam and all incoming scattered radiation (Figure 13.13). The pyranometer can be exposed continuously at an observing station. About 75 stations using the pyranometer are in operation in the continental United States and form a network sufficiently dense to allow maps of mean monthly radiation to be drawn.

**FIGURE 13.13.** Pyranometer for measurement of solar and sky radiation. (Photograph by courtesy of WeatherMeasure Corporation, Sacramento, Calif.)

Other types of instruments sense only infrared radiation. One instrument, the *net radiometer,* can measure the difference between incoming radiation from above and outgoing radiation from below.

## Seasonal radiation cycles

The discussion of radiant energy flow or *energy flux,* both incoming and outgoing, at the earth's surface has thus far dealt with annual averages only. Such annual figures would apply well to individual months only in equatorial regions where the sun is constantly at a high elevation and the days are about of equal length throughout the year. In middle latitudes strong seasonal effects are felt; these increase poleward, where great

**FIGURE 13.14.** A one-year record of incoming solar radiation at Inyokern, California. [From W. D. Sellers (1965), *Physical Climatology,* Chicago, Univ. of Chicago Press, p. 28, Figure 11; based on data of ESSA, Weather Bureau, Climatological Data, National Summary, vol. 13, 1962.]

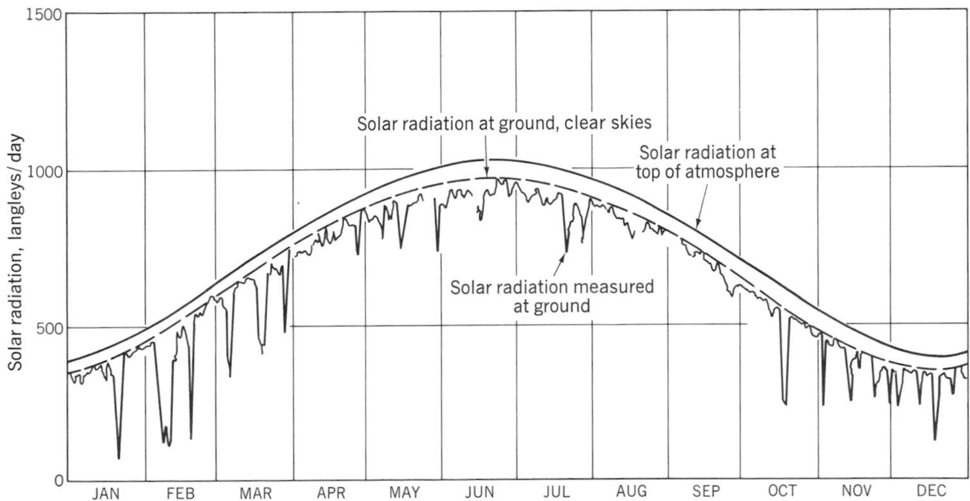

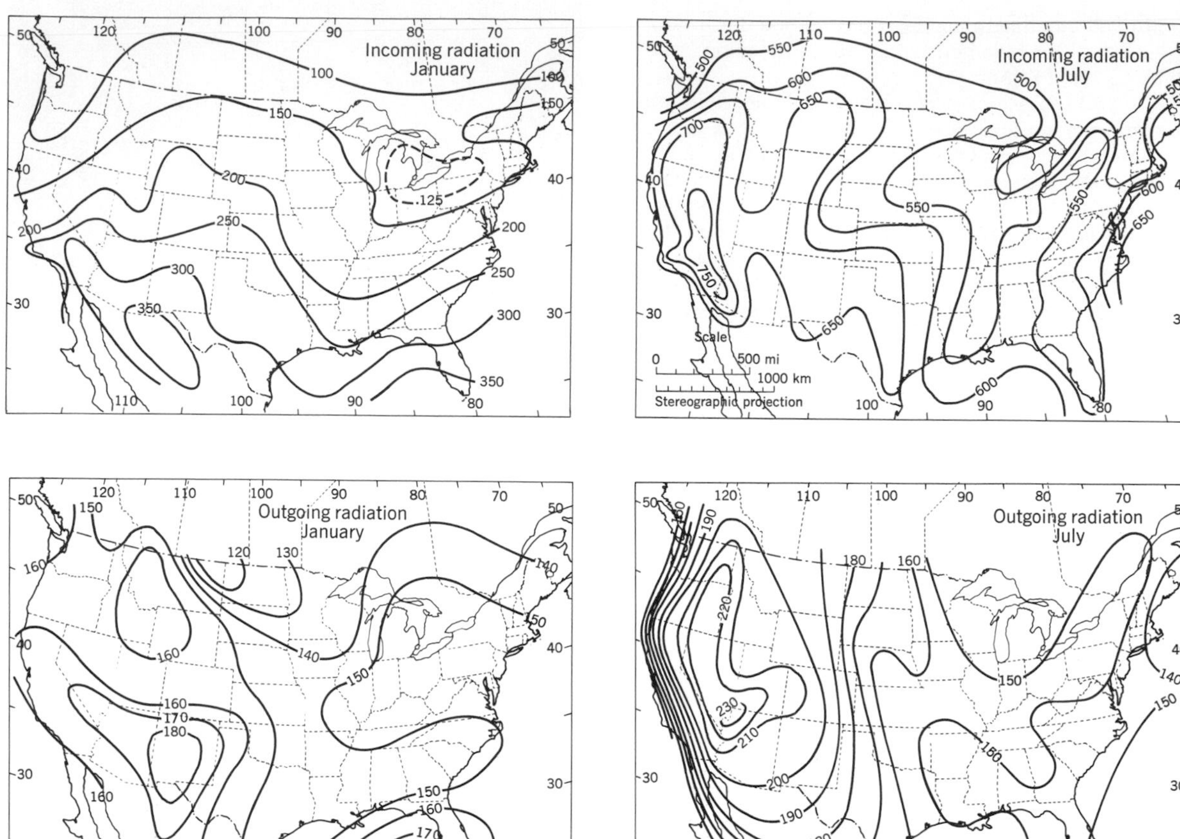


**FIGURE 13.15.** Maps of the United States showing mean solar radiation (ly/day) and mean effective outgoing radiation (ly/day) under conditions of clear skies for the months of January and July. [After W. D. Sellers (1965), *Physical Climatology,* Chicago, Univ. of Chicago Press, Figures 9, 10, 17, and 18.]

extremes exist. We have already considered how season affects the cycle of incoming short-wave radiation at the top of the atmosphere (Figures 13.2 through 13.4).

An example of the seasonal rhythm of incoming solar radiation is seen in the record of an entire year at a desert station in California (Figure 13.14). The actual record shows sharp dips, particularly in winter months, because of presence of cloudy days. A smoothly drawn curve over the highest points of the record shows the curve as it would look if clear skies persisted constantly. The upper curve is that of radiation at the top of the atmosphere.

The effect of season upon radiation at middle latitudes is well shown by maps of the United States and southern Canada. Figure 13.15 is a set of four maps, two for January and two for July. The upper map of each set shows incoming solar radiation for normal cloud-cover conditions, and the lower map shows outgoing long-wave radiation for clear-sky conditions.

Consider the January maps first. Incoming radiation is comparatively small in the north but increases evenly from north to south, showing the strong control of latitude. Outgoing radiation is, however, stronger over the desert regions of the Southwest than in the humid East. Although the quantities on the two maps cannot be directly compared, we can obtain a rough estimate of the radiation balance by subtracting values at any given location. We find that most of the northern half of the country has negative values, or a radiation deficit, while the Southwest and Florida maintain a radiation surplus. The line of zero difference runs east-west about on the 40th parallel of latitude.

Next, examine the July maps. Here the incoming radiation is everywhere very much greater than in January—as much as 5 times as large in the northern region. Because of persistent clear skies and lower water vapor content of the air, the desert Southwest receives very strong radiation (over 750 ly/day) compared with the East and Northeast (500 ly/day). Outgoing radiation in July is much less, on the average, than incoming radiation. Consequently there is strong radiation surplus over the entire nation. The surplus is greatest in the Southwest and diminishes northward and eastward.

## Net all-wave radiation

When all forms of radiation, both incoming and outgoing, can be measured simultaneously at an observing station, the *net all-wave radiation* can be calculated. This quantity represents the net exchange of energy by radiation

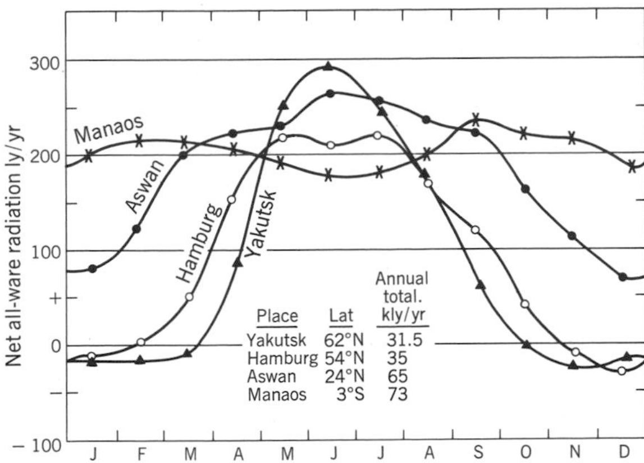


**FIGURE 13.16.** Net all-wave radiation throughout the year at four representative stations. (Data by courtesy of David H. Miller.)

between the surface and the atmosphere. Incoming radiation includes both direct and indirect short-wave radiation and downward long-wave radiation, while outgoing radiation consists of long-wave radiation from the ground and reflected short-wave radiation.

Net all-wave radiation ($R$), also referred to as the *radiation balance,* is rigorously defined as follows:

$$R = (Q + q)\ (1 - a) + I_d - I_u$$

where $Q$ is direct incoming solar radiation,
$q$ is indirect incoming solar radiation,
$a$ is the albedo of the receiving surface,
$I_d$ is downward counter-radiation,
and $I_u$ is outgoing long-wave radiation from the surface.

In the above equation the term $(1 - a)$ gives the percentage of incoming radiation that is actually absorbed by the surface.

## Annual cycle of net radiation

The annual cycle of net all-wave radiation is illustrated in Figure 13.16 by records of four observing stations ranging from close to the equator to a subarctic location. The two lower latitude stations show no deficit and have large annual totals. The two higher latitude stations have 3 and 6 months of radiation deficit, but nevertheless have substantial annual surpluses.

## Daily cycle of radiation

The cycle of incoming direct and diffuse solar radiation begins at sunrise. A maximum intensity is reached at noon by local apparent solar time, followed by a symmetrical decline and a cessation at sunset. Incoming radiation curves are illustrated in Figure 13.17 for the months of June and December at Hamburg, Germany, at 53½° N. latitude. Notice the enormous difference in total quantity of radiation received at summer solstice (June) as compared with winter solstice (December). The peak value at noon in June is more than

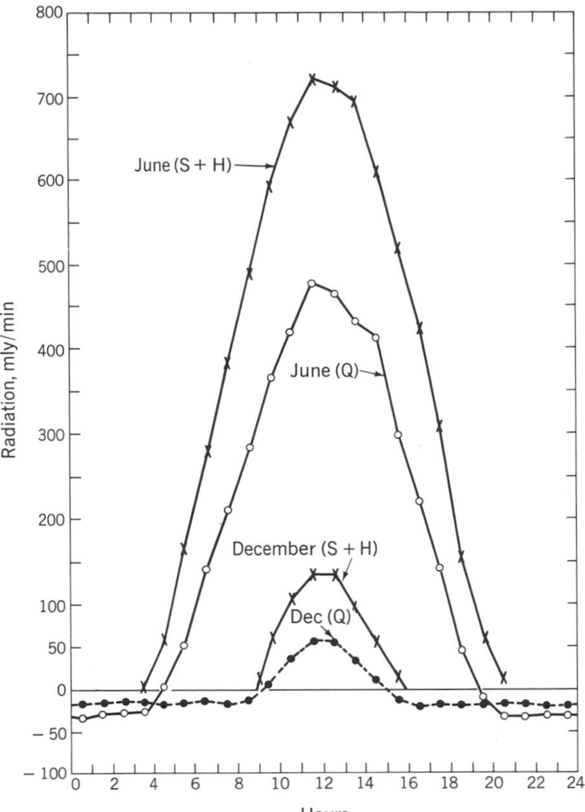


**FIGURE 13.17.** Mean daily cycles of June and December incoming and outgoing radiation at Hamburg, Germany. (Data by courtesy of Ernst Frankenberger.)

four times greater than at noon in December. Notice also that radiation commences about 5 hours earlier and ceases about 5 hours later in June than in December. Equinox curves, not shown, would fall between the June and December curves, beginning with sunrise at about 6 A.M. and ending with sunset at about 6 P.M.

Figure 13.17 also shows curves of net all-wave radiation for June and December at Hamburg. Radiation is given in units of thousandths of langleys per minute (mly/min). During hours of darkness energy loss from the ground continues by longwave radiation and a small deficit exists more or less uniformly throughout the night. This nocturnal deficit runs about 30 mly/min in June, but only half this amount in December. Net radiation becomes positive shortly after sunrise, rises sharply in the morning hours, and peaks at noon. Heat now flows from ground to atmosphere and a large surplus of radiation is accumulated during the day. Following a rapid decline in the late afternoon, net radiation becomes negative about an hour before sunset and thereafter heat flows from the air to the ground. In June, net radiation at noon is about 65% of the incoming radiation, whereas in December the proportion is only about 43%.

Radiation surplus for the entire day can be compared with deficit for the entire day by comparing the area lying above the zero line with that lying below the zero line. When this is done it will be seen that a very large net daily surplus is obtained in June, whereas for December there is a small net daily deficit. These observations are in agreement with the annual cycle of net all-wave radiation at Hamburg, Figure 13.16, which shows a June surplus of 210 ly/day and a December deficit of 30 ly/day.

The daily cycle of net radiation is examined in further detail in Chapter 14, along with the flow of heat into the ground by conduction and into the atmosphere by conduction and latent energy transfer.

## The global radiation balance

Returning to the average annual values of net all-wave radiation, we are in a position to evaluate the total global radiation budget.

Figure 13.18 is a world map of average annual net radiation. It shows that totals are very high (above 120 kly/yr) over equatorial oceans, but that over continents in the same belt the totals are not much over 80 kly/yr. The sharp break in isopleths at the shorelines indicates that the land and ocean surfaces behave very differently with respect to absorption and emission of radiation. At high latitudes, net radiation falls to values below 20 kly/yr. Although not shown on the map, negative values (deficits) occur poleward of about 75° latitude.

Figure 13.19 is a profile from pole to pole giving net all-wave radiation of the earth's surface (upper curve), of the atmosphere (lower curve), and of the combined earth-atmosphere system (middle curve). Where the curves lie above the zero line a surplus exists, and where they lie below the zero line a deficit exists. It is obvious that a huge global radiation surplus exists for the earth's surface, while a correspondingly large global deficit exists for the atmosphere alone. But when the two systems are combined into a single earth-atmosphere system, the net radiation is zero, a condition that must exist if the earth is not to be getting steadily warmer or colder.

The above relationships can be summarized in the following table—units are kilolangleys per year:

| | Radiation absorbed | Radiation lost | Net radiation |
|---|---|---|---|
| Earth's surface | 131 | 55 | +76 |
| Earth's atmosphere | 48 | 124 | −76 |
| Entire earth-atmosphere system | 179 | 179 | 0 |

Referring to Figure 13.19, you will find shaded areas labeled "surplus" and "deficit" between the middle curve and the zero line. The surplus area on the graph is equal to the combined areas of deficit. Thus the net radiation for the whole system is zero.

The radiation surplus of the earth's surface and the equal deficit of the atmosphere require that large quantities of heat shall flow from the earth's surface to the atmosphere. This vertical heat flux takes place in two ways, as already noted. First, heat is conducted from the surface to the adjacent air, then carried upward and mixed through the lower atmosphere by turbulent air motions. Second, the evaporation of water from land and ocean surfaces causes heat to pass into the atmosphere in the latent form. The processes of vertical heat transfer are explained in Chapters 14 and 18.

As Figure 13.19 shows, there exists a great radiation surplus between about 40° N. and 40° S. latitudes, and a corresponding deficit exists between 40° N. and S. latitudes and the poles. Unless heat is exported from the surplus zone to the deficit zone, the earth's low-latitude zone will become hotter and the polar zones will become colder. The necessity of poleward transport of heat is obvious, if average conditions are not to change. This poleward or *meridional* heat transfer must be at a

**FIGURE 13.18.** World map of mean annual net radiation. Values are given in units of kilolangleys per year. (Same data source as Figure 13.10.)

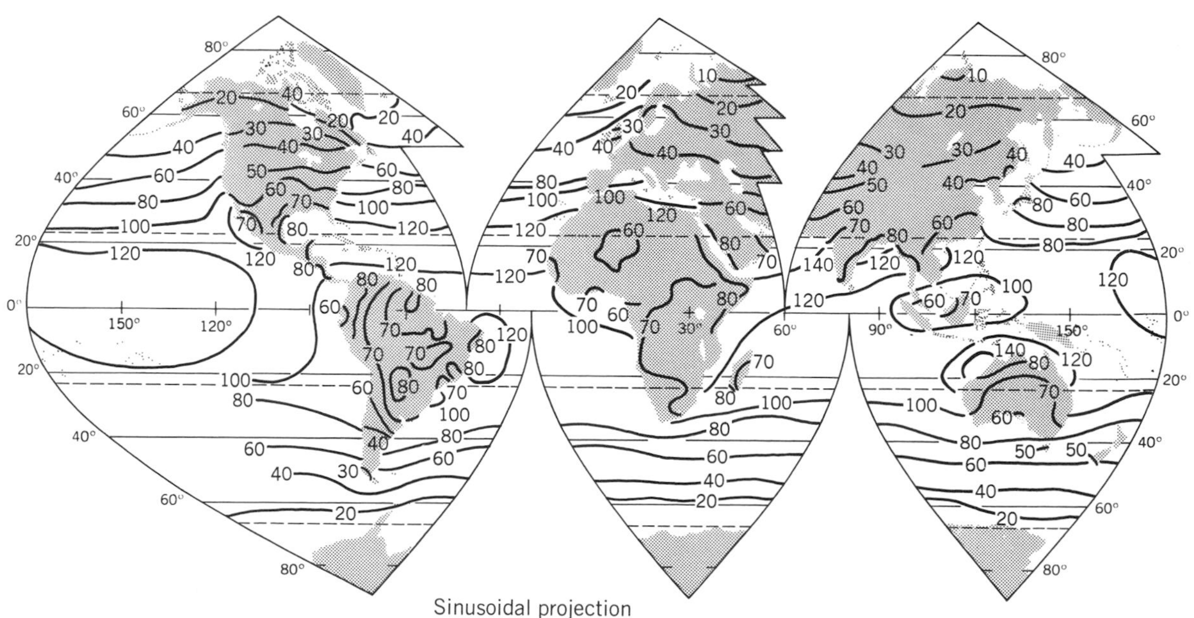

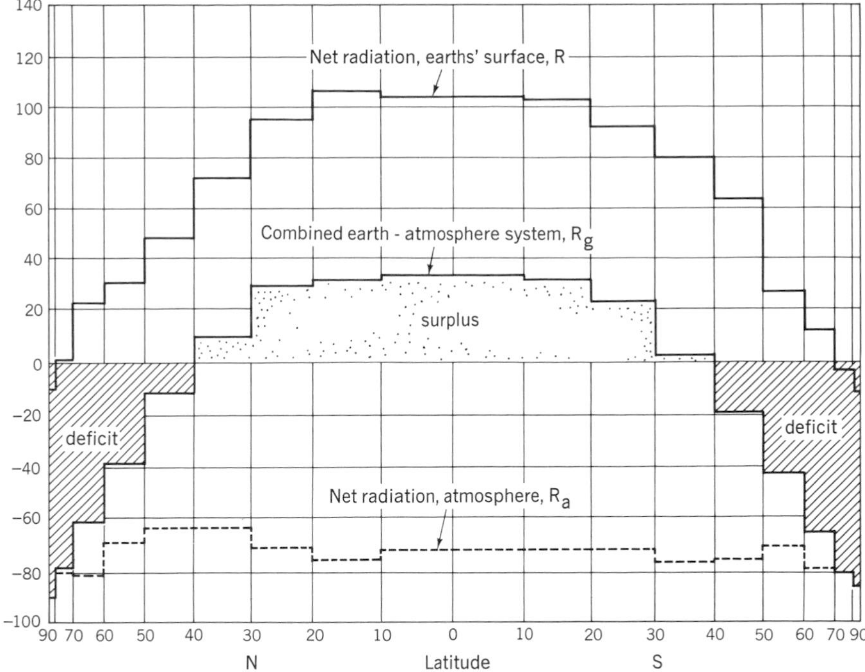


**FIGURE 13.19.** Meridional profiles of mean net radiation at earth's surface, from atmosphere, and from combined earth-atmosphere system. [Data from W. D. Sellers (1965), *Physical Climatology,* Chicago, Univ. of Chicago Press, p. 66, Figure 19.]

maximum value in the latitude belts of about 30° to 50° N. and S., but will be essentially zero at the equator and at both poles. The following figures are estimates of the yearly poleward heat transfer, or heat flux. The unit of heat is the kilocalorie (1000 calories), multiplied by ten raised to the 19th power:[3]

| Latitude (°N.) | Heat flux, kcal/yr × $10^{19}$ |
|---|---|
| 90 | 0.00 |
| 80 | 0.35 |
| 70 | 1.25 |
| 60 | 2.40 |
| 50 | 3.40 |
| 40 | 3.91 |
| 30 | 3.56 |
| 20 | 2.54 |
| 10 | 1.21 |
| 0 | −0.26 |

This meridional heat flow is accomplished by circulation of the atmosphere and oceans. Heat is carried both as sensible heat of the air and water, and as latent heat in water vapor contained in the air. When condensation of water vapor takes place, this latent heat is released and passes into the sensible form. These processes are explained in Chapters 15 through 19.

## Planetary temperatures

The effective temperature of the earth, its *planetary temperature,* is that single value which is required of a spherical body with a given albedo and emissivity in order for it to return to space exactly the amount of solar energy intercepted. For the earth, this temperature is estimated to be about 245° K (−28° C; −18° F). Effective planetary temperatures, in °K, are as follows:[4]

| | |
|---|---|
| Mercury | 616° K |
| Venus | 235 |
| Earth | 245 |
| Mars | 209 |
| Jupiter | 105 |
| Saturn | 78 |
| Uranus | 55 |
| Neptune | 43 |
| Pluto | 42 |

It is obvious that, in general, the closer a planet is to the sun, the higher its effective temperature, otherwise it could not radiate energy into space at a rate equal to the rate at which it is received. Differences in atmospheres and surface properties modify the effect of distance from the sun.

## References for further study

Budyko, M. I. (1958), *The Heat Balance of the Earth's Surface,* translated by N. A. Stepanova, Washington, D.C., U.S. Weather Bur., 255 pp.

Gates, D. M. (1962), *Energy Exchange in the Biosphere,* New York, Harper & Row, 151 pp.

Geiger, R. (1965), *The Climate Near the Ground,* 4th ed., Cambridge, Mass., Harvard Univ. Press, 611 pp.

Miller, D. H. (1965), "The Heat and Water Balance of the Earth's Surface," from *Advances in Geophysics,* vol. 11, pp. 175–302, New York, Academic.

Sellers, W. D. (1965), *Physical Climatology,* Chicago, Univ. of Chicago Press, 272 pp., chaps. 3, 4, 5, 6.

Petterssen, S. (1969), *Introduction to Meteorology,* 3rd ed., New York, McGraw-Hill, 333 pp., chap. 2.

[3] Data from W. D. Sellers (1965), *Physical Climatology,* Chicago, University of Chicago Press, Table 12.

[4] Data from S. I. Rasool (1967), *Encyclopedia of Atmospheric Sciences,* R. W. Fairbridge, Ed., New York, Reinhold, p. 734, Table 1.

# 14

# Heat and cold at the earth's surface

THE BASE OF THE atmosphere forms a continuous interface with the continental and interspersed ocean surfaces. In this chapter we investigate further the exchanges of energy across this global interface. The earth's energy budget involves not only the flow of energy in the form of electromagnetic radiation, which was the subject of the previous chapter, but also the flow and storage of energy in the form of sensible heat in the atmosphere, the continental surfaces, and the oceans.

Sensible heat, measured in terms of the temperature of a substance as indicated by a thermometer, constitutes an environmental factor of prime importance in the shallow layer of planet Earth in which life has evolved under stable conditions for more than a billion years of geologic history. We are all aware that our planet possesses extremes of thermal environment—from permanent frost of the great icecaps to permanent warmth of the equatorial belt. We are also aware that certain parts of the globe have a strong seasonal rhythm of severe winter cold alternating with summer heat. There is also a familiar daily rhythm of rising and falling temperatures. Obviously, these seasonal and daily thermal cycles are locked into the corresponding cycles of incoming and outgoing radiation analyzed in Chapter 13. The present chapter deals with the effects of latitude and of solar radiation cycles upon the earth's surface temperatures. This information will, in turn, be used in following chapters to explain the complex motions of the atmosphere and oceans, and thus to develop further the concepts of global systems of transport of energy and matter.

## Mechanisms of heat flow

A number of familiar principles of physics are applied in the analysis of rhythms of heat and cold within the air, the soil and rock of the land, and the water of lakes and oceans. Sensible heat can be gained by direct absorption of radiation falling upon an opaque ground surface or penetrating the partially transparent gas of the atmosphere and liquid of water bodies. Correspondingly, these same substances can lose sensible heat by radiating energy outward in the long wavelengths.

Heat can also be gained or lost by the process of *conduction,* in which sensible heat flows through the substance. For heat conduction to occur a *temperature gradient,* or *thermal gradient,* must exist; flow of heat is then from regions of higher temperature to regions of lower temperature. Heat flow (flux) increases as the thermal gradient increases. However, rate of heat flow by conduction also depends upon the *conductivity* of the substance, which is simply the relative ease with which heat flows through the substance.

In addition to heat exchanges by radiation and conduction, there occurs within fluids a transport of sensible heat through the movement of the fluid itself. This form of heat transport is sometimes referred to as *turbulent exchange*. To combine all of the above mechanisms of gain or loss of heat, the term *sensible heat flux* is used.

An important process by which liquid or moist surfaces lose sensible heat is evaporation. This heat loss may be called the *latent heat flux,* to distinguish it from the sensible heat flux. Note also that condensation of water vapor within the atmosphere liberates heat energy, a process that tends to raise the sensible temperature of the surrounding air. The condensation process will be treated in detail in Chapter 16. Latent heat flux is a highly important component of the heat budget over ocean and lake surfaces. It also operates in varying degrees from land surfaces, depending upon the moisture content of the exposed soil or rock. A related evaporative process, which can be included within the latent heat flux, is *transpiration* of water from plant foliage. In this process water drawn upward from the soil is evaporated through pores in the leaves. Importance of transpiration naturally depends upon the nature and density of the plant cover as well as upon the season. The combined evaporation from soil and transpiration from plants is termed *evapotranspiration.*

Other lesser forms of heat transfer involved in the heat budget can be mentioned. Melting of ice and snow absorbs substantial quantities of heat (latent heat of fusion) on land areas in the spring. Falling rain can add or withdraw heat from the surface upon which it falls, depending upon relative temperatures. Relatively small quantities of heat are exchanged through processes of mechanical friction of air and water currents and waves, by plant photosynthesis, by slow oxidation of organic matter, and by rapid combustion. Quantities of heat emerging from the earth's interior by slow conduction and volcanic eruptions can be neglected in our present discussion because of the extremely slow rates involved. Essential exchange processes are, therefore, radiation and the fluxes of sensible and latent heat.

## Specific heat

Storage of heat in air, water, soil, and rock is measured by the temperature of these substances, but the quantity of heat energy held in a unit mass of the substance depends not only on the sensible temperature shown by the thermometer, but also upon a property known as the *specific heat* of the substance. Specific heat is defined as that number of gram calories required to cause a temperature rise of one centigrade degree in a unit mass. For pure water the specific heat is, by definition, unity for one gram at a temperature of about 15° C (59° F). Some specific heats of common substances are:

| | |
|---|---|
| Water | 1.0 |
| Ice (−2° C) | 0.5 |
| Air (100° C, 1 bar) | 0.24 |
| Granite and basalt | 0.2 |
| Clay, dry | 0.2 |

It is important to keep in mind that the specific heat of water is four times greater than that of air and about five times greater than that of rock and dry soil. If heat is absorbed at the same rate by one gram of water and one gram of granite, the temperature of the granite will rise one degree in only one-fifth the time needed for a corresponding temperature rise in water.

The amount of heat required to increase the temperature of one cubic centimeter of a substance by 1 C° is known as its *heat capacity* (also *volumetric specific heat*). Because the densities of air, water, and rock are very different, the heat capacity of each substance requires separate calculation. One cubic meter of pure water weighs about 1000 kg, whereas one cubic meter of dry air at 1° C and a pressure of one atmosphere (1013 mb) weighs only 1.2 kg. A cubic meter of granite, density 2.6 g/cc weighs 2600 kg. Consequently, if heat were absorbed at a given rate by one cubic meter of pure dry air, its rate of temperature rise would be about 3000 times more rapid than for a cubic meter of water absorbing heat at the same rate. A cubic meter of granite would under similar circumstances experience a temperature rise about twice as fast as the water. Dry soils in a natural state of packing have densities roughly in the range of 1.0 to 1.5 g/cc and, with a specific heat of 0.2, would heat from three to five times faster than water in equal volumes.

These statements include the assumption that the applied heat is absorbed at the same rate by all substances. Actually, the factor of conductivity will be highly important in influencing the rate of heating if the distance to be penetrated is appreciable. Conductivity of dry soils and air is low, while that of water is high. A small amount of soil moisture greatly increases soil conductivity.

Differences in heating rates of unit volumes of air, water, and soil or rock are of great importance in understanding temperatures of the lower air layers, the surfaces of the oceans and lakes, and the land surfaces.

## The heat balance equation

Let us put together some of the principles of heat flow into a simple equation expressing the heat balance as it applies to a column of water or soil extending from the free upper surface downward to a depth where temperature changes are practically zero. This depth will generally be very much greater in water than in soil or rock. Figure 14.1 is a schematic diagram of the unit column and the various forms of heat flux that are involved in the equation.

The equation seeks to evaluate the rate at which the heat content of the unit column changes, stated, for example, as the number of calories of heat gained or lost per minute of time. This quantity is given the symbol $G$ in the equation

$$G = R - H - LE - F$$

where $R$ is net all-wave radiation at the surface (see Chapter 13 for details);
$H$ is transfer of sensible heat through the upper surface by conduction and turbulent exchange (positive when air is warmer than the surface, negative when air is cooler than the surface);
$LE$ is latent heat transfer by evaporation ($L$ is latent heat of vaporization, about 590 calories per gram of water; $E$ is the quantity of water evaporated);
and $F$ is horizontal transfer of heat out of the column.

Because we are interested in evaluating $R$, rather than $G$, these terms are transposed to give the following basic heat balance equation:

$$R = H + LE + G + F$$

The term $R$ is now a measure of the radiative energy available to warm the air or the column of soil or water and to evaporate water.

The term $F$ is a measure of the net horizontal flow of heat out of the column of water or soil below the surface. In the case of soil or rock, the value of $F$ is negligible, since there is no movement of matter and adjacent columns are subject to the same rates of gain or loss of heat through the upper surface. In the case of water bodies, however, currents readily transport heat out of or into the column, and the quantity $F$ is then important.

The heat balance equation can apply for any small unit of time, such as one second or one minute, or it may be applied to longer spans of time, such as a day, a month, a year, or a century. The equation may also be applied to the earth's surface as a whole, in which case the horizontal transport, $F$, is cancelled out through circulation of the oceans, leaving only the following terms:

$$R = H + LE + G$$

The global heat balance will be evaluated in Chapter 16, after the atmospheric and oceanic circulation patterns are described.

We will next examine the basic heat balance equation in daily and annual cycles of change.

**FIGURE 14.1.** Schematic diagram of the heat balance equation.

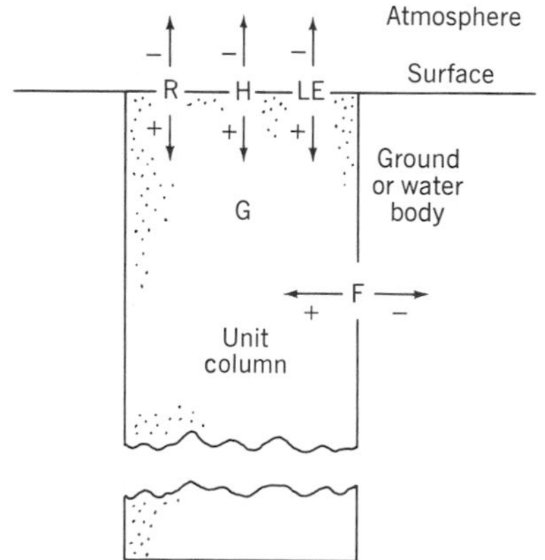


## The daily heat balance cycle

The components of the heat balance equation can be determined for each hour of the day by means of radiation- and temperature-sensing instruments placed close to the surface. When the hourly values of each component of the equation are plotted, a daily cycle is revealed. Figure 14.2 shows two examples of the heat balance throughout a summer day at middle latitudes. The upper example is typical of a humid climate with a dense vegetative cover, and the lower example is typical of a desert with bare dry soil forming the surface.

Only four terms are needed for the heat balance in these two examples: $R$, $G$, $H$, and $LE$, all defined in earlier paragraphs. The term $F$ is neglected, as no motion occurs beneath the soil surface. The curve of net all-wave radiation, $R$, resembles that shown in Figure 13.17; it is symmetrical about the noon-hour peak and is essentially flat during hours of darkness, when the value of $R$ is negative.

For any given hour of day the heat balance equation must be satisfied. Therefore the height of the $R$-curve with respect to zero is always equal to the combined values of $G$, $H$, and $LE$. This equality can be verified by applying a pair of dividers to the illustration along a vertical line drawn through any selected hour.

In the Wisconsin example (Figure 14.2*A*), the latent heat flux, $LE$, is the most important quantity throughout most of the day, because of evaporation and transpiration from plant foliage and moist soil. Sensible heat flux, $H$, is moderately great, but less than latent heat flux. Rate of heat gain by the soil through downward flow, $G$, is relatively small, but will cause a rise in soil temperature during the day. In hours of darkness, all components of the equation are small and of zero or negative value. Thus during the night the soil will become cooler. During the predawn hours the latent heat flux becomes negative, indicating the liberation of heat by condensation of dew.

In the California desert example (Figure 14.2*B*), the net all-wave radiation curve, $R$, is quite similar in form to that of the previous case, but the other three curves are very different. The sensible heat flux, $H$, rises to high values, peaking in the early afternoon because of maximum air turbulence at that time. Heat flow into the soil, $G$, reaches a maximum in the morning hours, but begins to fall off before noon. This curve indicates that the temperature of the surface soil rises rapidly early in the day. Latent heat flux is very small throughout the entire

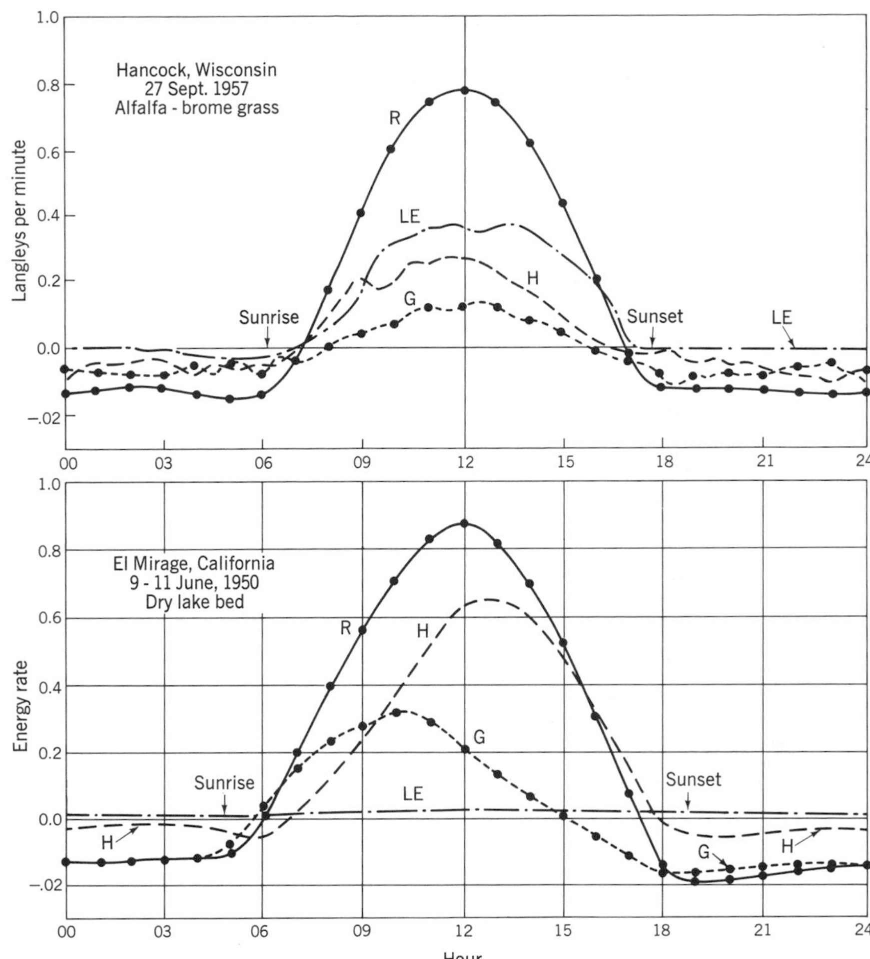


**FIGURE 14.2.** The daily heat balance cycle at two representative middle-latitude stations—Hancock, Wisconsin, in a humid climate, and El Mirage, California, in a desert climate. [Data from W. D. Sellers (1965), *Physical Climatology,* Chicago, Univ. of Chicago Press, p. 112, Figure 33.]

day, because soil moisture is very low and there is no plant cover to provide transpiration.

In both examples, the heat gained by the soil during the day closely approximates the heat lost at night.

## The annual heat balance cycle

In middle and high latitudes, where there is a strongly developed annual cycle of incoming solar radiation (see Figure 13.3), the heat balance runs through a corresponding cycle of change involving each of the four component terms. Figure 14.3 shows two examples. The first is for Madison, Wisconsin, the second for Yuma, Arizona, a desert station. Both stations show a maximum value of net all-wave radiation, *R,* near summer solstice and a minimum value near winter solstice. However, the radiation balance is positive throughout all months at Yuma, whereas negative values in the winter are experienced at Madison. The most striking difference in the two graphs is in the role played by the latent heat flux, *LE.* For reasons stated in connection with the daily cycle, latent heat flux is larger over moist soil and dense vegetation at Madison, but of only slight importance in the desert. Sensible heat flux, on the other hand, is predominant in the desert, but of small importance at Madison except in early spring before foliage appears. The flow of heat into and out of the soil follows a simple annual rhythm in both examples.

From the study of daily and annual cycles of the component terms of the heat balance equation we turn next to the resulting temperature changes in the soil, in water bodies, and in the lower air layer.

## Heating and cooling of the ground

Consider first the daily heating cycle of the soil in summer at Pavlovsk, U.S.S.R., 59½° N. lat. Figure 14.4*A* is a temperature graph showing time of day on the horizontal axis and temperature on the vertical axis. A separate curve is drawn for each depth below the surface, beginning with 1 cm (0.4 in.) at intervals doubling in depth to 160 cm (63 in.). Two important trends are shown as the temperature cycle is followed down into the soil: (1) The range of temperature rapidly decreases until, below 80 cm (31.5 in.), no daily change can be detected; (2) the hour of occurrence of highest temperature becomes later as depth increases. At the surface the soil temperature reaches its peak between 12 noon and 2 P.M., but at 20 cm (8 in.) the highest temperature is at 6 P.M. At 40 cm (16 in.) depth the daily cycle is exactly

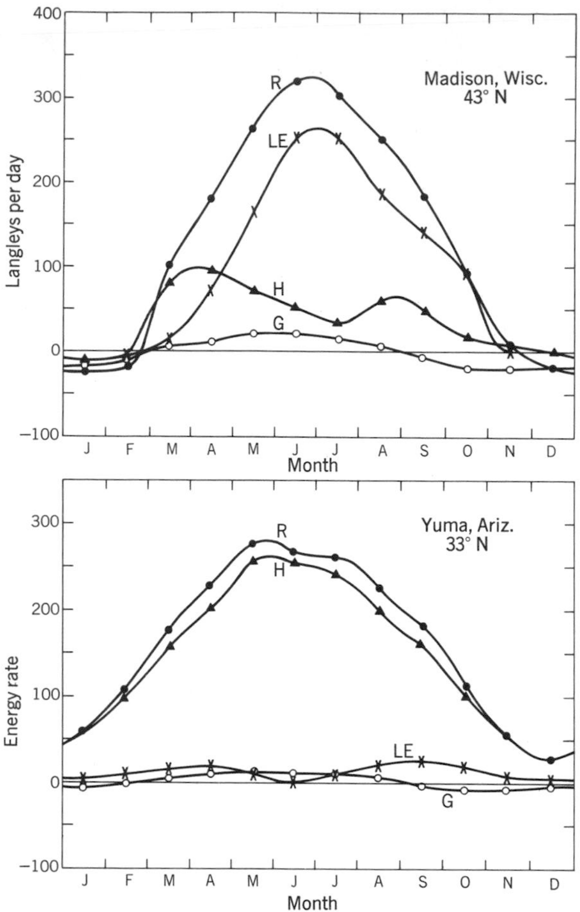


FIGURE 14.3. The annual heat balance cycle at a humid middle-latitude station (Madison, Wisconsin) and at a subtropical desert station (Yuma, Arizona). [Data from W. D. Sellers (1965), *Physical Climatology,* Chicago, Univ. of Chicago Press, p. 106, Figure 30.]

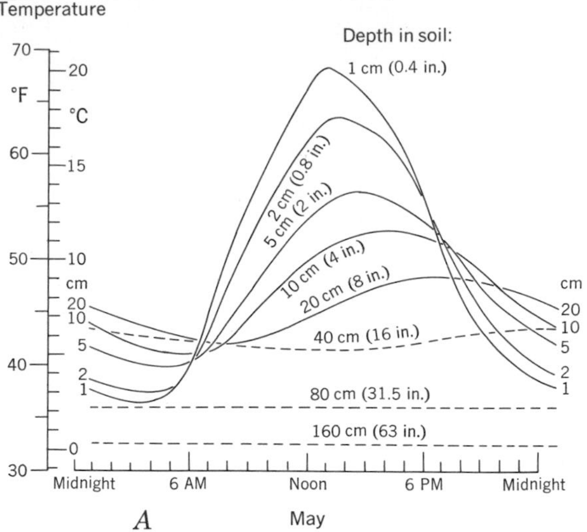


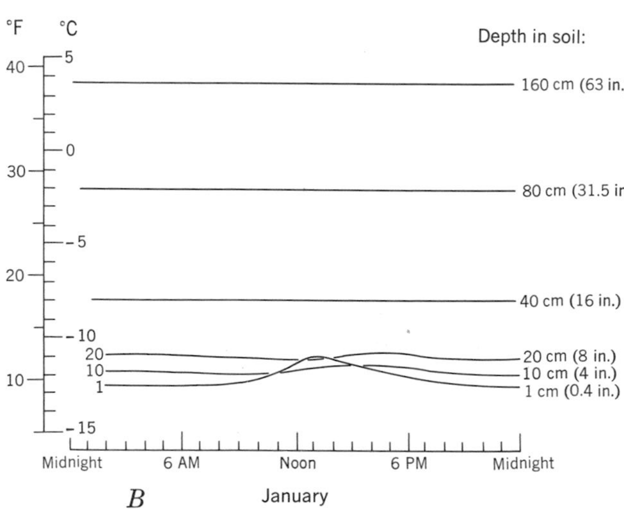


FIGURE 14.4. The daily cycle of temperature change during (*A*) May and (*B*) January at various depths in a sandy soil at Pavlovsk, U.S.S.R. [After R. Geiger (1965), *The Climate Near the Ground,* Cambridge, Mass., Harvard Univ. Press, p. 61, Figure 24 and p. 63, Figure 25.]

out of phase, so that the soil there is coldest just after noon. This increasing delay in time of the highest temperature is due to the slow rate of downward penetration of the daily heat wave.

In the intensely cold winters of the continental interiors in northerly latitudes a quite different daily temperature graph results. In Figure 14.4*B* is the daily cycle in January for Pavlovsk. First, note that the daily period of solar radiation is very short and produces only a slight warming of the soil near the surface. Cooling then continues for about 18 hours out of the 24. The daily cycle dies out rapidly between 20 and 40 cm (8 and 16 in.) depth. Whereas in May the soil becomes colder with depth, in January it becomes warmer. Notice particularly that at the 160-cm (63-in.) level the January temperature of the soil is warmer than at the same level in May, but that both temperatures are close to freezing. In winter the soil is frozen to a depth of 80 cm (31 in.).

It might be inferred from these data that a few feet below the ground we should enter a zone in which temperatures are nearly constant throughout the entire year. To study this principle, consider next the annual cycle of heating and cooling of the ground.

Figure 14.5 shows the yearly temperature cycle at Brookhaven, Long Island, New York, at lat. 41° N. Depths range down to 20 ft (6 m). Just as in the daily cycle, the annual range of temperature decreases rapidly with depth and the time of maximum temperature is increasingly delayed with depth. The logical conclusions from a study of these curves are that below a depth of, say, 50 ft (15 m)—depending on the annual range at the surface and soil type—the soil or bedrock remains at constant temperature throughout the year and that this temperature is identical with the average annual temperature of the surface air layer.

Proof of this principle may be found in limestone caverns, which are noted for their uniform air temperatures throughout the year. If there is restricted air circulation in the cavern, the cavern temperature should be the same as the average yearly air temperature. For ex-

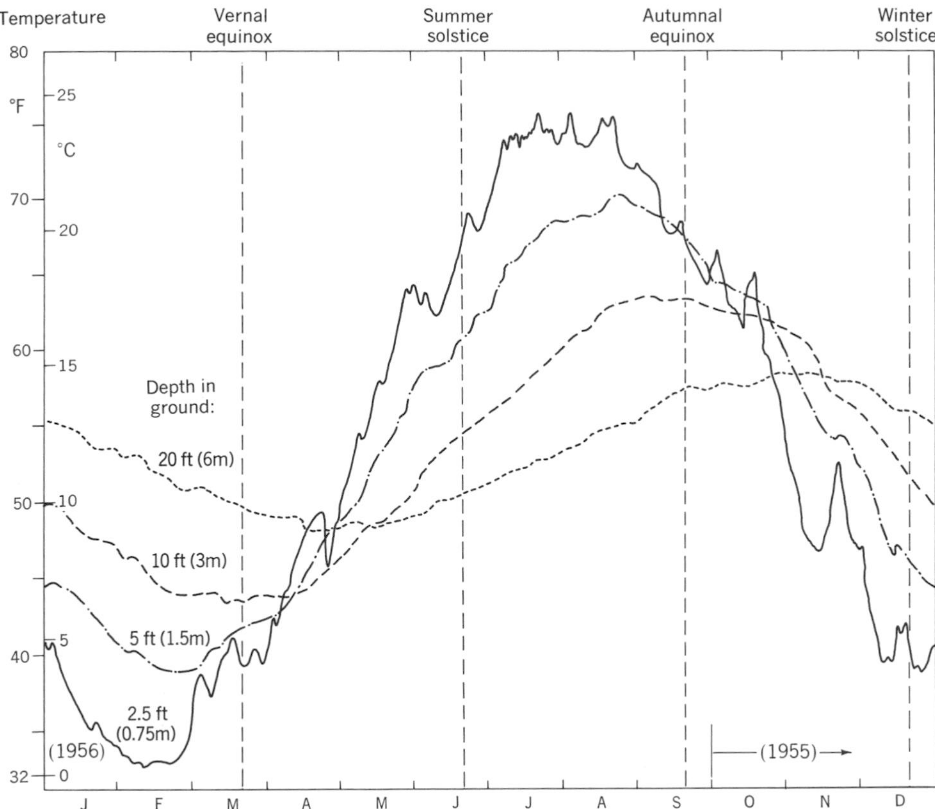


**FIGURE 14.5.** Soil temperatures throughout one year at various depths, North Station, Brookhaven, Long Island. [After Singer and Brown (1956)), *A.G.U. Trans.* 37.)

ample, in Endless Caverns, Virginia, the air temperature is a constant 56° F throughout the year, and the average yearly air temperature in this region is about 52° F. Of course, as explained in Chapter 22, if one went still deeper into the earth, a gradual rise of temperature would set in.

## Permafrost of the arctic regions

In the vast arctic regions of Siberia and North America the average annual temperature is below freezing. Examples are:

| | |
|---|---|
| Verkhoyansk, U.S.S.R. | 3° F (−16° C) |
| Dawson, Yukon Ter. | 23° F (5° C) |
| Point Barrow, Alaska | 10° F (−12° C) |

Here, in the tundra regions bordering the Arctic Ocean, ground temperatures below the depth of the annual heating and cooling cycle are constantly below freezing, so that all water in the soil and rock is continually frozen. This condition of perennially frozen ground is conveniently termed *permafrost.* Here one finds in the soil ice bodies in the form of horizontal layers, vertical wedges, and irregular masses (Figure 14.6). In Figure 14.7 the extent of permafrost in the Northern Hemisphere is shown, with diagrammatic cross sections through Alaska and Asia to give some indication of the thickness of the permafrost layer.

In the most northerly belt, that of *continuous permafrost,* the frozen layer is known to be as thick as 1000–2000 ft (300–600 m) and has temperatures generally from 15° to 20° F (−9° to −7° C). Ice is encountered within a few inches to 2 ft (0.6 m) of the surface, even in midsummer, and the frozen layer passes without any gaps under large lakes and rivers. To the south of the continuous belt lies a zone of *discontinuous permafrost* in which frozen patches are separated by the unfrozen ground underneath large rivers and lakes. In this

**FIGURE 14.6.** A V-shaped ice wedge surrounded by alluvial silt is seen here exposed in the banks of a stream near Livengood, Alaska. (Photograph by T. L. Péwé, U.S. Geological Survey.)

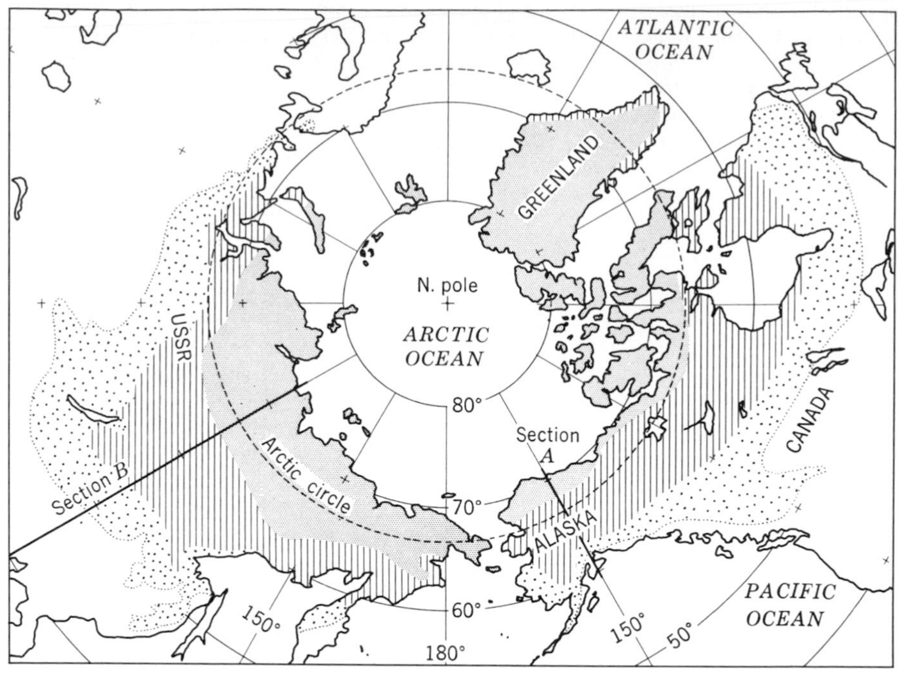


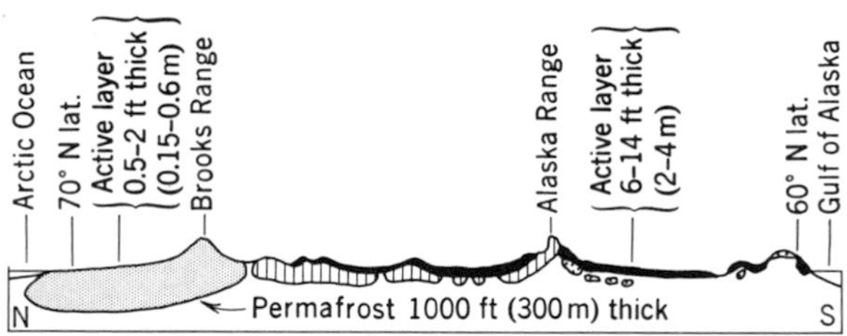


Section $A$: Alaska, on long. 150° W

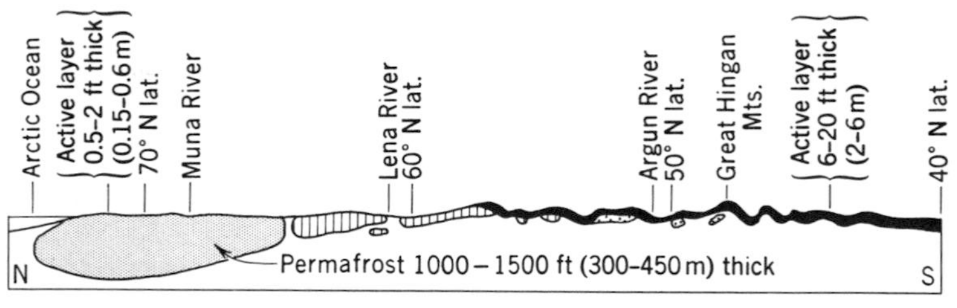


Section $B$: Asia, on long. 120° E
(Modified from I. V. Poiré)

Diagrammatic cross sections of permafrost

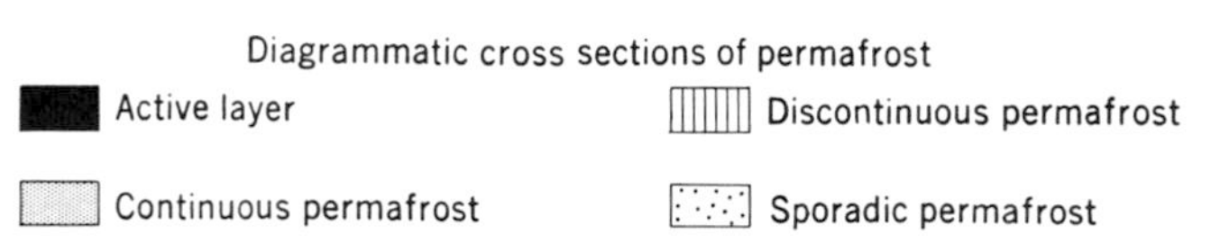


**FIGURE 14.7.** Permafrost distribution in the Northern Hemisphere, with cross sections along meridians in Siberia and Alaska. [© 1960, John Wiley & Sons, New York. After R. F. Black (1950), *Applied Sedimentation,* P. Trask, ed., New York, John Wiley & Sons, Chapter 14.]

warmer region the seasonal thawing extends down to depths of 1–10 ft (0.3–3 m). Fringing the permafrost region on the south in latitudes 50° to 60° N. is a zone of *sporadic permafrost* in which small shallow patches of frozen ground persist throughout the year on protected north-facing slopes. The profiles in Figure 14.7 also show an active layer of soil extending into the middle latitudes. This is a soil layer which is alternately frozen and completely thawed from winter to summer.

Traced northward under the Arctic Ocean, the permafrost zone thins abruptly and ends under the protective layer of ocean water. Very likely, the permafrost regions were more extensive southward during cold stages of the Pleistocene Epoch (Ice Age). This condition is inferred because soils of the middle latitudes now contain structures believed to have been formed by growth of ice bodies. The permafrost layer can be thought of as a reservoir of cold containing an excess quantity inherited from a colder period. Melting of ground ice requires absorption of great quantities of heat energy (heat of fusion) and is a very slow process, which makes the shrinkage of the areas of permafrost lag greatly behind any change to a warmer climate.

## Energy absorption by water bodies

When sunlight falls upon a body of clear water, such as a lake or ocean, the radiant energy is absorbed gradually through a surface layer many feet thick. The sun's energy spectrum at the earth's surface consists of about 10% ultraviolet rays, 40% visible-light rays, and about 50% infrared and heat rays of long wavelength. In what way is this energy absorbed by the water? Figure 14.8 shows the energy spectrum at the surface (top line) and at various depths below the surface. Although the graph is for distilled water, it is approximately correct for clear freshwater lakes. At 4 in. (0.1 meter) below the surface most of the long-wave radiation has already been absorbed, causing concentrated warming of the surface layer. At 40 in. (1 m) depth there remains very little but the visible rays and ultraviolet; about half of the total energy has already been absorbed. At 33 ft (10 m) only 10% of the original energy remains, and most of the red and orange wavelengths have been lost. At 330 ft (100 m) only 3% of the energy remains unabsorbed, and it consists mostly of blue and green wavelengths.

Here is an explanation for the blue-green color of deep bodies of clear water. The light which we see when we look down into the water is that of the blue-green wavelengths reflected back to the eye with little absorption or scattering. Still deeper in the water the last vestiges of light are absorbed and total darkness prevails. We now see that warming of water bodies by direct absorption of solar radiation is strongly concentrated near the surface and that warming of deep water can occur only by slow direct conduction of heat or by the much more rapid process of mixing, where various outside forces act to cause rising and sinking currents.

## Annual cycle of heating and cooling of a lake

In the middle and high latitudes, where warm summers and cold winters alternate, the heating and cooling of lakes follows an interesting series of changes which are of great importance in controlling the growth of aquatic plant and animal life. A convenient starting point is a time in early spring, when the ice cover of the lake has just melted and the entire body of water is at an almost uniform temperature, a few degrees above freezing (Figure 14.9*B*). As the rapid increase in solar radiation sets in, the surface-water layer is warmed, but because this warm water is less dense (lighter) than the cold water beneath, it cannot sink. The only way in which heat can be carried down, aside from very slow conduction, is by mixing action that the wind sets up. In blowing over the lake surface, the wind drags the surface layer along to make eddies or sets up waves in which the water moves in small orbits. Although the mixing gives the surface layer a uniformity of temperature, there is a rather abrupt change at a given depth where cold water is met. The term *thermocline* is given to the thin horizontal zone in which there is a rapid transition from warm water above to cold water below. The thermocline represents an extremely stable layer which strongly resists any vertical motion. In Figure 14.10 is a temperature graph such as one we might obtain in the spring by lowering a thermometer into the water and plotting the water temperatures with increasing depth.[1]

As the warm season progresses, the warm surface layer becomes deeper as well as warmer, pushing the thermocline down to greater depths. Meantime the cold water at the lake bottom may remain undisturbed, holding to a constant temperature of about 39° F (4° C), be-

[1] To the *limnologist* (scientist specializing in the study of lakes) the warm upper layer in which temperature is uniform is termed the *epilimnion,* and the uniformly cold layer below the thermocline is the *hypolimnion.*

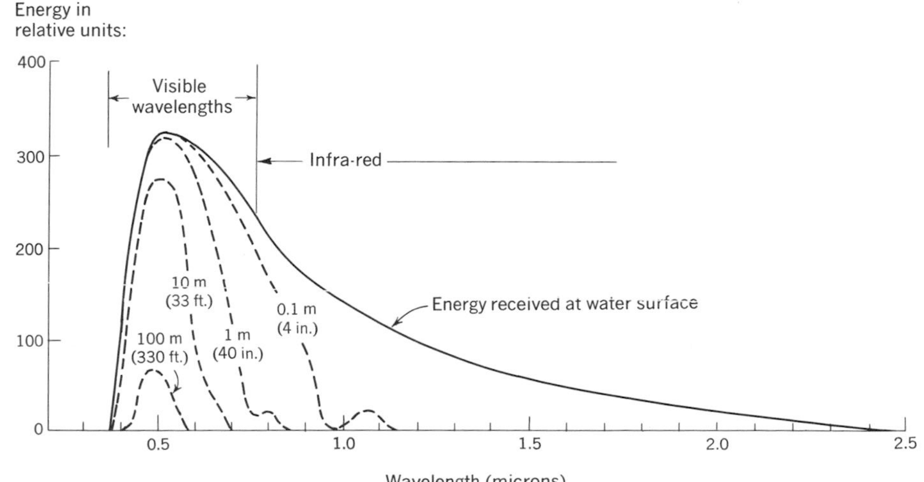


**FIGURE 14.8.** Energy spectrum of solar radiation at the water surface and at various depths. [After H. U. Sverdrup (1942), *Oceanography for Meteorologists,* Englewood Cliffs, N.J., Prentice-Hall, p. 54, Figure 8.]

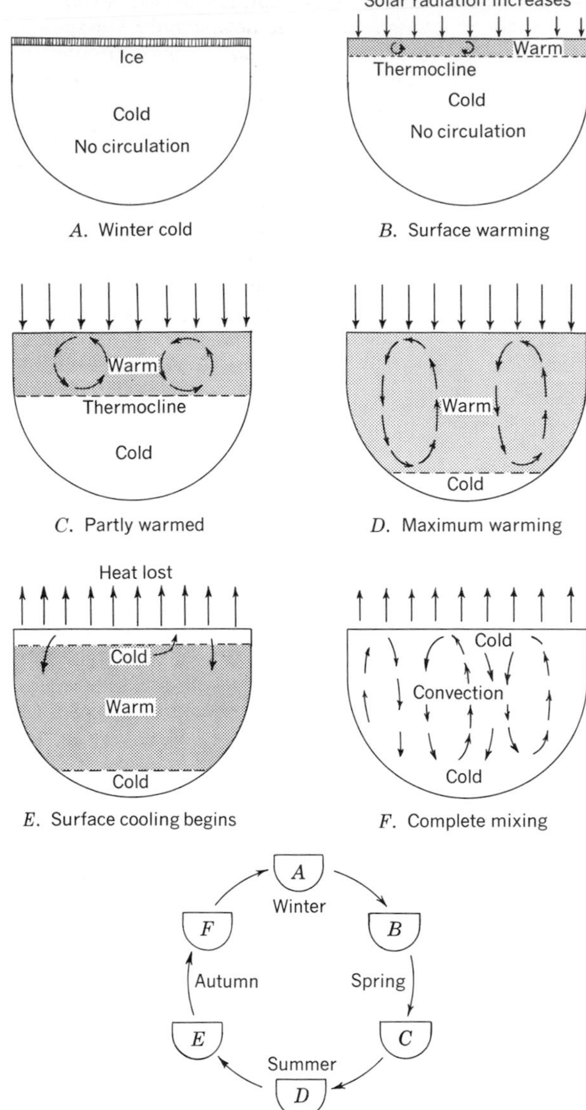


**FIGURE 14.9.** Annual cycle of heating, cooling, and mixing of water in a small fresh-water lake in middle latitudes.

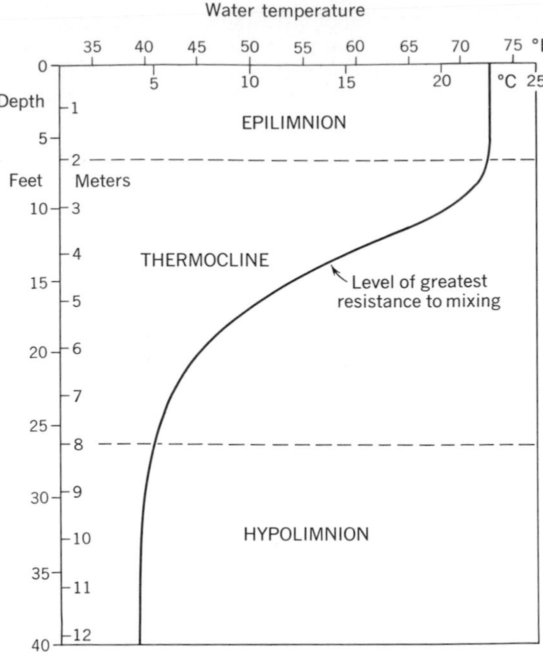


**FIGURE 14.10.** The summer-temperature profile of Little Round Lake, Ontario. [After J. R. Vallentyne (1957), *Amer. Scientist,* vol. 45.]

cause at this temperature pure water is more dense than at any other temperature and must remain at the bottom. In shallow lakes, less than 50–75 ft (15–23 m) deep, in regions of very windy conditions, the mixing of warm water may extend to the bottom of the lake, completely eliminating the cold layer. In addition, the influx of water from streams and springs may assist in mixing.

With the approach of winter (Figure 14.9*E*), incoming radiation decreases rapidly and the surface water is soon losing more heat than it receives. The cooler surface water, now denser than the warm layer below, begins to sink, forcing warm water to the surface, where it in turn is cooled. As the cooling intensifies, the surface water becomes increasingly dense and is continually sinking to replace lighter water. This causes a complete mixing, or convection, of the warm layer and destroys the thermocline, finally bringing the water to a uniform temperature of 39° F (4° C), its densest point. Now mixing ceases, because with further cooling water becomes less dense and this less dense water will tend to stay near the surface. At 32° F (0° C) the surface begins to freeze, and an ice cover soon seals over the lake.

In lakes of warm equatorial and tropical regions, water is relatively warm down to the lake bottom. This is because the tropical climates lack a winter, and the coolest water that can reach the lake bottom can be no colder than the average air temperature of the coolest part of the year. Yet, with each onset of a cool season associated with the low angle of the sun's rays a surface cooling and downsinking will, nevertheless, produce a complete circulation of the lake water.

## Heating and cooling of the sea surface

In Chapter 12, the temperature structure of the ocean was described in broad terms as a three-layer system in which the warm surface layer is separated from the cold deep water by a thermocline. We shall now examine the annual cycle of heating and cooling of the surface layer.

Temperature of sea water can be measured down to several hundred feet by means of the *bathythermograph,* a recording instrument towed behind a moving vessel (Figure 14.11).

The annual cycle of temperature changes in the uppermost 500 ft (150 m) of sea water is illustrated by the diagrams of Figure 14.12; the cycle applies generally to the middle latitudes, but not to oceans of equatorial or polar regions. Beginning with diagram *A,* showing winter conditions, we see that the surface water is at its

**FIGURE 14.11.** A scientist of the Lamont-Doherty Geological Observatory, on the research vessel *Vema,* examines a bathythermograph before it is released to be towed behind the vessel. A record of depth and water temperature is made within the instrument. (Courtesy of the National Academy of Sciences, International Geophysical Year.)

coolest and decreases in temperature only very slightly with depth. The temperature structure is therefore *isothermal.* In spring (diagram *B*) warm rains and increasing sun begin to warm the surface water. Mixing by wave action carries this heat downward by steps. In summer (diagram *C*), intense solar radiation causes warming of the shallow surface layer, but with relatively little mixing, and there is rapidly dropping temperature with depth. In the fall (diagram *D*) surface cooling again begins and mixing becomes more intense. This mixing produces a surface layer of uniform temperature (isothermal layer) which penetrates deeper as it is cooled. By winter the nearly uniform cool temperatures have been restored, as in the first diagram.

Note that throughout the entire year the complete range of surface-water temperature is only about 15 F° (8 C°). This small annual range of water temperature is typical of oceans generally, in contrast with the extreme annual changes of ground-surface temperatures on land in the middle latitudes (Figure 14.4). For example, off the Bay of Biscay (lat. 47° N.) the annual range of temperature in the surface water is only about 13 F°.

## Sea surface temperatures over the globe

Although a complete discussion of sea surface temperatures requires a knowledge of ocean currents, and these have not as yet been described (see Chapter 16), the general latitudinal variations in temperature can be understood in the light of the heat balance equation.

Global distribution of sea-surface temperatures is shown by means of isothermal maps (Figure 14.13). These maps are drawn for the months of February and August, which are the months of extreme temperatures over the oceans as a whole. In general, isotherms of sea-surface temperatures run east-west. At about the 60th parallel of latitude, sea-surface temperatures are

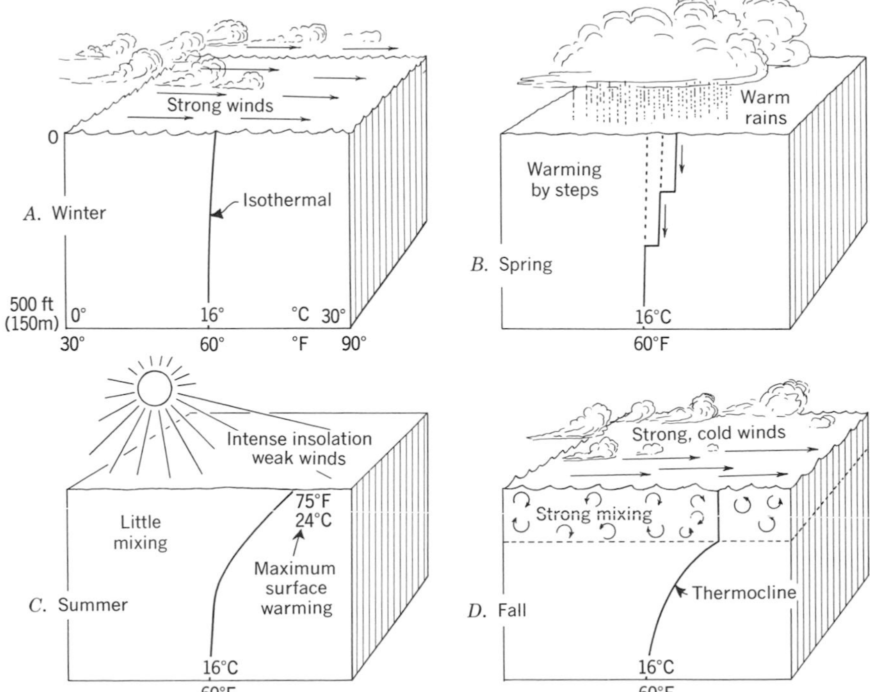


**FIGURE 14.12.** Seasonal changes of sea-water temperatures in middle latitudes. [After E. C. LaFond (1954), *Scientific Monthly,* April, 1954.]

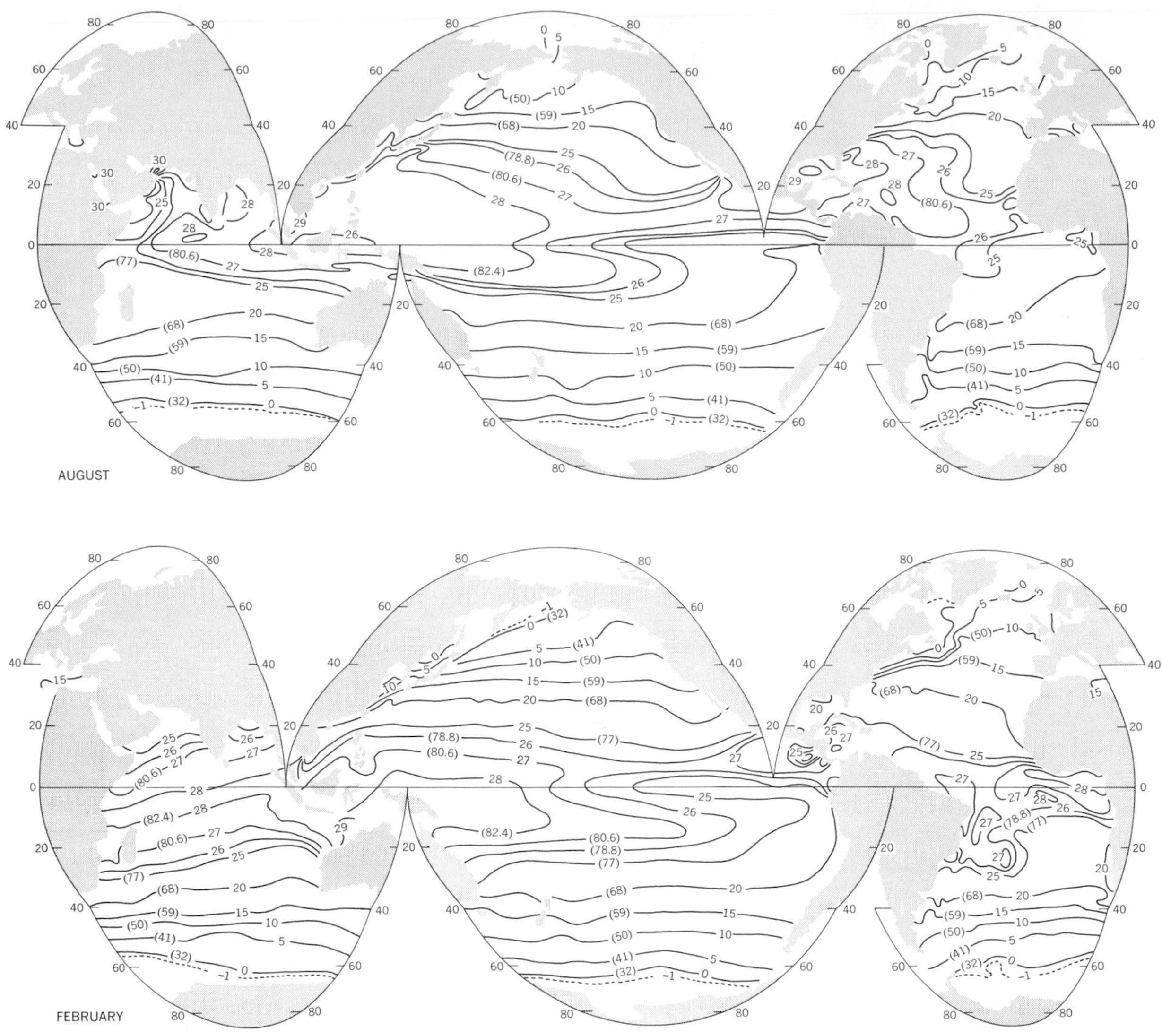


**FIGURE 14.13.** Sea-surface temperatures (°C) for the months of August and February. (Fahrenheit equivalents are given in parentheses.) [Simplified from H. U. Sverdrup (1942), *Oceanography for Meteorologists,* Englewood Cliffs, N.J., Prentice-Hall. Map based on Goode Base Map. Copyright by Univ. of Chicago; used by permission of Univ. of Chicago Press.]

0° C (32° F), or a little colder.[2] Southward they rise generally to reach a maximum of 28° to 29° C (83° to 84° F) over a broad belt of ocean in the equatorial latitudes.

Upsetting the east-west pattern of isotherms are marked equatorward bends in isotherms close to the west coasts of Africa, North America, and South America. As will be explained in Chapter 16, this deflection results from cool equatorward currents and the upwelling of cold subsurface water. Similar but opposite bends in isotherms off the eastern coasts of Asia and North America reflect north-moving warm currents without upwelling.

[2] The freezing point of sea water ranges from 28° to 31° F (—2.2° to —0.6° C), which means that sea water will remain liquid at temperatures somewhat lower than the freezing point of fresh water.

Annual range in sea-surface temperatures can best be appreciated by meridional profiles—one representing the Atlantic Ocean, the other representing the Pacific Ocean (Figure 14.14). Annual range is greatest between 35° and 50° N., where it is on the order of 8 to 10 C° (14 to 18 F°). In the Southern Hemisphere, maximum range occurs in a lower latitude belt (30° to 40° S.) and amounts to only 5 to 6 C° (11 to 13 F°).

Greater range over the Northern Hemisphere oceans is attributed to the influence of very cold air generated over the adjacent continents in winter. This cold air moving over the sea surfaces withdraws heat from the water by evaporation and convection. No comparable effect is found in the Southern Hemisphere, where the ocean surface forms a single circumglobal belt in middle latitudes.

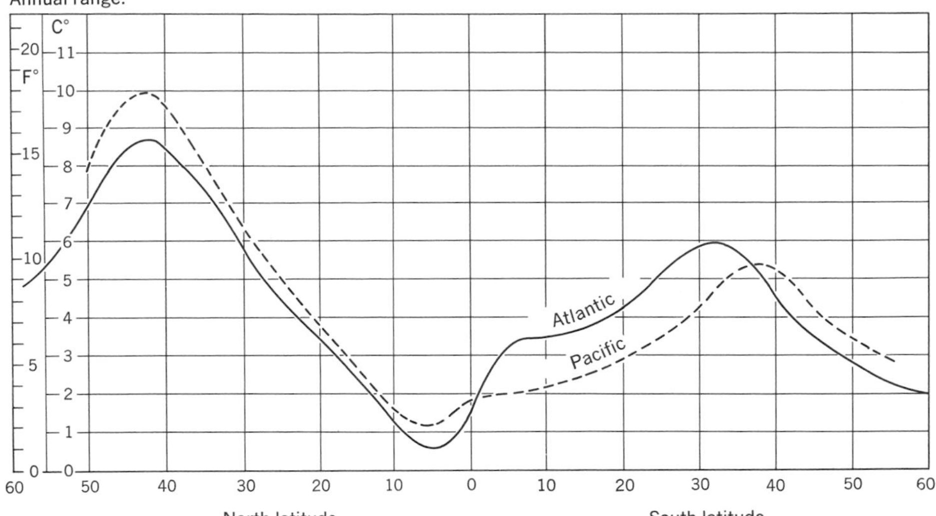


**FIGURE 14.14.** Meridional profiles of the mean annual range of surface-water temperatures in the Atlantic and Pacific Oceans. [After H. U. Sverdrup, M. W. Johnson, and R. H. Fleming (1942), *The Oceans*, Englewood Cliffs, N.J., Prentice-Hall, p. 130, Figure 31.)

Annual range is very small in the equatorial belt, falling to less than 1 C° (1.8 F°) at about 5° N. latitude in the Atlantic Ocean. The uniformly high incoming solar radiation in this belt explains the small temperature range.

## Daily cycle of air temperatures near the ground

Measurements of air temperatures are made at standard observing stations following the practice of placing the thermometer in a sheltered enclosure protected from direct sunlight but louvered to permit free air flow about the instrument (Figure 14.15). Height of the instrument is from 4 to 6 ft (1.2 to 1.8 m), which is approximately at eye-level for the observer. Readings can be taken at any hour, but much labor is saved by using the *maximum-minimum thermometer,* which permits readings of the highest and lowest temperature to be made at a single daily observation. For a continuous record, the *thermograph,* using a Bourdon-tube sensor, permits a temperature record to be drawn upon graph paper attached to a slowly rotating drum. Figure 14.16 shows typical thermograph traces.

Characteristically, the daily (diurnal) temperature cycle of air close to the ground follows a simple curve, with a minimum near the time of sunrise and a maximum in early to middle afternoon (Figure 14.17). The temperature cycle is not symmetrical, since the maximum occurs only about 8 to 10 hours after the minimum (equinox conditions) and the curve rises more steeply in the morning hours than it falls in late afternoon and early evening hours. The curve tends to flatten during night hours.

An explanation of the daily temperature cycle is found in the daily cycle of change in components of the heat balance equation. As the curve of net all-wave radiation, $R$, passes from negative to positive values after sunrise, the air begins to be warmed by long-wave radiation from the ground surface and temperature rises rapidly. Although the value of $R$ peaks at noon and begins to decline thereafter, a radiation surplus continues into the afternoon, causing air temperature to rise further. We might reason that the air temperature would not reach its peak until the value of $R$ declined to zero near sunset, but such is not typically the case. The reason for a decline in temperature in the latter part of the afternoon is to be found in the increased horizontal wind speed near the ground, which in turn increases the rate of upward transport of heat by air turbulence. Mixing of the heated lower air layer with cooler air from higher levels causes a temperature drop. That this mechanism is real is suggested by the curve of sensible heat flux, $H$, in Figure 14.2*B*. Note that the peak value of $H$ occurs in early afternoon, near the time of maximum wind speed.

Placement of the thermometer at a height convenient to the observer gives only a single curve of air temperature and tells little about variations in the layer closer to the ground. To tie in air temperatures with soil temperatures, readings must be taken at a number of points along the vertical. Figure 14.18 shows six temperature profiles—beginning with 5 A.M. and ending with 8 P.M.—in the vertical range from 14 in. (36 cm) below the soil surface to 8 ft (2.4 m) above the surface. The observations were made in July and August in Death Valley, California, and represent extreme conditions of a desert environment. Height above ground is indicated on the vertical axis of the graph, and temperature increasing from left to right is on the horizontal axis. Each line represents temperatures observed at a given hour, as labeled.

The maximum temperature occurs about 3 P.M. and is 17 F° (9.4 C°) higher close to the ground than at 50 ft (15 m) height. This effect would be much more pronounced were it not that heat is distributed upward by air currents, or eddies, in the warmest hours of the day. By about 6 P.M. the cooling process has occurred in such a way that temperatures are the same at all heights (called *isothermal* distribution), but by 8 P.M. the ground layer is cooler than the overlying air. By 5 A.M. the minimum temperature of the day is reached, and the air layer close to the ground continues to be colder than the air above. Such a condition is termed an *inversion,* that is, a reversal of the usual conditions of

**FIGURE 14.15.** A standard U.S. Weather Bureau thermometer shelter. (ESSA photograph, Weather Bureau.)

the normal lapse rate, in which air becomes cooler upward. By 8 A.M. air warming has set in and the isothermal condition again occurs.

The temperature profiles of Figure 14.18 will help tie together the daily thermal cycles of both soil and air. Notice that the temperature extremes, and hence also the maximum daily range (43 F°, 23 C°), is at the ground

**FIGURE 14.16.** These thermograph trace sheets show the daily variations in air temperature for a week's time at two observing stations. (© 1960, John Wiley & Sons, New York; Data of U.S. Dept. of Agriculture.)

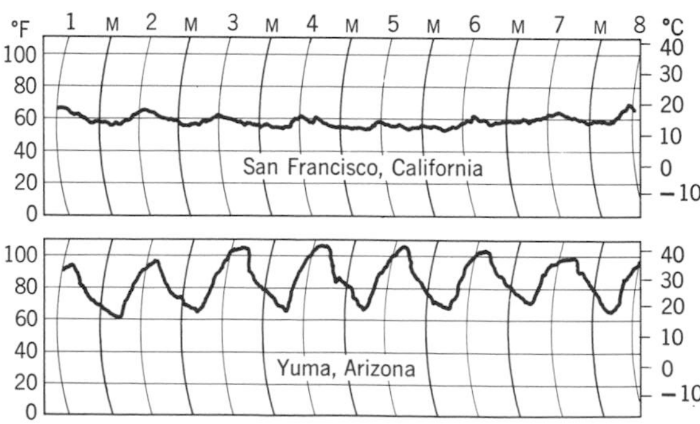


surface. The daily range diminishes much more rapidly downward into the soil than upward into the air, since heat can move into the ground only by slow conduction. In the atmosphere heat can move upward rapidly both by long-wave radiation and by mixing. In contrast to the air temperature peak at 3 P.M., the soil surface temperature peak occurs at noon in close conformity with the peak of incoming radiation (see also Figure 14.4).

One lesson that can be learned from the above illustration is that thermometer placement will make a great deal of difference if one is trying to give some sort of representative figure of air temperature. How high above ground should the thermometer be exposed? The standard U.S. Weather Bureau shelter (Figure 14.15) is set so that the bottom of the louvered box is 4 ft (1.2 m) off the ground, and we can surmise from the graph of temperatures at Death Valley that a shelter height even 2 ft (0.6 m) higher or lower would give quite different maximum and minimum temperatures.

The science of weather and climate close to the ground is called *microclimatology.* This rapidly developing branch of the earth sciences has shown the presence of startlingly great differences in the meteorological

**FIGURE 14.17.** Relationship of daily cycle of net all-wave radiation to air temperature. [After A. N. Strahler (1969), *Physical Geography,* New York, John Wiley & Sons, p. 146, Figure 8.21.]

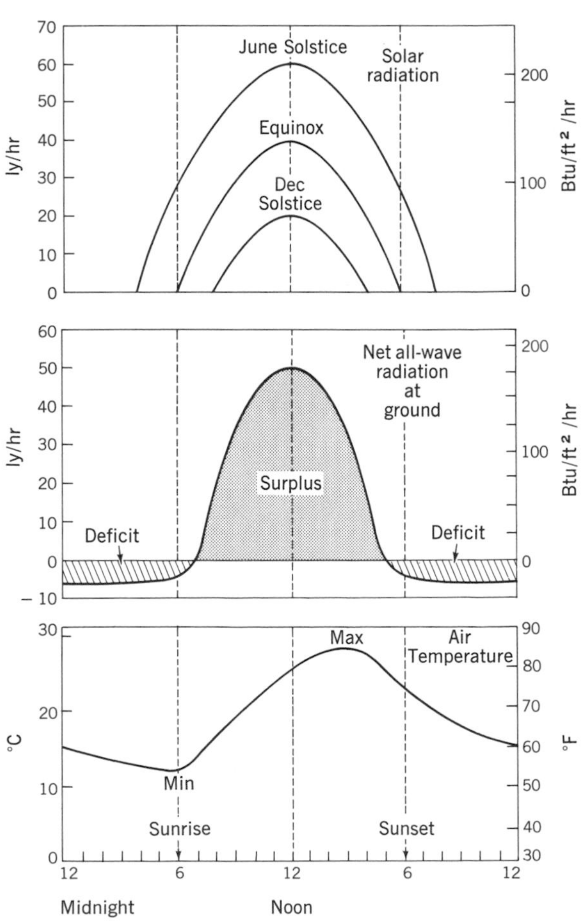

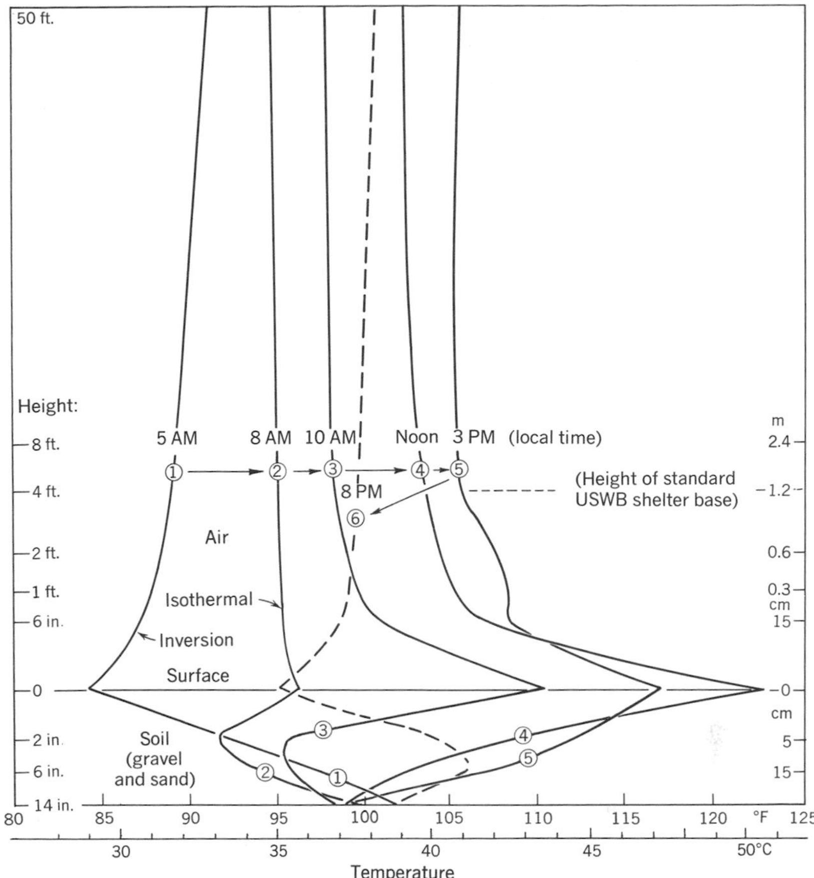


**FIGURE 14.18.** Air temperature at various levels above and below the ground surface throughout the day and night. Average values for July and August 1950 are shown here. Height is shown according to a square-root scale. [Data of Quartermaster Research and Development Branch, U.S. Army. After *Handbook of Geophysics* (1960), New York, Macmillan.]

variables within very short horizontal and vertical distances.

## Land and water contrasts in the daily temperature cycle

Air temperature cycles in the layer close to the earth's surface show quite different daily and seasonal characteristics, depending on whether the surface beneath is that of the ocean or of a continent. For a number of reasons, all of them explained in earlier paragraphs, the surface of any extensive deep body of water heats more slowly and cools more slowly than the surface of a large body of land, when both are subject to the same intensity of incoming radiation.

The slower rise of water-surface temperature can be attributed to (1) direct penetration of radiation, distributing the absorbed heat throughout a substantial water layer, (2) the higher specific heat of water, (3) mixing through eddy motions, which carry the heat to lower depths, and (4) cooling by evaporation from the water surface. In contrast, the more rapid rise of land surface temperature can be attributed to (1) opaqueness of the soil or rock, concentrating the heat in a shallow layer, (2) lower specific heat of mineral matter, (3) poor conductivity of the soil, if it is dry, and (4) absence of mixing. Lower albedo of water surfaces (6–10%) than of most natural ground surfaces (10–30%) will tend to favor more rapid heating of the water, but this effect is overcome by the other factors. As the capacity of a deep water body to hold heat is greater than that of a shallow layer of soil or rock, surface temperatures fall more gradually at the water surface than at the ground surface.

The effect of land and water contrasts is seen in the daily air temperature curves as recorded in the standard thermometer shelter (Figure 14.19), comparing stations of different situations. El Paso, Texas, exemplifies the

**FIGURE 14.19.** Average values of temperature throughout the day at El Paso, Texas, a desert station of the continental interior, and at North Head, Washington, a coastal station. (© 1960, John Wiley & Sons, New York. Data from U.S. Dept. of Agriculture.)

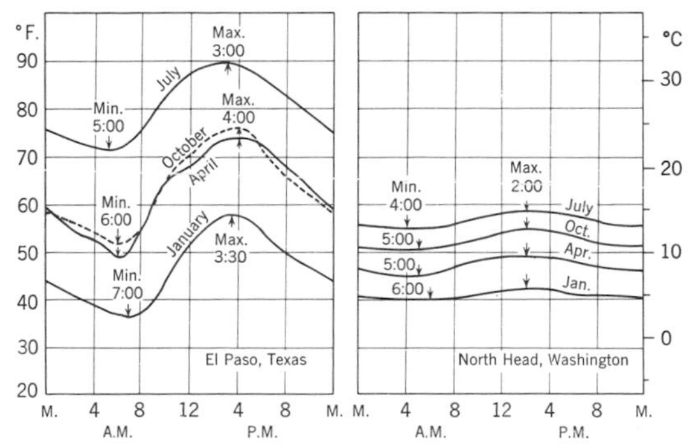

thermal regime of an interior desert in middle latitudes. Soil moisture content is low, vegetation sparse, and cloud cover generally light. Responding to intense heating and cooling of the ground surface, air temperatures show an average daily range of 20 to 25 F° (11 to 14 C°). North Head, Washington, is a coastal station strongly influenced by air brought from the adjacent Pacific Ocean by prevailing westerly winds, thus it exemplifies a maritime thermal evironment. The average daily range at North Head is a mere 5 F° (3 C°) or less. Persistent fogs and cloud cover also contribute to the small daily range. Refer also to Figure 14.16, which shows the same environmental contrast when the record of Yuma is compared with that of San Francisco.

## Seasonal cycle of air temperatures

The principle of contrasts in heating and cooling of water and land surfaces will explain not only the contrasts in daily temperature cycles between coastal and inland places, but also the contrasts in the seasonal or annual cycle of temperature of such places.

Consider first the effect of land and water properties on a seasonal temperature curve for two places at approximately the same latitude, where solar radiation is about the same for both. Two such places are Concordia, Kansas, located in the heart of the continent, and San Luis Obispo, California, on the Pacific Coast. In Figure 14.20 are shown the average daily temperatures through an entire year as well as the solar radiation curve for these two places. To understand such a graph, one must first know how temperature statistics are compiled. The unit building block of temperature data is the *mean daily temperature,* which the U.S. Weather Bureau obtains by averaging the daily maximum and minimum temperatures of the 24-hour period. To obtain a graph such as that in Figure 14.20, the mean daily temperatures for each calendar date of the year are averaged separately for the entire period of record, which may be 20–50 years or more. This gives the average of the mean daily temperatures for each date. Plotted on the graph and connected by a smooth curve, the daily values form a picture of the yearly cycle.

Returning now to the annual temperature graphs of Concordia and San Luis Obispo (Figure 14.20), we see two important differences. (1) Temperature extremes are much greater at Concordia than at San Luis Obispo, the Kansas station averaging about 13 F° (7 C°) higher at the summer maximum, but about 27 F° (15 C°) colder at the minimum point. Thus the *annual temperature range,* or difference between maximum and minimum monthly temperatures, is definitely greater in the heart of the land area than on the West Coast. (2) The inland station reaches its highest and lowest temperatures earlier in the year than the coastal station, although in both cases the extremes occur well after the solstice date. It is clear, then, that the land area both heats more rapidly and to a greater extreme than the coastal area and cools more rapidly and to a lower temperature than the coastal area. Generally speaking, the months of extreme temperature over land areas are July and January, whereas over oceans or on islands surrounded by large ocean areas the extremes are found in August or September and in February.

Notice in Figure 14.19, which reinforces the evidence of Figure 14.20, that the annual range at El Paso is about 35 F° (20 C°), while that at North Head is only about 15 F° (8 C°).

Another good example of the effect of continents and oceans on air temperature is shown in Figure 14.21, in which are plotted the observed highest and lowest daily air temperatures for the coldest and warmest months of a given year at three places on the 50th parallel of

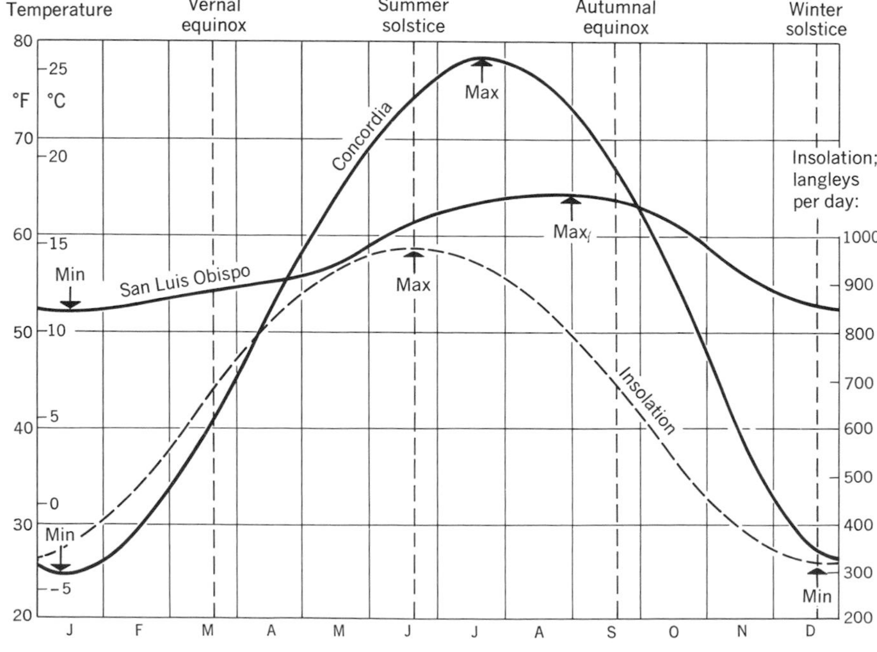


**FIGURE 14.20.** The annual cycle of average air temperatures at Concordia, Kansas, in a mid-continent location, contrasts strongly with that for San Luis Obispo, a west-coast station with strong marine influences. [Data from U.S. Dept. of Agriculture (1928), *Atlas of American Agriculture,* Washington, D.C., U.S. Govt. Printing Office.]

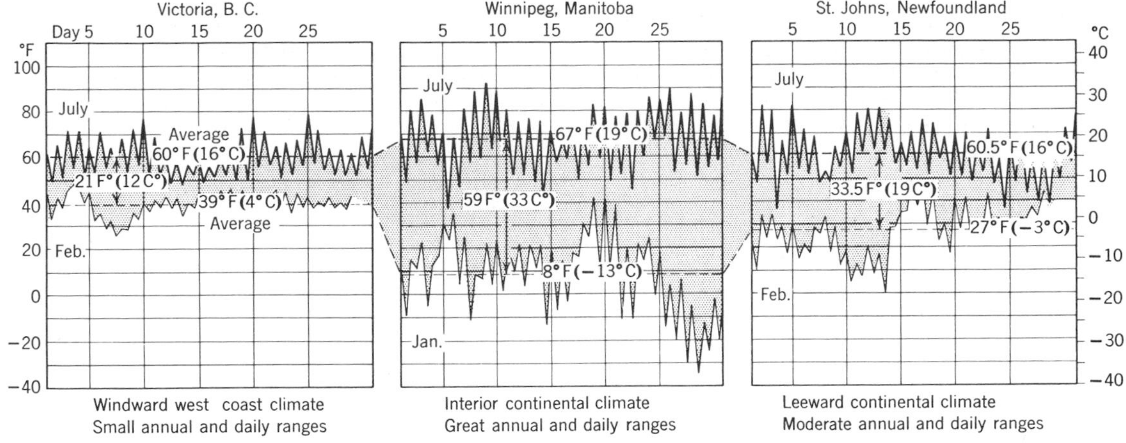


**FIGURE 14.21.** Actual daily maximum and minimum temperatures for selected months in winter and summer are shown here for three stations located about on the 50th parallel of latitude. (© 1965, John Wiley & Sons, New York. Data from Mark Jefferson.)

latitude in North America. Winnipeg, in the heart of the continent, shows not only the highest and lowest monthly averages, but also the greatest daily extremes. Of the two coastal stations—Victoria, British Columbia, and St. Johns, Newfoundland—the west-coast position has the smallest range, both annually and daily, because prevailing westerly winds cause air from over the North Pacific to drift over the coast. At St. Johns, on the eastern border of the continent, the same prevailing westerly winds bring air from the continental interior to the coast, thereby giving St. Johns somewhat more of a continental type of temperature cycle.

## Latitude and air temperature

We are all aware that latitude exerts a powerful control on both the average air temperature throughout the year and the seasonal extremes from summer to winter. Refer to Figure 13.3 showing the annual cycle of incoming solar radiation at key latitudes.

At the equator radiation has two maxima, one at each equinox, when the noon sun reaches the zenith point. The two minima occur at solstice, but even here radiation is intense. Thus in the equatorial belt we should expect not only high air temperatures throughout the year, but very little difference from month to month, so that there will be no summer or winter seasons. This point is illustrated very well in Figure 14.22. Panama, lying at lat. 9° N., has a remarkably uniform average temperature throughout the year. Indeed, the daily range is 15–20 F° (8–11 C°), whereas the extreme months of July and February have averages differing by only 0.3 F° (0.2 C°). Of course, the nearness of Panama to a large expanse of warm ocean also helps to keep the annual temperature differences to the minimum.

Returning to the radiation curves of Figure 13.3, note a great change in the range of the curves successively from 20° to 60° latitude. The maximum value becomes higher, but only moderately so, whereas the minimum value drops rapidly until poleward of the Arctic Circle

**FIGURE 14.22.** Observed daily maximum and minimum air temperatures at Panama (lat. 9° N.) during July and February. (© 1965, John Wiley & Sons, New York. Data from Mark Jefferson.)

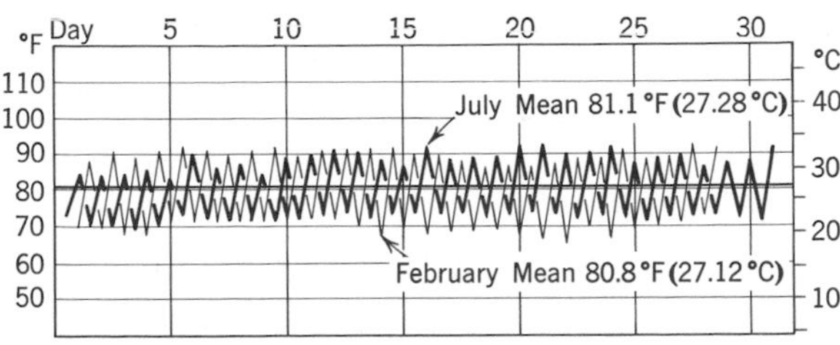


**FIGURE 14.23.** Monthly mean temperatures at semi-arid highland stations. (© 1965, John Wiley & Sons, New York. Data from G. T. Trewartha.)

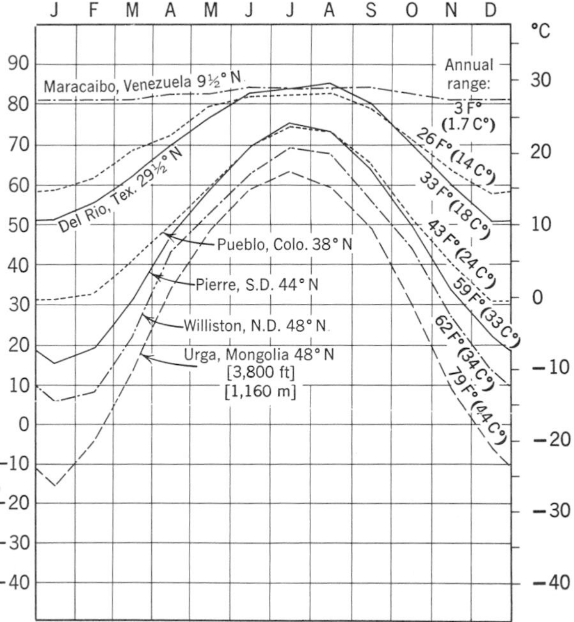

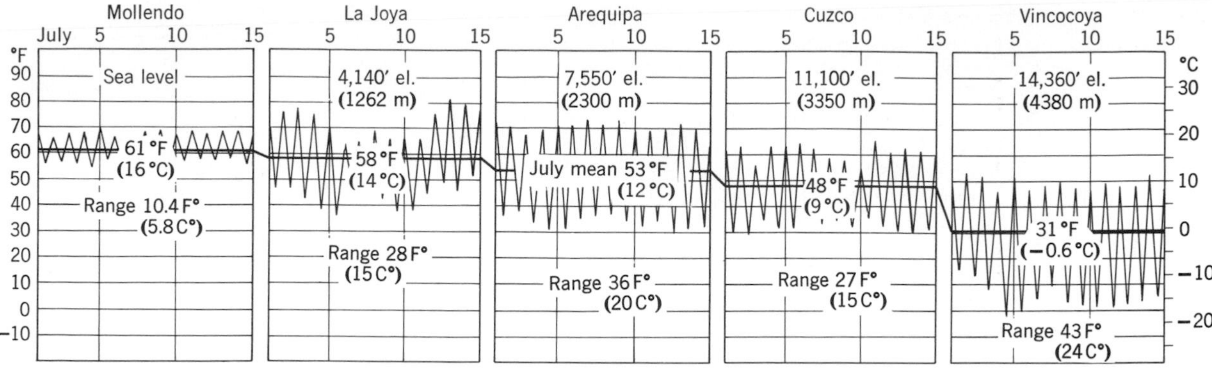


**FIGURE 14.24.** Observed daily maximum and minimum air temperatures for the month of July at five stations in Peru at progressively higher elevations. (© 1965, John Wiley & Sons, New York. Data from Mark Jefferson.)

there is no incoming radiation at all for a period ranging up to six months at the North Pole. These same changes are reflected in the annual air temperatures of stations progressively farther north, provided that one compares stations of similar location within the hearts of continents.

Figure 14.23 shows the annual air temperature cycle at stations of inland locations, all having a rather dry climate. Note that the annual range increases enormously with increasing latitude. The greatest latitudinal change is in the minimum temperatures. The graph for Urga, Mongolia, is abnormal in this comparison because of its high altitude, but the others are a fair illustration of the principle. Note that January is the coldest month and July the warmest in the most northerly four stations.

## Altitude and air temperatures

In Chapter 11 it was stated that, on the average, air temperature falls at the lapse rate of 3.5 F° per 1000 ft (6.4 C° per km) of increase in altitude and that this rate applies generally throughout the troposphere. It is thus normally true that places located at high altitudes have cooler air temperatures. A fine illustration of this principle is seen in the set of daily-temperature graphs for 15 days in July at several stations on the west side of South America at lat. 15° S. (Figure 14.24). These stations range in elevation from sea level to a maximum of over 14,000 ft (4.3 km).

Two effects of altitude are conspicuous. (1) The average temperature of the month decreases progressively with altitude, though not as rapidly as the standard lapse rate. (2) The daily range becomes much greater as altitude increases, because the clearer, more rarefied air at higher altitude permits more intense solar radiation to reach the ground, thus heating the ground more intensely during the day. At night the loss of heat by long-wave ground and air radiation into outer space is much more rapid at high altitude because of the lower amount of water vapor and carbon dioxide in a given air volume.

For the same reasons, during the daytime at high altitudes there is also a great difference in air temperatures taken on slopes exposed to the sun and on those in the shade. As far as average yearly temperature is concerned, then, the effect of increase in elevation is very much the same as a great poleward shift in latitude. One may reach the region of permanent snowbanks and glaciers by climbing above 15,000 ft (4.5 km) elevation in the equatorial belt just as surely as by traveling north to the arctic regions (Figure 14.25).

## Global pattern of air temperature distribution

The principles of air temperature control by land and water bodies, by latitude, and by altitude enable us to understand the general global air temperature pattern and its yearly changes. Distribution of temperatures over a large area is best studied by means of *isothermal maps,* on which lines are drawn to connect all places having the same temperature. (Maps of this type are explained in Appendix I.) Isothermal maps can be prepared not only for the temperatures observed at a given time, but also for the average monthly temperatures. Figures 14.26 and 14.27 show average monthly isotherms for the entire earth for the two months generally having

**FIGURE 14.25.** Zone of perpetual snow in the White Range of the high Andes mountains near Ancash, Peru. (Photograph by Aero Service, Litton Industries.)

the maximum and minimum temperatures over the continental areas: January and July. Isotherms have been generalized over the major mountain belts and high plateaus.

Notice first on these world air temperature maps that the isotherms trend generally east-west, following the trend of the parallels of latitude, as we should expect because of the diminishing solar radiation from equator to poles. The east-west trend is most clearly seen in the Southern Hemisphere, where a great expanse of ocean gives a single uniform type of surface around the entire globe in the middle latitudes. In the Northern Hemisphere, however, the two great land masses of Eurasia and North America disrupt the east-west pattern and cause centers of higher or lower temperature to develop seasonally.

In January a *cold pole,* averaging below −50° F (−46° C) forms over northern Siberia with somewhat less severely cold centers over the Greenland icecap and the Alaska-Yukon region. In contrast, in July the land areas heat intensely to produce high-temperature centers over North Africa, southern Asia, and the Sonoran Desert region of Mexico and the southwestern United States. A monthly mean exceeding 100° F (38° C) is found in a small part of the western Sahara. These hot centers are also very dry, for reasons explained in Chapter 18, and constitute the great tropical deserts. Their Southern Hemisphere counterparts are seen on the January map in the high-temperature zones over southwest Africa and central Australia, but mean values are not as high as in the Northern Hemisphere deserts.

Antarctica shows very well the effect of a continent centered on a pole and covered by a vast icecap. The isotherms run in roughly concentric circles around the South Pole and indicate bitterly cold winter averages. In summer (January) the snow-covered surfaces reflect so much radiation that temperatures average below −20° F (−30° C), even though the South Pole receives more radiation in a 24-hour day in January than the equator does in a day at equinox. The extreme cold is in an air layer close to the ground, for a few hundred feet above the surface the air may be as much as 50 F° (28 C°) warmer. Their high altitude is a major contributing factor to extreme cold of both Antarctica and Greenland.

Over the Arctic Ocean winter temperatures do not drop to the extreme low levels found in Siberia, Antarctica, or the Greenland icecap, because some heat is conducted to the air from the water, through the floating layer of sea ice. Thus the ocean shows its moderating influence, even at the North Pole.

FIGURE 14.28. Annual shift in latitude of an isotherm in middle latitudes. (© 1960, John Wiley & Sons, New York.)

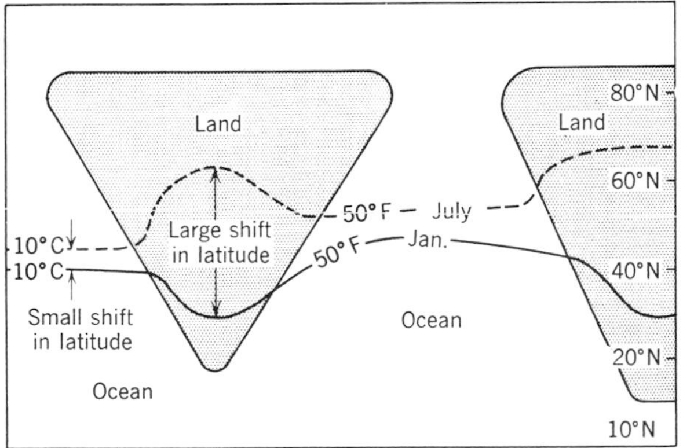


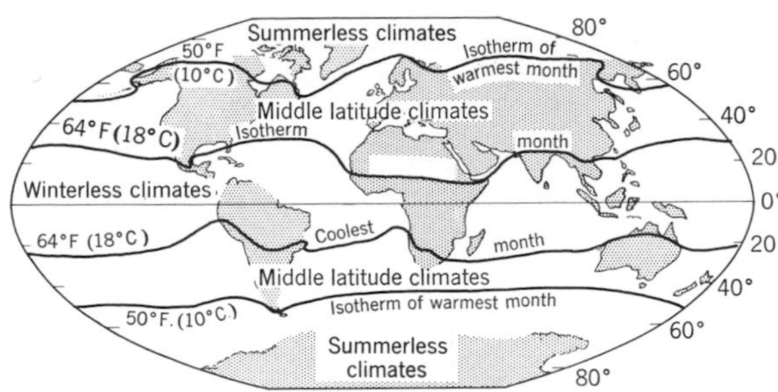


FIGURE 14.29. Three major world climate regions based on temperature. (© 1960, John Wiley and Sons, New York.)

A comparison of January and July temperatures at various points in the middle latitudes confirms the principle of land and water contrasts. Isotherms are deflected poleward over the continents in summer and equatorward over the continents in winter. Over the oceans a given isotherm shifts north and south through only about 5 degrees of latitude, whereas on land it migrates through 15–30 degrees of latitude. The schematic diagram in Figure 14.28 shows the nature of this seasonal shift in isotherms.

## Temperature as a basis of climate classification

The general east-west trend of isotherms, approximating the parallels of latitude, offers a means of dividing the earth into three climate zones, provided that the isotherms are selected with a definite purpose in mind. Figure 14.29 is a world map showing three such major climate groups: (1) *Tropical climates,* which have no winter season, are bounded on both north and south by the isotherm of 64° F (18° C) for the coolest month of the year—this means that nowhere in the tropical climates is there any month of the year in which the monthly mean temperature is lower than 64° F. (2) *Middle-latitude climates,* lying poleward of the tropical climates, are bounded on the poleward side by the 50° F (10° C) isotherms for the warmest month—thus no place in this region fails to have at least one month with a mean monthly temperature warmer than 50° F. Generally speaking, the middle-latitude climates have both summer and winter seasons. (3) *Polar climates,* lying poleward of the middle-latitude climates, have no month in which the mean monthly temperature rises higher than 50° F and are therefore said to have no true summer.

The system of world climate classification described in Appendix II makes use of the above temperature groups as the first order of climatic subdivision.

## References for further study

Byers, H. (1959), *General Meteorology,* New York, McGraw-Hill, 540 pp., chaps. 4, 5.

von Arx, W. S. (1962), *An Introduction to Physical Oceanography,* Reading, Mass., Addison-Wesley, 422 pp., chap. 7.

Geiger, R. (1965), *The Climate Near the Ground,* 4th ed., Cambridge, Mass., Harvard Univ. Press, 611 pp.

Miller, D. H. (1965), "The Heat and Water Budget of the Earth's Surface," pp. 175–302 of *Advances in Geophysics,* vol. 11, New York, Academic.

Sellers, W. D. (1965), *Physical Climatology,* Chicago, Univ. of Chicago Press, 272 pp., chaps. 8, 9.

Petterssen, S. (1969), *Introduction to Meteorology,* 3rd ed., New York, McGraw-Hill, 333 pp., chap. 3.

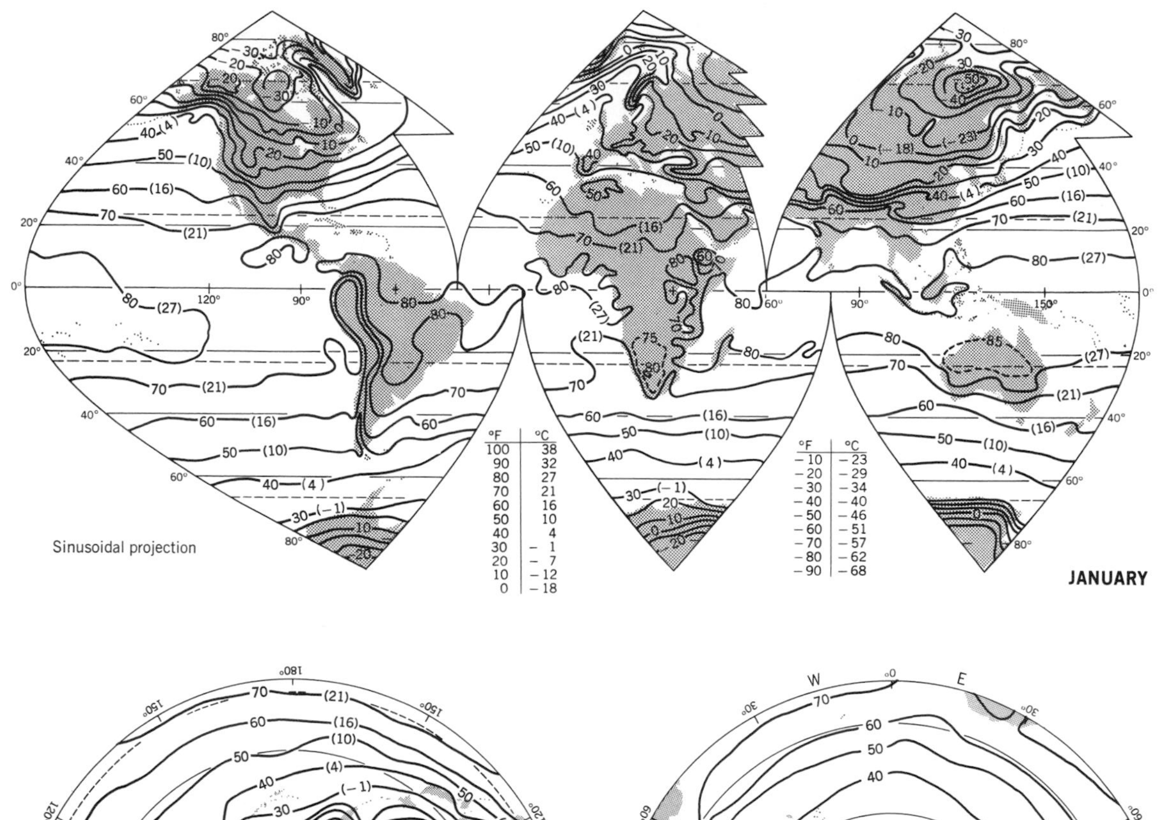


N. Hem

Azimuthal equal-area projection

S. Hem

**FIGURE 14.26.** Mean January surface air temperatures, °F. (Equivalent centigrade temperatures in parentheses.) [Isotherms compiled by John E. Oliver from data by World Climatology Branch, Meteorological Office, *Tables of Temperature, 1958,* Her Majesty's Stationery Office, London; U.S. Navy (1955), *Marine Climatic Atlas,* Washington, D.C.; and P. C. Dalrymple (1966), Amer. Geophys. Union. Isotherms reproduced by permission of John Wiley & Sons, New York.]

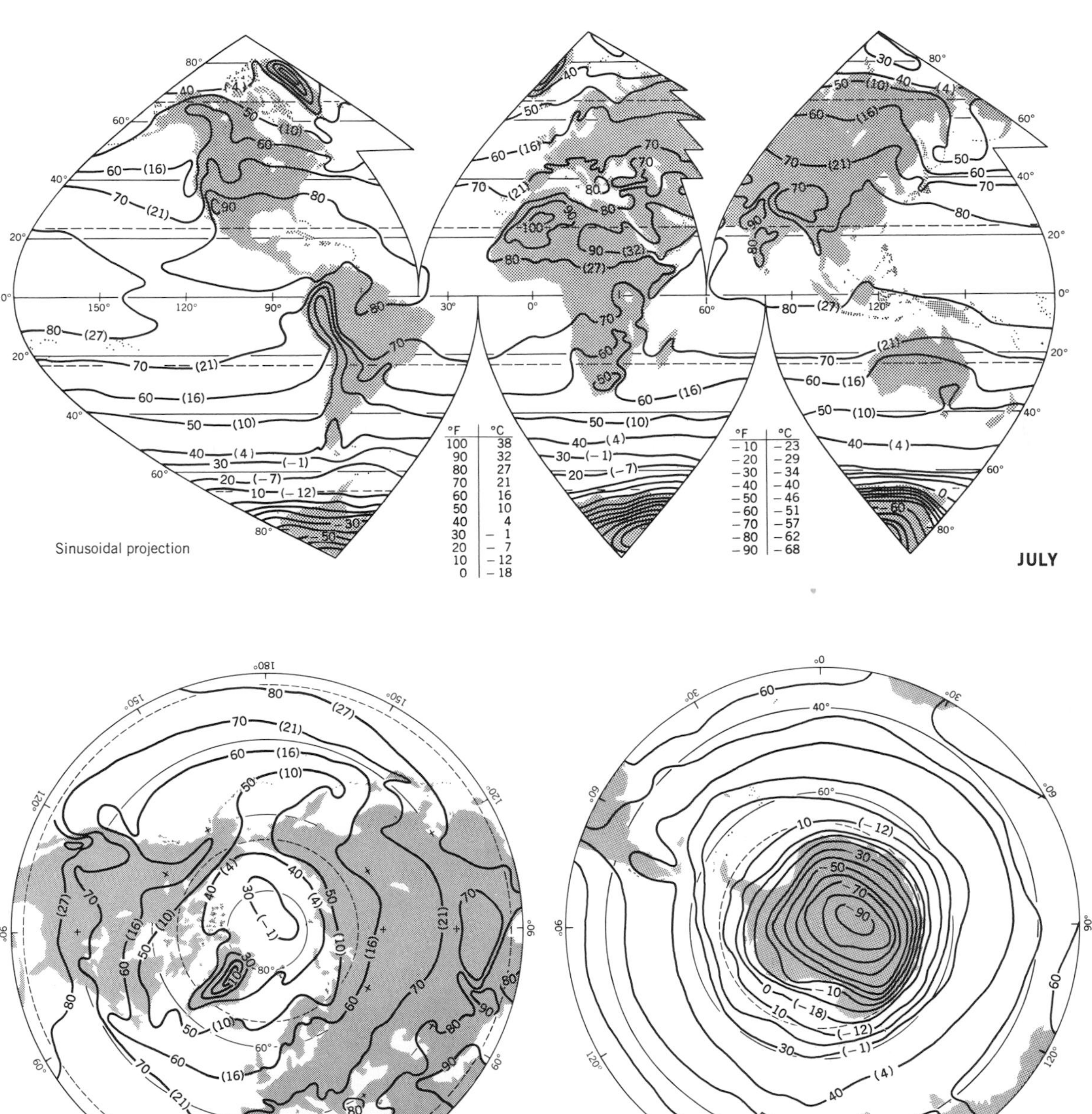


**FIGURE 14.27.** Mean July surface air temperatures, °F. (Equivalent centigrade temperatures in parentheses.) (Same data sources as Figure 14.26. Isotherms reproduced by permission of John Wiley & Sons, New York.)

# 15

# Atmospheric circulation

WE FOUND IN Chapter 11 that the earth's equatorial, tropical, and subtropical latitude belts[1] have an annual net radiation surplus, whereas from middle latitudes to the poles a net radiation deficit exists. Yet, within each latitude belt average annual temperatures of the lower air, the soil, and the ocean surface are practically constant from year to year, showing that surplus heat is exported from lower latitudes to higher latitudes by a meridional transport in just the right quantities to sustain those constant temperature levels (Figure 15.1). In this chapter and the next we examine the broad patterns of circulations of the atmosphere and oceans, whereby the global heat exchange is carried out.

Both the atmosphere and the ocean, as fluid layers, are capable of large-scale horizontal motions, designated by the general term *advection.* The term advection also includes large-scale rising and sinking motions accompanying the horizontal motions. Advection normally takes the form of closed loops of more or less circular pattern, going by such names as *gyres* in the oceans, or as *cyclones* and *anticyclones* in the atmosphere. Localized vertical motions within the atmosphere and oceans, taking the form of relatively small rising or sinking columns of fluid, constitute *convection.* Because both the atmosphere and ocean layers are of very small thickness compared with their horizontal dimensions, convectional motions are of much smaller dimension than advective motions. One might say that advective motions of the atmosphere are generally of one to two orders of magnitude larger (10 to 100 times larger) in scale than convectional motions.

[1] Arbitrary definitions of latitude belts for use in this and subsequent chapters are as follows: *Equatorial,* 10° N. to 10° S.; *tropical,* 10° to 25°; *subtropical,* 25° to 35°; *middle-latitude,* 35° to 55°; *subarctic,* 50° to 60°; *arctic* (*antarctic*), 60° to 75°; *polar,* 75° to 90°.

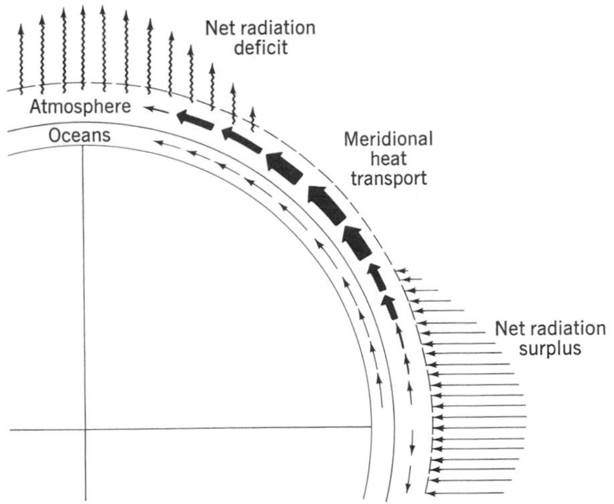


**FIGURE 15.1.** A schematic diagram of the earth's heat balance.

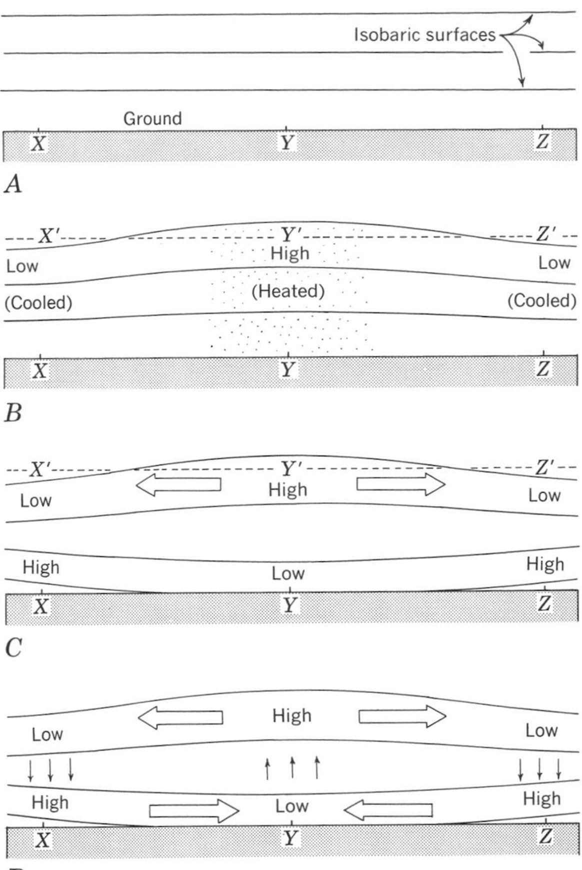


**FIGURE 15.2.** A simple convective system of winds produced by unequal warming and cooling of the atmospheric layer.

*Wind* is broadly defined as air motion relative to the surface of the earth. In meteorological practice, the word *wind* refers to air motions that are dominantly horizontal, vertical motions being designated by other terms, such as *updraft* or *downdraft.* Forces that cause winds are the first subject of inquiry in this chapter. The action of four basic forces must be taken into account to understand completely the directions and speeds of air motion throughout all parts of the atmosphere.

The basic energy source of global winds is solar radiation. Inequalities in temperatures within large masses of air result from different rates of heating and cooling according to the radiation balance, whether positive or negative. These thermal imbalances lead to action of a force tending to produce air motion. Once set in motion, other forces come into play and modify both the direction and speed of the motion. These secondary forces—which result from the earth's rotation, from air motion in a curved path, and from friction with the ground—complicate what might otherwise be a simple plan of planetary circulation. This chapter examines basic principles relative to air motion, proceeding from the simplest situation to more complex cases. From an understanding of these mechanical principles the earth's atmospheric circulation, with well-defined wind belts both at the surface and at high levels, will emerge as systematic and orderly.

## Simple convective circulation

A first step in understanding the cause of wind is to examine a simple convective circulation system caused by unequal heating of the atmosphere. Imagine first a layer of the atmosphere uniform in horizontal distribution of temperature and pressure at any level (Figure 15.2*A*). Barometric pressure is now exactly equal at surface points *X, Y,* and *Z.* Next suppose that solar heating warms the air layer above point *Y,* causing the layer to expand and increase in depth, while at the same time cooling by radiation occurs above *X* and *Z,* causing the layer there to contract. The top of the layer is now raised in elevation above *Y,* as shown in Figure 15.2*B.* Barometric pressure remains equal at surface points *X, Y,* and *Z,* because the mass of a column of air above each has not changed. But at any higher level we may choose to select (dashed line in diagram *B*), the pressure is higher at, say, *Y′* than at *X′* and *Z′.*

Thus a *horizontal pressure gradient* has been produced at higher levels by unequal heating and expansion of an air layer. (A pressure gradient is simply a change of barometric pressure along any selected surface.) In this case we are interested in the pressure gradient in a horizontal surface, such as the 5000-foot level, shown in Figure 15.3. Barometric pressure within a vertical cross section of the atmosphere can be shown by lines representing surfaces of equal pressure, or *isobaric surfaces.* Where a horizontal pressure gradient exists, the isobaric surfaces will appear as sloping lines, as in Figure 15.3*A.* If a map is drawn to show pressure conditions at a given level, such as the 5000-foot level, the isobaric surfaces will appear as lines of equal pressure, or *isobars,* as in Figure 15.3*B.* The pressure gradient on the map, shown by an arrow, is always at right angles to the isobars and in the direction from high to low pressure.

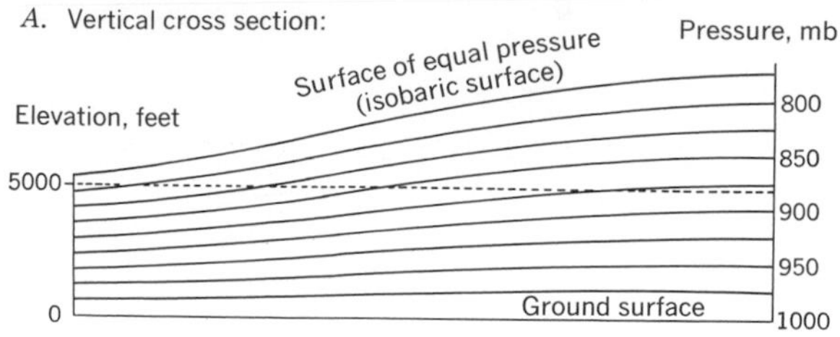


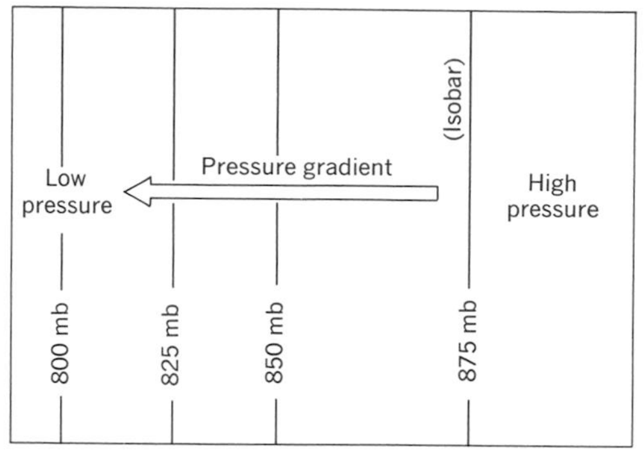


**FIGURE 15.3.** (*A*) Isobaric surfaces seen in vertical cross section. (*B*) An isobaric map corresponding with the profile above.

When a horizontal pressure gradient exists, there exists a *pressure-gradient force* acting in the direction of and proportiontal to the gradient. Hence the force is greatest where the isobars are most closely spaced on the map and least where they are most widely spaced, and it is directed at right angles to the isobars in the direction of lower pressure. Air will tend to move in response to this force with a speed which is greatest where the isobars are most closely spaced together.

Returning now to the sequence of events illustrated in diagram *C* of Figure 15.2, we find that air flows horizontally at high level from the region of high pressure to adjacent regions of lower pressure. As soon as motion begins, however, the transfer of mass from one area to another alters pressure conditions at surface points *X*, *Y*, and *Z*. The increase in mass of the air columns above *X* and *Z* causes the surface pressure at these points to become higher, while the reduction in mass of the air column over *Y* causes surface pressure there to become less. There now exists a pressure gradient from *X* and *Z* toward *Y* in the atmosphere close to the ground, and air begins to move toward *Y*, as shown in diagram *D* of Figure 15.2. Two winds have thus been developed, one at high level and one at low level, and are blowing in opposite directions. The convection system is completed by a general rising of air over *Y* and a general sinking of air over *X* and *Z*, and it continues until a uniform temperature distribution (and, consequently, a uniform pressure) is again produced.

## Sea and land breezes

An example of a simple convective circulation is found in the system of sea and land breezes commonly encountered along a coastline. On warm summer days when no strong winds of regional extent are blowing, rapid heating of the land surface adjacent to the sea causes the lower air layer to be expanded, setting off the chain of events already explained and resulting in a surface wind from sea to land—the *sea breeze* (Figure 15.4*B*). The entire circulation affects a layer only a few hundred feet in thickness, and the sea breeze is felt inland only a few miles from the shore.

At night, as the land loses heat more rapidly than water by radiation, the air layer over the land is cooled more than that over the water. Now the pressure gradients are reversed and a *land breeze* is set in motion (Figure 15.4*C*).

Sea and land breezes modify the climate of a narrow coastal belt a few miles wide, the sea breeze making particularly pleasant weather in summer. The sea breeze quickly reduces high afternoon temperatures and provides a flow of air when there might otherwise be oppressively stagnant conditions.

## Valley and mountain breezes

Essentially similar in origin and diurnal alternation is the system of *valley and mountain breezes.* When mountain slopes are heated by the sun, the overlying air layer is warmed and expanded, becoming warmer than air at the same level farther out over the valley. A pressure gradient is thus directed toward the slope, causing an upslope wind, the *valley breeze* (Figure 15.5). At night, air close to the slope is cooled, causing a pressure gradient directed away from the slope and generating a downslope wind, the *mountain breeze.*

**FIGURE 15.4.** Sea breeze and land breeze. [After S. Petterssen (1958), *Introduction to Meteorology,* New York, McGraw-Hill, p. 165, Figure 116.]

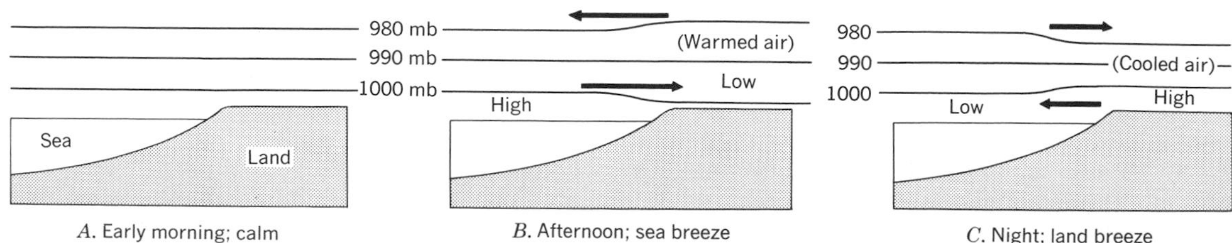

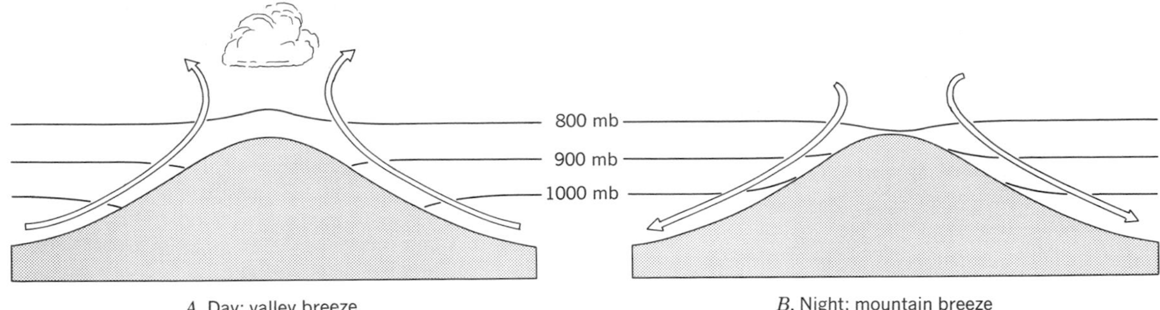


**FIGURE 15.5.** Valley breeze and mountain breeze. [After S. Petterssen (1958), *Introduction to Meteorology,* New York, McGraw-Hill, p. 166, Figure 117.]

## Forces acting to modify winds

Wind, which we limit here to predominantly horizontal air movements, is motion of air in response to unbalanced forces acting in the horizontal direction. Thus far we have examined one such force, the pressure-gradient force, disregarding for simplicity other possible forces that also act.

In addition to the pressure-gradient force, three other forces may act horizontally to affect air motion: (1) the *Coriolis force,* (2) *centrifugal force,* and (3) the *force of friction.* We shall consider the effect of each of these forces individually, adding its effect to the sum of those forces considered before it.

**Coriolis force and the geostrophic wind** In Chapter 2, the Coriolis effect was described as an apparent acceleration resulting from earth rotation. For an orbiting earth satellite whose path is a great circle fixed with respect to space coordinates, the satellite's earth track curves to the right in the Northern Hemisphere and to the left in the Southern Hemisphere because of eastward earth rotation.

For a small mass moving horizontally over the earth's surface, the Coriolis effect can be treated as a force directed at right angles to the path of motion. The velocity of the moving mass is a vector quantity in which the horizontal direction must be specified; the Coriolis force always acts at right angles to the velocity vector (Figure 15.6). Magnitude of the Coriolis force is directly proportional to the horizontal velocity, as well as to twice the angular velocity of earth rotation and to the sine of the latitude, as stated in the following equation:

$$\text{Coriolis force per unit mass} = V\, 2\, \Omega \sin \phi$$

where $V$ is the horizontal velocity (cm per sec),
$\Omega$ is angular velocity of earth rotation (0.00007292 radian per mean solar second),
and $\phi$ is geographic latitude (degrees).

Coriolis force is zero at the equator and increases to the maximum at either pole. At latitude 30° the force is 50% of the maximum value; at 60° latitude it is 86.7% of the maximum. In the Northern Hemisphere the Coriolis force acts to the right hand of the direction of motion, and in the Southern Hemisphere it acts toward the left hand (Figure 15.6).

In response to the Coriolis force, any particle of matter in motion the Northern Hemisphere will tend to be turned toward the right and will, if free to respond, follow a path curving toward the right (Figure 15.5). In the Southern Hemisphere the path is turned toward the left. Precisely on the equator there is no tendency for deflection. It is important to know that Coriolis force is entirely independent of the compass direction of the motion.

Air and water, as fluids which respond freely to unbalanced forces, are easily influenced by the Coriolis force. Turning of the flow paths to right or left, depending upon the hemisphere, is strongly evident in both winds and ocean currents.

Consider now a small parcel of air, starting from a position *A* at rest at some high level in the atmosphere, where surface friction can be neglected, and at a latitude other than the equator. A pressure gradient exists, as indicated by straight isobars (Figure 15.7).

**FIGURE 15.6.** Direction of application of the apparent Coriolis force is always at right angles to the direction of air motion.

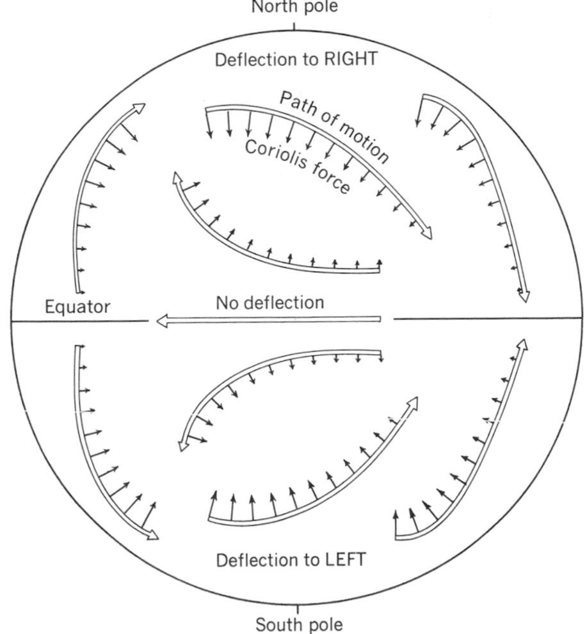

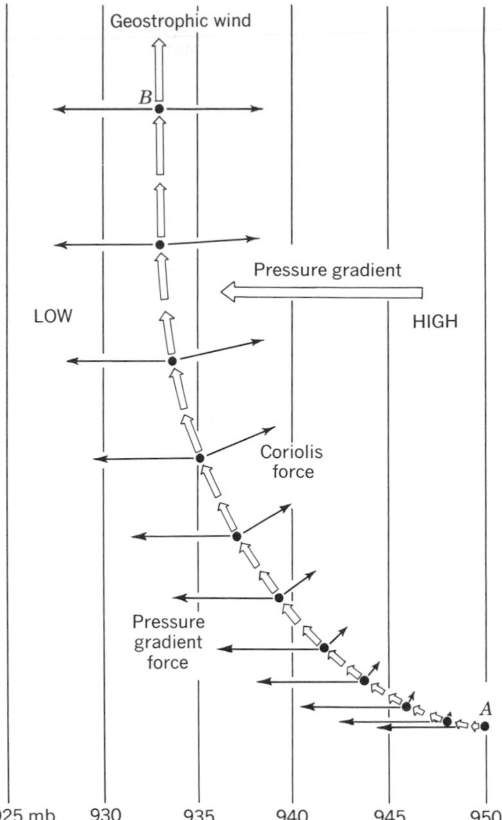


**FIGURE 15.7.** A parcel of air starting from a position of rest at *A* is deflected until it is moving parallel with the isobars at *B*. [After S. Petterssen (1958), *Introduction to Meteorology,* New York, McGraw-Hill, p. 152, Figure 105.]

In response to the pressure-gradient force the parcel begins to move at right angles to the isobars toward lower pressure. As soon as motion begins, the Coriolis force begins to act, increasing in strength as the speed of the parcel increases, but always directed at right angles to the path of the parcel. Turning ceases when the parcel is moving parallel with the isobars, with the Coriolis force equal and opposite to (and therefore just balancing) the pressure-gradient force.

The relation of pressure to wind is stated in the *law of Buys Ballot* (a Dutch meteorologist): In the Northern Hemisphere, if you stand with your back to the wind, arms outstretched to either side, the region of low pressure is toward your left hand, high pressure toward your right hand; in the Southern Hemisphere low pressure is toward your right hand, high pressure toward your left.

Wind blowing with steady speed and parallel to straight parallel isobars (hence not affected by any accelerations) and at upper levels (hence free of effects of friction with the ground) is described as the *geostrophic wind.* The speed of the geostrophic wind is directly proportional to the steepness of the horizontal pressure-gradient, thus it is stronger where isobars are closely spaced than where they are widely spaced. The geostrophic wind is rarely a truly accurate description of actual winds because isobars are usually curved, and flow is rarely in a straight line for any appreciable distance. Also, isobars frequently are not parallel for any great distance but converge or diverge appreciably. Hence the pressure-gradient force is usually either increasing or decreasing along the path of travel of the parcel, causing it to be accelerated or decelerated.

**The gradient wind** Consider next the effect of motion of an air parcel in a horizontal but curved path, as it would follow to conform to a set of curving isobars. As explained in Chapter 2, motion in a curved path is accompanied by centripetal acceleration. A centripetal force must be applied to cause the body to follow a curved path because the natural tendency is for the body to follow a straight path tangent to the curve (see Figure 2.7). For purposes of discussion we shall substitute for the centripetal force an equal and opposite centrifugal force directed radially outward from the center of curvature. The centrifugal force, which varies as the square of the linear speed and inversely as the radius, will thus be added to, or subtracted from, the pressure-gradient and Coriolis forces, depending upon whether the path curves clockwise or counterclockwise and whether it lies in the Northern or Southern Hemisphere. A low-pressure center, delineated by roughly concentric isobars, is termed a *cyclone,* and a high-pressure center is an *anticyclone.*

Four possible cases of curved isobars at low levels in the atmosphere are illustrated in Figure 15.8:

Case *A:* Counterclockwise turning about a center of low pressure (cyclone) in the Northern Hemisphere.

Case *B*: Clockwise turning about a center of high pressure (anticyclone) in the Northern Hemisphere.

Case *C:* Clockwise turning about a center of low pressure (cyclone) in the Southern Hemisphere.

Case *D:* Counterclockwise turning about a center of high pressure (anticyclone) in the Southern Hemisphere.

For each of the four cases are shown the various vector combinations of pressure-gradient force (open arrow), Coriolis force (diagonal-shaded arrow), and centrifugal force (black arrow). Geostrophic wind for straight isobars is also shown. Note first that the pressure-gradient force arrow (Pr) is the same length in all four cases, because the isobars are equally spaced in all.

In Case *A,* a low-pressure center (cyclone) in the Northern Hemisphere, the pressure-gradient force is opposed to and exactly balances the sum of the Coriolis and centrifugal forces. The parcel of air moves along the isobar in a counterclockwise motion about the center of low pressure.

Case *B,* a high-pressure center (anticyclone) in the Northern Hemisphere, presents a quite different force arrangement than Case *A.* Here the pressure-gradient force is directed radially outward from the center and is added to by centrifugal force, hence their sum is greater than that of the pressure-gradient force alone in Case *A.* The Coriolis force, directed toward the center of the high, must be greater to balance the greater opposed forces, and as a result the parcel of air must move

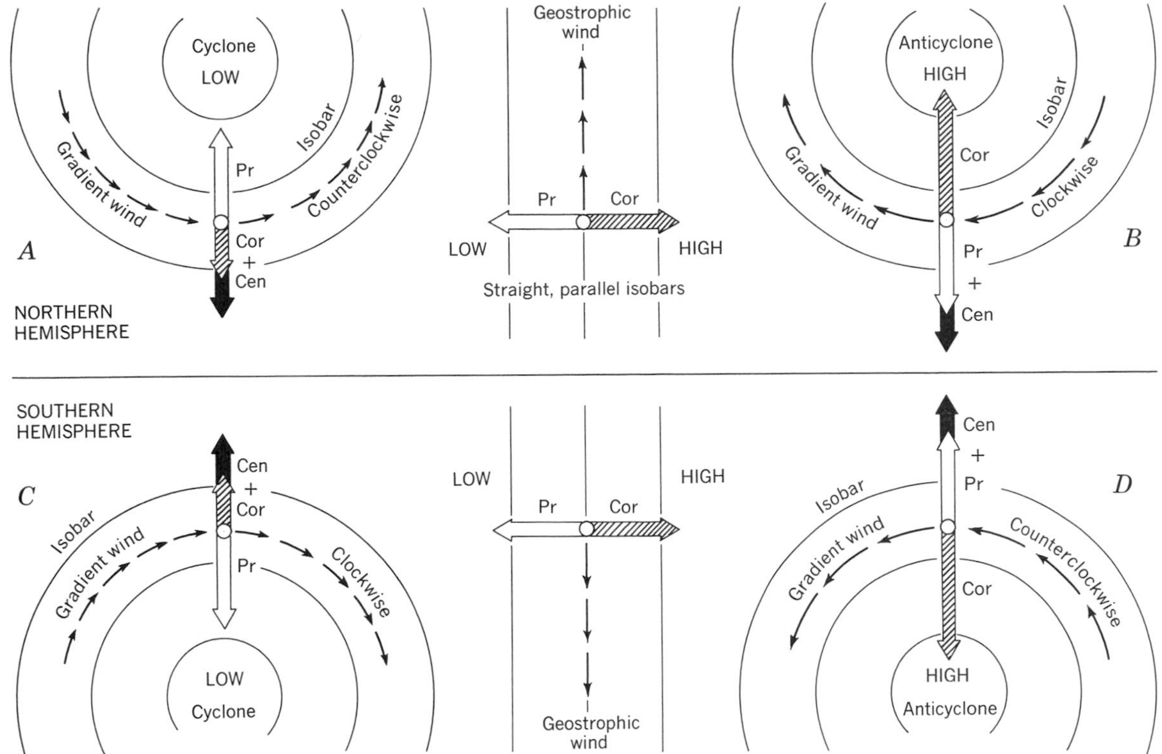


**FIGURE 15.8.** Balance of forces in cyclonic and anticyclonic motion in the Northern and Southern Hemispheres. [After S. Petterssen (1958), *Introduction to Meteorology,* New York, McGraw-Hill, p. 154, Figure 107.]

faster. Therefore the resulting wind will be of higher speed around the anticyclone (Case *B*) than around the cyclone (Case *A*).

Case *C,* in the Southern Hemisphere, is essentially the same as Case *A*, but reversed in direction of turning. In both *A* and *C* the resulting wind is the same in speed for isobars of equal spacing and equal radii of curvature and located at equal latitudes. Case *D* is essentially the same as Case *B,* but with direction of turning reversed.

The wind described above, following curved parallel isobars and having no accelerations in the direction of motion, is known as the *gradient wind.* Although representing a special situation, it is a close approximation to the wind actually found in the atmosphere at levels exceeding 3000 ft (900 m), where surface friction is negligible. In Figure 15.9 is a map of pressures and winds at high elevation. Note that the wind speed is greatest where the isobars are closest, slowest where they are farthest apart.

A knowledge of the gradient wind is important in air navigation, since it is possible, by means of an isobaric map, to determine the direction and speed of air flow at a given level and thus to plot a course avoiding head winds and utilizing tail winds to the maximum. In the Northern Hemisphere such a course would be steered counterclockwise around the cyclones, keeping low pressure always to the left.

**Surface winds** Finally, we turn to the effect of a fourth force, that of friction with the ground surface. To examine the principle involved, consider initially a geostrophic wind—that is, the case in which isobars are straight and parallel—but imagine that the elevation selected is within a few tens of feet above the ground (Figure 15.10). The flow of air over the ground is met by frictional resistance, which may be thought of as a force acting opposite to the direction of movement of the air parcel and proportional to the parcel's speed and to roughness of the surface. Reduction in wind speed caused by friction is accompanied by a reduction in the Coriolis force (which is proportional to wind speed), hence the pressure-gradient force, which is not changed, is more effective and turns the wind direction somewhat toward the direction of lower pressure. A balance of forces, shown by the arrows in Figure 15.10, is reached in which the wind is blowing diagonally across the isobars and is not of as high a speed as the equivalent geostrophic wind with the same pressure-gradient at higher altitude.

As we should expect, the effect of surface friction is greatest near the ground and decreases rapidly upward. Moreover, the effect of friction is greater for rough ground than for smooth. Over a relatively smooth level surface, such as a prairie or a body of water, surface wind is deflected to an angle about 20–25° left of the geostrophic direction (Northern Hemisphere) and may have a speed of 60–70% of the geostrophic wind. In contrast, surface winds over a rough surface may be turned as much as 45° to the left of the isobar and reduced to one-third of the geostrophic wind speed. Surface frictional effect largely disappears at heights

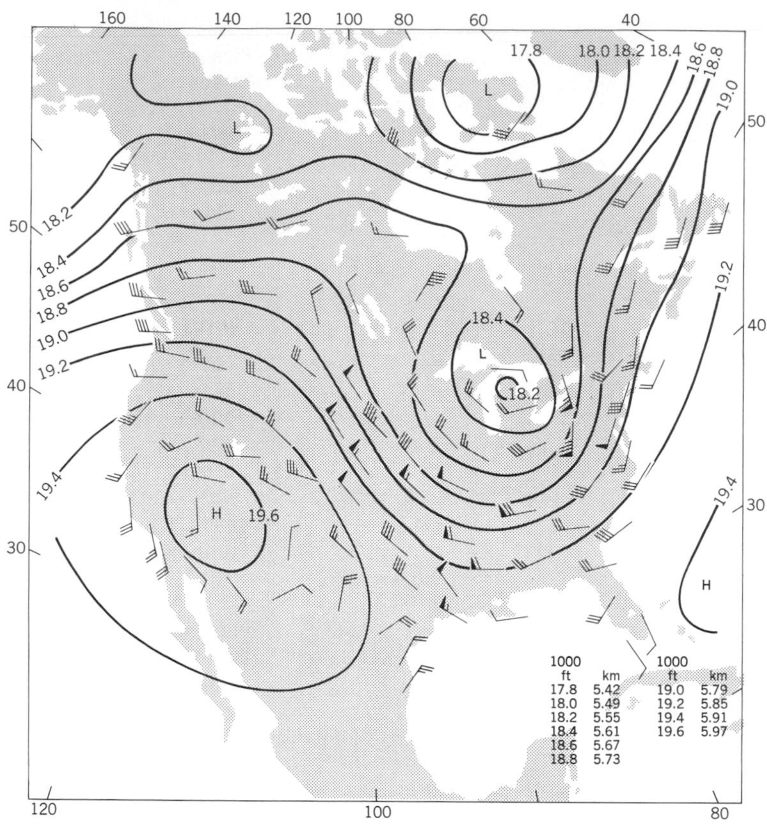


**FIGURE 15.9.** On this upper-air map for a day in late June air flow closely parallels contours drawn on the 500-millibar pressure surface. Elevations in thousands of feet. Refer to Figure 15.12 for interpretation of wind arrows. (Data from ESSA, Weather Bureau.)

upward of 2000–3000 feet (600–900 m), so that at higher levels air flow closely parallels the isobars and becomes a gradient wind. Other frictional forces act in high-speed air flow at upper levels in the jet stream region, described in later paragraphs.

## How winds are measured

Wind velocity is a vector quantity, requiring statement of both direction and speed. Wind direction is stated as the direction from which the wind is blowing and may be indicated either by 8 or 16 compass points or by azimuth in degrees (see Figure 15.13). Thus a north wind comes from the north point of the compass—the air is traveling southward. Of all weather-observing instruments, perhaps the oldest and simplest is the familiar wind vane,

**FIGURE 15.10.** Resolution of forces in surface winds. [After S. Petterssen (1958), *Introduction to Meteorology,* New York, McGraw-Hill, p. 156, Figure 108.]

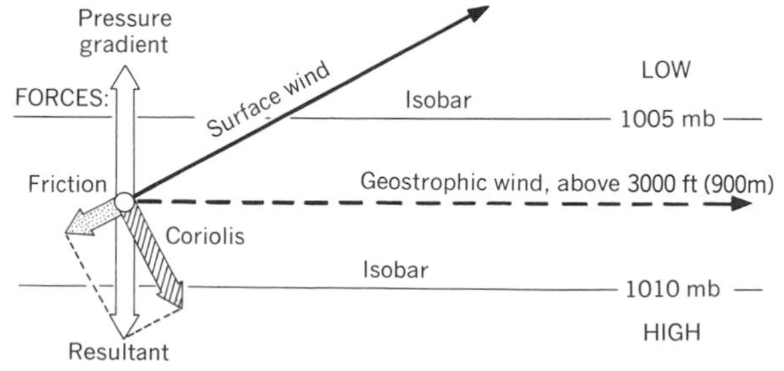


from which the direction of surface winds is determined. Most wind vanes have a point, or arrow head, which faces into the wind. Therefore one may simply read the compass direction toward which the arrow is pointing.

The instrument which measures wind speed is the *anemometer.* Several types are in use. The cup anemometer consists of three or four cups mounted at the tips of wheel-like spokes turning horizontally on a delicate bearing (Figure 15.11). The cups travel at a speed approximately equal to the wind speed. The instrument can be so calibrated that the number of turns per minute is exactly equal to the wind speed in miles per hour. In other cup anemometers the turning shaft drives a small dynamo whose varying current is read on a sensitive ammeter calibrated in units of wind speed. Other types of anemometers measure the wind force on an exposed surface or against the air column in a tube whose open end is pointed into the wind.

To determine wind direction and speed in the air layer from near the ground surface up to about 15,000 ft (5 km), pilot balloons filled with hydrogen or helium are released at the weather-observing station and tracked, as they ascend, by use of a telescopic instrument known as a *theodolite.* The rate of rise of the balloon is known and is constant. Consequently, if the vertical angle of sight is read at intervals of, say, 1 minute, the horizontal distance of travel and wind speed can be calculated (Figure 15.12). The azimuth will indicate wind direction. Larger balloons carrying a reflective target are also tracked by radar, making possible observations above overcast layers or during precipitation.

Modern weather science requires accurate knowledge

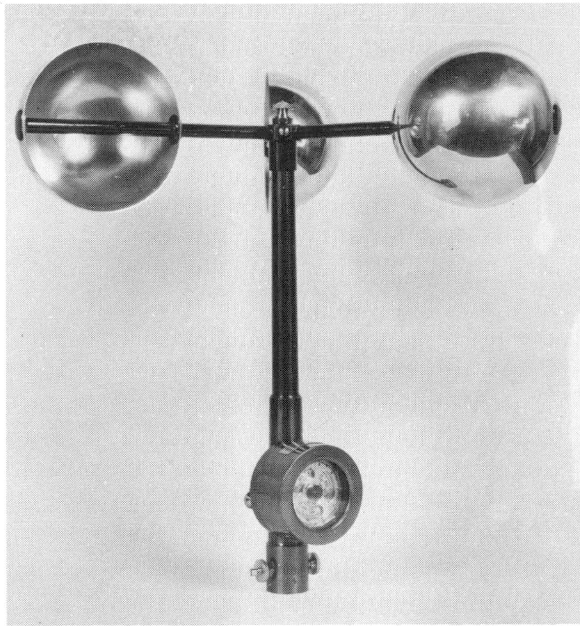

**FIGURE 15.11.** A three-cup anemometer. Dial below gives count of revolution. (ESSA Weather Bureau photograph.)

of wind direction and speed to the top of the troposphere and higher. To obtain this information—along with information on air temperature, air pressure, and water vapor content—the upper atmosphere must be sounded by sending up balloons carrying compact sensing instruments and a radio transmitter, which sends the information by code to a ground receiving station. This apparatus is named the *radiosonde.* An extension of this system, *rawinsonde,* uses a ground radio station to track the position of a radiosonde and thus to determine the direction and speed of winds at various levels up to great heights.

**FIGURE 15.12.** Down-wind speed of a rising balloon can be calculated from the angle of a sight line upon it. (© 1960, John Wiley & Sons, New York.)

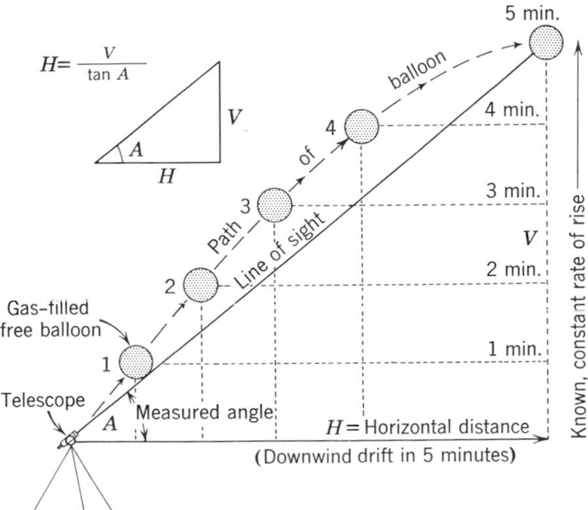


Wind speed is stated in statute miles per hour, in meters per second, or in knots (nautical miles per hour), knots being the preferred units for stating wind speeds in the troposphere. On weather maps wind direction and speed are indicated by a symbol resembling an arrow shaft with feathers, or barbs (Figure 15.13). On upper-air charts the direction is measured clockwise from geographic north, using the azimuth (full-circle bearing) system used in navigation.

## A simple model of the earth's wind systems

In attempting to deduce the general nature of the earth's atmospheric circulation, consider first a simple model of a wind responding only to the pressure-gradient force. We must assume the earth to be nonrotating, hence with no Coriolis force. (We must also disregard the effect of nonrotation on solar radiation—at this point we are concerned only with eliminating the deflective effects of rotational motion.) *A* in Figure 15.14 indicates the initial half-envelope of atmosphere, perfectly uniform throughout. The *B* half shows the effect of solar heating of the atmosphere in equatorial latitudes and cooling over the poles. The air layer expands and thickens over the equatorial belt, but contracts and thins over the poles. A pressure-gradient from the equatorial region toward the poles is set up at a high level, and air begins to flow poleward at high level because of the pressure-gradient force.

It should by now be evident that we are describing the same chain of events used previously in this chapter to explain a simple convective circulation (Figure 15.2). At *C* in Figure 15.14 the transfer of air poleward has increased the surface weight of a column of the atmosphere at the poles, creating higher barometric pressure near the ground, and has correspondingly decreased the surface pressure at the equator. Thus we have two polar highs and an equatorial belt of low pressure. Surface air moves equatorward following this low-level pressure gradient, completing the flow circuit. At *D* is shown the complete circulation with subsidence at the

**FIGURE 15.13.** Direction and speed of winds is given by means of standard map symbols. (© 1960, John Wiley & Sons, New York.)

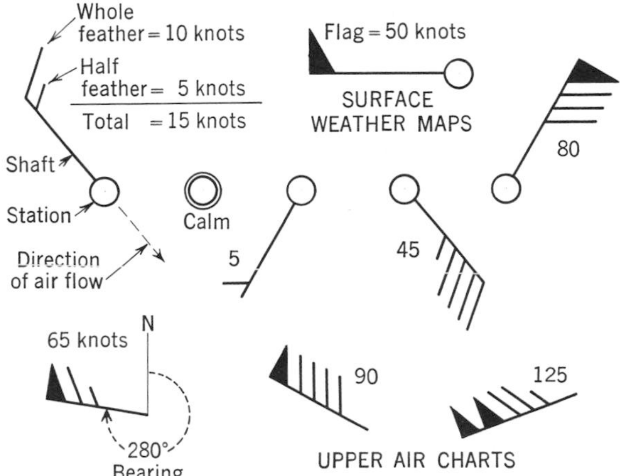

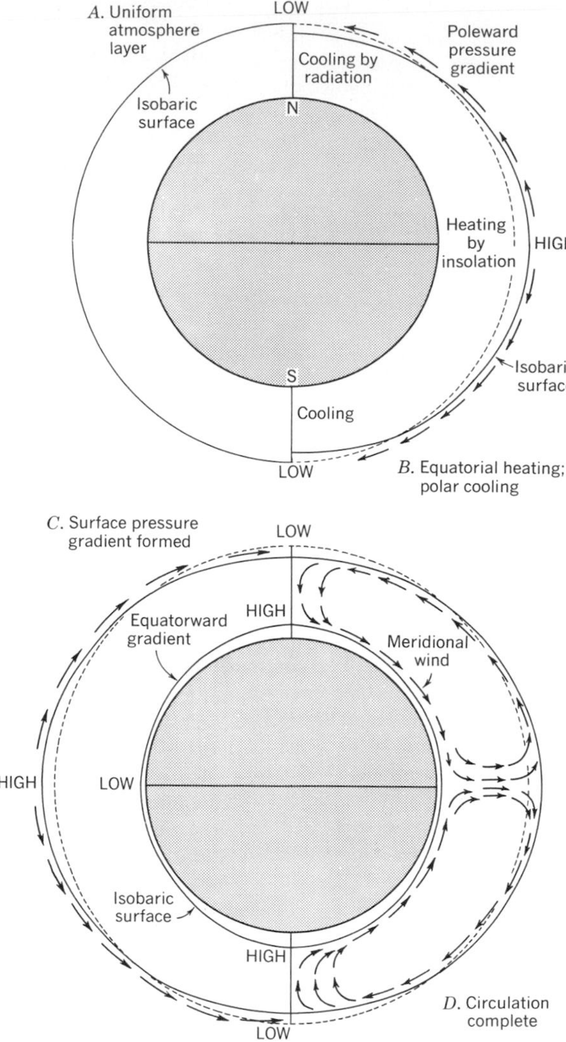


**FIGURE 15.14.** Simple wind system on an imagined nonrotating earth.

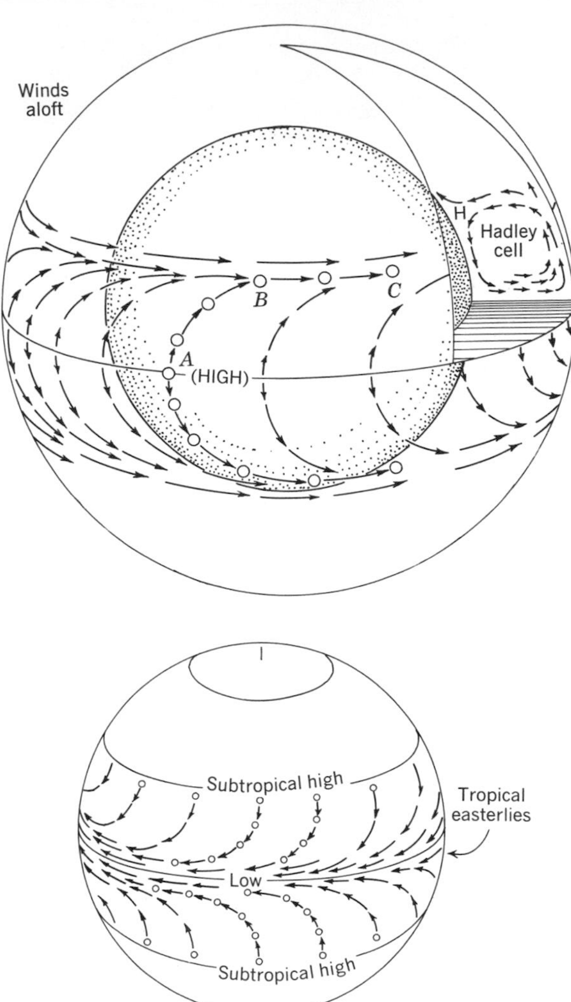


**FIGURE 15.15.** At high levels a parcel of air starting northward from a position at rest at *A* over the equator would be deflected to the right until moving due eastward at *B* (upper figure). Near the earth's surface air starting to travel equatorward from the subtropical highs is turned westward to produce the tropical easterlies (lower figure).

poles and ascent of air at the equator. All motion is north-south in direction, i.e., *meridional circulation.* The system in each hemisphere is single-celled, or *unicellular.*

The simple convectional wind system on a hypothetical nonrotating earth serves to explain certain of the observed features of the earth's circulation. There is, in fact, an equatorial belt of low barometric pressure, the *equatorial trough.* Furthermore, there exist at high atmospheric levels two great, strongly developed lows, one centered over each pole. These features, the *polar lows,* will be described in more detail later.

The next step in developing our simple model of atmospheric circulation is to introduce the Coriolis force, to yield the geostrophic motion on a rotating globe (Figure 15.15). As the high-level air over the equatorial belt begins to move poleward, it is deflected to the right (Northern Hemisphere) to become a system of upper westerly winds paralleling the isobars at about the 30th parallel. Correspondingly, in the Southern Hemisphere deflection to the left also turns the poleward flow at high level into a westerly wind system.

But now still another phenomenon can be anticipated. Because air moving at high levels poleward from the equatorial belt has been turned into westerly flow, following the earth's parallels of latitude, the air here tends to accumulate more rapidly than it can escape poleward. This accumulation, or banking up, of air constitutes a *convergence* and takes place in zones between lat. 20° N. and 30° N. and between lat. 20° S. and 30° S.—the tropical zones. Here convergence aloft produces at the surface two belts of high barometric pressure known as the *subtropical high-pressure belts,* one in each hemisphere.

Air subsiding within the subtropical high-pressure zone spreads both equatorward and poleward, producing systems of prevailing surface winds. That air which follows the barometric pressure gradient from subtropical high to equatorial low is deflected westward to create a system of prevailing winds known as the *tropical easterlies,* or *trade winds* (Figure 15.15). The tropical easterlies form a broad, steady, and deep air stream moving around the earth over the equatorial regions and extending to high altitudes. As shown in Figure 15.15, the tropical easterlies at low level tend to converge from both hemispheres upon the equatorial zone of low pressure. This zone is designated as the *intertropical convergence zone* (abbreviated to *ITC*).

The atmospheric circulation system of equatorial and tropical latitudes thus consists of two cells, one in each hemisphere. Seen in cross section, and neglecting east-west components of motion, the meridional circulation within each cell consists of horizontal and vertical motions, together forming a complete circuit. The existence of such a circulation system was first postulated by George Hadley in 1735 and is now designated as the *Hadley cell* by meteorologists.

Figure 15.16 shows an analysis of meridional air motions within the Northern Hemisphere Hadley cell based on a single day's observations. The atmospheric cross section shown here is an average for the entire earth circumference. (This example is believed to be typical of prevailing conditions.) In Figure 15.16 latitude is scaled on the horizontal axis, elevation on the vertical axis. Obviously the vertical scale is greatly exaggerated and the diagram is purely schematic. Shown on the graph are *isotachs,* which are lines of equal velocity. The solid isotachs represent horizontal motion, or winds. The arrows at the centers of the concentric isotach configurations show cores of fastest wind speed. The equatorward maximum speed at low level was 3 meters per second (7 mph), and the poleward maximum speed at high level was 4 m/sec (9 mph). These maximum values are located at about 10° N. latitude. The dashed isotachs show air speed in the vertical direction. Arrows show an equatorial core of maximum upward speed and a tropical core of maximum downward speed located at about 15° N. Maximum speeds of rising and sinking air are on the order of about 1 cm/sec (0.02 mph), which is only about 1/300 to 1/400 as fast as the maximum horizontal speeds.

Mass rate of equatorward air flow within the Hadley cell on the day referred to in the preceding paragraph was calculated to be 255 million tons (230 metric tons) per second; poleward flow at high level was the same. Heat is transported both poleward and equatorward within the Hadley cell in the form of sensible heat and latent heat. The low-level flow, which comprises the trade winds, carries large amounts of water vapor equatorward, where much of it condenses as rain, with an accompanying liberation of latent heat.

The Hadley cell is not a closed system, for if it were closed there could be no exchange of air and water vapor with the middle and high latitudes of the two hemispheres. At the poleward limit of the Hadley cell, about at latitude 25°, part of the low-level air migrates poleward, carrying with it sensible heat and water vapor. Of the total quantity of water vapor moving within the cell about one-third escapes poleward, constituting the latent energy flux required to satisfy the global energy balance.

## Transport of angular momentum by atmospheric motions

Thus far, the discussion of winds has been treated in terms of four forces. Of these, the Coriolis force was called upon to explain why air traveling poleward across the parallels of latitude is deflected to the right (Northern Hemisphere) and becomes a westerly wind, whereas air traveling equatorward, also deflected to the right, becomes an easterly wind. We shall now introduce the concept of *transport of angular momentum* as a basis for understanding the global atmospheric circulation.

Angular momentum was discussed in Chapter 5 in an explanation of the changing speeds of planetary revolution in elliptical orbits. Recall that angular momentum, $L$ is defined as follows:

$$L = M \cdot V \cdot R$$

where $M$ is mass of the object in motion
$V$ is the instantaneous linear velocity,
and $R$ is the radius of the circular path of motion.

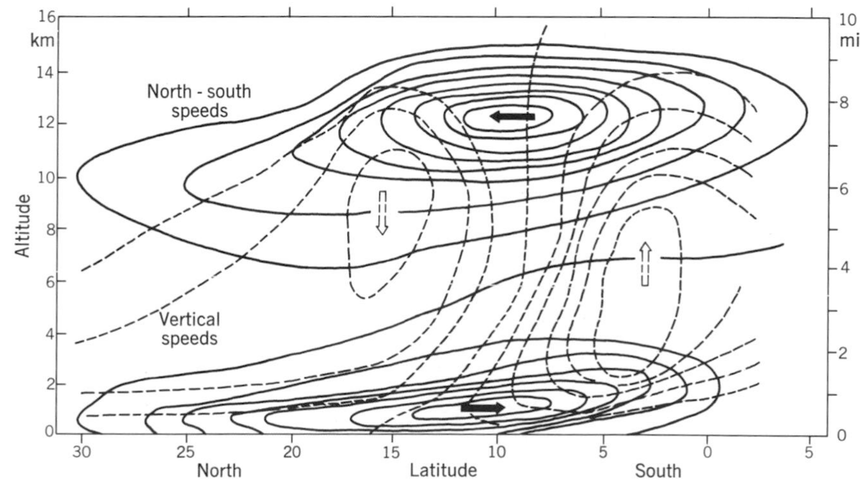


**FIGURE 15.16.** Hadley-cell circulation observed on a day in December. Lines are isotachs showing globally-averaged meridional components (solid lines) and vertical components (dashed lines). Maximum meridional speeds are about 3 m/sec (6 knots) southward and 4 m/sec (8 knots) northward. Maximum vertical speeds are on the order of 1 cm/sec (1/5 knot). (IGY 1957 data analyzed by H. M. E. van de Boogaard and F. Defant as shown in *NCAR Quarterly,* October 1964, Issue No. 8, Boulder, Colo.)

In the present discussion, we are concerned with small masses on or close to the earth's surface traveling in horizontal paths. Thus the paths of motion conform with a spherical surface (disregarding oblateness). At any instant, then, a small parcel of air has one component of its motion in a circle whose plane is at right angles to the earth's axis of rotation (Figure 15.17). This circle has the radius of the parallel of latitude with which it is identical. In the case of the rotating earth, angular momentum is a vector quantity directed toward the north polar axis. The angular momentum of a stationary particle at point *B* in Figure 15.17 will be less than that of a particle at point *A* because both radius and linear velocity are less than at *A*. For the earth as an entire planet, the total angular momentum must remain constant, in accordance with the law of conservation of angular momentum. In discussing circulation of the atmosphere and oceans, we can consider the total angular momentum to be the sum of three parts:

$$L_{\text{total}} = L_{\text{earth}} + L_{\text{oceans}} + L_{\text{atmosphere}}$$

The term $L_{\text{earth}}$ denotes the solid earth, or lithosphere, which can be regarded (for short periods of time) as a rigid body within which there is no transfer of mass from one place to another. In both the atmosphere and the oceans mass transfer occurs readily. Should the angular momentum of any one of the three parts be changed by mass transfer, there must be compensating changes in one or both of the other parts.

Consider that a parcel of air is located at point *A* on the equator (Figure 15.17) and has no motion relative to the earth's surface, which is to say that there is no wind at this point. Let the parcel of air be of unit mass, which remains unchanged throughout the analysis. The only two variables will then be radius and velocity.

As the air parcel begins to move poleward from the equator, its horizontal path, paralleling the earth's curvature, traverses parallels of latitude of decreasing radius. (Radius of parallels decreases proportionately to the cosine of the angle of latitude.) Consequently the value of *R* in the equation of angular momentum decreases with poleward travel, whereas the angular momentum of the parcel must remain a constant. Therefore the linear velocity (*V*) from west to east must increase, with the result that the parcel of air moves eastward at a rate faster than the eastward motion of a point beneath it on the earth's surface. Consequently a westerly wind component is generated and angular momentum is transported poleward across the parallels.

In reverse motion, toward the equator, the air parcel at Point *C* in Figure 15.17 will cross parallels of both increased radius and increased linear velocity. The parcel will tend to drop behind the surface motion of the earth beneath it and will develop a relative westward motion—which is to say, an easterly wind component. The transfer of angular momentum across the parallels is now a negative quantity.

In the case of the Hadley cell circulation, the necessity for conservation of angular momentum requires that upper air, moving poleward in the cell, acquire a west-to-east motion. The result is a strong westerly wind at high levels in the troposphere in subtropical latitudes, about over the 30th parallels north and south. This high-speed flow will be discussed in later paragraphs. Air moving equatorward at low levels in the Hadley cell circulation is required to develop into an easterly wind, but because of friction with the earth's surface it attains only moderate speeds.

We have now accounted for both the meridional (north-south) and zonal (east-west) components of motion in the atmospheric circulation system of low latitudes. We turn next to global circulation at middle and high latitudes.

**FIGURE 15.17.** Angular momentum and zonal winds.

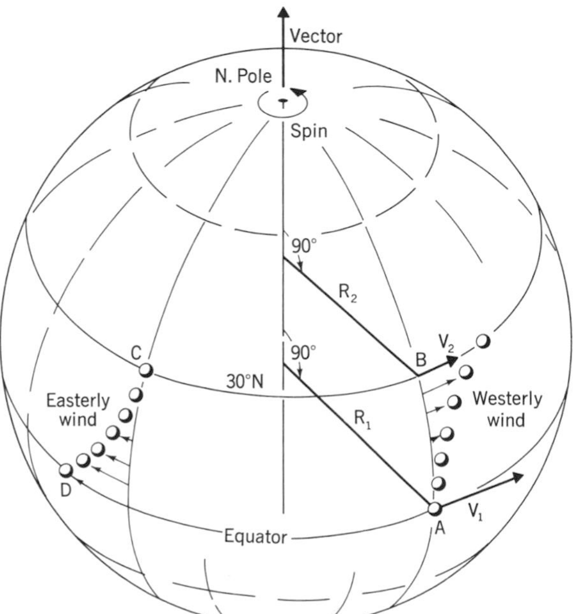


## Global circulation in middle and high latitudes

Poleward of the subtropical high pressure belts, average circulation in the troposphere takes the form of a prevailing system of *upper-air westerlies,* shown schematically in Figure 15.18. This flow constitutes a great vortex moving counterclockwise (Northern Hemisphere) around a prevailing center of low barometric pressure, the *polar low.* A corresponding system of upper air westerlies exists in the Southern Hemisphere.

The simple zonal flow of the westerlies is disturbed by a ceaseless succession of wave-like undulations and by the formation and dissolving of large eddies, which are lows or highs of barometric pressure. Thus advection occurs on a large scale in the troposphere. Figure 15.19 is a map of the Northern Hemisphere showing the distribution of barometric pressure and winds at high altitude on a particular day. Gradient winds parallel the isobars and are strongest where the isobars are most closely spaced. Notice, first, that the isobars in middle latitudes are sinuous in pattern and form large waves, of which some five or six can be identified. These undulations are *upper-air waves,* or *Rossby waves* (named for C.-G. Rossby, a meteorologist who developed the

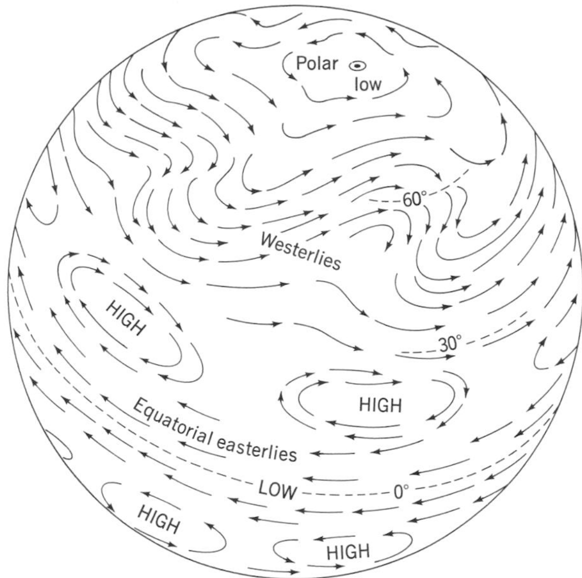


**FIGURE 15.18.** Generalized pattern of global circulation at high levels in the troposphere.

mathematical equations for parameters governing the waves).

The upper-air waves may grow, change in form, and dissolve. They may remain essentially stationary for many days, and may also drift slowly in the east-west direction. An upper-air wave may deepen to the extent that the crest, bulging equatorward, is detached and becomes a *cut-off low* (several are depicted by concentric isobars labeled "L" on Figure 15.19). A wave trough may also become detached to form a *cut-off high.* Where the isobars of upper air-waves are closely spaced, a narrow meandering band of high-speed air flow is generated, a phenomenon known as the *jet stream.* Notice that a ring of weak anticyclones surrounds the earth at subtropical latitudes; these are the subtropical high pressure centers of subsiding air on the poleward side of the Hadley cell.

Upper-air westerly wind patterns are vividly revealed by the track of a horizontal sounding balloon of the GHOST type, released at Christchurch, New Zealand, and tracked by radio as it traveled around the world several times at a level of about 40,000 feet (12 km) (Figure 15.20). Notice the undulations of the path, following troughs and crests of Rossby waves.

Speed of the upper-air westerly winds varies greatly from time to time and place to place. Maximum speeds in the range of 180 to 230 miles (290 to 370 km) per hour are found in the jet stream. Average values of wind speed in the west-east direction for the Northern Hemisphere along the meridian of 80° W. are shown in Figure 15.21 for winter and summer. The core of maximum speed is found at an altitude of about 35,000 to 40,000 ft (11 to 12 km). The speed is about twice as fast in winter as in summer and the core in winter lies at somewhat lower latitude than in summer.

Notice in Figure 15.21 that in winter, poleward of about 70° N. latitude, average winds are shown as moving from east to west. These winds are referred to as the

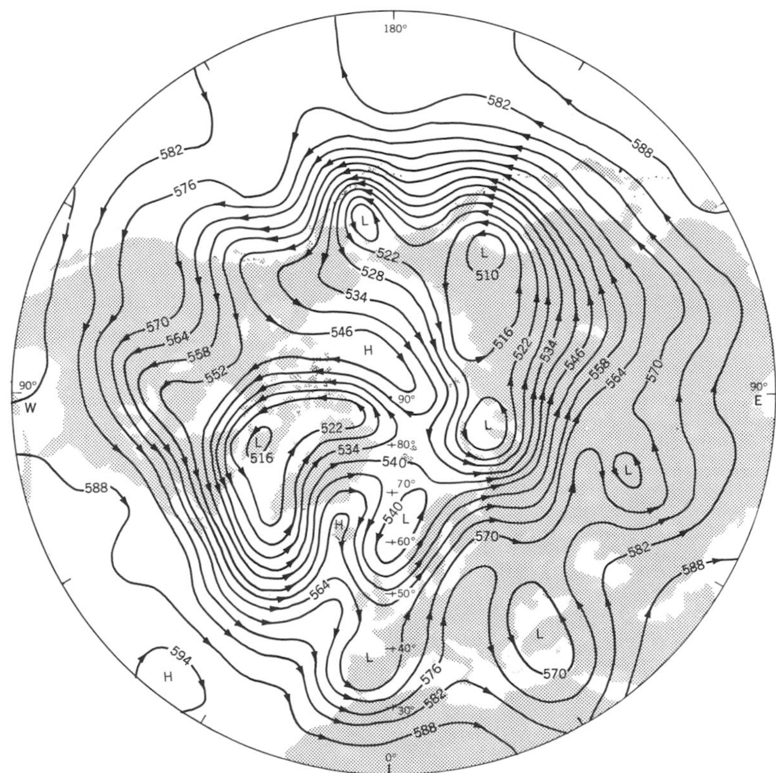


**FIGURE 15.19.** Isobaric map at the 500-mb (18,000-ft) level for 28 April 1969, drawn from infrared spectrometer data obtained by *Nimbus III* satellite. Pressures in millibars. Arrows show upper-air winds. (Data from ESSA and NASA. See *Amer. Meteorological Soc. Bull.*, vol. 50, no. 7, July 1969, cover and p. 544.)

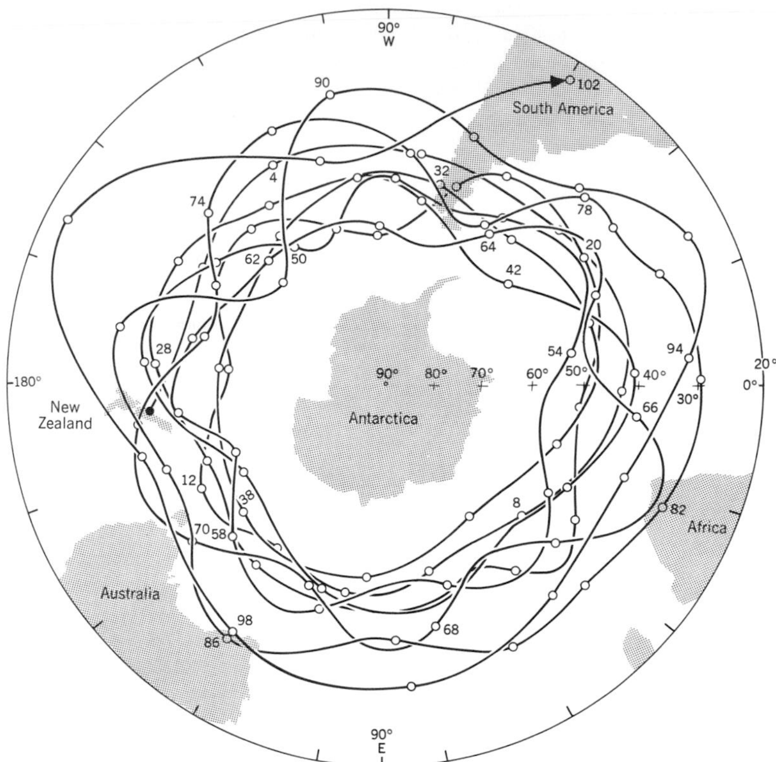


FIGURE 15.20. Trajectory of a GHOST balloon launched on 10 April 1966 from Christchurch, New Zealand. Its positions on 102 consecutive days of travel at the 200-mb (40,000-ft) level are shown by circles. (Data of V. E. Lally and E. W. Lichfield, NCAR, as reported in *Amer. Meteorological Soc. Bull.,* 1969, vol. 50, no. 11, p. 868, Figure 1.)

*polar easterlies.* Their average speed is small and they are not as persistent as the tropical easterlies, shown in Figure 15.21 as located south of latitude 30° N.

Figure 15.22 is a schematic diagram of the general east-west, or *zonal,* components of winds in the troposphere. This diagram does not show the north-south, or *meridional,* components of the circulation, nor does it suggest the changing patterns of Rossby waves, cyclones, and anticyclones.

## Cause of the westerlies

Driving mechanism of the upper-air westerlies and polar easterlies was for many years attributed to two circulation cells, resembling the Hadley cell and lying poleward of it (Figure 15.23). Within one hemisphere the circulation is therefore three-celled, or *tricellular.* The northernmost cell was thought to be driven by the sinking of cold polar air which spread southward and was deflected by

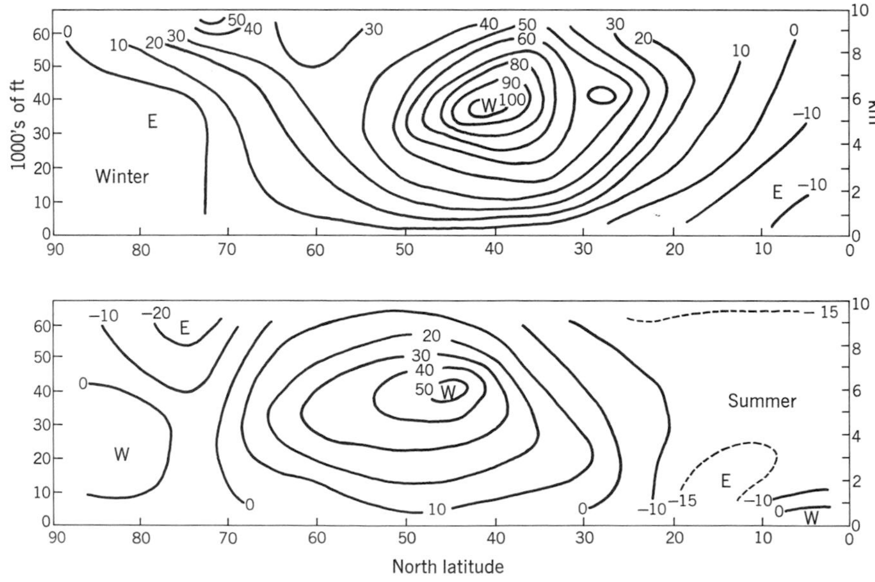


FIGURE 15.21. Mean zonal wind speeds (knots) along the 80th meridian west in winter and summer. [Data of A. Kochanski (1955), *Journal of Meteorology,* vol. 12, pp. 95–106.]

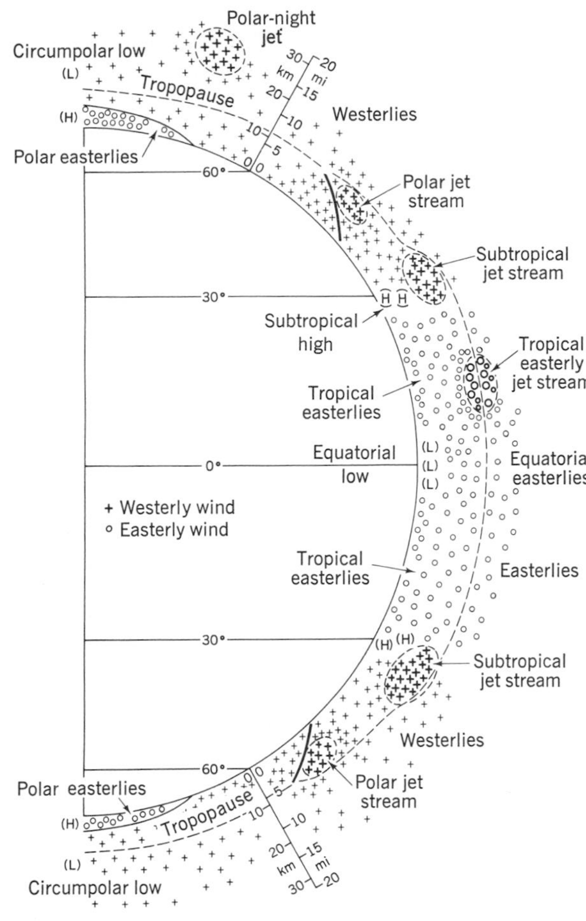


**FIGURE 15.22.** Schematic diagram of zonal wind directions and jet streams along a meridian from pole to pole.

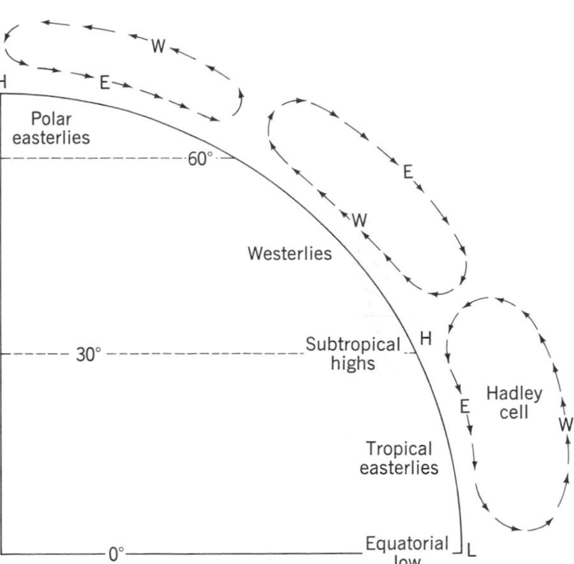


**FIGURE 15.23.** Schematic diagram of the tricellular theory of global atmospheric circulation.

the Coriolis force to become the polar easterlies. Warmer air, moving poleward at high levels to replace the subsiding air, would require high-level polar westerly winds. The intermediate cell was thought to be driven by the action of the two adjacent cells. It was supposed that part of the air subsiding on the poleward side of the Hadley cell moves north, and is deflected toward the east, becoming the westerly winds of middle latitudes. A requirement of this hypothesis is that upper-level winds in middle latitudes should be easterlies to complete the circulation of the intermediate cell.

We have already seen that upper-level air flow does not conform with the three-cell hypothesis. This discrepancy was not observable until about the time of World War II, when extensive observations of upper-air winds became commonplace and the jet stream was discovered. The model of tricellular circulation has now been replaced for middle latitudes by a circulation system in which angular momentum is transferred from low latitude to high latitudes by the action of cyclones and anticyclones.

The system of tropical easterlies is a westward air flow, opposite to the direction of the earth's eastward rotation. Friction of these winds with the earth's surface must tend to slow the earth's rotation. Angular momentum is transferred from the solid earth into the tropical easterlies by this friction. On the other hand, the same friction draws energy from the easterlies at low levels, and these winds are much weaker than would be predicted on the basis of angular momentum transfer. In contrast, in the westerlies the atmosphere is rotating faster than the earth's surface beneath and the earth will thus draw angular momentum from the atmosphere. Such withdrawal of angular momentum would quickly slow the westerly winds and reduce them to nothing unless momentum were brought into the westerlies at a rate equal to its withdrawal. It is therefore necessary that a mechanism be present whereby angular momentum can be transferred poleward across the parallels of latitude from the easterlies into the low-level westerlies. Such transfer must be sustained if the general atmospheric circulation is to be maintained in the form we find it.

Transfer of angular momentum is accomplished by the mechanism of large-scale cyclones and anticyclones of the middle latitudes and takes place largely at about the 30th parallel of latitude. Figure 15.24 shows how momentum transfer operates. An upper-air wave in the westerlies lies toward the left and appears as a trough of low pressure whose axis is slanted from southwest to northeast. Adjacent to the low trough is a center of high pressure, or anticyclone, whose axis of elongation is also from southwest to northeast. This orientation is typical in the Northern Hemisphere. Air crossing the 30th parallel of latitude at the point *A* has both northward and eastward components of motion, while air crossing the same parallel at point *B* has both westward and southward components of motion. Whereas the northward and southward components are equal at *A* and *B* respectively, the eastward component at *A* is greater than the westward component at *B*, because of the earth's eastward rotation. The vector sum of the eastward and westward components will therefore give a net difference that is directed eastward and represents the transport of angular momentum northward across the parallel of latitude. Thus the kinetic energy is furnished

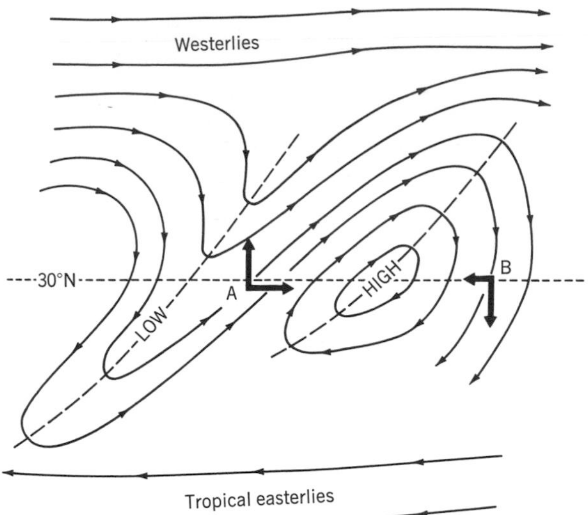


**FIGURE 15.24.** Wave theory of angular momentum transfer to sustain westerly winds. [Based on a diagram by R. L. Pfeffer (1967), in *Encyclopedia of Atmospheric Sciences and Astrogeology,* R. W. Fairbridge, Ed., New York, Reinhold, p. 74, Figure 6.]

for the driving of the westerly winds. This hypothesis of westerly winds is designated the *wave theory* and has replaced the cellular theory. This form of poleward transport of angular momentum is described as an *eddy transport mechanism.*

The polar easterlies, which are comparatively weak winds and occur largely at low levels, may be explained through the spreading of dense, cold polar air toward lower latitudes, with deflection toward the west by the Coriolis force. This explanation represents a recourse to the cellular convection theory.

It is interesting to note that model experiments have proved successful in reproducing the main features of the general circulation of the troposphere (Figure 15.25). A circular pan of fluid is used to represent a hemisphere. Heat is applied to the fluid around the periphery, or equatorial zone, while the fluid in the center of the pan is cooled. The entire apparatus, together with an attached overhead motion picture camera, is rotated clockwise. Particles of aluminum powder moving with the fluid permit flow paths to be photographed.

When the thermal gradient and rate of rotation are properly adjusted in the model, a westerly flow sets in and develops a number of waves resembling the Rossby waves. Anticyclonic centers ring the westerly current zone in a manner analogous to the subtropical highs. Experimentation has shown that when the rotation rate is sufficiently slow and the temperature gradient is sufficiently high, a single convectional cell resembling the Hadley cell extends from equator to pole. These results suggest that our earth owes its atmospheric circulation pattern to a unique combination of rotation rate and thermal imbalance. Perhaps on Venus, a planet with very slow rotation and a strong thermal gradient from equator to poles, a Hadley cell circulation dominates the entire planet and strong westerlies do not exist.

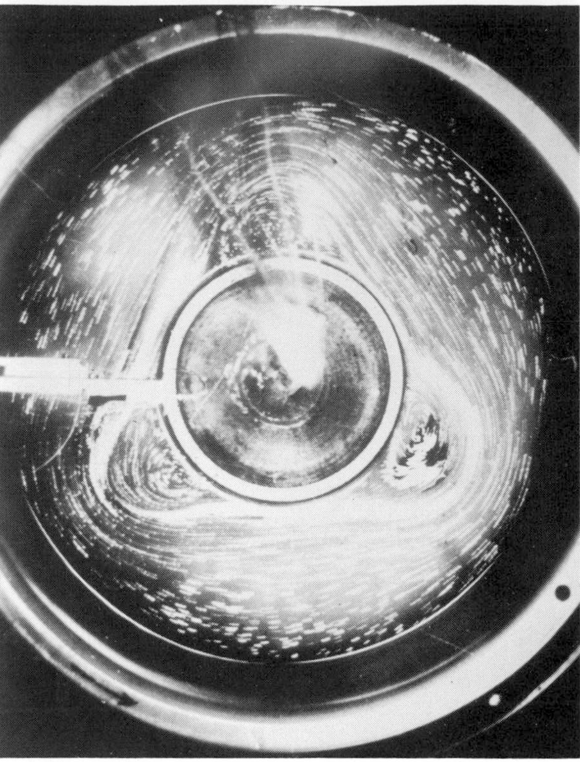

**FIGURE 15.25.** Photograph of a laboratory "dishpan" experiment showing waves generated in a fluid in a rotating container. Flow pattern is revealed by particles of aluminum scattered on the water surface. (Photograph by courtesy of Dr. Dave Fultz, Hydrodynamics Lab., Univ. of Chicago.)

## Development of upper-air waves

Let us analyze further the patterns of development of upper-air, or Rossby, waves and their relation to atmospheric temperatures. Figure 15.26 is a schematic diagram showing wave evolution in four stages. Long heavy arrows show the location of a jet stream whose axis defines the position of the waves. Conditions shown are those existing near the top of the troposphere, which ranges in elevation from about 30,000 ft (5.5 mi, 9 km) over the poles to about 50,000 ft (10 mi, 17 km) over the equator (see Figure 12.12).

The troposphere lying poleward of the jet axis consists of cold polar air, whereas that on the equatorward side consists of warm tropical air. Such large bodies of the atmosphere are referred to by the term *air mass.* Air masses are identified on the basis of both temperature and water-vapor content. As will be explained in greater detail in Chapter 19, polar air masses, because they are cold, can hold little moisture, whereas warm tropical air masses can hold comparatively large quantities. The jet stream in middle latitudes occupies a position at the contact between the polar air mass and the tropical air mass. A contact surface between adjacent air masses is termed a *front,* and in the case under discussion the front lying beneath the jet stream is known as the *polar front.*

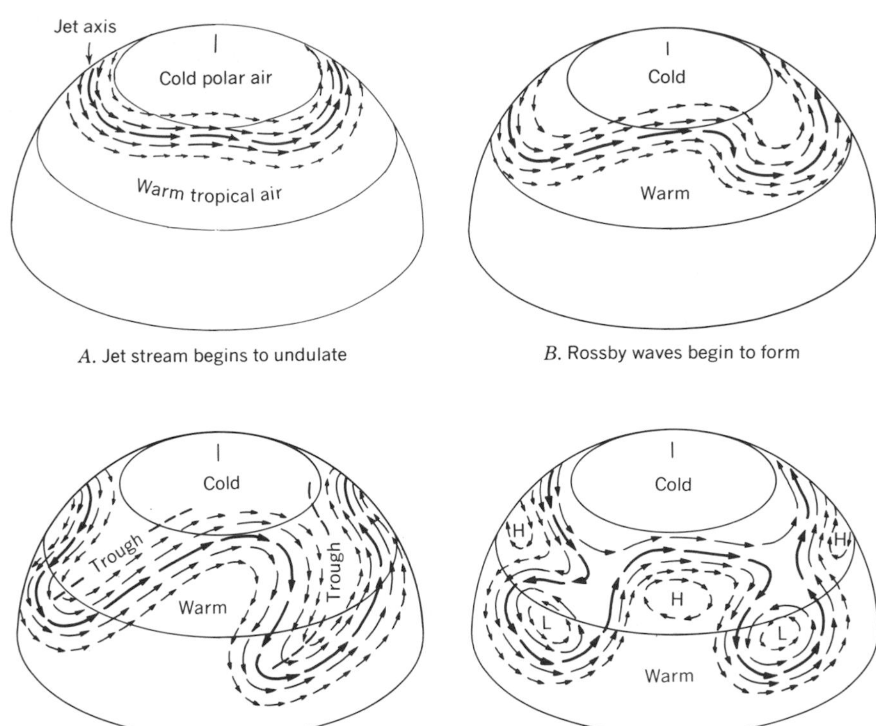


**FIGURE 15.26.** Four stages in the development of upper-air waves in the Northern Hemisphere. (After J. Namias, ESSA, Weather Bureau.)

Figure 15.26*A* shows the jet stream lying over the high latitudes and with only small undulations. As waves form (Figure 15.26*B*), the polar air pushes south at one place and the tropical air moves north at another. Soon great tongues of air form an interlocking pattern, with the jet stream taking a sinuous path between them (Figure 15.26*C*). Finally, a wave constricts at the base, and a mass of cold or warm air is detached, forming an isolated mass, or *cell.* A cell of stranded cold air aloft at subtropical latitudes forms a low-pressure center with counterclockwise circulation. An isolated cell of warm air aloft at the higher latitude becomes a high-pressure center with clockwise air flow. At the close of the wave-development cycle, which takes 4 to 6 weeks to complete, the isolated cells dissolve, and the jet stream resumes its simple course over the high latitudes, as shown in Figure 15.26*A*.

The cycle of upper-air wave development explains how great quantities of heat are transferred from equatorial regions to polar regions. North-moving tropical air carries heat to the high latitudes where the heat is lost, whereas south-moving tongues bring cold air to the low latitudes where it absorbs part of the excess heat. Although this form of heat and moisture transfer is fluctuating in intensity and location, the average effect, year in and year out, is to maintain in balance the earth's heat budget. Transfer of heat and water vapor throughout the middle and high latitudes by the growth of upper-air waves and the formation of cyclones and anticyclones is dominantly a process of advection; the horizontal movements are vast and take place within a relatively thin troposphere. In contrast, Hadley cell mixing of air in equatorial and tropical latitudes is dominantly by convection in a relatively thick troposphere.

## The jet stream

We now return to a more detailed consideration of the jet stream phenomenon. During World War II American pilots flying B-29 aircraft at high altitude in bombing missions over Japan occasionally reported that above 20,000 ft (6 km) westerly winds of such high speed were encountered as to equal the forward air speed of the planes and hence to reduce ground speed to zero. Transport planes bound eastward at high altitudes over the Pacific were sometimes aided by tail winds which doubled the ground speed of travel. These were the first indications of the nature of the *jet stream* as a powerful, but narrow stream of fast-moving air in the westerlies of the upper troposphere. One might think of this jet stream as resembling the high-pressure flow of water from a hose nozzle held submerged and pointed horizontally in the direction of flow of a slowly moving stream (Figure 15.27). Rather than being a layer, the jet stream is shaped more like a tube which lies roughly horizontally, but which may be curved in plane to change direction from, say, northwest to west to southwest.

Within the past decade or so, an enormous expansion in information about winds and temperatures of the upper air has revealed the existence of three important jet stream systems in the troposphere of the Northern Hemisphere.

The jet stream described in previous paragraphs as associated with the Rossby waves is known as the *polar front jet.* Its core lies at the top of the troposphere and it is classified as a *tropopause jet stream.* Figure 15.28 shows the broad band in which the principal activity of the polar front jet takes place during the winter. Figure 15.29 is a map of the United States showing wind speeds

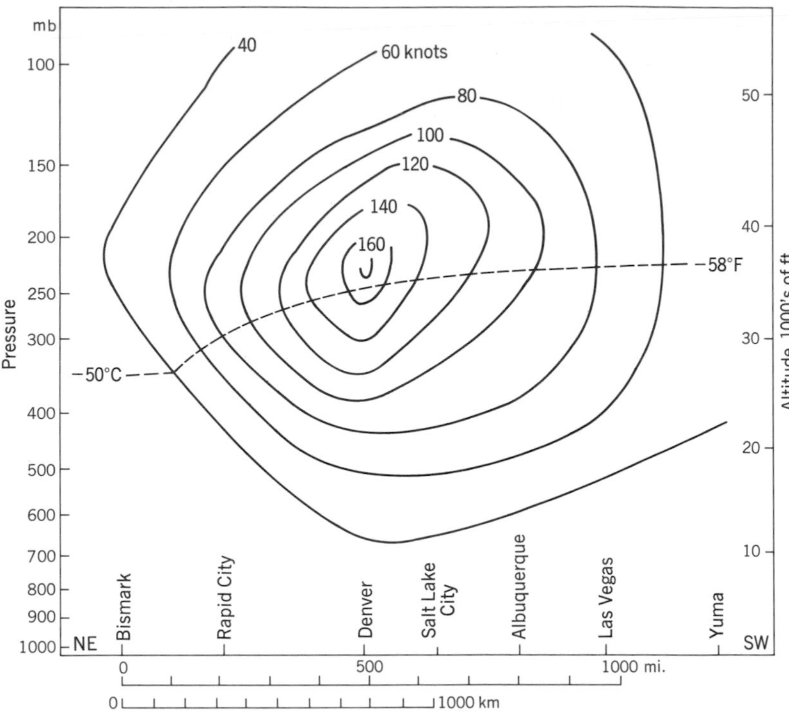


**FIGURE 15.27.** Cross-sectional diagram through a jet stream over the western United States. See Figure 15.29 for line of section and accompanying map data. [After H. Riehl (1962), *Jet Streams of the Atmosphere,* Fort Collins, Colo., Colorado State Univ., p. 12, Figure 2.16.]

at the 30,000 ft (9 km) level on a particular day. The heavy arrows show the jet core as making a great loop southward over the central United States, then curving north over New England. Wind speed is over 200 mi (320 km) per hour in the fastest section of the stream.

A second westerly jet system is found in subtropical latitudes and occupies a position at the tropopause level, 43,000–46,000 ft (13–14 km), on the poleward sides of the subtropical high pressure centers. The mean axis of this *subtropical jet stream* is shown in Figure 15.28. A third system, discovered more recently at still lower latitudes, differs from the first two in that it runs in the opposite direction, namely from east to west. This *tropical easterly jet stream* occurs only in the summer (high-sun) season and is limited to Northern Hemisphere locations over southeast Asia, India, and Africa. In a typical example, in late July an easterly jet stream was found over Madras, India (latitude 13° N.), at an altitude of about 50,000 ft (15 km). Wind speed in the core was over 115 mi (185 km) per hour. At the same time, the subtropical jet stream was situated in an adjacent position to the north, at latitude 25°, but at a lower level and traveling in the opposite direction.

**FIGURE 15.28.** Mean winter position of the axis of the subtropical jet stream and the belt of principal winter activity of the polar front jet stream. [After H. Riehl (1962), *Jet Streams of the Atmosphere,* Fort Collins, Colo., Colorado State Univ., p. 2 Figure 1.2.]

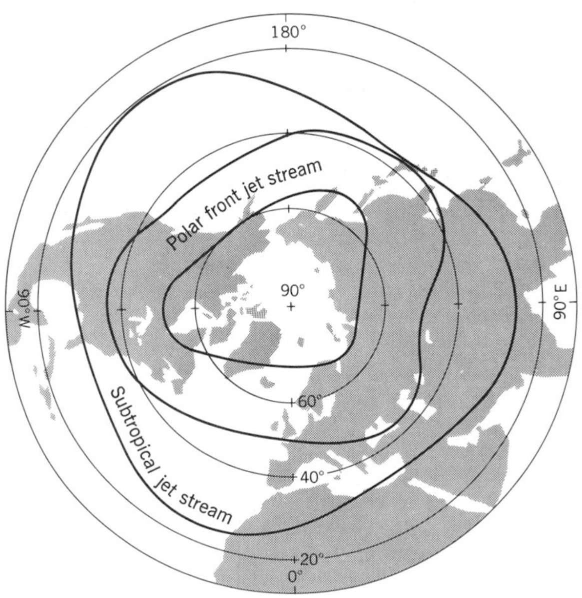


For an understanding of the driving mechanism of the polar jet stream we must look into the distribution of both temperature and pressure in a north-south cross-section through the atmosphere in the region of the jet stream. Figure 15.30 is such a cross-section of the polar front region. The polar front is shown by a shaded band, the tropopause by a narrow band above it. Two sets of lines are superimposed—isothermal surfaces (dashed lines) and isobaric surfaces (solid lines). From south to north, temperatures drop sharply across the front, as shown by the steplike bend in an isothermal surface where it crosses from warm air to cold air. Correspondingly, barometric pressure drops sharply at the front, but this effect is present only in the upper troposphere and above the tropopause. Where the isobaric surface makes its steep descent the pressure gradient is greatly strengthened in a narrow zone. Because wind speed depends upon pressure gradient, the gradient wind paral-

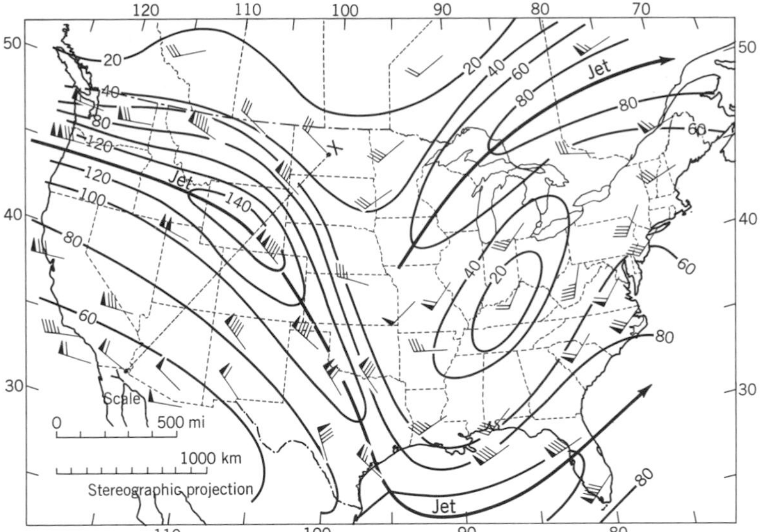


FIGURE 15.29. Isotachs (knots) and wind arrows at the 300-mb (30,000-ft) level on 22 April 1958. See Figure 15.13 for explanation of symbols. Solid arrows mark jet stream axis. Cross section along the line X–Y is shown in Figure 15.27. [After H. Riehl (1962), *Jet Streams of the Atmosphere,* Fort Collins, Colo., Colorado State Univ., p. 9, Figure 2.12.]

leling the isobars is greatly intensified and forms the jet stream core, indicated in the diagram by a circle placed at the steepest point on the isobaric surface.

To understand the existence of the subtropical jet stream, we return to the principle of conservation of angular momentum and the Hadley cell circulation. It can be calculated that air moving poleward from the equator to latitude 30° (N. or S.) will, because of conservation of angular momentum alone, attain a speed of west-to-east motion relative to the earth surface of about 300 mi (480 km) per hour. This speed is even greater than that observed in the subtropical jet stream, which reaches maximum core speeds of 215 to 240 mi (345 to 385 km) per hour. Thus, although the principle of conservation of angular momentum explains the existence of a subtropical jet stream, there must be found a reason that air speed is substantially less than the theoretical value. An explanation lies in the banking up of air, or convergence, which takes place at the tropopause in the region of maximum westerly wind speed. This convergence sets up a force (pressure force) that resists westerly air flow and detracts from the theoretical speed, as well as limiting further poleward extension of the upper-air westerlies in the Hadley cell.

FIGURE 15.30. Schematic cross section through a frontal zone, showing jet axis in relation to isothermal and isobaric surfaces. [After E. R. Reiter (1967), *Jet Streams,* Garden City, N.Y., Doubleday, p. 122, Figure 57.]

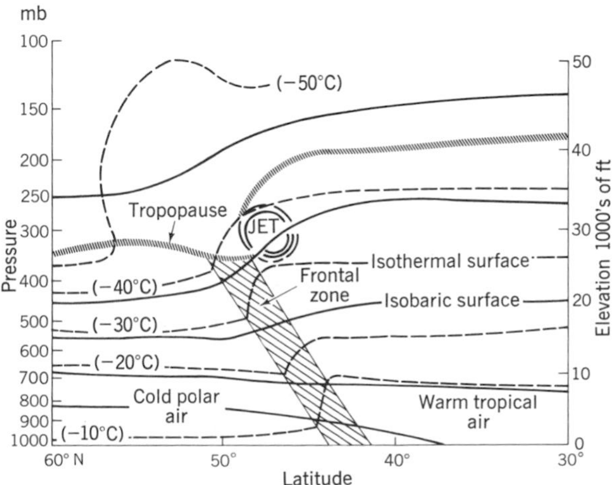


**The jet stream and seasonal changes in earth rotation**
In Chapter 3 it was pointed out that there are marked seasonal changes in speed of earth rotation, clearly seen in Figure 3.4. The speed of rotation slows during winter of the Northern Hemisphere but increases in summer. We are now prepared to offer an explanation of this phenomenon.

As previously explained, the total angular momentum of the earth must remain constant. A change in angular momentum of the atmosphere or of the oceans, or of both, must be met by a compensating change in angular momentum of the solid earth.

The polar jet stream in the Northern Hemisphere shows strong seasonal variations in strength, being intense in winter but weak in summer. In the Southern Hemisphere corresponding seasonal changes in jet stream strength occur, but are less marked. The net global total west-to-east atmospheric motion rises above the annual average during the winter of the Northern Hemisphere. In compensation for this increase in angular momentum of the atmosphere, the earth's rotation slows. Correspondingly, in the Northern Hemisphere summer west-to-east atmospheric motion is below the average value of the year and the earth's rotation speeds up. West-to-east ocean currents in the Northern Hemisphere show small seasonal changes in speed corresponding with the prevailing westerly winds which drive them. Thus changes in angular momentum of the oceans correspond with those of the atmosphere and tend to supplement the seasonal effect on earth rotation.

## Global circulation in the stratosphere

Data on air temperatures and winds above the tropopause have been accumulated in large quantities only since the first concerted efforts were made during the International Geophysical Year, 1957–1958. Data are obtained by two methods. Sounding balloons, rising to heights of 20 to 25 mi (30 to 40 km), are tracked by radar to reveal wind direction and speed, while at the same time they transmit data on barometric pressure and temperature. For information on conditions above 25 mi (40 km), meteorological rockets are used. These rockets eject radar targets whose motions are tracked from the ground. Temperature measurements are also derived from rocket soundings. During the IGY about 250 stations in the Northern Hemisphere launched balloons twice daily, while rocket measurements numbering in the hundreds gave data for conditions at high levels. As a result of these and subsequent programs of investigation, the general patterns of atmospheric circulation in the stratosphere and mesophere have become known, although data for equatorial regions and the Southern Hemisphere remain incomplete.

During winter in the Northern Hemisphere westerly winds of high speed are found at an altitude range of about 25–45 mi (40–70 km) over middle latitudes. The highests speeds occur in a core situated at about 30 mi (50 km), known as the *stratospheric polar-night jet stream.* The words "polar-night" denote the period of total darkness that covers much of the arctic region for a period of months during the winter season.

Speed of the polar-night jet stream averages some 160 mi (280 km) per hour, which is on the order of twice that of the polar jet stream in the troposphere below. However, it must be kept in mind that air density at 30 mi (50 km) is about 1/100 as great as that at the level of the tropopause, hence angular momentum and transport of sensible heat for a given volume of air in motion at this altitude are much less than at lower levels.

Figure 15.31 shows average zonal (east-west) wind speeds from equator to pole in the Northern Hemisphere for winter and summer. Mean position of the polar-night jet stream coincides with the stratopause and is closely related to the temperature maximum found at that level.

The polar-night jet stream can be explained by the temperature gradient from equator to pole that exists during the winter. When sunlight does not fall upon the stratosphere, there is no warming of the air in the ozone layer, which lies at the stratopause. Instead, radiational cooling takes place and upper air temperatures fall to low values over the north polar region. As a result, there is a pressure gradient from equator to pole in the winter, causing westerly winds.

During the summer season of the Northern Hemisphere, solar warming of the stratosphere over the polar region takes place, causing temperatures there to become warmer than at equivalent levels over the equatorial belt. Consequently the pressure gradient is reversed and stratospheric winds reverse in direction, becoming easterlies. Figure 15.31 shows these summer easterly winds by a core situated at about 40 mi (65 km) elevation over latitude 35° N. Speed of the summer easterly stratospheric wind is markedly less than that of the polar-night westerlies and it is not designated as a jet stream.

In the Southern Hemisphere a corresponding system of stratospheric winds, reversing in direction from summer to winter, is thought to exist, although data for this hemisphere are not yet adequate to document the circulation.

Stratospheric winds over the equatorial region display a curious pattern of change. The presence of stratospheric easterlies in this belt was recognized as long ago as 1883, when fine dust emitted by the explosion of the volcano *Krakatoa,* in Indonesia, traveled around the world from east to west at levels above 12 mi (20 km). The name *Krakatoa easterlies* was applied to these winds. Subsequent observations have shown the easterly wind to be fastest at about the 20 mi (35 km) level, where speeds are on the order of 70 mi (110 km) per hour.

The Krakatoa easterlies can be explained by the necessity for momentum transport across the equator,

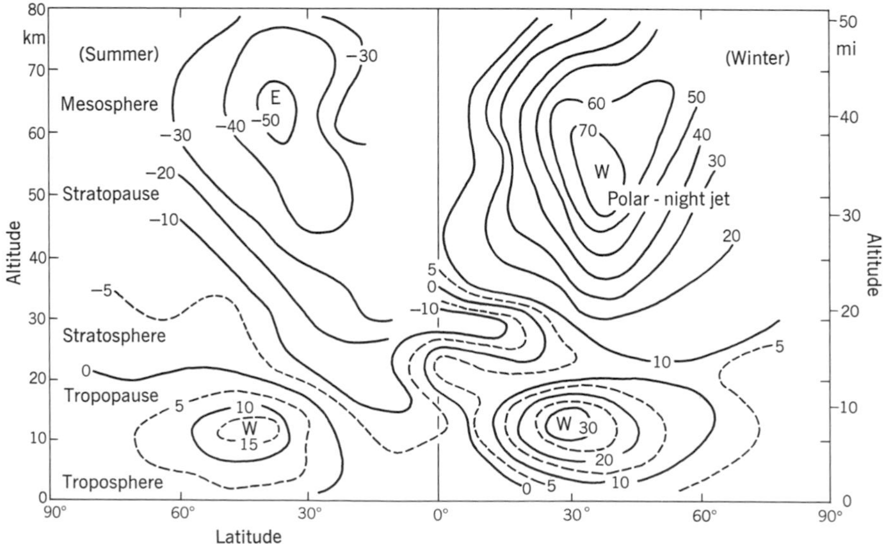


**FIGURE 15.31.** Average zonal wind speeds over the Northern Hemisphere in summer (left) and winter (right) up to levels of 80 km (50 mi). Speeds are in meters per second. Multiply by two to obtain approximate speed in knots. [After R. E. Newell (1964), *Scientific American,* vol. 210, p. 66.]

from one hemisphere to the other, in response to seasonal reversals of the stratospheric winds at higher latitudes.

In the early 1960s a surprising discovery was made concerning the stratospheric winds over the equator. At a given level a reversal of direction occurs in approximately alternate years. The easterly wind sets in at very high levels and works down to lower levels, replacing the westerly wind about every other year. Actually, the period of alternation is not 24 but 26 months, a phenomenon that has not as yet been explained.

## Surface wind systems of the earth

Long before man could probe the atmosphere above him, a fairly detailed knowledge of winds close to the earth's surface had been built up by navigators of sailing vessels as they extended their explorations and trade routes over the world's oceans. Because of surface friction and the contrasting thermal properties of land and ocean areas, surface winds show a number of important differences from the broadly flowing patterns of the troposphere and stratosphere.

Figures 15.32 and 15.33 are world maps showing average barometric pressure and surface winds for the months of January and July. These months are chosen because they represent the extremes of summer and winter temperature seasons in the middle and high latitudes. Moreover, during these months the sun's declination changes but slightly and the conditions represented are maintained for a long period.

Perhaps the most striking feature of the world pressure pattern is the presence of a belt of high-pressure centers, or anticyclones, centered on the subtropical belts in the latitudes of 30° to 35°, both north and south. These centers, which are relatively permanent features, are the surface expression of the subtropical high-pressure cells already referred to as lying on the poleward side of the Hadley cell. The Southern Hemisphere, with little land, shows their development best. The cells are located over the oceans and shift a few degrees north and south from solstice to solstice, being strengthened in the season of most intense incoming radiation. From the centers of these anticyclones surface winds blow outward with a spiralling pattern, clockwise in the Northern Hemisphere, counterclockwise in the Southern Hemisphere, as shown in Figure 15.34. Within the center of each cell, where the pressure gradient is very slight, there occur calms and light, variable winds. For this reason the belt of subtropical high-pressure cells has long been designated in marine terminology as the *subtropical belt of variable winds and calms.* The more picturesque term *horse latitudes* applied to this belt is said to have been given because in Colonial times traders' vessels transporting horses from New England to the West Indies were sometimes becalmed there and some of the horses had to be thrown overboard to conserve drinking water.

To the equatorward side of the subtropical high-pressure belt lies a belt of the earth's most reliable and persistent surface winds, the *trades,* which are the expression of the tropical easterlies at higher levels. The trades are best developed over the Pacific and Atlantic Oceans. From the Northern Hemisphere high-pressure cells, these winds blow from the northeast and are therefore called the *northeast trades.* Those from the Southern Hemisphere high-pressure cells blow from the southeast and are the *southeast trades.*

The trades are noted for their persistence, for their frequency of calm is less than 2 percent in most areas. The trades are accompanied by generally fair weather and little rainfall over the oceans. A notable exception is the season of high sun, when occasional violent tropical storms, known as hurricanes or typhoons (see Chapter 19), develop in and pass through the trade-wind belt.

The trades converge equatorward and meet in the equatorial trough, a zone in which the average pressure is just slightly below the normal standard sea-level pressure of 29.9 in. (1013 mb), but which is strongly defined when compared with the high pressures of the tropical anticyclones. Air converging into this region from both northeast and southeast must escape by rising.

The equatorial trough, or intertropical convergence zone (ITC), has an axial region of weak pressure gradients, which causes some parts to have long periods of calms. Such portions of the equatorial oceans are known as the *doldrums.* Typical doldrum belts lie off the west coasts of Central America and Africa a few degrees north of the equator, but the principal occurrence is in a belt straddling the equator and extending from the Indian Ocean, through the East Indies, and well out into the mid-Pacific Ocean.

Poleward of the subtropical highs lie the belts of *prevailing westerlies.* Disregarding for the moment the Northern Hemisphere with its great land areas, the westerlies are clearly shown at lat. 40° to 65° S. over the great expanse of the Southern Ocean, which girdles the globe. Because of the frequency of winds of gale force in these waters, mariners referred to these latitudes as the *roaring forties,* the *furious fifties,* and the *screaming sixties.* Although the westerlies in the Southern Hemisphere blow most frequently from the northwest, other compass quandrants are well represented. It will become apparent in Chapter 19 that the wide variability of wind direction in the westerly wind belt is the result of frequent, rapidly moving pressure centers (cyclonic and anticyclonic), which bring about rapid changes in wind direction.

Over the oceans the westerly winds are clearly a part of the outflowing air from the subtropical high-pressure centers (Figure 15.34), which air is deflected toward the east as it travels to the high latitudes.

Continuing southward in the Southern Hemisphere, we find that the westerlies give way, poleward of lat. 65° S., to a system of southeasterly winds blowing outward from the Antarctic continent. These are the *polar easterlies* and represent the anticlockwise outward-spiraling flow of air from the permanent *polar high* intensified by the extreme cold of the antarctic icecap. In the region where westerlies and polar easterlies meet, at about lat. 60° to 65° S., the world pressure maps (Figures 15.27 and 15.28) show a belt of extremely low barometric pressure, averaging below 29.1 in. (987 mb). This zone, termed the *subpolar low,* is one in which intense low-pressure centers (cyclonic storms) are frequent. Although the pressure is not constantly low, the

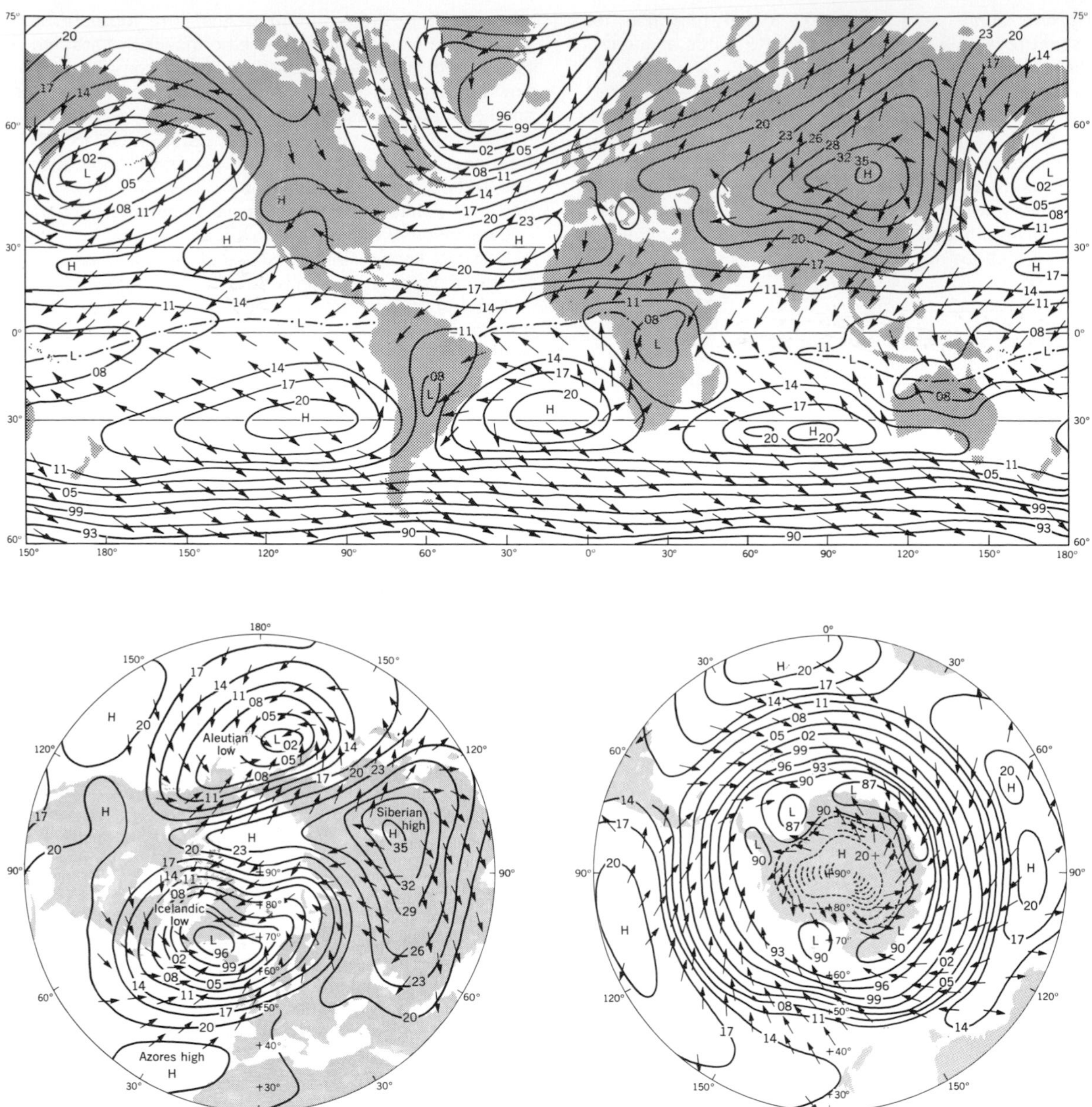


**FIGURE 15.32.** Average January surface barometric pressures in millibars, reduced to sea level. Only the last two digits are shown. Arrows showing prevailing winds are drawn to agree with isobars. (Map compiled by John E. Oliver from data by Y. Mintz, G. Dean, R. Geiger, and J. Blüthagen. Isobars reproduced by permission of John Wiley & Sons, New York.)

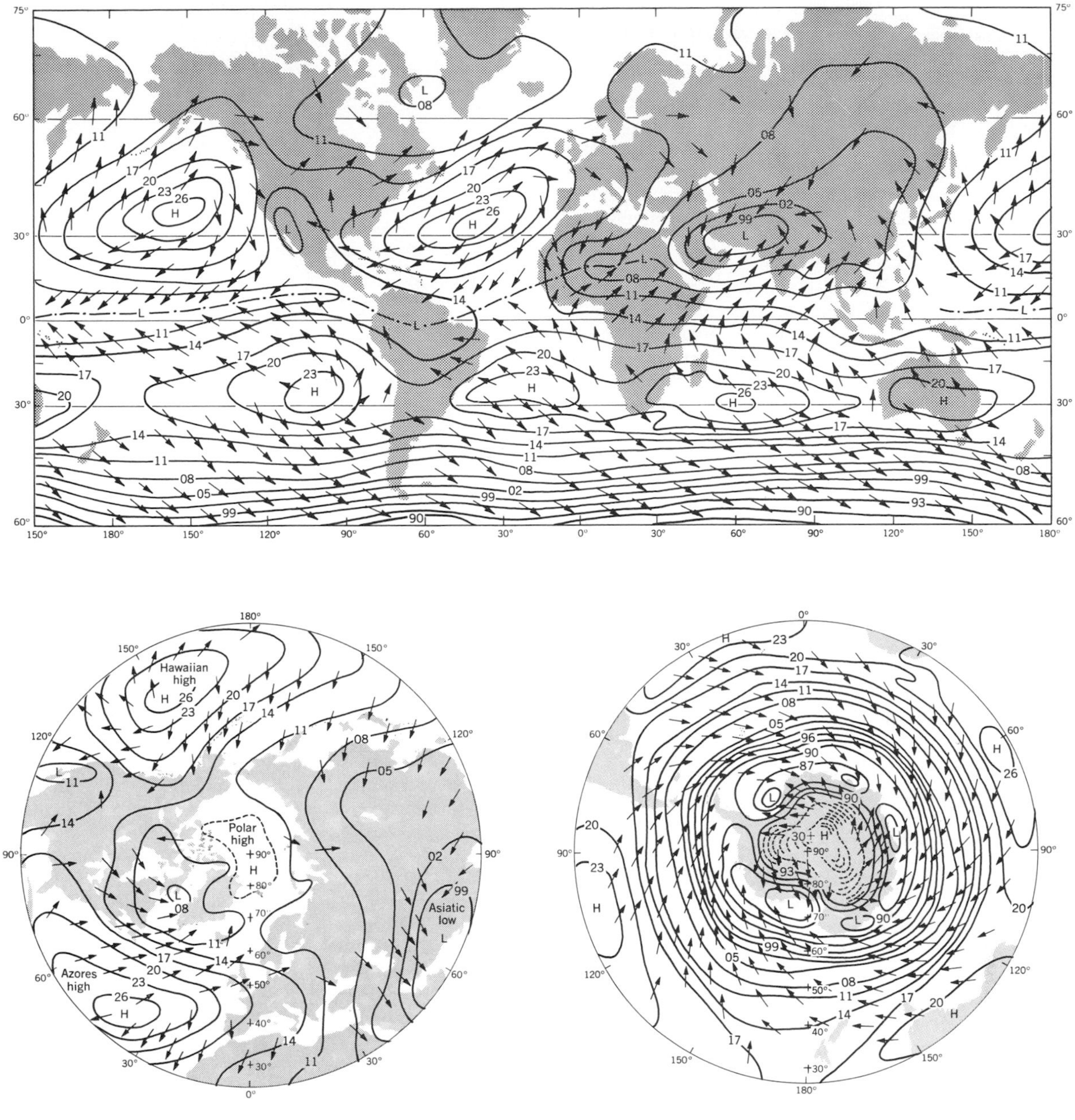

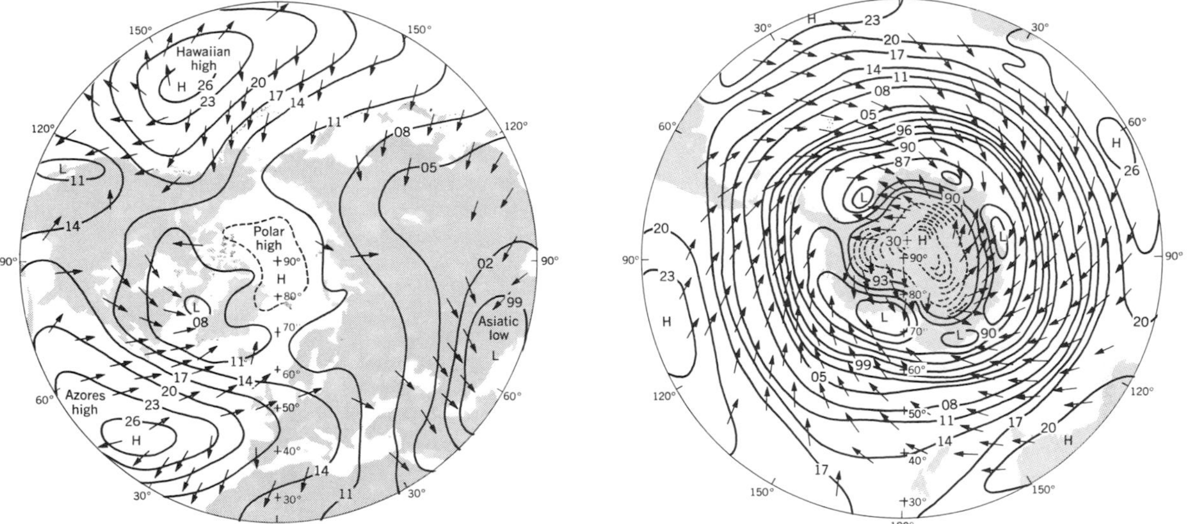


**FIGURE 15.33.** Average July surface barometric pressure in millibars, reduced to sea level, and surface winds. (Same data sources as Figure 15.32. Isobars reproduced by permission of John Wiley & Sons, New York.)

frequent occurrence of very low values yields a low average, and thus the monthly average isobars show a low-pressure trough.

Latitude belts of pressure and winds, so well developed in the Southern Hemisphere, are missing over the Northern Hemisphere, because the great landmasses of North America and Eurasia lie between the North Atlantic and North Pacific oceans. Thus there are four quadrants in the Northern Hemisphere—two of land, two of ocean (Figure 15.35). Applying the principles of fundamental differences in heating and cooling between land and ocean areas, we find that large pressure centers develop instead of parallel belts. The January map of pressure and winds (Figure 15.32) shows that Asia is dominated by a great center of high pressure, the *Siberian high,* and that a small but distinct counterpart, the *Canadian high,* lies over northwestern Canada. These highs are produced by the intense cooling of the land areas in winter. In contrast, the intervening oceans are relatively warm and develop large lows. The *Icelandic low,* centered over Iceland and southern Greenland in the North Atlantic, is one, and the other is the *Aleutian low,* centered over the Aleutian Islands of the North Pacific. In Figure 15.35 the four winter pressure centers are shown as alternating in the four Northern Hemisphere quadrants.

In July (Figure 15.33) the land areas heat rapidly and intensely, developing low-pressure centers over southern Asia and North America, while the subtropical high-pressure cells of the intervening oceans shift northward, enlarge, and intensify. Over the North Atlantic lies the *Azores high,* and over the North Pacific the *Hawaiian high.*

## Monsoon systems

Development of a summer low and a winter high over the large Asiatic landmass in middle latitudes creates a seasonally alternating system of pressure gradients and with it a seasonally reversing set of surface winds which we call a *monsoon system.* The idealized wind system for an imaginary circular continent in the middle latitudes of the Northern Hemisphere is shown in Figure 15.36. In summer (diagram *A*) the low-pressure center tends to develop in the southern part of the continent. This is a low associated with heating of the lower levels of the atmosphere; it does not extend high into the troposphere. Nevertheless pressure gradients at low levels are radially inward from sea to land, so that a cyclonic circulation forms. This is the *summer monsoon,* which in southern and eastern Asia is associated with the rainy season of the year.

In winter, intense cooling produces the center of higher pressure in the northerly part of the landmass (Figure 15.36*B*). Now an anticyclonic circulation is set up with surface winds blowing from continental interior toward the coast. In southern and eastern Asia this *winter monsoon* is associated with a period of dry, cool weather.

Turn now to the world maps of pressure and winds (Figures 15.32 and 15.33), to examine the monsoon system of Asia. Notice that the pressure contrast between land and water is far more intense in January than July. Note also that, as our idealized diagram (Figure 15.36) shows, the summer low lies far south in Asia, whereas the winter high is centered in Siberia.

A monsoon wind system also affects northern Australia, but here the seasons are opposite to those in Asia. Air flows into northeastern Australia in January, but flows outward, from south to north, over the same region in July. Some suggestion of a seasonal monsoon is also seen in the central part of the United States. In the summer the predominant direction of air flow is from the Gulf of Mexico northward into the central plains region. In winter winds from Canada reverse this flow much of the time.

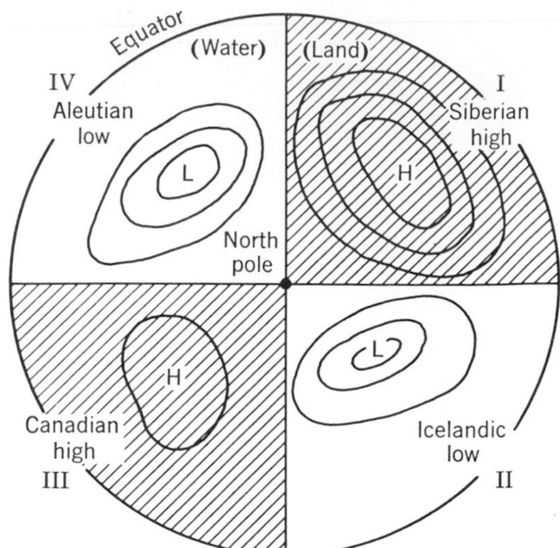


**FIGURE 15.35.** Schematic diagram of the Northern Hemisphere in winter showing centers of high and low pressure. (© 1960, John Wiley & Sons, New York.)

**FIGURE 15.34.** Generalized pattern of surface winds about the subtropical high-pressure centers. (© 1960, John Wiley & Sons, New York.)

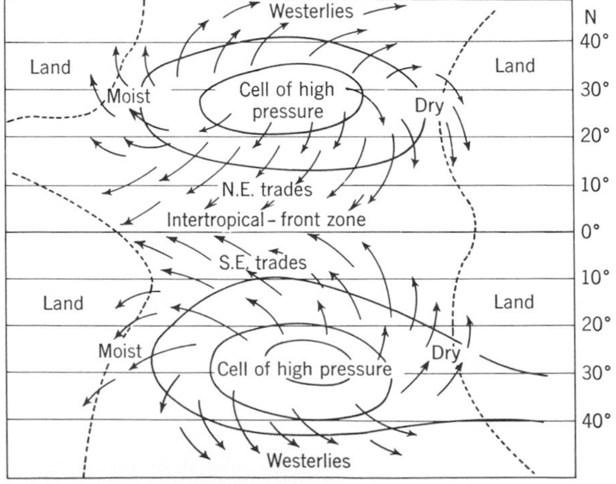


## Global atmospheric circulation in review

A thermally-driven atmospheric system serves to transport sensible heat and latent heat from equatorial to polar regions. Together with an oceanic circulation sys-

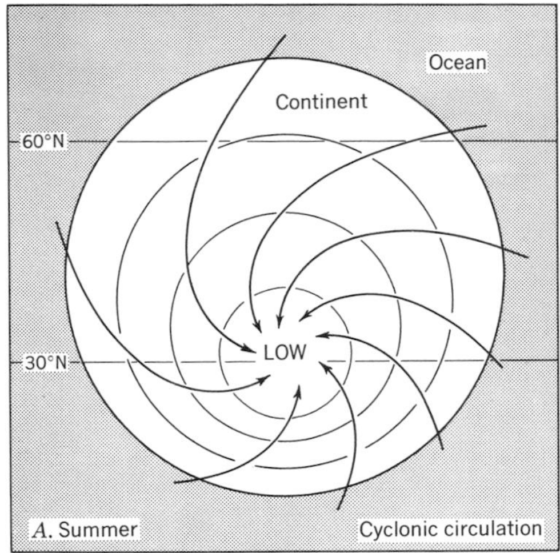


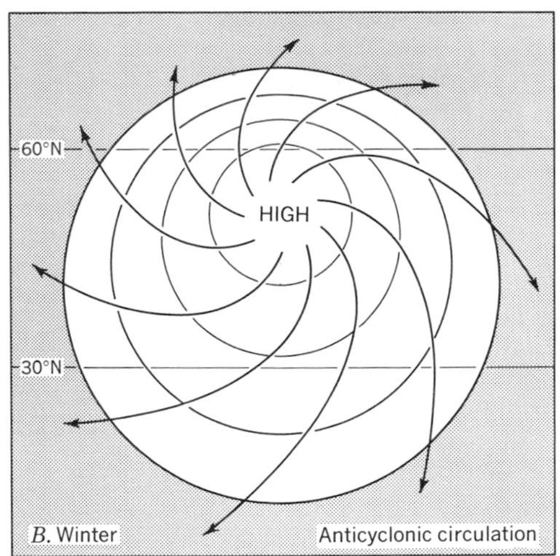


**FIGURE 15.36.** Schematic diagram of yearly alternations in surface pressure and air flow over a large middle-latitude continent in the Northern Hemisphere. [After S. Petterssen (1958), *Introduction to Meteorology,* New York, McGraw-Hill, p. 173, Figure 121.]

tem, which is itself largely wind-driven, this circulation maintains the earth's heat balance. In low latitudes the Hadley cell, with its rising and sinking motions, moves heat toward higher latitudes, at the same time transferring angular momentum poleward across parallels of latitude. At subtropical latitudes the westerlies, extending through the troposphere, take over the circulation, transporting heat and angular momentum farther poleward in large-scale horizontal eddies. The total angular momentum of the earth is maintained at an average constant value by a balance between the easterlies of low latitudes and the westerlies of middle and high latitudes.

The complex characteristics of the Earth's atmospheric circulation result from a unique combination of a dense atmosphere, radiation imbalances varying with latitude and season, and a relatively rapid rate of planetary rotation. No other planet even closely approaches Earth in matching this combination of atmospheric circumstances.

## References for further study

Riehl, H. (1962), *Jet Streams of the Atmosphere,* Tech. Report No. 32, Dept. of Atmospheric Sci., Colorado State Univ., Fort Collins, Colo., 117 pp.

Fairbridge, R. W., ed. (1967), *Encyclopedia of Atmospheric Sciences and Astrogeology,* New York, Reinhold, 1200 pp. See Atmospheric circulation, Coriolis force, Ferrel's law, Geostrophic wind, Gradient wind, Jet streams, Monsoons, Rossby wave, Trade winds, Wind—principles, Winds—local.

Reiter, E. R. (1967), *Jet Streams,* Garden City, N.Y., Doubleday, 189 pp.

Petterssen, S. (1969), *Introduction to Meteorology,* 3rd ed., New York, McGraw-Hill, 333 pp.

# 16

# Oceanic circulation

CONTINUING OUR STUDY of the earth's heat balance we turn next to the circulation of the oceans as a mechanism for the transport of sensible heat from equatorial regions of radiation surplus to arctic regions of radiation deficit. Although the total quantity of sensible heat transported poleward by ocean currents is only about one-fifth to one-fourth of the quantity transported by atmospheric circulation, the contribution of ocean transport to the maintenance of the earth's heat balance is important. We shall find that the surface water motions, which accomplish most of the meridional heat transfer taking place in the oceans, are themselves driven by the prevailing surface winds. This ocean circulation is therefore a secondary system, dependent upon the primary heat transport system of the atmosphere.

Further examination of oceanic circulation requires detailed study of the vertical dimension. Although the average ocean depth, about 2½ mi (4 km), is a very small fraction of the horizontal extent of a great ocean—the Pacific Ocean spans 10,000 mi (16,000 km)—the differences in temperature and salinity encountered with depth are matters of great importance to the oceanographer in interpreting sluggish vertical and horizontal motions that affect great masses of water. Thus in the latter part of this chapter the vertical scale of the ocean will be enormously magnified as we examine oceanic circulation in meridional cross-sections penetrating to the ocean bottom.

## Ocean currents

An *ocean current* may be defined as any predominantly horizontal water movement. Currents range in scale from oceanwide flow systems to local currents of small extent, and are generated by a variety of causative mechanisms. Most important as causes of the great ocean current systems are the drag of winds over the sea surface and the unequal forces set up by differences in water density.

Quite different from the above class of ocean currents are tidal currents, discussed in Chapter 9. Tidal currents are not only localized phenomena, but are unique in being alternating or rotatory in nature.

Current direction is stated in terms of the compass direction toward which the water is moving. Thus a *north current* consists of water traveling northward. The terminology is exactly opposite to that used in designating wind direction. To illustrate, the prevailing tropical easterly winds (trades) would produce a westerly water drift, and the prevailing westerly winds would set up an easterly water drift. Direction may be given in compass points (N, NNE, NE, ENE), in compass bearings referred to quadrant (N. 30° E., S. 45° W.), or as azimuth in degrees from 0° to 360° measured clockwise with respect to north (50°, 130°, 320°).

Because even the most rapid currents of the open oceans are slow-moving in comparison with winds or rivers, publications on navigation give the current speed in nautical miles per 24 hours—a motion of 12 nautical miles per day would therefore be equivalent to a current of half a knot. For scientific purposes, current speeds are stated in meters per second.

Despite their low speeds, ocean currents move enormous volumes of water in a given time because the cross-sectional area of the current is great. For example, the Gulf Stream in the region opposite Chesapeake Bay has a total water transport of from 75 to 90 million cubic meters per second. Because a cubic meter is a little more than a cubic yard, we can try to visualize this flow as between 75 and 90 million cubes of water, each a yard on a side, passing each second through an imaginary vertical plane placed across the current. The Gulf Stream current extends to a depth of not more than about 1 mi (1.6 km) and across a width of roughly 150 mi (240 km). In comparison, the Mississippi River averages no more than 50 ft (15 m) deep and about 0.5 mi (0.8 km) wide and is discharging water at about 20,000 cubic meters per second.

Ocean currents are difficult to measure because there is no solid bank or fixed surface platform to serve as a reference point in deep water far from land. Much information on surface directions and speed of ocean currents has been built up from ocean navigation. How this is done is shown in Figure 16.1. A ship located at *A* has its position determined precisely by celestial navigation. Suppose that the ship is pointed in the direction of *B* and travels for 24 hours headed constantly in that direction. As the ship travels, the ocean current, shown by dashed arrows, shifts the vessel sidewise with respect to its intended course, giving an actual track *AC*. When the position is again taken by celestial navigation and found to be point *C*, the sidewise drift *BC* can be calculated. This solution gives an average surface speed and direction of the current during the period of travel.

In shallow seas, such as those present over continental shelves and in straits, currents can be measured over long periods of time from an anchored ship, such as a lightship. Floating markers released from the fixed vessel can be followed and their direction and velocity recorded. Methods of tracking floating objects over long

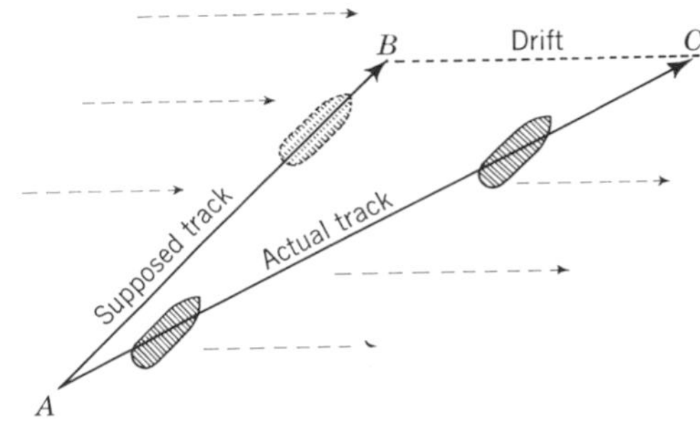


**FIGURE 16.1.** Estimates of ocean drift may be made from navigational calculations. (© 1960, John Wiley & Sons, New York.)

distances are referred to in general as *drift methods.* Because very light floating objects such as pieces of cork are dragged along by winds, which do not necessarily coincide with the general water movement, the float should lie low in the water with little or no projecting surface. Oceanographers have long used sealed *drift bottles,* weighted down with enough sand so that they float nearly submerged. Each bottle is released at a selected point and contains a card giving information on the experiment and requesting the finder to return the card by mail with information on the date and place it was found. Drift-bottle information is useful in giving the over-all long-range pattern and average speed of surface-water movement of the broad oceans, but the actual path of the bottle is uncertain.

In contrast to the drift methods is direct flow measurement with meters or gauges lowered into the water from anchored ships. One example is the *Ekman current meter,* which has several unique features designed to meet the special problems of ocean-current measurement (Figure 16.2). Like current meters used in rivers,

**FIGURE 16.2.** This current meter, an improved type based on the principles of the Ekman meter, measures current speed by totaling the revolutions of a propeller (left). The cylindrical box below at regular intervals receives metal balls in radial compartments to give information on current direction. (Courtesy of the G. M. Manufacturing Co., New York.)

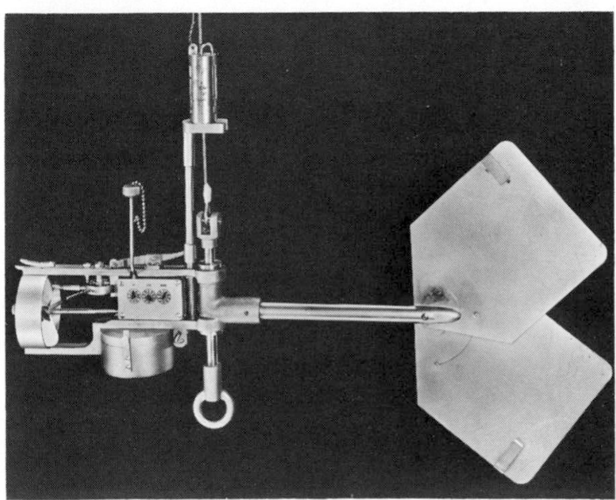

this meter has a propeller that turns at a speed proportional to the water velocity and a tail fin that keeps the propeller pointed into the current. A cylindrical shield protects the propeller from responding to vertical motions. After the meter has been lowered to the desired depth on a steel wire, a messenger (sliding weight) is sent down on the wire. It releases the propeller, which begins to turn. The number of turns is recorded on a set of dials. After the propeller has turned for a fixed number of minutes, a second messenger is released and trips a lever that stops the propeller. During this time the direction of the current has been recorded by an ingenious magnetic-compass mechanism. Current meters have also been placed on the ocean bottom, suspended from tripods, so as to study the current force acting to move silts and sands on the ocean bottom. A type of current meter adapted to deep currents is described at a later point in this chapter.

**Wind as a cause of surface currents** Persistent large-scale circulation of the oceans is caused in two principal ways: (1) by the force of prevailing winds blowing over the sea surface and (2) by differences in density of sea water from place to place. Almost all important surface ocean currents are powered by wind, directly or indirectly.

Air flowing over a water surface exerts a dragging force upon the water surface, setting the surface water in motion. The amount of this dragging force on each unit area of sea surface can be estimated from a knowledge of the wind speed a few meters above the water surface. The force increases roughly as the square of the wind speed.

Prevailing winds, such as the tropical easterlies (trades) and middle-latitude westerlies, exert a one-way drag on the sea surface over vast expanses of the oceans, setting in motion a system of currents on a gigantic scale. These so-called *drift currents* merge with currents caused by density differences to produce a continuous ocean circulation.

A remarkable feature of ocean currents set up by wind drag is that the water does not move in the same direction as the wind. This fact was observed by the arctic explorer Fridtjof Nansen during the years 1893–1896, when his ship, the *Fram,* was held fast in the pack ice of the polar sea. Nansen noted that the direction of the drift of the ice was some 20–45 degrees to the right of the direction of the wind. He rightly attributed this difference in direction to the Coriolis effect, causing the surface water to be deflected to the right because of the earth's rotation.

Now, each imaginary layer of drifting sea water exerts a drag upon the layer below, setting it in motion but at diminished speed. Consequently each successively lower layer will be deflected still more to the right (Northern Hemisphere) and the direction of drift gradually swings around until it is actually opposite to that at the surface.

Changing velocity (speed and direction) with depth is shown by a diagram known as the *Ekman spiral* (Figure 16.3), after the oceanographer who developed Nansen's observation mathematically and showed the full extent of the turning effect. In Figure 16.3 the column on the left is marked off into units of depth. At the top of the column an arrow shows the wind direction at the sea surface. The uppermost long broad arrow shows the surface-water drift.

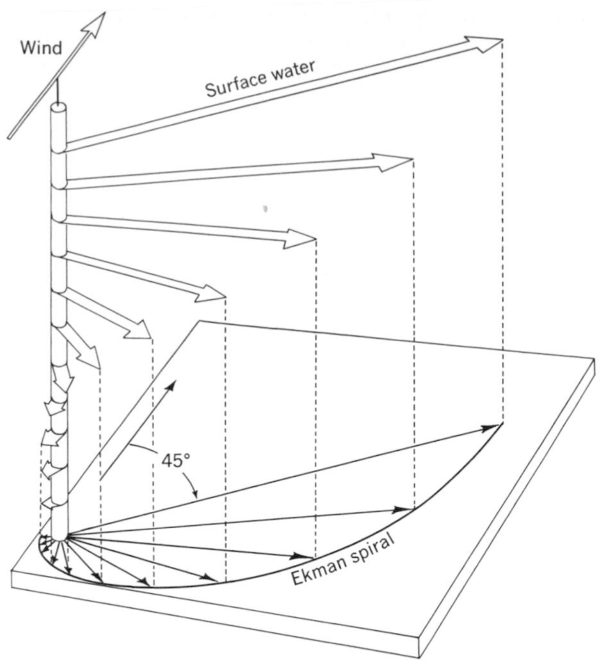


**FIGURE 16.3.** The Ekman spiral. Open arrows show current direction and relative speed from the surface downward for equal depth units. The projection of these arrow points upon a horizontal plane, below, produces the Ekman spiral. [After H. U. Sverdrup (1942), *Oceanography for Meteorologists,* Englewood Cliffs, N.J., Prentice-Hall, p. 125, Figure 30.]

The horizontal angle between surface motion and wind direction is about 45°. Thus if the wind is a west wind (that is, blowing eastward), the drift will be toward the southeast. The successive lower arrows show the drift directions at successively lower levels in the water. These arrows, whose position resemble the steps on a spiral staircase, become shorter with depth, showing that the speed decreases rapidly as the depth increases. On the graph at the base of the diagram the dashed line connecting the ends of the arrows form a curve of a type known as a *logarithmic spiral.* At the depth where the direction is exactly opposite to the wind, the drift speed is only one twenty-third that of the surface speed and is therefore of little importance. This depth of opposite flow, called *friction depth,* is commonly about 300 ft (90 m) and rarely deeper than 600 ft (180 m). Although the logarithmic spiral does, in theory, continue downward to the bottom of the ocean, its effect is too minute to be considered below the friction depth.

Because of the changing direction of drift with depth, as the Ekman spiral shows, the direction of average transport of water for the entire moving layer above the friction depth will be at an even greater angle to the wind than water drift at the surface. Actually the average direction of water motion in the layer moved by wind is about at right angles to the wind direction. In the Northern Hemisphere the direction of water motion is to the right of the wind direction, while in the Southern Hemisphere it is to the left.

**Currents produced by density differences** We have seen that density of sea water depends both upon its temperature and its salinity (Chapter 12). Differences in water density from place to place may produce both horizontal and vertical movements and thus modify the oceanic circulation based upon wind-driven drift currents. Water circulation powered by density differences is described by the adjective *thermohaline,* a word implying by its components the combined effect of temperature and salinity upon water density.

Two ways in which a surficial layer of less dense water may be produced and maintained are by solar warming and by the addition of much fresh water by heavy rainfall. The area of less dense water thus produced will stand at a higher surface elevation than adjacent water areas of greater density, and hence will assume a surface slope in the direction of the denser water.

Figure 16.4 shows an idealized case in which denser and lighter water masses lie side by side—the lighter water forms a layer resting on the denser and tapers to a wedge. At the level *P* and below all forces are balanced, with no tendency for water to flow in any direction. On the extreme right- and left-hand sides of the block there is no current-producing force within the denser and lighter areas. Between the two, in the area of the tapering water wedge, the sea surface slopes from lighter to denser water. A force, analogous to the pressure-gradient force in the atmosphere, tends to move the water down this slope in the direction of the large arrow labeled *F.* Now, however, we bring into play the Coriolis effect, which tends to turn the flow toward the right in the Northern Hemisphere. Turning occurs to the point that the water current is parallel to the sea-surface slope, as in the case of the geostropic wind paralleling the isobars in a wind system. We thus arrive at the general rule: Current in the Northern Hemisphere flows in such a direction that the less dense water lies on the right-hand side of the current and the denser water on the left. For Southern Hemisphere the words "right" and "left" must be interchanged.

**FIGURE 16.4.** Difference of density in adjacent water layers tends to produce a current at right angles to the slope of the water surface. [After H. U. Sverdrup, 1942, *Oceanography for Meteorologists,* Englewood Cliffs, N.J., Prentice-Hall, p. 105.]

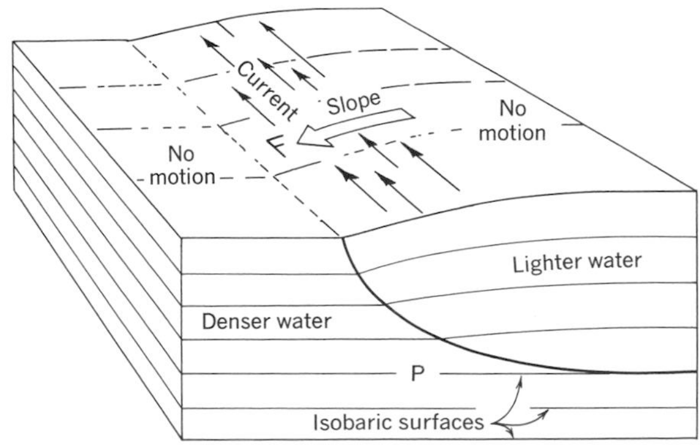


## General scheme of surface ocean currents

The Atlantic and Pacific Oceans have a simple and orderly pattern of surface-water movement which can be generalized in a schematic diagram (Figure 16.5). Both oceans extend unbroken from high latitudes north and south across the equator and are bounded by continents on both sides. The dominant features are two great circular water motions called *gyres,* each of which is centered on a subtropical high-pressure region. Within each gyre the water turns clockwise in the Northern Hemisphere and counterclockwise in the Southern Hemisphere (Figure 16.6). Each gyre is formed by two sets of prevailing winds: the trades (tropical easterlies) on the equatorward side and the prevailing westerlies on the poleward side. The westward drifts of water in equatorial latitudes are referred to as the *North Equatorial Current* and *South Equatorial Current.* These are separated by the *Equatorial Countercurrent* that moves eastward and is caused by the return of lighter surface water which has been piled up on the western side of the ocean basin by the equatorial currents. The Equatorial Countercurrent is best developed in the Pacific Ocean,

**FIGURE 16.5.** Schematic diagram of an ocean with an idealized system of surface currents.

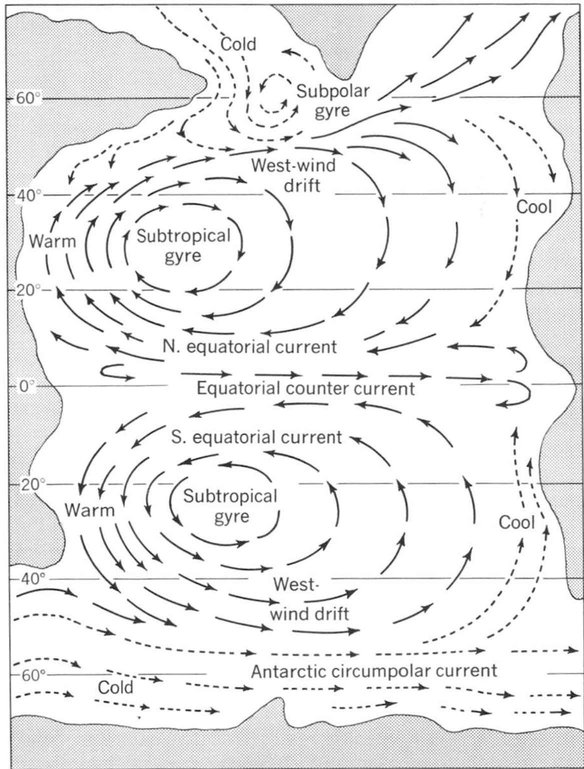

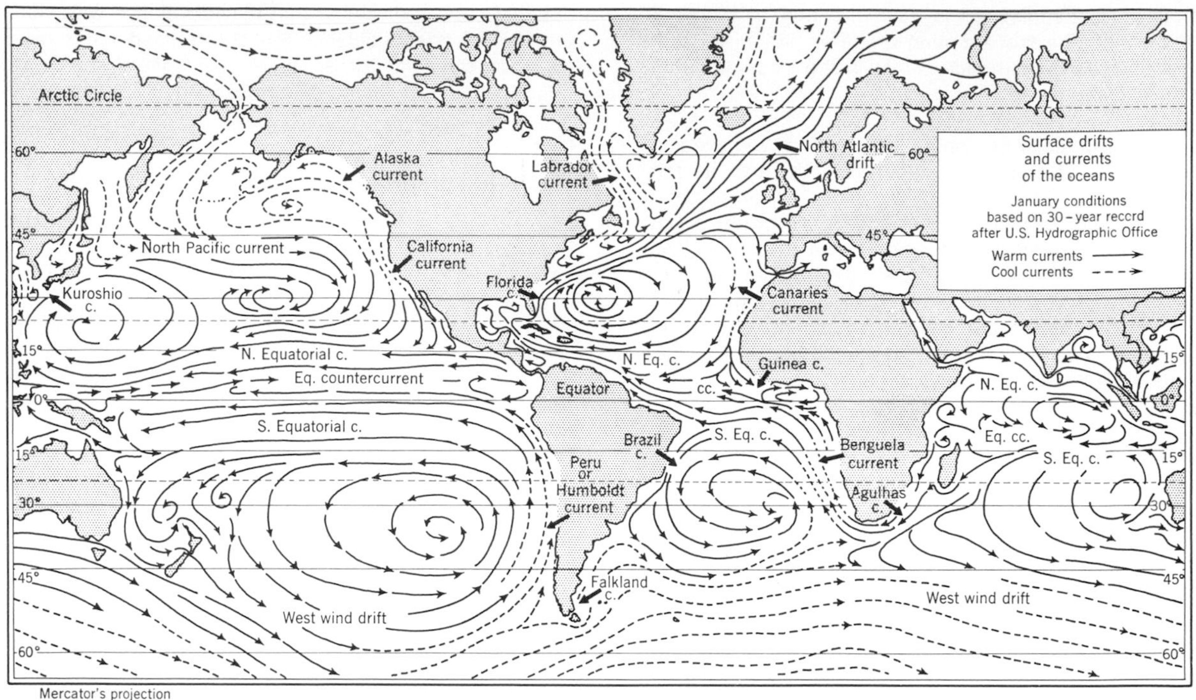


**FIGURE 16.6.** World map of average surface drifts and currents of the oceans for the month of January. (Based upon data of the U.S. Navy Oceanographic Office. © 1960, John Wiley & Sons, New York.)

but is also found in the Atlantic and Indian Oceans (Figure 16.6).

An essential feature of the great gyres is that the current is greatly narrowed and intensified in velocity on the western side of the ocean, whereas on the eastern side the current is diffused into a slow drift spread over a broad zone. This asymmetry results from the Coriolis effect—on an eastward-rotating earth the gyre is deflected westward and forced to be compressed against the western boundary of the ocean.

The intensification of poleward currents on the western sides of the North Atlantic and North Pacific Oceans results in two powerful warm currents, the *Gulf Stream* in the Atlantic and *Kuroshio Current* in the Pacific. Speeds up to 5 knots (2.6 m/sec) are developed in these narrow streams. Perhaps most familiar of all currents to Americans is the Gulf Stream, which flows northward from the Caribbean, passing close to Florida and the southeast Atlantic coast, then curving northeast to spread over the North Atlantic. The Kuroshio Current is a similar warm current of the western Pacific. It sets in close to the Philippines, running northeastward past Formosa and the southern islands of Japan. In the Southern Hemisphere similar but less intensively developed currents flow southward off the coasts of Australia (*East Australia Current*) and South America (*Brazil Current*).

Upon turning eastward, each warm poleward current becomes part of the *west-wind drift,* produced by the highly variable prevailing westerly winds in lat. 40° to 65°. The gyre is then completed by a cold coastal current moving equatorward close to the western coast of the bordering continent. The four most important examples are the *California Current, Canary Current, Peru* or *Humboldt Current,* and the *Benguela Current,* shown in Figure 16.6. Upwelling, explained by the drift of water away from the coast as well as the importation of cold water from the high latitudes, makes these coastal currents unusually cold, considering their low-latitude locations. Fog produced by condensation of water vapor in air cooled close to the sea surface hangs over these currents for long periods of time. Air temperatures are surprisingly cool throughout the year for latitudes at which we find the world's hottest deserts not far inland. The 70° F isotherm for January and July (Figures 14.27 and 14.28) shows a strong equatorward bend in crossing the cool current, but a poleward bend in crossing the warm current on the western side of the ocean.

The *North Atlantic drift,* an eastward movement of warm water, divides upon approaching western Europe. While part turns southward to form the Canary Current, most continues northeast to the British Isles, where a strong current passes just north of Scotland and thence northeast along the Norwegian coast, as the *Norway Current,* to the Arctic Ocean well above the Arctic Circle. Murmansk, an ice-free port on the Arctic Circle, owes its year-round navigability to the Norway Current, for the polar sea would otherwise freeze over solidly in winter at this high latitude.

Surface-water movements in the arctic and antarctic regions must be considered separately from one another because of the exactly opposite relationship between land and water. The Arctic Ocean is an open ocean centered approximately on the North Pole and fringed by lands between which straits provide a connection with the Pacific and Atlantic basins. On the other hand, the Southern Hemisphere extremity consists of a pole-centered landmass, Antarctica, about the same size as the Arctic Ocean but completely surrounded by an open ocean, the Southern Ocean.

Currents in the Arctic Ocean take the form of a single large gyre of clockwise motion centered at about 80° N. latitude in the Beaufort Sea directly north of Alaska. Arctic water flows south in vigorous cold currents entering the North Atlantic. One of these is the *Labrador Current,* which flows south through Baffin Bay and Davis Strait to reach the Labrador coast and Newfoundland. It is this cold water, meeting the warm water of the Gulf Stream in the vicinity of the Grand Banks of Newfoundland, that gives rise to great advection fogs (Chapter 18). Along the east side of Greenland is another stream of cold arctic water flowing south. This is the *East Greenland Current,* a rapid stream which passes between Greenland and Iceland to mix with the North Atlantic drift. Outflow of cold water is largely equalled by inflow of warmer water by the Norwegian Current.

The Southern (Antarctic) Ocean, which is simply the southern part of the Pacific, Atlantic, and Indian Oceans in the region of the 50th and 60th parallels, forms a continuous circular ribbon of ocean, scarcely interrupted by land (Figure 16.7). Here the *Antarctic Circumpolar Current* flows eastward in an uninterrupted path following the parallels of latitude. This current represents the joining of west-wind drifts of the individual ocean basins under the prevailing westerly winds.

## Equatorial undercurrents

In the Pacific Ocean, running directly beneath the west-flowing South Equatorial Current but moving in the opposite (eastward) direction, is an *undercurrent* named the *Cromwell Current.* It was first explored in 1952 and has since been traced approximately along the equator for about 3500 mi (4800 km); it seems to disappear at the Galapagos Islands.

About 250 mi (400 km) wide, the Cromwell Current has a speed of about 3½ miles per hour (1.5 m/sec). Surprisingly, this speed is considerably greater than that of the westward surface current flowing above it. The undercurrent sets in about 100 ft (30 m) below the surface and has its core of most rapid motion at about 300 ft (90 m) depth, which is at the level of the thermocline. Total vertical thickness is about 700 ft (210 m).

Oceanographers have estimated that the Cromwell Current transports a flow of water approximately equal to that moved by the Gulf Stream through the Straits of Florida. Beneath the Cromwell Current is a weak westerly current. There thus seem to be here three ribbon-like currents superimposed and alternately opposed in direction of flow.

Equatorial undercurrents like the Cromwell Current

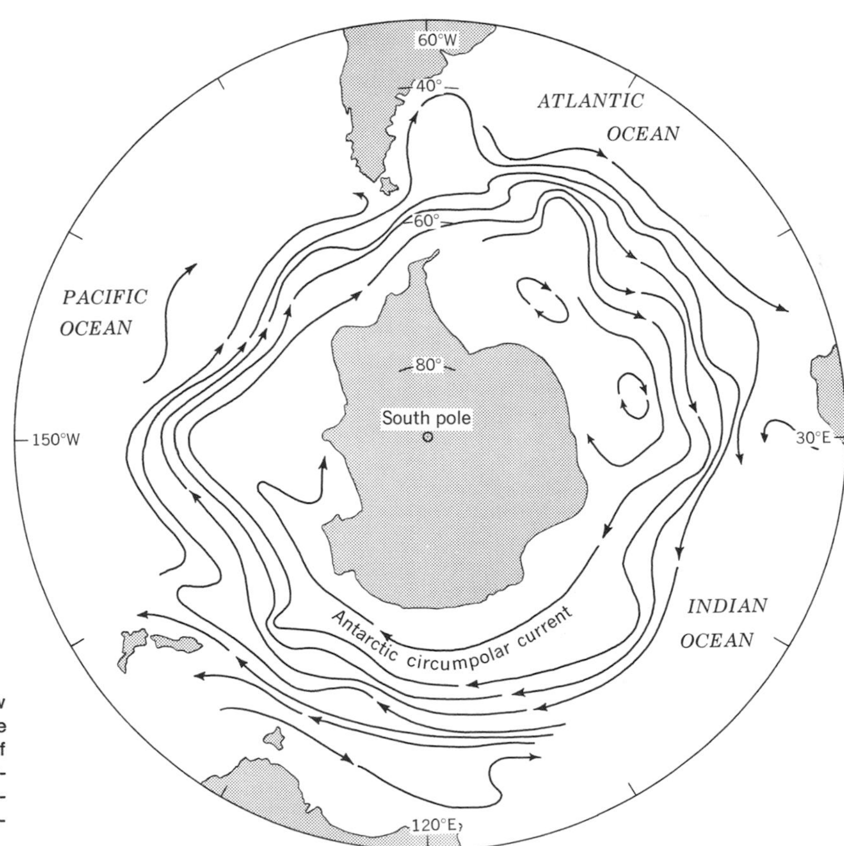


**FIGURE 16.7.** Streamlines of water flow about the Antarctic continent. Where lines are most closely spaced, rate of flow is most rapid. [After H. U. Sverdrup (1942), *Oceanography for Meteorologists,* Englewood Cliffs, N.J., Prentice-Hall, p. 206, Figure 57.]

exist also in the Atlantic and Indian Oceans. Origin of the equatorial undercurrent remains obscure.

## Deep countercurrents

On theoretical grounds oceanographers reasoned that the strong poleward flow of water in the Gulf Stream and Kuroshio Currents must be equalized by equatorward flow at considerable depths. It was predicted that the return flow of colder water would take the form of a narrow fast current lying close to the continent on the western side of the ocean basin. Confirmation of these predictions long remained wanting because of the difficulty of detecting and measuring deep currents.

About the time of the International Geophysical Year (1957–1958) floats, or buoys, of adjustable densities had been devised, which meant that the density of the float could be matched to that of sea water at a given level and therefore could remain suspended at that level. Tracking of such floats may be done by *sonar,* the sound-reflection system used to track submarines, or by other types of sound systems. A particularly successful device is the *Swallow float,* which emits sound pulses by which it can be followed.

During the IGY oceanographic program the new equipment was used with various other types of oceanographic data collection in the deep water lying at the base of the continental slope (Chapter 23) in the vicinity of Cape Hatteras. Here a narrow swift current, named the *Gulf Stream Countercurrent,* was discovered, or more accurately, its presence at depths between 8000 and 10,000 ft (2400 and 3200 m) was confirmed. The current flows southwestward along the base of the Blake Escarpment and apparently skirts the Bahamas. Maximum current speed is about one-third knot (0.18 m/sec).

Figure 16.8 is a pair of maps showing the postulated deep countercurrent of the western Atlantic Ocean, as compared with the established surface currents.

## Convergence and sinking, divergence and upwelling

We turn next to consider ocean water motions that are predominantly vertical, corresponding to convective motions of the atmosphere. Vertical water motions must be coupled with horizontal motions, hence two combinations of motions can exist (Figure 16.9). Where water volumes tend to move closer together, a process of *convergence,* there must be escape of water downward by *sinking.* Where water volumes tend to move apart, a process of *divergence,* there must be replacement by rising of water from below, or *upwelling.* A number of persistent zones of convergence and divergence, with corresponding zones of sinking and upwelling, can be identified in the world ocean and define the large-scale patterns of convectional motion in which water follows paths from ocean surface to ocean floor and return to surface.

Causes of sinking and upwelling are several and

**FIGURE 16.8.** Surface circulation (left) and deep circulation (right) of the Atlantic Ocean. Arrows trace flow paths from a number of starting points. [After H. Stommel (1957), *Deep-Sea Research,* vol. 4.]

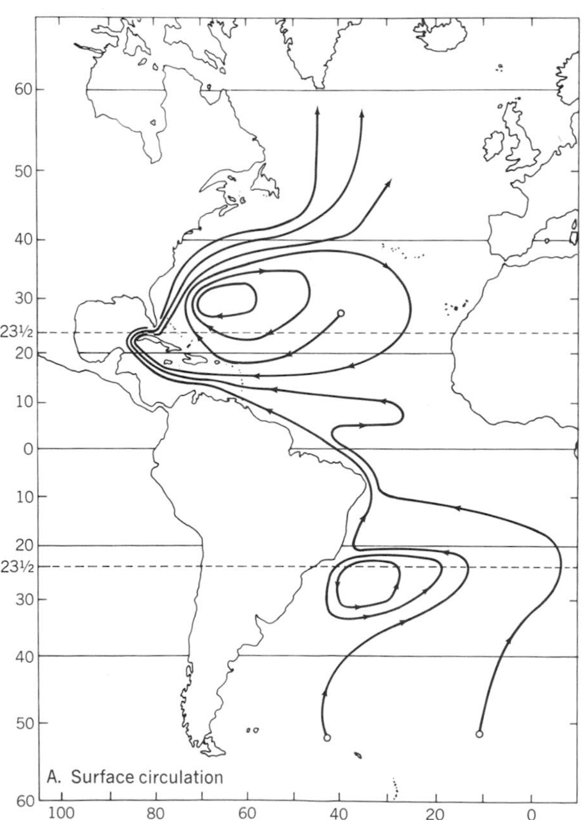


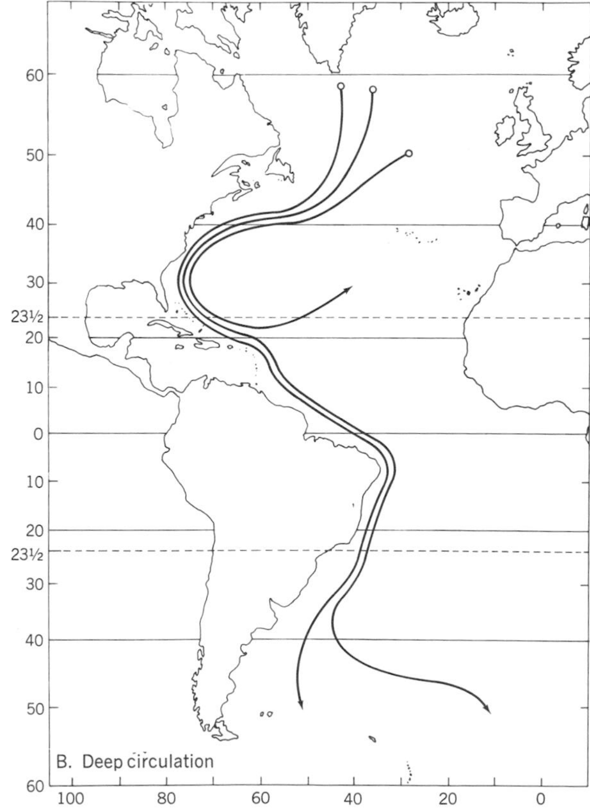

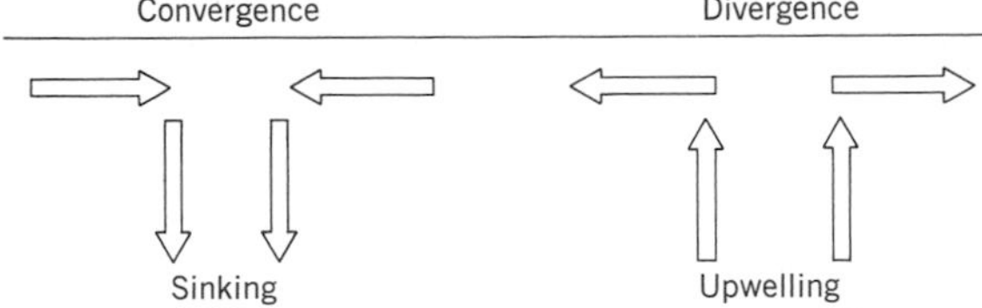


**FIGURE 16.9.** Convergence and sinking; divergence and upwelling.

relate to wind action, evaporation and rainfall, and temperature change.

Prevailing winds blowing approximately parallel with the coast of a continent may cause either upwelling or sinking. In Figure 16.10 the principle is illustrated for the west coast of a continent in the Northern Hemisphere. For relatively deep water, prevailing northerly winds cause an average surface water transport westward at about right angles to both winds and coast line. A water drift having a component of motion away from the shoreline, but moving obliquely (northwestward) with respect to it, would be expected if the winds were northeasterly, blowing from land to ocean and crossing the coast line obliquely.

Surface motion with a westward component away from the land acts as a divergence and tends to lower the water level near the coast. The deficiency of water is made up by upwelling of deeper water. Because water rising from below is normally colder than surface water, such coastal zones of upwelling will be cool in climate, even in the low latitudes, and will be characterized by fogs.

**FIGURE 16.10.** Winds blowing parallel with a coast line in the Northern Hemisphere tend to produce a surface drift of water away from the land and thus to cause upwelling of cooler water. [After H. Panofsky (1960), *Oceanography for the Navy Meteorologist,* NWRF 32-0360-030, Norfolk, Va., U.S. Naval Weather Research Facility.]

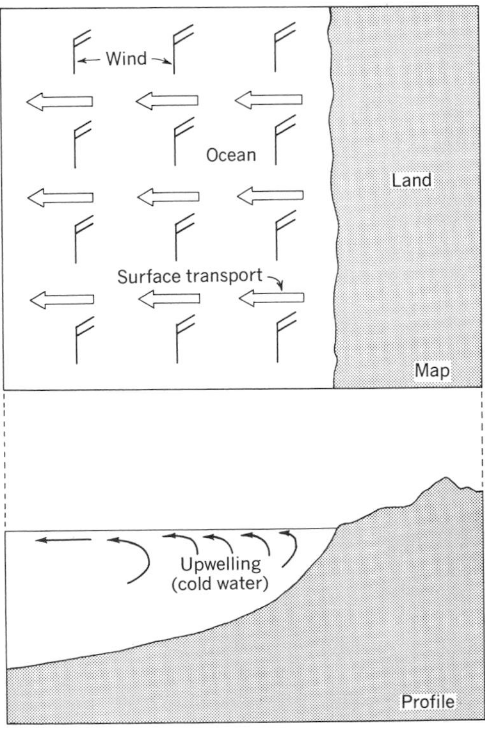


Among the best-known examples of coasts bordered by cool upwelling currents are the subtropical west coasts of southern California, Morocco, Southwest Africa, and Peru. An examination of the world maps of pressure and surface winds (Figures 15.32 and 15.33) shows that prevailing winds along these coasts are directed equatorward, roughly paralleling the coast lines, when the subtropical highs are strongly developed. Water drift at right angles to these winds (to the right in the Northern Hemisphere) will move the water away from the continents.

Prevailing winds blowing approximately parallel with a coast or obliquely toward a coast may cause drift currents toward the land. Such is the case where in the Northern Hemisphere the land lies to the right-hand side with respect to direction of the wind, exactly the reverse situation from that in Figure 16.10. Surface water thus moved landward must escape by sinking and flowing seaward at greater depth.

Applying the principle of surface water transport at right angles to prevailing wind direction, consider the case of an anticyclonic cell in the Northern Hemisphere (Figure 16.11). Prevailing southwesterlies on the poleward side of the cell, coupled with northeast trades on the equatorward side, tend to direct water transport toward the center of the cell, where it will constitute a convergence and lead to sinking. We can further envision that the sinking water would, near the ocean bottom, spread outward and then rise in peripheral regions to complete the convective circulation. This type of circulation was proposed as a theoretical model by Ekman, but does not actually operate in nature because other factors, causing changes in water density, do not permit the circulation to be completed.

An entirely different mechanism leading to sinking of surface water falls within the thermohaline category of effects. Intensive evaporation of water from the sea surface within the subtropical high pressure belt increases the salinity of the upper water layer. As the water density is thus increased, it tends to sink and to develop a convergence zone (Figure 16.12).

**FIGURE 16.11.** Schematic diagram of surface winds and induced water transport in a subtropical high pressure cell.

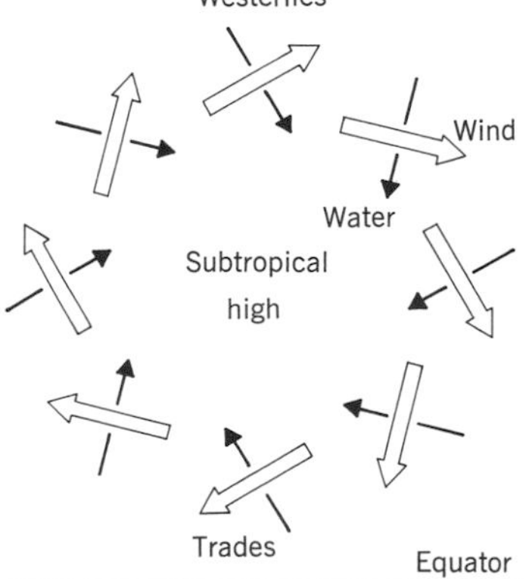

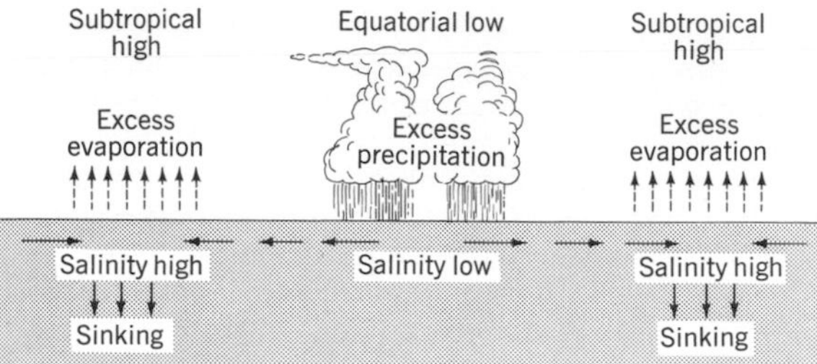


**FIGURE 16.12.** Excess evaporation under the dry subtropical highs increases surface water salinity; excess precipitation over the equatorial low tends to reduce salinity.

Figure 16.13 is a graph showing the way in which evaporation and precipitation influence surface water salinity. In the latitude zone 20° to 30°, under the aridity imposed by the subtropical high pressure belt, evaporation exceeds precipitation by a large margin, and salinity correspondingly rises to values over 35.5 ‰. In the intertropical convergence zone, located slightly north of the equator, heavy rainfall and prevailingly high relative humidity of the air result in a large surplus of precipitation over evaporation. The surface water thus tends to become diluted with fresh rainwater and salinity is lowered. Poleward of the subtropical high pressure belt, precipitation again exceeds evaporation so that salinity declines with increasing latitude.

The *subtropical convergence,* explained by the combined influences of anticyclonic winds and excessive evaporation, is an important zone in the convective system of the oceans. Located on the poleward side of the high pressure belt, the subtropical convergence can be found between 30° and 40° latitude in the oceans of both hemispheres.

Finally, we come to the most important mechanism in convectional circulation of the oceans, that of surface cooling by radiation of heat into the atmosphere. Throughout the long winter of high latitudes, net long-wave radiation from both ocean surface and atmosphere experiences a prolonged and severe deficit. Relatively warm surface waters brought poleward by ocean currents are chilled and increase in density. This water, which may be close to the freezing point, sinks to the deep ocean floor. A surface convergence zone is thus created in both arctic and antarctic latitudes.

In the North Atlantic, the *arctic convergence zone* lies between Iceland and southern Greenland in an area into which the relatively more saline water arriving from tropical latitudes via the Gulf Stream is cooled and becomes unusually dense. The *antarctic convergence zone,* roughly concentric about the continent of Antarctica, is the most important zone of sinking of cold water, from a global standpoint. The principal convergence lies in the latitude belt between 50° and 60° S. and forms a relatively narrow and well-defined line (Figure 16.7). Closer to Antarctica, chilling of the surface water is even more severe and results in sinking of dense water down the continental slope of that landmass.

With the major causes of both surface currents and vertical motions established, we can turn to the structure and circulation of the oceans as seen in vertical cross sections.

**FIGURE 16.13.** A strong correspondence exists between ocean-water salinity and the difference between precipitation and evaporation over a wide range of latitude. [Based on data of Sverdrup. © 1960, John Wiley & Sons, New York.]

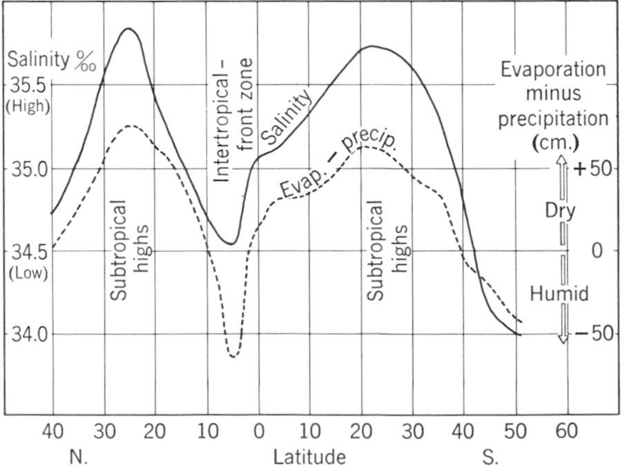


## Water masses

In modern oceanography, as in modern meteorology, study has progressed from analyses of surface conditions to a three-dimensional study of the entire layer of fluid. Through deep-sea soundings, in which water temperatures are taken and samples of water are collected for measuring salinity, it has been possible to extend our knowledge of the nature of great bodies of ocean water, just as the use of sounding balloons has permitted a study of the temperature, pressure, humidity, and winds in the upper atmosphere.

By recognizing unique combinations of temperature and salinity, large water bodies can be distinguished from one another. Such bodies are known as *water masses.* Identification of a particular water mass cannot be made on the basis of density alone, because, as stated in Chapter 12, density depends simultaneously upon both temperature and salinity. Therefore water of a given density can be produced by a wide range of combinations of temperature and salinity.

For example, the water mass lying close to the ocean floor in the antarctic region has a low salinity of 34.6 ‰ and a very low temperature of 28.6° F (−1.9° C). This combination gives a density of 1.0279, which is high for sea water, when pressure is neglected. In contrast, the water 1000–1500 ft (300–450 m) deep in the Mediterranean has a relatively high temperature of 52–55° F (11–13° C) and a high salinity of 38 ‰. For this water mass the density is 1.0275.

Unlike air masses, in which strong convection and turbulence can mix the air rapidly, water masses move sluggishly and tend to spread out into stable layers, one above the other, arranged in order of their density. For this reason water masses are described according to position from the surface downward as *upper, intermediate, deep,* and *bottom* water masses. In addition, water masses are classified in terms of latitude and the particular ocean basin, according to the geographical area in which they are formed.

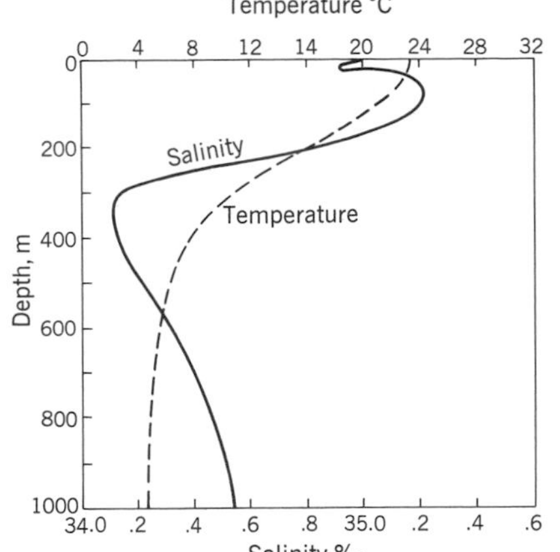


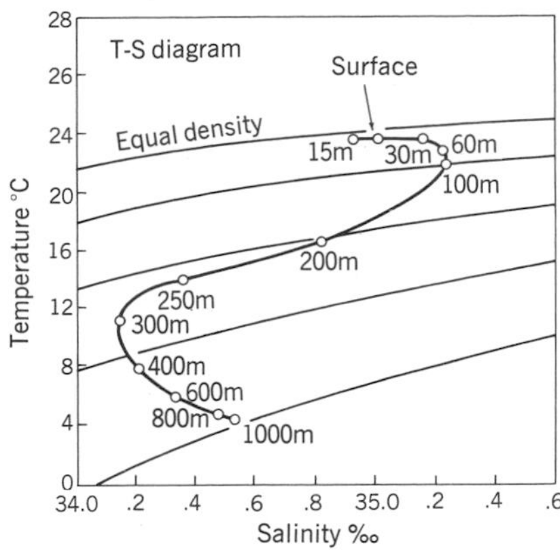


**FIGURE 16.14.** Changes in temperature and salinity with depth measured near the Hawaiian Islands (left). The same data are plotted as a temperature-salinity diagram (right). [After J. Williams, *Oceanography,* Copyright © 1962, Boston, Little, Brown, p. 104, Figure 8-2.]

Thus, in order from equator to poles, there are *equatorial, central* (in subtropical latitudes), *subarctic* and *subantarctic, arctic* and *antarctic* water masses.

Simultaneous plotting of temperature versus salinity places a water sample as a single point on the field of a graph and establishes the distinctive character of the water. Such a graph is known as a *temperature-salinity diagram,* or *T-S diagram.* The left-hand graph of Figure 16.14 shows temperature and salinity plotted separately with respect to depth. Notice that the two curves are quite independent of one another. The right-hand graph is the T-S diagram obtained from the same data. Points are plotted for depth intervals of 100 m and connected by a line in order of increasing depth. Various portions of the curve are identified as comprising a single water mass. Mixing of water of different temperature-salinity combinations takes place on a large scale so that sharp surfaces of demarcation between water masses do not, as a rule, exist in the oceans in a manner analogous to the sharp boundaries of air masses in the troposphere.

Figure 16.15 is a T-S diagram illustrating several kinds of water masses encountered in a typical sounding at a middle-latitude position in the Atlantic Ocean. The upper water layer, identified as *central water,* shows a decline in both salinity and temperature with increasing depth. Below the upper layer is a layer of *antarctic intermediate water* within which salinity reaches a minimum value, then begins to increase with depth. Below this intermediate layer is a layer of *North Atlantic deep water* in which the salinity curve reaches a maximum value, then reverses with depth. The lowest layer is one of *antarctic bottom water,* throughout which both temperature and salinity decrease with depth.

Notice that the T-S diagram in Figure 16.15 has superimposed upon it a set of approximately parallel curving lines sloping down to the left. These are lines of equal water density (neglecting the effects of pressure) and are labeled accordingly. Stability of the water layers requires that density increase progressively with depth. For the upper and intermediate layers the plotted T-S curve cuts downward across the constant-density lines, showing increase of density with depth. In the lower deep layer and bottom layer, the plotted T-S curve parallels the constant-density lines, which means that density neither increases nor decreases with depth. Should the T-S curve cross upward through the constant-density lines, density would be decreasing with depth, an unstable condition leading to overturning and mixing of water layers.

## Deep ocean circulation

Figure 16.16 is a schematic diagram showing the meridional (north-south) flow of deep water in the Atlantic Ocean. The *Atlantic central water mass* is produced at the surface in the region of the subtropical convergence, where it sinks and moves northward toward the equator. Sinking of cold water in the antarctic convergence produces the *antarctic intermediate water mass,* which moves northward as it sinks, passing beneath the central water layer, then reversing to southward flow as

**FIGURE 16.15.** Temperature-salinity diagram of data obtained by sounding in middle-latitude waters of the South Atlantic Ocean. [After H. U. Sverdrup, M. W. Johnson, and R. H. Fleming (1955), *The Oceans,* Englewood Cliffs, N.J., Prentice-Hall.]

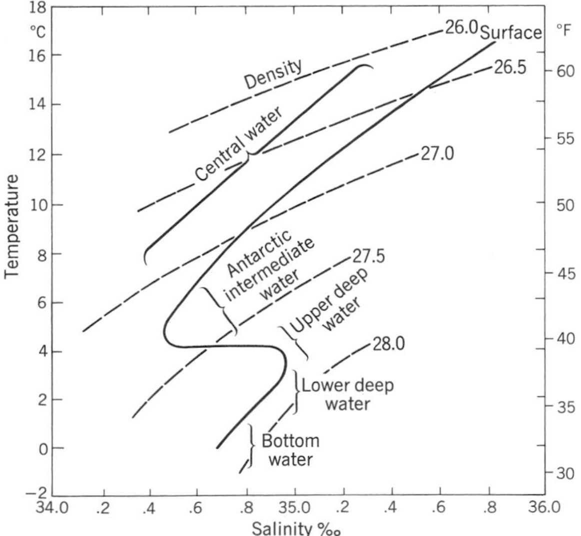

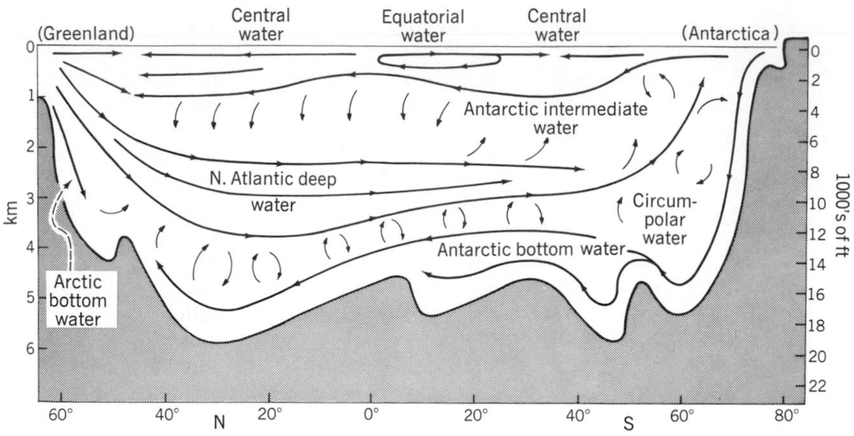


FIGURE 16.16. Meridional cross section of the Atlantic Ocean showing water masses and their movement. [After J. Williams, *Oceanography*, Copyright © 1962, Boston, Little, Brown, p. 121, Figure 9-9.]

it encounters and mixes with *North Atlantic deep water* and *North Atlantic bottom water.* The resulting mixture is a *circumpolar water mass* surrounding the Antarctic continent. Very cold water produced close to the coast of Antarctica moves down the continental slope and spreads out upon the ocean floor as *antarctic bottom water.* Because it is colder, and therefore denser, than the water mass produced in arctic regions of the North Pacific and North Atlantic Oceans, antarctic bottom water travels across the equator and far into the Northern Hemisphere, reaching to 35° to 40° N. Above this bottom layer, North Atlantic deep water flows in the opposite direction (southward) to arrive in the region of circumpolar water, at about 60° S.

Flow of deep water is extremely slow in comparison with surface currents above the thermocline and amounts to less than a few centimeters per second. Because a water mass develops its characteristics at the ocean surface, the surface provides a convenient starting point for tracing the flow path of a water particle. The elapsed travel time from this initial point is termed the *water age.* Estimates of water age for deep masses have been made by taking water samples and determining their age by the radiocarbon method (see Chapter 41). When this is done, ages of from 750 to 1000 years are obtained for Atlantic bottom water. Ages of Pacific bottom water run higher, 1500 to 2000 years. On this evidence, a complete cycle of movement of a water particle from surface to deep ocean and back to the surface might require a time span on the order of some 2000 to 4000 years. We can conclude that oceanic transport of sensible heat across the parallels of latitude from equatorial to arctic regions is carried out largely by surface currents moving at relatively high speeds in the layer above thermocline in the great oceanic gyres, since deep water moves much too slowly to contribute to the global heat balance.

## Oceanic circulation and the earth's heat balance

In Chapter 14 the following heat balance equation was developed for a unit column of soil or water:

$$R = H + LE + G + F$$

where $R$ is net all-wave radiation at the earth's surface, $H$ is transfer of sensible heat through the upper surface by conduction and turbulent exchange, $LE$ is latent heat transfer by evaporation, $G$ is the net warming or cooling of the column, and $F$ is horizontal transfer of heat out of the column by mass transport.

FIGURE 16.17. Latitudinal distribution of components of the global heat balance equation. [Data from W. D. Sellers (1965), *Physical Climatology,* Chicago, Univ. of Chicago Press, p. 115, Figure 34.]

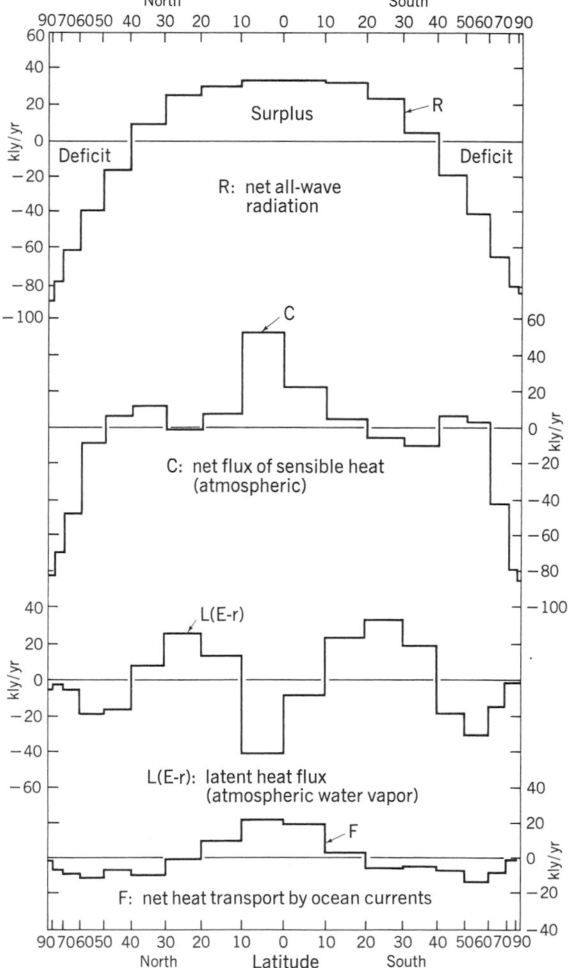

The global circulation systems of both the atmosphere and the world ocean have been described in this and the preceding chapters. Therefore it is appropriate to consider the heat balance equation as it applies to the earth-atmosphere system. The unit column now includes the entire thickness of both atmosphere and ocean.

First, the net warming or cooling will be very small for the annual cycle at a given place, which means that the term $G$ can be eliminated from the equation. Second, instead of the term $H$, which refers to upward heat flux from the earth's surface, we will substitute the term $C$, defined as the net flux of sensible heat out of the column by atmospheric motion. The term $F$ will now refer to the net transport of heat out of the column by ocean currents. Instead of the term $LE$, it will be necessary to use for latent heat flux a corresponding term $L\ (E - r)$, in which the smaller letter $r$ is the annual precipitation (rain or snow). Therefore the quantity $(E - r)$ is the difference between water evaporated and water precipitated and represents the net quantity of water that enters or leaves the atmospheric column in vapor form. A positive value of $(E - r)$ indicates that evaporation is in excess and that water vapor must be exported from the atmospheric column.

With terms thus redefined, the global heat balance equation becomes:

$$R = C + L(E - r) + F$$

Notice that the three terms on the right represent the three mechanisms of meridional heat transport by (1) sensible heat carried by moving air, (2) latent heat carried in atmospheric water vapor, and (3) sensible heat carried by moving water.

Figure 16.17 shows the average annual values of all four terms of the heat balance equation for each 10-degree belt of latitude from pole to pole. Figure 16.18 corresponds to the preceding figure, but shows annual total meridional transport of heat for each term in the heat balance equation. The units used in Figure 16.18 are kilocalories per year times $10^{19}$. Smooth curves are used in this illustration, instead of step graphs, because flow is continuous across the parallels of latitude. Where the curves lie above the zero line, flow is northward, while below the zero line flow is southward.

The explanations of each curve in the two figures have been fully explored in this chapter and preceding chapters. Notice that the net radiation graph ($R$) in Figure 16.17 is identical with that shown as the middle graph in Figure 13.19, conveying the information that there is a radiation surplus between latitudes 40° N. and 40° S. and a radiation deficit poleward of those parallels.

Consider next the distribution of the term $C$, representing sensible heat flux (Figure 16.17). A sharp peak between the equator and 10° N. latitude shows that a great surplus of atmospheric heat is generated in a narrow zone. Appropriately named the "firebox" of the earth's atmosphere, this zone obtains its heat surplus both from radiation and from the conversion of latent heat into sensible heat in cloud condensation (a process explained in Chapter 18). Negative values of sensible heat flux occur in two subtropical latitude belts. For an explanation, we look to the graph for latent heat flux, $L(E - r)$. At a glance, it is evident that this graph is opposite in phase with the graph above it. A strong negative value of latent heat flux in the zone 0° to 10° N. shows that water vapor is imported into the equatorial trough, there to be converted into sensible heat by condensation. Recall that in discussion of the Hadley cell (Chapter 15) it was stated that large amounts of

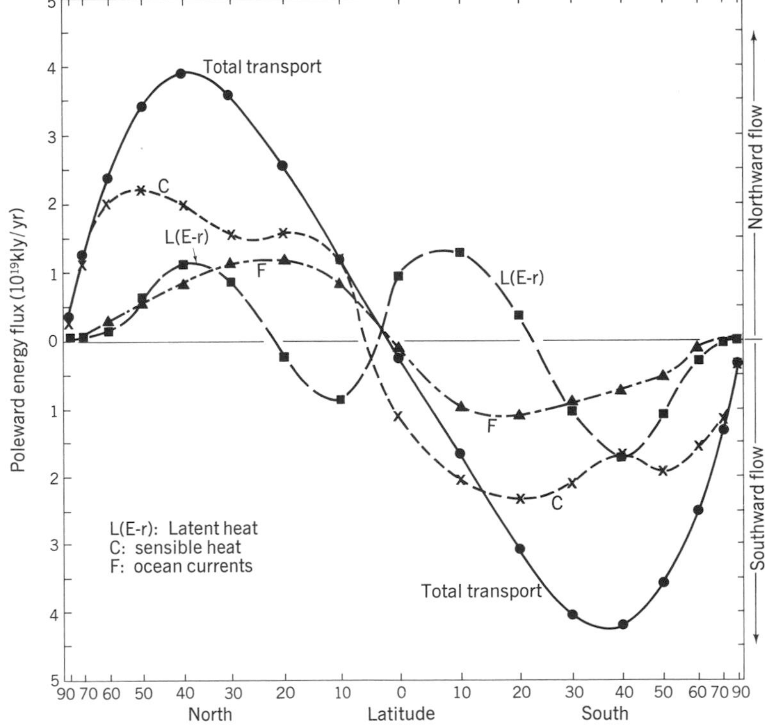


**FIGURE 16.18.** The earth's meridional heat transport. [Data from W. D. Sellers (1965), *Physical Climatology*, Chicago, Univ. of Chicago Press, p. 115, Figure 34.]

water vapor are brought equatorward in the converging trades (tropical easterlies).

Over the subtropical high pressure belts, peaking in the belt 20° to 30°, a surplus in the latent heat flux signifies that water vapor is entering the atmosphere by evaporation from the sea surface (Figure 16.17). In the graph of sensible heat flux, above, these same belts show slightly negative values, for here air in the descending limb of the Hadley cell divides and flows out of the belt both poleward and equatorward.

The middle latitude belts, 40° to 60°, gain sensible heat by poleward air movement in the westerlies, but lose latent heat by condensation in cyclonic storms, which are common in this belt. (See Chapter 19.) In the two polar zones, sensible heat is lost by transformation into radiant energy, which leaves these regions by long-wave radiation into outer space.

Finally, the meridional transfer of sensible heat from equatorial latitudes to middle latitudes by ocean currents is clearly evident in the lowermost graph of Figure 16.17 and in Figure 16.18. Transport out of the belt between 20° N. and 20° S. occurs largely in the poleward water movements on the western sides of the great oceanic gyres. As shown in Figure 16.18, peak values of poleward transport by ocean currents occur at about 20° to 25° latitude.

We have now completed an evaluation of the earth's heat balance, including estimates of the quantities of energy flux involved. Keep in mind that these estimates will be revised from time to time and should serve only as a guide to relative amounts. The heat balance is, of course, entirely an energy budget and includes no evaluation of masses in motion except with regard to their roles as transporters of sensible heat and latent heat.

There exists a second great global budget, a *mass balance,* consisting of transport systems of both air and water. The latter is referred to as the *water balance* and will be developed further in Chapter 18, following a discussion of atmospheric moisture and its changes of state. Final details of the water balance must be deferred until the flow of water upon the lands and below the ground surface are treated in Chapters 33 and 34.

## References for further study

Defant, A. (1961), *Physical Oceanography,* vol. 1, New York, Pergamon, 729 pp.

von Arx, W. S. (1962), *An Introduction to Physical Oceanography,* Reading, Mass., Addison-Wesley, 422 pp., chaps. 5, 6, 7, 8, 9.

Williams, J. (1962), *Oceanography, An Introduction to the Marine Sciences,* Boston, Little, Brown, 242 pp. chaps. 8, 9, 10, 11.

Pickard, G. L. (1963), *Descriptive Physical Oceanography,* New York, Pergamon, 200 pp., chaps. 6, 7.

Sellers, W. D. (1965), *Physical Climatology,* Chicago, Univ. of Chicago Press, 272 pp., chap. 8.

Fairbridge, R. W., ed. (1966), *Encyclopedia of Oceanography,* New York, Reinhold, 1021 pp. See: Convergence, currents by names, Dynamics of ocean currents, Equatorial currents, Heat transport by ocean currents, Ocean-atmosphere interaction, Ocean currents, Oceanic circulation, Oceanography—physical, oceans by names, Upwelling.

# 17

# Ocean waves and sea ice

INTERACTION BETWEEN ATMOSPHERE and ocean, a persistent concept throughout the preceding chapters of Part Two, is further developed by consideration of two quite dissimilar forms of interaction. First is the mechanical transfer of energy from atmosphere to ocean surface to produce waves and related motions of the sea surface. Study of these waves is a logical extension of our inquiry into prevailing planetary winds and the wind-driven ocean currents (Chapters 15 and 16). Second is the transfer of sensible heat out of the ocean into the atmosphere, leading to the formation of sea ice, a phenomenon logically extending our study of heating and cooling of the atmosphere and oceans (Chapter 14).

Ocean waves, as well as waves of large fresh-water lakes, transport enormous quantities of kinetic energy toward their shores, where further energy transformations take place and the wave forms of deep water are modified to become surges and local currents of primary importance in shaping the configuration of the coastlines, as well as in transporting sediment derived from wasting of the continents. So in examining the transformations of waves in shallow water, we take a first step in linking the fluid processes of the atmosphere and oceans with geologic processes of the solid earth.

## Progressive oscillatory waves

By far the most important class of ocean waves, in terms of their abundance and persistence over the world ocean, are those waves generated by the action of wind. Quite different in origin are the rare seismic sea waves, or tsunamis, generated by earth movements. These are discussed in Chapter 23. Different also, by reason of origin and dimensions, are the true tidal waves described in Chapter 9. In the deep water of the oceans, both seismic sea waves and tidal waves produce changes in water level of such small amounts over such long periods of time that they would pass undetected by persons on a vessel at sea.

Ocean waves produced by wind belong to a class described as *progressive waves* because the wave form moves rapidly through the water. In contrast are stationary waves, seen in rapids of swiftly moving rivers, in which the wave form remains stationary while the water flows rapidly through it.

Before proceeding further with the explanation of waves, it will be useful to review the standard scientific terminology applied to them (Figure 17.1).

Description of ocean waves uses the same terms as those applied to waves of the electromagnetic wave spectrum (see Chapter 6 and Figure 6.5). *Wave length* is the horizontal distance from crest to crest or from trough to trough, and *wave height* is the vertical distance between crest and trough. Wave length and height are commonly expressed in feet or meters. The wave form travels in the direction of the wind with a speed commonly expressed in feet or meters per second or in knots. The time elapsed between the passage of two successive wave crests with respect to some fixed reference point is termed the *wave period,* expressed in seconds. Thus a wave 200 feet long traveling at a rate of 20 feet per second has a period of 10 seconds.

Stated formally, wave length, $L$, is related to both wave period, $T$, and wave speed, $C$, as follows:

$$C = \frac{L}{T}$$

$$T = \frac{L}{C}$$

$$\text{and } L = C \cdot T$$

Progressive waves produced by wind are of a type described as *oscillatory,* because as each wave passes the water particles travel through a cycle of motion and return approximately to their original positions. Progressive oscillatory waves moving over the surfaces of deep water bodies are controlled by gravity and forces of inertia; they are also known as *Rayleigh waves.* Particle motion within such a wave is greatest at the surface and dies out rapidly at depth. Figure 17.2 shows that each water particle travels in a circular vertical orbit, making one circuit with each wave period—on the wave crest all particles are moving forward, in the direction of wave travel, while in the trough all particles are moving backward, opposite to the direction of wave travel, and halfway between crest and trough the particles move vertically, up or down.

**FIGURE 17.1.** Elements of a water wave. (© 1960, John Wiley & Sons, New York.)

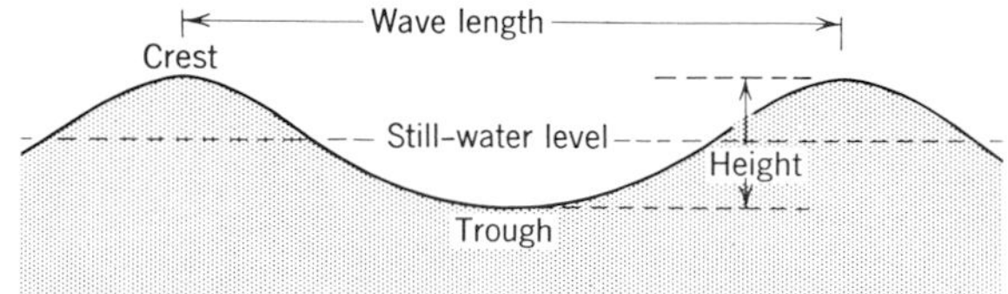


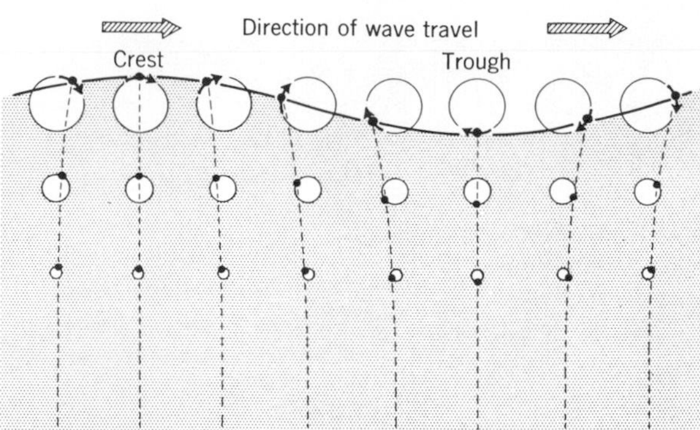


**FIGURE 17.2.** Circular orbits in simple waves of low steepness in deep water. (© 1960, John Wiley & Sons, New York.)

The upright lines in Figure 17.2 connect particles at various depths from the surface downward at a given instant. From the way in which these lines bend toward the crests and away from the troughs, we can see that the progressive oscillatory wave is a traveling series of convergences and divergences. Water, being incompressible, cannot respond by changing volume, as air might, thus the converging water is forced to rise in level to make a crest, then as it flows away from the line of divergence the water drops in level to form a trough. It is this combination of horizontal and vertical movements that produces a circular particle orbit.

The orbits die out rapidly with depth. At a depth equal to one-half of the wave length the orbit diameter is reduced to about 1/23 of its surface diameter, and at a depth equal to one wave length the orbit diameter is only 1/535 of the surface diameter. This decrease explains how submarines can travel underwater in relative calm, even though storm waves agitate the water above. Scientists wishing to measure the force of gravity over the ocean basins have used this principle to advantage by taking their delicate pendulum instruments to sea in submarines, which provide the stable platform required for their extremely precise measurements (Chapter 10).

## Wave steepness and profile form

Form and physical behavior of ocean waves depend in large part upon a descriptive property known simply as *wave steepness, $H/L$,* which is the ratio of wave height, $H$, to wave length, $L$.

Oceanographers have set up the following definitions of degrees of wave steepness:

| | *Steepness ratio, $H/L$* |
|---|---|
| Low steepness | less than 1/100 |
| Moderate steepness | more than 1/100, less than 1/25 |
| Great steepness | more than 1/25, but not over 1/7 |

Steepness does not take into account actual wave size. Thus a wave 1 ft high and 50 ft long has the same steepness as a wave 10 ft high and 500 ft long.

Water depth is a second property of major importance in determining wave behavior. The definition of *deep water* is a strict one and is given in relative terms as follows: Deep water is water of depth, *d*, greater than one-half of the wave length, *L*, or

$$d > \tfrac{1}{2} L$$

*Shallow water,* also defined in relative terms, is water of depth less than 1/25 of the wave length, or

$$d < 1/25\, L$$

Wave form and speed are determined by both wave steepness and relative water depth, and it is therefore important to state these parameters in discussing the laws that apply to the wave motion.

In their simplest form, progressive oscillatory waves of low steepness in deep water are perfectly symmetrical, hence the crests and troughs form mirror-images of each other with respect to the still-water line (Figure 17.3). The profile of such waves describes a *sine curve.* (Refer to Chapter 9 and Figure 9.8 for analysis of the sine curve.)

Speed of a wave of low steepness in deep water is governed by two variable quantities: acceleration of gravity, *g,* and wave length, *L.* The equation is as follows:

$$C = \sqrt{\frac{g}{2\pi} L} \quad \text{or} \quad C = \sqrt{\frac{g}{2\pi}} \cdot \sqrt{L}$$

Now, because *g* is very nearly a constant value at sea level over the globe, and $\pi$ has a constant value of 3.1416, the value of the first term on the right can be given as a numerical constant and the equation becomes

$C = 2.26\sqrt{L}$ for units of feet and seconds,

and $C = 1.25\sqrt{L}$ for units of meters and seconds.

Relationship of length to period can be obtained by use of the equation

$$L = C \cdot T$$

We substitute for *C* the right-hand term of the previous equation to arrive at

$$L = \sqrt{\frac{g}{2\pi} L} \cdot T$$

Square both sides to obtain

$$L = \frac{g}{2\pi} T^2$$

Thus we find that the length is proportional to the square of the wave period. Substituting the numerical values for *g* and $\pi$ the equation becomes

$L = 5.12\, T^2$ for units of feet and seconds,
and $L = 1.56\, T^2$ for units of meters and seconds.

Speed of waves of low steepness in shallow water follows a quite different equation:

$$C = \sqrt{gd} \quad \text{or} \quad C = \sqrt{g} \cdot \sqrt{d}$$

Considering the value of *g* to be a constant, the equation becomes

$C = 5.80\sqrt{d}$ in units of feet and seconds,
and $C = 3.13\sqrt{d}$ in units of meters and seconds.

On the oceans only one class of waves, known as *swell,* has sufficiently low steepness to conform closely to the equations for waves of low steepness in deep water. For most ocean waves steepness falls in the "moderate" to "great" categories and the profile form approximates more closely that of a *trochoid* shown in Figure 17.3. A trochoid is produced by rolling a disk along a line and letting a curve be traced by a point part way between the center of the disk and its circumference. The important fact about the trochoidal wave form is that the wave crests have steeper sides and the troughs are broader and more flat-bottomed than those of the sine-wave form.

For waves of moderate and great steepness in deep water, the equation for velocity given above requires some modification. For example, waves of steepness ratio 1/10 travel about 5% faster than given by the formula for waves of low steepness. For a steepness of 1/8, which is close to the breaking point, the speed is about 8% faster. A steepness ratio of 1/7 represents the limit of stability of a simple wave—any tendency to increase this ratio is met by breaking of the wave crest.

## Mass transport in wave orbits

Although the orbits of water particles in the trochoidal wave are essentially circular, the forward speed in the

**FIGURE 17.3.** The trochoidal wave form can be drawn by use of a disk rolled along a reference line. (After U.S. Navy Oceanographic Office, Misc. Publ. 11,275.)

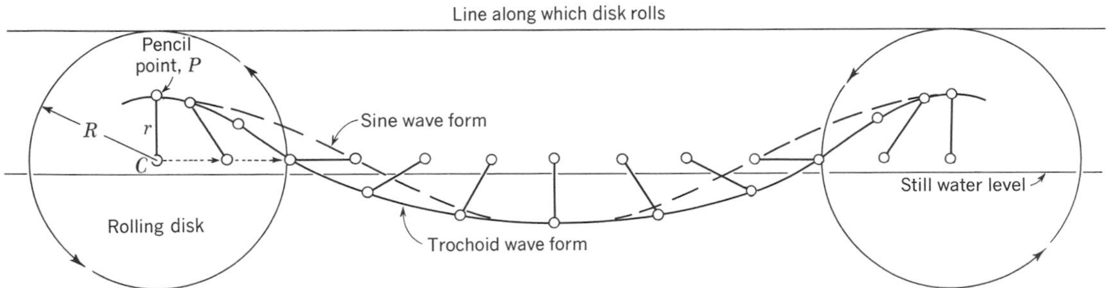

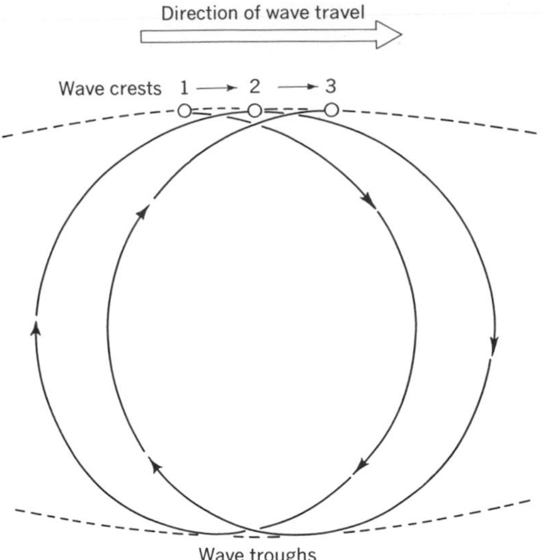


**FIGURE 17.4.** Orbit of a surface particle during passage of two successive trochoidal waves. (After U.S. Navy Oceanographic Office, Misc. Publ. 11,275.)

crest is slightly greater than the backward speed in the trough. This difference results in orbits which fail to close in a perfect circle, but instead creep forward in the direction of wave motion. In Figure 17.4 are shown two complete orbits with the water particle successively at points 1, 2, and 3. The result of such distorted orbits is to give the water a very slow motion in the direction of the wave travel. The rate and direction of water motion constitute the *mass-transport velocity,* a phenomenon quite distinct from the drift of water, discussed in Chapter 16, caused by drag of air over water. Mass transport velocity increases rapidly in speed as the waves become steeper. For example, for waves 82 ft (25 m) long 10 ft (3 m) high the mass-transport velocity is almost 2 knots (100 cm/sec), whereas for a wave 500 ft (150 m) long and 10 ft (3 m) high it would amount to only 0.1 knot (5 cm/sec). For a low swell of sine-curve form the mass transport velocity would, in theory, be zero. Mass transport velocity is important near coasts because the creep of water toward the shore tends to raise the water level and the excess water is forced to escape in the form of currents parallel to the shore.

## Interference of waves

Rarely does a single train (a succession of waves in the same direction) of perfectly uniform waves exist on a water body, although waves sent out into a calm lake from the bow of a moving ship might appear to be almost perfect. Suppose, however, that there exist two wave trains traveling in the same direction, but of two different wave lengths, as shown in Figure 17.5. The result is *interference,* or a combination of the two wave trains to form a distorted series of crests and troughs. Where two crests happen to coincide, the wave is reinforced and its height is the sum of the two crests. Where a crest in one train is superimposed upon the trough of the other train, the wave is canceled out. The result is a combined wave train in which the waves first increase in height then almost die out.

Still another kind of interference is produced by two wave trains traveling in somewhat different directions, as shown in Figure 17.6. Again, where the crests cross each other, the wave height is doubled, whereas in the zone where crests are separated so that the crest of one train coincides with the trough of the other, the waves tend to be canceled out. For this case, however, the result is an assemblage of short-crested waves. We can imagine the two wave groups traveling at right angles to each other, in which case the waves would take the form of sharp peaks with intervening basinlike hollows.

Wave forms on any storm-tossed sea are extremely irregular and complex because there are many wave trains of differing lengths and directions interfering with one another (Figure 17.7). At a point where the waves reinforce one another a wave becomes so steep that the crest overturns, sliding off as a *breaking wave* or *whitecap.* It is generally considered that when the side slopes of a wave crest become steeper than 30° from the horizontal, the wave will break.

## Waves and wind

Oceanographers distinguish between *wind waves,* which are formed or sustained by winds, and *swell,* which consists of waves moving through a region of weaker winds or calms and therefore decreasing in height and steepness. Wind waves grow under the influence of wind through two kinds of mechanism. First, the wind exerts

**FIGURE 17.5.** Combination of two wave trains of different wavelengths. (After U.S. Navy Oceanographic Office, Misc. Publ. 11,275.)

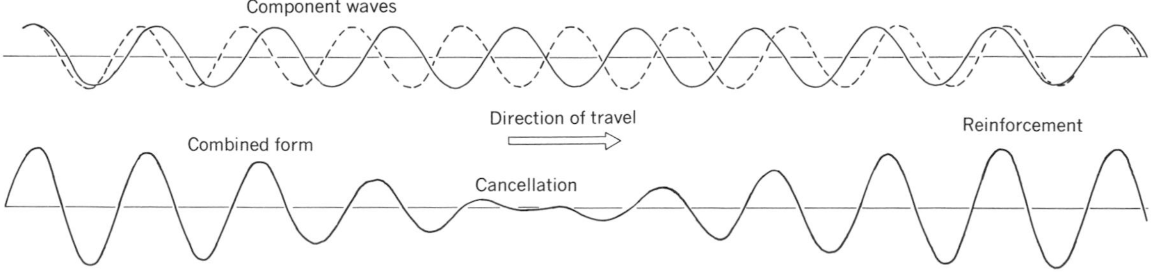

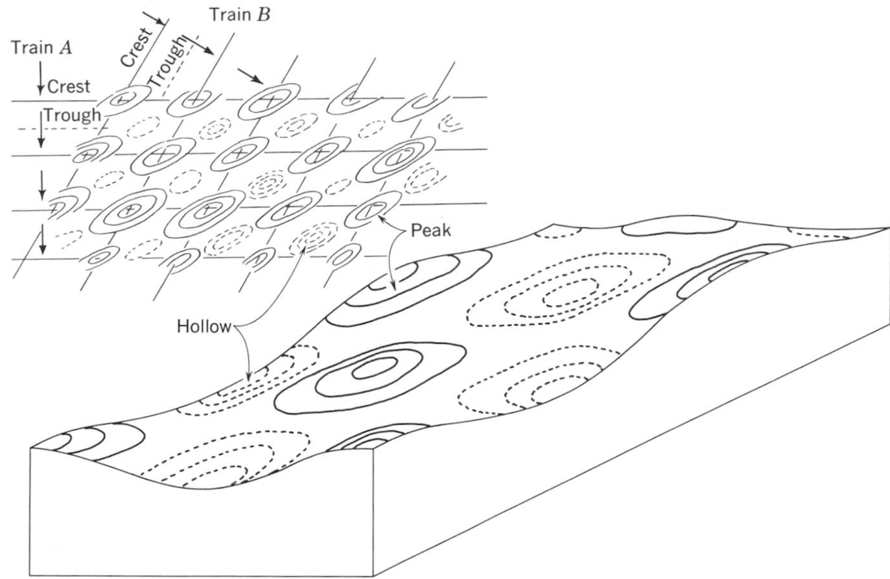


**FIGURE 17.6.** Short-crested waves, taking the form of peaks and hollows, result from intersection of two wave trains. (After U.S. Navy Oceanographic Office, Misc. Publ. 11,275.)

a direct pressure upon the exposed windward sides of the wave crests. This force, which may simply be called *push,* is essentially the same as that which propels a ship by filling the sails (Figure 17.8).

But this explanation is not enough, because in many cases the waves are traveling faster than the wind which generates them. Under such conditions the forward sides of the wave crests would push against the air, and this would tend to slow the wave, just as air resistance acts to slow down a glider or rocket. The second source of wave energy is through *drag,* the friction of the moving air against the water surface. As shown in Figure 17.8, drag tends to pull the surface-water layer in the direction of the wind. On the crests this drag augments the orbital movement of the water, tending to add energy to the circular motion and thereby produce a higher wave. In the troughs drag opposes the orbital motion, but here the surface is better sheltered from the wind. The net result for the entire surface will be a gain in strength by the waves.

In general, the maximum height of waves that will be produced by the wind depends upon three factors: (1) wind speed, (2) wind duration, and (3) *fetch,* the distance of open deep water over which the wind can blow unimpeded. Table 17.1 gives wave height data in relation to the three factors. Because successive waves differ greatly in size, wave height is given in three forms: (a) average of all waves, (b) average of the highest one-third of all waves (*significant height*), and (c) average of the highest one-tenth of all waves. Occasional waves will be of still greater heights, with the probability that about one wave in one thousand will exceed twice the significant height.

The second column of Table 17.1 gives the minimum wind duration required to produce waves of the heights given in the body of the table. Waves are slow in building up to their maximum heights, and the time requirement becomes greater for winds of increasing speed. As the table shows, 10 hours are required for full development of waves under a 20-knot wind, but more than four times this duration is required for development under wind twice that strong.

The third column of Table 17.1 gives the minimum length of fetch required for full development of waves under stress of a given wind speed. A small lake or bay cannot produce large waves, no matter how strong the wind or how long it blows. For distances exceeding 1000 mi (1600 km) the fetch ceases to be a factor except for the strongest winds. Within severe cyclonic storms the path of action of very strong winds is limited to a fetch

**TABLE 17.1. WAVE HEIGHTS AS RELATED TO WIND SPEED, DURATION, AND FETCH***

| Sustained Wind Speed | | Duration, | Fetch Length | | Average Height | | Significant Height | | Average of Highest 10% | | Wave |
|---|---|---|---|---|---|---|---|---|---|---|---|
| knots | km/hr | hours | nautical miles | km | ft | m | ft | m | ft | m | period, seconds |
| 10 | 18 | 2.4 | 10 | 18 | 0.9 | 0.3 | 1.4 | 0.4 | 1.8 | 0.5 | 4 |
| 15 | 28 | 6 | 34 | 63 | 2.5 | 0.8 | 3.5 | 1.1 | 5 | 1.5 | 6 |
| 20 | 37 | 10 | 75 | 140 | 5 | 1.5 | 8 | 5.5 | 10 | 3.0 | 8 |
| 25 | 46 | 16 | 160 | 300 | 9 | 2.7 | 14 | 4.3 | 18 | 5.5 | 10 |
| 30 | 55 | 23 | 280 | 520 | 14 | 4.3 | 22 | 6.7 | 28 | 8.5 | 12 |
| 40 | 74 | 42 | 710 | 1300 | 28 | 8.5 | 44 | 13 | 57 | 17 | 16 |
| 50 | 92 | 69 | 1420 | 2600 | 48 | 15 | 78 | 24 | 99 | 30 | 20 |

* Data from W. Bascom (1964), *Waves and Beaches,* Garden City, N.Y., Doubleday, Table 3, p. 53.

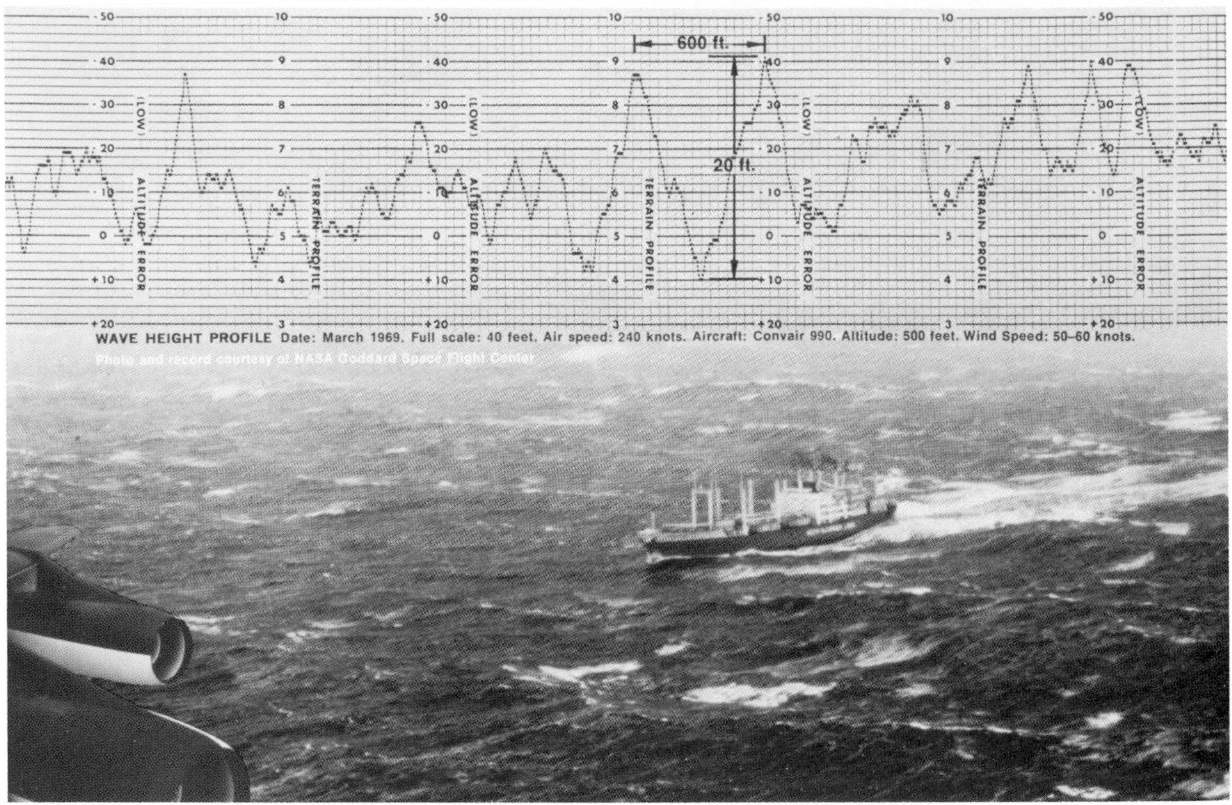


**FIGURE 17.7.** This profile of large, complex storm waves in the North Sea was made by a precision airborne laser altimeter (Spectra-Physics, Inc. *Geodolite* 3A). Waves ranging in height from 0.5 to 46 ft (0.15 to 14 m) were profiled with 4-in. (10-cm) resolution. (Photo and record courtesy of NASA Goddard Space Flight Center.)

that does not often exceed 300 or 400 mi (500 or 650 km).

The last column of Table 17.1 gives the wave period associated with the greatest concentration of kinetic energy in the spectrum of waves associated with a given wind speed.

Estimates of heights of great storm waves are difficult to make from a moving vessel, but a record height may have been obtained from a tanker, the *U.S.S. Ramapo,* during a Pacific typhoon in 1933. With winds clocked up to 68 knots a single wave-height measurement of 112 ft (34 m) was obtained by reasonably reliable sighting methods. Heights of from 60 to 75 ft (18 to 23 m) are considered as not unusual in severe storms developed under hurricane-force winds. Normally, where such great waves are formed in regular succession and have long wave lengths (600 to 800 ft, 180 to 240 m) a ship can ride easily despite the great wave height. However, when high waves are of great steepness, so that the crests break away, huge masses of water are hurled at the ship with destructive force.

**FIGURE 17.8.** Development of wind waves by pressure and surface drag.

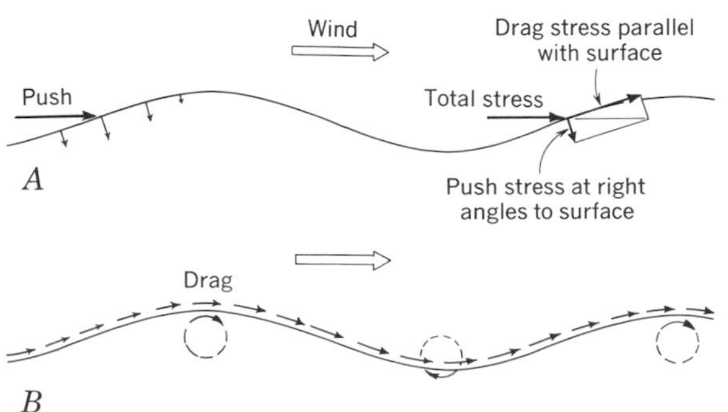


## The Beaufort scale

Strength of wind and height of waves have been the constant concern of seafaring men since time immemorial. The need for having some standard of measuring and expressing these quantities became strongly felt as large navies of sailing vessels were organized to operate under uniform regulations and control. In 1806 Admiral Sir Francis Beaufort of the British Navy devised a standard series of numbers, ranging from 0 to 12, to express wind force and its effect upon the surface of the sea. Table 17.2 gives the Beaufort scale and the corresponding wind speeds, average wave heights, and a system of sea-disturbance numbers which may be

**TABLE 17.2. THE BEAUFORT SCALE OF WIND (NAUTICAL)**

| Beaufort No. | Name of Wind | Wind Speed knots | Wind Speed km/hr | Description of Sea Surface | Sea Disturbance Number | Average Wave Height ft | Average Wave Height m |
|---|---|---|---|---|---|---|---|
| 0 | Calm | <1 | <1 | Sea like a mirror. | 0 | 0 | 0 |
| 1 | Light air | 1–3 | 1–5 | Ripples with appearance of scales are formed, without foam crests. | 0 | 0 | 0 |
| 2 | Light breeze | 4–6 | 6–11 | Small wavelets still short but more pronounced; crests have a glassy appearance but do not break. | 1 | 0–1 | 0–0.3 |
| 3 | Gentle breeze | 7–10 | 12–19 | Large wavelets; crests begin to break; foam of glassy appearance. Perhaps scattered white horses. | 2 | 1–2 | 0.3–0.6 |
| 4 | Moderate breeze | 11–16 | 20–28 | Small waves becoming longer; fairly frequent white horses. | 3 | 2–4 | 0.6–1.2 |
| 5 | Fresh breeze | 17–21 | 29–38 | Moderate waves taking a more pronounced long form; many white horses are formed; chance of some spray. | 4 | 4–8 | 1.2–2.4 |
| 6 | Strong breeze | 22–27 | 39–49 | Large waves begin to form; the white foam crests are more extensive everywhere. Probably some spray. | 5 | 8–13 | 2.4–4 |
| 7 | Moderate gale | 28–33 | 50–61 | Sea heaps up and white foam from breaking waves begins to be blown in streaks along the direction of the wind. Spindrift begins to be seen. | 6 | 13–20 | 4–6 |
| 8 | Fresh gale | 34–40 | 62–74 | Moderately high waves of greater length; edges of crests break into spindrift. The foam is blown in well-marked streaks along the direction of the wind. | 6 | 13–20 | 4–6 |
| 9 | Strong gale | 41–47 | 75–88 | High waves. Dense streaks of foam along the direction of the wind. Sea begins to roll. Spray affects visibility. | 6 | 13–20 | 4–6 |
| 10 | Whole gale | 48–55 | 89–102 | Very high waves with long overhanging crests. The resulting foam in great patches is blown in dense white streaks along the direction of the wind. On the whole the surface of the sea takes on a white appearance. The rolling of the sea becomes heavy. Visibility is affected. | 7 | 20–30 | 6–9 |
| 11 | Storm | 56–65 | 103–117 | Exceptionally high waves. Small- and medium-sized ships might be for a long time lost to view behind the waves. The sea is covered with long white patches of foam. Everywhere the edges of the wave crests are blown into foam. Visibility is affected. | 8 | 30–45 | 9–14 |
| 12–17 | Hurricane | above 65 | above 117 | The air is filled with foam and spray. Sea is completely filled with driving spray. Visibility very seriously affected. | 9 | over 45 | over 14 |

Source: After R. C. H. Russell and D. H. Macmillan (1954), *Waves and Tides*, London, Hutchinson's Sci. and Tech. Publ., p. 54, Table 7; and N. Bowditch (1958), U.S. Navy Oceanographic Office Publ. No. 9.

used as a code to convey information on wave height.

Although designated for marine use, the Beaufort scale was adopted about a century later for expressing wind velocities over land. It has, however, been replaced for land observations by the system of knots described in Chapter 15.

## Young and old waves

Waves which are in the process of rapid growth under the force of wind are characterized by having a high steepness ratio. Large waves of great steepness are commonly experienced in intense storms of a few hours duration. As the wind continues to blow over the sea surface, however, changes take place. The height gradually reaches its maximum value, but the length increases and with it the wave period. Thus the wave normally becomes less steep with the passage of time.

Still another change occurs. The wave speed becomes greater as the duration of wind increases. Speed increase is proportional to square root of length increase, as stated in the equation governing speed of deep-water waves. There comes a point in time when the waves are not merely traveling at the same speed as the wind, but even faster. Figure 17.9 shows how these changes are related. The life cycle of an average wave begins at the left. As it grows rapidly to maximum height its steepness increases to a maximum, but its speed of travel may be only half that of the wind. Later the steepness decreases and becomes moderate at about the point at which the waves and wind have the same speed. Finally the steepness reaches a constant value as the waves travel from perhaps 1½ to 2 times the speed of the wind.

We might expect to find young steep waves produced by rapidly moving middle-latitude or tropical storms, whereas the old waves would be found in the trade-wind belts where persistent winds blow from a constant direction for many days at a time.

## Swell

Waves that have passed beyond the region of the winds which formed them and that are therefore dying out as they travel are designated as *swell.* Height of the swell decreases in such a way that about one-third of the height (in feet) is lost each time the wave has traveled a distance in nautical miles numerically equal to its length in feet. Lessening height means reduced energy in each foot of wave length and is explained in part by the lateral spreading (stretching) of the wave crest as it assumes a progressively greater length of arc of a circle.

Besides losing height, the waves of a swell seemingly increase both in length and in period. This phenomenon can be explained by the fact that the wind-generated waves include a broad spectrum of wave lengths and periods. The longer waves travel faster than those of shorter length. Consequently, the first waves to arrive at a distant point are those of greatest length and longest period. The sorting out of waves by length and period is referred to as *dispersion.* Many swells that have originated from regions 3000–4000 mi (4800–6400 km) distant have periods as long as 15–20 seconds, compared with storm waves, whose average period might range from 6 to 10 seconds. Figure 17.10 shows how the height and period of a swell changes at increasing distance from the storm area.

Because a swell in deep water consists of waves of low steepness of approximate sine-wave form, the equations for wave speed, length, and period can be applied with good results. Table 17.3 gives data based on solution of the equations $C = 2.26\sqrt{L}$ and $L = 5.12\,T^2$.

**TABLE 17.3. SWELL IN DEEP WATER**

| Period seconds | Wave length ft | Wave length m | Wave speed mph | Wave speed km/hr |
|---|---|---|---|---|
| 6 | 184 | 56 | 21 | 38 |
| 8 | 326 | 99 | 28 | 45 |
| 10 | 512 | 156 | 35 | 56 |
| 12 | 738 | 225 | 42 | 68 |
| 14 | 1000 | 305 | 49 | 79 |
| 16 | 1310 | 400 | 56 | 90 |
| 18 | 1660 | 506 | 63 | 102 |
| 20 | 2050 | 625 | 70 | 112 |

**FIGURE 17.9.** Relation between wave steepness and wave age. [After H. U. Sverdrup and W. H. Munk (1947), U.S. Navy Oceanographic Office, Publ. No. 601.]

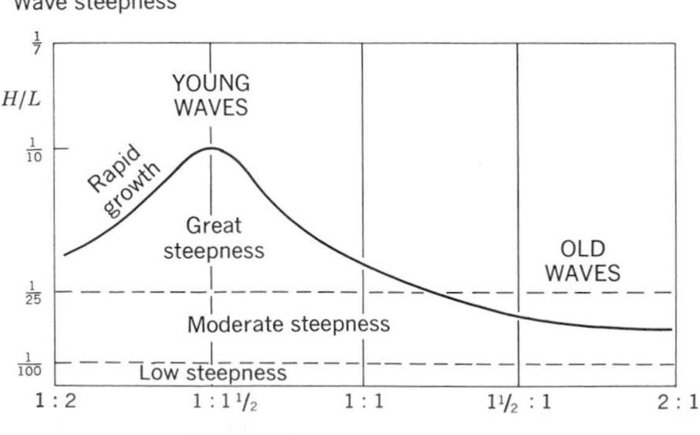


**FIGURE 17.10.** Height of swell diminishes while period increases with increasing distance of travel from a storm area. [After H. U. Sverdrup and W. H. Munk (1947), U.S. Navy Oceanographic Office, Publ. No. 601.]

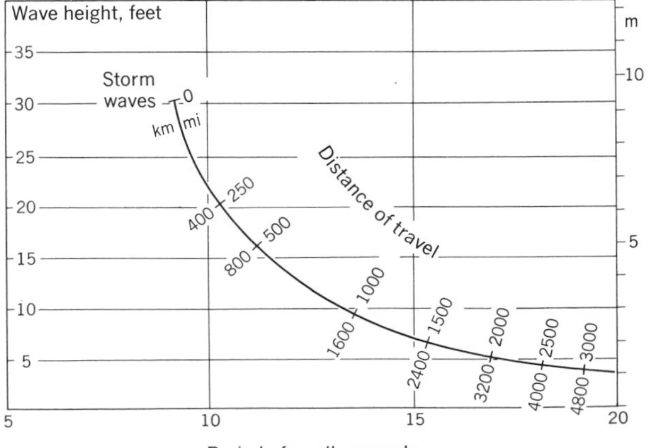

## Wave groups

As a swell travels into calm regions from the generating area of a storm it consists of a *wave train,* which can be visualized as a moving *wave group.* The ideal model of such a wave group can be studied in a wave trough (wave tank) in which wave action can be started and stopped instantly. A closely similar model of the wave group is seen when a ship moves through a calm sea, generating a train of bow waves moving away on either side.

If the leading wave of the group is closely observed, it will be seen to diminish in height and disappear, its place being taken by the wave behind it. This diminution in height results from the expenditure of energy required to set the still water in orbital motion. Correspondingly, if the rear of the wave train is observed, new waves will be seen to form in succession to assume a trailing position. Consequently, the number of waves in the train remains the same, but the train as a whole moves more slowly than individual waves within the train.

The term *group speed* (*group velocity*) is applied to the rate of motion of the wave train as a whole, in distinction from the wave speed, which refers to rate of motion of a single wave. According to the theory of gravity waves in deep water, group speed is one-half that of wave speed. This fact must be taken into account in forecasting the time of arrival of a swell at a distant shore, a matter of possibly great concern in scheduling the landing of amphibious military forces upon a beach.

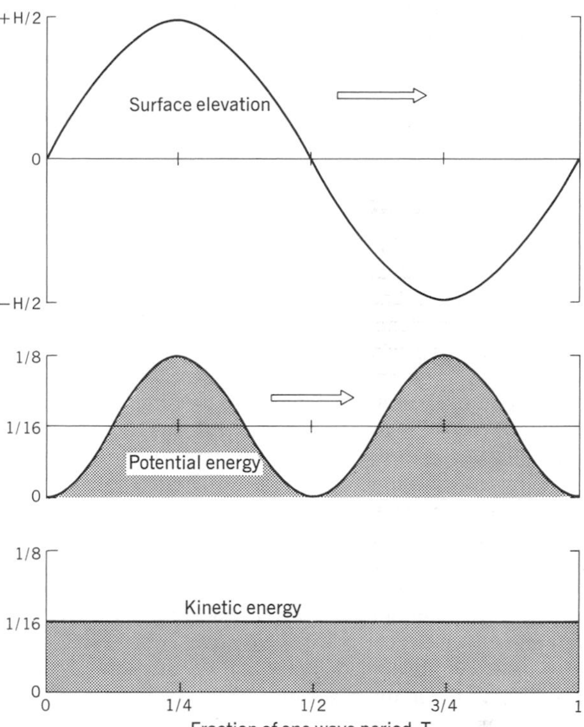


**FIGURE 17.11.** Energy in one wave length. [After H. U. Sverdrup and W. H. Munk (1947), U.S. Navy Oceanographic Publ. No. 601.]

## Wave energy

Looking further into the question of energy within waves, it is important to know how energy is transported in the direction of wave travel. For an ideal wave of low steepness within a prism one wave length long and of a unit width, one-half of the energy is potential and one-half is kinetic. The potential energy exists because, on the average, part of the water surface lies above still-water level and part lies below. Changes in potential energy with wave passage are illustrated in Figure 17.11. The upper curve shows the rise and fall of surface elevation in one wave period, *T.* The middle curve shows the rise and fall of potential energy during one wave period. As one wave moves past a fixed point, the potential energy attains maximum value as the crest passes and again as the trough passes. Potential energy also falls to zero twice in the passage of one wave length.

The remaining half of the energy within one wave length is in the form of kinetic energy present because of the orbital motion shown in Figure 17.2. Assuming the orbits to be perfectly circular, speed of every water particle in its orbit is constant, hence kinetic energy is uniform. The constant level of kinetic energy is shown by the horizontal line in the lower graph of Figure 17.11.

The total energy within a unit width of the ideal sine wave is given by the following equation:

$$E = \tfrac{1}{8}\, w \cdot H^2 \cdot L$$

where $E$ is total energy in foot-pounds in a belt one foot wide and one wave length long,
$w$ is unit weight of water, about 64 lb/cu ft,
$H$ is wave height in feet,
and $L$ *is* wave length in feet.

In metric units, energy would be given in joules, unit weight of water in kg/m$^3$ (about 1000 kg/m$^3$ for pure water), and height and length in meters.

Using the above formula, the energy within a single wave length can be roughly computed. For example, a storm wave 500 ft (150 m) long and 10 ft (3 m) high has a total energy of 400,000 ft-lbs per foot width (about $10^6$ joules per meter width).

For steeper waves of trochoidal form the formula requires modification but is approximately the same, in that the energy is proportional to the square of wave height. The influence of length is somewhat reduced.

Because half of the wave energy moves forward at the speed of the wave, one can reason that the rate at which the total quantity of energy present in the wave moves forward is half the speed of the wave. In other words, the speed of energy transport is equal to the group speed.

We have thus far examined an energy system in which kinetic energy of atmospheric motion is transferred to the sea surface and flows forward in the direction of wave motion. Notice that this form of energy flux involves no net mass transport and is different from both the mass transport velocity of water due to creep of noncircular wave orbits and the motion of the surface layer (Ekman principle) due to surface drag of winds. Whereas the latter two forms of mass movement are extremely sluggish, the flow of energy at the group speed of waves is extremely fast. One has only to take one-half of the wave speed shown in Table 17.3 to calculate the speed of energy flow in a swell of long period—e.g., 20 to 35 mi (35 to 55 km) per hour. As already stated, the speed of old waves can reach almost double the wind speed, in which case group speed approaches equality with wind speed.

The next step in analyzing the wave energy flux is to consider what changes take place as a wave enters shallow water and eventually expends its energy upon the shore.

## Waves in shallow water

Inevitably a wave train arrives at the coast of a continent or island, where shallow water is encountered and the presence of the bottom begins to interfere with the progress of the wave. New principles come into play in the shallow-water zone.

Consider first a simple series of waves entering a zone of gently shoaling water. The wave is said to *feel bottom* when the water depth relative to the wave length is such that the orbital motions of water particles are appreciably interfered with by the solid bottom. As a rule of thumb, it is assumed that when water depth is one-half the wave length, the effect of the bottom produces appreciable changes in the wave form and speed (Figure 17.12).

Wave orbits in shallow water are modified into ellipses (Figure 17.13) which become progressively flatter as the bottom is approached. Immediately adjacent to the bottom, water particles move in flat paths paralleling the bottom, alternately shifting landward (under the passing crest) and seaward (under the passing trough). Such motion is a frictional drag, or shear, against the bottom and causes loss of wave energy. Wave speed is decreased, and certain changes in wave height and length occur as the wave travels shoreward into even shallower water.

Although wave speed diminishes shoreward, the wave period must remain constant—that is, the same number of waves must pass a fixed point each minute. The obvious result is that the wave crests become more and more closely spaced, which is to say that the wave length diminishes (Figure 17.12). This effect is quite nicely illustrated by the flow of automobile traffic as a toll gate is approached. As the cars slow down they become more closely spaced, until at the toll gates they are creeping along bumper to bumper.

Wave height also undergoes a change as the wave moves into shoaling water. The first effect is to decrease slightly the wave height, but when the water has shoaled to a depth about one-twentieth of the deep-water wave length, the wave height begins to increase rather sharply, continuing to do so to the point of wave breaking. A height increase of more than 50 percent may ultimately result. Perhaps this is why, when a low swell is approaching the shore and the sea is otherwise calm, the swell seems to rise mysteriously from the water only a few yards from the beach. Actually the swell came from deep water, but was so low there as to be scarcely noticeable.

## Wave refraction

If waves were approaching a perfectly straight shoreline with crests parallel with the shore and if the bottom were uniformly sloping seaward at all points, the sea surface as viewed from directly above would show parallel wave crests, which become more closely spaced as they approach the shoreline. Such conditions are most unlikely in nature, however, because wave crests usually approach the shore at an angle, or the shore is irregularly curved or has unequal bottom slopes and depths from place to place. In nature, then, the water depth under a single wave crest is different from point to point, and the reduction of wave speed does not take place evenly. As a result the wave becomes curved, or *refracted,* in plan view (Figures 17.14 and 17.15).

The case of a straight shoreline with uniformly sloping bottom is shown in Figure 17.14. That part of the wave which has arrived first has been slowed most, hence the wave crest is bent into a curve that is convex toward the shore. Although the waves tend to be turned to approach the shoreline directly, the degree of turn-

**FIGURE 17.12.** A shoaling wave undergoes changes in form and finally breaks. (© 1960, John Wiley & Sons, New York. Data from U.S. Navy Oceanographic Office, Publ. No. 234.)

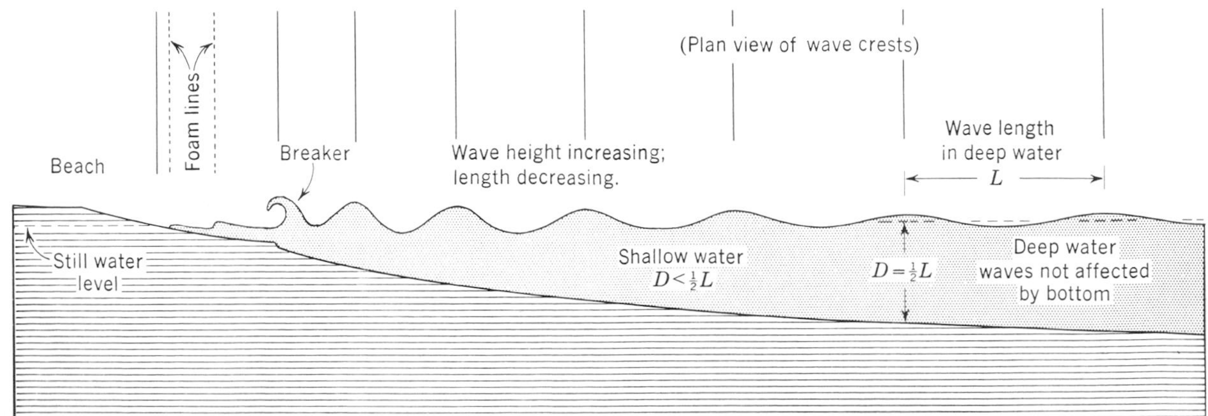

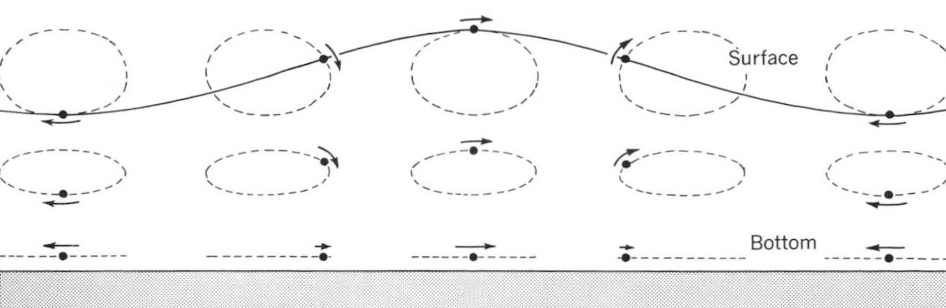


**FIGURE 17.13.** Elliptical wave orbits in shallow water. [After H. A. Panofsky (1960), *Oceanography for the Navy Meteorologist,* NWRF 32-0360-030, Norfolk, Va., U.S. Naval Weather Research Facility.)

ing is not normally sufficient to achieve this limit and the waves break obliquely on the beach.

The case of an irregular shoreline, illustrated in Figure 17.15, is that of refraction about a promontory, or *headland,* flanked by bays on either side. Notice that the wave crests are bent concavely toward the projecting headland, but convexly toward the axis of the bay. From the close spacing of the wave crests opposite the headland it is evident that shallow water is encountered there and that the wave speed is reduced, whereas the waves are able to travel into the deeper water of the bays with little delay. In a general way the wave crests are being bent into rough conformity with the features of the shoreline.

Because of refraction the distribution of energy contained in the waves is strikingly changed as the shore is approached. This phenomenon is illustrated in Figure 17.15. Assume, first, that the waves in question are large uniform swells with even crests parallel to one another in deep water, as at the bottom of Figure 17.15. We can now divide the wave into equal units, shown by the points *a, b, c, d,* etc. Each segment of the wave will now contain the same amount of energy, about half of which is traveling landward with the wave form.

From each of the lettered points an orthogonal line (dashed) is drawn landward in such a way that the line always crosses the wave crests at right angles. Between any two orthogonals lies the zone of landward travel of the original quantity of wave energy. Where the orthogonals converge, as they do in front of the headland, wave energy is crowded into a narrower zone and concentrated, much as a convex lens gathers the sun's rays to a focal point. Here the waves increase greatly in height and produce large breakers upon the shore.

**FIGURE 17.14.** Wave refraction along a straight shoreline. (© 1960, John Wiley & Sons, New York.)

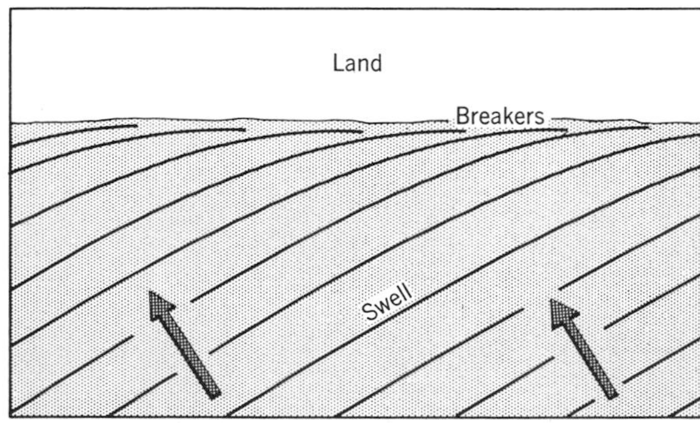


In contrast, where orthogonals diverge, as they do in the bays, the original unit of wave energy is spread more thinly along a greater length of wave crest, causing the wave to be weakened, or attenuated, and to lose height, despite the normal tendency of shoaling waves to increase in height. As a result, waves break with little force along the head of the bay. If the bay is a sufficiently long body of water it may have little or no surf on its beaches. This sheltering effect of a bay is simulated or increased by the construction of breakwaters in a harbor.

As we shall see in Chapter 38, dealing with landforms made by wave action upon the shores, refraction explains a great deal about the changes that take place in a coast line through erosion and deposition.

One interesting application of the principles of wave refraction has been to calculate the water depths and bottom configuration from the refraction patterns of waves shown on air photos. Such knowledge may be of crucial importance in military operations, where the ability to reach the beach with landing craft must be assured in advance, but where no direct survey can be made.

## Solitary waves

When a heavy block, such as a brick, is dropped into one end of a long narrow water trough, a single wave is

**FIGURE 17.15.** Wave refraction along an embayed coast. (© 1960, John Wiley & Sons, New York.)

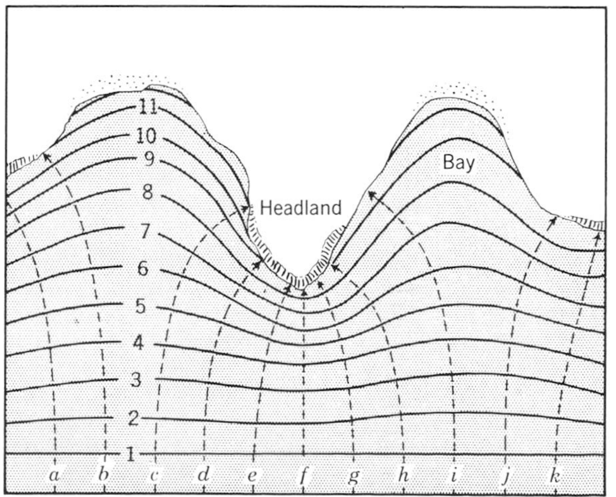

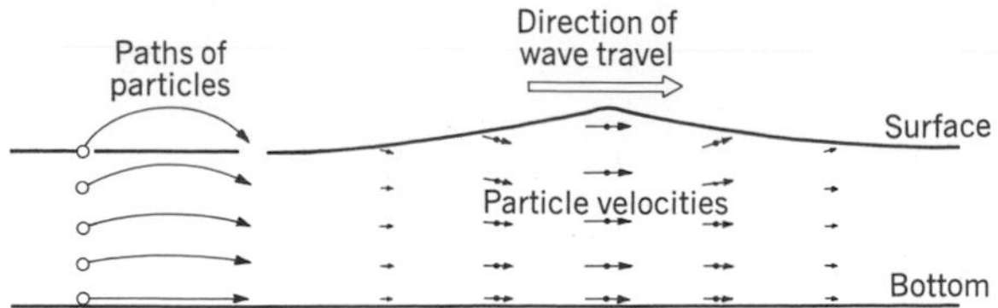


**FIGURE 17.16** Particle motions and velocities in a solitary wave. [After R. C. Russell and D. H. Macmillan (1954), *Waves and Tides*, London, Hutchinson's Sci. and Tech. Publ., p. 44, Figure II, 2.]

generated and travels down the length of the trough. In its ideal form, such a wave is known as a *solitary wave,* or *wave of translation*, and is unique in that the water particles move forward in a single short leap, but not back again. Therefore in the solitary wave the total wave energy moves forward at the speed of the wave. Figure 17.16 shows, at the left, the paths followed by particles during the passage of one solitary wave, and at the right the flow directions in various parts of the wave. Notice that particles at the bottom move the same distance as those at the surface.

The formula which describes the speed of a solitary wave is essentially that of the gravity wave of sine form in shallow water, namely,

$$C = \sqrt{gd}$$

where $g$ is acceleration of gravity and $d$ is water depth.

Like tidal waves in an estuary, which follow the same law of speed, solitary waves tend to develop a steepened front as they travel, because the crest of the wave travels faster than the base of the wave.

Where, in nature, are solitary waves generated? One example might be the falling of a huge mass of rock into a long narrow lake or fiord. This type of landslide has on occasion generated a destructive wave capable of breaking a dam or wiping out a town situated at the opposite end of the water body.

However, we are primarily concerned here with the changes which take place in ocean waves as they enter shallow water. Observation has shown that the typical wave, as it gains height in increasingly shallow water, tends to be transformed into a solitary wave. Although this transformation is not complete, a forward thrust of water becomes the dominant motion. At the bottom, this forward thrust exerts a powerful landward drag capable of moving sediment in the landward direction.

The degree to which solitary wave motion is developed in shallow water depends upon wave steepness in deep water, as well as upon the bottom slope. Generally speaking, waves of low steepness (including a long swell) passing over a gently sloping bottom are most likely to be transformed into the solitary wave, whereas the change is not evident in waves of great steepness on a steeply-sloping bottom.

## Breakers

As the steepening wave continues to travel shoreward, encountering still shallower water, the crest height in-

**FIGURE 17.17.** Development of a plunging breaker. (After W. M. Davis. © 1960, John Wiley & Sons, New York.)

creases sharply and the forward slope of the wave becomes greatly steepened. At a critical point the wave crest seems to leap forward and the wave form disintegrates into a mass of turbulent water, the *breaker* (Figure 17.17).

Despite many attempts to explain wave breaking, the mechanism is not well understood. One point to consider is that the kinetic energy of a shoaling wave becomes concentrated into a smaller and smaller depth of water, so that the radius of the wave orbit must increase greatly. Collapse seems to occur when there is insufficient water to fill the enlarged orbit. A cavity develops on the forward side, and the crest, lacking support, quickly collapses. Furthermore, as the wave orbit enlarges, there comes a point in time when the increasing forward velocity of water at the top of the orbit exceeds the forward velocity of the wave form as a whole, which may account for the apparent sudden shoreward leap of water at the breaker crest.

Two basic varieties of breakers can be recognized. One is the *spilling breaker,* in which the steepened crest collapses rather gradually, the water spilling down continuously over the advancing wave front (Figure 17.18). Spilling breakers may retain their form throughout a relatively long distance of wave travel and are the best type for surfboarding.

The *plunging breaker* is characterized by the sudden rise of a smoothly curved arch of water which encloses a cylindrical air space at the instant preceding collapse (Figures 17.17 and 17.19). Collapse is often accompanied by a booming sound and is immediately followed by complete disintegration of the wave into a mass of turbulent foaming water which surges forward into shallower water or rides swiftly up the sloping beach.

Although it is not feasible to assign simple causes to spilling and plunging types of breakers, it may be noted that waves that are already steep in deep water tend to produce the spilling type of breaker, because such waves approach the shallow water in a condition already close to breaking. Breaking begins rather far from shore and continues as the wave travels landward, the continued spilling keeping the breaker height suffi-

**FIGURE 17.18.** Spilling and plunging breakers.

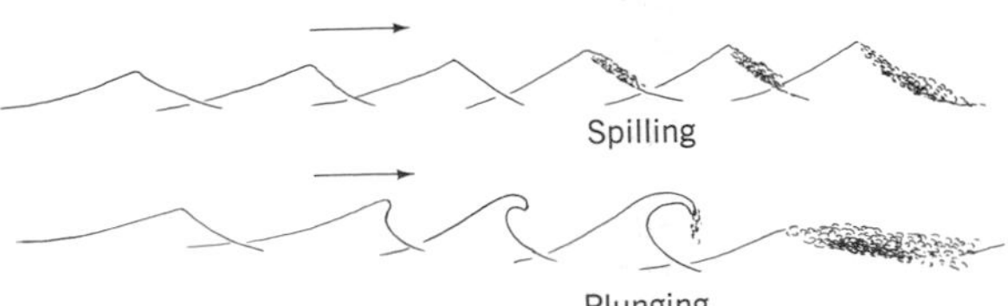

**FIGURE 17.19.** A plunging breaker from a low swell along the Atlantic coast of New Jersey. (Photograph by Douglas Johnson.)

ciently reduced to preserve the wave form. Plunging breakers are well illustrated by the breaking of swells of low steepness, which do not reach the critical steepness until they are in relatively shallow water. Steepness of the bottom slope and direction of the wind, whether onshore or offshore, may also influence the manner of breaking.

Breakers may occur at a single line or may form two or three or more parallel breaker zones, depending upon wave characteristics and bottom configuration. A submerged low ridge of sand or pebbles, the *offshore bar,* commonly lies a few tens of yards from shore. This obstacle may cause the breakers to form directly over the bar. If no such barrier exists, breaking may not occur until the waves have arrived at the foot of the beach.

In terms of the energy system we are investigating, the breaker represents the final step in a series of changes in mode of energy transport. From a purely orbital motion in deep water in which almost no net forward mass motion occurs, the wave has evolved into a nearly horizontal surge in which the water mass itself moves forward at the same speed as the wave form. Kinetic energy of the moving mass is dissipated both by internal turbulence and by friction with the bottom over which it rides. Part of the energy is expended in transporting rock particles from place to place, but most is transformed into sensible heat and eventually returns to the atmosphere by long-wave radiation.

## Currents set in motion by shoaling waves

In the nearshore zone of steepening and breaking waves certain local currents are set up. Although of great importance in shaping the shoreline and in transporting sand from one place to another, in terms of global extent and quantity of water transported these currents are in no way to be compared with the large-scale currents described in the preceding chapter.

The oblique approach of waves wind-driven toward a uniformly sloping straight shore sets up a current parallel with the shore and most strongly developed within the breaker zone (Figure 17.20). Termed the *longshore current,* this flow owes its development to the shoreward mass transport of surface water by steep waves, such as those of young age developing under strong onshore winds. Water thus brought to shore tends to raise the water level and escapes by flowing parallel to the shore. The shoreward drift of water by surface drag of the wind may also contribute to the rise of water level. Velocities of 1 to 2 knots (½ to 1 m/sec) are commonly developed by the longshore current.

Also, where wave refraction increases the wave height at one point along the shore but decreases it at an adjacent point, a current will be set up parallel to the shore in the breaker zone and will move from the region of high breakers to that of low breakers (Figure 17.21). Since higher waves bring more water landward by mass transport than lower waves do, water level is raised higher in the region of high breakers, setting in motion a current toward the region of low breakers.

A third variety of current flows in narrow, jet-like streams directly seaward at nearly right angles to the shoreline. This flow, named the *rip current*[1] (Figure

[1] Erroneously called the *rip tide* in popular usage.

**FIGURE 17.20.** Longshore currents set in motion by oblique approach of waves. (© 1960, John Wiley & Sons, New York.)

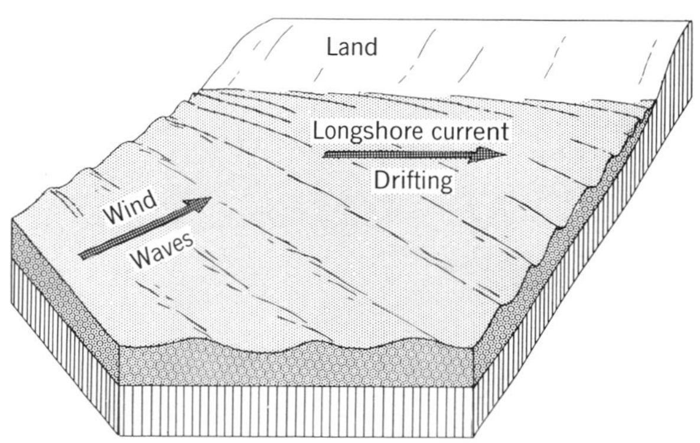

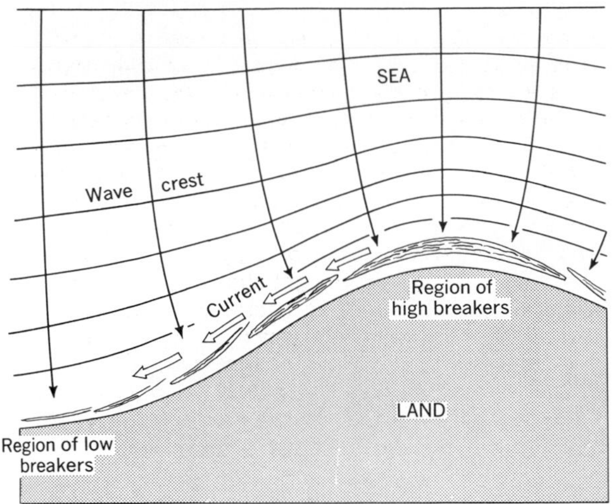


**FIGURE 17.21.** Local currents paralleling the shore set up by differences in breaker height.

17.22), crosses the breaker zone at irregular intervals of time and of horizontal spacing, although sometimes occurring with a rather regular period and even spacing. Upon reaching deeper water, the rip current slackens and spreads out into a broadened *rip head.* Flow of a rip current may last only a few minutes, or it may continue for an hour or two. Rip currents represent the surge-like escape of water brought laterally along the shore zone by feeder currents set up by unequal breaker heights. Where feeder currents converge from both directions at a point of low breaker height, the flow is diverted seaward in a narrow jet. A single rip current may have a length of 200–2500 ft (60–760 m) and speeds as high as 2 knots (1 m/sec). Unwary swimmers may be carried out to sea by the rip current. Erosive effects of the current are often seen in shallow channels scoured through submarine bars.

Is the *undertow* a form of current to be considered in this list? Most surf bathers have felt at one time or another the strong seaward pull of water between breakers. This surge is best explained as the seaward flow in that part of a wave orbit under a passing wave trough. In the breaker zone near the foot of the beach, undertow is the return flow of the mass of water that has been thrust landward by the previous breaker. The undertow is therefore not a continuously flowing current, but rather a series of pulses.

Important currents in shallow water near a coast, particularly where bays and estuaries exist, are set in motion by tides. These tidal currents are discussed in Chapter 9 and should be reviewed in connection with this chapter.

## Storm surges

Meteorological conditions affect the sea level by setting up varying degrees of disturbance (apart from wind waves and swell), ranging from scarcely perceptible water-level fluctuations to catastrophic inundations. Consider first the effect of onshore winds in raising water level. The mass-transport velocity phenomenon, already mentioned as important for steep waves generated by strong winds, causes a piling up of water along a coast. Similarly, strong winds blowing offshore tend to lower the water level.

To the mass transport velocity is added drift-current

**FIGURE 17.22.** Sketch map of rip currents and longshore currents. Distance from shoreline to farthest extent of rip head may be up to 0.5 mi (0.8 km). [After U.S. Department of the Navy (1960), *Oceanography for the Navy Meteorologist,* NWRF 32-0360-030, Norfolk, Va., U.S. Naval Weather Research Facility.)

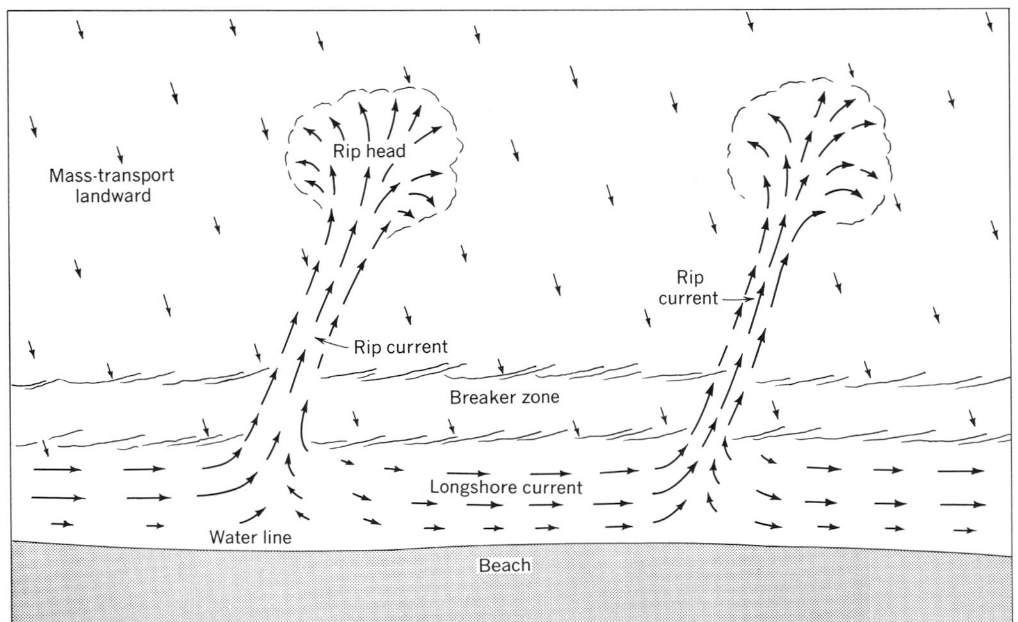

movement set up by wind drag. In calculating drift currents, correction should be made for the deflection of surface-water drift to the right of the direction of wind (Northern Hemisphere). We have seen in the preceding chapter that the direction of surface drift over deep water is about 45° to the right of the wind direction, and that the average direction of motion in the moving layer is at 90°. In shallow water of most coasts and bays the frictional effect of the bottom reduces the surface-movement angle to about 20°, while in very shallow water the induced flow is essentially in the same direction as the wind. The mass-transport velocity of steep waves is in the same direction as the wind. Changes of sea level of as much as 5 to 10 ft (1.5 to 3 m) may be attributed to water movement by winds of gale force.

Persistent strong winds are usually associated with cyclones of rather low barometric pressure. Neglecting effects of wind, tides, or other disturbances, sea level fluctuates as a barometer does, but in reverse. A change of 1 inch of mercury (13 times as dense as water) is equivalent to 13 inches of change of sea level (Figure 17.23). A middle-latitude cyclone in the United States occasionally develops a pressure as low as 29.1 in. (73.9 cm) or 0.8 in. (2 cm) below normal sea-level pressure, which would raise the sea level by about 10 in. (25 cm). Traveling anticyclones of the middle latitudes occasionally attain pressures as high as 30.7 in. (78.0 cm), which would lower the sea level by about 10 in. (25 cm). Thus a range of perhaps 20 in. (50 cm) can be the most caused by the barometric effect alone with the passage of most weather disturbances.

The tropical cyclone, however, may have pressures well below 28.5 in. (72 cm) in the central eye, giving still greater increases in sea level. Combined with winds of hurricane force favorably directed with respect to the coast, a tropical cyclone may raise water levels several feet. Where the maximum effect of winds and low pressure coincides with high tide and particularly with the exceptionally high water of spring tides, the effect is to inundate low-lying coastal areas which would normally be well above sea level. The danger of such inundations is stressed in hurricane warnings, and the evacuation of low-lying areas is strongly urged as a precaution.

FIGURE 17.23. Sea level acts as a barometer in reverse.

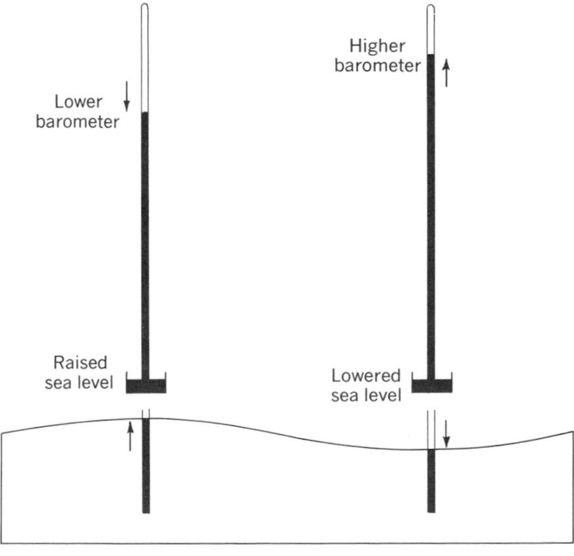


In terms of loss of life, few natural disasters can match the destructiveness of the *storm surge,* a sudden rise in sea level occurring during the progress of a tropical cyclone or an unusually severe extra-tropical cyclone as it approaches a coast and passes from sea to land. The storm surge is brought about by a resonance effect relating a storm and the water body over which it travels. The surge develops when the speed of the storm equals the speed of the natural, or free, wave of the water body. Because the natural wave speed in shallow water varies as the square root of water depth, a particular storm speed must match an appropriate water depth to induce a surge. The water level at a given coastal point may rise several feet in only a minute's time or even less, representing the greatly steepened forward slope of a large wave traveling landward.

Extreme surges raise the water level 20 ft (6 m) or more, perhaps even as much as 40 ft (12 m), if accounts of great storms are to be believed. Drowning of vast numbers of humans, trapped without warning in the suddenly rising waters, is the natural consequence of a storm surge inundating a heavily populated coastal region, such as a deltaic plain, whose elevations are at best only a few feet above mean sea level. One such region which has repeatedly suffered major disasters is the deltaic coast of the Ganges and Brahmaputra Rivers, east of Calcutta in the West Bengal province and in East Pakistan. Cyclones reaching this coast from the Bay of Bengal set up severe storm surges. One such surge at the mouth of the Hooghly River in 1737 is said to have caused a surge 40 ft (12 m) high which drowned some 300,000 persons. Similar conditions exist on the deltaic coastal plain of Louisiana. Here hurricane Audrey in 1957 set up storm surges, taking many lives and doing great property damage. Similarly the hurricane of 1900 at Galveston, Texas, brought a sudden storm surge of 4 ft (1.2 m) and a subsequent water-level rise of 15 ft (6 m) above mean high-water level. Within a few hours some 6000 persons had perished.

In many ways the action of a storm surge upon a coast resembles that of the seismic sea wave (Chapter 22). The causes are entirely different, however, and the two phenomena should not be confused. Unfortunately, the American press, including even the most reputable newspapers and magazines, persists in referring to both storm surges and seismic sea waves as "tidal waves," a misnomer for either one. The correct use of the term *tidal wave* is explained in Chapter 9 as an everyday and little-noticed occurrence of tidal estuaries and tidal rivers.

## Sea ice and icebergs

Ice formed by freezing of sea water at the ocean surface is termed *sea ice* and is distinct from an *iceberg,* which is a floating mass of glacial ice formed on land then broken off from a tide-level glacier. Vast areas of sea

**FIGURE 17.24.** Distribution of sea ice in the Arctic Ocean. Heavy arrows show common tracks of icebergs derived from tide-water glaciers. Tilted homolographic projection. (Based on data of Nat. Research Council.)

ice exist in both arctic and antarctic seas (Figures 17.24 and 17.25). Sea water will begin to freeze when its temperature falls to about 28½° F (−2° C). The floating ice layer is limited to a thickness of about 10 to 13 ft (3 to 4 m) in the Arctic Ocean, because it constitutes an insulating layer which becomes more effective as the thickness increases—beyond a given thickness the rate at which heat is brought to the water surface by current movements balances the rate at which heat is lost by conduction through the ice. In this equilibrium condition the rate at which new ice is formed at the base equals the rate of loss by melting and evaporation at the upper surface.

Sea ice covering the water surface completely is termed *pack ice* (Figure 17.26). Being brittle, the ice is subject to cracking under the forces of winds and currents and breaks up into individual patches, which are called *ice floes.* These may be separated by long narrow strips of open water, termed *leads,* or may be forced together with such great pressure that the ice margins buckle and turn up to form wall-like *pressure ridges* and hummocks. (See Figure 17.29.) It is these rugged features of the ice pack, rising 15 ft (6 m) or more in height, that have made north polar explorations by foot and dog sledge such terrible ordeals.

Because the force of the wind varies from place to place, open leads are formed in some places, and buckling and overriding of one flow upon another occur in other places. In general the pack ice of the Arctic Ocean is more subject to compression and piling up than that of the Antarctic Ocean, because the former is a land-locked sea with many bays and islands that tend

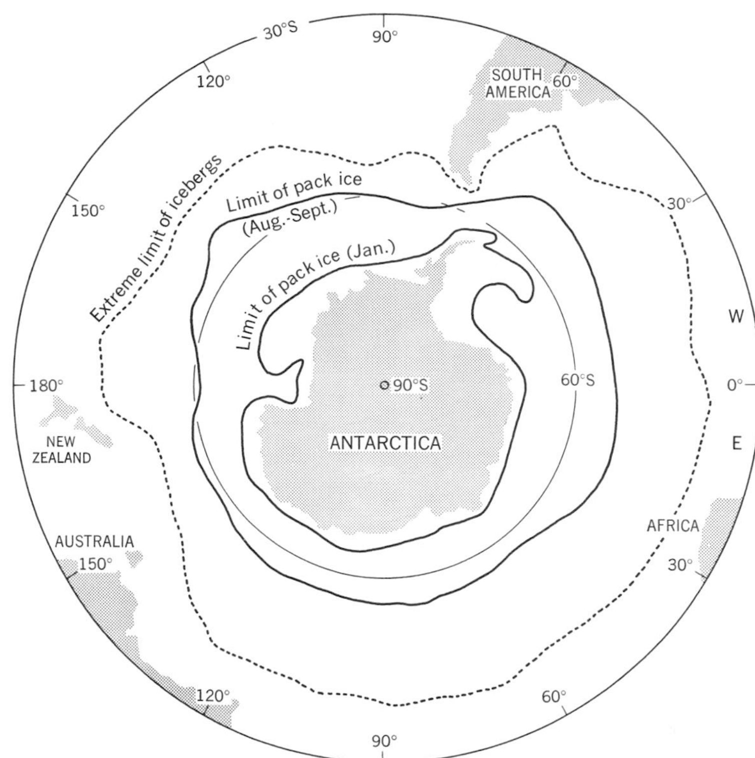


**FIGURE 17.25.** Distribution of sea ice in the Antarctic region. (Data from Nat. Acad. of Sciences and Amer. Geog. Soc.)

to constrain the ice. The antarctic pack ice, surrounded by a warmer ocean, is free to shift outward where the floes can separate and melt. There is a rather distinctly defined northern limit to the antarctic pack ice, roughly coinciding with the 55th parallel at its greatest extent in October, but shrinking to a narrow zone bordering Antarctica in March, at the close of the warm season of the year (Figure 17.25).

The Arctic Ocean is largely covered by pack ice throughout the year, except for a path bordering the northern coast of Norway, which remains ice-free throughout the year because of the relatively warm North Atlantic drift. Although winds open up leads in the pack ice at any season of the year, the leads freeze over rapidly in winter. In summer the leads remain open, and the ice floes may separate to provide extensive passageways for ships or for the surfacing of submarines. Rapid melting takes place on the arctic ice floes in summer, producing pools and ponds of standing water. During a two- or three-month melting period some 3 ft (1 m) of ice may melt from the upper surface. This water is fresh or nearly so, since there is a gradual exclusion of the sea salts between the time that the ice is first formed on the lower side of the floe and the time that it gradually arrives, by melting of the overlying ice, at the upper surface.

Icebergs, being pieces of valley glaciers or icecaps, are limited in size only by the depth of the parent glacier and may therefore be as much as several hundred feet in vertical dimension. Glacial ice is only a little less dense than the sea water in which it floats, thus the iceberg lies very low in the water, with about five-sixths of its volume below the water line (Figure 17.27). Unlike sea ice, icebergs are formed of compacted and recrystallized snow (or melted and refrozen). Therefore the water of the icebergs is fresh from the start. Morainal debris (see Chapter 35), consisting of broken rock, may be embedded in the ice and will increase the over-all density of the berg, causing it to float lower in the water.

Icebergs of the Northern Hemisphere are formed almost entirely from ice tongues of the Greenland icecap and are released into the Labrador and East Greenland Currents, which carry them south into the Atlantic to points in the vicinity of the Grand Banks of Newfoundland. From March through July they peril North Atlantic

**FIGURE 17.26.** Floating sea ice in Whale Sound, Greenland, about 100 mi (160 km) north of Thule Air Base. The black areas are leads of open water. (U.S. Air Force photograph.)

**FIGURE 17.27.** A large iceberg in Baffin Bay. (Official U.S. Coast Guard photograph.)

shipping and are watched carefully by the International Ice Patrol, whose duty it is to warn ships of the presence of bergs. Although small icebergs are produced by glaciers of Alaska, Spitzbergen, Northern Land, and Franz Josef Land, they are unimportant compared with the Greenland bergs. In Figure 17.24 is shown the route of travel of the Greenland bergs, which reach as far south as the 40th parallel.

Icebergs of the Antarctic Ocean are quite different in form from the Greenland bergs, which are often sharp-crested and irregularly peaked. A distinctive feature of the Antarctic is the presence of *shelf ice,* the floating margin of the great continental icecap which has spread beyond the land margins. This shelf ice breaks off into enormous *tabular* icebergs with flat top and bottom surfaces and steep cliff-like sides. A single berg may be tens of miles across and more than 2000 ft (600 m) thick. The ice wall may rise 250–300 ft (75–90 m) above the water's surface (Figure 17.28). The slow melting of such great masses of ice permits tabular bergs to drift as far equatorward as the 40th parallel south before disappearing entirely.

## Ice islands of the Arctic Ocean

With the advent of extensive military flying over the Arctic Ocean, some extremely large flat-topped masses of floating ice were discovered in the ice pack. These bodies, termed *ice islands,* are much too thick to have been produced as floating pack ice by freezing of sea water under present conditions. One example, *Island T-3,* has a width of 20 mi (32 km) and an area of 59 sq mi (775 sq km) (Figure 17.29). A thickness of 200 ft (60 m) or more is indicated by the bordering ice cliff rising 20–30 ft (6–9 m) above the surrounding pack ice. Ice islands commonly show a ribbed or corrugated surface resembling a sea of low waves 300–900 ft (90–270 m) from crest to crest and 5–15 ft (1.5–4.5 m) high. The crests are covered with clean white snow, and clear blue ice or ponded meltwater forms contrasting dark bands in the troughs.

Ice island *Arlis II,* discovered in the spring of 1961 northwest of Point Barrow, Alaska, and occupied shortly thereafter as the site of an arctic research laboratory, measured at that time about 2 by 4 mi (3 by 6 km) in surface extent and had an estimated ice thickness of 70 ft (20 m). Surface elevations of the ice ranged from 5 to 7 ft (1.5 to 2 m) above sea level. A remarkable feature of this ice island is the presence of mounds of fragmented rock up to 50 ft (15 m) in height and isolated flats of frozen mud. These deposits testify to the terrestrial origin of the ice island.

Ice islands resemble the great tabular bergs of shelf ice of the Antarctic but are neither so large nor so thick. A source for ice islands has been found along the shores of Ellesmere Island, about lat. 83° N., where a belt of similarly corrugated shelf ice is attached to land in a zone 50 mi (80 km) wide (Figure 17.24). Unlike antarctic shelf ice, which is fed by the continental icecap, the Ellesmere Island shelf ice has no land glaciers to feed it. It seems likely, therefore, that the ice shelf was formed by continued thickening of what was originally pack ice attached to land and is a relic of a much colder period in the recent past.

Since the discovery of the first ice island by the crew of a U.S. Air Force weather reconnaissance plane in 1946, ice islands have been under constant study. They have been used as aircraft landing fields and as permanent sites of polar research laboratories, for which they provide excellent stable platforms for studies of polar meteorology and oceanography and a wide range of geophysical problems.

**FIGURE 17.28.** This vast tabular berg of the Antarctic is a detached portion of an ice shelf. Bay of Whales, Little America. (Official U.S. Coast Guard photograph.)

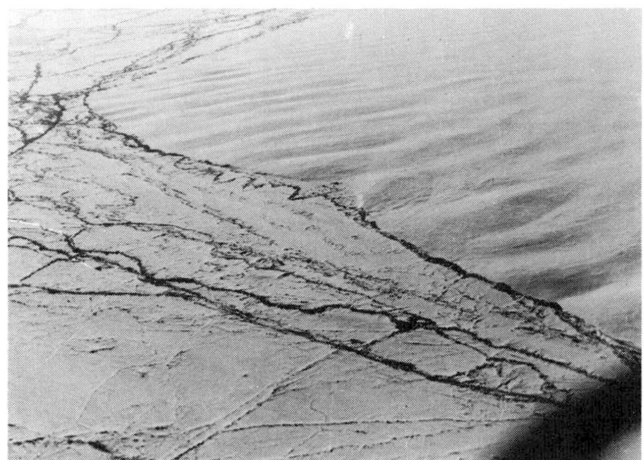

**FIGURE 17.29.** This aerial view of Ice Island T-3 (Fletcher's Ice Island) was taken from a height of 1000 ft (300 m). The undulating, wave-like ridges of the ice island (upper right) contrast with the irregular pressure ridges of the ice pack. (U.S. Air Force photograph.)

## References for further study


Bigelow, H. B., and W. T. Edmondson (1947), *Wind Waves at Sea; Breakers and Surf,* Washington, D.C., U.S. Navy Oceanographic Office, Publ. 602, 177 pp.

Russell, R. C. H., and D. H. Macmillan (1954), *Waves and Tides,* London, Hutchinson's Sci. and Tech. Publ., 348 pp.

U.S. Navy (1957), *Oceanographic Atlas of the Polar Seas,* Part I; *Antarctic,* Washington, D.C., U.S. Navy Oceanographic Office, Publ. 705, 70 pp.

Von Arx, W. S. (1962), *An Introduction to Physical Oceanography,* Reading, Mass., Addison-Wesley, 422 pp., chap. 3.

Williams, J. (1962), *Oceanography,* Boston, Little, Brown, 242 pp., chaps. 14, 15.

Bascomb, W. (1964), *Waves and Beaches,* Garden City, N.Y., Doubleday, 260 pp.

Fairbridge, R. W., ed. (1966), *Encyclopedia of Oceanography,* New York, Reinhold, 1021 pp. See: Ocean waves, Sea ice, Sea state, Storm surge, Wave refraction, Wave theory.

# 18 Atmospheric moisture

THE IMPORTANCE OF moisture in the earth's atmosphere is so great that one might well consider evaporation and condensation to be the most significant of all meteorological processes. Whether in the invisible gaseous form of water vapor, in minute suspended droplets or ice crystals which constitute clouds and fog, or as larger falling particles of precipitation, water never ceases to play the leading role in changing patterns of weather.

Atmospheric moisture may exist in three possible states: *gas, liquid,* and *solid* (Figure 18.1). In the gaseous state, known as *water vapor,* the water molecules diffuse perfectly and freely among the molecules of nitrogen, oxygen, and the other gases of the atmosphere. We cannot see water vapor, but we can feel its effects. When water vapor is present in large proportions in the air in winter, heat is conducted rapidly from our bodies, and winds seem to chill us to the marrow. In summer a high content of water vapor in the air slows evaporation of perspiration from the skin, thus inhibiting body cooling, and we feel sticky, warm, and uncomfortable, while doors and windows swell and stick, and mildew may begin to coat objects stored in poorly ventilated places.

Whereas the gases of the pure dry atmosphere remain almost perfectly constant in proportions within the troposphere, water vapor may constitute as little as 1/1000 of the weight of the air in the cold winter air of Canada or Siberia or as much as 18/1000 of the total weight in the hot sultry air of an equatorial rainforest. There is thus about a twentyfold range in water-vapor content of the atmosphere when all parts of the globe are considered.

We frequently say that air has the capacity to "contain" water vapor. Actually this concept is incorrect. Rather, air is replaced by water vapor. For equal volumes of dry and wet air, the volume of dry air is the heavier of the two, because the density of water vapor is less than that of dry air. This principle is important in meteorology because masses of

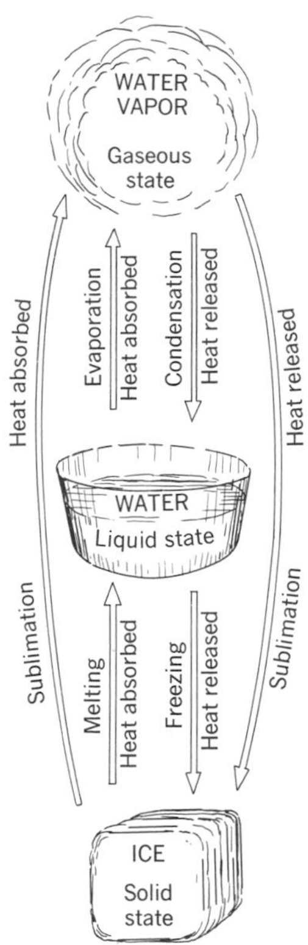


**FIGURE 18.1.** Three states of water.

moist air will tend to rise and, by spontaneous cooling described below, produce condensation products.

Water-vapor content of the air is referred to in general as the *humidity* and may be expressed by using any one of several forms of measures, such as vapor pressure, relative humidity, and absolute humidity.

*Vapor pressure* is simply the partial barometric pressure attributable to the presence of the water vapor. Recall that standard barometric pressure at sea level is 1013 mb (29.92 in., 76 cm). For cold dry air, vapor pressure may be a mere 2 mb (0.06 in., 0.15 cm), but for very warm humid air it is as high as 30 mb (0.9 in., 2.3 cm) or nearly one-thirty-fifth the entire mercury column.

The liquid form of water is found in the atmosphere in the tiny particles that make up the greatest proportion of fog and clouds. The process of change of water from the gaseous vapor form to the liquid form is termed *condensation,* and the change from liquid to vapor is *evaporation.* Condensation to form clouds and fog requires the presence of extremely tiny foreign particles, or impurities, to serve as *nuclei,* or cores, around which a water film can grow. Another form of condensation is *dew,* the growth of water droplets upon exposed surfaces of plants, soil, or rock. Much of this chapter is concerned with the causes of rapid condensation on a large scale in the atmosphere, leading to *precipitation,* the falling of liquid drops or ice particles too large to remain suspended in the air.

Water in the solid state is found in the atmosphere in the form of tiny hexagonal crystals in the very high clouds of the upper part of the troposphere. At temperatures far below the freezing point of water (32° F, 0° C) water droplets may change into ice crystals, a process termed simply *freezing,* or water vapor may change directly into crystalline ice by the process of *sublimation* (Figure 18.1). The reverse process, that of ice passing directly into water vapor, is also termed sublimation and is analogous to evaporation. Sublimation is illustrated by the formation of *hoarfrost* (often called simply *frost*) on the ground on cold clear nights and on windowpanes during very cold weather. Snowflakes and high clouds are also produced by sublimation.

## Latent energy of water vapor

When water changes its state from gas to liquid and back, from gas to solid and back, or from liquid to solid and back, heat is given off or absorbed in the process of change. The physical nature of these changes can be deduced by considering the activity of the water molecules.

Evaporation consists of the flight of the more energetic, more rapidly moving water molecules from the free surface of a liquid. Molecules thus passing from the liquid state to the gaseous state carry with them a great amount of kinetic energy of molecular motion. The average velocity of motion of the molecules remaining in the liquid form is correspondingly reduced, reducing the total kinetic energy and resulting in a lowering of the temperature of the liquid surface. Sensible heat within the liquid has thus passed into the form of latent heat within the gas. Consequently evaporation is a cooling process. Perspiration evaporates to cool the skin, and the desert water bag made of coarsely woven flax allows water to seep through and evaporate from the fabric, cooling the water remaining inside. The amount of heat taken up by the evaporation of 1 gram of water (or of heat given up when enough vapor condenses to produce 1 gram of water) is about 600 calories. The precise amount varies according to the temperature at which the process is taking place.

In the reverse process, condensation, rapidly moving gas molecules condense into a liquid, their motions becoming greatly reduced. The kinetic energy of gas molecule motion must change into another form—in this case sensible heat—since a basic law of physics states that energy cannot simply disappear and be lost. Condensation is therefore accompanied by the change of latent heat into sensible heat (Figure 18.1). Consequently condensation is a warming process, causing the temperature of the air to rise as cloud droplets grow in size. This important principle will be used repeatedly to explain weather processes.

In like manner, the change from liquid to solid state (freezing) causes heat to be given up, and heat is taken up when melting occurs. The *heat of fusion,* as this is called, amounts to about 80 calories for each gram of water. Sublimation requires even larger quantities of heat to be given out or taken up than evaporation or condensation, because the change is from highly energetic flights of gas molecules to the very quiet repose of the molecules locked in the crystalline solid (680 calories are required to be gained or lost, since sublimation combines the heat of condensation/evaporation and heat of fusion in a single step).

## Saturation vapor pressure

Consider what will happen to dry air in a sealed glass jar about half full of water left to stand without any change in the temperature of the surroundings. Evaporation will cause water molecules to leave the water surface and to enter the air as vapor. After a time the number of water molecules leaving the water will be balanced by an equal number returning to the water surface from the vapor state. There is no further increase in the quantity of water vapor, and the space above the water is said to be *saturated.*

For a given temperature there is a fixed quantity of water vapor that can occupy a given volume of space. Now, if the temperature of the glass jar is allowed to rise to a higher point, additional evaporation takes place and the condition of saturation is again reached, but this time with a greater quantity of water vapor per unit volume. Similarly, a colder temperature allows saturation with less water vapor.

These points are summarized in a principle of fundamental importance to the understanding of weather and climate: The quantity of water vapor that can be held in a given volume of space depends only upon the temperature of the gas occupying that space.

Vapor pressure, already explained, gives a direct measure of the quantity of water vapor present in a given volume of the atmosphere. In Figure 18.2 is a graph showing the maximum possible vapor pressure for any given air temperature from −40° to 120° F (−40° to 50° C). A vapor pressure of 35 mb, or about 1 in. (2.5 cm) of the mercury column of the barometer, occurs at 80° F (27° C) and might represent coastal conditions in the wet equatorial climates. A value of 3 mb (0.1 in., 0.25 cm) at 20° F (−7° C) might represent conditions on a damp cold winter day in the northeastern United States.

**FIGURE 18.2.** Vapor pressure of saturated air and the equivalent values of absolute humidity.

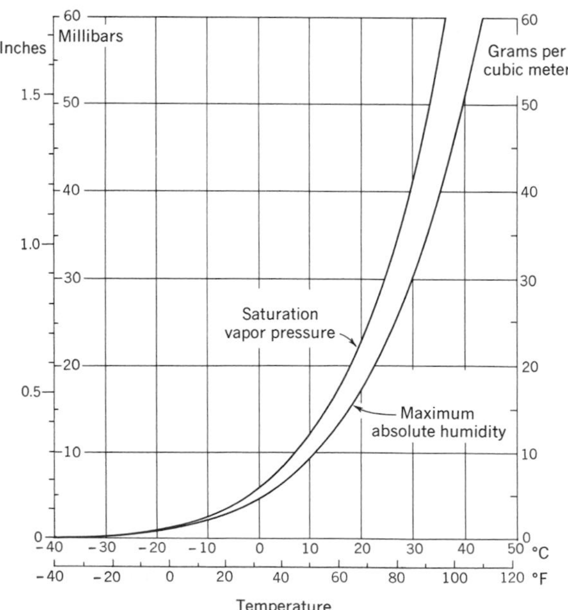


## Absolute humidity; specific humidity

Another way to state the quantity of water vapor in the atmosphere is in terms of *absolute humidity,* defined as the weight of water vapor in a given volume of air. Because the water-vapor weight is extremely small, it is given in grams per cubic meter. Figure 18.2 includes a curve of maximum absolute humidity for a given air temperature. For example, a value of about 47 grams per cubic meter occurs at a temperature of 100° F (37° C), but such a value is not likely to be found in free air in nature because air of such warmth is usually found over dry continental areas.

One lesson which the graphs teach is that the warm atmosphere of tropical and equatorial regions can hold roughly 10 times as much water vapor as the air of the cold arctic and polar regions. The former can also give up vastly more precipitation, and incidentally release 10 times the latent heat, when this water vapor is condensed. Recall that in Chapter 16 the equatorial belt was described as the "firebox" of the earth's atmosphere because of the release of vast amounts of latent heat by condensation taking place there.

One shortcoming of absolute humidity as a means of stating water-vapor content is that air expands, or becomes more rarefied, as it rises in elevation. Air contracts, or becomes denser, as it descends. Therefore absolute humidity changes automatically as the air moves up or down or moves horizontally from areas of higher barometric pressure to areas of lower barometric pressure. To avoid dealing with changes in humidity due only to pressure changes, meteorologists prefer to use a third measure of moisture content of the air, the *mixing ratio,* defined as the ratio of density of the water vapor to density of the dry air. In practice the mixing ratio is stated in weight of water vapor in grams to weight of air in kilograms. A similar measure is *specific humidity,* the ratio of weight of water vapor to total weight of air, including the water vapor. It, too, is given in grams per kilogram.

Mixing ratio and specific humidity do not change when air pressure alone changes. Consequently these parameters enable the meteorologist to follow or trace a given body of air as it travels from place to place. As long as no moisture is lost by condensation or added by evaporation, the mixing ratio and specific humidity remain constant. Under extreme conditions in the humid equatorial regions a mixing ratio as high as 20 grams per kilogram can occur, whereas in arctic regions it may be as low as 1 gram per kilogram. (Note that numerical values of both mixing ratio and specific humidity are almost identical.)

## Relative humidity

The fourth and best-known way of stating moisture content of the air is as *relative humidity,* defined as the ratio of the actual quantity of water vapor present to the maximum quantity possible in the state of saturation, or, more simply, as the percentage of saturation. Relative humidity is given in percent, 0% being absolutely dry air, and 100% being completely saturated.

Relative humidity can be increased by evaporation from water surfaces or moist ground or by transpiration of plants. The reverse process, direct condensation upon ground or water surfaces, is not of great importance in its effect on humidity.

Change of air temperature alone results in important changes in relative humidity. We have shown that the maximum quantity of water vapor that can be contained in a given volume of the atmosphere increases with temperature. Therefore the relative humidity will automatically drop as air temperature rises, even though no moisture is added or lost. Conversely, relative humidity rises as air temperature drops.

For example, suppose that the air at a particular place has a relative humidity of 50% at a temperature of 60° F (15° C). If this air is heated by the sun to 90° F (32° C), the relative humidity automatically drops to 20%. But if by radiation at night the same air cools down to 40° F (5° C), the relative humidity automatically increases to 100%, or the saturation point.

Because the daily temperature cycle normally consists of a maximum in the early afternoon and a minimum at about sunrise, there is also a normal daily cycle of rise and fall of relative humidity. In this case, however, the humidity reaches its high point when temperature is lowest, and vice versa. In Figure 18.3 the two curves are superimposed. The relation will hold only if there are no important changes in general weather conditions. Obviously, if winds shift in direction so as to import moist air, the relative humidity may rise even during the middle of the day.

## Measurement of humidity

Instruments for the measurement of the water-vapor content of air may use one of two principles. The *hygrometer,* on whose scale relative humidity is read directly, makes use of a human hair, or other suitable fiber, which lengthens as humidity increases and shortens as it decreases. Change in length of the hair can be made to activate an arm to which a pen is attached, thus drawing a continuous line on a slowly turning drum. Such an apparatus is known as a *recording hygrograph.*

The principle of varying rates of evaporation is made use of in the *sling psychrometer,* an instrument consisting of two liquid-in-glass thermometers mounted side by side (Figure 18.4). One thermometer has its bulb exposed to the air, as usual, whereas the other has a piece of water-saturated cloth wrapped around its bulb. The thermometer pair is swung through the air by means of a handle and swivel joint, so that evaporation cools the wet bulb, depressing its temperature somewhat below that of the dry bulb. The degree of cooling of the wet bulb depends upon the dryness of the air. For fully saturated air no evaporation will occur and both thermometers will read the same. In dry air the wet-bulb thermometer will register a temperature several degrees below that of the dry bulb. By means of standard tables or by using a specially calibrated slide rule it is possible to estimate relative humidity from the temperature difference of the two bulbs.

FIGURE 18.3. Curves of mean hourly air temperature, dew point, and relative humidity for the month of May at Washington, D.C. (Data of ESSA, Weather Bureau.)

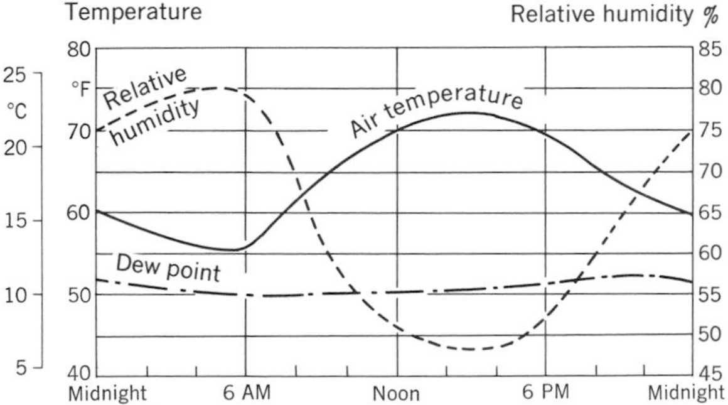


## Dew point temperature

The temperature to which air would need to be cooled for water vapor to reach the saturation condition (relative humidity 100%) is the *dew point.* Should any further cooling occur, condensation may begin to occur in the form of clouds, fog, dew, or frost. If the dew point is below freezing, direct sublimation into tiny ice crystals, snowflakes, or hoarfrost can be expected. The actual situation in nature may not be so simple, however. The tiny droplets of which clouds and fog are composed can exist in the liquid state at below-freezing temperatures. Such water, said to be *supercooled,* will turn into ice if the air is subjected to mechanical shock or if tiny ice crystals are added to the cloud.

An example is the formation of ice on aircraft. As the plane passes through a cloud composed of supercooled water the shock of the plane disturbs and deflects the air, causing sudden changes of water droplets to ice, which coats the plane. If allowed to accumulate, the ice reduces the lift of the wings, increases the weight of the plane, and increases the drag of air, thereby creating a very dangerous situation in which the plane cannot maintain altitude.

In what ways can the atmospheric temperature be lowered to the dew point, resulting in condensation?

FIGURE 18.4. A sling psychrometer. (Photograph by ESSA, Weather Bureau.)

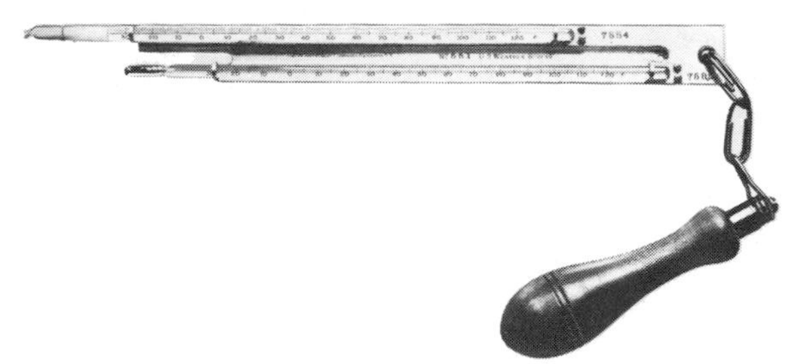

Three mechanisms are available. First, the air may lose heat by long-wave radiation (as explained in Chapter 13), which commonly occurs at night when the sky is clear and heat readily passes out to higher air layers and thence into space. A second mechanism is the rising or lifting of large masses of air to higher altitudes, a process which automatically results in lowering of air temperature. A third is the cooling of air by mixing with colder air.

## Fog and smog

Fog is simply a cloud at the earth's surface. Dense fog is an indication that the air is at or close to the dew-point temperature and that sufficient moisture has condensed to produce abundant cloud droplets or ice particles. Perhaps the simplest type of fog is *radiation fog,* produced at night when a cold land surface conducts heat away from the lowermost inch or so of the atmosphere. For a moist atmosphere, calm air induces dew or frost, light winds cause fog by stirring, but strong winds dissipate the condensation product, thereby maintaining good visibility.

On calm clear nights, because of air drainage the coldest air tends to collect in valley bottoms, and it is here that the radiation fog is usually seen, often appearing as a lake of fog when viewed from higher ground. Radiation fogs disappear by evaporation when air temperature increases soon after sunrise, when they are said to "burn off".

Another type of fog is *advection fog.* Advection simply means horizontal transfer of air. One type of advection fog is formed where moist warm air blows over a colder surface, whether land or water. Air passing close to the surface loses heat by conduction to the colder surface beneath and its temperature is thus brought to the dew point. A second type, known as an *evaporation fog,* results when cold dry air passes over a warm moist surface. Evaporation is accompanied by rapid upward diffusion of water vapor, with almost immediate condensation in the cold air. Evaporation fog in arctic waters goes by the name of *sea smoke.*

Among the most famous of advection fogs is that over the Grand Banks off Newfoundland, where warm, moist air overlying the Gulf Stream is close to the cold Labrador Current. Depending upon wind direction, an advection fog of either type may be formed, making this the foggiest region in the world.

Another common example of advection fog in the northeastern United States develops in winter during a period of unusually mild rainy weather, when moist air from southerly sources passes over a frozen or snow-covered ground surface.

Fog is most frequent in its occurrence close to sunrise, because this is the normal time of minimum air temperature and highest relative humidity. Several other distinct types of fogs are recognized besides those mentioned here.

The subject of fog is one of extreme importance in our modern life because of the effect of fog upon the operation of aircraft. Fog at a busy metropolitan airport will cause thousands of airline passengers to be rerouted, to miss connecting flights, or to have their flights canceled. In military operations a dense and prolonged fog allows ground forces to move without being observed or attacked from the air. The near-disastrous counterattack of the German forces in the Battle of the Bulge in World War II was conducted under a persistent cover of fog and low-lying clouds which prevented the Allied air forces from attacking.

*Smog,* a nuisance and health hazard of increasing severity in some metropolitan areas, is found in a low-lying layer of air in which smoke and water-vapor droplets containing various dissolved chemical substances have accumulated to the point of producing a serious obstruction to vision. A temperature inversion lasting several days is conducive to the development of smog, since an inversion strongly inhibits vertical motion and smog dissipation. Toxic and irritating products of combustion, including that from automobiles, heating systems, and incinerators, cannot escape by mixing with the upper air. The word smog is a combination of *smoke* and *fog* and thus suggests its origin.

## The adiabatic process in rising and descending air

Any gas allowed to expand by reduction of the confining pressure will become cooler, and it becomes warmer if compressed into a smaller volume. Such temperature changes are termed *adiabatic,* because heat is neither brought in from outside sources nor lost to the surrounding area. Instead, the change in temperature of the gas reflects a change in the degree of crowding of the gas molecules. If the gas is allowed to expand into a larger space its molecules are more widely separated and have less frequent collisions, causing a drop in sensible temperature. Compression causes more frequent molecular collisions and raises the sensible temperature.

The principal cause of important and sustained increase or decrease in temperature of vast masses of air is the adiabatic process in sinking or rising air. In general, such vertical motion is described as convection. When unsaturated air rises, its temperature falls at a rate of approximately 5½ F° per 1000 feet of rise (1 C° per 100 meters). This rate is termed the *dry adiabatic temperature lapse rate.*[1] Figure 18.5 shows how temperature falls in a rising body of air.

As the air continues to rise, adiabatic cooling also continues, thus the air temperature gradually approaches the dew point. Relative humidity is automatically increasing, and condensation can begin as soon as the dew point is reached. But the dew-point temperature itself decreases at the rate of 1 F° per 1000 feet of rise (0.2 C° per 100 meters), hence the dew point and air temperature approach each other at the rate of 4½ F° per 1000 feet (0.9 C° per 100 meters).

No set figure can be given for the amount of altitude rise required to begin condensation, because this depends upon the dryness of the air at the start. In the example shown in Figure 18.5, air near ground level has

[1] Do not confuse the adiabatic temperature lapse rate with *normal temperature lapse rate* of nonrising air, which has an average value of 3½ F° per 1000 feet. The word *adiabatic* will imply temperature changes due to rising or sinking.

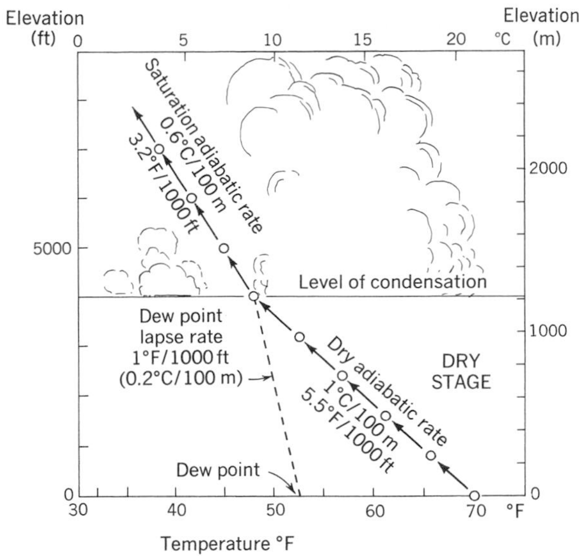


**FIGURE 18.5.** Dry adiabatic lapse rate and dew-point lapse rate.

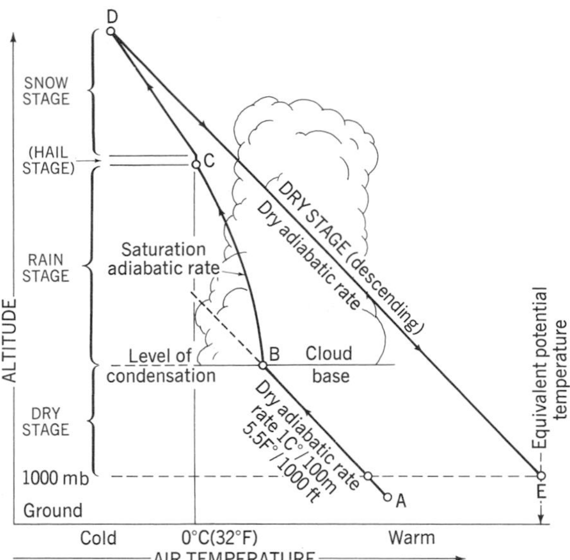


**FIGURE 18.6.** Schematic diagram (not to scale) of moisture stages in a rising air mass. [After War Department (1940), *Weather Manual for Pilots,* Technical Manual 1-230, Washington, D.C., p. 35, Figure 34.]

a temperature of 70° F (21° C) and a dew-point temperature of 52° F (11° C). A rise of 4000 ft (1200 m) is required, with a temperature drop of 22 F° (12 C°), to bring it to the new dew-point temperature of 48° F (9° C). In this example the air was relatively dry at ground level, or at about 53% relative humidity. Had the air at ground level possessed a high relative humidity (therefore a higher dew-point temperature initially), it would have required a lesser amount of lift to bring it to the dew point.

When rising air is lifted to an elevation at which its dew point is reached, condensation begins, producing a cloud. Most convectional clouds show a flat base, marking the level at which condensation starts.

As already stated, condensation of water vapor releases latent heat in the amount of 600 calories per gram of water, generating sensible heat. This process tends to warm the air in which condensation is taking place. Consequently the adiabatic rate is partially offset by the production of sensible heat and takes on a reduced value, known as the *saturation adiabatic temperature lapse rate* (the word *wet* is commonly used in substitution for "saturation").

Figure 18.6 shows the stages of decrease in air temperature as air rises. Starting at Point *A,* the rising air is in the *dry stage* described above. After condensation has set in, above the Point *B,* the temperature-altitude curve steepens abruptly, representing the change from dry adiabatic rate to saturation adiabatic rate.

No single value can be given for the saturation adiabatic rate because it varies with moisture content and temperature of the air. For very moist warm tropical air the saturation adiabatic rate may be reduced as low as 35% of the dry rate, *i.e.,* to about 2 F° per 1000 ft (0.35 C° per 100 m). In cold air with low moisture content the release of heat by condensation is small, and the saturation adiabatic rate is only slightly less than the dry adiabatic rate.

Figure 18.6 shows that between Points *B* and *C* condensation occurs at above-freezing conditions. This portion of the ascent is referred to as the *rain stage.* Notice that the curve bends to a smaller angle of slope when followed upward through the rain stage. This curvature reflects an increase in value of the saturation adiabatic rate as the rate of release of latent heat becomes less important because of reduced temperature and reduced moisture content of the rising air.

When the rising air has cooled to the freezing point (Point *C*) water droplets suspended in the cloud begin to freeze. Release of latent heat of fusion (80 calories per gram) momentarily prevents a further drop of temperature until all liquid water is frozen. The result is a *hail stage* in which the curve takes a short vertical segment. Above the hail stage is the *snow stage,* in which water vapor passes by sublimation directly into ice. The saturation adiabatic rate in the snow stage gradually decreases to a value only slightly less than that of the dry adiabatic rate, since little water vapor remains in the very cold rising air.

In theory, further rise of the air would ultimately cause all water vapor to be condensed. Let Point *D* in Figure 18.6 represent this condition of absolutely dry air. If, now, the air is caused to descend, its temperature will increase at the dry adiabatic rate in a continuous dry stage. Upon reaching a low elevation (Point *E*) the air will be considerably warmer than when the ascent was begun, and it will also have a substantially reduced water vapor content.

In tracing the rise and descent of a mass of air we have thus described a process that is crudely analogous to squeezing water out of a sponge. The condensation process is like the squeezing of a saturated sponge, while the dry stage of descent is like the expansion of the sponge to its original dimensions, but with little or no water remaining in the pores.

Meteorologists derive a quantity known as the *potential temperature,* which is the temperature a mass of air at any given initial temperature and pressure would have if it were brought down to the 1000-mb pressure level. Under standard conditions, the 1000-mb level lies at about 350 ft (105 m) above sea level. Air descending from high elevations to the 1000-mb level follows the dry adiabatic rate of temperature increase. In Figure 18.6 the potential temperature is reached at Point *E.*

Extending the concept of potential temperature further, an important identifying property of a mass of air can be derived by supposing that the air is first lifted and subjected to adiabatic cooling until all water vapor is condensed (Points *A* through *D* in Figure 18.6), then brought down to the 1000-mb level at the dry adiabatic rate. The resulting temperature (Point *E*) is termed the *equivalent potential temperature.*

Naturally occurring air masses exhibit a wide range of equivalent potential temperatures, the span being on the order of 180 F° (100 C°). If the temperature and pressure of the air at any elevation are measured by sounding instruments, it is possible to derive the equivalent potential temperature by means of specially prepared charts. This information is valuable in ascertaining the origin and path of travel of the air mass, a subject discussed in further detail in Chapter 19.

## Clouds

Clouds and fog are composed of tiny water droplets or ice crystals on the order of 20–60 microns (0.02–0.06 mm, 0.0008–0.0024 in.) in diameter. Under a microscope they look like tiny spheres. Each droplet forms by condensation of water upon a tiny *nucleus,* usually a bit of salt or other chemical compound which is *hygroscopic,* that is, which has an affinity for water. Common table salt is hygroscopic, unless specially treated, and turns damp and sticky in moist weather.

Salt particles are abundant in the atmosphere because the turbulent winds blowing over ocean waves lift bits of salt spray into the air. Evaporation of these spray particles leaves salt particles that travel easily into all parts of the troposphere and make excellent nuclei, or cores, upon which cloud particles can be formed. Growth of cloud droplets begins while air is still not fully saturated, and the droplets become rapidly larger when the saturation point is reached.

Minute particles of water can remain in the liquid state at temperatures far below the normal freezing point of 32° F (0° C). Such liquid water is said to be *supercooled* (also *undercooled*). At temperatures down to about 14° F (−10° C) cloud particles are almost entirely in the liquid state; between 14° F (−10° C) and about −22° F (−30° C) a mixture of liquid and ice particles exists; down to −40° F (−40° C) the particles are predominantly of ice; below −40° F (−40° C) the cloud consists entirely of ice crystals. In general, the highest forms of clouds, above about 4 mi (6½ km) high, are composed entirely of ice crystals because here air temperatures are very low.

Clouds have such a very high capacity to reflect sunlight that reflection of the entire visible spectrum occurs, accounting for their brilliant snowy appearance when lighted by the sun. Dense cloud masses appear gray or black on the underside because sunlight is unable to pass through. Thin layers transmit enough sunlight to appear gray, whereas some of the thinnest veil-like clouds seem scarcely to weaken the intensity of direct sunlight.

Apart from their major role as producers of rain, snow, sleet, and hail, clouds are excellent indicators of the general weather situation, the direction and speed of air movement, and the moisture state of the air.

When formed into blanketlike layers, clouds are described as *stratiform.* Obviously such layers could not exist with large-scale vertical motions of the air. Thus stratiform clouds may indicate that air is moving in layers, one sliding over the other. However, the air within the layer may be engaged in rather turbulent motion, as evidenced by the fact that a plane passing through a layered cloud often experiences a series of dips and rises resembling the undulations experienced in a roller-coaster ride.

Flat-based clouds of massive globular shape, often higher than wide, are described as *cumuliform.* These forms generally indicate strong rising air currents, or updrafts, carrying moist air rapidly to higher levels and causing continued adiabatic cooling and condensation.

Clouds are grouped into classes and named according to height and general form, whether stratiform or cumuliform. An international system of classification recognizes four families of clouds: *high clouds, middle clouds, low clouds,* and *clouds of vertical development* (Figure 18.7).

The high-cloud family above 23,000 ft (7 km) includes individual types named *cirrus, cirrocumulus,* and *cirrostratus.* All are composed of ice crystals. Cirrus is a wispy, feather-like cloud, commonly forming streaks or plumes named *mares' tails* (Figure 18.8*A*). Cirrus clouds are so thin as to make no barrier to sunlight. Cirrocumulus is a layer composed of small cumulus masses looking like tiny bits of cotton (Figure 18.8*B*). The regular geometric pattern formed by these cloud masses is sometimes described as a *mackerel sky.* Cirrostratus is a thin veil-like cloud, commonly causing a halo around the sun or moon but too thin to dim sunlight appreciably. The halo is evidence that the cloud particles consist of ice rather than of liquid water. Cirrus clouds, particularly the streaked cirrus bands, on occasion indicate the presence of a high-altitude jet stream, with the wind direction paralleling the long lines of the cloud.

The middle-cloud family, extending from 6500 to 23,000 ft (2 to 7 km) in height, includes two cloud types—*altocumulus* and *altostratus.* Altocumulus consists of grayish cumuliform cloud masses lying in a distinct layer, with blue sky visible in breaks between masses (Figure 18.9*A*). Altocumulus is usually associated with fair weather. Altostratus is a rather uniform thick grayish blanket, usually with a smooth underside, and is a frequent precipitation producer. It will shut out sun-

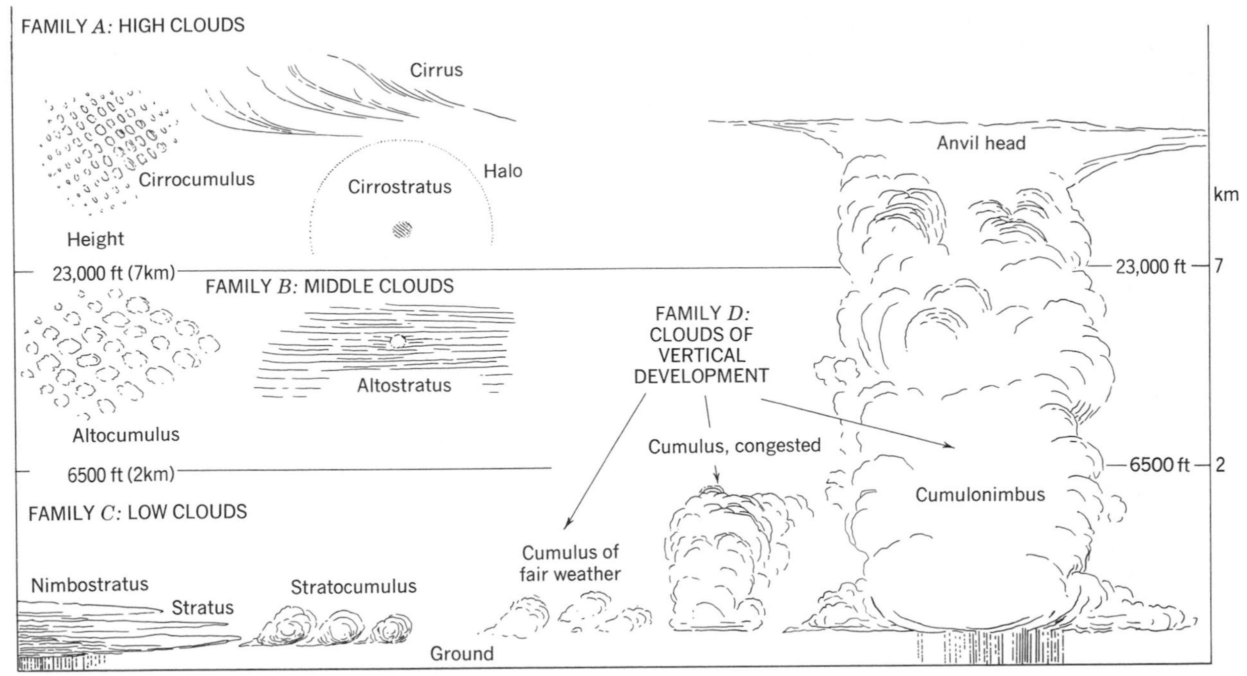



**FIGURE 18.7.** Cloud forms are classified into families based on height and vertical development.

light, but the sun can be seen as a bright spot through the cloud (Figure 18.9*B*).

The low-cloud family, found from ground level to a height of 6500 ft (2 km) above the earth's surface (not necessarily measured from sea level), includes three types: *stratus, nimbostratus,* and *stratocumulus.* Stratus is a uniform cloud sheet at low height and usually completely covers the sky. The gray undersurface is fog-like in appearance. Where stratus thickens to the point that rain or snow begins to fall from it, the cloud becomes designated nimbostratus, the prefix "nimbo" meaning rain. Normally, nimbostratus will be dense and

**FIGURE 18.8.** High-cloud forms. (*A*) Fibrous form of cirrus clouds. (*B*) Cirrocumulus (above) and tufted cirrus (below). (Photographs by F. Ellerman; ESSA, Weather Bureau.)

*A*

*B*

A

B

C

**FIGURE 18.9.** Middle and low clouds. (*A*) Active form of altocumulus. (Photograph by C. F. Brooks; ESSA, Weather Bureau.) (*B*) Thin altostratus with fractostratus patches below. The sun shows as a bright spot of light. (Photograph by G. A. Clarke; ESSA, Weather Bureau.) (*C*) Stratocumulus seen from above. (Photograph by Lois Bowen; ESSA, Weather Bureau.)

dark gray, shutting out much daylight. The cloud may extend upward many thousands of feet into the middle-cloud height range (altostratus can also be nimbostratus). Ragged cloud patches beneath the nimbostratus are named *fractostratus* or *scud.*

Stratocumulus consists of low individual masses of dense cloud often in large cigar-shaped rolls, the masses forming a distinct layer with an approximately uniform base. The masses are dark gray on the shaded sides, but white on the illuminated sides, often with narrow breaks between them through which blue sky is visible. Stratocumulus is produced by rather intense turbulent motions of the air rising and sinking within the cloud layer. Stratocumulus is best developed in the clearing period following a storm, when gusty cold winds are blowing. Minor rain or snow squalls may develop from the cloud masses. Viewed from above, in sunlight, stratocumulus is like a vast white quilt (Figure 18.9*C*).

Clouds of the fourth family, those of vertical or upright development, are all the cumuliform type. The smallest and most pleasant are the simple *cumulus of fair weather.* These are snow-white cotton-like clouds, generally with rounded tops and rather flattened bases (Figure 18.10*A*); their shaded undersides are gray. On the whole the accompanying weather is fair with much sunshine. Small cumulus may grow larger and denser to form *congested cumulus* with rounded tops resembling heads of cauliflower and flat dark-gray bases (Figure 18.10*B*). These larger cumulus in turn may grow into gigantic *cumulonimbus* clouds, or thunderheads, from which come violent rain, hail, wind gusts, and thunder and lightning (Figure 18.10*C*). Cumulonimbus clouds on occasion extend upward to heights of 60,000 ft (18 km)

A

B

C

FIGURE 18.10. Cumuliform clouds. (*A*) Cumulus of fair weather. (Photograph by H. T. Floreen; courtesy of ESSA, Weather Bureau.) (*B*) Congested cumulus (*cumulus congestus*). (Courtesy of ESSA, Weather Bureau.) (*C*) Cumulonimbus. This isolated thunderstorm has heavy rain falling from the central region. (Photograph by Air Service, U.S. Navy. Courtesy of ESSA, Weather Bureau.)

in the tropics and thus occupy low-, middle-, and high-cloud zones simultaneously. A more detailed description of cumulonimbus clouds is given under the descriptions of convectional rainfall and thunderstorms.

**Wave clouds** A class of cloud quite different in origin and significance from those described above is the *wave cloud,* distinguished by the fact that the cloud itself remains stationary with respect to some topographic feature on the ground, while at the same time air moves rapidly through the cloud form. Air motion is in the form of a *stationary wave.* Most persons have seen stationary waves in rapids of a swift river, the crests and troughs of such waves remaining motionless while water flows through them at high speed.

Figure 18.11 illustrates two occurrences of wave clouds. With strong winds present, air is forced to ascend while passing over a topographic obstacle such as a hilltop or ridge (Figure 18.11*A*). Under favorable combinations of temperature and humidity, moisture in the rising air condenses to produce a *lenticular cloud* (Figure 18.12). As the air descends to the lee of the obstacle, adiabatic warming causes the cloud to evaporate. The cloud is thus constantly in a state of both condensation on its windward side and evaporation on its leeward side while remaining in a fixed position.

Where strong winds blow over a high mountain crest, the air flow is thrown into a succession of stationary waves to the lee of the crest (Figure 18.11*B*). Here, again, conditions may be favorable for the development of the lenticular cloud, one at each wave crest. *Mountain waves,* as this form of air disturbance is often termed, constitute a severe hazard to aircraft, both because of the extreme turbulence that may be present and because of a strong downdraft immediately in the lee of the range.

FIGURE 18.11. (*A*) Lenticular cloud over a hilltop. (*B*) Wave clouds in lee of a mountain crest. [Modified from diagrams by F. H. Ludlam and R. S. Scorer (1957), *Cloud Study: A Pictorial Guide,* London, John Murray, p. 13, Figure 3 and p. 64, Figure 8.]

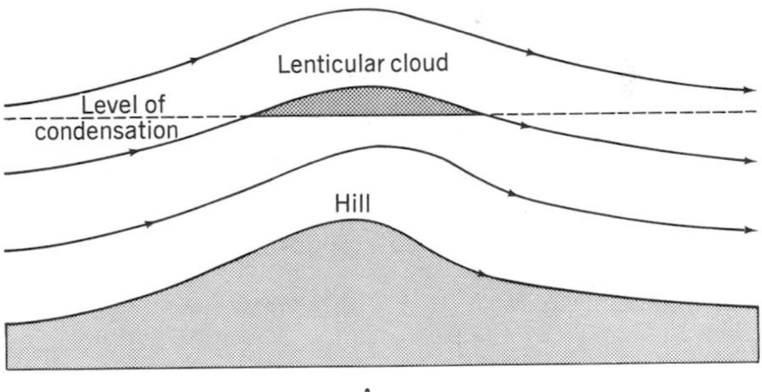


A

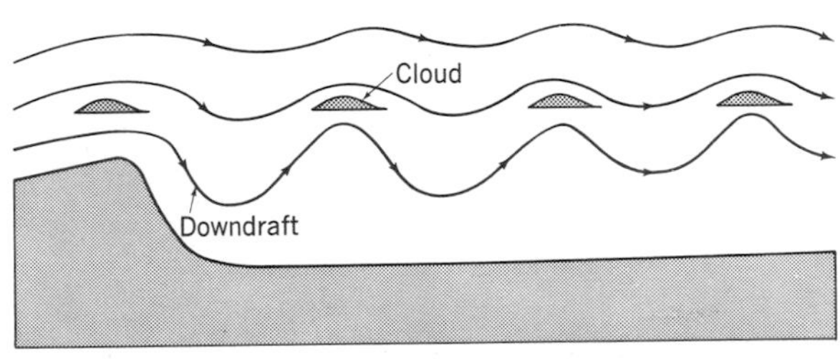


B

**FIGURE 18.12.** A lenticular cloud, holding a stationary position over a hill summit. (Photograph by ESSA, Weather Bureau.)

**Clouds and moisture in the upper atmosphere** Although atmospheric moisture and clouds lie almost entirely in the troposphere, there is evidence of the presence of small amounts of condensed water vapor in faint high-altitude clouds called *nacreous clouds* because of their pearly luster. The nacreous clouds form in the stratosphere at heights of 15–20 mi (24–32 km), where temperatures are very low (−60° to −70° F, −50° to −57° C) and therefore where even a small amount of water vapor might condense to form a cloud. The amount of water vapor at higher levels is not known but must be extremely minute.

Still higher, in the air layer at about 50 mi (80 km) altitude, are faint silvery or bluish clouds termed *noctilucent* (night-shining) *clouds* because they may be seen in arctic and subarctic latitudes about an hour after sunset. Although the nature of the cloud particles is not known, it is suspected that they are of dust rather than of moisture. The dust may be either volcanic or formed by condensation of gases in meteor trails. However, the observed temperature of −120° F (−84° C) of the mesopause at this level is sufficiently low to permit condensation of even traces of water vapor on minute dust particles.

## Forms of precipitation

Precipitation consists of any or all forms of water particles that fall from the atmosphere and reach the ground. Excluded from precipitation are dew and hoarfrost, which are produced when moisture condenses directly upon the ground surface. Precipitation is usually considered as reaching the earth's surface, but it is possible in hot deserts or elsewhere for rain to evaporate completely while falling through lower layers of dry air. Streaks of such falling rain are referred to as *virgae,* from the Latin *virga* for "twig" or "wand".

Commonly recognized forms of precipitation are rain, snow, hail, and sleet. *Rain* consists of water droplets larger than 1/50 in. (0.5 mm) in diameter. The droplets form by rapid condensation and grow by joining with other droplets in frequent collisions. The average raindrop contains roughly one million times the quantity of water found in a single cloud particle and may grow as large as 1/5 in. (5 mm) in diameter. Above this size the drop is unstable and will break apart as it falls. *Drizzle* is simply precipitation composed of tiny droplets, each less than 1/50 in. (0.5 mm) in diameter. Drizzle falls from low-lying nimbostratus clouds.

**FIGURE 18.13.** Tiny hexagonal ice crystals such as these become grouped into aggregates to produce snowflakes. (Photographs by W. A. Bentley; ESSA, Weather Bureau.)

*Snow* is a form of ice in tabular or branched hexagonal (six-sided) crystals (Figure 18.13), which may mat together to form large snowflakes if the air temperature is close to the freezing point. *Sleet* (American usage)

**FIGURE 18.14.** Hailstones, larger than a hen's egg (center foreground). (Courtesy of ESSA, Weather Bureau.)

consists of small grains or pellets of ice formed by the freezing of raindrops falling through a cold air layer.

*Hail* consists of rounded pieces of ice, often made up of concentric ice layers much like the layers of an onion (Figure 18.14). They are formed only in cumulonimbus clouds and indicate powerful updrafts and great turbulence within the clouds, because the ice layers are formed either by repeated lifting of hailstones upward through a moist air layer where subfreezing temperatures exist or by a long, delayed fall through such a layer.

Related to precipitation is the *ice storm,* or *glaze,* a coating of clear ice that forms on branches, wires, pavements, and all exposed surfaces (Figure 18.15). Glaze forms when rain falls through a cold air layer lying close to the ground, causing the droplets to freeze as they touch exposed surfaces. Ice storms cause great damage in the form of broken wires and tree branches and make travel by foot or automobile extremely hazardous.

## Measurement of precipitation

Precipitation is stated in terms of depth in inches or millimeters and represents the depth of water that would be caught in a straight-sided flat-bottomed pan from which there is no loss by evaporation. The *rain gauge,* one of the simplest of weather instruments, consists of a cylinder 4 or 8 in. (10 or 20 cm) in diameter leading into a funnel which collects the water in a long narrow tube in which small amounts can be measured easily by inserting a calibrated stick (Figure 18.16). Some types are able to weigh the water and record the amounts automatically.

Snow may be measured by sampling the snow depth and converting the average figure into the equivalent of water, which is commonly one-tenth the depth of the snow. Very loose freshly fallen snow may, however, reduce to as little as one-thirtieth of its depth as water. If the funnel of the rain gauge is taken out, the cylinder can be used to catch a snowfall, which is then melted to determine its water equivalent. For estimates of snow equivalents on mountain slopes where snow has accumulated over long periods and has layers varying in degree of density, a thin-walled cylinder is forced into the snow to obtain a sample, which is then weighed.

In describing precipitation amount, not only must the depth be given, but the period of time must be given as well. Thus the cumulative total depths to fall in a month or year constitute the *monthly* or *yearly* (*annual*) *precipitation,* respectively. Total depth for single storms is also commonly given. The *intensity* of precipitation is determined by the amount falling in very short periods of time, as in one hour, or in one 10-minute period. Intensity of 0.1 in. (2.5 mm) per hour would be considered a moderate rain, whereas 1 in. (25 mm) per hour would constitute a real cloudburst, causing storm drains to back up and flood city streets and causing much damage by gully erosion on cultivated lands.

**FIGURE 18.16.** A tipping-bucket rain gauge of standard design used in a weather-observing station. (Courtesy of ESSA, Weather Bureau.)

**FIGURE 18.15.** This heavy glaze of ice caused many tree limbs and power lines to break at Cherry Valley, N.Y., December, 1942. (Courtesy of ESSA, Weather Bureau, and N.Y. Power & Light Co., Albany.)

## Conditions that produce precipitation

Precipitation can occur only if large masses of moist air are cooled rapidly below the dew-point temperature, causing condensation to continue until large droplets or ice particles are formed. Only through the vertical rise of large air masses can such continued cooling take place. Therefore a study of conditions leading to precipitation is a study of the ways in which large masses of air (many tens of miles across and thousands of feet thick) are made to rise several thousands of feet in altitude. The rise of large masses of air may be either *spontaneous* or *forced.* Commonly a forced rise triggers spontaneous rise. Precipitation resulting from spontaneous rise of air is commonly termed *convectional.* Forced ascent of air is of two quite different types: *orographic,* the forced ascent of air in crossing a mountain barrier, and *frontal,* the forced rise of air occurring when dissimilar air masses meet. The last of these mechanisms is discussed in Chapter 19, along with the explanation of weather fronts and cyclonic storms.

**Convection and thunderstorms** Convectional rainfall forms from rising columns of moist warm air and may take the form of the torrential downpour of a thunderstorm, with its massive cumulonimbus cloud and associated lightning, thunder, and occasionally hail. Mechanically the rising convection column is similar to the updraft in a chimney caused by the rise of the less dense heated air produced in a fireplace or stove.

In their simplest form small convection units are formed by uneven heating of an air layer near the ground (Figure 18.17). A mass of warmer air detaches itself from the ground layer, to rise as a bubble of air might rise in a vessel of water. Cooled adiabatically, the rising air soon arrives at the level at which the dew-point temperature is reached, and a cumulus cloud begins to form. Commonly the cumulus cloud is small

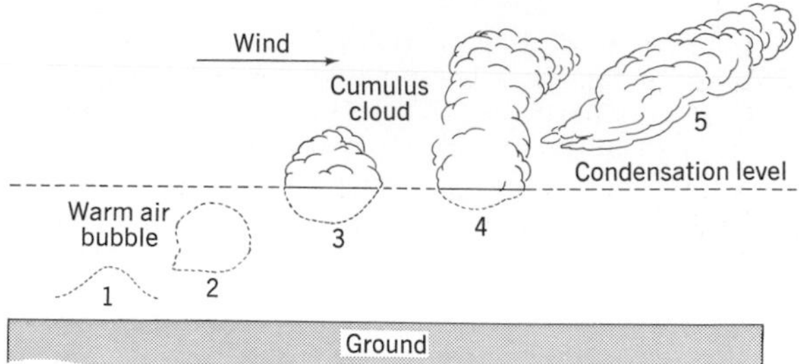


**FIGURE 18.17.** Rise of a bubble of heated air to form a cumulus cloud. [Modified from a drawing by F. H. Ludlam and R. S. Scorer (1957), *Cloud Study: A Pictorial Guide,* London, John Murray, p. 12, Figure 2.]

and subsequently dissolves. In other cases the condensation triggers the growth of a shower-producing cloud, or even the great cumulonimbus storm cloud.

How can convection, once initiated, intensify itself into a thunderstorm? Actually, heating of the ground layer may be only one of several triggering mechanisms which may set off spontaneous growth of convection columns. Another source of energy needs to be called upon to explain the continued rise of air for thousands of feet—namely, the latent heat of condensation present in the moist air and spontaneously released, much as the heat of a fire is obtained by release of energy stored in another form in the fuel. A tiny match can start a great conflagration, similarly a small rising air current can grow into a violent storm.

Under what may be considered normal conditions, air has no tendency to rise spontaneously; it is in a condition described as *stable.* The principle is illustrated in the left hand graph of Figure 18.18. The upper straight line represents the normal temperature lapse rate of the still air. Suppose, now, that we should

**FIGURE 18.18.** Stable and unstable air conditions. (© 1965, John Wiley & Sons, New York.)

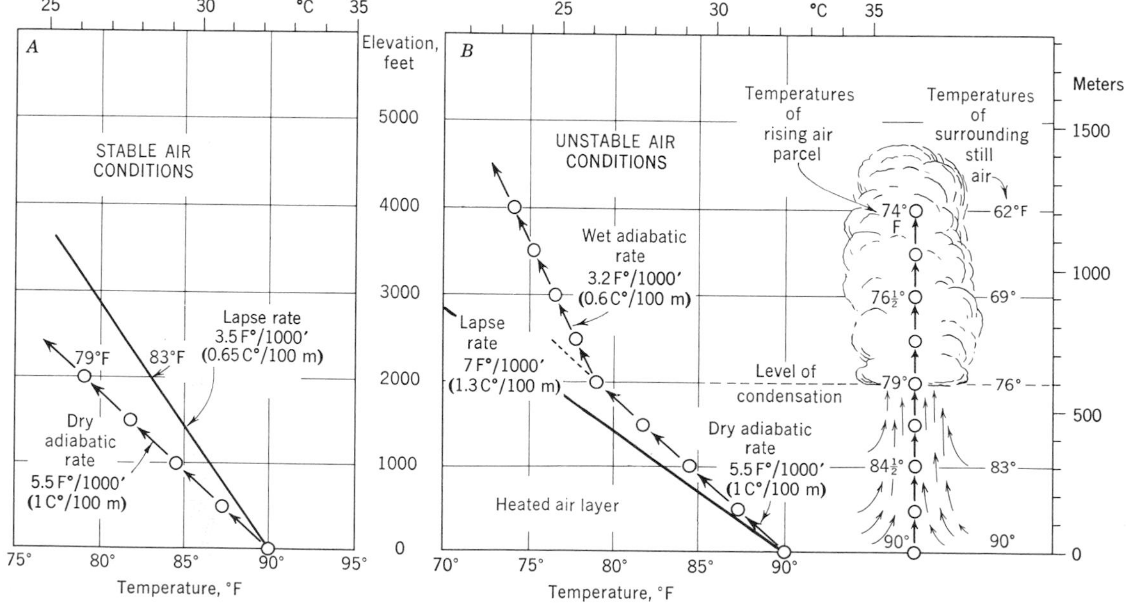

take a parcel of air at ground level and force it to rise. As the lower line of circles shows, the rising air will cool at the dry adiabatic rate, which has a larger value than the normal lapse rate. At all levels, then, the rising air will prove to be colder and denser than the surrounding air. If allowed to move freely, the air parcel would sink back to ground level.

When a mass or layer of air is in a condition favorable to overturning or vertical motion and to the spontaneous growth of convectional storms, it is said to be *unstable.* This principle is illustrated in the right-hand graph of Figure 18.18. Suppose that a rising air column is set in motion by heating of the air layer near the ground. Through heating, the lapse rate has been raised to 7 F° per 1000 ft (1.3 C° per 100 m), which is a larger value than the dry adiabatic rate of 5.5 F° per 1000 ft (1 C° per 100 m). As the air rises, it is adiabatically cooled at the dry rate. If we now examine the air temperature in the surrounding still air, we shall find that at any given level the air in the rising column remains several degrees warmer than the still air adjacent to it. The rising air therefore continues to rise.

When condensation begins, the wet adiabatic rate takes over and liberated heat is added to the rising air, and it continues to be warmer than the surrounding air. Consequently the convection becomes more violent and the upward currents intensify, causing a violent storm with heavy bursts of rain. Finally, at elevations of perhaps 20,000–40,000 ft (6–12 km), condensation in the rising air becomes greatly reduced, and its temperature falls to the same level as the surrounding air. The rising air now being of the same density as the surrounding air, the upward movement of the convection system ceases and the air spreads sideways.

Detailed studies show that thunderstorms consist of individual parts, called *cells.* Within each cell air rises in a succession of bubble-like masses, rather than in a single continuous column. At all levels air is brought into the cell from the sides in the wake of the rising bubble by a process called *entrainment.*

Vertical air speeds up to 3000 ft (900 m) per minute commonly develop. Condensation goes on rapidly and ranges in type from droplets of water in the lower and middle parts, through mixed rain and snow, then wet snow, to dry snow in the extremely cold upper part.

As the rising air bubble travels upward to high levels, heavy precipitation occurs. The top of the cloud, above the freezing level, spreads laterally to form an *anvil top.* Falling ice particles, cooling and seeding the cloud, cause rapid condensation. Falling drops or ice particles actually drag the air downward to produce a strong downdraft of cold air which strikes the ground at the time of the heavy initial burst of rain (Figure 18.19). This gusty squall wind spreads out horizontally along the ground.

The downdraft creates an area of higher barometric pressure at ground level, the *thunderstorm high.* Air turbulence within the storm is violent and will seriously damage or destroy light aircraft that venture into the cell. Raindrops may be caught in the updraft and carried above the freezing level, where they become frozen pellets. Coated by supercooled water, these pellets grow into hailstones (Figure 18.14). Hailstones up to 3 in. (8 cm) in diameter fall in rare cases—the

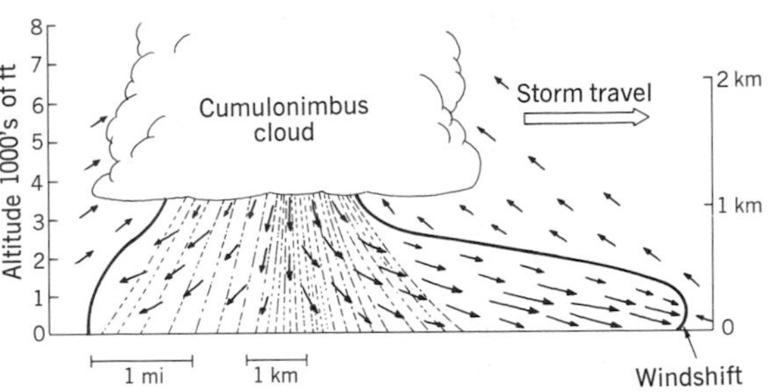


**FIGURE 18.19.** Schematic diagram of downdraft beneath a thunderstorm. A cold air wedge with strong wind gusts spreads along the ground in advance of the cloud. [After H. R. Byers and R. R. Braham (1949), *The Thunderstorm,* Washington, D.C., U.S. Govt. Printing Office.]

maximum on record in the United States was a single hailstone 5.2 in. (13.2 cm) in diameter and weighing 1.58 lb (0.72 kg).

Another familiar effect of the mature stage of the thunderstorm is *lightning,* an electrical discharge—or simply a great spark, or arc—from one part of a cloud to another or from the cloud to the ground. In a manner not yet established, but subject to a number of hypotheses currently under intensive investigation, regions of positive and negative electrical charges accumulate in the cumulonimbus cloud (Figure 18.20). Generally

**FIGURE 18.20.** Distribution of electrical charges inside a typical thunderstorm cell. [After U.S. Dept. of Commerce (1955), *C. A. A. Technical Manual 104,* Washington, D.C., U.S. Govt. Printing Office, p. 60, Figure 95.]

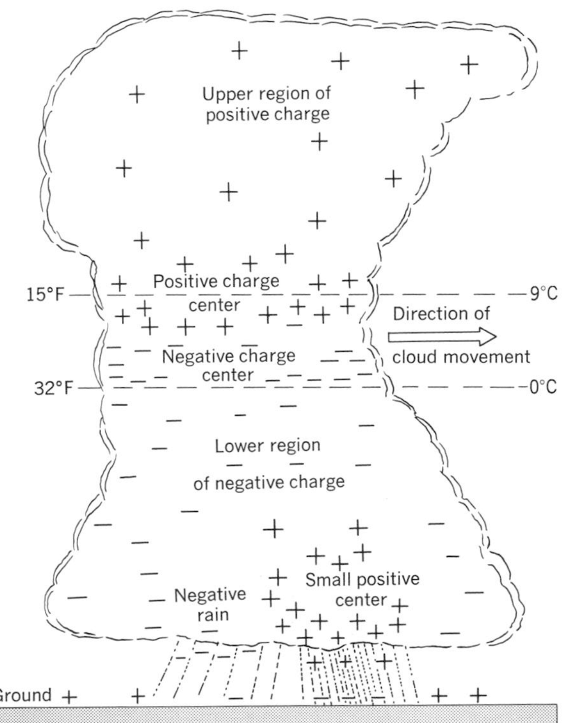

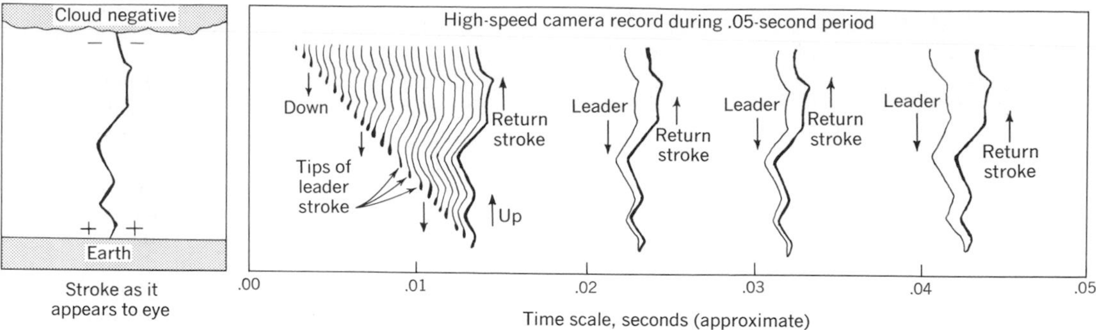


**FIGURE 18.21.** A lightning stroke analyzed by high-speed camera photograph. [After U.S. Dept. of Commerce (1955), *C. A. A. Technical Manual 104,* Washington, D.C., U.S. Govt. Printing Office, p. 62, Figure 96.]

the upper portion of the thunderstorm is positively charged, whereas centers of negative and positive charges form below this.

The ground beneath the negatively charged parts of cloud in turn develops a positive charge. When the electrical potential has reached sufficient magnitude (some 20–30 million volts), a lightning stroke occurs, traveling first from cloud to ground (Figure 18.21), then returning to the cloud. Several alternations between cloud and ground eliminate the difference in electrical pressure. The whole process takes less than one-tenth of a second and appears as a single flash.

An electric current of perhaps 60,000–100,000 amperes may flow during a lightning discharge. The thunder which we hear is the shock wave of sound sent out by the lightning stroke, whose great heat causes a sudden expansion of the air along the path of the stroke. Because sound travels at a rate of roughly 1 mile for every 5 seconds (330 m per sec), the thunder follows the lightning flash by a time interval depending upon distance. If both seem to occur at the same instant, the strike is very close by, whereas a delay of 5 seconds in the sound would indicate a strike roughly 1 mile away. Very distant diffuse flashes reflected from high cumulonimbus clouds may be too far away to be heard, because sound waves die out rapidly as they travel.

After a thunderstorm has experienced the rise of a number of successive bubble-like air masses, the uppermost portion of the thunderstorm has developed an anvil top in the altitude zone 40,000 to 60,000 ft (15 to 18 km). The anvil, formed of ice crystals, drifts downwind in the prevailing upper air flow and may result in an extensive cirrus layer (Figures 18.22 and 18.23).

Large thunderstorms may consist of several cells, developing in succession at adjacent positions, thus giving the storm long duration and repeated bursts of heavy rain. When many thunderstorms occur along a broad belt, it is not feasible to distinguish individual storms. As a general rule, a single-celled thunderstorm will have a width of perhaps 3–5 mi (5–8 km). In the following chapter on air masses, fronts, and cyclonic storms, the characteristic conditions for occurrence of thunderstorms are explained.

Because convectional, or thunderstorm, rainfall requires favorable air conditions in the form of moist, usually warm, unstable air, it is a dominant type in equatorial and tropical regions. It generally becomes less important in the higher latitudes and is conspicuously absent in the polar regions. Thunderstorms are also most frequent in summer. Because convectional rainfall is formed in cells, the rainfall pattern is spotty—some localities receive as much as 1–3 in. (25 to 75 mm) of rain in a single storm, whereas localities a few miles away may have none at all. Although convectional rainfall is produced in storms of small areal extent, these in turn can constitute the numerous parts of much larger atmospheric disturbances.

**FIGURE 18.22.** An anvil-topped cumulonimbus cloud. (Sketched by A. N. Strahler from a photograph by ESSA, Weather Bureau.)

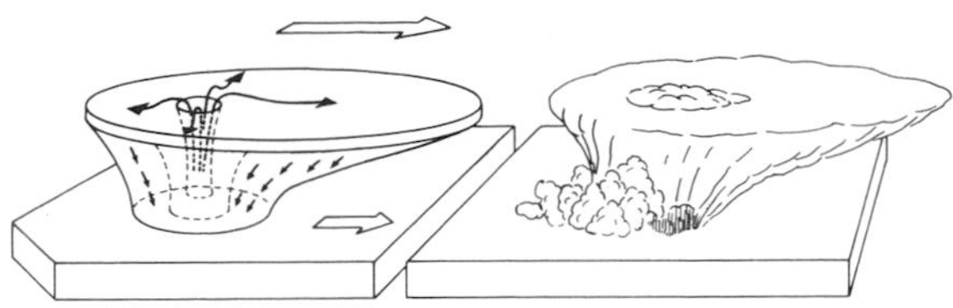

**FIGURE 18.23.** Schematic diagram (left) and sketch (right) of anvil cloud formation. Underside of anvil overhang is formed of trails of ice and snow crystals falling from the spreading cloud top. [Modified from drawings by F. H. Ludlam and R. S. Scorer (1957), *Cloud Study: A Pictorial Guide,* London, John Murray, p. 16, Figure 5.]

**Orographic precipitation** The word orographic is an adjective meaning "relating to mountains." Orographic precipitation is therefore related to the existence of a mountainous terrain. The principle of orographic rainfall is explained in Figure 18.24. Where prevailing winds blow from an ocean across a mountainous coast, air is made to rise, often through many thousands of feet. If the moisture content is high, as is the case of most air originating over an ocean, the dew-point temperature is quickly reached and further ascent of the air produces rain or snow which falls on the windward slopes and crest of the range.

Orographic precipitation can take two forms: (1) a persistent light rain resulting from the steady lift of stable air, or (2) heavy convectional showers or thunderstorms set off by the forced rise of unstable air.

In equatorial and tropical regions particularly, orographic rainfall is usually convectional in form and brings frequent violent downpours when the rainy monsoon is on. The world's record of great rains probably goes to Cherrapunji, India, a station at 4300 ft (1300 m) elevation on the southern slopes of the Khasi Hills in Assam. Here, in the single month of August, 1841, 241 in. (612 cm) of rain fell, and of this 150 in. (380 cm) fell on five consecutive days, 40.8 in. (104 cm) in one 24-hour period!

Orographic rainfall is also great along the western coasts of both North America and Europe wherever mountains lie close to the sea and are exposed to prevailing westerly winds (Figure 18.25). This precipitation is partly in the form of snow, which piles up to depths of many feet in winter. Compared with tropical coasts, rain along these northerly west coasts tends to be lighter and much more prolonged, with many more rainy days per year. The Scottish Highlands, for example, may have 200–250 days per year with rain, whereas the figure is about half this in the wet tropics. (See Figure 18.28.) On the Pacific Coast, the Olympic Mountains of Washington are an outstanding example of a locality with high orographic rainfall. Here the yearly total precipitation is well over 100 in. (250 cm).

**FIGURE 18.24.** Cooling, condensation, and subsequent warming within a mass of air forced to pass over a mountain barrier.

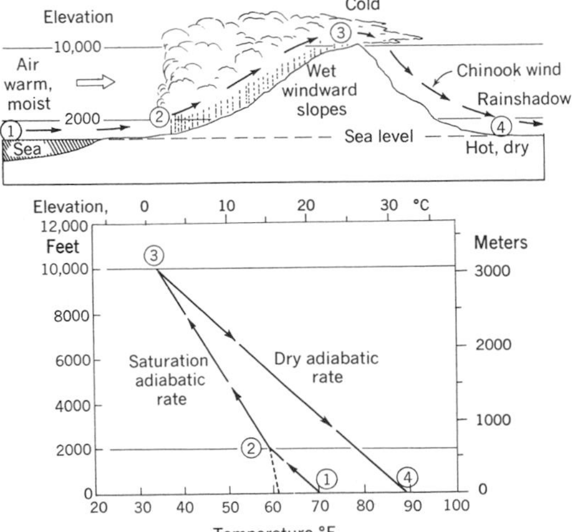


**FIGURE 18.25.** Relation between mean annual precipitation (above) and major topographic features (below) for the State of California. (© 1965, John Wiley & Sons, New York. Precipitation data from U.S. Dept. of Agriculture.)

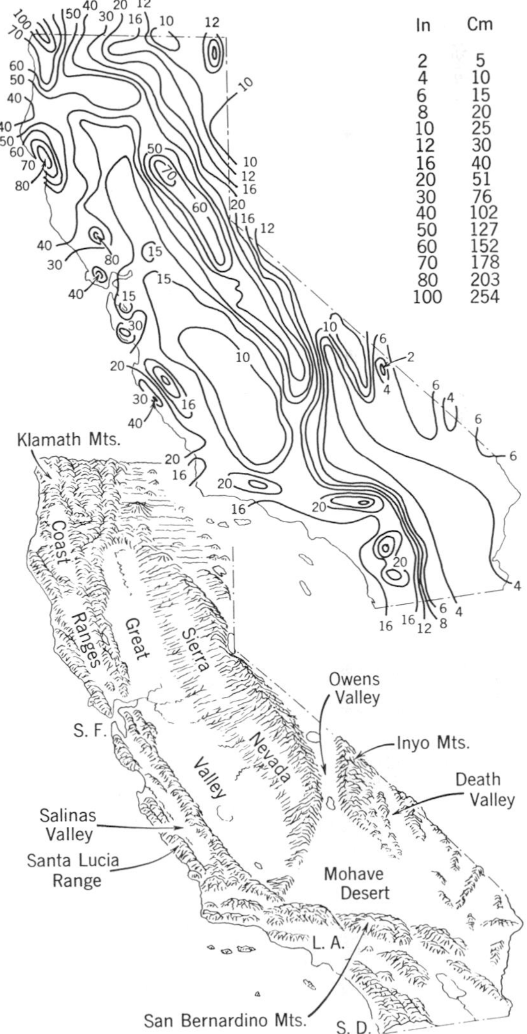

## Rain-shadow deserts

We have seen that subsiding air is warmed at the dry adiabatic rate. As Figure 18.24 shows, air descending the lee slope of a range warms rapidly, the relative humidity falls below saturation, and the remaining water droplets of the clouds quickly evaporate, clearing the air. Since no more moisture is available, the air temperature continues to increase at the dry adiabatic lapse rate of 5½ F° per 1000 ft (1 C° per 100 m). Relative humidity continues to decrease. Notice that the graph informs us that at any given level, say 200 ft (600 m), the descending air is considerably warmer than the rising air at the same level on the windward slope of the mountain range.

By the time the air has reached the valley floor at sea level on the lee side of the range, it is hot and very dry. A desert, commonly called a *rain-shadow desert,* will exist here if winds blow prevailingly from the ocean toward the continent throughout the year. Where winds alternate in direction with season of year, as in a monsoon system affecting a narrow landmass in low latitude, each side of the range has its alternate seasons of rainfall and drought.

Yet another weather phenomenon explained by subsiding air is a warm, dry wind which occasionally blows from high mountains down upon the adjoining plains. In Europe, this wind is named the *foehn* from its occurrence in Swiss valleys bordering the Alps on the north. Locally named a *chinook* in the United States, it blows down from the Rocky Mountains upon the Great Plains in a belt extending from Colorado into Alberta.

Actually a foehn, or chinook, wind is essentially identical with the subsiding drying air which produces a rain-shadow desert, illustrated in Figure 18.24, and is explained in much the same way. What makes the foehn wind noteworthy is that it often occurs in late winter or spring, when snow covers the ground on the plains. The dry air has great evaporating ability and may cause the snow to disappear by sublimation in a remarkably short time. A rapid rise of temperature, sometimes as great as 30 or 40 F° (17 or 22 C°) may occur within a few hours of the onset of a foehn.

## Aridity in high-pressure cells

Another important example of dryness associated with sinking air is seen in the high-pressure cell, or anticyclone, explained in Chapter 15. Air in a high-pressure center is slowly sinking and spreading outward toward areas of lower barometric pressure. Such air is warmed adiabatically and becomes drier as it descends. This process tends to produce fair skies and sunny weather.

The subtropical high-pressure cells centered on tropical oceans are especially dry in their central and eastern portions, producing rainless conditions that extend from the west coast of continents far out to sea. (See Figure 18.28.) Figure 18.26 shows diagrammatically a set of conditions commonly present along the west coasts of Chile, Peru, and southern California. Dry, warming air descends upon a coastal lowland hemmed in on the landward side by mountain ranges. At the same time a cold upwelling ocean current, such as the California or Humboldt currents, chills a layer of air within a few hundred feet of the surface, producing dampness and fog. At the top of the cool-air layer is warmer air. There results a *temperature inversion* or increase of temperature with altitude. The cool, heavy surface air remains at ground level. Such conditions are ideal for the formation of smog, because pollution products cannot escape from this trap.

Farther out to sea (Figure 18.26) in the region of the trade winds the temperature inversion persists, with warmer air above cooler. The moist air above the sea surface tends to condense into cumulus, or wool-pack, clouds, but these cannot rise through the inversion lid, and the air is thus prevented from undergoing the great vertical rise necessary to produce sufficient adiabatic cooling for precipitation (Figure 18.27). Consequently the climate is relatively rainless over large expanses of the ocean under the influence of the subtropical high-pressure cells.

## World precipitation patterns

The areal extent of precipitation can be shown on a map by means of lines of equal amounts of precipitation, or *isohyets.* A given isohyet connects all points on the map having a specified quantity of rainfall in a given period of time. Isohyets might, for example, tell how the rainfall in a given storm of three days duration was distributed. In Figure 34.21 isohyets are drawn for a storm over Ohio. More commonly, however, isohyets are used to show climatological information, such as monthly or yearly precipitation averaged over many years of observations. Figure 18.28 is such a map, showing average annual precipitation for the entire world, exclusive of the polar regions. The map is generalized and does not show details of precipitation differences, but it will serve to show a global pattern of seven types:

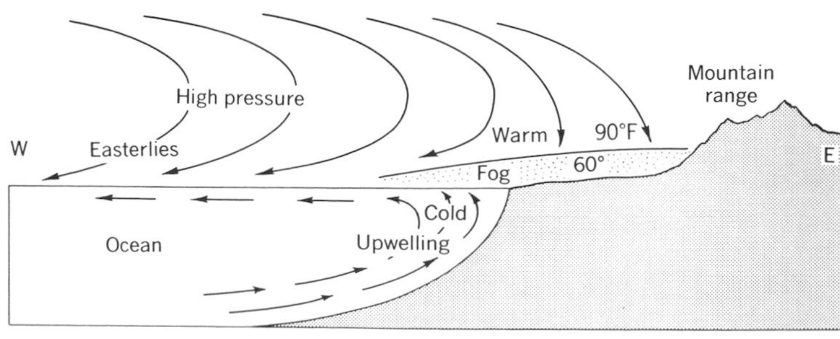


**FIGURE 18.26.** Schematic diagram of descending air over a desert west coast and formation of a coastal temperature inversion.

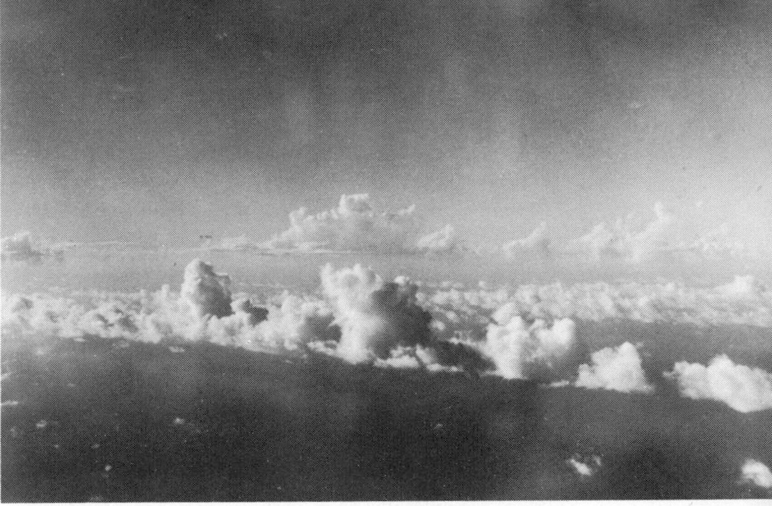

FIGURE 18.27. Trade-wind cumulus clouds of the Pacific Ocean seen from the air. The clouds are arranged in rows. (Photograph by courtesy of Joanne Simpson.)

(1) The *wet equatorial belt* of heavy rainfall, over 80 in. (2030 mm) annually, straddles the equator and includes the Amazon River basin in South America, the Congo River basin of equatorial Africa, much of the African coast from Nigeria west to Guinea, and the East Indies. Here the prevailingly warm temperatures and high moisture content of the air favor abundant convective rainfall. Thunderstorms are frequent and their great cumulonimbus clouds extend upward to heights as great as 50,000–60,000 ft (15–18 km).

(2) Narrow coastal belts of high rainfall, 60–80+ in. (1520–2030+ mm) per year, extend from near the equator to latitudes of about 25° to 30° N. and S. on the eastern sides of every continent or large island. For examples, see the eastern coasts of Brazil, Central America, Madagascar, and northeastern Australia. These are the *trade-wind coasts,* or *windward tropical coasts,* where moist air from warm oceans is brought over the land by the trades. Encountering coastal hills, escarpments, or mountains, these winds produce heavy orographic rainfall.

(3) In striking contrast to the wet equatorial belt astride the equator are the two zones of huge *tropical deserts* lying approximately upon the Tropics of Cancer and Capricorn. These hot, barren deserts, with less than 10 in. (254 mm) of rainfall annually and in many places with less than 2 in. (50 mm), are located under and caused by the subtropical cells of high pressure where the subsiding air is adiabatically warmed and dried. Note that these deserts extend off the west coasts of the lands and out over the oceans. Such rain as these areas experience is largely convectional and extremely unreliable.

(4) Farther northward, in the interiors of Asia and North America between lat. 30° and lat. 50°, are great continental *middle-latitude deserts* and expanses of semi-arid grasslands known as *steppes.* Dryness here results from remoteness from ocean sources of moisture. Located in a region of prevailing westerly winds, these arid lands occupy the position of rain shadows in the lee of coastal mountains and highlands. Thus the Cordilleran Ranges of Oregon, Washington, British Columbia, and Alaska shield the interior of North America from moist air originating in the Pacific. Upon descending into the intermontane basins and interior plains, this air is warmed and dried.

Similarly, mountains of Europe and the Scandinavian peninsula serve to obstruct the flow of moist air from the North Atlantic into western Asia. The great southern Asiatic ranges likewise prevent the entry of moist tropical air from the Indian Ocean and the western Pacific.

The Southern Hemisphere has too little land in the middle latitudes to produce a true continental desert,

FIGURE 18.28. World map of mean annual precipitation. Isohyets in inches of water; metric equivalents in table. (Isohyets modified and simplified from *The Times Atlas,* 1958, *World Climatology,* Volume 1, Plate 3, London, The Times Publ. Co.)

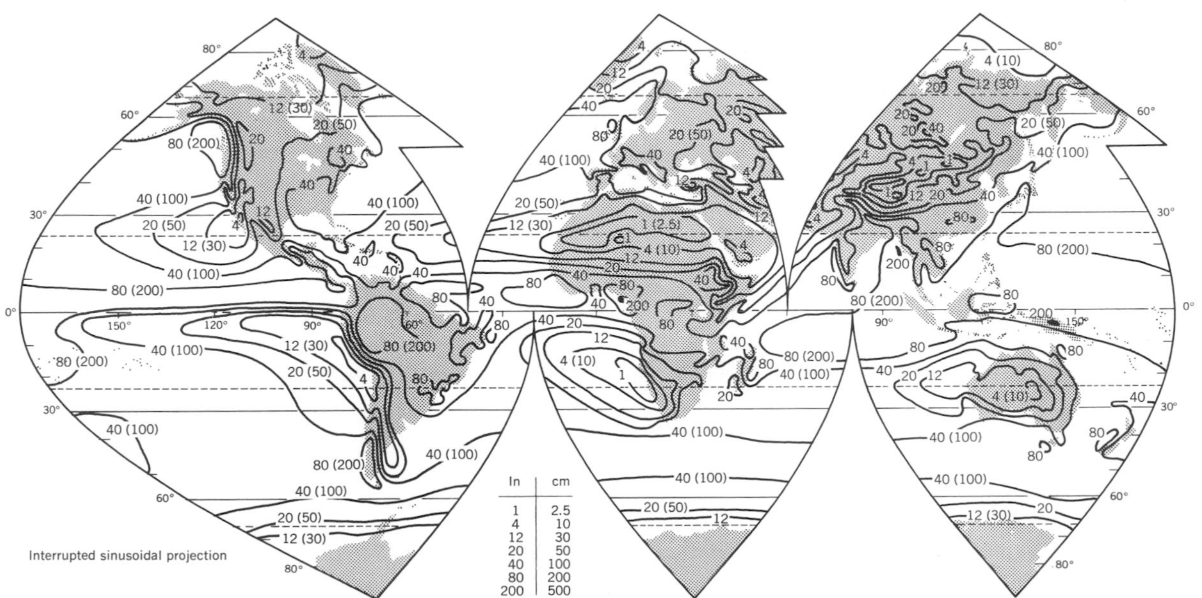

but the dry steppes of Patagonia lying on the lee side of the Andean chain are roughly the counterpart of the North American deserts and steppes of Oregon and northern Nevada, which lie in the rain shadow of the Sierra Nevada and the Cascade Range.

(5) On the southeastern sides of the continents of North America and Asia, in lat. 25° to 45°, and to a less marked degree in these same latitudes in the Southern Hemisphere in Uruguay, Argentina, and southeastern Australia, are the *humid subtropical* regions with 40–60 in. (1020–1520 mm) of rainfall annually. These regions lie on the moist western sides of the subtropical high-pressure centers in such a position that humid air from the tropical ocean is carried poleward over the adjoining land. Commonly, too, these areas receive heavy rains from tropical storms.

(6) Still another distinctive wet location is on *middle-latitude west coasts* of all continents and large islands lying between about 35° and 65° in the region of prevailing westerly winds. These zones have already been explained as good examples of coasts on which abundant orographic precipitation falls. Where the coasts are mountainous, as in Alaska and British Columbia, Patagonia, Scotland, Norway, and South Island of New Zealand, the annual precipitation is over 80 in. (2030 mm). Small wonder that these coasts formerly supported great valley glaciers which carved the deep bays known as fiords, so typically a part of their scenery.

(7) The seventh precipitation region is formed by the *arctic* and *polar deserts.* Northward of the 60th parallel, annual precipitation is largely under 10 in. (254 mm), except for the west-coast belts. Cold air cannot hold much moisture, consequently it does not yield large amounts of precipitation. At the same time, however, the relative humidity is high and evaporation is low. Consequently these arctic and polar regions have abundant moisture in the air and soil and are not to be considered as dry in the same sense as the tropical deserts.

## Natural vegetation and precipitation

Plants are highly sensitive indicators of climatic conditions. Plants assume characteristic physical forms and dimensions associated with particular limits of temperature and precipitation. (Refer to the world map of natural vegetation, Appendix II.)

Where temperatures are sufficiently high and precipitation ample, at least in one season of the year, the natural vegetation is *forest.* Certain varieties of forests are composed of evergreen trees, others are composed of deciduous trees. For example, in the uniformly warm and wet environment of the equatorial belt, forests consist of tall broad-leaved trees that undergo no recognizable seasonal shedding of leaves. In tropical latitudes experiencing a very wet monsoon season alternating with a very dry season, forests consist of trees that shed their leaves in the dry season to prevent death by water loss. In middle latitudes experiencing a warm moist summer but a very cold winter, forest trees shed their leaves in winter to prevent destruction of tissues by freezing. In still colder climates, forests consist largely of needle-leaved evergreens that can withstand the effects of long cold winters.

Extreme aridity prevailing throughout the year imposes a severe stress upon plants. Forests are lacking and the few conspicuous desert plants are shrubs whose leaf structures are adapted to low rates of water loss. In the semi-arid regions, where annual evaporation exceeds precipitation, grasses are a dominant plant form, since they are able to withstand a prolonged dry season and high soil temperatures. The extreme cold and frost action of the arctic regions produces yet another form of desert, the *tundra,* in which plants are very small.

Appendix II includes a brief description of the principal types of natural vegetation assemblages, together with a world map showing their distribution in a highly generalized way. A careful comparison of maps in this appendix will show that climate has a strong control over both natural vegetation and soils.

## Water balance of the atmosphere

This chapter has dealt with basic principles of evaporation, condensation, and precipitation, so it is appropriate at this point to take another step in evaluating the global balance of energy and matter developed in Chapters 13, 14, and 16. The role of latent heat in the earth's energy balance has already been treated (Chapter 16). Figure 16.17 shows the latent heat flux for each belt of latitude, and Figure 16.18 the transport of latent heat across the parallels of latitude. That analysis dealt with energy alone, not with mass, the units used for energy transfer being kilocalories per unit of time.

The earth's water balance is concerned with the transfer of mass in the form of water from place to place in the atmosphere, oceans, and lands. Units used in water balance analysis are kilograms of water, thus the transport of water is given in kilograms per unit of time (hour, day, month, or year).

At this point, let us consider only the water balance of the earth's atmosphere, deferring to Chapter 33 a consideration of the water balance of the total global system, involving continents and oceans as well as the atmosphere.

A simple equation can be developed for the water balance of the atmosphere by considering the ways in which water can enter and leave a unit column of the atmosphere extending from the earth's surface to the top of the atmosphere. For practical purposes, the atmosphere above the 400 mb level (which lies at about 24,000 ft, or 7.4 km) can be disregarded.

Water can enter the atmospheric column by evaporation from the ocean or land surface beneath; let this quantity be designated by the symbol $E$ (kilograms per year). Second, water may be imported horizontally into the column in vapor form by atmospheric circulation; let this quantity be designated as $c$. Water may also be exported from the column by the same process, and a negative value of $c$ will suffice to denote a loss. Another form of water loss is by precipitation (dew and hoarfrost can be included); designated by $P$.

The rate of increase or decrease of water vapor within the atmosphere column, designated by the term $g$, can be grouped with the four terms in the preceding paragraph into the following water balance equation:

$$g = E - P - c$$

Consider, next, that the average annual value of $g$ will be close to zero, therefore

$$0 = E - P - c$$
$$\text{and } c = E - P$$

Consequently, on an annual basis the horizontal transport of water through atmospheric circulation must equal the difference between evaporation and precipitation. The principles of evaporation from continental surfaces, as well as the disposal of precipitation by flow of water over and beneath the ground surface, are treated in Chapters 33 and 34.

Consider at this time only the term *c*, as the net annual transport of water across the parallels of latitude for the entire earth. Figure 18.29 is a graph resembling the graph of the meridional energy transport of Figure 16.18, except that the units on the vertical axis are in kilograms of water per year, rather than kilocalories per year. Where the curve lies above the zero line, transport is northward; where below the line, transport is southward. Notice that from about 20° latitude north and south transport is toward the equator. This transport represents movement of water vapor in the Hadley cell circulation, in which the tropical easterlies meet in the intertropical convergence zone. Here the vapor is condensed, largely as convectional precipitation, and leaves the atmosphere to become water on the lands and oceans. Above latitude 25° north and south, water vapor transport is poleward, as descending air in the poleward limb of the Hadley cell is transferred across parallels of higher latitude by advection in cyclones and anticyclones of middle latitudes. Poleward of 40° latitude losses of water vapor through precipitation are large and evaporation is reduced by cold. Thus the transport of water vapor drops off sharply, to become zero at each pole.

**FIGURE 18.29.** Graph of mean annual meridional transport of water vapor. A smooth curve has been drawn through values calculated for each 10-degree parallel of latitude. [Data from W. D. Sellers (1965), *Physical Climatology*, Chicago, Univ. of Chicago Press, p. 94, Figure 29.]

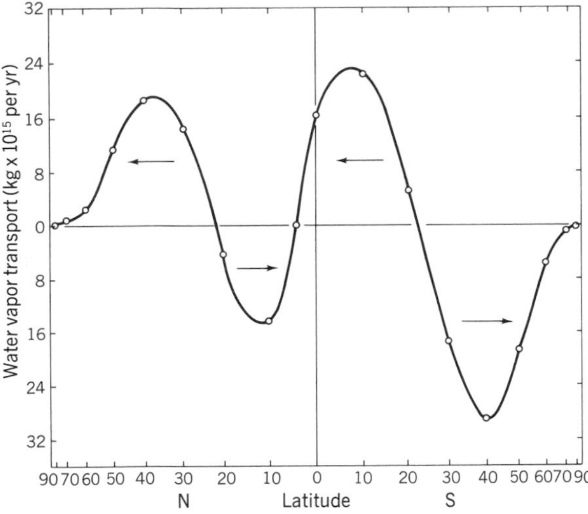


It should be pointed out that the values shown by the curve in Figure 18.29 are estimates. A number of different estimates have been made, and we must be prepared for further changes as more data are available. Such changes will not, however, alter the basic global pattern of atmospheric water vapor transport.

## References for further study

World Meteorological Organization (1956), *International Cloud Atlas,* 2 vols., English ed., Geneva, Switzerland.

Ludlam, F. H., and R. S. Scorer (1957), *Cloud Study: A Pictorial Guide,* London, John Murray, 80 pp.

Battan, L. J. (1961), *The Nature of Violent Storms,* Garden City, N.Y., Doubleday, 158 pp., chaps. 2, 4.

Battan, L. J. (1962), *Cloud Physics and Cloud Seeding,* Garden City, N.Y., Doubleday, 144 pp.

Riehl, H. (1965), *Introduction to the Atmosphere,* New York, McGraw-Hill, 365 pp., chaps. 4, 5.

Sellers, W. D. (1965), *Physical Climatology,* Chicago, Univ. of Chicago Press, 272 pp., chap. 7.

U.S. Dept. of Commerce (1965), *Aviaticn Weather for Pilots,* Fed. Aviation Agency and Civil Aeronautics Admin., Washington, D.C., U.S. Govt. Printing Office, 299 pp., chaps. 5, 6, 7, 8, 11, 12.

Petterssen, S. (1969), *Introduction to Meteorology,* 3rd ed., New York, McGraw-Hill, 333 pp., chaps. 4, 5, 6, 7, 8, 16.

# 19

# Air masses, fronts, and storms

WITH THE INTRODUCTION of the telegraph, making possible instantaneous communication between cities, it first became possible for meteorologists to prepare current weather maps, showing the surface distribution of pressure, temperature, winds, and weather. Such weather maps are termed *synoptic maps,* because they give a synopsis, or picture, of weather elements at a given moment over a large area. The first American synoptic maps and forecasts were prepared in 1857 by Joseph Henry of the Smithsonian Institution in Washington, D.C. After a period of inactivity during the Civil War, preparation of the daily synoptic map was resumed by Cleveland Abbe. This activity progressed into systematic weather reporting under the U.S. Signal Corps and finally led to organization of the U.S. Weather Bureau in 1890.

The examination of maps drawn at 12- or 24-hour intervals demonstrated that bad weather —involving cloudiness, precipitation, and strong winds—was associated with centers of low barometric pressure, or cyclones, which move across country, generally from west to east. Most cyclones are not dangerous in character and few would be called severe storms by the average person. Clear skies and fair weather were seen to be associated with centers of high barometric pressure, or anticyclones.

By anticipating the speed and direction of movement of lows and highs, meteorologists developed the principles of weather forecasting, initially a mixture of science and art based on long experience with correlating weather and pressure patterns. At the time of World War I rapid advances in weather theory were made as a result of the study of much new information on conditions in the upper air provided by the first aircraft. Not until World War II, however, did the nature of large-scale weather systems become really apparent. At that time military aircraft operations were extended into the equatorial, tropical, and arctic regions on a vast scale. A great network of weather-observing stations accompanied the construction of military bases and airfields. Synoptic charts of the entire Northern Hemisphere became possible, not only for surface weather conditions, but for upper levels as well.

## Air masses

A basic idea, upon which the understanding of modern weather science depends, is that of *air masses.* A single, or individual, air mass is simply a large body of air that may have the horizontal extent of some large fraction of a continent or ocean and is characterized by a sameness of temperature and humidity at a given altitude level. In vertical extent most air masses include the lower part of the troposphere from ground level to heights of 2–4 mi (3–6 km). In some places it will be found that one air mass lies above another.

Air masses usually have distinct boundaries and have properties different from those of adjacent air masses. The meteorologist can distinguish between adjacent masses by noting differences in temperature or in moisture content or in both at the same elevation. A boundary between two air masses is termed a *front.* Most unsettled weather occurs along fronts rather than deep within the boundaries of an air mass.

**Air-mass source regions** An air mass acquires its characteristic properties of temperature and humidity from its *source region,* which is the land or sea surface over which it originates. When a portion of the troposphere remains stagnant or moves very slowly over a given area of land or ocean of uniform surface properties, the air gradually takes on the properties of this surface.

For example, air accumulating over a cold snow-covered arctic landmass will lose heat by radiation on long winter nights and become extremely cold. Being cold, its moisture content will be small. Here, then, is formed an air mass with the properties of its source region. In contrast, air which stagnates over a warm tropical ocean not only will be warmed by radiation, but will absorb water vapor by evaporation from the sea surface. This vapor will diffuse upward until the entire layer has a high moisture content.

In general, air-mass source regions coincide with the earth's large bodies of land and water. The properties of these source regions may change greatly from winter to summer, especially in the middle latitudes, therefore the air mass developed in winter may be quite different from that formed in summer. Over oceans at low latitudes air masses will be quite similar year around.

Because of the earth's prevailing circulation, air masses tend to travel, or migrate, passing out of their source regions and over areas with different surface characteristics. When this happens, the moving air mass will be gradually modified by the surface over which it travels. For example, a cold dry air mass from a northern continent may move southward over a tropical ocean. Here the air is steadily warmed, and its moisture content rises until it is eventually completely transformed into an air mass typical of the new source region.

**Classification of air masses** An international system of air-mass classification has been generally accepted. It is based on two categories of classification: (1) latitudinal position of the source area and (2) surface condition of the source area—whether land or water. The first basis of classification, initial temperature, depends in a general way upon latitude. Four types of air masses are thus recognized on a temperature basis:

| | | |
|---|---|---|
| A | Arctic air masses | Formed over Arctic Ocean and fringing lands. |
| or AA | Antarctic air masses | Formed over Antarctica. |
| P | Polar air masses | Formed over lands and oceans of lat. 50° to 65° N. and S. |
| T | Tropical air masses | Formed over lands and oceans under the subtropical high-pressure cells at lat. 20° to 35° N. and S. |
| E | Equatorial air masses | Formed principally over oceans near the equator. |

As one might guess, arctic and polar air masses are cold, and tropical and equatorial air masses are warm.

The second important factor in classifying air masses is humidity. Whether air masses are moist or dry depends upon whether the source region is land or water; hence the following subdivisions:

| | | |
|---|---|---|
| m | Maritime air masses | Formed over oceans, relatively moist. |
| c | Continental air masses | Formed over large landmasses, relatively dry. |

In combining the two sets of symbols the lower-case letters *m* and *c* are written in front of the capital letters *A, P, T,* and *E,* thus: *mT* (maritime tropical air mass), *cP* (continental polar air mass), etc.

The air-mass classification scheme also provides for symbols that indicate the temperature and humidity modifications an air mass may undergo. To designate whether air masses are warmer or colder than the surface over which they are passing, the lower-case letters *w* and *k* are added after the air-mass symbol. The letter *w* means that the air mass is warmer than the surface over which it is passing, and *k* that it is colder than the surface. The letters *w* and *k* are used on synoptic charts. For example, *cPk* designates a continental polar air mass which is colder than the surface over which it is passing.

The relation of air mass to surface is most important in meteorology, because entirely different weather conditions, ranging from stability to instability, will result, depending upon whether the air mass is warmer or colder than the surface over which it is passing. Humidity changes within an air mass may be indicated on the weather map by a symbol meaning that transformation of an air mass from one classification to another is occurring. For example, the symbol *mP* → *cP* means that a maritime polar air mass is being transformed by reduction in moisture content into a continental polar air mass during travel across the continental interior.

**World-wide distribution of air masses** A general picture of the earth's air masses and their source regions is given in Figure 19.1, which shows a hemisphere of the earth with land and ocean areas greatly generalized. Source regions are outlined by ovals, centered over either the ocean or land, but not straddling both. Also shown are frontal zones of conflict between air masses of adjoining unlike source regions. These frontal zones represent only the average or typical location of the conflict zones, which actually shift rapidly and widely.

Starting in the vicinity of the Tropics of Cancer and Capricorn (lat. 23½° N. and S.), we observe a double chain of tropical air-mass source regions encircling the globe. Those on land are the sources of *continental tropical air masses* (*cT*), which coincide with the great tropical deserts resulting from the adiabatic warming of air subsiding in the centers of the subtropical high-pressure cells. Desert surfaces have little or no surface water or vegetation to supply moisture. Specific humidity is rather large (11 g/kg in the example shown in Figure 19.2), but with high daytime air temperatures the relative humidities can become very low.

Over the oceans at this same latitude are source regions for *maritime tropical air masses* (*mT*). On the west side of each source the air is particularly moist and may contain as much as 18–20 grams of water per kilogram of air, which can yield heavy rainfall. Figure 19.2 shows data for Miami, Florida, as a typical example of the *mT* air mass in summer. Much of the world's rainfall comes from maritime tropical air masses. The eastern sides of the *mT* source regions are quite dry, by contrast, for here the air is subsiding on the eastern side of the high-pressure cells. Located over cool ocean currents, these air masses are stable and dry, causing an extension of the continental deserts far out over the oceans (see Figure 18.26). On the other hand, advection fog is commonly formed over the cold water surface. The symbol *mTs* is applied to this subsiding air mass.

Between the two belts of tropical air-mass source regions lies the equatorial trough of low pressure where the trade winds, or tropical easterlies, come together in the intertropical convergence zone (*ITC*). At certain places, however, the trade winds are not well defined in the equatorial trough, and there exist doldrum regions of stagnant air where the *maritime equatorial air masses* (*mE*) are produced. In a typical example, the *mE* air mass at Djakarta, Indonesia, registered a temperature of 80° F (27° C), a specific humidity of

**FIGURE 19.1** Schematic diagram of climate groups in relation to frontal zones, air masses, and source regions. (© 1960, John Wiley & Sons, New York. Data from Petterssen and others.)

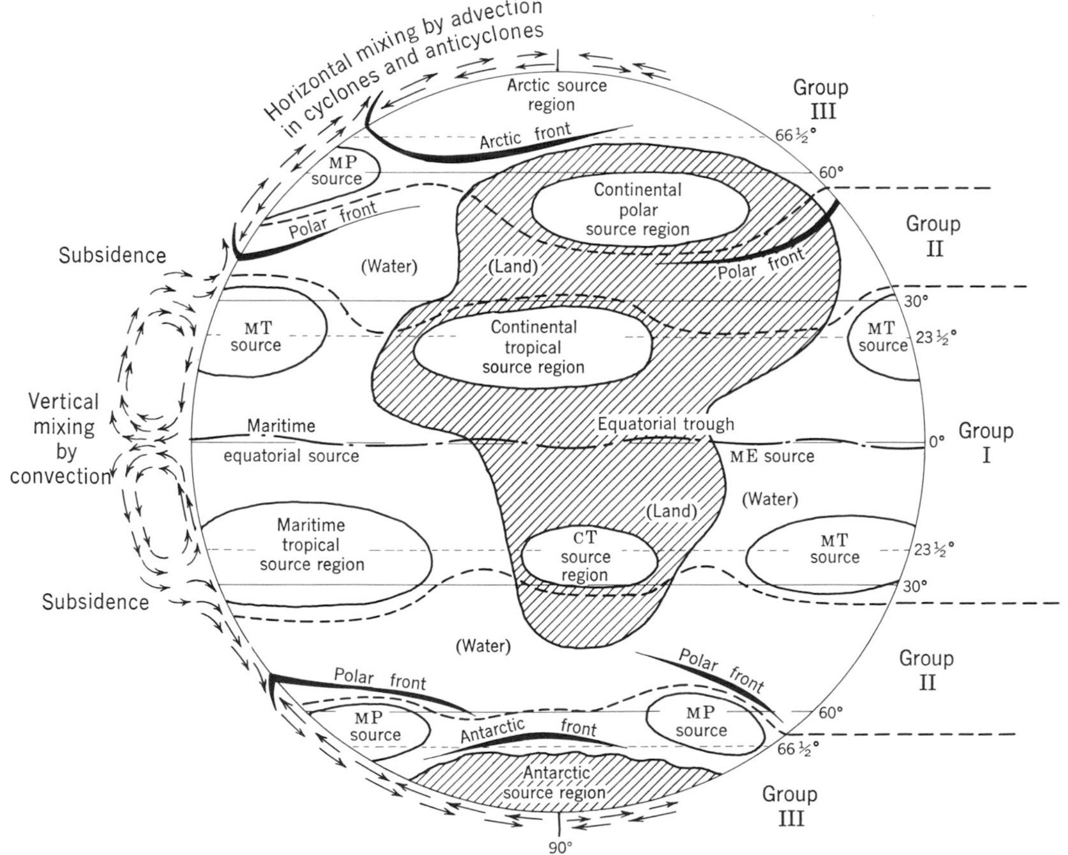

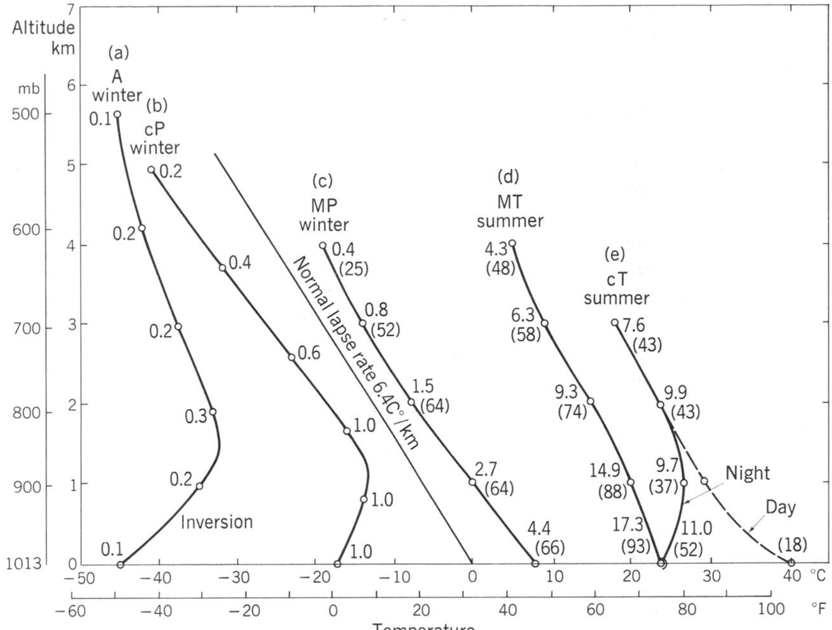


**FIGURE 19.2.** Soundings of representative air masses. (a) Extreme arctic, Siberia. (b) Seattle, Washington. (c) Miami, Florida. (d) El Paso, Texas. (e) Moscow, U.S.S.R. Figures give specific humidity, with relative humidity in parentheses. (Based on data of S. Petterssen and H. C. Willett, from various sources.)

18.7 g/kg, and a relative humidity of 86%. Maritime equatorial air, being warm and moist, is similar to maritime tropical air, and some climatologists make no distinction between them, recognizing only a tropical air mass. A distinct equatorial front is recognizable at that time of year when the meeting of tropical and equatorial air masses occurs some distance north or south of the geographic equator.

Over the vast land surfaces of northern North America and Eurasia, roughly between lat. 55° and 65° N., lie source regions of the *continental polar air masses* (*cP*). In winter especially, when these source regions form the cold poles of the Northern Hemisphere (Chapter 14), there develop here extremely cold air masses with very small moisture content. The winter example (Moscow) shown in Figure 19.2 is typical; specific humidity is about 1 g/kg. Notice the temperature inversion below 3000 ft (1 km). These air masses periodically burst southward in tongues called *polar outbreaks,* generating severe storms and blizzards when displacing moist tropical air. In general, the zone of conflict between polar and maritime air masses is called the *polar frontal zone.*

Over the North Atlantic and North Pacific Oceans (coinciding with the Icelandic and Aleutian lows) and in the Southern Ocean at lat. 55° to 65° lie the source regions for *maritime polar air masses* (*mP*). These air masses are both cool and moist. Formed over ocean bodies, they lack the intense chilling found in the winter *cP* air masses. In the winter example (Seattle) shown in Figure 19.2, specific humidity is 4.4 g/kg at sea level, temperature is 46° F (8° C), relative humidity 66%. Maritime polar air supplies much of the moisture which falls as orographic precipitation on the west coasts of continents between lat. 40° and 60°.

Arctic air masses originate in the region of the Arctic Ocean and its bordering lands. Unfortunately, the use of the words *polar* and *arctic* in describing air masses had gradually grown up and been accepted in exactly the reverse of the geographical meanings of those words. In the strict sense *arctic* means the latitude region near the Arctic Circle (66½° N.), and *polar* means the region surrounding the North Pole. Therefore, strangely, the arctic air masses originate nearer the North Pole than the polar air masses do. In general the arctic air masses are colder than the polar air masses, particularly in winter, as illustrated in Figure 19.2 by the example of extreme arctic air mass. Here the inversion extends to 5000 ft (1.5 km).

Meteorologists sometimes subdivide the arctic air masses into two types: *continental arctic* (*cA*), which form over the islands and land fringes bordering the polar basin, and *maritime arctic* (*mA*) formed over the Arctic Ocean.

In Figure 19.1 is shown an *arctic frontal zone,* the meeting place of arctic and polar air masses. This is a zone of conflict along which frequent weather disturbances are developed, but it may actually represent a variation in position of the polar front rather than a distinctly different frontal zone.

In the Southern Hemisphere the pole-centered continent of Antarctica, with some 5,000,000 sq mi (13 million sq km) of ice and snow surface, forms the source region for a *continental antarctic* air mass (*cAA*) colder than any other on earth and with very low moisture content. Spreading equatorward (northward), this antarctic air mass meets maritime polar air masses of the Southern Ocean along the *antarctic frontal zone.* Here violent storms are frequent. Continental polar air masses are absent here because there is little land to provide a source region.

**Air masses of the United States and Canada** Most of the United States and southern Canada does not lie

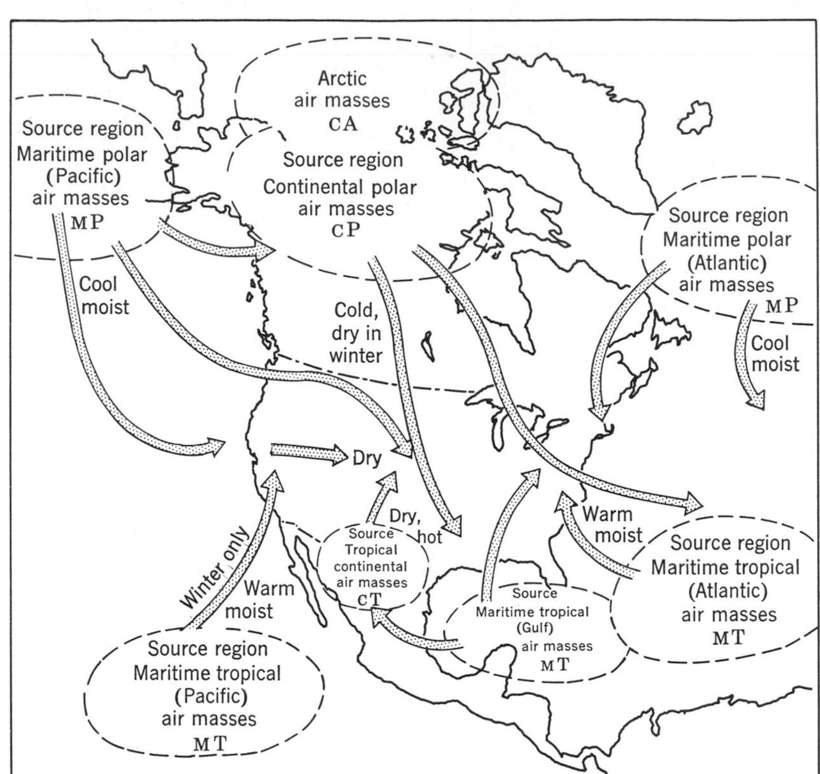


**FIGURE 19.3.** Source regions and trajectories of air masses affecting North American continent. (© 1960, John Wiley & Sons, New York. Modified from a map by Haynes, U.S. Department of Commerce.

in any air-mass source region, but instead represents a polar frontal zone which is invaded continually by air masses from source regions lying both north and south. A knowledge of these air masses, their paths of travel or *trajectories,* and their changes en route will be of great use in understanding our day-to-day weather changes and seasonal climate.

In Figure 19.3 are shown very diagrammatically the sources and trajectories of air masses which commonly visit the United States and southern Canada. Of the invading air masses, consider first the polar and arctic continental air masses (*cP* and *cA*), which originate in a vast source area north of the 50th parallel from Hudson Bay to Alaska. Winter is the season in which these air masses make their most important invasions into the United States, passing down the Central Plains region into the Mississippi Valley and across the Great Lakes region to bring cold waves to the nation. Both air masses are cold and have low moisture content (on the order of 0.5 gram of water per kilogram of air), but of the two the arctic air mass is the colder and drier. Within tongues of these air masses in winter one commonly finds clear blue skies and good visibility, along with high barometric pressure, for the cold air layer is relatively dense. An important exception is seen in the behavior of the *cP* air masses which cross the Great Lakes. Here, as shown in Figure 19.4, the air picks up moisture from the relatively warm lake surface. By the time it reaches the southern and eastern lake shores, the air is unstable and very moist, giving snowfalls which

**FIGURE 19.4.** Passage of a *cP* air mass across the Great Lakes is accompanied by a gain in water vapor, resulting in snow flurries over the adjacent land. [After U.S. Department of Commerce (1955), *C.A.A. Technical Manual 104,* Washington, D.C., U.S. Govt. Printing Office, p. 42, Figure 70.]

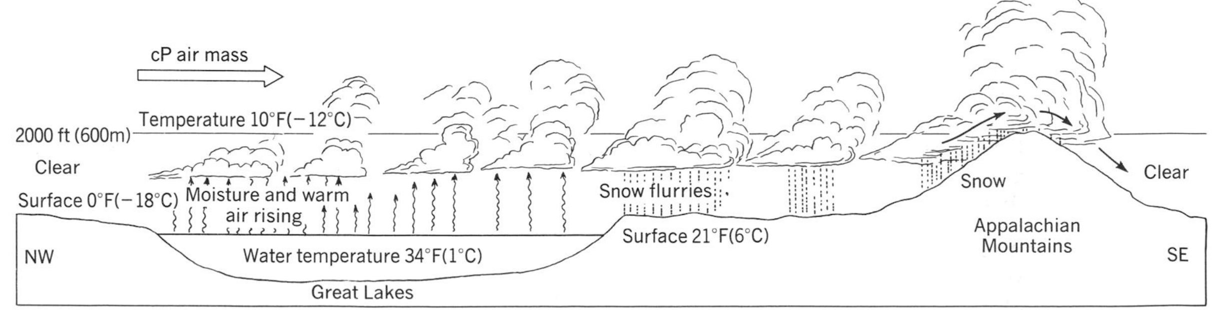

may pile up to depths of many inches of snow in a few hours along the shores. As it continues southeast across the Appalachians, this *cP* air mass will produce strato-cumulus clouds and more snow flurries over the mountains.

From the North Pacific Ocean, in the vicinity of the Aleutian low, come cool moist maritime polar air masses (*mP*). Near the surface this air is usually well above freezing temperature, even in winter, and has moderately high moisture content (some 3–6 g/kg) and a high relative humidity (Figure 19.2). It may bring heavy showers to the coast or snow in the colder, higher mountains. As the *mP* air mass travels eastward across the western mountain ranges, it loses moisture by orographic precipitation and therefore reaches the Great Plains as a relatively dry air mass. Over the eastern United States and southeastern Canada, *mP* air masses from the Pacific in the winter season bring fair pleasant weather that is especially mild in temperatures.

The maritime tropical air mass (*mT*) developed over the eastern Pacific Ocean off the Central American coast is an infrequent visitor to the United States. Spreading northeast to the California coast only in winter, this warm moist air brings heavy rains to the coastal region of southern California.

Of great importance to the entire central and eastern United States are the maritime tropical (*mT*) air masses which originate in the Gulf of Mexico, Caribbean Sea, and adjoining parts of the Atlantic Ocean (Figure 19.3). Warm, moist, and unstable, this air moves northward into the country up the Mississippi Valley and supplies the water vapor for most of the precipitation. With a specific humidity at low levels running about 15–17 g/kg, this air mass contrasts strongly to the cold dry *cP* and *cA* air masses from the north and to the mild but dry *mP* air which has come across country from the West Coast. Therefore, where these unlike air masses meet in the general region of conflict of the polar frontal zone, frequent and sometimes violent disturbances are formed.

From the North Atlantic come maritime polar (*mP*) air masses to invade the Maritime Provinces and the northeastern United States on occasions when a storm known as a *northeaster* is in progress. This cool moist air mass brings drizzling rains in the warmer seasons and often heavy snowfalls in the winter. Because of the prevailingly westerly winds the *mP* air masses of the North Atlantic normally drift toward Europe and rarely are brought westward farther than the New England states.

Only one small air-mass source region lies within the United States, that of warm to hot continental tropical (*cT*) air masses situated over the Sonoran Desert region of northern Mexico, the southern parts of Arizona and New Mexico, and western Texas (Figure 19.3). In summer this air mass is important in producing the hot dry climate of the southwestern United States and is a small-scale American representative of the huge *cT* air-mass source region of the Sahara-Arabian desert region. In winter this source region is inactive and unimportant.

With this brief description of the principal air masses of the North American region we are ready to study their conflicts and resulting weather disturbances in the zone where they meet.

## Weather fronts

A weather *front* is the boundary separating two air masses of unlike properties. Air masses do not mix easily, but because of their different properties tend to have distinct boundaries between them, just as oil and water tend to remain in separate layers or drops without mixing. In most weather fronts one mass of air is moving into, or invading, a region occupied by an unlike air mass, so that not only is the air on both sides of the front in motion, but also the front itself is moving over the earth's surface beneath it. The primary rule of weather fronts is that the air of the colder mass, being the denser, stays close to the ground, forcing the warm (or less cold) air to slide over it and to rise upward.

Putting these principles to use, consider the three basic types of fronts that may develop. The *cold front,* shown in Figure 19.5, is formed by a cold air mass invading the region occupied by a warm (or less cold) air mass. Staying close to the ground, the cold air forms a wedge, pushing the warm air upward from its advancing edge. Ground friction slows the advancing cold air close to the ground, so that it may develop a steep or blunt leading edge. The lifting of the warm air is therefore abrupt and violent on occasions.

Of course, the vertical scale in Figure 19.5 is very greatly exaggerated. Actually the cold air forms a thin wedge whose slope may be from 1 in 40 to 1 in 80. This means that (using the ratio of 1:40) the cold air layer would be 1 mile thick at a distance of 40 miles back from the line where the front touches the ground, but in meteorological terms this is steep. The front itself is the entire surface of contact between the two air masses, not just the trace of this surface on the ground.

If the warm air is of maritime tropical (*mT*) type, as is most often the case, it may be unstable and break into spontaneous convection, producing dense cumulus and cumulonimbus clouds (thunderstorms) extending to extreme heights. Often a cold front produces a long line of thunderstorms 200–500 mi (300–800 km) in length. Such fronts are of great significance to pilots, for the storms often rise too high to be surmounted and extend too low to be flown beneath. The pilot must try to pass between

**FIGURE 19.5.** Diagram of a cold front. (© 1960, John Wiley & Sons, New York.)

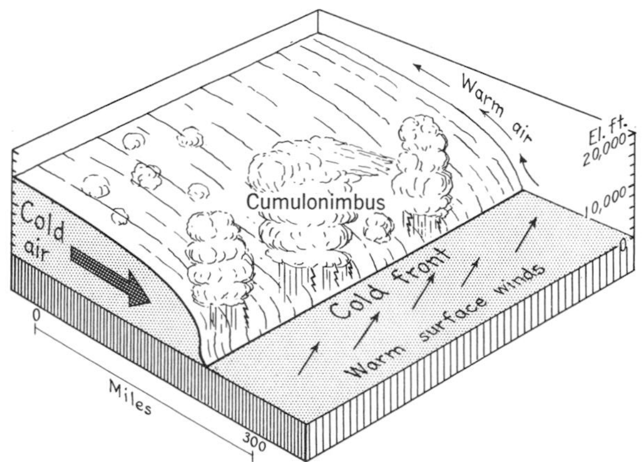

individual convection units. Radar is most useful for this purpose, for this screen will show the active convection cells (Figure 19.6). Not all cold fronts are accompanied by violent weather, however, but cloudiness will normally be present and the passage of the front will bring a marked drop in temperature and humidity, together with a quick shift in wind direction.

The *warm front,* shown in Figure 19.7, is formed by a relatively warm air mass moving into a region occupied by colder air. The cold air will remain close to the ground, while the warm air slides up over it on a broad gently sloping front that may have a slope ratio of 1:100 or smaller. If the warm air mass is stable, stratiform clouds mark the overriding air layer, for the forced ascent of air causes steady adiabatic cooling and condensation. The highest fringe of advancing warm air is marked by cirrus and cirrostratus clouds. As the front comes nearer, these clouds are replaced by altostratus, then by a dense stratus, and finally by nimbostratus, with a broad zone of light, steady, and prolonged precipitation. On the other hand, if the warm air is unstable, it will break into heavy showers or into thunderstorms rising above the stratus layer.

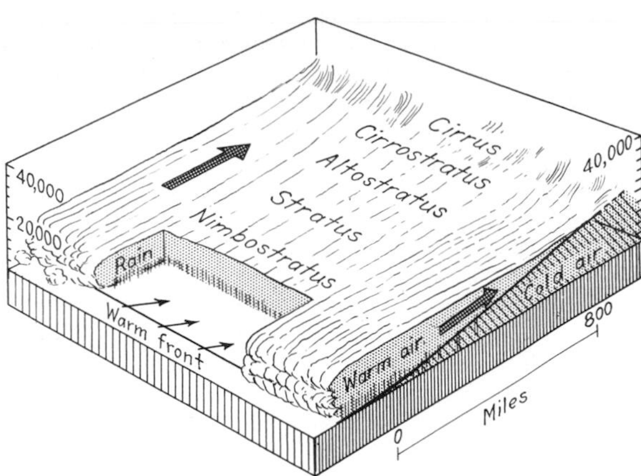


**FIGURE 19.7.** Diagram of a warm front. (© 1960, John Wiley & Sons, New York.)

**FIGURE 19.6.** Lines of thunderstorms show as light patches on this radar screen. The heavy circles are spaced 50 nautical mi (70 km) apart. (Courtesy of ESSA, Weather Bureau.)

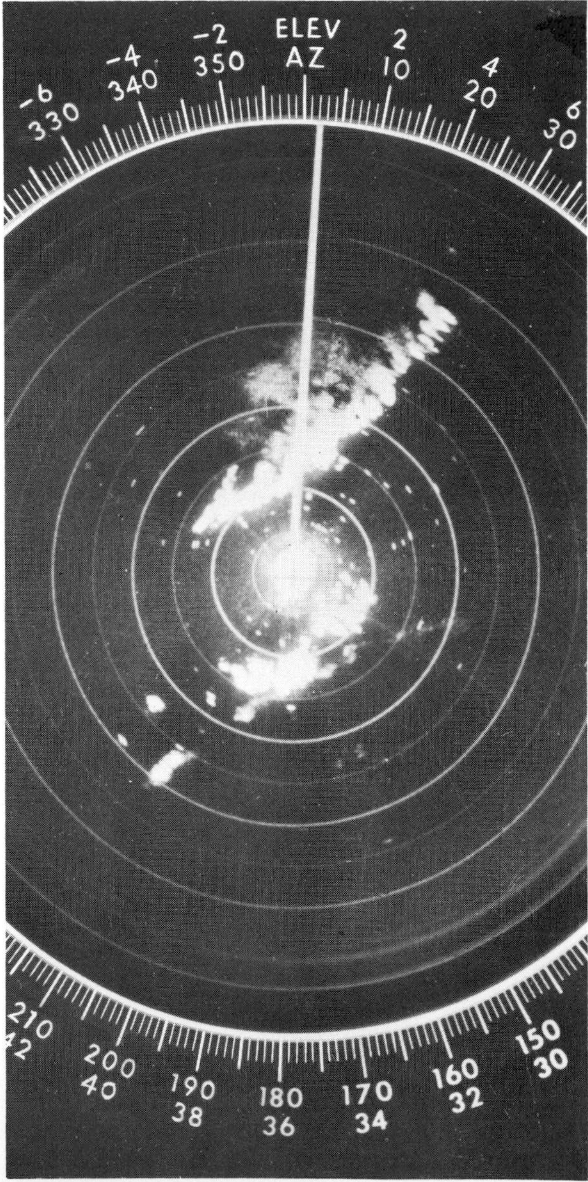


If the cold air beneath a warm front is below freezing, rain originating in the warm air above may freeze to form ice pellets (sleet) as it falls through the cold air layer, or the drops may freeze upon contact with the ground, producing a glaze or ice storm. In contrast to cold fronts, which are usually fast-moving and narrow, a warm front may move slowly and cover a belt 200–400 mi (300–600 km) wide, bringing a long period of precipitation and cloudiness. As the warm front passes, air temperatures rise gradually, and winds will normally shift to a southerly or westerly direction.

A third type of front is the *occluded front,* diagrammed in Figure 19.8. Here a cold front has caught up with and pushed into a warm front, completely lifting the warm air off the ground. The invading cold air remains close to the ground and comes in contact with less cold air under the warm front. The warm front is now said to be

**FIGURE 19.8.** Diagram of an occluded warm front. (© 1960, John Wiley & Sons, New York.)

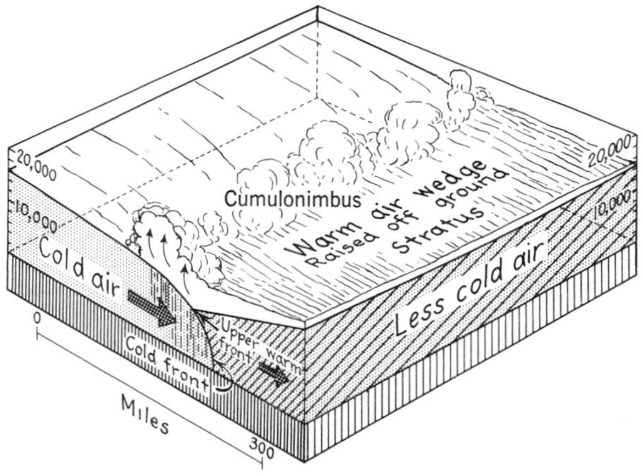

*occluded,* that is, cut off from contact with the ground. The warm front would then not show on a weather map of surface conditions, but is found at higher altitudes and produces precipitation reaching the ground. Again, as with both cold and warm fronts, an occluded front may contain relatively stable warm air, which forms a dense stratus cloud with steady rain or snow, or it may contain unstable warm air that breaks into cumulonimbus clouds as the cold air pushes under, as illustrated in Figure 19.8.

Cold, warm, and occluded fronts form in the middle and high latitudes wherever unlike air masses meet in conflict. Fronts will be most frequent in the regions of conflict between polar and maritime air masses (labeled "polar frontal zone" on Figure 19.1) and between arctic and polar air masses (the lines labeled "arctic frontal zone" and "antarctic frontal zone" in Figure 19.1). In the equatorial belt, however, fronts are usually not clearly defined, because the air masses on the two sides of the equator differ but slightly in temperature and humidity.

## Air masses and frontal zones as bases for climate classification

Climate may be defined as the characteristic combination of meteorological variables (temperature, moisture, precipitation, winds) at a given place. A climate is described in terms of average values as well as extreme values, based upon long periods of observation. The annual rhythm of seasons—hot or cold, wet or dry—is particularly important in the description of a climate.

We have seen that weather is controlled by air masses and their interplay along fronts and in cyclonic storms. It is reasonable to devise a classification of climates based upon the characteristic air masses, their source regions, typical movements, and frontal zones of conflict. Such a classification has the advantage of explaining climate rather than merely exhibiting a collection of facts.

Figure 19.1 shows in a diagrammatic way how the world's climates can be placed in three major groups according to the air-mass source region or frontal zone which dominates in a given region.

*Group I* consists of climates dominated by tropical and equatorial air masses. Source regions of subsiding continental tropical (*cT*) and maritime tropical (*mT*) air masses form great deserts lying upon the Tropics of Cancer and Capricorn. Between these desert belts is the equatorial trough where maritime air masses converge to produce wet climates. Climates of Group I are warm or hot throughout the year—no winter season exists.

*Group III* consists of cold climates dominated by polar, arctic, and antarctic air masses. These climates have a short summer or no true summer at all, whereas winters are long and severely cold. Continental polar (*cP*) air-mass source regions fall in this group, as do the ice-covered regions of Antarctica, Greenland, and the Arctic Ocean. Although convection is at a minimum in these high latitudes, advection is intense in cyclonic storms that sweep eastward along a frontal zone termed the *arctic front* (*antarctic front*) lying between the sources of moist maritime polar air (*mP*) located over the oceans and the colder and drier arctic (*A*) and antarctic (*AA*) air masses.

*Group II* consists of climates in the middle-latitude zone lying between the tropical climates of Group I and the cold arctic and polar climates of Group III. Climates of Group II are thus controlled by both tropical and polar air masses and occupy areas swept over by the polar front, a zone of intense interaction between polar and tropical air masses. Frequent cyclonic storms traveling eastward in this zone bring first tropical, then polar air masses over a given place, often in rapid alternations which give highly varied weather from day to day and from season to season.

In all, 14 distinctive types of climate are included in the three world zones. Appendix II provides a brief description of each of the 14 climate types, together with monthly temperature and precipitation data for a representative station of each type. A world map shows the distribution of the climate types, but only in a generalized way. Highland areas, in which climates change rapidly with increasing elevation, are left unclassified.

## Cyclones of the middle and high latitudes

We define a cyclone as a center of low barometric pressure which, in the Northern Hemisphere, has a counterclockwise flow of winds about its center. Near the ground the air will spiral inward toward the center of the cyclone (Chapter 15). Cyclones occur at all latitudes and vary greatly in size and intensity. Some cyclones of the tropics are of a violent type, such as the hurricane or typhoon. A special type of cyclone is

**FIGURE 19.9** Surface conditions typically associated with the formation of a wave cyclone. (© 1960, John Wiley & Sons, New York.)

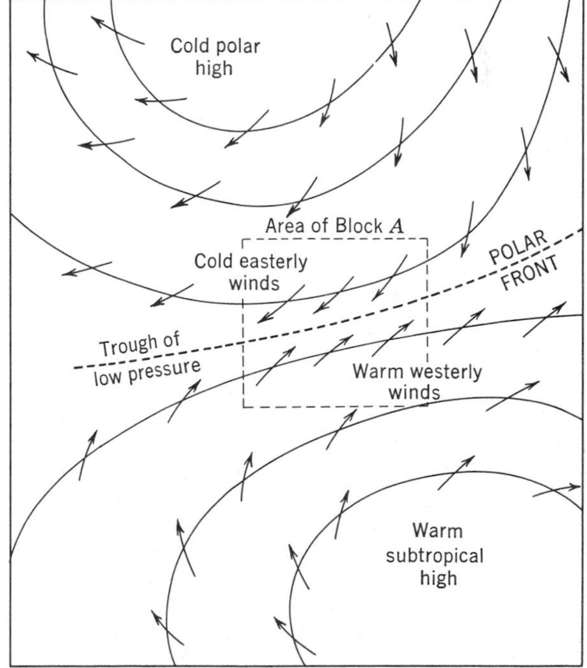

the tornado, a very small but intense storm restricted in occurrence to a few special locations. The tornado will be discussed later in this chapter. The great majority of cyclones in the middle and high latitudes (referred to as *extra-tropical cyclones*) with which we are here concerned are produced by wavelike kinks that develop on the fronts separating cold from warm air masses. These disturbances may therefore be called *wave cyclones* or *frontal waves.*

An understanding of the cause of cyclone formation (*cyclogenesis*) must be searched for in movements within the entire troposphere including upper-air waves (Rossby waves) and the jet stream. However, we first examine surface weather conditions, in order to become familiar with the development of the cyclone as it appears to a surface observer.

Consider first the conditions shown on the surface weather map in Figure 19.9 in which a mass of cold polar air on the north adjoins a mass of warm tropical air on the south, with a front lying between. The front lies in a trough of low pressure between the two highs. Air flow is approximately opposite on either side.

Stages in the development of a wave cyclone are shown in Figure 19.10. Stage *A* shows a portion of the front described in Figure 19.9. Because the air flow on the two sides of this front is in opposite directions, a shearing or dragging action is set up between the air masses. Under such conditions the front cannot remain

**FIGURE 19.10.** Four stages in the life history of a wave cyclone of middle latitudes. (© 1960, John Wiley & Sons, New York.)

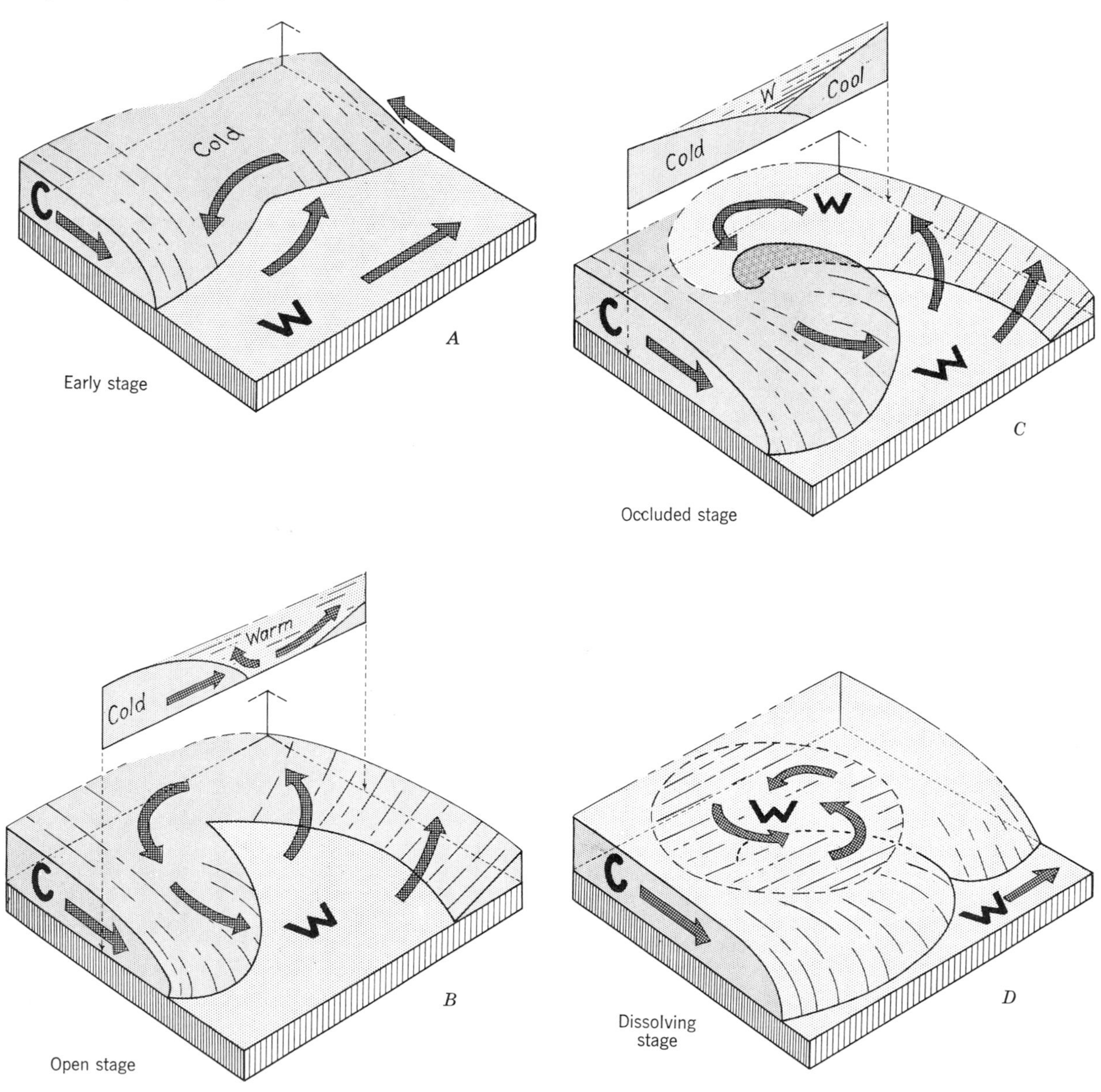

smooth, but will tend to develop a bend or kink, such as that shown beginning to form in Stage *A*. Imagine that we are studying the development of a water wave as it nears a beach where it steepens and finally breaks. If we could produce such a water wave in a glass-walled trough, the profile of the wave could be watched from the side, seen through the glass wall. The development of the cyclone is somewhat analogous to that of the steepening water wave seen through the glass, except that the atmospheric wave is turned horizontally and is seen by means of a synoptic chart.

As the frontal wave in Stage *A* (Figure 19.10) develops, the flow of air is modified so that cold air begins to push into the region of the warm, and the warm begins to move into the region occupied by the cold. This motion resembles a revolving door, with one person going out of a building while another enters.

In Stage *B*, the *open stage*, the frontal wave is well developed and forms a sharp point toward the region of cold air. To the left of this point, or crest, lies a cold front with cold air actively pushing south. To the right lies a warm front curved in a great arc bowed to the east. A synoptic chart at this stage would look like Map *A* of Figure 19.11. Notice that the sharp point of the wave coincides with the center of lowest barometric pressure and that the winds are spiraling in toward this center in a counterclockwise manner.

A cross section of the atmosphere drawn along the line *AA′*, passing through the cyclone south of its center, is shown just below Map *A*. Note that the cold front and warm front are both present and that precipitation is falling along both fronts. Between the two fronts is a sector of the cyclone which is relatively clear, or open, at this stage. Into this sector warm moist air is moving northeastward. Just back of the cold front, however, cold air is moving southward rapidly on a system of northwest winds. The cold front marks a line of abrupt wind shift and a replacement of the warm air by cold.

Returning to Stage *C* of Figure 19.10, we note that the wave has now steepened to the point that the crest has been cut off. Here the cold front has caught up with the warm front to produce an occluded front separating a

**FIGURE 19.11.** Surface-weather maps showing two stages in the development of a cyclonic storm. Isobars are labeled in millibars. The figure beside each station gives air temperature in degrees Fahrenheit. Arrows fly with the wind. Diagonal shading shows areas experiencing precipitation. These maps are modified from daily weather maps of the U.S. Weather Bureau. (From *Climates of the World*, copyright A. K. Lobeck, reproduced with permission of the publisher, Hammond Incorporated.)

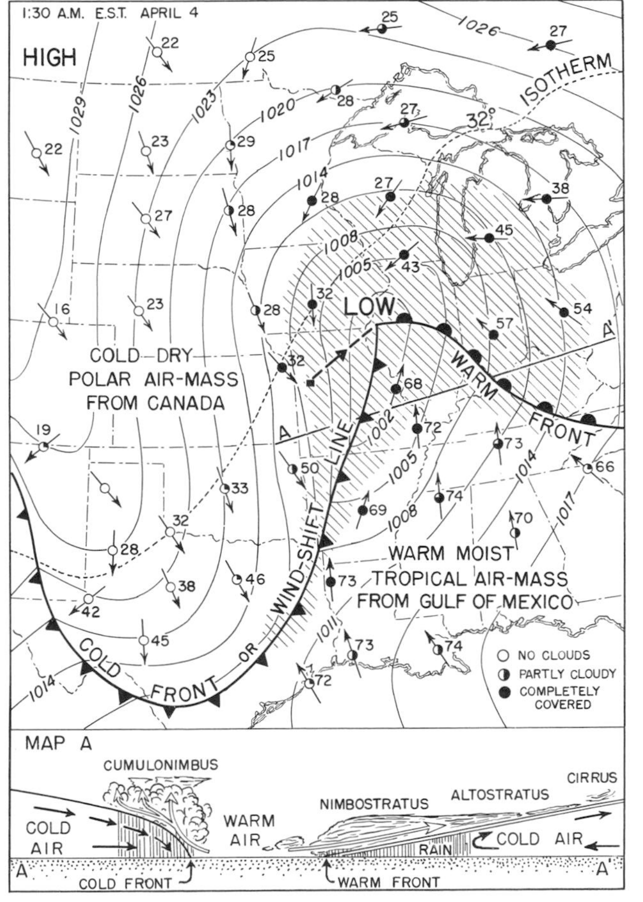


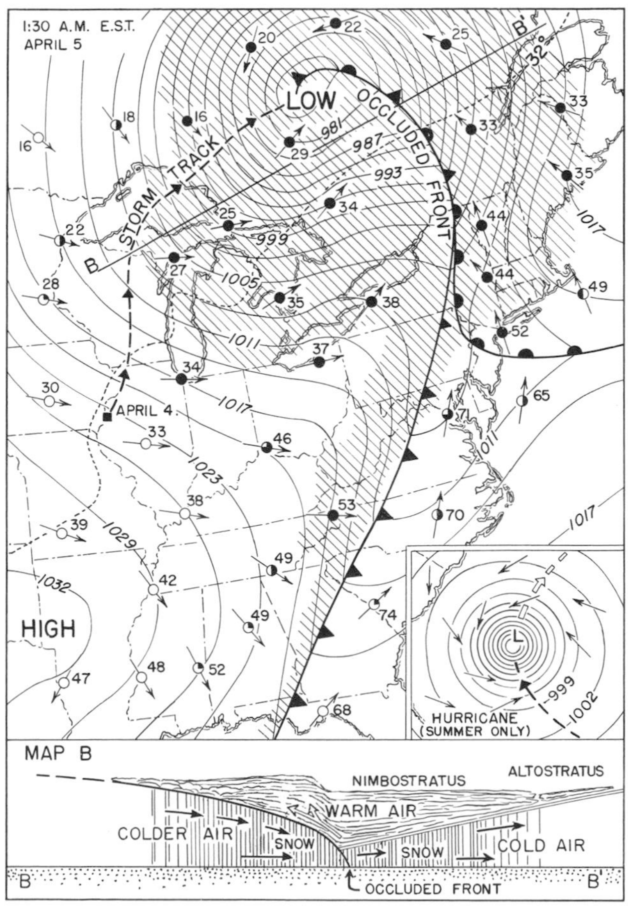

layer of warm air from contact with the ground. This *occluded stage* is illustrated by Map *B* of Figure 19.11. Note that the center of the cyclone has traveled far to the northeast in the 24-hour period between the two maps. The cyclone has deepened—that is, its barometric pressure has fallen still lower. The occluded front extends out from the cyclone center in a broad spiral curve. A cross section of the atmosphere along *BB′* through the occluded part is shown below Map *B*. A great saucer-like mass of warm air lies above the cold air and is producing snow from stratiform clouds.

After the occluded stage the cyclone enters the *dissipating stage* (Figure 19.10*D*). No longer supplied with moist warm air, whose condensation would furnish latent heat energy, the cyclone dies out, and the front is reformed as a smooth line between polar and tropical air masses.

Cyclones travel in a generally easterly direction in the Northern Hemisphere at speeds ranging from 20 to 40 mi (32 to 64 km) per hour. Some travel a distance of one-third to one-half of the way around the earth during their life cycle. The intensity of these cyclones is extremely varied. Considering that a cyclone is experienced every few days throughout the year by persons living in North America and Europe, it is obvious that most cyclones pass almost unnoticed as spells of cloudy or rainy weather. On the other hand, a large intense wave cyclone can be a powerful and devastating storm involving winds up to 70 mi (112 km) or more per hour and can bring flooding rains or deep snows. At sea, over the North Atlantic and Pacific Oceans and over the Southern Ocean in lat. 40° to 70°, cyclonic storms tend to deepen and to become extremely severe in the winter season, causing high seas and great peril to shipping. A cold air mass pushing from the northwest with great strength into an occluded storm can build up mountainous seas which lash the western coasts of North America and Europe with great fury.

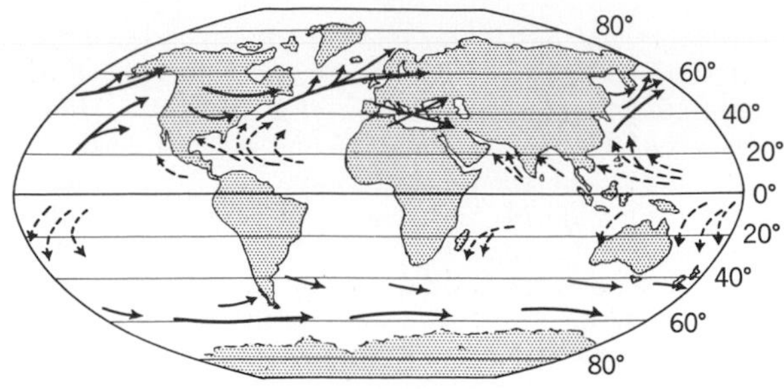


**FIGURE 19.12.** Solid lines on this world map show principal tracks of middle-latitude cyclones, and dashed lines the characteristic tracks of tropical cyclones. (© 1960, John Wiley & Sons, New York. Based on a map by Petterssen.)

From long observation of the tracks of wave cyclones it was established that they tend to follow certain paths with greater frequency than others. In Figure 19.12 are shown the principal tracks of cyclones of the middle latitudes. Whereas in the Southern Hemisphere the storms are rather uniformly distributed around the Southern Ocean, the Northern Hemisphere shows a definite concentration into two characteristic paths: one originating in eastern North America and crossing the North Atlantic to northern Europe; another originating in easternmost Asia and the Japanese Islands and extending across the North Pacific to Alaska and the northwestern coast of North America. Along these two tracks wave cyclones tend to form in succession as *cyclone families* (Figure 19.13), in which the stage of development ranges from open wave to occlusion, from southwest to northeast. Thus many a storm begins in the southern plains

**FIGURE 19.13.** Schematic weather map showing two families of wave cyclones in the Northern Hemisphere. Surface fronts are shown by dashed lines. Solid arrows show streamlines of flow of cold air, and open arrows the flow of warm air. [After S. Petterssen (1958), *Introduction to Meteorology,* New York, McGraw-Hill, p. 223, Figure 163.]

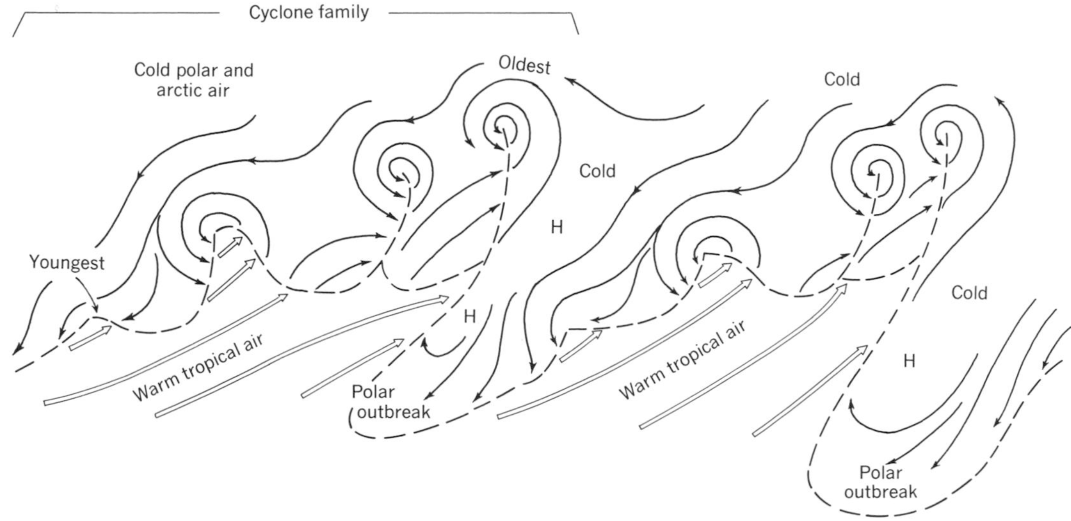

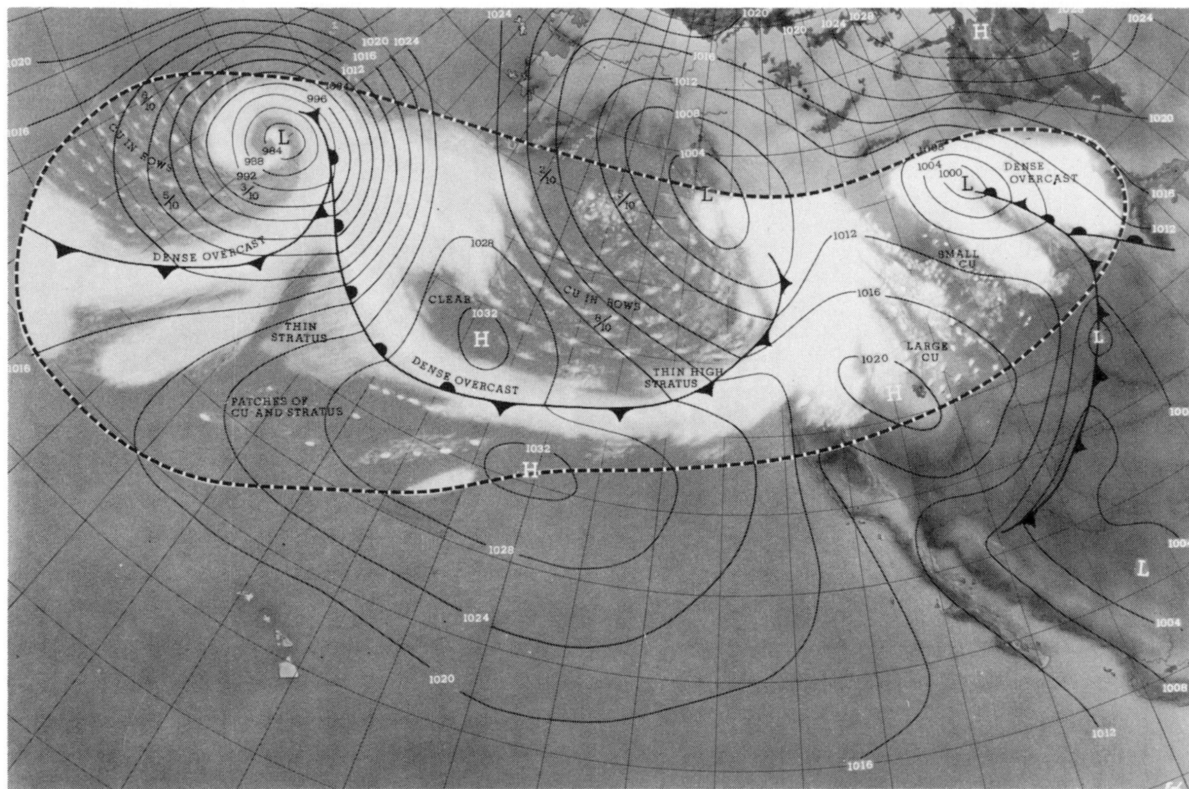


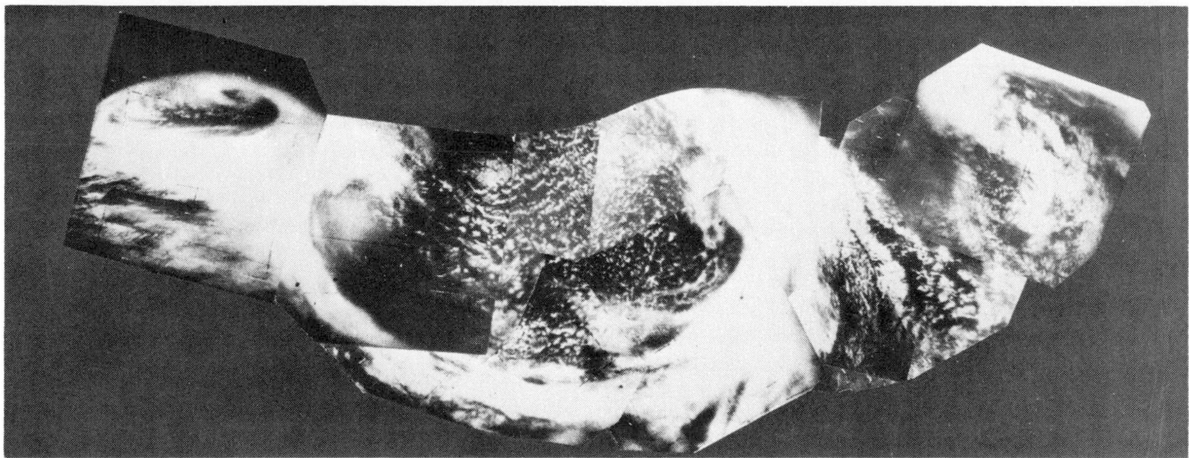

**FIGURE 19.14.** The lower figure, a composite of individual photographs taken by a Tiros weather satellite, shows the actual cloud formations of cyclonic storms. The upper figure is a weather map of the North Pacific Ocean upon which cloud formations from the Tiros pictures have been superimposed. (Courtesy of ESSA, Weather Bureau.)

of the United States, travels northeast, deepens and becomes occluded as it passes out over the Atlantic Ocean, and arrives in the British Isles in a late stage of development.

Figure 19.14 shows photographs taken by a Tiros weather-observing satellite of a cyclone family over the eastern North Pacific Ocean and North America.

Figure 19.15 is a weather map of the entire world, showing a number of wave cyclones in both the Northern and Southern hemispheres. Those of the Southern Hemisphere bear a mirror-image relation to those of the Northern Hemisphere, because all travel from west to east. Note the cyclone families located over the North Pacific, North Atlantic, and western Asia.

Figure 19.16 is a surface weather map of the Southern Hemisphere for a day late in February, which is in the late summer of that hemisphere. Cyclones, eight in number, form a circumglobal ring over the Southern

**FIGURE 19.15.** On a typical day in July or August a surface-weather map of the entire world might have weather systems such as those shown here. (© 1960, John Wiley & Sons, New York. Data modified after M. A. Garbell.)

Ocean between 40° and 65° S. latitude. This ring is surrounded in turn by a ring of subtropical high pressure cells centered over the latitude belt 30–35° S. A peripheral belt of low pressure lies close to the equator.

## Vorticity and winds

In Chapter 15 the upper-air (troposphere) flow in the middle and high latitudes was explained as a continuous system of westerlies in which a jet stream of extremely high speed develops from time to time along certain zones. It was shown that at times the westerly winds at these high altitudes develop a sinuous flow pattern with great loops, or upper-air waves (Figure 15.26). Such loops projecting equatorward are cold-air tongues and form troughs of low pressure at high levels. The questions now arise: What causes these large upper-air waves? How are they related to the wave cyclones and fronts whose development has just been discussed? A close relation between the two systems does exist, but the explanation requires us to make use of certain principles of air flow not previously discussed.

Refer back to Chapter 2, in which the motion of the Foucault pendulum was explained by analogy with an automobile running eastward around the earth at various latitudes. On all parallels between the equator and pole in the Northern Hemisphere the car wheels must be turned left; the floor of the car thus slowly rotates counterclockwise with respect to an axis perpendicular to the earth's surface. Recall that the rate of turning is zero at the equator, but increases with latitude at a rate which is equal to the sine of the latitude times the constant of 15° per hour. At the pole, the rate of turning of the car floor is the same as the angular velocity of the earth, 15° per hour.

The turning, or *spin,* of a small horizontal element of the earth's surface is referred to as the *vorticity of the earth's surface,* or *planetary vorticity,* and is equal to

**FIGURE 19.16.** Sea-level weather map of Southern Hemisphere for February 27, 1958. (Same symbols as in Figure 19.24.) [Simplified and modified from a map by J. J. Taljaard and H. Van Loon (1964), *Amer. Meteorological Soc. Bull.,* vol. 45, p. 89, Figure 1.]

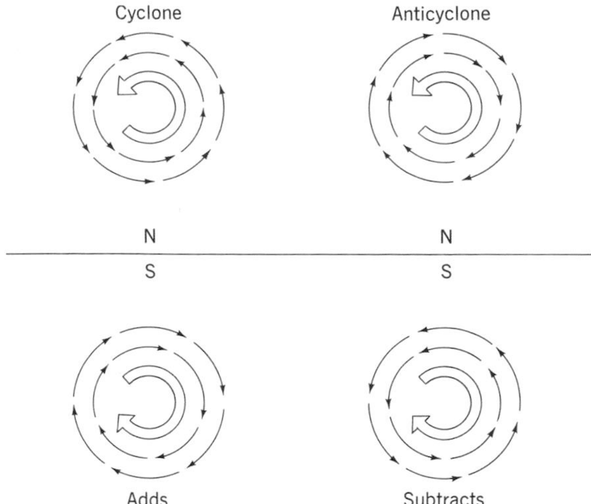


**FIGURE 19.17.** Addition and subtraction of vorticities. The bold arrow in the center of each figure represents vorticity of the earth's surface (planetary vorticity). Surrounding thin arrows represent vorticity of air moving in cyclones and anticyclones (relative vorticity).

twice the angular velocity of rotation of the earth times the sine of the latitude at a given location.[1] Any particle at rest on the earth's surface possesses the planetary vorticity, except at the equator, where there is no such spin relative to the earth's axis.

Consider, next, the motion of air in a small cyclone in the Northern Hemisphere (Figure 19.17, upper left). Here the vortex of air has a counterclockwise spin with respect to the center; this spin is in the same direction as the planetary vorticity at that place. The rotation, or spin, of the moving air with respect to the earth's surface constitutes *relative vorticity.*

In the case of the anticyclonic vortex (Figure 19.17, upper right) the spin is opposite to the spin of the earth's surface, which is to say that the relative vorticity is opposite to the planetary vorticity.

The algebraic sum of the two forms of vorticity (planetary vorticity plus relative vorticity) is termed the *absolute vorticity.*

We can also conclude that wherever air is moving in a horizontal path curved toward the left in the Northern Hemisphere (right in the Southern Hemisphere) the air possesses *cyclonic relative vorticity,* which is a positive quantity to be added to the planetary vorticity (Figure 19.18). When the path is curved to the right in the Northern Hemisphere (left in the Southern Hemisphere) it possesses *anticyclonic relative vorticity,* which is a negative quantity to be subtracted from the planetary vorticity.

Rotation, or spin, of a small element of air (or any fluid) also exists wherever the fluid motion is in a state of *shear.* The meaning of shearing is illustrated in Figure 19.19. The parallel arrows represent velocities of motion within layers of the fluid. These layers are infinitely thin and slide past one another freely like playing cards in a deck. The upper example represents the case of an increase in speed of flow equatorward (southward) in the Northern Hemisphere. A particle of fluid at the point $P_1$ engages in a continual spinning motion, which is anticlockwise. If a very tiny rod were suspended in the fluid, it would turn end-over-end as the drawing to the right suggests. In the middle example, all layers are moving at the same speed, and there is no shear and no rotation. In the lower example speed of flow is increasing poleward and rotation within the fluid is clockwise. It is now apparent that the upper case is one of cyclonic relative vorticity, while the lower case is one of anticyclonic relative vorticity. Note that in neither case are the flow lines curved.

In summary, relative vorticity—or intensity of spin about a vertical axis—is contributed both by curvature of path in horizontal motion and by shearing; it can be

[1] Identical with terms included in the equation for Coriolis force per unit of mass, as given in Chapter 15. The expression $2\ \Omega \sin \phi$ is known as the *Coriolis parameter.*

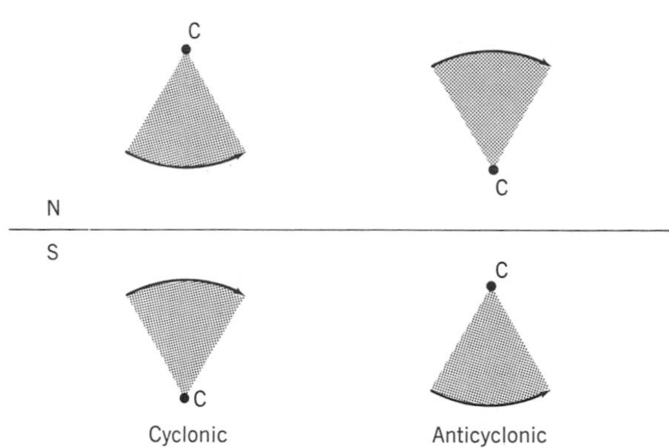


**FIGURE 19.18.** Schematic map to illustrate cyclonic and anticyclonic relative vorticity about a center of rotation, *C.*

**FIGURE 19.19.** Shear, rotation, and vorticity.

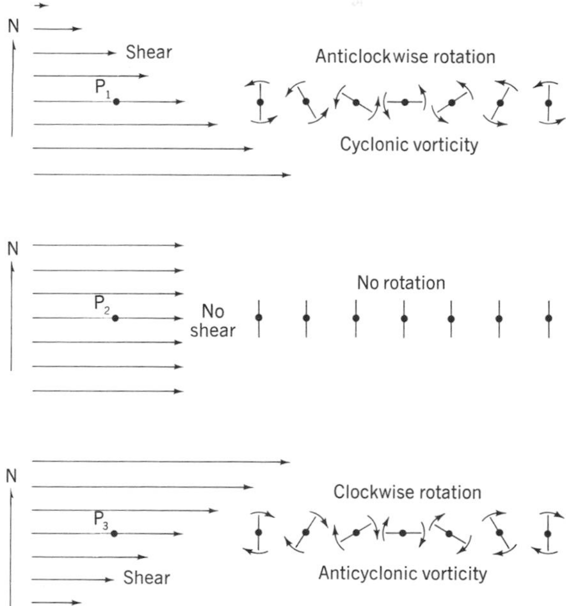

either cyclonic (positive) or anticyclonic (negative). Relative vorticity is added to or subtracted from the planetary vorticity to yield the absolute vorticity. We can now apply the principle of absolute vorticity to the upper-air westerlies and their configuration into Rossby waves.

**Conservation of absolute vorticity** Carl-Gustav Rossby, the meteorologist who developed equations for wave motions in the atmosphere, applied the principle of *conservation of absolute vorticity* to explain the large-scale upper air waves, later named *Rossby waves* in his honor. The principle can be grasped through a step-by-step examination of vorticity of an imaginary small cylindrical column of air moving over the earth's surface within a Rossby wave.

Figure 19.20 shows the undulating path of the column of air as it travels eastward. At Point *A* the air is moving from southwest to northeast in a straight path—it is assumed to be a true geostrophic wind for which the isobars are straight and parallel (see Figure 15.7). Without curvature of path or shearing, the air at this point has no relative vorticity, it has only the planetary vorticity, suggested in the figure by a broad arrow curved into an arc of 180°.

As the air column travels northeastward, it crosses parallels of higher latitude, where the planetary vorticity becomes greater. In order to conserve the total or absolute vorticity, the air column must develop anticyclonic vorticity in sufficient quantity to offset the increase in planetary vorticity. This effect is accomplished by curvature of the path of travel toward the right. At Point *B* the column is traveling due eastward. The dashed arrow, curved clockwise around Point *B*, represents the relative vorticity, which is here opposite in direction to the planetary vorticity.

Now traveling toward the southeast in a curving path, the column moves into lower latitudes. As planetary vorticity decreases, anticyclonic relative vorticity also must decrease, and this is accomplished by a straightening of the path's curvature. At Point *C* the path is again straight and relative vorticity is again zero. As equatorward travel continues, cyclonic relative vorticity must be developed to compensate for further reduction in planetary vorticity, consequently the path now bends to the left.

**FIGURE 19.20.** Conservation of absolute vorticity along the path of an upper-air wave. [Based on a diagram of H. Riehl (1965), *Introduction to the Atmosphere,* New York, McGraw-Hill, p. 128, Figure 6.7.]

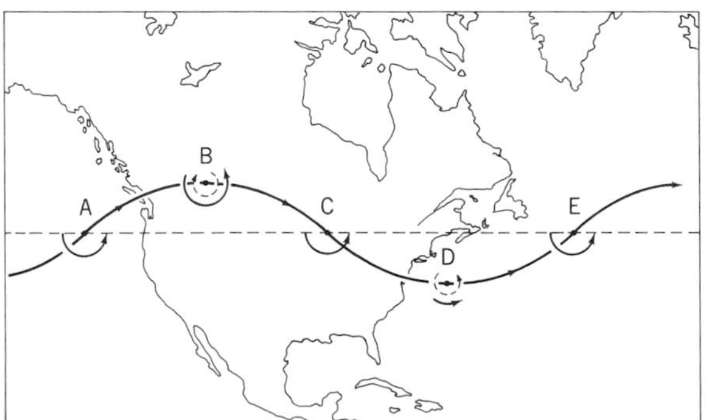


When Point *D* is reached, cyclonic relative vorticity has reached a maximum and the direction of motion is again due east. Path curvature continues and the air column is now again moving poleward into higher latitudes. Relative vorticity again decreases and becomes zero at Point *E,* where the path is again straight. Conditions at Point *E* are identical with those at Point *A,* after completion of one full wave length.

We have explained why a series of waves should form within the upper-air westerlies. These waves of relatively great length and only moderate amplitude are the expected pattern, provided that the conditions are approximately geostrophic, meaning that the isobars associated with the wind are essentially parallel and that path curvature radius is so large that it can be neglected. The situation is about as depicted in Figure 15.26*B*. The number of such waves present at any one time is normally from three to six.

## The circulation index

Because shearing is very slight and wind speed is fairly uniform in the long open waves described above, they comprise a regime of relatively mild weather disturbances lacking in intense cyclones. Such a flow regime is described by meteorologists as a strongly zonal flow and is designated as a *high-index circulation.* Under such conditions there is little exchange of heat between low and high latitudes. Instead, heat exchange between ocean bodies and adjacent land bodies at about the same latitude takes place readily.

As the third and fourth diagrams of Figure 15.26 show, the upper air flow typically changes in character throughout a period ranging in length from three to six weeks. The amplitude of the upper-air waves increases, while their wave length decreases. In this condition intense cyclones develop and there is a large heat exchange across the parallels of latitude. Under such conditions, designated as a *low-index circulation,* the meridional flow is relatively strong. Toward the end of the low-index period waves become occluded, to form centers of high and low pressure. These ultimately dissolve and the circulation returns to the high-index form with a few long waves of low amplitude.

Our next problem is to explain how the intensification of upper-air waves can lead to formation of strong wave cyclones.

## Convergence and divergence

The subject of convergence and divergence within fluids has already been brought up in connection with oceanic circulation (Chapter 16). There it was pointed out that a surface convergence of ocean water must be accompanied by sinking, and a surface divergence by upwelling. To examine conditions at the base of an atmospheric column we must now turn this oceanic configuration upside-down.

Figure 19.21 illustrates convergence and divergence. In the uppermost diagram, which is a plan-view (map-view) looking down upon the earth's surface, a column of air centered at position *A* moves horizontally to posi-

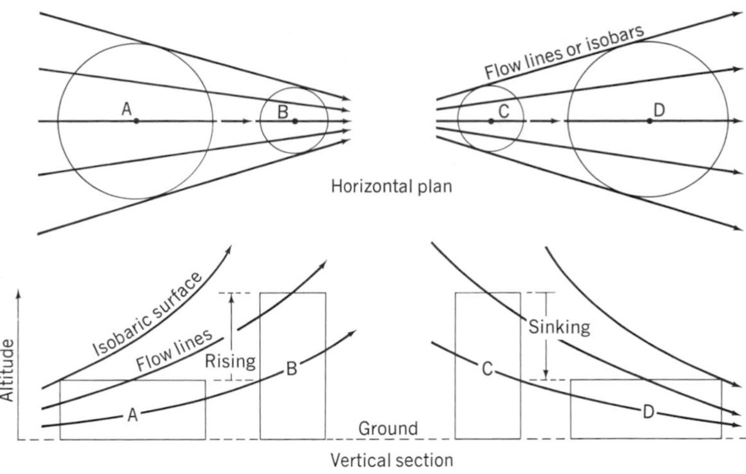


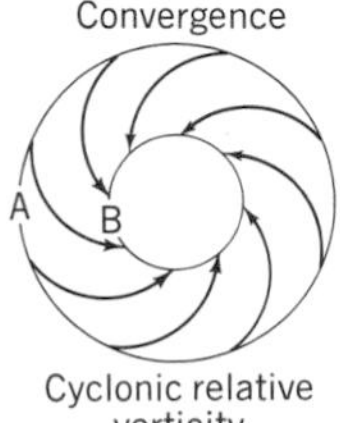


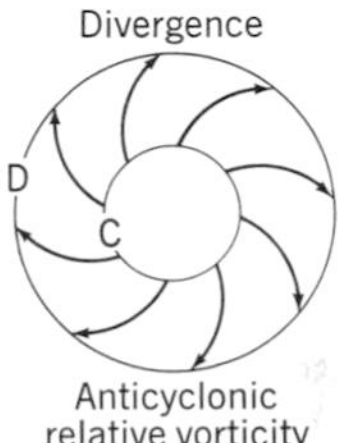


**FIGURE 19.21.** Horizontal convergence (left) and divergence (right), causing an increase or a decrease in the absolute vorticity of an air column. [Based on a diagram of H. Riehl (1965), *Introduction to the Atmosphere,* New York, McGraw-Hill, p. 130, Figure 6.8.]

tion *B.* As the flow lines converge toward the right, the column shrinks in horizontal cross-sectional area. In the middle diagram the same air column is shown as a cylinder undergoing an increase in height as its cross-sectional area shrinks. Flow lines must therefore slope upward and diverge as they undergo convergence in the horizontal plane. At the right in Figure 19.21 are shown the reversed effects of divergence.

Consider now the changes in relative vorticity accompanying convergence and divergence, shown in the lower part of Figure 19.21. As the basal area of the cylinder contracts, air moves inward (centripetally) and is deflected by the Coriolis force into an anticlockwise inspiralling motion. A cyclonic relative vorticity develops and is added to the planetary vorticity, giving an increase in the absolute vorticity in the air column. With divergence, an anticyclonic relative vorticity is generated and subtracts from the planetary vorticity, yielding a decrease in the absolute vorticity.

**FIGURE 19.22.** Effect of divergence and convergence upon flow paths in upper-air waves. Compare with Figure 19.20. [After H. Riehl (1965), *Introduction to the Atmosphere,* New York, McGraw-Hill, p. 132, Figure 6.9.]

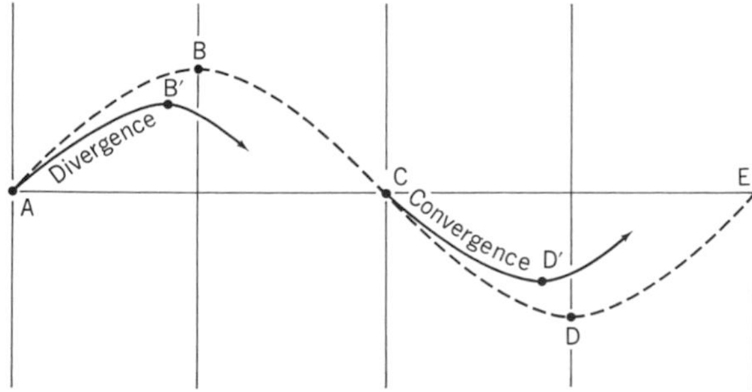


**FIGURE 19.23.** Coupling of upper-air zones of convergence and divergence with surface anticyclones and cyclones, respectively. The upper drawing is a schematic weather map. The lower drawing is a cross section on the line *x–y,* extending up to 10 km (33,000 ft). [After H. Riehl (1965), *Introduction to the Atmosphere,* New York, McGraw-Hill, p. 154, Figure 7.7.]

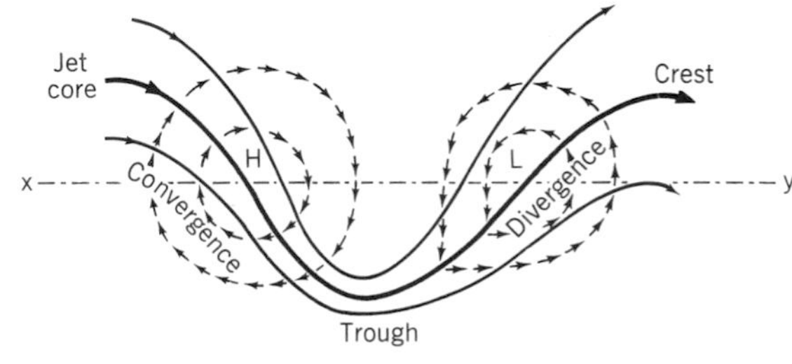


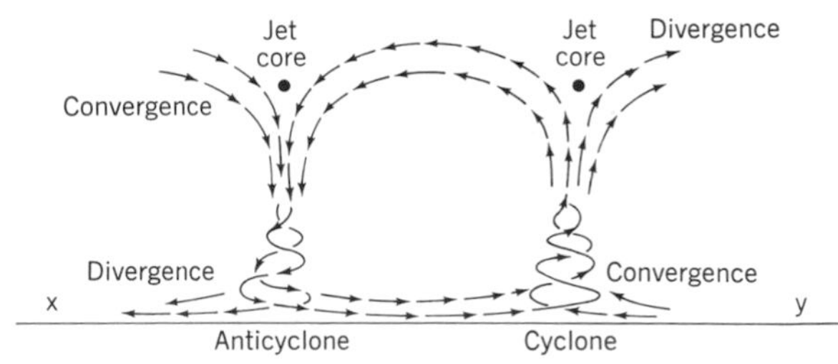

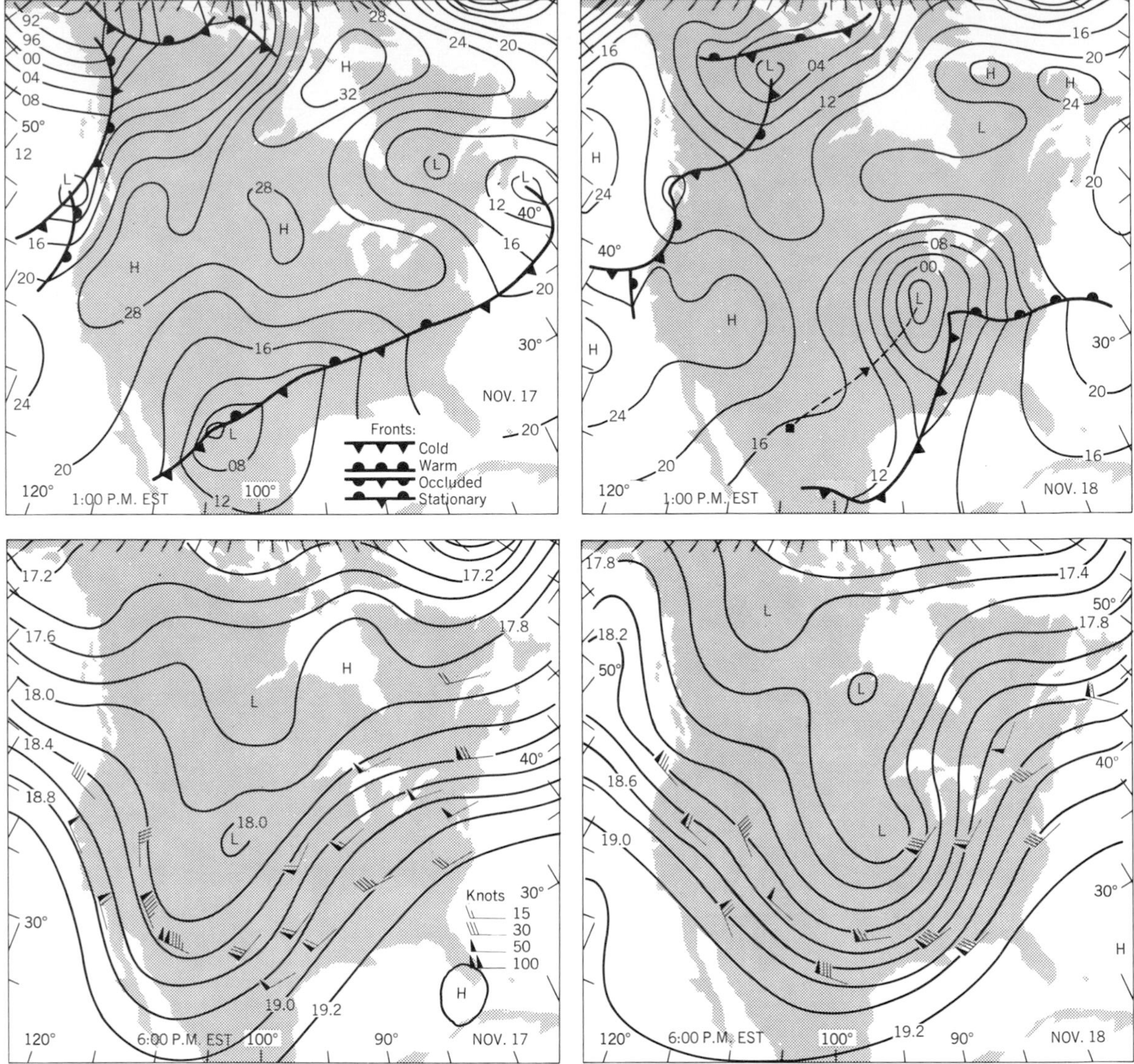


**FIGURE 19.24.** Weather maps for four consecutive days showing evolution and movement of an intense cyclonic storm and its relation to upper-air pressure and winds. *Upper row:* Surface maps for 1:00 p.m. EST. Isobars in millibars, labeled with last two digits. *Lower row:* Pressure and winds in the altitude range 17,000 to 19,000 ft. Contours drawn on the 500-mb surface, labeled in thousands of feet. Note that data for upper-air maps are gathered 6 to 10 hours later than that for surface maps. (Redrawn and simplified from ESSA, U.S. Weather Bureau daily weather maps.)

From what has been said above, we conclude that during convergence of an air mass absolute vorticity is increased, during divergence it is decreased. Actually, it is more accurate to say that the absolute vorticity is either concentrated by convergence into a smaller horizontal area, or spread out more thinly by divergence, since neither convergence nor divergence can by itself generate vorticity.

The next step is to look for horizontal convergences and divergences within upper-air waves and deduce the consequences. Figure 19.22 shows the same map as in Figure 19.20, except that the path of constant absolute vorticity is shown by a dashed line. Assume that in traveling northeastward from Point *A* the air column encounters horizontal divergence along its path. Under the Rossby principle of conservation of absolute vorticity a decrease in absolute vorticity caused by the divergence must be met by a sharper curvature of the path toward the right, as shown by the solid line. The crest of the wave will thus be achieved at Point *B′* and the wave length will be shortened.

Suppose that an air column starting southeast at Point *C* undergoes horizontal convergence, which by itself tends to increase absolute vorticity. In order to conserve absolute vorticity, the path must be turned more sharply to the left. The trough of the wave is reached at Point *D′*, rather than at Point *D*, and the wave is thus shortened.

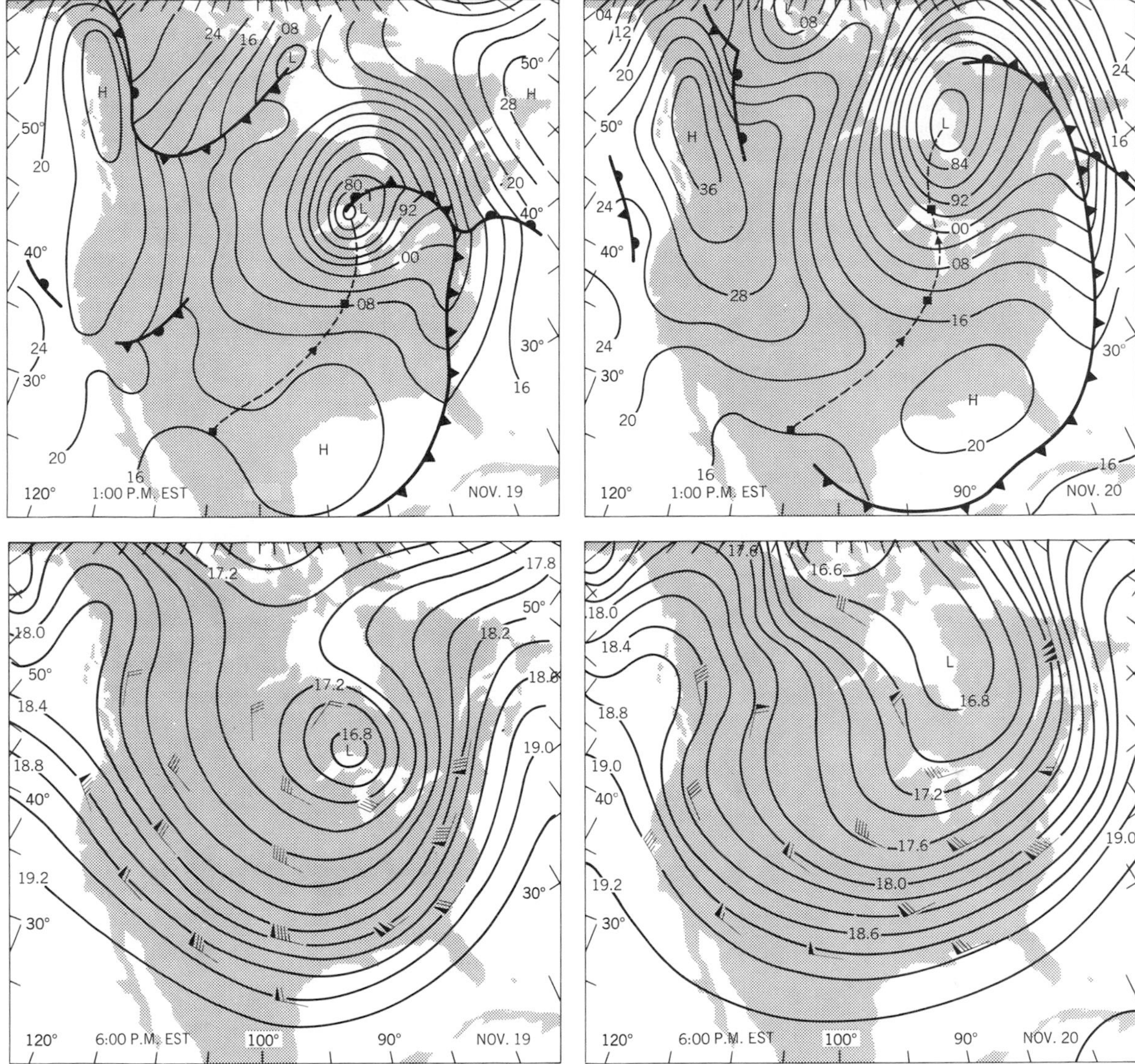


We can therefore attribute the shortening of wave length associated with the low-index circulation to the development of divergences and convergences of flow paths occurring alternately within the waves. As wave lengths shorten and flow lines intensify their meridional pattern, conditions become favorable for the genesis of cyclonic storms.

Whereas the longer waves of high-index circulation have lengths on the order of 3000 to 5000 mi (5000 to 8000 km), the shorter and steeper waves of low-index circulation have lengths of only 1000 to 2000 mi (1600 to 3200 km).

Referring again to Figure 19.21, observe that convergence requires vertical rise of the shrinking air column—divergence requires sinking of the spreading air column. The Coriolis effect is to generate cyclonic flow in the converging column and anticyclonic flow in the diverging column. But rising air must be disposed of at high levels by divergence, while sinking air must be replaced by air drawn in from all sides at high level and this requires high-level convergence.

The coupling together of high-level convergences and divergences with their opposites at low level is schematically illustrated in Figure 19.23. An upper-air wave, its axis marked by the jet stream core, shows convergence in the zone between crest and trough of the upper-air wave (left). Beneath this upper-air convergence is a surface divergence, represented by an anticyclone, or high. Between trough and crest of the wave (right) is a zone of divergence, beneath which is a surface convergence represented by a cyclone, or low. While idealized and simplified, this model of coupling offers a coherent explanation for the occurrence of cyclonic storms and explains their control by upper-air flow. The column of rising air above the surface cyclone is, of course, subject to adiabatic cooling, causing cloudiness and precipitation, whereas the sinking column of air over the surface anticyclone is subjected to adiabatic warming, with reduced humidity and resulting clear skies.

Our coupling model shows a true vortex of wind to exist only in the air layer close to the ground. Traced upward, this vortex dies out and is not seen in the converging and diverging high-level flow lines, which follow broadly curving patterns. We shall see, however, that in the advanced (occluded) stages of development of a large intense cyclone the vortex is extended into the troposphere and becomes an upper-level low.

## Cyclone development under an upper-air wave

Figure 19.24 is a series of weather maps of North America illustrating the relation between wave cyclones and the larger upper-air waves. The lower line of charts shows conditions at about 17,000–19,000 ft (5.2–5.8 km). The continuous lines on the map are not actually isobars, but may be considered equivalent to isobars for purposes of comparing the two maps. Actually, the pressure lines on the upper-air map are contours, representing the elevation of the 500-mb pressure surface. In a way this is a map of the topography of an imaginary surface at which the pressure is everywhere the same. Thus high altitude corresponds to high pressure. The upper-air charts show conditions several hours later than the surface charts, but this does not greatly alter the general points of comparison.

On November 17 an upper-air wave trough lies over the western United States. The air in this trough is very cold, −30° F (−34° C) over Wyoming at 18,000 ft (5.5 km). At the ground surface there is an east-west stationary front oriented from Texas to North Carolina. This is the line between cold (*cP*) air on the north and warm (*mT*) air on the south and represents the conditions, shown in Figures 19.9 and 19.10*A*, at the outset of the life cycle of the wave cyclone. A wave is already beginning to form over the Rio Grande Valley, as shown by a weak low-pressure center with cold and warm fronts. This low lies on the southeast margin of the upper-air wave.

On November 18 the upper-air wave has deepened and has shifted eastward. Note that the air flow at high levels parallels the isobars and that there is very little suggestion of the well-developed wave cyclone that is now in the open stage of development and is centered over the Ohio Valley. The cyclone at low levels is located on the eastern side of the upper-air wave but is traveling rapidly northeast, as if dragged along and steered by the strong northeastward air flow at high levels. Note the divergence shown above the center of the low.

On November 19 the cyclone is in the occluded stage, centered over Lake Superior. Over this same position on the upper-air map is a nearly circular low with counterclockwise air flow. This represents the cutting off of the upper-air wave to form an isolated pocket of cold air. Meantime the tongue of the cold *cP* air mass which in-

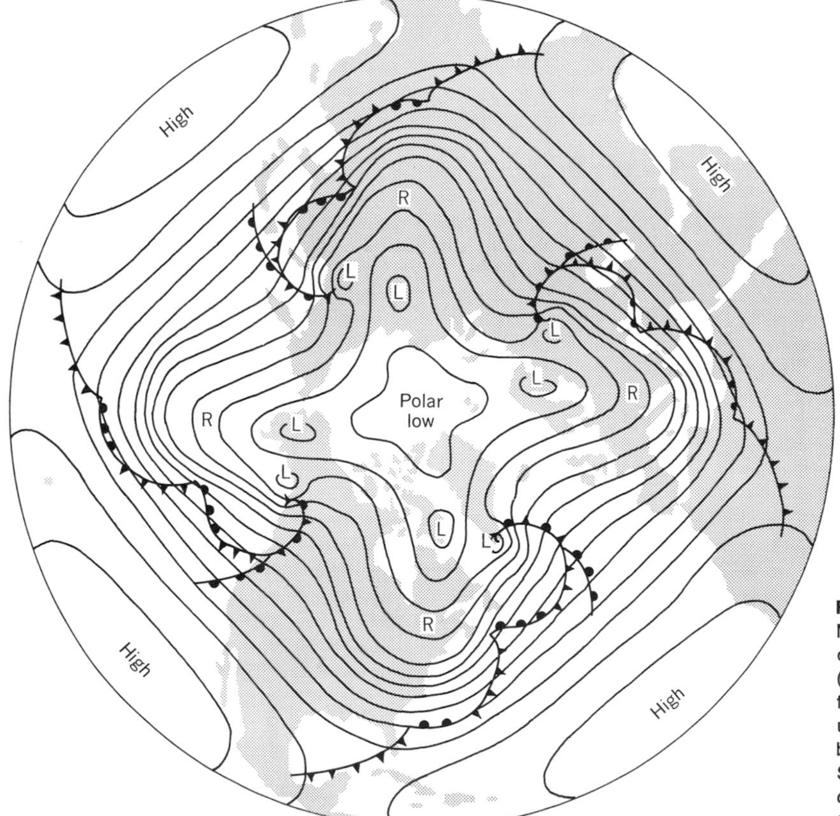


**FIGURE 19.25.** This map, centered on the North Pole, shows four families of wave cyclones associated with four Rossby waves (labeled *R*). Cyclones are indicated by frontal systems at sea level, whereas the upper-air waves are shown by high-level isobars (smoothly curving, solid lines). [After S. Petterssen (1958), *Introduction to Meteorology*, New York, McGraw-Hill, p. 226, Figure 166.]

vaded the Central States behind the surface cold front of the wave cyclone has now spread far over the Gulf of Mexico, but nevertheless the upper-air winds are westerly in this same area. On the final map, November 20, the wave cyclone has moved over Labrador, heading for the North Atlantic, while the upper-air wave has also moved farther east.

Figure 19.25 is a diagrammatic map of the Northern Hemisphere showing four families of wave cyclones superimposed on four upper-air waves. Notice that the youngest member of the cyclone family lies about at the bottom of a wave trough, while the oldest member has migrated to a position close to the wave crest.

## Thunderstorms and tornadoes

Thunderstorms are frequently found in large numbers in a wave cyclone. As we have seen, thunderstorms may occur along both cold and warm fronts where the lifted air is unstable. Those along the cold front are often extremely violent, with powerful squall winds. In extreme cases the tornado, the most violent of all storms, is produced.

Thunderstorms also occur along a *squall line,* paralleling the cold front, but moving in advance of it in the warm sector. In Figure 19.26 is a portion of the U.S. weather map showing a squall line in the region of *mT* air. The thunderstorms of a squall line may be recognized as such by the weather observer because their passage is not usually accompanied by a shift of winds to the northwest or sharp temperature drop, as is normal for the cold front. Instead the cold front arrives several hours later and may produce little precipitation.

The *tornado* is a small but very intense wind vortex which extends down from a cumulonimbus cloud, taking the form of a tapering funnel (Figure 19.27). Although but a few hundred feet in diameter, the funnel cloud contains winds with speeds up to 500 mi (800 km) per hour. Within the center of the funnel cloud is a vortex in which air pressure is but a fraction of normal pressure. Tornadoes commonly move northeastward across country at 25–40 mi (40–65 km) per hour, following the general motion of thunderstorms and associated cold fronts. Where the funnel cloud touches ground, there is complete destruction along a swath on the order of 1000 ft (300 m) wide and often many miles long. Not only does the great wind speed prove irresistible, but the sudden lowering of air pressure as the vortex passes may cause buildings to explode from the expansion of air entrapped within (Figure 19.28).

**FIGURE 19.27.** A tornado funnel cloud seen at Hardtner, Kansas. (Photograph by Blacklock, courtesy of ESSA, U.S. Weather Bureau.)

Tornadoes are the small eddies of intense turbulence generated by the mixing of dry polar air masses (*mP*) with unstable moist maritime tropical air (*mT*). The region most favorable for such tornado-producing interactions between unlike air masses is the Great Plains region and the Mississippi Valley. The states of Kansas, Oklahoma, and Texas have the highest frequency of tornadoes—over 1000 per year—with Iowa, Missouri and Arkansas in a second bracket—400 to 600 per year. Tornadoes are most likely to occur in those months in which the greatest contrast exists between polar and tropical air masses. These months are from early spring to late summer, with May leading, followed by June and April. Tornadoes are typically an American

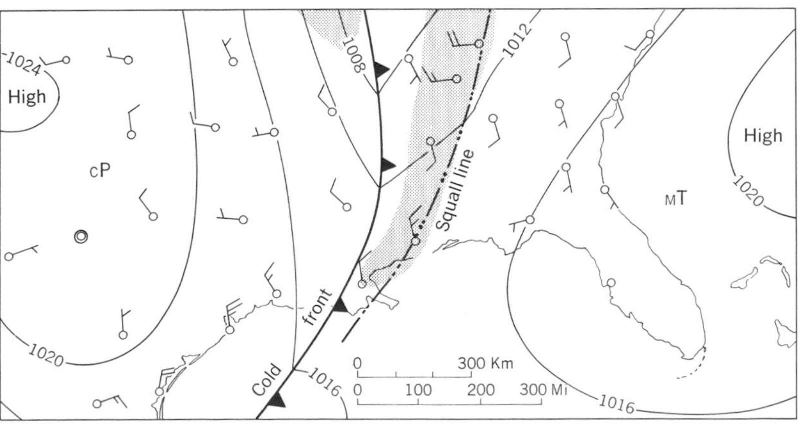


**FIGURE 19.26.** A squall line and its associated precipitation (shaded areas) are shown on this portion of the daily surface-weather map for May 9, 1961. (After ESSA, U.S. Weather Bureau.)

**FIGURE 19.28.** Two persons died in the wreckage of this store at Ionia, Iowa, struck by a tornado on April 23, 1948. (Courtesy of *Des Moines Register* and ESSA, U.S. Weather Bureau.)

weather phenomenon. Although reported in other parts of the world, they are nowhere so frequent as in the United States.

*Waterspouts,* which are funnel-like clouds of water droplets over the sea surface, are much like tornadoes in structure. Some large and violent waterspouts are actually tornadoes formed over the Gulf of Mexico and off the southeastern coast of the United States at times when the cold front of a continental air mass is spreading across the tropical water. More commonly, however, waterspouts are small vortexes produced by turbulent whirls associated with convective movements of the air. They are often formed during the squalls associated with thunderstorms, consequently small water spouts are common over the tropical oceans. Rapid condensation of water vapor in the spout accounts for the dark aspect of the funnel, which is not formed of water drawn up from the sea surface as commonly imagined.

## Weather disturbances of low latitudes

In contrast to our detailed weather knowledge of the middle latitudes of the Northern Hemisphere, knowledge of weather systems in the low latitudes is not yet sufficient for developing a complete and generally acceptable set of explanations of the weak atmospheric disturbances which produce rainy periods.

The fundamental differences between the low-latitude belt of the troposphere and that of the middle and high latitudes are these: (1) Barometric pressure differences are generally small from place to place in the low latitudes (except in violent tropical storms), whereas extremely strong barometric pressure gradients frequently occur at the higher latitudes in connection with wave cyclones and fronts. Consequently most weather disturbances producing clouds and rain in the low latitudes are very mild and are difficult to define on the weather maps. (2) Because the Coriolis effect is very weak in the low latitudes, there is far less tendency for air flow to be deflected into small and intense cyclones and anticyclones, which form readily in the middle and high latitudes. (3) Air masses of tropical and equatorial regions tend to be very much alike in temperature properties, hence there do not exist strongly defined fronts along which violent disturbances can occur. Although some meteorologists have recognized such air masses as *mT, cT, mE* as distinctly different from one another in these regions, others doubt that any real differences exist to the point that an air mass can be named and its boundaries sharply drawn. (4) Rainfall in the low latitudes is almost entirely from cumuliform clouds and takes the form of showers and thunderstorms, whereas in the middle and high latitudes much of the precipitation, particularly in the cold seasons of the year, is from stratus clouds associated with fronts of wave cyclones without strong convection. (5) General flow of air of the troposphere is easterly in the low latitudes and is weaker than the powerful westerlies with their associated jet streams in the higher latitudes. (An exception is the very high tropical easterly jet stream.)

These basic differences combine to give an important point of contrast between these two regions of the globe: Weather processes of the low latitudes are dominantly those of vertical rising and sinking air motions, or convection, whereas weather processes of the middle and high latitudes are dominantly those of horizontal mixing, or advection, in great flat plate-like eddies formed by moving cyclones and anticyclones.

**Easterly waves** Much of the rain of the trade-wind belt over the Atlantic and Pacific Oceans may be caused by a type of moving disturbance termed an *easterly wave.* Figure 19.29 is a weather map of the region of northeast trades in the West Indies where these waves have been studied in detail. The isobars oriented generally east-west show that the pressure is decreasing from the subtropical cell of high pressure on the north to the equatorial trough of low pressure on the south. Winds several thousand feet above sea level follow the isobars with the air moving from east to west. These are the prevailing tropical easterlies. A shallow wave, or trough, of slightly lower barometric pressure has developed in the easterlies, as shown by the bending of isobars along the axis of the wave marked by the dashed line.

The wave trough travels slowly westward. In advance of the trough the winds shift from east to northeast, then, as the trough passes, swing to southeast. In the rear of the trough is a belt of convectional showers and thunderstorm rain, produced from cumulonimbus clouds. Stratus clouds may also be present and may produce some of the rain.

**FIGURE 19.29.** An easterly wave, shown by a northward bend in the streamlines of air flow, moves slowly westward over the West Indies. (© 1960, John Wiley & Sons, New York. Based on a map by Riehl.)

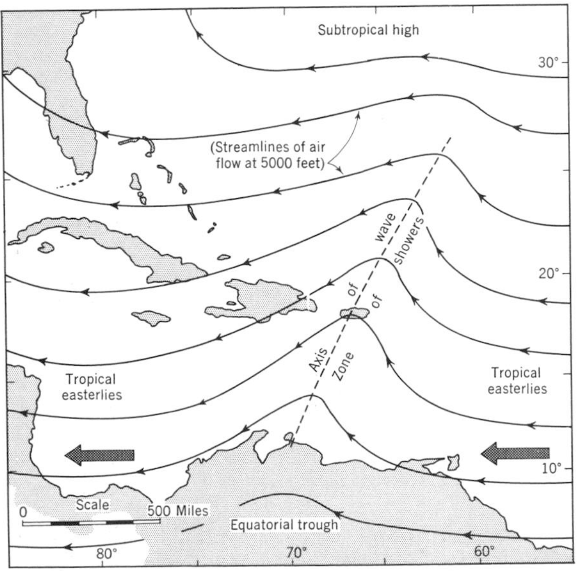


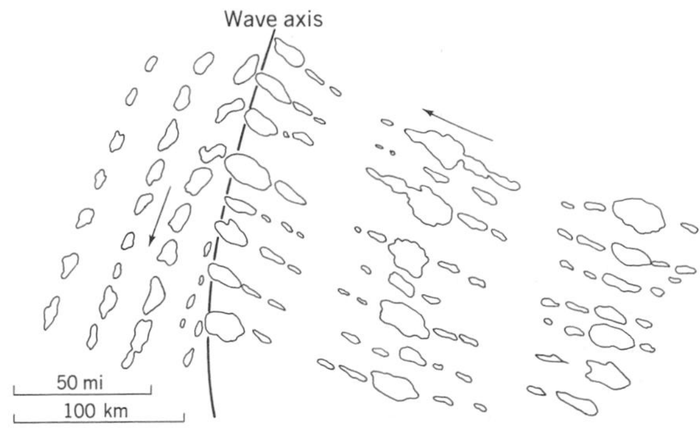


**FIGURE 19.30.** Sketch map of cumulus clouds in an easterly wave in the central Pacific Ocean. Compare with Figure 19.29. Clouds of similar form are pictured in Figure 18.27. [After J. S. Malkus (1963), *Science,* vol. 141, p. 767, Figure 3a.]

Patterns of air flow within an easterly wave are revealed by cloud formations (Figure 19.30). Small trade-wind cumulus clouds form in parallel rows oriented northeast–southwest in the region west of the trough axis. To the east of the axis, rows of heavy shower-producing cumulus follow a very different trend.

A single easterly wave may cover a zone roughly 1000 mi (1600 km) broad from east to west and will move slowly westward at a rate of perhaps 250–300 mi (400–500 km) per day, or at a speed of about 12 mi (20 km) per hour. The period of rain may last one to two days.

Easterly waves are thought to travel across the Atlantic and Pacific Oceans. They have been traced across the Atlantic from the Guinea coast of Africa to the Caribbean.

**Equatorial waves and monsoon depressions** In the equatorial trough the easterly air flow may run uniformly from east to west. This is shown in the eastern part of the weather map of Figure 19.31, which may be considered to represent air movement at low levels in the equatorial and tropical region of the Pacific Ocean. At other times a clockwise eddy may form in the easterlies, reversing the air flow from westward to eastward in the vicinity of the equator, as shown on the western side of the map. When this happens, an *equatorial wave* develops. Convergence of moist air masses into a slowly moving weak low on this wave causes convectional rainfall. Note that the clockwise eddy produces westerly winds, running counter to the easterlies.

Meteorologists designate as *equatorial westerlies* any westerly winds in the equatorial belt separated from the westerlies of the middle and high latitudes by the tropical easterlies. Equatorial westerlies are said to be typically formed in the hemisphere having its high sun, or summer season, and are best developed in summer of the Northern Hemisphere.

A related weather disturbance is the *monsoon depression,* a weak cyclone that develops in the monsoon (high-sun) season over southeast Asia and the Indian Peninsula (Figure 19.32). Barometric pressure in a monsoon depression is only from 2 to 4 mb lower than that of the surrounding region, but convectional rainfall

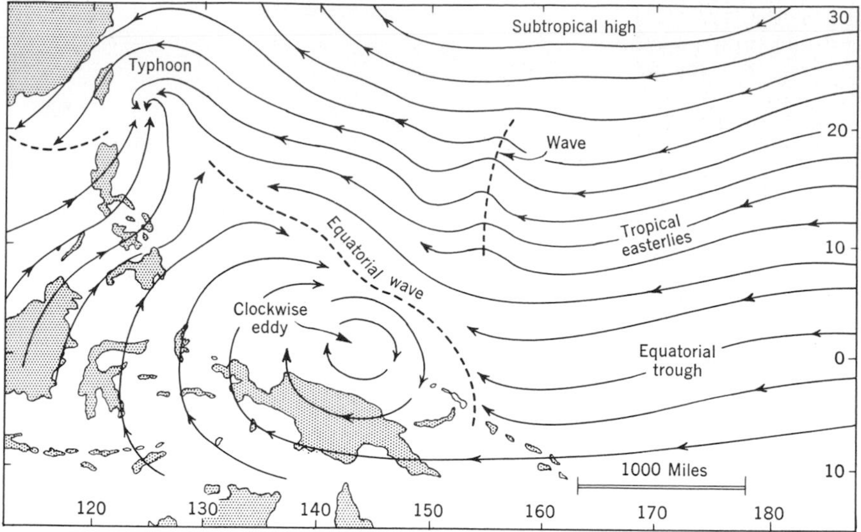


**FIGURE 19.31.** Streamlines of air flow at an elevation of 1000 ft (300 m) show an equatorial wave and associated eddy in the zone of tropical easterly winds. (© 1960, John Wiley & Sons, New York. Based on a map by Riehl.)

is heavy. The depressions move slowly westward, 10 to 12 mi (16–20 km) per hour, and are apparently steered by the tropical easterly jet stream, which has its development at the same season.

Greatly increased knowledge of weather elements in the equatorial trough and bordering tropical zones will be needed before the nature and form of weather disturbances prevalent in the equatorial regions are understood. A large number of weather-observing stations from which upper-air soundings can be made simultaneously and at frequent intervals is needed to obtain this knowledge. Detailed synoptic charts will eventually yield answers to many puzzling questions about this little-known belt of air.

**Tropical cyclones** In contrast to the weakly defined disturbances considered above, the belt of tropical easterlies breeds the most violent of all large cyclonic storms, the *tropical cyclone,* a nearly circular storm with extremely low pressure at the center, accompanied by high winds, dense clouds, and heavy precipitation (Figure 19.33). The terms *hurricane* (West Indies) and *typhoon* (western Pacific) are acceptable equivalent names for severe tropical cyclones.

Tropical cyclones originate in easterly waves and equatorial waves of the type already described, but only over oceans. At some point in the wave a distinct center of low pressure forms and, if conditions are favorable, deepens rapidly, with the isobars taking on the form of nearly concentric circles. Not all such tropical cyclones deepen into severe storms—some die out quickly, others travel long distances as mild disturbances. If, however, the pressure becomes extremely low in the storm center, winds may increase to speeds of 75 mi (120 km) per hour or much higher, with the accompaniment of dense clouds, extreme air turbulence, and heavy rain. The storm is then commonly designated as a hurricane or typhoon and is a serious menace to ships at sea and to islands or continental coasts over which it may pass. The storm normally travels westward or northwestward at a rate of 6–12 mi (10–20 km) per hour.

Figure 19.34 is a surface-weather chart showing details of a hurricane of the West Indies. Although based on an actual hurricane, several wind arrows have been

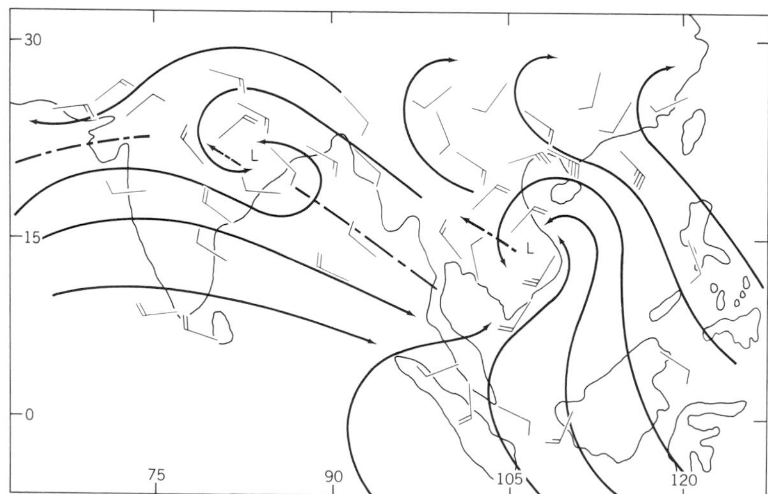


**FIGURE 19.32.** Weather map for southeast Asia for a day near autumnal equinox. Bold arrows represent streamlines of air flow at 10,000 ft (700-mb level). Dashed line is equatorial trough. Monsoon depressions (L) located over India and Indochina are moving slowly toward the northeast. [After H. Riehl (1965), *Introduction to the Atmosphere,* New York, McGraw-Hill, p. 177, Figure 8.5.]

**FIGURE 19.33.** Hurricane Gladys located about 150 mi (240 km) southwest of Tampa, Florida, on October 8, 1968, photographed from Apollo 7 spacecraft at an altitude of about 110 mi (180 km). View is southeast, toward Cuba. (NASA photograph.)

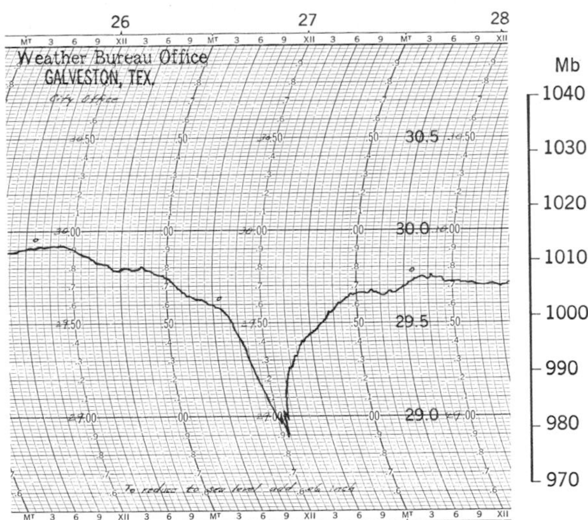


**FIGURE 19.35.** During the hurricane of July 27, 1943, a barograph in Galveston, Texas, recorded this trace of the fall and rise of pressure. (Courtesy of ESSA, U.S. Weather Bureau.)

added and the precipitation pattern is inferred from similar examples. The pressure of 952 mb in the storm center is equivalent to about 28.3 in. (72 cm) of mercury, a low pressure rarely found in even the deepest of middle-latitude cyclones. The barograph trace shown in Figure 19.35 is a sample of the low pressure produced by the passage of a hurricane, but much lower values have been observed. Surface winds blow in toward the center with a counterclockwise spiral (Northern Hemisphere), making an angle of about 30–40 degrees with the isobars. Wind speeds are commonly from 75 to 125 mi (120 to 200 km) per hour, but much higher gusts have been reported. These extreme winds may affect a circle of radius as great as 200 mi (300 km) for a very large storm.

Precipitation occurs in spiral bands, as shown in Figures 19.33 and 19.34. Air temperatures in the central part of the storm are abnormally high, from 9 to 18 F° (5 to 10 C°) higher than the average value of the tropical atmosphere. This fact shows that large quantities of heat are being absorbed into the storm from the ocean surface below.

Figure 19.36 is a schematic cross-section through a tropical cyclone, showing cloud formations and rain bands. Upon reaching high levels, air flows outward, producing a cirrus cloud cap. Figure 19.37 shows the rain bands as registered on the radar scope.

The passage of a severe tropical storm at sea usually follows the same pattern of events. On the day preceding the storm, the weather is fair and calm, with barometric pressure somewhat above normal and fewer cumulus clouds than normal. A long sea swell, produced by great storm waves which have outrun the slowly moving storm, gives warning of what is to come. Where this swell reaches a coast, the breakers are powerful, but less frequent than usual, breaking perhaps 4 or 5 to the minute. The sky in this period preceding the storm shows a sequence of clouds much like that of an approaching warm front—cirrus bands reach across the sky, then thicken to form cirrostratus and altostratus. The cirrus layer is carried downwind in the high-level easterlies. The clouds continue to thicken; congested cumulus forms; showers begin. Now the barometer falls rapidly and the wind increases. Finally, a great dark wall of dense clouds approaches; when it reaches the observer, the storm is unleashed in full fury. Great waves break over the ship and seawater spray is blown in sheets that reduce visibility almost to zero.

**FIGURE 19.34.** Surface weather map of a typical hurricane of the West Indies. Eye of storm is located over the western tip of Cuba. [After A. N. Strahler (1969), *Exercises in Physical Geography,* New York, John Wiley & Sons, p. 110.]

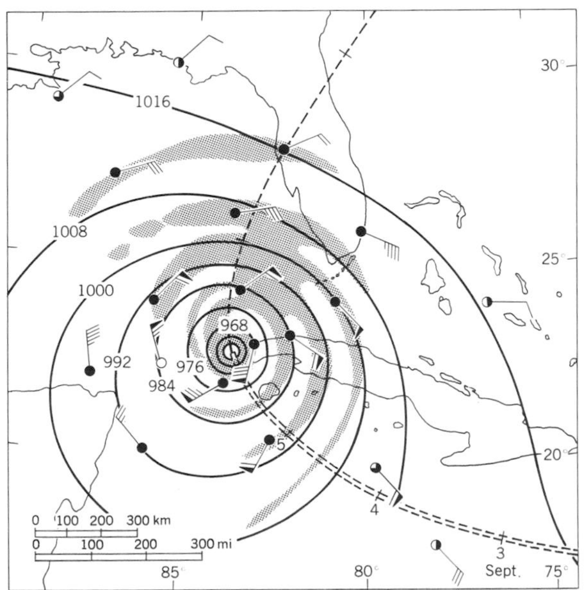

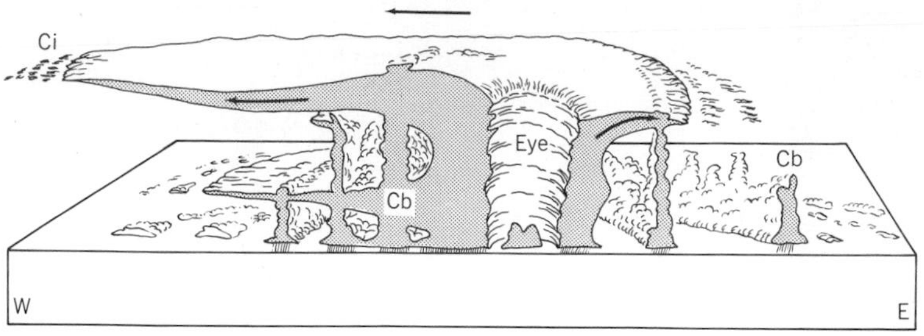

**FIGURE 19.36.** Schematic diagram of a hurricane. The cross section cuts through the eye. Cumulonimbus clouds in concentric rings rise through dense stratiform clouds in which the air spirals upward. Width of the diagram represents about 600 mi (1000 km). Highest clouds are at elevations often over 30,000 ft (9 km). [Redrawn from ESSA, U.S. Weather Bureau, R. C. Gentry (1964), *Weatherwise*, vol. 17, p. 182.]

After several hours of raging storm an abrupt calm sets in. This is the *central eye* of the storm, a strange hollow vortex several miles wide surrounded by a dense cloud wall (Figures 19.36 and 19.37). Although the air is almost calm and the sky may clear, waves are mountainous and especially perilous to the ship because they intersect in great peak-like masses. In the central eye, air is subsiding rapidly and at the same time is being adiabatically heated. This process explains the remarkably rapid warming often reported in the eye, as well as the tendency for clouds to evaporate and skies to clear. The period of calm may last perhaps a half hour, then the dark cloud wall of the eye approaches and the ship is again enveloped in violent storm, except that now the wind direction is exactly reversed from that in the first part of the storm. After many hours the winds lessen and subside, the clouds break up, and the storm is over.

Tropical cyclones occur in seven ocean regions of the world (Figure 19.38): (1) Caribbean Sea and Gulf of Mexico, (2) western North Pacific, including the Philippine Islands and China Sea, (3) the Arabian Sea and Bay of Bengal, (4) eastern Pacific Ocean, off the coast of Mexico and Central America, (5) the South Indian Ocean, east of Madagascar, (6) the western South Pacific, in the region of Samoa, the Fiji Islands, and the northeast coast of Australia, and (7) off the northwest coast of Australia. Severe tropical storms are not known in the South Atlantic.

**FIGURE 19.37.** Hurricane Hilda seen on radar, September 15, 1958. The concentric circles on the radar screen are spaced at intervals of 50 nautical mi (70 km). (Official U.S. Navy photograph.)

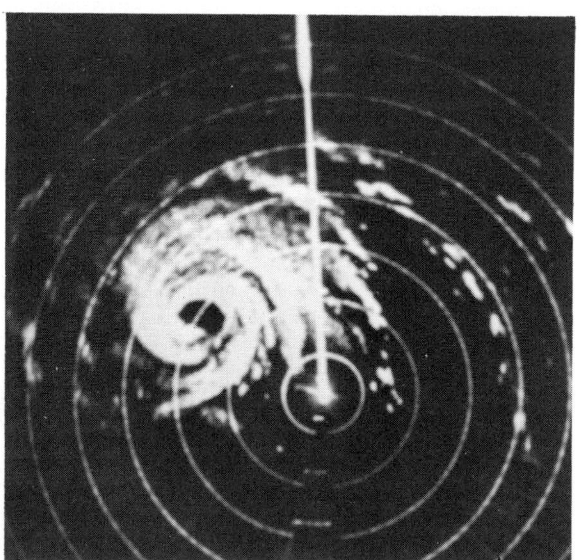

If the paths of many Atlantic tropical cyclones are plotted on a chart (Figure 19.39), it will be seen that they tend to originate in lat. 10° to 20° N. and to travel westward, following the tropical easterlies. The paths then turn more northwestward (Northern Hemisphere) bringing the storms into the region of westerlies. There they turn north, then northeast, become broadened and weakened into middle-latitude cyclones, and are carried eastward across the ocean. In taking this curving path, many storms stay entirely over the ocean, but others travel over the eastern margin of the adjoining continent.

Tropical cyclones occur in that part of the year including and immediately following the period of high sun, or summer season, in the hemisphere in question. Thus the hurricanes and typhoons of the Caribbean and northwestern Pacific occur from June through November. Those of the western South Pacific and South Indian Oceans occur from December through March.

The reasons for development of an intense tropical cyclone from the much more frequent weak tropical disturbances are not yet fully understood. As Figure 19.38 shows, high sea-surface temperatures are an important contributing factor, permitting a high rate of heat flow from ocean surface to atmosphere.[2] That tropical cyclones do not occur in the South Atlantic, which does not attain maximum temperatures over 82° F (28° C), seems to confirm the importance of the temperature factor. Only a small fraction of the weak cyclonic disturbances of low latitudes develop into intense tropical cyclones, and the number of storms per season in each locality varies greatly from year to year. Perhaps the controlling factors will be revealed through analysis of upper-air winds.

Vast destruction and loss of life brought about by tropical storms cause them to rank among the great catastrophes which nature inflicts upon man. Although of prime importance as a hazard to ships at sea, these storms do their greatest damage when passing over densely inhabited islands and coasts. Destruction of harbor facilities and small craft is especially great because the great waves may be accompanied by abnormally high tides, bringing both wave attack and

[2] Estimates from hurricane *Carla*, 1961, gave a total energy flux from sea surface to storm of $21.5 \times 10^{17}$ calories in one 24-hour period, which is an average rate of $6 \times 10^{13}$ calories per second. As a result, the sea surface temperature was lowered by more than 3 F° (1.5 C°) in the path of the storm.

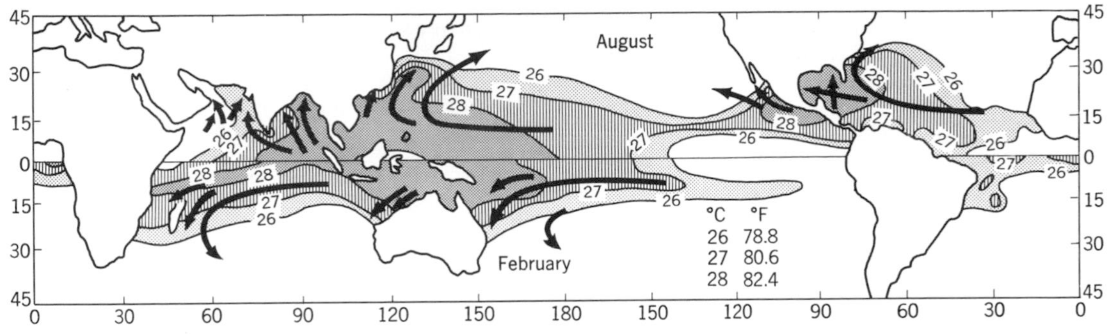


**FIGURE 19.38.** Common paths of tropical cyclones as related to sea surface temperatures (°C) in summer of the respective hemisphere. [© 1965, John Wiley & Sons, New York. After Palmen (1948).]

storm surges (Chapter 17) upon places usually far above the reach of the sea (Figure 19.40).

Another important effect of tropical cyclones reaching land is the heavy fall of rain, which may total as much as 6–12 in. (15–30 cm) in a 24-hour period. Summer floods of the Gulf Coast and eastern seaboard states are usually of this origin. A striking example was provided by hurricane Diane in August, 1955. This storm, which took altogether about 200 lives and did property damage amounting to 1½ million dollars in its sweeping path over the eastern states, passed eastward over southern New England. Torrential rains on the watersheds of New England rivers produced unprecedented floods by the rivers of Connecticut, Rhode Island, and Massachusetts. Similar flooding rains are brought to Japan and the coast of China by summer typhoons. An occasional tropical storm formed off the west coast of Mexico will pass inland over the Sonoran Desert region of southeastern California and southern Arizona, causing torrential rains which flood desert stream channels and wash out highways and railroad bridges.

## Atmosphere and oceans in review

In Part Two the atmosphere and oceans have been treated as dynamic systems of planet Earth. Emphasis has been upon the global flux of energy and matter through the complex motions of air and water. Planet Earth possesses a unique combination of a thick oceanic layer and a dense atmosphere. The uniqueness is obvious when we look at the other planets of our solar system. Mercury and Mars are totally, or almost totally, devoid of both oceans and atmospheres. The same can be said of our Moon. Venus has a dense atmosphere but no ocean and practically no free water. The great outer planets have dense atmospheres, but cold surfaces which cannot maintain water in the liquid state.

Combined with the remarkable endowment of ocean and atmosphere is a rotation rate that strongly controls the circulatory systems of planet Earth. The oceanic gyres as well as the convective and advective circulation systems of the atmosphere exist in the scales we find them because a particular rate of planetary rotation is combined with a particular degree of imbalance between incoming radiation in equatorial latitudes and outgoing radiation in polar regions.

There remains to be considered another major control

**FIGURE 19.39.** Hurricane tracks for the month of August illustrate typical storm paths in the western North Atlantic. (© 1960, John Wiley & Sons, New York. Based on data of U.S. Navy Oceanographic Office.)

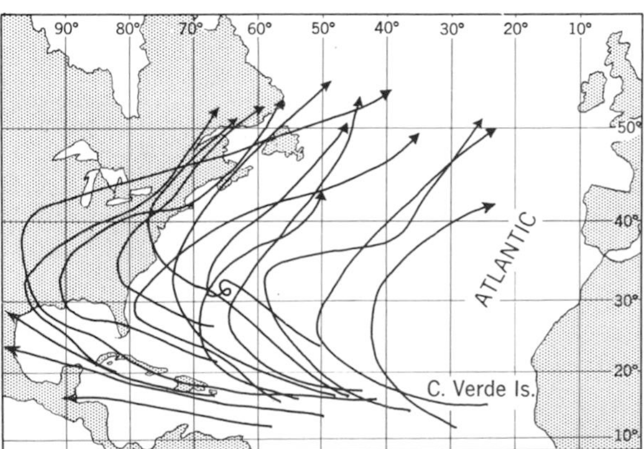


**FIGURE 19.40.** Palm trees and storm surf along the Miami, Florida, waterfront at the height of a severe hurricane. (Courtesy of ESSA, U.S. Weather Bureau.)

of the circulatory system of planet Earth, namely a configuration of ocean basins and continents which gives a unique arrangement of unlike surface elements beneath the atmosphere and a compartmentation for the world ocean. The configuration of the solid earth is controlled largely by internal processes depending upon energy sources quite unrelated to solar energy. Consequently the trends of mountain ranges, ocean deeps, and other relief features of the globe cut across the parallels of latitude in an accidental manner, interrupting the symmetrical flow systems of oceans and atmosphere.

Part Three, to follow, is concerned with the processes, materials, and forms of the solid earth, and with the history of the continents and ocean basins. In connection with a review of hypotheses of origin of the earth it will also be appropriate to speculate about the origin of the earth's atmosphere and oceans and the salt constituents of the ocean waters.

## References for further study

Flora, S. D. (1954), *Tornadoes of the United States,* Norman, Univ. of Oklahoma Press, 221 pp.

Riehl, H. (1954), *Tropical Meteorology,* New York, McGraw-Hill, 392 pp.

Tannehill, I. R. (1956), *Hurricanes,* Princeton, N.J., Princeton Univ. Press, 308 pp.

Battan, L. J. (1961), *The Nature of Violent Storms,* Garden City, N.Y., Anchor Sci. Study Series, Doubleday, 158 pp.

Dunn, G. E., and B. I. Miller (1964), *Atlantic Hurricanes,* Baton Rouge, Louisiana State Univ. Press, 377 pp.

Fed. Aviation Agency, and Civil Aeronautics Admin., U.S. Dept. of Commerce (1965), *Aviation Weather,* Washington, D.C., U.S. Govt. Printing Office, 299 pp.

Riehl, H. (1965), *Introduction to the Atmosphere,* New York, McGraw-Hill, 365 pp., chaps. 7, 8.

Petterssen, S. (1969), *Introduction to Meteorology,* 3rd ed., New York, McGraw-Hill, 333 pp., chaps. 12, 13, 14.

# THREE

# The solid earth

*Volcanic eruption at the birth of the island of Surtsey. Courtesy Icelandic Photo & Press Service.*

# 20

# Introduction to rocks and minerals

IT MIGHT SEEM most logical to begin a study of the solid earth, or *lithosphere,* by taking the largest features first, then working down to smaller and smaller details. In that case we should consider first the earth's interior, then the nature of its continents and ocean basins, then such relief features as volcanoes or mountain ranges, and finally the individual varieties of rocks and minerals. But there are good reasons to consider minerals and rocks first. We cannot discuss meaningfully the earth's interior, the structure of the crust, or the development of relief features except through reference to the chemical composition and physical structure of the forms of mineral matter comprising these larger features. The development of Man's understanding of the earth has required attention to small details which he has been able to observe directly and to test in his laboratories. The cumulative development of detailed surveys and geological maps has enabled the geologist to visualize the arrangements of rocks into larger patterns. Observed differences in chemical composition and physical structure of rocks from place to place have led directly to inferences as to process and origin, and these inductively derived principles have served to control speculation concerning the formation of continents and the larger events of geologic history.

By the word *rock* the geologist generally means the solid, undisturbed mineral matter lying beneath the thin layer of soil and vegetation. Rock is usually hard enough that it cannot easily be broken except by use of a hammer or pick. Some rock is, however, soft enough to pulverize easily with the fingers. Usually, also, rock is extremely old in comparison with living matter and man-made objects on the surface. By far the greatest part of all solid rock forming the earth's surface zone is at least a million years old, and much of it is billions of years old. Here too there are striking exceptions, such as the molten lava being erupted at this very moment from one volcano or another and solidifying into an extremely hard dense rock almost before our eyes.

Rather than labor for a precise definition of "rock," let us turn next to some practical distinctions among varieties of earth materials close to the surface of the ground.

## Bedrock and its overburden

Examination of a freshly cut cliff, such as that in a new highway excavation or quarry wall, may reveal several kinds of earth materials (Figure 20.1). Solid hard rock that is still in place and relatively unchanged is called *bedrock.* It grades upward into a zone where the rock is partly decayed and has disintegrated into clay and sand particles. This material may be called the *residual overburden,* or *regolith.* At the top is a layer of true *soil,* often called *topsoil* by farmers and gardeners. The soil scientist refers to this layer as the *solum.* It is usually less than 3 ft (1 m) thick and in humid regions may be relatively dark in color in comparison with the regolith below. A distinctive feature of the soil is the presence of a layered structure formed of two or three *horizons.* Horizons are designated in Figure 20.1 by letters $A_1$, $A_2$, *B,* and *C.* Over the soil may be a protective layer of grass, trees, or other vegetation.

In some places the soil and regolith have been stripped off down to the bedrock, which then appears at the surface as an *outcrop* (Figure 20.2). In other places, after cultivation or forest fires, only the true soil is stripped off, exposing the regolith, which is infertile.

The thicknesses of soil and regolith are variable. Although the true soil is rarely more than a few feet thick, the regolith of decayed and fragmented rock may extend down tens or even hundreds of feet. Formation of the regolith is greatly aided by the presence of innumerable cracks, termed *joints,* in the bedrock (Figure 20.1).

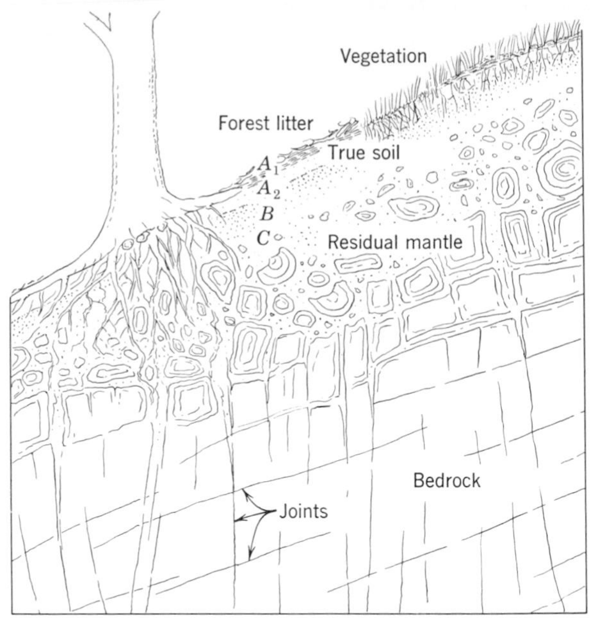


**FIGURE 20.1.** Soil and residual overburden overlying bed rock. (© 1960, John Wiley & Sons, New York.)

The term overburden[1] is broad in scope and may refer to any sort of relatively loose or soft mineral particles lying on the bedrock. Thus gravels, sands, or floodplain silts laid down by streams or rubble left by a disappearing glacier are also forms of overburden, but are unique in having been transported by such agents as streams, ice, wind, or waves. Such material is called *transported overburden* to distinguish it from *regolith,* formed in place by decay and disintegration of the bedrock below it. In Figure 20.2 is shown a deposit of transported overburden of a type known as *alluvium,*

[1] *Overburden* is a miner's term, signifying the unwanted mineral matter, whether soil or rock, overlying a deposit of value. Its use as a general term in the earth sciences signifies unconsolidated material lying above the bedrock.

**FIGURE 20.2.** Residual and transported overburden. (© 1960, John Wiley & Sons, New York.)

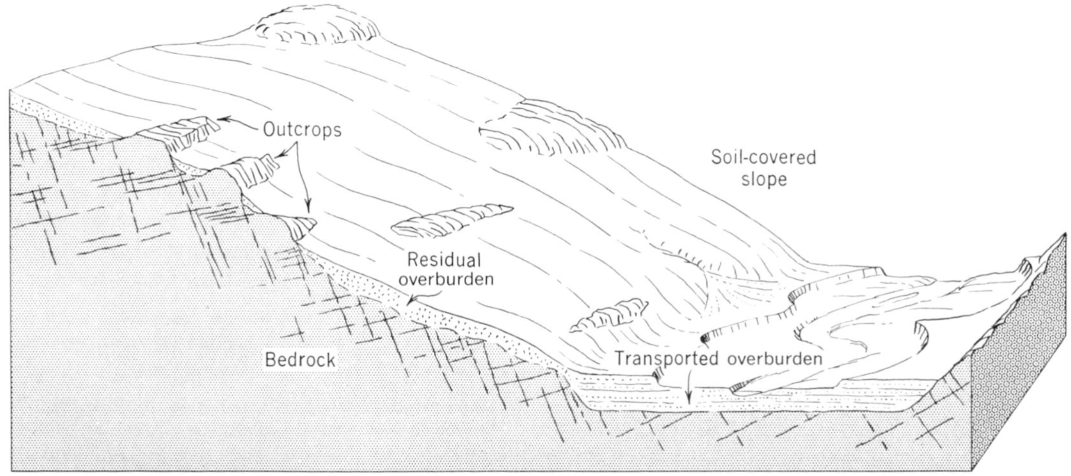

covering the bottom of a valley, where it has been left by a stream.

## The major rock classes

In the study of rocks, a branch of geology known as *petrology,* it has been found convenient to classify all rocks into three major classes: igneous, sedimentary, and metamorphic.

*Igneous rocks* are those which have solidified from a molten or partially molten state. The molten material is referred to as *magma* within the earth or *lava* on the surface. Igneous rock originates deep within the earth in an environment of very high temperatures and confining pressures. The magma is forced upward to invade, or *intrude,* the solid brittle rock of the earth's outer crust and to solidify there as bodies of *intrusive igneous rock.* The magma may reach the earth's surface, where it emerges as lava in volcanic eruptions to solidify as *extrusive igneous rock.*

*Sedimentary rocks* are those composed of mineral matter derived from decomposition, disintegration, and dissolution of previously existing rock, or produced by biological activity, or precipitated from solution in bodies of standing water. This finely divided mineral matter, known as *sediment,* is deposited in layers upon the ocean floor, or on the lands in such locations as floodplains or lake beds. The wide variety of processes, compositions, and environments encompassed by the sedimentary rocks as a group are treated in detail in Chapter 22.

At this point it is important to know that sedimentary rock layers have accumulated to great total thicknesses in certain favorable areas of shallow ocean floor throughout the geologic past. Such accumulations, which have amounted to many thousands of feet, have necessarily produced a series of physical changes in the sediment. The uppermost, freshly-deposited layers consist of soft muds, clays, and silts, or of incoherent sands and gravels saturated with water. As new layers are added, the underlying layers experience progressively deeper burial. Under increasing pressures imposed by the overlying load, water is excluded from the sediment and it becomes denser and more strongly coherent. Ultimately, hard rock layers are produced, a process termed *lithification.* A more general term for the sum total of all processes of physical and chemical change affecting sediment during its conversion into solid rock is *diagenesis.*

*Metamorphic rocks* are created by alteration of previously formed rocks, whether igneous, sedimentary or metamorphic, while the rock remains in the solid state. The processes of change in physical texture and sometimes in chemical composition of the rock constitute *metamorphism.* The rock alteration is a deep-seated activity, typically occurring in an environment of high temperatures and high pressures, but not as high as in igneous processes. Metamorphism is aided by the presence of fluids. Changes may be caused by a deforming of the rock accompanying mountain making, or by introduction of new chemical substances or heat from adjacent sources, or by a combination of these. The nature of these changes is discussed in Chapter 26.

This threefold classification is generally satisfactory for most of the abundant and commonly seen rock types. With study the distinctive qualities of each group become readily recognizable to the geologist, often by rapid inspection with the unaided eye, and in some cases at distances of many miles from the outcrop or from a plane or satellite thousands of feet in the air.

## The cycle of rock transformations

Of the three major rock classes no one class necessarily precedes the other as the original material. Any of the sedimentary or metamorphic rocks may be partially melted to produce an igneous rock, and it is thought by some geologists that certain of the igneous varieties are largely of this origin. Any igneous, sedimentary, or metamorphic rock may be altered in the course of mountain making to yield a metamorphic rock. It is also evident that any igneous or metamorphic rock or an older sedimentary rock can disintegrate to produce soil and regolith and that this material can be transported to the ocean as sediment to produce a new sedimentary rock.

Although we may reason that the original rock of the earth's crust was igneous, having been solidified from a molten state, no rocks thus far studied can be identified as being this original igneous rock. Over all continents the rocks we find today consist of mineral matter which has passed through one or more cycles of transformation from one rock group to another since the beginnings of geologic time.

A schematic model relating the three rock classes in the various possible sequences of transformations is known as the *rock cycle.* In its simplest form, the cycle of rock transformations is depicted by a triangular diagram, not unlike that which illustrates the changes of state of water among its gaseous, liquid, and solid states (Chapter 18). Each rock class occupies a corner of the triangle and can be transformed into the rock class occupying either of the other two corners (Figure 20.3). Sequences of change are labeled on all three sides of the triangle.

Notice that both the igneous-to-sedimentary and metamorphic-to-sedimentary transformations involve a chain comprised of three activities: (1) The initially hard (lithified) rock may be broken down physically into small particles (disintegration) and/or chemically altered (decomposed), or dissolved. (2) The resultant particles of sediment, ranging in size from boulders down to ions in solution, must be transported and deposited by a fluid medium, such as streams, glaciers, winds, or ocean currents. (3) The sediment is buried and perhaps eventually lithified (diagenesis). Sufficiently deep burial can bring sedimentary rock into an environment of relatively high temperatures and confining pressures, through which it may be transformed into metamorphic rock.

The sedimentary-to-igneous and metamorphic-to-igneous transformations involve partial melting by application of heat at depth. The liquid magma can be expected to move from one place to another (*intrusion*), under pressure and because of lower density. This movement is generally considered to be upward from

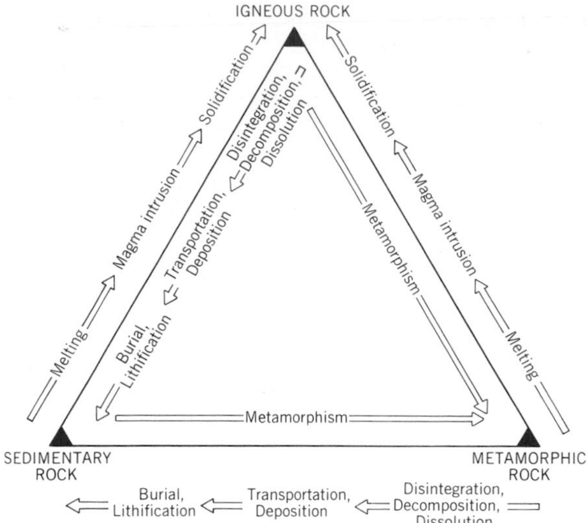


**FIGURE 20.3.** The three major rock classes.

an environment of high temperatures and pressures toward one of relatively lower temperatures and pressures. In the extreme case, where magma emerges upon land surface by *extrusion,* it comes into direct contact with the atmosphere.

Notice that metamorphism of both sedimentary and igneous rocks does not involve transportation or dislocation of the rock mass itself. Changes within the rock can be either wholly self-contained or can involve the importation of chemical substances by invasion of solutions.

Let us relate the rock cycle to the contrasting physical-chemical environments found at depth within the earth and at the earth's surface (Figure 20.4). The modified diagram now represents a schematic vertical cross section of the outer zone of the earth, say to a depth of about 20 mi (30 km). Throughout the rock cycle, large masses must be moved from the deep environment of high temperatures and pressures to the surface environment of low temperatures and pressures. We see that this change of environment can be accomplished by two processes: (1) Rise of magma brings igneous rock to various intermediate positions, where it solidifies into intrusive igneous rock bodies, or by extrusion it may reach the surface to form volcanic igneous rocks. (2) Rock formed at depth can appear at the surface of the earth by uncovering as a result of the combined processes of crustal uplift and denudation. *Denudation* is a general term describing the removal of rock at the earth's surface by the combined action of weathering and erosion. (These processes are treated in detail in Chapters 32 through 36.) Thus large bodies of igneous, metamorphic, or sedimentary rock can migrate upward from the deep environment to the surface environment.

Transition from the surface environment to the deep environment can be accomplished by burial and downsinking of the earth's crust. Both sedimentary layers and extrusive volvanic rocks can eventually reach the deep environment where either metamorphism or partial melting can take place.

The cycle of rock transformation can operate only because sources of energy exist. Energy is required both to partially melt solid rock and to raise enormous liquid masses. This energy comes from internal sources, probably largely from the process of spontaneous decay of radioactive substances, which produces radiogenic heat (see Chapter 23). The internal energy source has been inherited from the time of origin of the earth as a planet. Energy required to break down surface rocks into sediment and to transport that sediment to sites of deposition is supplied by solar radiation. In earlier

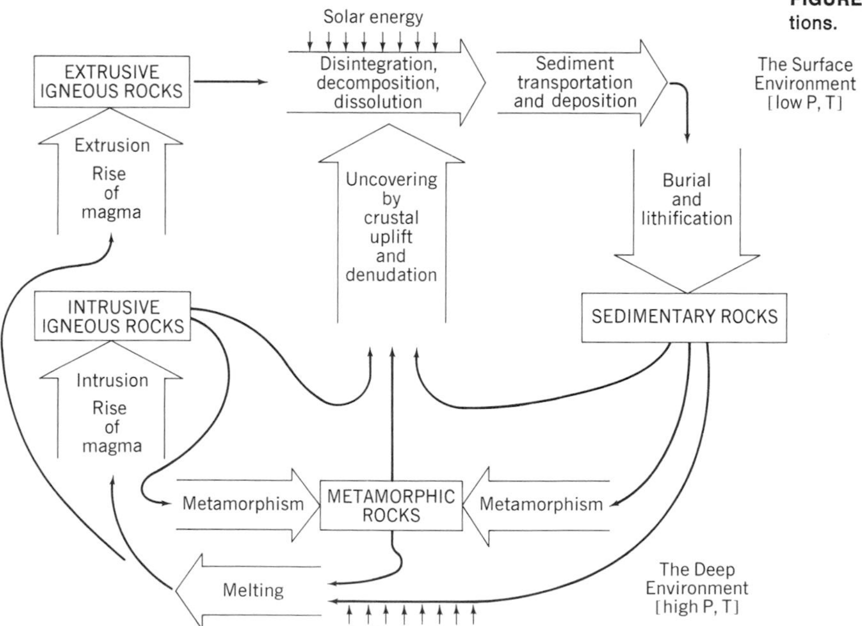


**FIGURE 20.4.** The cycle of rock transformations.

chapters of this book the atmospheric and oceanic transport systems powered by solar energy have been examined in detail. The flow of water and ice over the land surfaces and the work of waves and associated currents, all powered by solar energy, are analyzed in later chapters.

In summary, we find that any rock is the product of its physical-chemical environment at the time of formation. When transported to a different set of environmental conditions, the rock undergoes physical or chemical changes that bring the minerals of which it is composed into an appropriate equilibrium with those new conditions. With this generalized model of rock-changing processes in mind, we can turn to an investigation of the composition and structure of matter comprising each of the three rock classes.

## Chemical composition of the earth's crust

Before beginning a study of the principal minerals comprising the igneous rocks, it is instructive to examine data on the abundance of elements in the earth's crust. The term "earth's crust" is defined in Chapter 23. At this point it should suffice to explain that the crust is the outermost of the earth's solid shells and has an average thickness of about 10 mi (17 km). Important differences in thickness and composition of the crust exist between the continents and ocean basins. Although the rocks of the crust constitute only about four-tenths of one percent of the total mass of the earth, they are the only rocks available to the geologist for direct examination and chemical analysis. The great bulk of the crust (about 95 percent) is composed of igneous rock, including metamorphic rock derived from igneous rock. Sedimentary rock, including metamorphosed sedimentary rock, comprises the remaining 5 percent and is for the most part only a thin veneer overlying portions of a dominantly igneous crust.

Table 20.1 lists the eight most abundant elements in the earth's crust. The order of listing is according to percentage by weight. Values for percent by volume and percent of atoms present are also shown. Keep in mind that these proportions are estimates based on analyses of rock samples and will be subject to minor changes in the light of revised estimates.

**TABLE 20.1. THE EIGHT MOST ABUNDANT ELEMENTS IN THE EARTH'S CRUST***

| Element | Symbol | Percent by weight | Percent by volume | Percent of atoms present |
|---|---|---|---|---|
| Oxygen | O | 46.6 | 93.8 | 62.6 |
| Silicon | Si | 27.7 | 0.9 | 21.2 |
| Aluminum | Al | 8.1 | 0.5 | 6.5 |
| Iron | Fe | 5.0 | 0.4 | 1.9 |
| Calcium | Ca | 3.6 | 1.0 | 1.9 |
| Sodium | Na | 2.8 | 1.3 | 2.6 |
| Potassium | K | 2.6 | 1.8 | 1.4 |
| Magnesium | Mg | 2.1 | 0.3 | 1.8 |

* Data from Brian Mason, 1966, *Principles of Geochemistry*, 3rd ed., New York, Wiley, Table 3.4, p. 48. Figures have been rounded to nearest one-tenth.

Several points are of interest in the data of Table 20.1. Notice, first, that the eight elements comprise between 98% and 99% of the crust by weight and that almost half of this weight is oxygen. Measured in other ways, the importance of oxygen is even greater—in numbers of atoms it makes up over 60% of the total and, being an atom of comparatively large radius, it represents almost 94% by volume. Notice that silicon is in second place with about 28% by weight, or roughly half the value for oxygen. Aluminum and iron occupy intermediate positions, while the last four elements—calcium, sodium, potassium and magnesium—are subequal in the range of 2–4% by weight.

To extend the table we add that the ninth most abundant element is titanium, followed in order by hydrogen, phosphorus, barium, and strontium. It is interesting to note that the metals copper, lead, zinc, nickel, and tin, which play such an important role in our modern technology, are present only in very small proportions and are indeed scarce elements. Fortunately, these and other rare but important elements have been concentrated locally into ores from which they can be extracted in useful quantities.

The list of abundances of elements in the crust should be compared with that for the earth as a whole (see Table 27.2). Notice that iron assumes first place in the earth list, while magnesium gains fourth place. Nickel and sulfur, which do not appear in the crustal table, are in fifth and sixth places for the entire earth. Evidently the crust represents a selected assortment of particular elements as compared with the average earth composition. Therefore, an important problem in earth history is to explain how the various shells of our planet acquired unique combinations of abundances of elements. This problem will be considered in later chapters, in connection with the origin and early history of the earth.

## Minerals

Minerals are the constituent chemical substances of which rocks are composed. A *mineral* can be defined as a naturally occurring homogeneous inorganic substance, usually having a definite chemical composition and a characteristic atomic structure. A particular mineral variety can usually be recognized by a distinctive set of physical properties, such as color, hardness, density, and manner of fracturing into smaller fragments. Our problem is that hundreds of minerals—each bearing a different name and displaying a different set of characteristics—have been identified, whereas it is possible in this brief introduction to geology to consider only a very few. Fortunately, this problem is greatly simplified if we consider only those minerals making up the bulk of common rocks.

Although rocks are composed of mixtures of particles of one or more kinds of minerals, as it happens only a few combinations commonly occur in nature. In this chapter seven important minerals, which together comprise most of the bulk of the igneous rocks, are selected for description. Only a few additional minerals of secondary importance need be mentioned in connection with the

**TABLE 20.2. SOME CHEMICAL CLASSES OF COMMON MINERALS**

| Chemical Group | | Representative Mineral | | Symbol |
|---|---|---|---|---|
| NATIVE ELEMENTS | Metals | Native copper | | Cu |
| | | Gold | | Au |
| | Nonmetals | Native sulfur | | S |
| | | Diamond | | C |
| | **Description** | **Representative Mineral** | **Composition** | **Formula** |
| COMPOUNDS | | | | |
| *Oxides* | Elements in combination with oxygen | Quartz | Silicon dioxide | $SiO_2$ |
| | | Hematite | Sesquioxide of iron | $Fe_2O_3$ |
| | | Ice | Solid state of water | $H_2O$ |
| *Sulfides* | Elements in combination with sulfur | Galena | Lead sulfide | PbS |
| | | Sphalerite | Zinc sulfide | ZnS |
| *Carbonates* | Elements in combination with carbonate ion ($CO_3$) | Calcite | Calcium carbonate | $CaCO_3$ |
| | | Dolomite | Carbonate of calcium and magnesium | $CaMg(CO_3)_2$ |
| *Halides* | Compounds of the halogen elements: chlorine, bromine, iodine, fluorine | *Halite* (*rock salt*) | Sodium chloride | NaCl |
| | | Fluorite | Calcium fluoride | $CaF_2$ |
| *Sulfates* | Elements in combination with sulfate ion ($SO_4$) | Anhydrite | Calcium sulfate | $CaSO_4$ |
| | | Gypsum | Hydrous calcium sulfate | $CaSO_4 \cdot 2H_2O$ |
| *Silicates* | Elements in combination with silicate ion ($SiO_4$) | Orthoclase feldspar | Aluminosilicate of potassium and sodium | $(K,Na)AlSi_3O_8$ |
| | | Olivine | Silicate of magnesium and iron | $(Mg,Fe)_2 SiO_4$ |
| *Hydrous silicates* | (Clay minerals) Compounds derived by union of water with silicate minerals | Kaolinite | Hydrous aluminosilicate derived from feldspars | |
| | | Illite | Complex hydrous aluminosilicate derived from micas | |
| *Hydroxides* | Compounds derived by union of water with oxides of the metals iron, aluminum, manganese | Limonite | Hydrous sesquioxide of iron | $2Fe_2O_3 \cdot 3H_2O$ |
| | | Bauxite | Hydrous sesquioxide of aluminum | $Al_2O_3 \cdot 2H_2O$ |

igneous rocks. Several other mineral species are important constituents of the sedimentary and metamorphic rocks, but their number is not large.

**Chemical grouping of minerals** Minerals can be classified according to chemical composition as well as by certain physical properties, such as crystal form and atomic structure. In terms of an understanding of the origin and distribution of rock varieties, the chemical grouping of common minerals will be the more meaningful approach. If, however, one's purpose is to be able to identify a given mineral or rock specimen by name, a knowledge of the mineral classifications based upon physical properties will be essential.

Minerals may be composed of single elements, or of compounds of those elements. Almost the entire bulk of rock-forming minerals are compounds, the single-element minerals being comparative rarities. Table 20.2 lists several classes of inorganic compounds to which the most abundant minerals can be assigned. Representative examples of common minerals are given for each group. The groups as listed do not conform with a strictly formalized chemical classification, nor is the list of groups by any means complete. The information presented in Table 20.2 is intended only to give insight into the wide variety in chemical compositions and degrees of complexity to be expected among the common minerals.

## Physical properties of minerals

An intensive laboratory course using mineral specimens and the equipment needed to perform various tests would be required to gain even a rudimentary understanding of the physical properties of the commonest minerals. In these paragraphs we can only suggest the types of physical properties that serve to differentiate minerals according to species.

*Crystal form* Most minerals occur in the crystalline solid state, in which the various component atoms, as ions, occupy regular positions in a characteristic geometrical arrangement known as a *crystal lattice.* The nature of crystalline structure is treated in later

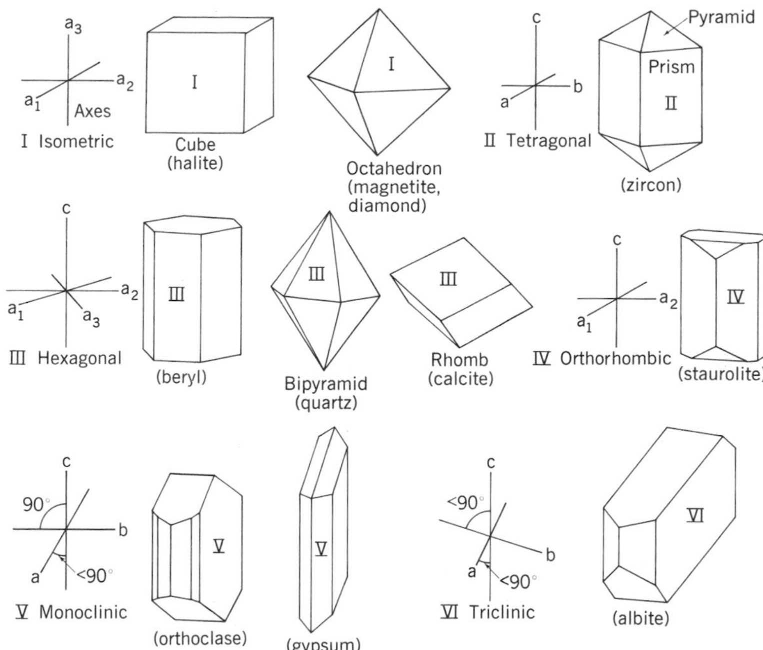


**FIGURE 20.5.** Axes and representative external crystal forms of the six crystal systems.

paragraphs of this chapter. When a crystalline mineral grows without inhibition or interference from other minerals about it (for example, crystal growth in an aqueous solution or in soft mud) a distinctive geometric configuration of the mineral surfaces appears and is known as the *external crystal form.* Normally a crystal presents smoother planar surfaces, or *faces,* which together form a distinctive geometrical solid, such as the cube, prism, octahedron, or tetrahedron (Figure 20.5). Because the angles between various sets of crystal faces is constant for a given mineral species, measurements of the crystal configuration permits the mineral to be identified.

On the basis of symmetry, the crystal forms of minerals fall into *crystal systems,* of which there are six (Figure 20.5). For example, the mineral *diamond* falls into the *isometric system* and assumes the geometrical form of an octahedron. (The crystals of magnetite in Figure 22.7*A* are octahedrons.) The mineral *quartz* falls into the *hexagonal system* and typically takes the form of a six-sided prism, terminating at each end in a hexagonal pyramid (Figure 20.6).

*Cleavage* Many minerals show a pronounced tendency to split along smooth planar surfaces of weakness. These surfaces, known as *cleavage planes,* bear a close relationship to the external crystal form. One set of cleavage planes may be very strongly developed, as in the familiar case of mica, which can be split easily into thin sheets (see Figure 20.9). In other minerals there are three intersecting sets of parallel cleavage planes, enabling the mineral to be broken into similar prisms or rhombs of many sizes (see Figures 20.11 and 22.12). The key to an understanding of mineral cleavage lies in the atomic structure of crystals.

Minerals lacking cleavage break along various characteristic forms of fracture surfaces. For example, the curved fracture surfaces of glass constitute *conchoidal fracture,* seen in quartz (Figure 20.6). Other fracture types are described as even, uneven, splintery, or hackly.

*Specific gravity, or relative density* For a given chemical composition, each mineral species has a fixed specific gravity, which is the ratio of its density to the density of water at 4° C (39.2° F). Most of the abundant minerals in igneous rocks have densities in the range of 2.7 (quartz) to 3.4 (olivine). Other minerals have much higher specific gravities—for example, hematite is about 5.0, galena 7.5, and native copper 8.8. Mineral specific gravity is a property of great importance because it determines the specific gravity of a given rock, which is a mixture of minerals, and rock specific gravity determines the gross layered structure of the earth.

*Hardness* The degree to which a mineral surface resists being scratched is known as its hardness and is a geologically important property because it determines how easily a mineral is worn away by abrasive action of streams, waves, wind, and glaciers in the processes of erosion and transportation. Minerals themselves provide a set of tools of differing hardness by means of which other minerals can be tested. Ten standard minerals constitute the *Mohs scale* of hardness, ranging from the softest, talc (No. 1) to the hardest, diamond (No. 10). The complete scale is as follows:

1. talc (Softest)
2. gypsum (2½, fingernail)
3. calcite (3, copper coin)
4. fluorite
5. apatite (5½ to 6, knife blade, plate glass)
6. orthoclase (6½ to 7, steel file)
7. quartz
8. topaz
9. corundum
10. diamond (Hardest)

**TABLE 20.3. SILICATE MINERALS ABUNDANT IN IGNEOUS ROCKS**

| Mineral or Group | Composition, Formula | Specific Gravity | Hardness, Mohs scale |
|---|---|---|---|
| Quartz | Silica (silicon dioxide) $SiO_2$ | 2.65 | 7 |
| Potash feldspar group (Orthoclase, microcline) | Aluminosilicates of potassium, also with sodium $(K,Na)Si_3O_8$ (orthoclase) $KAlSi_3O_8$ (microcline) | 2.5–2.6 | 6 |
| Plagioclase feldspar group | Aluminosilicates of sodium and calcium. $NaAlSi_3O_8$ (albite) $CaAl_2Si_2O_8$ (anorthite) | 2.62–2.76 | 6 |
| Mica group (Biotite, muscovite) | Aluminosilicates of potassium, magnesium, and iron, with water. (Complex formulas) | 2.9 | 2½–3 |
| Amphibole group (Hornblende) | Silicates of aluminum, calcium, magnesium, and iron. (Complex formulas) | 3.2 | 5½ |
| Pyroxene group (Augite) | Silicates of aluminum, calcium, magnesium, and iron (Complex formulas) | 3.3 | 5½ |
| Olivine | Silicate of magnesium and iron $(Mg,Fe)_2SiO_4$ | 3.3 | 6½–7 |

A

B

**FIGURE 20.6.** Two forms of quartz. (*A*) Crystals, about half natural size. (*B*) Crystalline quartz with broken surfaces. The thin, needlelike objects within the quartz are crystals of tourmaline. (Courtesy of Ward's Natural Science Establishment, Inc., Rochester, N.Y.)

Each mineral on the scale will scratch all those of lower number, but will be scratched by those of higher number.

*Luster* The appearance of a mineral surface under reflected light is referred to as its luster, described by several descriptive adjectives, such as metallic, adamantine (diamond-like), vitreous, resinous, pearly, or silky.

*Color* Certain minerals possess a distinctive color that facilitates recognition, but many minerals have varieties that differ conspicuously in color. Among the rock-forming minerals the range is from colorless (quartz, calcite, gypsum) and white (orthoclase feldspar), through olive green (olivine) to black (biotite, hornblende). Reddish-brown and yellow-brown colors are typical of iron oxides such as hematite and limonite. These minerals lend earth-red coloration to many sedimentary rocks (red sandstones, red shales).

*Streak* When a mineral specimen is rubbed across the unglazed surface of a white porcelain plate, it may leave a streak of powdered mineral of distinctive color. This "streak" is consistently useful in identifying the mineral. An example is hematite, with a red-brown streak. Most common rock-forming minerals give a white streak of no particular help in identification.

*Optical properties* A completely different group of mineral properties relate to the effect of a transparent mineral upon light rays which pass through it. These optical properties are of great value in mineral identification and are evaluated by means of a polarizing microscope. A particularly important diagnostic property is the degree to which the mineral bends (refracts) light rays passing through it.

## The silicate minerals

The igneous rocks are composed preponderately of minerals that are compounds of silicon. These are the *silicate minerals,* in which various metallic ions are com-

| Crystal System | Cleavage or Fracture | Luster | Color |
|---|---|---|---|
| Hexagonal | No cleavage<br>Conchoidal fracture | Vitreous or greasy | Colorless and various colors |
| Monoclinic (orthoclase)<br>Triclinic (microcline) | Good prismatic cleavage at right angles | Vitreous | White, gray, or pink; also green |
| Triclinic | Good prismatic cleavage at 86° angle | Vitreous | White or gray |
| Monoclinic | Perfect cleavage in one plane | Vitreous to pearly | Black or dark brown |
| Monoclinic | Imperfect prismatic cleavage at 56° and 124° angles | Vitreous or silky | Dark green to black |
| Monoclinic | Imperfect prismatic cleavage at 87° angle | Vitreous | Dark green to black |
| Orthorhombic | No cleavage | Vitreous | Yellowish green to bottle green |

bined with the silicate ionic group, with the exception of quartz, an oxide of silicon. Based upon a statistical study of about 700 rock samples covering the entire range of igneous varieties, it has been found that the principal silicate minerals comprise close to 92 percent by weight of the igneous rocks. Consequently the silicate minerals determine, by the varieties present and the proportions of those varieties, the names and classifications of the individual rock varieties within the igneous group.

Table 20.3 gives details of properties of the principal silicate minerals of the most common igneous rocks.

*Quartz* consists of silica, an oxide of silicon ($SiO_2$). It is one of the commonest of minerals among rocks of all three major groups. A hard mineral (hardness 7) lacking in cleavage, quartz when clear has an outward resemblance to broken glass, as seen in the massive state (Figure 20.6*B*). The characteristic pyramid-topped hexagonal prism is seen only in quartz that has undergone crystal growth in open rock cavities (Figure 20.6*A*).

The *potash feldspars* are a mineral group, of which *orthoclase* and *microcline* are abundant in certain of the igneous rocks (Figure 20.7). The word "potash" refers to the element potassium, which is the ingredient distinguishing these from other feldspars. Although commonly white or gray in color, potash feldspar may be salmon pink (or, rarely, green), giving a distinctive pink color to certain granites.

The *plagioclase feldspars* comprise a chemically related group of minerals of paramount importance in the composition of the igneous rocks. Altogether six mineral species are recognized by name in the plagioclase group, but one grades into the other in terms of proportions of the two end components—*albite,* a sodium aluminosilicate with the composition $NaAlSi_3O_8$, and *anorthite,* a calcium aluminosilicate with the composition $CaAl_2Si_2O_8$. Albite is pictured in Figure 20.8. Albite and anorthite can exist in combination in the solid crystalline state in any proportions.

The six plagioclase feldspars with proportions of the end components and percentages of sodium, calcium, alumina, and silica are described in Table 20.4. The figures in this table deserve close attention, because the changes in composition from one end of the plagioclase series to the other are of fundamental importance in understanding the igneous rocks. The mineral names are

**FIGURE 20.7.** Microcline feldspar, showing cleavage surfaces. (Courtesy of Ward's Natural Science Establishment, Inc., Rochester, N.Y.)

**FIGURE 20.8.** Albite feldspar, showing cleavage surfaces. (Courtesy of American Museum of Natural History.)

**TABLE 20.4. THE PLAGIOCLASE FELDSPAR GROUP**[1]

| | Name | Percent Albite | Percent Anorthite | Percent Sodium as $Na_2O$ | Percent Calcium as CaO | Percent Alumina $Al_2O_3$ | Percent Silica $SiO_2$ |
|---|---|---|---|---|---|---|---|
| Alkalic (Sodic) | Albite | 100–90 | 0–10 | 11 | 0.0–0.8 | 20 | 67 |
| Alkalic (Sodic) | Oligoclase | 90–70 | 10–30 | 10 | 3 | 23 | 64 |
| Intermediate | Andesine | 70–50 | 30–50 | 6 | 8 | 26 | 58 |
| Intermediate | Labradorite | 50–30 | 50–70 | 4 | 12 | 30 | 53 |
| Calcic | Bytownite | 30–10 | 70–90 | 3 | 15 | 32 | 49 |
| Calcic | Anorthite | 10–0 | 90–100 | 0.2–0.8 | 19 | 35 | 44 |

[1] Based on data of W. A. Deer, R. A. Howie, and J. Zussman (1966), *An Introduction to the Rock-Forming Minerals,* New York, Wiley, pp. 324–325, Table 31.

of secondary importance and may be disregarded. As the series progresses from albite toward anorthite, that is to say, from the *alkalic* (*sodic*) end to the *calcic* end, not only do the proportions of sodium and calcium reverse position, but there are important changes in the content of aluminum (as *alumina,* $Al_2O_3$) and silicon (as *silica,* $SiO_2$). The percentage of alumina almost doubles, while the percentage of silica decreases by about one-third. We shall see in later pages that plagioclase feldspar, at the alkalic end of the series, is associated with quite different igneous rocks than those associated with the calcic end.[2]

For purposes of simplification, this list of silicate minerals does not include a group known as the *feldspathoids,* which are aluminum silicates of potassium and sodium with less silica than the feldspars. These minerals take the place of the feldspars in igneous rocks that have a deficiency of silica. One of the feldspathoid group, the mineral *nepheline,* assumes importance in one group of igneous rocks and is referred to in Chapter 21. Its formula is $NaAlSiO_4$. Notice the lower silica content (43%) as compared with the formula for albite (67%).

The *mica group* consists of silicates of aluminum, commonly with potassium, and in the case of the dark mica *biotite,* described in Table 20.3, also contains iron and magnesium. In addition, a distinctive feature of the chemical composition of the micas is the presence of small amounts of water locked into the crystal structure. In the chemical formulas of the micas the water can be represented by the *hydroxyl ion* (OH). The most striking physical feature of the micas is their perfect cleavage in one plane only. As a result, mica can be split into thin, flexible sheets (Figure 20.9*A*). Biotite is a common constituent of the igneous rocks. *Muscovite,* a pale-colored mica which appears clear in thin sheets or flakes, is also a common mica and occurs in various metamorphic rocks and in some igneous rocks (Figure 20.9*B*). Iron and magnesium are absent from the composition of muscovite, a fact that explains its light color.

The *amphibole group* consists of minerals which are silicates of aluminum, calcium, magnesium, and iron. *Hornblende* is the common variety described in Table 20.3 and is an important constituent of the igneous rocks. Notice that this mineral is relatively dense (specific gravity 3.2) and is dark in color. It has imperfect prismatic cleavage in which the planes have angles of intersection of 56° and 124°.

The *pyroxene group* is closely similar in chemical and physical properties to the amphiboles. The group includes a dozen mineral species of quite varied composition. All are silicates and contain important amounts of calcium, magnesium, and iron; some also have substantial amounts of aluminum, titanium, or sodium. The common variety *augite,* described in Table 20.3, is not easily distinguished from hornblende, but the prismatic cleavage angle of 87°, close to a right angle, can serve as a distinguishing criterion (Figure 20.10).

*Olivine,* treated here as a single mineral, is also one of a mineral group bearing that name. A silicate of magnesium and iron, this greenish mineral has a simple chemical formula. Magnesium is usually present in greater proportion than iron and in some analyses magnesium (calculated as MgO) comprises half the total content. Specific gravity of olivine is approximately the same as for pyroxene, about 3.3. Absence of any cleavage is an important physical property of olivine, contrasting with the well-developed cleavages of the amphiboles and pyroxenes.

[2] The term *alkali feldspars* is used to include the potash feldspars and albite, all of which contain potassium or sodium or both, but little or no calcium.

A

*B*

**FIGURE 20.9.** (*A*) Biotite mica is black, with highly lustrous cleavage surfaces. (Courtesy of Ward's Natural Science Establishment, Inc., Rochester, N.Y.) (*B*) Muscovite mica is light in color. Surfaces on the top and sides of this specimen are crystal surfaces. (Courtesy of the American Museum of Natural History.) Vertical surfaces facing the observer are cleavage planes.

**FIGURE 20.10.** A crystal of pyroxene, about half natural size, showing natural parting (top surface). (Courtesy of Ward's Natural Science Establishment, Inc., Rochester, N.Y.)

**Felsic and mafic mineral groups** The silicate minerals have been presented in a purposeful order in which specific gravity increases down the list. Notice also that in a general way the list runs from light-colored to dark-colored minerals, and that there is a corresponding increase in calcium, magnesium, and iron. Geologists have found it convenient to refer to the minerals forming igneous rocks, as being composed of two groups, *felsic* and *mafic.* Minerals assigned to each group are as follows:

| *Felsic* | *Mafic* |
|---|---|
| Quartz | Biotite |
| Feldspars | Amphiboles |
| Feldspathoids | Pyroxenes |
| Muscovite | Olivine |
| | (Magnetite) |
| | (Ilmenite) |

The term "felsic" is derived from the word "feldspar" and connotes light-colored minerals of relatively low specific gravity. The term "mafic", derived from "magnesium" and "ferric," connotes dark-colored minerals of relative high specific gravity. Notice that two minerals on the mafic list are not silicates: *magnetite* (an iron oxide, $Fe_3O_4$) and *ilmenite* (iron-titanium oxide, $FeTiO_3$). (See Chapter 22 and Figure 22.6.) Both are found in small grains as accessory minerals in a wide variety of igneous rocks. Synonymous with mafic is the word *ferromagnesian.*

The terms felsic and mafic are also applied to igneous rocks composed predominantly of minerals in the respective lists and will be referred to again in dealing with igneous rocks in Chapter 21.

## Atomic structure of crystalline minerals

We have learned that cleavage is an important internal physical property of many minerals, and that among the silicate minerals the cleavage varies considerably: Quartz and olivine exhibit no cleavage; the feldspars and pyroxenes have prismatic cleavage varying in perfection and angle; the micas have remarkably perfect cleavage in one direction only. An explanation of these differences lies in an understanding of the manner in which the component atoms, as ions, are fitted together in a crystal structure.

One of the simplest examples with which to begin is that of the mineral *halite,* or rock salt, with the formula NaCl. It has been noted that halite belongs to the isometric crystal system (Figure 20.5) and that its natural external crystal form is the cube. When halite is crushed, the cleavage is found to be excellent in three sets of perpendicular planes, yielding innumerable cleavage cubes. In this mineral, then, cleavage and

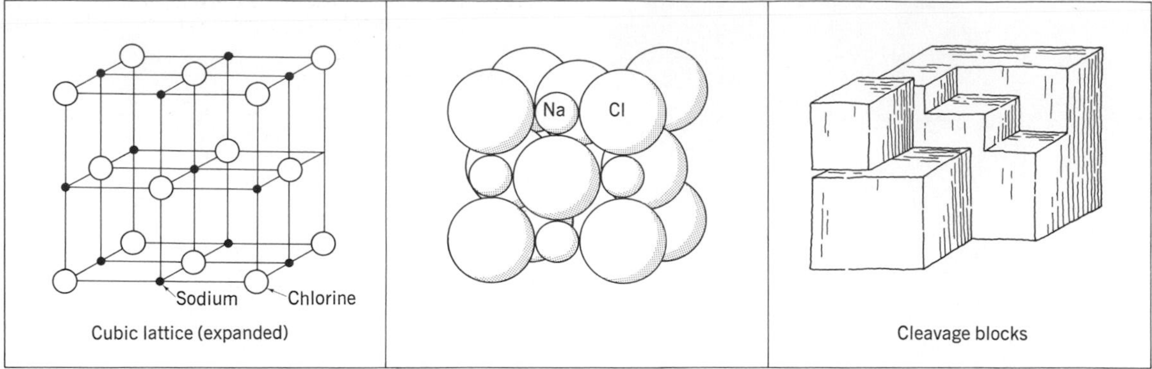


**FIGURE 20.11.** Structure of halite.

external crystal form are alike, reflecting the atomic results (left part of Figure 20.11).

Within a crystal structure, elements exist as *ions* or as *ionic groups* bearing either a negative or a positive electrical charge. Ions of unlike charge tend to be attracted together and to be held by *ionic bonds*. In the case of halite, the positively charged sodium ion ($Na^+$) is bonded to the negatively charged chlorine ion ($Cl^-$). Because the charges are of equal magnitude for both ions, they must be arranged in space so that each ion of a given charge is surrounded by six equidistantly spaced ions of the opposite charge. This arrangement is illustrated in Figure 20.11. If we connect the centers of the ions with straight lines, a *cubic space lattice* results (left part of Figure 20.11).

The ionic bonds in halite are not particularly strong, thus the lattice can be easily split in three sets of planes passing between the ions. Bonding is of equal strength in all three planes, hence a cubical cleavage results. The comparatively low hardness of halite (2.5) and ease of crushing are also explained by this form of atomic structure.

Notice in Figure 20.11 that the space lattice is shown in two forms. In the center diagram, ions are depicted as spheres scaled in size in proportion to the *atomic radius* of the ions they represent. In angstrom units (see Chapter 6 and Figure 6.6), the atomic radius of the sodium ion is 0.98, and that of the chlorine ion is 1.8. The smaller sodium ions are fitted as closely as possible among the larger chlorine ions. In the left part of Figure 20.11, the ionic arrangement has been expanded graphically and the bonds are depicted by line segments in order that the lattice can be seen.

Three other kinds of bonds exist in crystalline solids. In *van der Waal's bonding,* molecules of the compound retain their identity and are rather weakly bonded to their neighbors. An example is ice, which, as we all know, is easily crushed. *Metallic* bonding, found in malleable and ductile metals, is not applicable to the rock-forming minerals. The fourth kind, in which *covalent bonds* exist, is of primary importance here, since the main bonding found in the silicate minerals is partly ionic and partly convalent.

**The silicon-oxygen tetrahedron** The essential building-block of lattice structure of all of the silicate minerals is the *silicon-oxygen tetrahedron,* pictured in unexpanded form in Figure 20.12. It consists of four oxygen ions ($O^{2-}$) surrounding a single silicon ion ($Si^{4+}$). The expanded form of this tetrahedron is shown in Figure 20.13. In its central position, the small silicon ion fits neatly into the space between the four surrounding large oxygen ions.

Table 20.5 gives the necessary data on the charges and ionic radii of the eight elements, listed in the same order as in Table 20.1. Weights of single atoms are also given. Notice that the ionic radius of silicon (0.42Å) is less than one-third that of oxygen (1.40Å). This ratio of sizes is just right to enable the silicon ion to occupy the space between the four enclosing oxygen ions.

**FIGURE 20.12.** Unexpanded silicon-oxygen tetrahedron.

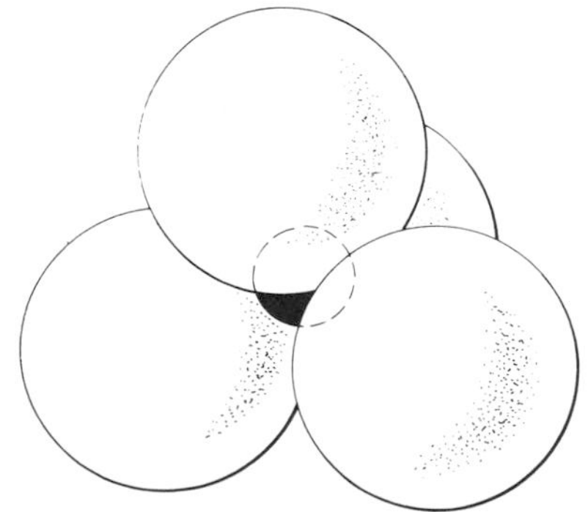

**FIGURE 20.13.** Expanded silicon-oxygen tetrahedron.

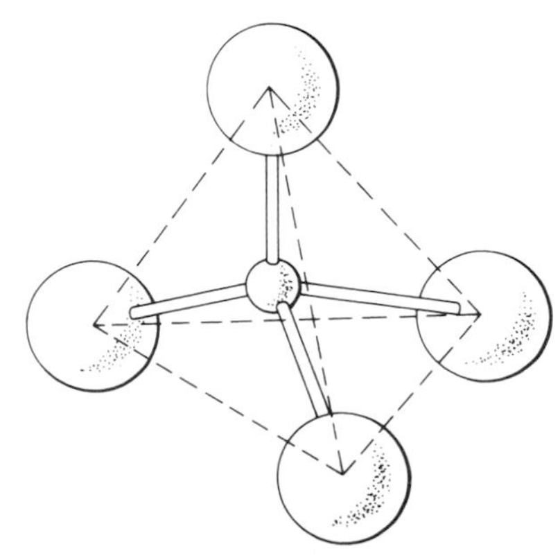

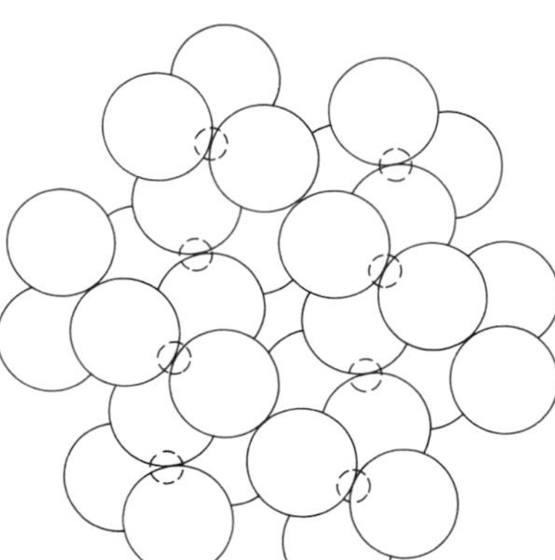

**FIGURE 20.14.** Arrangement of tetrahedra in a quartz crystal.

The combined unit charges of the four oxygen ions is $8^-$, whereas that of the silicon ion is $4^+$. It is obvious that, isolated by itself, the silicon-oxygen tetrahedron cannot constitute a stable compound. However, these tetrahedrons can be arranged in such a way that all charges are balanced, which case is represented by quartz.

**TABLE 20.5. IONIC RADII AND CHARGES OF THE MOST ABUNDANT ELEMENTS OF THE EARTH'S CRUST***

| Element | Symbol | Ionic Radius, angstroms | Unit Charge | Weight of One Atom $\times 10^{-24}$ grams (rounded) |
|---|---|---|---|---|
| Oxygen | O | 1.40 | 2− | 27 |
| Silicon | Si | 0.42 | 4+ | 47 |
| Aluminum | Al | 0.51 | 3+ | 45 |
| Iron | Fe | 0.74 or 0.64 | 2+ or 3+ | 93 |
| Calcium | Ca | 0.99 | 2+ | 20 |
| Sodium | Na | 0.97 | 1+ | 38 |
| Potassium | K | 1.33 | 1+ | 65 |
| Magnesium | Mg | 0.66 | 2+ | 40 |

* Data from Jack Green (1953), *Bull. of the Geol. Soc. of Am.,* vol. 64, p. 1001, Table 3.

The lattice structure of quartz is illustrated in Figure 20.14. The tetrahedra are so arranged that each oxygen ion is common to two tetrahedra, in other words, that the oxygen ions are *shared.* In effect, the one silicon ion within the tetrahedron is equated to only four units of negative charge. In this way the charges are balanced

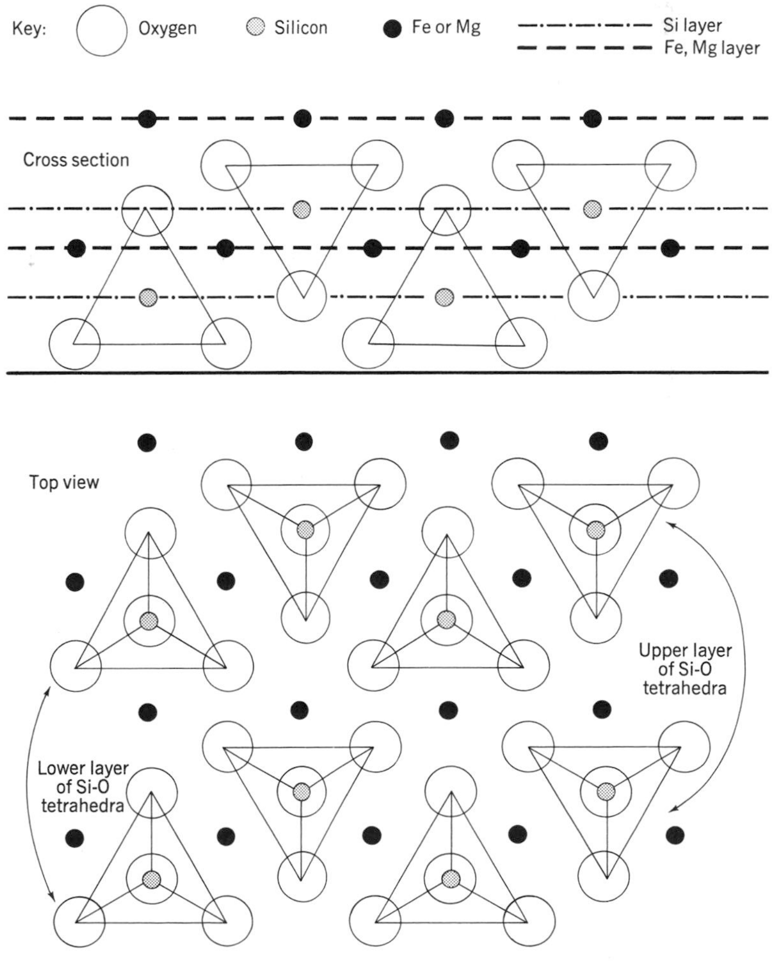

**FIGURE 20.15.** Crystal lattice structure of olivine.

FIGURE 20.16. Single chain of silicon-oxygen tetrahedra.

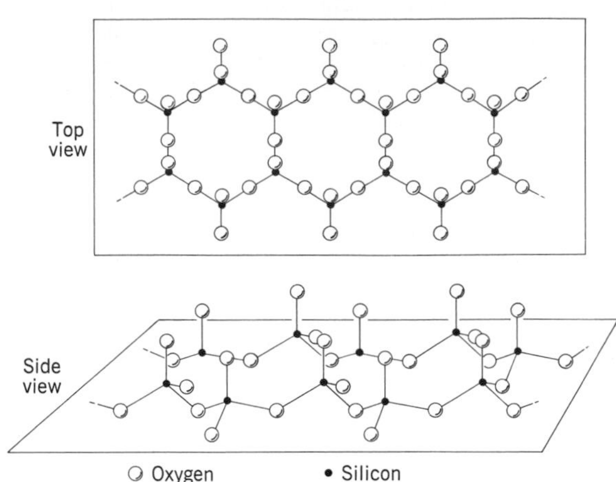


FIGURE 20.17. Perspective drawings of a double chain of tetrahedra in the structure of amphibole. [Modified from W. F. de Jong (1959), *General Crystallography,* San Francisco, W. H. Freeman, p. 173, Figure 140.]

and a stable compound is produced. Because the ionic bonds are equally strong in all directions, no planes of weakness exist in the structure of quartz, and it exhibits no cleavage.

We turn next to the last mineral on the list, olivine, to

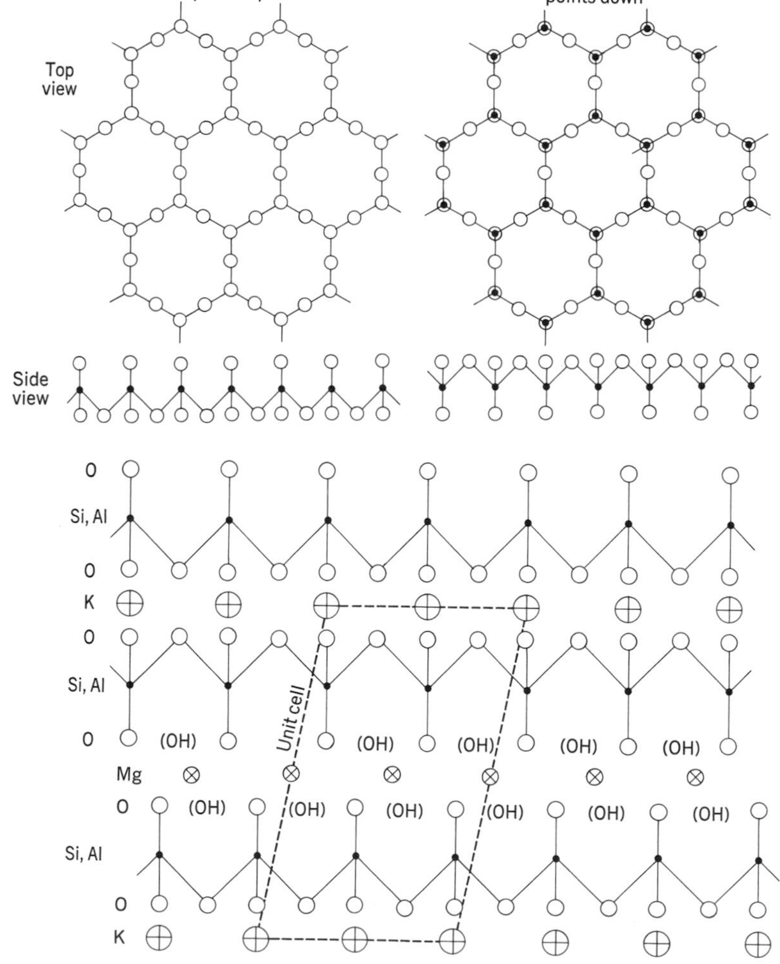


FIGURE 20.18. Crystal lattice structure of mica. Upper diagram shows sheets of silicon-oxygen tetrahedra. Lower diagram is a cross section through three sheets of tetrahedra with intervening layers of potassium and magnesium ions. [Modified from W. A. Deer, R. A. Howie, and J. Zussman (1966), *An Introduction to the Rock-Forming Minerals,* New York, John Wiley & Sons, pp. 194–195, Figures 69, 71.]

illustrate a different arrangement of silicon-oxygen tetrahedra, which, together with other ions, are so arranged as to produce strong bonding in all directions. Figure 20.15 shows the lattice structure of olivine. In the top view, tetrahedra are equidistantly separated and the intermediate positions are occupied by ions of iron or magnesium. The formula for olivine is $(Mg,Fe)_2$ $SiO_4$. Both iron and magnesium ions have two positive unit charges each, so that within the compound the eight negative charges of oxygen are balanced by the total of eight positive charges. In the lattice structure this balance is achieved by an arrangement in which alternate layers of tetrahedra are inverted (upside-down), the points thus fitting into space between the opposed tetrahedra, as shown in the upper part of Figure 20.15, with ions of either magnesium or iron occupying spaces intermediate between the tetrahedra. Thus linked to the oxygen ions, an ion of magnesium or iron shares the double unit charge of each oxygen ion with the silicon ion inside the tetrahedron. The lattice structure of olivine lacks planes of weakness, and consequently there is no cleavage.

Lattice structures of the other silicate minerals are more complex and are treated here in more generalized descriptions. The structures can consist of either *chains* or *sheets.* A single chain of tetrahedra, linked by their shared oxygen ions, is the basic arrangement of the pyroxenes (augite), as shown in Figure 20.16. Adjacent chains are linked by ions of magnesium, iron, calcium, or aluminum. The arrangement is such that two planes of weaker bonding exist at about right angles (87°), giving the prismatic cleavage seen in augite.

A double chain of silicon-oxygen tetrahedra characterizes the amphiboles (hornblende), as shown in Figure 20.17. In this arrangement the tetrahedra alternately share two and three oxygen ions. Ions of magnesium, iron, calcium, sodium, or potassium occupy positions between chains. This arrangement results in two directions of weaker bonding and yields two sets of cleavage planes at an angle of 56° and 124°, as seen in hornblende.

The micas possess an interesting sheet structure, pictured in Figure 20.18. The silicon-oxygen tetrahedra are arranged in sheets in which each of the three basal oxygen ions is shared with an adjacent tetrahedron. A single layer, seen from above the plane of the sheet, forms a pattern of hexagonal cells. Alternate sheets of tetrahedra are inverted, as seen in the side view of Figure 20.18. Sheets are alternately separated by layers of positively charged ions, but these intervening layers alternate in composition. Between those pairs of sheets in which the tetrahedra points are opposed lies a layer of magnesium ions, forming a strong bonding between sheets. Hydroxyl ions (OH) occupy spaces in the plane of the tetrahedron points. Between those pairs of sheets in which the bases of the tetrahedra are opposed there is a layer of potassium ions. Here the van der Waal's bonds are weak, forming a natural set of parallel parting planes. This sheet structure explains the remarkably perfect cleavage of biotite and muscovite micas in a single set of parallel planes.

The feldspars present a still different structural arrangement of silicon-oxygen tetrahedra. In a framework somewhat similar to that of quartz, the tetrahedra are linked in a continuous network in which all oxygen ions are shared. The principal difference is that in the feldspars a certain proportion of the silicon ions have been replaced with aluminum ions (three positive units of charge). There is thus a net negative charge, resulting from the replacement, and this is equalized by ions of sodium, potassium, or calcium, which are distributed through the network. Because certain sets of bonds are weaker than others, cleavage is developed in two intersecting sets of planes.

Using the basic information on the silicate minerals given in this chapter, we are prepared to study in a meaningful way the igneous rocks, which make up most of the earth's crust and from which most sedimentary rock has been derived.

## References for further study


Loomis, F. B. (1948), *Field Book of Common Rocks and Minerals,* New York, Putnam's, 352 pp.

Dana, E. S., revised by C. S. Hurlbut, Jr. (1949), *Minerals and How to Study Them,* New York, Wiley, 323 pp.

Dana, E. S., revised by C. S. Hurlbut, Jr. (1959), *Manual of Mineralogy,* 17th ed., New York, Wiley, 609 pp.

Spock, L. E. (1962), *Guide to the Study of Rocks,* 2nd ed., New York, Harper & Row, 298 pp.

Mason, B. (1966), *Principles of Geochemistry,* 3rd ed., New York, Wiley, 329 pp., chap. 5.

Simpson, B. (1966), *Rocks and Minerals,* New York, Pergamon, 292 pp.

# 21

# Igneous activity and the igneous rocks

IN THE PRECEDING chapter we found that the list of the eight most abundant crustal elements provides all of the essential components of seven important silicate minerals or mineral groups. (See Tables 20.1 and 20.3.) Igneous rocks, which together with metamorphic rocks comprise about 95 percent of the mass of the earth's crust, are composed almost entirely of the seven silicate minerals or mineral groups, other minerals being of secondary importance, and it is estimated that the seven comprise as much as 99 percent of all igneous rocks.[1]

One of the first questions that can arise in reviewing these facts concerns the number of minerals involved. Why, with eight elements available, should there exist in abundance only eight minerals or basic mineral groups (including the feldspathoids), instead of the 300-odd possible combinations of groups of two through eight elements? Even assuming that silicon and oxygen will always be linked as a single component, giving six components instead of seven, there exists a possibility of 120 combinations, each representing one hypothetical mineral. The answer lies in the *mineralogical phase rule,* which states that for a given number of components (elements) not more than that same number of *phases* (mineral compounds) can coexist in stable form at a given combination of temperature and pressure. In fact, a magma composed principally of eight elements is not likely to yield the maximum of eight abundant minerals because certain of the component elements have the tendency to replace certain others on an ion-for-ion basis.

[1] Brian Mason (1966), *Principles of Geochemistry,* 3rd ed., New York, Wiley. See p. 120.

## Crystallization of magma

Much of our theoretical knowledge of the formation of silicate minerals from a magma comes from laboratory experiments in which pure mineral ingredients are melted and allowed to crystallize under carefully controlled conditions of temperature and of pressures of different kinds. This type of investigation is one branch of the science of *geochemistry,* which applies the principles of chemistry to solving problems relating to all forms of natural matter in the lithosphere, hydrosphere, and atmosphere.

Magma that upon solidifying yields rock composed of silicate minerals is referred to as a *silicate magma.* The nature of silicate magma as it exists deep within the earth is not, of course, known from direct examination, but much can be inferred from studies of magmas that emerge from volcanoes as lavas and from observations made from silicate melts in the laboratory. Silicate magmas at great depth probably have temperatures in the range of from 900° to 2200° F (500° to 1200° C). At depths of 12 to 25 mi (20 to 40 km) magmas may be under pressures as high as 6 to 12 kilobars (6000 to 12,000 times the value of atmospheric pressure at sea level). The following figures relate confining pressure to depth below the surface:

| Depth, mi | km | Pressure, kilobars | Pressure, atmospheres |
|---|---|---|---|
| 0 | 0 | 0.0 (approx) | 1 |
| 5 | 8 | 2.4 | 2,400 |
| 10 | 16 | 4.8 | 4,800 |
| 15 | 24 | 7.2 | 7,200 |
| 25 | 40 | 12.0 | 12,000 |

As a magma rises, it passes into regions of progressively declining confining pressure.

Although a silicate magma is in a liquid or near-liquid state, the elements are by no means completely separated into individual ions of those elements. Instead, the silicon-oxygen tetrahedra probably remain largely intact and may be linked to one another in rather complex but irregular chains and networks. The fact that silicate magmas have a high viscosity (resistance to flow) may be explained by the presence of these atomic structures.

All silicate magmas contain additional chemical substances, over and above the elements that yield silicate and non-silicate minerals. These substances are termed *volatiles,* because they remain in a liquid or gaseous state at much lower temperatures than the mineral-forming compounds and therefore are separated from the magma as temperatures drop and the silicate minerals crystallize into the solid state.

Although we do not know a great deal about the content of volatiles in magmas at depth in the earth, much has been learned by sampling of substances emitted from volcanoes along with the eruption of molten rock (lava). Water is the preponderant constituent of the volatiles emitted as gases from volcanoes. It has been inferred that about 90% by volume of the gas contained in an average magma is water, although some of this may be ground water taken in from near the surface. (The various other volatile substances are discussed in Chapter 27.) Estimates of the proportion of water present in magmas ranges from 0.5% to 8%. Fresh igneous rocks commonly contain about 1% of water entrapped within the minerals during their crystallization.

The importance of water in magma is very great, because even a small amount of water can greatly lower the temperature at which the silicate compounds remain melted. Thus a rising magma experiencing a progressive lowering of temperature can remain molten at considerably lower temperatures with water present than if it consisted only of silicate compounds without water. As a result intrusions of magmas can reach closer to the earth's surface, and can pour out upon the surface in greater amounts, than would be possible without the presence of water.

**Crystallization of a silicate magma** Crystallization, the process of change from liquid state to solid state, begins to take place in a silicate magma at a certain critical combination of temperature and pressure. However, all minerals do not begin to crystallize at the same time. Moreover, a mineral, once formed, does not necessarily remain intact and unchanged from that point on. Instead, the early-formed minerals may subsequently be changed in composition or dissolved and reformed as temperatures continue to fall. This process of change is referred to as *reaction,* and the orderly series of such changes is referred to as a *reaction series.* A further complexity in the crystallization process may be introduced by the removal of crystallized minerals from the silicate melt, a process termed *fractionation.* For example, early-formed crystals may be left behind as the magma migrates upward, or the crystals may simply settle or rise in the magma body and accumulate. Removal of crystallized minerals changes the average chemical composition of the remaining fluid magma and consequently modifies the series of reactions that can follow.

Reaction can take one of two forms. First, there is *continuous reaction,* in which the earlier-formed mineral is gradually changed in composition by the substitution of ions of one element in the magma for another in the mineral. An example is the plagioclase feldspar series (see Table 20.4). The first feldspar to crystallize is of calcic composition near the anorthite end of the series. As the temperature of the magma continues to fall, sodium ions in the magma are substituted for calcium ions in the crystallized feldspar, causing a gradual change in the plagioclase toward the alkalic (sodic) end of the series. Second, there may be *discontinuous reactions,* in which case a given mineral is dissolved and reconstituted as another mineral at the lower temperature. An example is olivine, which crystallizes at comparatively high temperature. As temperature falls, the olivine is dissolved and pyroxene is formed in its place.

**The Bowen reaction series** Assuming a silicate magma of average crustal composition to start with, it is possible to recognize a complete reaction series that will take place during crystallization. Named the *Bowen reaction series*—after N. L. Bowen, the scientist who developed the concept—the total series consists of two converging branches, one of continuous, the other of discontinuous reactions (Figure 21.1).

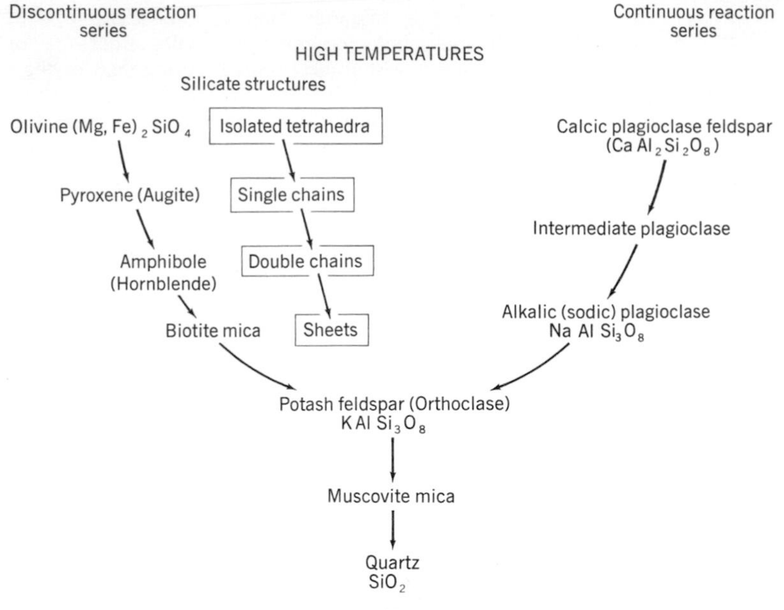


**FIGURE 21.1.** The Bowen reaction series.

The mafic minerals follow the discontinuous reaction series, starting with olivine and ending in biotite mica. The feldspars follow a continuous series, in which calcic plagioclase forms about the same time as does olivine, while alkalic (sodic) plagioclase is formed about at the same time as the amphiboles and biotite mica.

Let us consider how the Bowen reaction series is related to the formation of igneous rocks of various mineral compositions. Suppose that fractionation takes place after olivine and pyroxene have been formed. These minerals form a distinctive rock type known as *peridotite.* If the reaction series is allowed to progress to the stage in which pyroxene (augite) and intermediate plagioclase feldspar are formed, a rock known as *gabbro* can result.

The remaining components of the magma are now comparatively richer in silicon, aluminum, and potassium because most of the calcium, iron, and magnesium have been used up. This remaining magma may crystallize after migrating to a different physical location from the earlier-formed minerals. The result may be an igneous rock predominantly composed of quartz and potash feldspar. *Granite* is such a rock. The final residual matter of the magma, remaining fluid at comparatively lower temperatures, is a watery solution rich in silica. From this solution are deposited rock veins of a type known as *pegmatite,* which consists of large crystals of quartz, potash feldspar, and muscovite or biotite mica. Ultimately, the water and other minor volatile constituents may reach the earth's surface, to escape in fumaroles (vents emitting hot gases) and hot springs.

It is interesting to note the progression of silicon-oxygen tetrahedra arrangements in the discontinuous reaction series of the mafic minerals (Figure 21.1). Olivine, with its independent tetrahedra, has the simplest arrangement. This is followed by the single-chain structure of the pyroxenes, the double-chain structure of the amphiboles, and finally by the highly complex sheet structure of the micas. This arrangement suggests that stability of the simpler structures is greater at high temperature, and that more complex structures, in order of their complexity, are stable only at lower temperatures.

The general process whereby the original magma with its full range of component elements is separated into rocks of quite different mineral composition is known as *magmatic differentiation.* This process can be responsible for an arrangement of igneous rocks into a series ranging from a *mafic* group rich in iron, magnesium, calcium and silica, to a *felsic* group rich in aluminum, sodium, and potassium, and with excess silica. The classification of igneous rocks which we are about to present is thus based upon principles of the Bowen reaction series and processes of mineral fractionation and magmatic differentiation.

## Textural basis of igneous rock classification

In setting up a classification of igneous rocks, two variables of classification are needed. The first, which has been outlined in preceding paragraphs, is based upon mineral composition and is chemical in nature. The second is *textural* and relates to the sizes of the component mineral crystals and to the patterns of arrangements of those crystals. Texture also encompasses the noncrystalline state.

Crystal size is largely dependent upon the rate of cooling of the magma through the stages of crystallization. As a general rule, rapid cooling results in small to very minute crystals, while extremely sudden cooling produces a natural glass. Very slow cooling, on the other hand, tends to produce large crystals. From this principle we can deduce that the *plutonic* intrusive igneous rocks, cooling in huge masses at great depths where escape of heat is extremely slow, will tend to de-

**FIGURE 21.2.** A coarse-grained granite, typifying phaneritic texture. The light-colored grains are quartz and feldspar, and the dark grains are largely biotite mica. (Photograph by A. N. Strahler.)

velop a texture of large crystals, whereas the *extrusive* igneous rocks, which cool rapidly on contact with the atmosphere or ocean water, will be fine-grained or glassy.

Among the crystalline igneous rocks texture falls into two classes: (1) *Phaneritic texture* consists of crystals large enough to be seen with the unaided eye or with the help of a small hand-lens (Figure 21.2). (2) *Aphanitic texture* consists of crystals too small to be distinguished as individual particles without the aid of the microscope. Where all crystals in the rock are about

**FIGURE 21.3.** This andesite porphyry has large feldspar phenocrysts scattered through an aphanitic ground mass. Specimen is 3 in. (7.6 cm) wide. (Photograph by A. N. Strahler.)

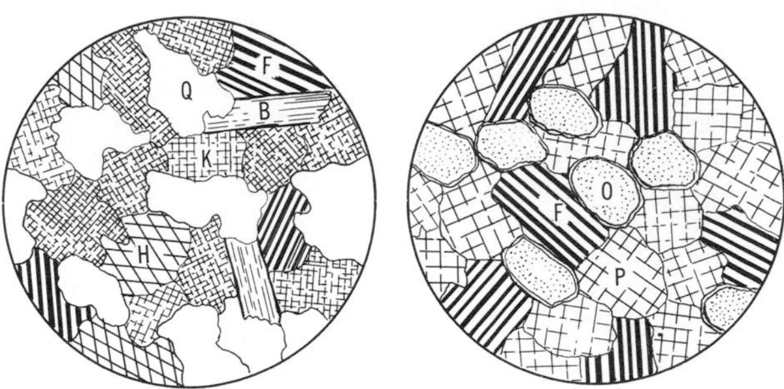


**FIGURE 21.4.** Diagrammatic sketch of mineral grains as seen in microscopic thin section, enlarged about five times. *Left:* granite. *Right:* olivine gabbro. *Q*—quartz, *K*—potash feldspar, *F*—alkali feldspar, *B*—biotite, *H*—hornblende, *P*—pyroxene, *O*—olivine.

of the same size range, the texture is described as *equigranular.* Quite different is the case where a few large crystals, called *phenocrysts,* are embedded in a coarse- or fine-grained or glassy matrix, or *groundmass.* Such texture is *porphyritic* and the rock is designated as a *porphyry* in addition to its proper name (Figure 21.3).

The crystalline fabric of the phaneritic rocks is best studied under a specialized microscope in which very thin slices of the rock are examined under transmitted light (Figure 21.4). For the most part, external crystal forms are lacking or only poorly developed. On the other hand, evidences of cleavage show up well as linear markings within the grains. The use of polarized light makes possible mineral identification based upon distinctive optical properties. This branch of petrology is known as *petrography.*

The phaneritic igneous rocks with equigranular textures have crystal grains ranging in diameter from 0.002 in. (0.05 mm) to over 0.4 in. (10 mm). An accepted grade scale is as follows:

| | |
|---|---|
| Fine-grained | 0.002–0.04 in. (0.05–1 mm) |
| Medium-grained | 0.04–0.2 in. (1–5 mm) |
| Coarse-grained | 0.2—0.4 in. (5–10 mm) |
| Pegmatitic texture | 0.4 in.–1 ft (10 mm–0.3 m) |

Particles under 0.002 in. (0.05 mm) are too small to be separated by the unaided eye and fall into the aphanitic texture class. A few enormous crystals found in pegmatites run to many feet in length, with a maximum known length of over 30 ft (6 m).

**FIGURE 21.5.** Scoria (*left*); volcanic glass, or obsidian (*right*). (Photograph by A. N. Strahler.)

The extrusive igneous rocks have distinctive textures resulting from the rapid expansion of volatile gases as confining pressure is reduced and cooling occurs. The specimen of volcanic *scoria* shown in Figure 21.5 is full of cavities formed by gas bubbles, and this texture is described as *scoriaceous.* In contrast, the *volcanic glass* (or *obsidian*), also pictured in Figure 21.5, is dense and free of such cavities. Notice the conchoidal fracture of the obsidian. In an extreme case of scoriaceous texture, the magma is frothed by expanding gases to solidify into a rock of very low density known as *pumice.*

## The granite–gabbro series

Figure 21.6 organizes the commoner varieties of the igneous rocks into an orderly classification based upon mineral composition. The graph is partly quantitative, in that percentages by volume of the component minerals or mineral groups are suggested by a set of numbers for each named rock variety. It is particularly important to be aware that the numbers given here are to serve only as approximate guide values. The continuous curved boundary lines on the field of the graph suggest the manner in which one rock variety can grade into the next. Consequently the assigned rock name can apply to transitional zones between it and the adjacent varieties. Two sets of rock names are given. One set applies to the intrusive plutonic rock bodies, usually of medium to coarse crystal grain texture, and the second set applies to the extrusive rocks, largely rocks formed by the solidification of magma (lava) that has poured out upon the surface. Lavas are typically aphanitic or glassy and often scoriaceous in texture.

In terms of bulk composition, most igneous rock of the earth's crust belongs to members of the *granite–gabbro series,* which follow closely upon the mineral order of the Bowen reaction series. Customarily, these rocks are presented in sequence from the felsic end toward the mafic end. We shall follow this practice, although with the knowledge that it is the reverse of the order suggested by the reaction series and magmatic differentiation.

*Granite* is dominated in composition by the feldspars and quartz. Potash feldspar of the orthoclase variety is the most important mineral, while alkalic plagioclase may be present in moderate amounts or absent. Quartz, which accounts for perhaps a quarter of the rock, reaches its most abundant proportions in granite. Biotite and hornblende are common accessory minerals. Magnetite, not shown on the chart, is also a common accessory.

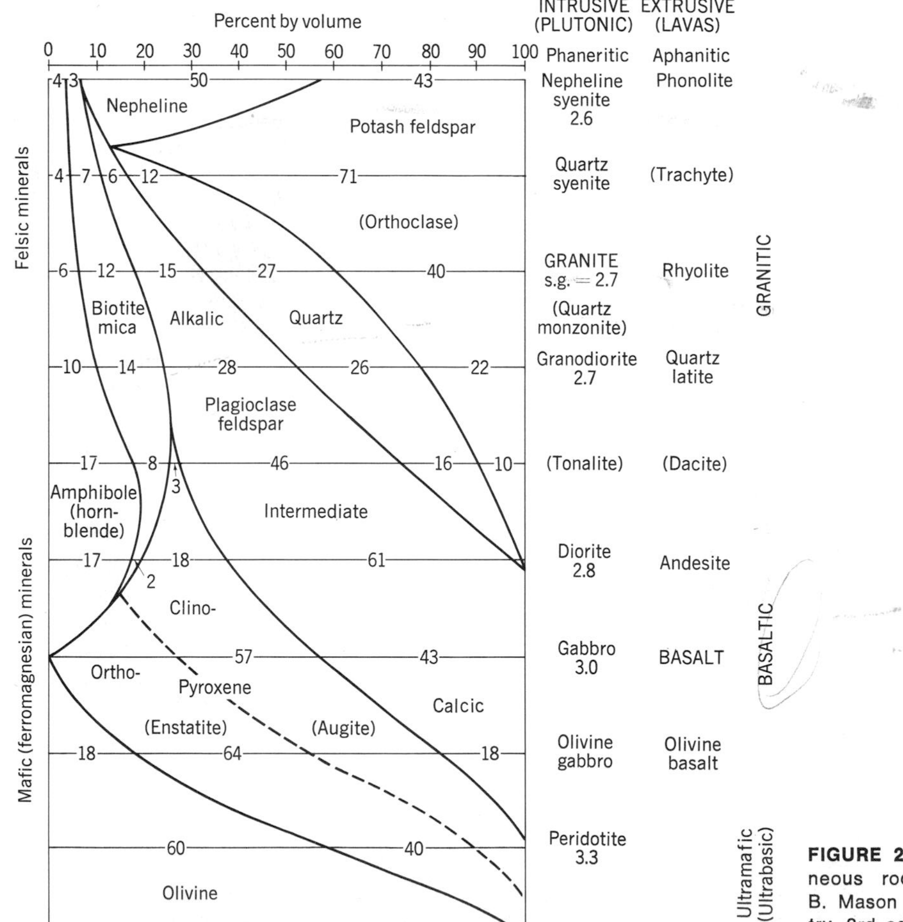


**FIGURE 21.6.** Mineral compositions of igneous rocks. [Based on a diagram by B. Mason (1966), *Principles of Geochemistry*, 3rd ed., New York, John Wiley & Sons, p. 101, Figure 5.3.]

Granite is described as a light-colored igneous rock and is grayish to pinkish, depending upon the variety of potash feldspar present. Its specific gravity, about 2.7, is comparatively low among the igneous rocks. Most granites are sufficiently coarse in texture for the component minerals to be identified with the unaided eye. (Granite is pictured in Figure 21.2.) The grayish cast of the quartz grains, with their glassy luster, sets them apart from the milky white or pink feldspars. Black grains of biotite or hornblende contrast with the light minerals. The extrusive equivalent of granite is *rhyolite,* a light-gray to pink form of lava.

Granite grades into the relatively less important rocks *granodiorite* and *tonalite,* including their extrusive equivalents *quartz latite* and *dacite,* respectively. These rocks may be given only brief consideration, noting that potash feldspar and quartz decrease in proportion, while plagioclase feldspar increases and moves from the alkalic end toward the intermediate varieties.

*Diorite* is an important plutonic rock, and its extrusive equivalent, *andesite,* occurs very widely in lavas associated with volcanoes. Diorite is dominated by plagioclase feldspar of intermediate composition, while quartz is a very minor constituent. At this point in the granite–gabbro series pyroxene makes its appearance and is of the augite variety. Amphibole, largely hornblende, is also important, and some biotite is present.

*Gabbro* is an important though not abundant plutonic rock, but it is greatly overshadowed in importance by its extrusive equivalent, *basalt,* which comprises huge areas of lava flows and is the predominant igneous rock underlying the floors of the ocean basins. Gabbro and basalt are composed almost entirely of pyroxene and intermediate to calcic plagioclase feldspar with or without minor amounts of olivine. As olivine increases, at the expense of reduced plagioclase and pyroxene, *olivine gabbro* and *olivine basalt* appear in the series. Gabbro and basalt are dark-colored rocks—dark-gray, dark-green, to almost black—and of relatively high specific gravity, 3.0. They are designated as being of *basaltic* (or *mafic*) affiliation, in contrast to the *granitic* (or *felsic*) rocks related to granite.

## The ultramafic rocks

Continuing the igneous rock series depicted in Figure 21.6 we arrive at *peridotite,* a rock composed almost entirely of two mineral constituents, olivine and pyroxene. Although widespread in occurrence, peridotite occurs in relatively small plutonic bodies. It is a dark-colored rock of high specific gravity, 3.3, and belongs to a group designated as *ultramafic* (*ultrabasic*) rocks.

The ultramafic rocks include three other varieties, only one of which is shown in Figure 21.6. All three are *monomineralic* in composition, meaning that a single mineral or mineral group comprises most of the rock. The three monomineralic rocks, together with peridotite, are shown in a triangular diagram (Figure 21.7). *Dunite,* a rock composed largely of olivine, and *pyroxenite,* composed largely of pyroxene, are relatively rare rocks. *Anorthosite,* composed mostly of intermediate or calcic plagioclase, usually occurs in very large masses. Although dunite, peridotite, and pyroxenite are of high

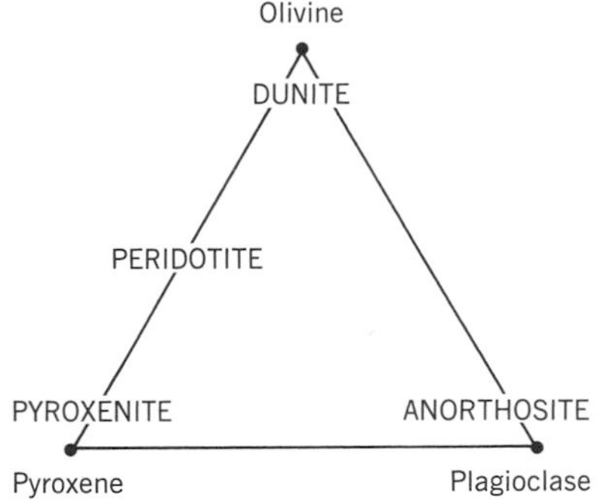


**FIGURE 21.7.** The ultramafic (ultrabasic) rocks. [After L. E. Spock (1962), *Guide to the Study of Rocks,* 2nd ed., New York, Harper & Row, p. 66, Figure 4.3.]

specific gravity, 3.3, anorthosite has both a lower specific gravity, 2.7, typical of the granitic rocks, and a light color as well. In these respects, anorthosite is quite unlike the other three ultramafic rocks.

## The syenite group

Figure 21.6 shows the igneous rock series extended beyond granite in the direction of the felsic minerals. In this part of the graph we find a group of rocks of considerable interest scientifically, despite their relatively limited or rare occurrence. *Quartz syenite* and its extrusive equivalent, *trachyte,* are dominated by potash feldspar and contain relatively minor amounts of quartz, plagioclase feldspar, biotite, and hornblende. As the syenite series is extended further, quartz disappears entirely and its place is taken by *nepheline* or other feldspathoid minerals. This composition results from a deficiency of silica in the magma. Quartz and nepheline cannot be found together in the same igneous rock, and this is shown in the arrangement of boundary curves in Figure 21.6. The extreme end of the syenite series is represented by *nepheline syenite* and its extrusive equivalent, *phonolite.* The syenite rocks are light-colored and of relatively low specific gravity, around 2.6.

## Primary magmas

Based upon the consideration that igneous rocks can be arranged into a more-or-less continuous series in which the mineral composition grades from one rock to another, one might be led to reason that there exists at depth a single source magma, or *primary magma.* By fractionation this primary magma could be differentiated into magmas of the compositions of the individual igneous rock species which we find in the solid state. Geologists who have reasoned in this way have supposed that the composition of the primary magma is probably basaltic. By differentation processes, the felsic minerals contained in the basaltic magma have been separated in sufficiently large quantities to provide secondary magmas of the granitic composition.

The hypothesis of a single primary magma of basaltic

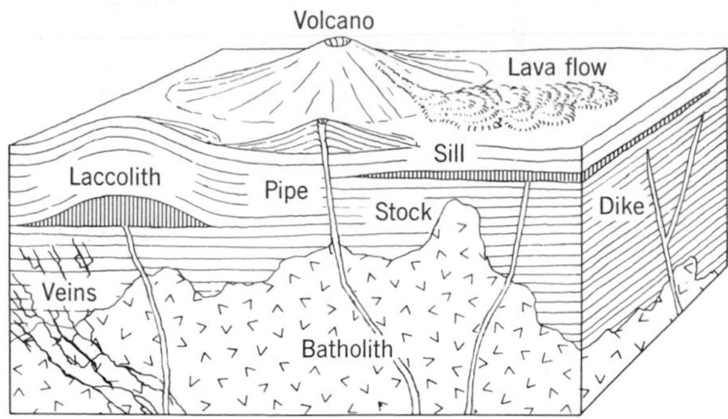


FIGURE 21.8. Forms of occurrence of the igneous rocks. (© 1960, John Wiley & Sons, New York.)

FIGURE 21.10. Basalt sill with columnar jointing intruded into sedimentary rocks. Yellowstone River near Town Creek Bridge, Yellowstone National Park. (U.S. National Park Service photo by George A. Grant.)

composition finds support in the great abundance of basaltic rocks in the earth's crust. Not only are the oceanic floors largely underlain by a basaltic layer, but there are extensive outpourings of basaltic lavas upon the continents. As we shall find in an analysis of the earth's crust (Chapter 23), a basaltic crustal layer forms a continuous shell around the earth, while the granitic rocks are in the form of overlying continental fragments of much smaller areal extent.

In the case of granite, we should be aware of a completely different scientific point of view held by some geologists as to the origin of this widespread rock of the continents. While it has been assumed in this chapter that granite is an igneous rock solidified from a magma, there are those who explain granite as a metamorphic rock. In Chapter 26 we will return to this controversy over the origin of granite.

FIGURE 21.9. Xenoliths of various kinds of igneous and metamorphic rocks enclosed in granite. Prescott, Arizona. (Photograph by A. N. Strahler.)

## Forms of intrusive rock bodies

Intrusive rock bodies assume a wide range of sizes and shapes. The larger masses, referred to as *plutons,* consist of rock of phaneritic texture, usually of medium- to coarse-grained crystal sizes. A large variety of smaller intrusive bodies are fine-grained or aphanitic in texture because of rapid cooling in contact with surrounding rock.

Largest of the plutonic bodies is the *batholith* (Figure 21.8), usually of granitic rock composition, but in certain cases consisting of anorthosite. A single batholith may have an areal extent of several thousand square miles. An example is the Idaho batholith, of which 16,000 sq mi (40,000 sq km) is exposed, equal to the combined areas of New Hampshire and Vermont. Another example is the Sierra Nevada batholith of California, underlying much of the Sierra Nevada range. (See Figure 30.21.)

Batholiths are formed at considerable depth within the crust and are therefore seen only after the erosion of millions of years has removed the overlying mountain masses, exposing the mountain roots. (See Figure 37.24). As a batholith is uncovered, there appear first smaller bodies of the plutonic rock known as *stocks,* which occupy areas of less than 40 sq mi (100 sq km) (Figure 21.8). Remnants of the *country rock* (rock into which the igneous rock was intruded) will be found extending down into the batholith as *roof pendants,* but with continued denudation of the land surface a vast expanse of uninterrupted plutonic rock will appear.

Close examination of plutonic rock exposures will often reveal the presence of irregularly-shaped inclusions of country rock, which may be of almost any variety (Figure 21.9). These inclusions, termed *xenoliths,* suggest that the emplacement of a batholith is in part at least a mechanical process, known as *stoping* (stōp•ing), in which masses of the brittle country rock are wrenched loose and become incorporated into the magma. Batholiths are of sufficient thickness to prevent the bottom being exposed to observation. However, from evidence relating to the layered structure of the earth's crust we must suppose that a batholith is limited to a depth of a few miles.

Figure 21.8 shows other forms of intrusive rock bodies. The country rock is depicted as having a layered structure, as would be the case for sedimentary strata. Magma intruding these layers may spread out into a

**FIGURE 21.11.** Dike of basalt cutting granite. Cohasset, Massachusetts. (Photograph by John A. Shimer.)

thin sheet of relatively great horizontal extent named a *sill* (Figure 21.10). Where magma pressure lifts the overlying layers into a dome, a *laccolith* results. In thick sills and large laccoliths the rock texture is that of a pluton.

Fractures in previously formed solid rock may be invaded by magma, which forces the enclosing rock mass apart, resulting in more-or-less vertical *dikes,* wall-like igneous rock bodies (Figure 21.11). Dikes are typically of small thickness—from a few inches to a few yards—and have a fine-grained crystalline texture. Shrinkage in cooling of thin sills and dikes results in a system of joint fractures that produces long rock columns of prismatic form with four, five, or six sides. This structure is termed *columnar jointing* (Figure 21.10). The columns are oriented with the long dimension at right angles to the enclosing country-rock surfaces. Consequently columns are typically vertical in orientation in sills and horizontal in dikes.

Watery silica-rich solutions that remain after a magma has largely crystallized are forced to penetrate fractures in either the newly-formed igneous body or the adjacent country rock. Minerals deposited from such solutions take the form of *veins* (Figure 21.8). One important class of veins consists of *pegmatite,* already described as having a rock texture of unusually large crystals. Other types of veins contain concentrations of uncommon minerals, among them the ores of various metals.

## Forms of igneous rock extrusion

Magma erupting at the earth's surface gives rise to a wide variety of igneous phenomena with a wide range of external forms as well as of the internal structures and texture of material composing those forms.

Basically, we can distinguish forms constructed of lava from those constructed of ejected solid particles. Lava consists of magma behaving as a viscous fluid after it has arrived at the surface. Lava may emerge from the localized central vent of a volcano, in which case the lava flows away from the vent as a narrow tongue following any one of a number of radial paths. In other places lava (usually of basaltic composition) emerges from a long crack, or *fissure,* in the brittle surface rock and flows out as a succession of thin sheets covering considerable surface area (Figure 21.12). The latter lavas are known as *fissure flows.* One flow is built upon another and they may accumulate in thicknesses totaling hundreds to thousands of feet spread over tens of thousands of square miles. A further description of

*A*

*B*

**FIGURE 21.12.** (*A*) Vertical air photograph of the King's Bowl Rift, Snake River Plain, Idaho. Long dimension of the photograph spans about 2000 ft (600 m); north is toward the top. Dark areas are basaltic lava flows. The fissure is 6 to 8 ft (1.4 to 2.4 m) wide and over 800 ft (240 m) deep. An explosion crater lies near the center (light-colored slope). (U.S. Dept. of Agriculture photograph.) (*B*) View south along the rift, with a spatter cone in the distance. (Photograph by Martin Prinz.)

**FIGURE 21.13.** Basaltic lava flow from Mauna Loa moving toward the village of Hoopuloa, Hawaii, April, 1926. (U.S. Air Force photograph.)

**FIGURE 21.14.** Ropy lava of a recent basalt flow at Craters of the Moon National Monument, Idaho. (U.S. Department of the Interior.)

these accumulations, which are also referred to as *plateau basalts,* will be found in Chapter 25 (see Figures 25.2, 25.3, and 25.4). In highly fluid basalts, liquid lava may be seen exposed in the central zone of the flow and close to the vent. But because of rapid cooling, the surface and margins of a lava flow usually appear to be encrusted with solid blocks of lava. (See Figure 21.16*A*.) Lava flows move under the force of gravity in the downhill direction, occupying any available valley or topographic depression (Figure 21.13). Where the solidified crust of a flow forms a strong structural arch, fluid lava beneath may flow out to lower levels, leaving a hollow lava tube or tunnel within the flow.

Lavas of basaltic composition flow more easily and more rapidly than do those of felsic mineral composition (andesite, rhyolite). Lower viscosity (higher fluidity) of basaltic lava may be due in part to higher temperature. Although direct measurements have been few, temperatures of basaltic lavas have been observed in the range of 2000° to 2200° F (1100° to 1200° C). Temperatures of felsic lavas may be somewhat less, 1650° to 1830° F (900° to 1000° C). Another cause of greater fluidity of basaltic lavas may lie in the fact that the silicon-oxygen tetrahedra are fewer and structures of the mafic compounds are less complex and therefore offer less resistance to flowage. Flow surfaces may be extremely rough (*aa* texture) where the lava is highly charged with gases and produces a scoriaceous texture. Other basalt flows have rather smooth outer surfaces convoluted into billowy and ropy configurations (*pahoehoe* texture) (Figure 21.14).

Upon solidification, the interiors of many lava flows exhibit the same type of columnar jointing previously mentioned as characteristic of thin sills and dikes (Figure 21.15). Lavas which reach the ocean, or which erupt from vents or fissures beneath the ocean or intrude shallow water or muddy sediments, upon cooling develop a characteristic *pillow structure* and are known as *pillow lavas.*

In contrast with the lava flows is a class of extruded igneous material known collectively as *volcanic ejecta,* or *tephra.* This material consists of rock and mineral fragments blown out from a vent under pressure of gases present in the magma. The fragments are either in the solid state or in a plastic state immediately prior to solidification. Fragments of the country rock are commonly included with the ejecta.

Volcanic ejecta are classified in terms of the sizes of the fragments. The largest fragments are huge solid blocks, and the smallest range down in size to the finest dusts. Spindle-shaped masses a few inches to a foot or more in diameter, known as *volcanic bombs,* result from the congealing of blebs of fluid lava thrown high into the air (Figure 21.17*B*). Blebs of plastic lava falling close to a small vent may build a small *spatter cone* (Figure 21.16). Smaller particles of scoriaceous lava, ranging in diameter from 0.15 to 1 in. (4 to 25 mm), are *lapilli,* and particles under about 0.15 in. (4 mm) constitute *volcanic ash* (Figure 21.17*D*). Ash particles range downward in size to the finest dusts (smoke particles) and can be transported for thousands of miles in the troposphere. Upon microscopic examination,

**FIGURE 21.15.** Columnar structure in basaltic lava. Palisades of the Columbia River, Washington. The columns are about 15 ft (5 m) long. (Photograph by G. K. Gilbert, U.S. Geological Survey.)

**FIGURE 21.16.** A spatter cone at the base of Sunset Crater, northern Arizona. (Photograph by A. N. Strahler.)

particles of fine ash will be found to take the form of minute *shards* (angular fragments) of volcanic glass.

Deposits built of volcanic ejecta are classified as *pyroclastic deposits* and are intermediate in class between igneous and sedimentary rocks because the rock material, although igneous, is transported by or falls through air or water. *Volcanic breccia,* a crude mixture of large and small ejecta that have fallen close to a vent, represents one form of rock more closely allied to the igneous class than to the sedimentary class. On the other hand, volcanic ash that has been transported by winds or water currents is deposited in layers which may become compacted into *tuff,* a stratified rock sometimes classed as sedimentary.

A unique form of volcanic material is that carried in *glowing avalanches* (*nuées ardentes*), or *ash flows,* consisting of a highly heated mixture of gases and frothed lava. Moving as a dense cloud-like tongue down the slopes of a volcano, the glowing avalanche leaves a fine-textured rock layer resembling tuff but fused into hard layers by the high temperature. This rock is described as a *welded tuff.*

The extremely high gas pressures causing a volcano to explode huge quantities of pyroclastic materials and to emit lavas are thought to develop in a *magma reservoir* situated below the volcano at a depth on the order of perhaps 2 to 3 mi (3 to 5 km). Here the magma is in the process of slow cooling and partial crystallization.

**FIGURE 21.17.** Sakurajima, a Japanese volcano, erupted violently in 1914. These pictures show various scenes from the eruption. (Photograph by T. Nakasa.)
*A.* Distant view of Sakurajima showing the great cauliflower cloud of volcanic gases and condensed steam.
*B.* A blocky lava flow advanced slowly over a ground surface littered with volcanic blocks and bombs.
*C.* The hot lava made clouds of steam upon reaching the sea.
*D.* Volcanic ash buried a village.

*A*

*B*

*C*

*D*

It is known from laboratory experimentation with cooling of silicate melts that, as crystallization proceeds, the water contained in the melt increases in proportion in the remaining solution, causing an enormous rise in pressure. This pressure increase is believed to be of an order of magnitude easily capable of causing volcanic explosion. Because basaltic lavas have lower viscosity, gas can escape more easily than from felsic lavas with higher viscosity. Hence felsic lavas retain gases and are the more explosive of the two classes.

## Landforms built by volcanic activity

When igneous extrusion takes place repeatedly from a single vent, or from closely grouped vents, the igneous matter accumulates to form a mound or peak. All such centralized accumulations come under the broad classification of *volcanoes.* There is a wide range in the sizes and shapes of volcanoes, as well as a wide range in the forms of extrusive rock of which they are constructed.

The more viscous felsic lavas solidify rapidly and thus build up large masses with steep slopes close to the vent. Moreover, the felsic magmas tend to plug the vent upon cooling, so that a subsequent eruption is extremely violent and may greatly alter or destroy the cone previously built. The coarser pyroclastic fragments blown from a vent fall nearby, building up steep slopes of loose consistency that attain a uniform angle of repose and thus contribute to smoothness and perfection of the conical form.

In general, then, the form of a volcano depends upon the viscosity of the lava, whether highly fluid or highly viscous, and the degree to which gases are present under confining pressure in the emerging magma. Volcanoes range in a series from those formed almost entirely of highly fluid lavas to those formed entirely of pyroclastic materials.

**Basaltic domes** The continued outpouring of great quantities of highly fluid basaltic lavas from a radiating series of fissures produces the *basaltic dome,* or *shield volcano.* Unquestionably the greatest assemblage of basaltic domes is the Hawaiian Islands, each island formed of one or more such volcanoes (Figure 21.18). Another locality famous for its lava domes is Iceland. The Hawaiian domes were built upward from the floor of the Pacific Ocean basin, now averaging about 16,000 ft (4900 m) below sea level in this region. The highest volcano, Mauna Loa, rises to an elevation over 13,000 ft (4000 m) above sea level. Thus with respect to their bases on the ocean floor these volcanoes are on the order of 5 mi (8 km) high, which is vastly greater than the height of most other forms of volcanoes. Side

**FIGURE 21.18.** Hawaii Volcanoes National Park. Upper left, Aerial view of Mokuaweoweo, the broad central depression on the summit of Mauna Loa, March, 1962. The volcano Mauna Kea is on the distant skyline. Upper right, Halemaumau, a pit crater on Mauna Loa, seen in 1952. Below, A fire fountain on the floor of Halemaumau during the eruption of July, 1961. (Courtesy of National Park Service, U.S. Department of the Interior.)

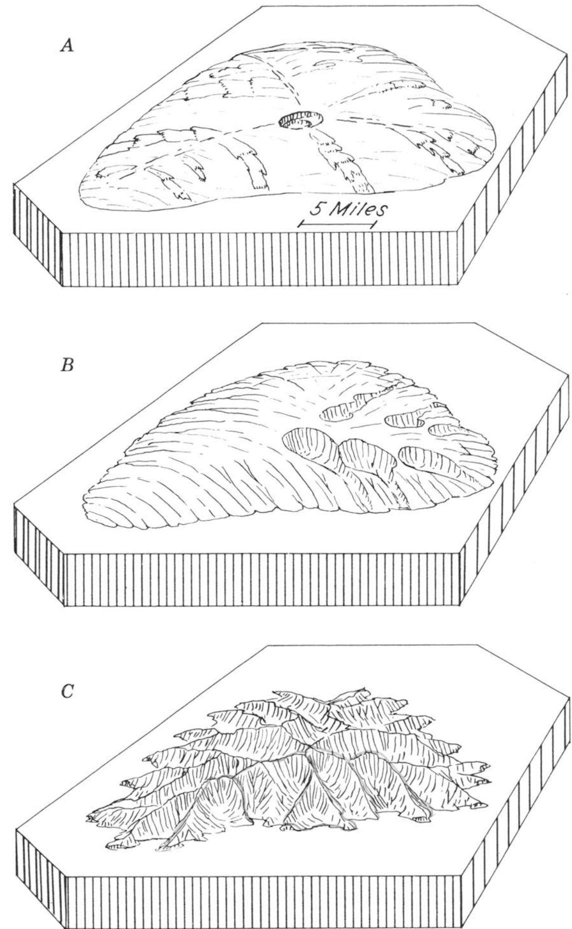


FIGURE 21.19. Schematic diagrams of stages in erosion of Hawaiian shield volcanoes. (*A*) Initial stage, lava dome with central depression and fresh flows. (*B*) Valley heads deeply eroded. (*C*) Mature stage of fluvial dissection. (© 1960, John Wiley & Sons, New York. Based on data of H. T. Stearns and G. A. Macdonald.)

**FIGURE 21.20.** Amboy Crater, a cinder cone with lava flow in San Bernardino County, California. (Copyright Spence Air Photo.)

slopes of the Hawaiian lava domes are usually not more than 4° to 5° in the freshly built condition. Lava flows emerge from fissures on the flanks of the dome and travel long distances before solidifying (Figure 21.13). There is comparatively little explosive activity and little pyroclastic material.

A characteristic feature of the Hawaiian form of lava dome is the broad steep-walled *central depression,* or *sink,* up to 2 mi (3.2 km) or more wide and several hundred feet deep (Figure 21.18). The central depression is produced by a subsidence that follows withdrawal of basaltic magma from below. Upon the floor of the depression are smaller *pit craters,* 0.5 mi (0.8 km) across or less, in the bottoms of which molten basalt is often exposed (Figure 21.18).

Various stages of lava-dome dissection by erosion processes are illustrated in Figure 21.19. After volcanic action has ceased, streams begin to carve radial valleys.

**FIGURE 21.21.** Summit and crater of an active composite volcano in central Java. (Photograph by Luchtvaart-Afdeeling, Ned. Ind. Leger., Bandoeng.)

**FIGURE 21.22.** Volcan de Agua, an extinct composite volcano 25 mi (40 km) southwest of Guatemala City. Radial streams have begun to dissect the cone. (Aero Service Corporation, Division of Litton Industries.)

Deepening and enlargement of the valley heads produce characteristic amphitheater-like hollows, as shown in Block *B* of Figure 21.19. An example is East Maui. In time the dome is steeply dissected and possesses steep slopes and strong relief (Block *C*), as in the case of West Maui. Steep marine cliffs are cut by wave action. Ultimately the dome will be reduced to a submarine bank.

**Basaltic cinder cones** We turn now from the largest volcanoes to the smallest—the *basaltic cinder cones* (Figure 21.20). These small cones, usually but a few hundred feet high and less than 1 mi (1.6 km) in basal diameter, are formed entirely of pyroclastic materials. They have a relatively large central depression, or *crater.* Scoriaceous basalt is ejected from a small pipe.

Solidification of the magma as it is blown out results in solid fragments of many sizes, from large angular blocks and bombs through lapilli to ash. The larger fragments accumulate close to the vent, building up a cone, whereas the finer particles of ash are carried in the wind to fall in a surrounding apron. An ash layer up to several inches deep may be found within a radius of a few miles. In some cases a basaltic lava flow emerges from the same vent, spreading in a tongue-like stream away from the cone and continuing for several miles down the nearest stream valley.

Cinder cones commonly occur in groups of as many as several dozen. One of the best examples of a cinder-cone field is that surrounding the San Francisco Peaks in northern Arizona. Other fine groups of cinder cones lie north and east of Mt. Lassen in northern California and in Craters of the Moon National Monument, Idaho.

**Stratovolcanoes** Most of the world's great steep-sided volcanic cones are composed of both lava and pyroclastic layers, producing what is termed a *composite volcano,* or *stratovolcano.* The lava is commonly of felsic composition—andesite or rhyolite—and is of relatively high viscosity, which means that it does not flow readily and congeals close to the vent. The lava may emerge from a set of radial fissures extending down the flanks of the cone. Pyroclastic materials are blown from the central crater and rain down upon the surrounding slopes of the cone, which are built up to angles of 20° to 30° (Figure 21.21). There results an internal structure consisting of alternating layers of lava and pyroclastics. A composite cone may grow to heights of several thousand feet and have a basal diameter of several miles. Typically the cone steepens toward the summit, giving the beautiful proportions so greatly admired in such large stratovolcanoes as Fujiyama in Japan and Mayon in the Philippines (Figure 21.22). The great elevation of many great stratovolcanoes causes them to extend above the snowline and to accumulate small glaciers. The mantle of snow about the summit contributes to the beauty of the peak.

A characteristic of the behavior of stratovolcanoes is their highly explosive eruption. During periods of dormancy lava solidifies in the upper central part of the volcano, beneath the crater, forming a *plug* that strongly resists renewed extrusion until great pressures have been built up. Eruption throws out huge blocks of broken lava and showers of lapilli and ash. A great cloud of dust and condensed steam hangs over the crater. (Figure 21.17*A*.)

**Explosion depressions** The explosive eruption of a volcano occasionally blows out an enormous mass of previously solidified lava as well as magma from a considerable depth. This event may be accompanied by a collapse or subsidence of the central part of the cone to produce a deep steep-sided crater. Thus we may distinguish between a crater produced by the gradual construction of a pyroclastic rim (as in the cinder cone) and a crater produced by destruction in a violent eruption. Explosion craters of a large stratovolcano are commonly less than 1 mi (1.5 km) in diameter and represent only a small proportion of the diameter of the cone at its base.

A much larger explosion depression, the *caldera,* may be from 3 to 10 mi (5 to 16 km) or more in diameter and represents a large proportion of the total cone diameter. Formation of a caldera is one of the most violent of natural catastrophes. Perhaps the best-known event of this kind to have occurred in historic time was the explosive destruction in 1883 of the Indonesian volcano, Krakatoa. Some 18 cu mi (80 cu km) of rock are estimated to have disappeared from the volcano, demolishing the cone and leaving a caldera about 4 mi (6 km) across. Much of this lost material is believed to have disappeared by subsidence into a cavity left by

**FIGURE 21.23.** Crater Lake, Oregon. Wizard Island, a cinder cone surrounded by its lava flows, is seen in the lower right. (U.S. Air Force photograph.)

the loss of magma, but enormous quantities of volcanic dust and pumice spread outward. The explosion produced a great seismic sea wave, or tsunami, that caused the death of many thousands of coastal inhabitants of the islands of Java and Sumatra.

In 1912 another such explosion demolished the volcano Katmai, on the Alaskan Peninsula, producing a caldera 3 mi (5 km) wide and 2000–3700 ft (600–1130 m) deep. As far away as Kodiak, 100 mi (160 km) distant, the ash fall from this explosion totaled 10 in. (25 cm), and the sound of the explosion was heard at Juneau, 75 mi (120 km) away.

Of the older calderas, those produced in prehistoric time, perhaps the best known is the basin of Crater Lake, Oregon (Figure 21.23). The caldera is about 5.5 mi (9 km) in diameter and surrounded by steep cliffs, rising to heights of 500–2000 ft (150–600 m) above the lake. The lake is up to 2000 ft (600 m) deep and covers 20 sq mi (52 sq km). The original volcano, given the name Mt. Mazama, probably rose 4000 ft (1200 m) higher than the present caldera rim and was an imposing stratovolcano resembling Mt. Hood and other volcanoes of the Cascade Range. An interesting feature of the Crater Lake caldera is that the rim is notched with the cross sections of valleys and glacial troughs truncated by destruction of the cone (Figure 21.23). More recently a small cinder cone, Wizard Island, and its associated lava flow were built up in the floor of the caldera.

## Rocks and minerals in a changing earth

In this chapter and the one before it we have begun an analysis of the inorganic matter comprising almost the entire crust of the earth. This study has ranged in scope from a broad plan of classification of all rocks, through details of chemical composition and physical properties of common silicate minerals and the igneous rocks, down to the level of atomic structure of those minerals.

In concentrating upon differences between individual varieties of minerals and rocks and their identification, we should not lose sight of the fact that a collection of mineral and rock specimens in the laboratory is a collection of cold, static objects usually far removed from the environments of their formation. To be able to identify these specimens and recite their chemical compositions and physical properties is no more of an intellectual achievement than to identify collections of stuffed birds or invertebrate shells.

Although it is essential in the pursuit of science to name, describe, and classify things, the goal of science is to interpret and to explain phenomena in terms of processes of their origin and development. In the chapters to follow emphasis will be upon explanation of the structure of the earth, its origin, and its changes throughout recorded geologic time.

The cycle of rock transformations, outlined in the previous chapter, serves as a useful dynamic conceptual model for unifying the geological processes that go on within the earth's crust. In this chapter the cycle has been entered at the point where magmas invade the crust or break out upon the earth's surface, solidifying into igneous rock. Yet we should be aware that this is an arbitrary point at which to enter the rock cycle. Rocks of each of the three major groups can be produced from rocks of any of the other groups. Age is no criterion of precedent, for we have no knowledge of the primeval rocks of our planet. At this very moment, somewhere on or within the earth, lava is solidifying into igneous rock, mud layers are compacting slowly into sedimentary rock, and sedimentary strata are being gradually transformed into metamorphic rock. All parts and phases of the rock transformation are in continuous operation. Energy is being transformed, masses are being transported, physical and chemical changes are in progress. Let us keep these dynamic considerations at the forefront of our study.

## References for further study


Cotton, C. A. (1944), *Volcanoes as Landscape Forms,* Christchurch, N.Z., Whitcombe & Tombs, 416 pp.

Wahlstrom, E. E. (1950), *Introduction to Theoretical Igneous Petrology,* New York, Wiley, 365 pp.

Bullard, F. M. (1962), *Volcanoes, in History, in Theory, in Eruption,* Austin, Univ. of Texas Press, 441 pp.

Spock, L. E. (1962), *Guide to the Study of Rocks,* 2nd ed., New York, Harper & Row, 298 pp.

Mason, B. (1966), *Principles of Geochemistry,* 3rd ed., New York, Wiley, 329 pp., chap. 5.

Simpson, B. (1966), *Rocks and Minerals,* New York, Pergamon, 272 pp.

# 22

# The sedimentary rocks

THE INTERFACE BETWEEN lithosphere and atmosphere represents a specialized environment as far as minerals and rocks are concerned. This surface environment is one of relatively low temperature and low confining pressure in contrast to the high-temperature and high-pressure environment in which plutonic igneous rocks are formed deep within the earth's crust.

The surface environment is one of instability for the silicate minerals, for they succumb readily to the presence of free oxygen, carbon dioxide, and water. We may like to think that no substance is more enduring than the granite we use in monuments to signify an everlasting tribute, yet in fact granite is one of the most decay-susceptible of mineral assemblages to face the "elements." Much the same statement can be made of most varieties of metamorphic rocks, for they too were produced in an environment of high pressures and temperatures and are not well adapted to endure exposure to atmospheric conditions.

The alteration of minerals in the presence of water, oxygen, and various natural acids is greatly aided by a group of physical forces of disintegration. These forces can break apart and fragment the hard well-knit minerals of igneous and metamorphic rocks, thereby increasing the mineral surface area exposed to chemical reagents. Were it not for the forces of physical disintegration, rock alteration would have proceeded very slowly throughout the geological past and the course of earth history would have been quite different.

Geologists use the term *weathering* for the total of all processes acting at or near the earth's surface whereby rock undergoes physical disintegration and chemical decomposition. The physical processes of weathering will be considered in later chapters, but the chemical processes of rock alteration must be studied here if we are to understand the origin and composition of sedimentary rocks.

## Chemical weathering

*Chemical weathering,* essentially a synonymous term with *mineral alteration,* consists of several important chemical reactions, all of which may occur more-or-less simultaneously. Consider first that all surface water—whether it be in the form of raindrops, soil water, ground water, or water in streams, lakes, and the oceans—contains in solution ions of the gases of the atmosphere. Disregarding nitrogen, the major atmospheric component but a comparatively inactive element, the principal gases of interest are oxygen and carbon dioxide. Oxygen ions in water are readily available for the process of *oxidation,* in which the oxygen ion combines with such metallic ions as may be available. Carbon dioxide in solution in water forms a weak acid capable of reacting with certain susceptible minerals. Other acids of organic origin are also active in the water found in soil and rock. Water itself is capable of dissolving minerals directly, a process we see daily in the solution of table salt (the mineral halite). All of these chemical processes require water, and the earth's surface is abundantly endowed with water. There is no truly dry environment on the earth's surface. Even the most nearly rainless deserts are easily supplied with water vapor that diffuses through the troposphere. While water is not obviously present much of the time in many deserts, rain does occasionally fall and the processes of mineral alteration do act. If there is any surface environment in which rocks can escape the chemical processes of decay, it is in the perpetually frozen layer found below the surface in arctic and antarctic lands.

**Products of hydrolysis and oxidation** Chemical union of water with mineral compounds is termed *hydrolysis.* The process is a true chemical change and is not reversible in the surface environment. It is not merely a form of water absorption, which can be followed by desiccation. Hydrolysis produces a new mineral compound from the original mineral.

A simple example of hydrolysis is found in the change of potash feldspar of the microcline variety into the clay mineral *kaolinite* (Table 22.1). In the formula for kaolinite the union with water is represented by the hydroxyl ion (OH). Notice that kaolinite does not contain potassium, present in the original feldspar. The potassium is released as a free positive ion in the soil water or is used by plants. In the alteration of feldspar to kaolinite, free silica ($SiO_2$) is also released and may remain in solution. Kaolinite is a soft white mineral with a greasy feel. It becomes plastic and exudes a distinctive "clay" odor when moistened. Kaolinite is an important ceramic material used in the manufacture of chinaware, porcelain, and tile. Under the electron microscope kaolinite proves to be composed of small tabular crystals (Figure 22.1), which possess a sheet structure very much like that of muscovite mica. Muscovite with the formula $KAl_3Si_3O_{10}(OH)_2$ differs from kaolinite principally in the inclusion of potassium. Muscovite can, in fact, be formed by the hydrolysis of potash feldspar and in turn can be converted to kaolinite by the loss of the potassium ion. Hydrolysis of the sodic plagioclase feldspar can also yield kaolinite and free silica (Table 22.1).

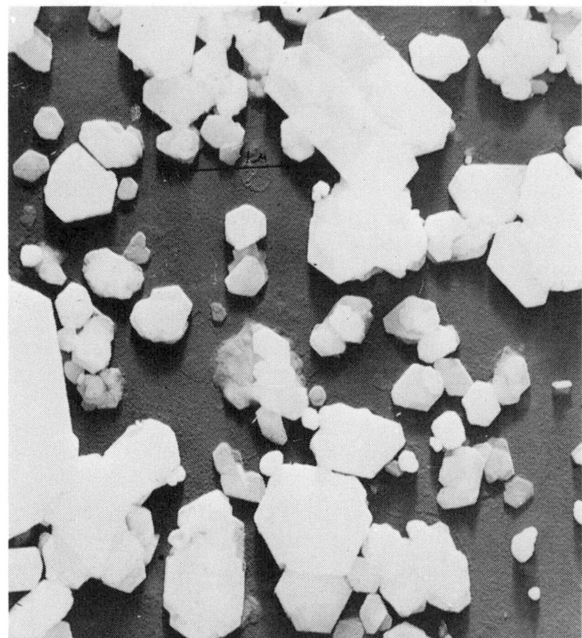

**FIGURE 22.1.** Electron microscope photograph of kaolinite crystals, magnified about 20,000 times. (Photograph by Paul F. Kerr.)

Under conditions of prevailingly warm and wet environments such as are found in equatorial and tropical wet–dry climate zones (see Appendix II), alteration of the feldspars leads to formation of *bauxite,* composed

**TABLE 22.1. ALTERATION PRODUCTS OF SILICATE MINERALS**

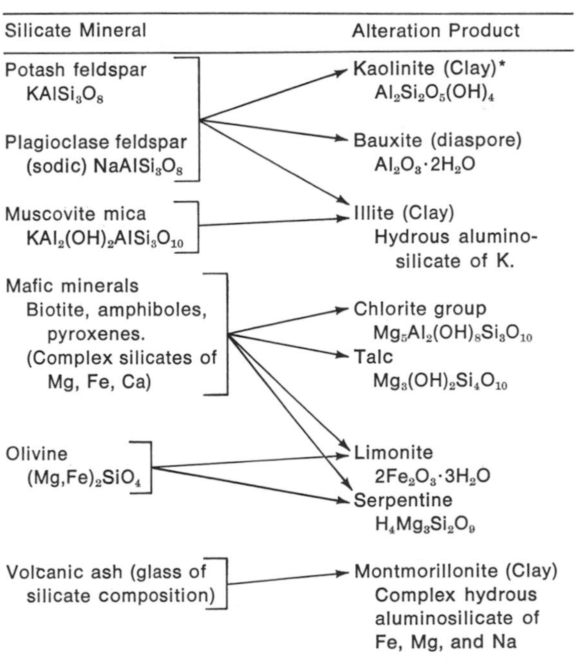

| Silicate Mineral | Alteration Product |
|---|---|
| Potash feldspar $KAlSi_3O_8$; Plagioclase feldspar (sodic) $NaAlSi_3O_8$ | Kaolinite (Clay)* $Al_2Si_2O_5(OH)_4$ |
| | Bauxite (diaspore) $Al_2O_3 \cdot 2H_2O$ |
| | Illite (Clay) Hydrous aluminosilicate of K. |
| Muscovite mica $KAl_2(OH)_2AlSi_3O_{10}$ | Illite (Clay) Hydrous aluminosilicate of K. |
| Mafic minerals Biotite, amphiboles, pyroxenes. (Complex silicates of Mg, Fe, Ca) | Chlorite group $Mg_5Al_2(OH)_8Si_3O_{10}$ |
| | Talc $Mg_3(OH)_2Si_4O_{10}$ |
| | Limonite $2Fe_2O_3 \cdot 3H_2O$ |
| | Serpentine $H_4Mg_3Si_2O_9$ |
| Olivine $(Mg,Fe)_2SiO_4$ | Limonite $2Fe_2O_3 \cdot 3H_2O$ |
| | Serpentine $H_4Mg_3Si_2O_9$ |
| Volcanic ash (glass of silicate composition) | Montmorillonite (Clay) Complex hydrous aluminosilicate of Fe, Mg, and Na |

* "Clay" denotes a clay mineral.

of sesquioxide of aluminum ($Al_2O_3$) and water (Table 22.1). Union of aluminum with oxygen represents the process of oxidation accompanying hydrolysis. Bauxite is not actually a single mineral, but probably consists of several related clay minerals (principally *diaspore*) and is usually contaminated with iron oxide and silica. Bauxite is clay-like in appearance and typically has small spherical structures. Where it has accumulated in large quantities it is an important ore of aluminum (Figure 22.2). Bauxite is also the principal constituent of a rock-like material known as *laterite* which forms in layers and irregular bodies within the regolith in tropical and equatorial regions. Laterite can be easily cut into building blocks, which harden upon exposure to the air. Many examples of this use of laterite as a building material are found in southeast Asia.

*Illite,* a very abundant clay mineral in sedimentary rocks, is derived through the alteration of feldspars and also from muscovite mica, which it closely resembles in crystal lattice structure. A hydrous aluminosilicate of potassium, illite occurs as a soft clay-like substance mixed with other clay minerals (Figure 22.3).

Through hydrolysis the mafic minerals can yield *chlorite* and *talc.* Both are hydrous magnesium silicates. They are soft scaly substances usually grayish to greenish in color. Talc is familiar to most persons for its soapy or greasy feel ("talcum powder") and was widely used in cut slabs for laboratory table tops and sink tops.

The mafic minerals also normally release iron during decomposition and this oxidizes to take the form of the mineral *limonite,* a hydrous sesquioxide of iron (Table 22.1). An earthy substance largely noncrystalline in structure, in color limonite is usually brown to yellow-brown and sometimes black. It yields a characteristic yellowish-brown streak when rubbed across an unglazed porcelain plate. Limonite can be derived from the weathering of any mineral containing iron and is a very widely distributed mineral. It has served as a poor-grade iron ore (bog ore). It is closely associated with bauxite in the soil and regolith of the warm humid equatorial and tropical climates. Both bauxite and limonite are almost immune to further chemical change under conditions of a warm wet climate. Limonite gives a typical chocolate brown to red color to soils of those climates and is conspicuous also as a coloring agent in rocks and soils exposed in dry regions.

Olivine, along with pyroxenes and amphiboles, is commonly altered by hydrolysis into *serpentine,* a hydrous magnesium silicate (Table 22.1). A soft greenish mineral with greasy feel, serpentine is commonly massive in structure without apparent crystal form. A fibrous variety, one of the forms of *asbestos,* consists of delicate flexible crystal fibers which can be easily separated and can be woven into fabric (Figure 22.4).

One of the most important clay minerals[1] produced by alteration of igneous rock is *montmorillonite,* actually a group of related minerals. This complex hydrous aluminosilicate of iron, magnesium, and sodium is produced by the alteration of feldspar, some mafic minerals, and volcanic ash, which itself consists of shards of glass of silicate composition. Montmorillonite is soft and clay-like, without any crystal form evident to the naked eye (Figure 22.3).

**Mineral susceptibility to alteration** The Bowen reaction series (Figure 21.1) can now be applied to the relative susceptibility of the silicate minerals to chemical alteration by hydrolysis and accompanying oxidation. It is a well-known phenomenon to geologists that in humid climates the mafic minerals decompose more rapidly than the felsic minerals. This fact is strikingly illustrated by rock exposures in which a dike of felsic rock is

[1] Of the alteration products named here, only three are classed as clay minerals: kaolinite, illite, and montmorillonite. Clay minerals are those that give a plastic property to earth materials composed of particles of clay size and have a sheet or layered atomic structure.

**FIGURE 22.2.** Oblique air photo of Babelthuap Island, Palau Group (lat. 7½° N., long. 134½° E.). The light-colored patches are bauxite strip mines operated during World War II by the Japanese. The bauxite ore, averaging 7 ft (2 m) thick, was derived by weathering of volcanic rock under a warm wet equatorial climate. (U.S. Geological Survey photograph.)

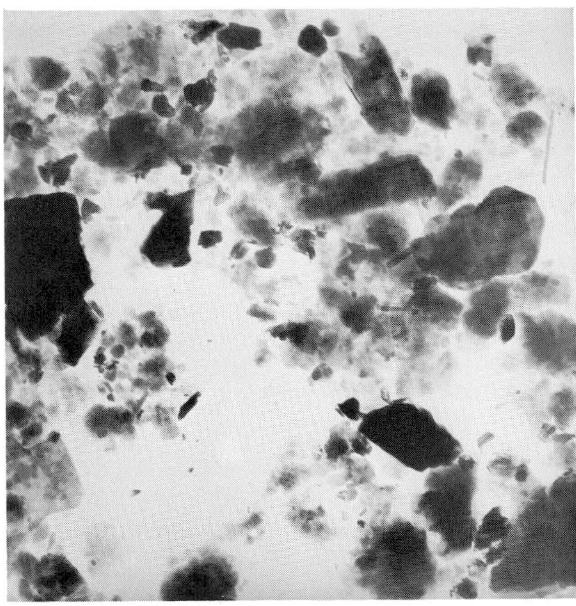

**FIGURE 22.3.** Fragments of the clay minerals illite (sharp outlines) and montmorillonite (fuzzy outlines) which have settled from suspension in tidal waters of San Francisco Bay. Enlargement about 20,000 times. (Photograph by Harry Gold. Courtesy of R. B. Krone, San Francisco District Corps of Engineers, U.S. Army.)

surrounded by a pluton of mafic rock (Figure 22.5). The dike rock in this illustration is fresh in appearance and has sharp corners and edges on the exposed joint blocks. By contrast, the surrounding mafic rock has softened into a friable mass of partly altered crystals. The centers of a few joint blocks remain intact as spheroidal bodies.

Susceptibility to alteration follows the same order as the order of crystallization in the Bowen reaction series. Olivine and calcic feldspar are the most easily altered, followed by the pyroxenes, amphiboles, biotite, and sodic plagioclase feldspar. Potash feldspars are generally, although not always, less susceptible than the last group, and muscovite is comparatively resistant to alteration. Quartz is in a class by itself and almost immune to chemical change beyond direct solution in water. An explanation of the relationship between mineral susceptibility to alteration and the order of crystallization is found in the environment of mineral crystallization. Olivine and calcic plagioglase were crystallized at the highest temperatures and pressures and consequently the environment of their formation is the farthest removed with respect to atmospheric conditions. Muscovite, crystallized at the lowest temperature and pressure, stands the least removed from atmospheric conditions.

**FIGURE 22.4.** Specimen of asbestos variety of the mineral serpentine. (Photograph by courtesy of Ward's Natural Science Establishment, Rochester, N.Y.)

**FIGURE 22.5.** Felsic dike (angular blocks at center) in deeply altered mafic rock, Sangre de Cristo Mountains, New Mexico. (Photograph by A. N. Strahler.)

The several minerals or mineral groups formed by alteration of the silicate minerals make up much of the bulk of regolith and soil overlying igneous rock bodies. From this environment of origin on the continents the alteration products are transported by running water, wind, and glaciers to distant sites of sediment deposition. The alteration products of weathered rocks, together with unaltered minerals (principally quartz and feldspar) and small unaltered rock fragments, become the sediment from which one major group of sedimentary rocks is formed. We therefore turn next to a study of the sedimentary rocks.

## Classification of the sedimentary rocks

A classification of the sedimentary rocks follows logically in terms of the possible origins of the sediment comprising the rock. Figure 22.6 attempts to organize sedimentary rocks according to sediments, minerals, and textures. The first order of classification is into *clastic* and *nonclastic* divisions. The adjective "clastic" comes from the Greek word *klastos,* meaning "broken," and describes a sediment consisting of particles removed individually from a parent rock source. The

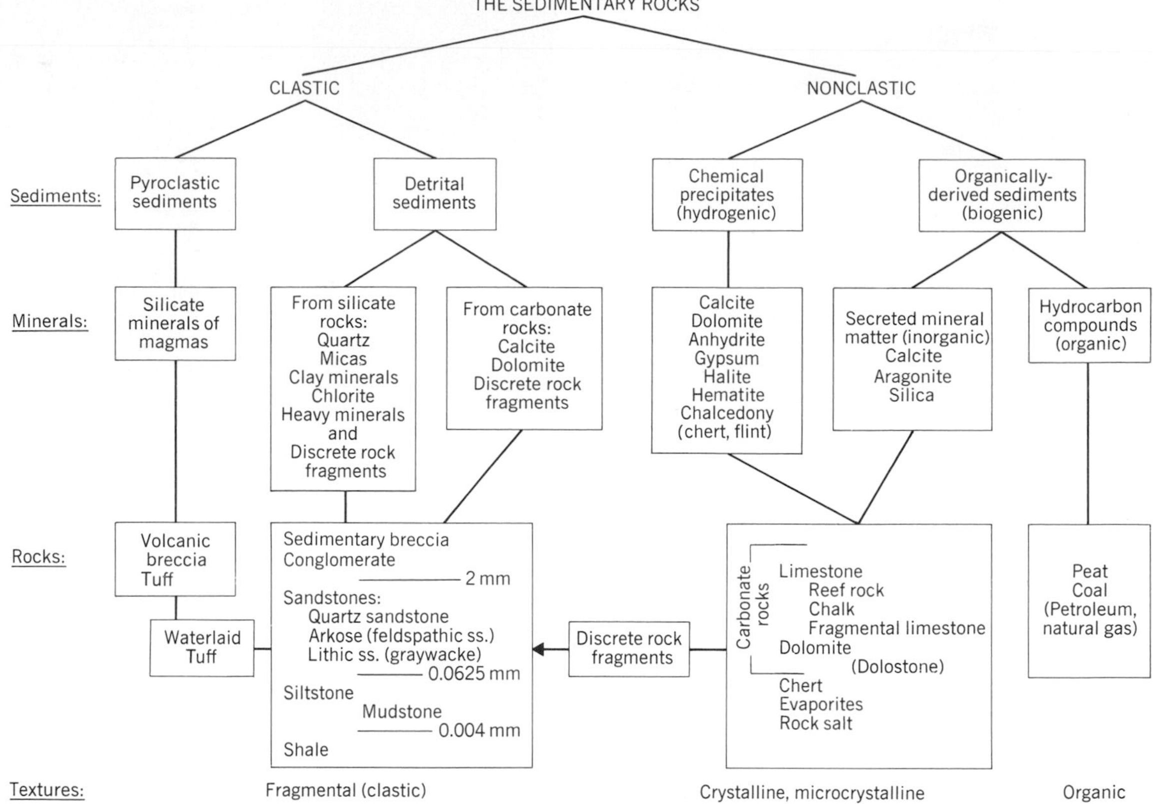


**FIGURE 22.6.** Composition and classification of the sedimentary rocks.

clastic rocks are in turn subdivided into those made up of *pyroclastic* sediments (Chapter 21) and those made up of *detrital* sediments. The latter are mineral fragments derived by the weathering of preexisting rocks of any classification.

The nonclastic division itself includes two basic subdivisions, *chemical precipitates* and *organically derived sediments.* Chemical precipitates (hydrogenic sediments) are inorganic compounds representing solid mineral matter precipitated from an aqueous solution in which that matter has been transported. The organically derived (biogenic) sediments consist of both the remains of plants or animals and mineral matter produced by the activities of plants and animals. For example, the shell matter secreted by animals is a crystalline inorganic substance and therefore a true mineral. Separated from the organic matter of these animals, shells constitute an inorganic sediment. On the other hand, accumulating plant remains, consisting of hydrocarbon compounds, form a truly organic sediment. As used here, the adjectives "organic" and "inorganic" agree in meaning with the chemist's classification of compounds as well as with the mineralogist's definition of a mineral. We shall need to be careful to distinguish between organically derived mineral matter and organic sediment (hydrocarbon compounds).

Once the sediments are classified and understood, the essential component minerals can be listed (Figure 22.6). Minerals that have not been previously described can be treated in the discussion of the appropriate sediment group. The naming of a particular sedimentary rock depends not only upon its mineral composition but also upon the texture of the rock, chiefly the size of the component mineral grains. Clastic sediments having fragmental textures are named primarily on the basis of the mineral composition of those fragments. For example, *sandstone* is a detrital rock in which the grains range between 0.0625 mm (1/16 mm) and 2 mm in diameter. Sandstones are further subdivided according to the mineral composition of those grains. In the case of the nonclastic sediments formed by chemical precipitation and by the secretion of mineral matter by organisms, the rock texture is classified as *crystalline* and is in some cases quite like the crystalline structure of an igneous rock. Organic textures, found in peat and coal, depend upon the way in which plant matter is deposited and compacted. Sedimentary rocks are usually recognizable through the presence of distinct layers resulting from changes in particle size and composition during the period of deposition. These layers are termed *strata,* or simply *beds.* The planes of separation between layers are *planes of stratification,* or *bedding planes.* The rock is described as being *stratified,* or *bedded* (see Figure 22.12). Bedding planes in their original condition are nearly horizontal, but they may have become steeply tilted (see Figure 22.14) or otherwise distorted into wavelike folds by subsequent movements of the earth's crust.

## The clastic sediments

Of the clastic sediments, the pyroclastic varieties have been discussed in connection with volcanic rocks and the structure of volcanic cones. We shall therefore turn, instead, to the detrital sediments and rocks derived from them.

The most abundant particles of detrital sedimentary rocks consist of (1) quartz, (2) rock fragments, and (3) feldspar. Fragments of unaltered fine-grained parent rocks can easily be identified in coarse sandstones by microscopic examination. Such fragments are typically second in abundance to quartz grains and are the chief component in the coarser grades of detritus. Mica and other minerals generally make up less than 3 percent of an average sandstone. Clay minerals, principally kaolinite, montmorillonite, and illite, may be abundant in the finer-grained detrital sediments.

**The heavy detrital minerals** There are, in addition to quartz, feldspar, and muscovite a number of minor minerals, found in the igneous and metamorphic rocks, which are highly resistant to physical abrasion and chemical alteration, and which therefore remain intact during transportation. Because of their relatively greater specific gravity, as compared with that of quartz and other felsic minerals, these detrital minerals are referred to as the *heavy minerals.* In Table 22.2 four heavy

**TABLE 22.2. HEAVY DETRITAL MINERALS COMPARED TO QUARTZ**

| Mineral | Composition | Specific gravity | Hardness |
|---|---|---|---|
| Quartz | $SiO_2$ | 2.65 | 7 |
| Magnetite | $Fe(FeO_2)_2$, also $Fe_3O_4$ | 4.9–5.2 | 5.5–6.5 |
| Ilmenite | $FeTiO_3$ | 4.3–5.5 | 5–6 |
| Zircon | $ZrSiO_4$ | 4.4–4.8 | 7.5 |
| Garnet group | Aluminosilicate of Ca,Mg, Mn,Fe | 3.4–4.3 | 6.5–7.5 |

minerals are compared with quartz in terms of specific gravity and hardness.

*Magnetite,* an oxide of iron, is a dense mineral of iron-black color and submetallic luster. It crystallizes in the isometric system and typically displays the octahedral crystal form (Figure 22.7). Magnetite is strongly attracted to a magnet, thus a magnet dragged through dark-colored sands of beach or stream bed will usually emerge with a coating of magnetite grains.

*Ilmenite,* an oxide of iron and titanium, resembles magnetite in outward appearance but is only slightly magnetic. It is a common associate of magnetite in black beach sands. *Zircon,* a silicate of zirconium, is even harder than quartz and has a density comparable to that of magnetite. Unlike the dark metallic minerals magnetite and ilmenite, zircon can be transparent and of pale color. A highly durable mineral, zircon is important in providing a means of radiometric age determination, explained in Chapter 25. Minerals of the *garnet group*—aluminosilicates of calcium, magnesium, manganese, or

*A*

*B*

**FIGURE 22.7.** (*A*) Octahedral (eight-sided) crystals of magnetite from the Magnet Cove locality, Arkansas. (Courtesy of the American Museum of Natural History.) (*B*) This variety of magnetite, known as lodestone, attracts iron filings much as does a bar magnet. (Courtesy of Ward's Natural Science Establishment, Inc., Rochester, N.Y.)

iron—are abundant in the metamorphic rocks but also occur in igneous rocks. (A description of garnet will be found in connection with the metamorphic rocks, Chapter 26.) Although not as dense as the three detrital heavy minerals named above, garnet is a durable mineral and will be found in company with those minerals in the dark sands of beaches and stream beds.

Because of their greater relative density, the heavy detrital minerals are easily separated from the less dense quartz and mica by processes of water transportation or by winds. Consequently these minerals form local concentrations as dark layers in many types of sand accumulations.

**Grade scale of mineral particles** Because the naming of clastic rocks depends in part upon the sizes of component mineral grains, it is important to establish a system of size grades. Among geologists the *Wentworth scale* is widely accepted (Table 22.3). The units of length are millimeters and, for the finer grades, microns. English units are given for comparison only. In scanning down the list of numbers forming the limits of the successive classes, it is immediately evident that each number is half the value of that which precedes it and twice the value of the number that follows it. The Wentworth scale is therefore a *constant-ratio scale,* or *logarithmic scale.* One can assign an integer series of numbers to the grade class limits, as indicated in the right-hand column, labeled *phi units.* Numbers on the *phi scale* give the negative logarithm to the base 2 of the millimeter values in the first column.

In the study of sediments and sedimentary rocks, the size grades of the component particles coarser than silt are determined by the use of sieves, the openings of the sieve mesh being spaced according to the Wentworth scale. Particles that pass through a given sieve opening but are caught upon the sieve of the next smaller mesh are referred to the named size grade given in Table 22.3. The sizes of gravel particles are generally determined by direct measurement, whereas silt and clay particle sizes are determined indirectly by the rate at which they settle in a still column of water.

**TABLE 22.3. THE WENTWORTH SCALE OF SIZE GRADES**

| Grade Name | | mm | in. | Phi units |
|---|---|---|---|---|
| | | 4096 | 160 | −12 |
| Boulders | Very large | | | |
| | | 2048 | 80 | −11 |
| | Large | | | |
| | | 1024 | 40 | −10 |
| | Medium | | | |
| | | 512 | 20 | − 9 |
| | Small | | | |
| | | 256 | 10 | − 8 |
| Cobbles | Large | | | |
| | | 128 | 5 | − 7 |
| | Small | | | |
| | | 64 | 2.5 | − 6 |
| Pebbles | Very coarse | | | |
| | | 32 | 1.3 | − 5 |
| | Coarse | | | |
| | | 16 | 0.6 | − 4 |
| | Medium | | | |
| | | 8 | 0.3 | − 3 |
| | Fine | | | |
| | | 4 | 0.16 | − 2 |
| | Very fine | | | |
| | | 2 | 0.08 | − 1 |
| Sand | Very coarse | | Microns | |
| | | 1 | 1000 | 0 |
| | Coarse | | | |
| | | 0.5 | 500 | + 1 |
| | Medium | | | |
| | | 0.25 | 250 | + 2 |
| | Fine | | | |
| | | 0.125 | 125 | + 3 |
| | Very fine | | | |
| | | 0.0625 | 62 | + 4 |
| Silt | Coarse | | | |
| | | 0.0312 | 31 | + 5 |
| | Medium | | | |
| | | 0.016 | 16 | + 6 |
| | Fine | | | |
| | | 0.008 | 8 | + 7 |
| | Very fine | | | |
| | | 0.004 | 4 | + 8 |
| Clay | Coarse | | | |
| | | 0.002 | 2 | + 9 |
| | Medium | | | |
| | | 0.001 | 1 | +10 |
| | Fine | | | |
| | | 0.0005 | 0.5 | +11 |
| | Very fine | | | |
| | | 0.00024 | 0.24 | +12 |
| | (Colloids down to 0.001 microns) | | | |

## The detrital sedimentary rocks

Coarsest of the detrital sedimentary rocks are the *sedimentary breccias,* consisting of large angular blocks in a matrix of finer fragments. These rocks often represent ancient submarine landslides, or terrestrial flows of mud, and are comparatively rare rocks. *Volcanic breccias* are equivalent rocks in the pyroclastic group.

*Conglomerate* consists of pebbles or cobbles, usually quite well rounded in shape, embedded in a fine-grained matrix of sand or silt (Figure 22.8). The principal distinction between a conglomerate and a breccia is that the large fragments in the breccia are angular. Rounding of the conglomerate pebbles is a result of abrasion during transportation in stream beds or along beaches. Essentially, then, conglomerates represent lithified stream gravel bars and gravel beaches.

The *sandstones* are composed of grains in the range

**FIGURE 22.8.** A conglomerate, consisting of well-rounded quartzite pebbles in a matrix of fine sand and silt. (Photograph by A. N. Strahler.)

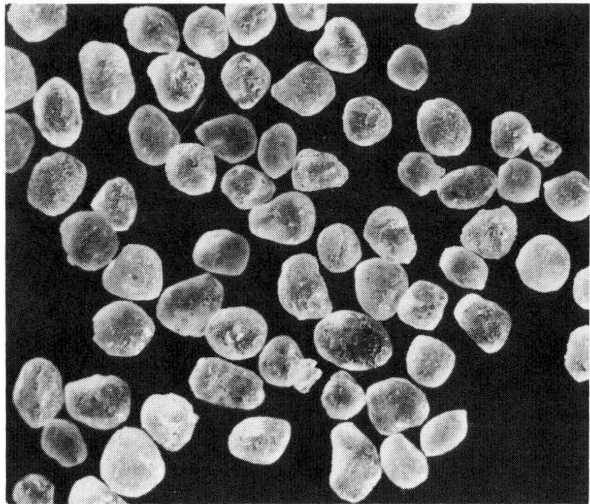

**FIGURE 22.9.** Well-rounded quartz grains from the St. Peter sandstone of Ordovician age. The grains shown here average about 1 mm (0.04 in.) in diameter. (Photograph by A. McIntyre, Columbia University.)

from 2 mm down to 0.0625 mm (1/16 mm) and are designated as coarse-, medium-, or fine-grained in accordance with the grade sizes on the Wentworth scale. Sandstones can be differentiated into at least four types on the basis of mineral content. Perhaps the most abundant and familiar form is *quartz sandstone,* in which quartz is the predominant constituent. Beautifully rounded quartz grains, many of spherical form, from a sandstone rock are pictured in Figure 22.9. In this example rounding was perfected by wind transport in ancient sand dunes. Quartz sandstones contain minor amounts of the heavy detrital minerals, and frequently small flakes of muscovite mica and some grains of feldspar, and rock fragments. The quartz sandstones are commonly lithified sediment deposits of the shallow oceans bordering a continent or of shallow inland seas. The quartz grains have survived a long distance of travel and finer particles have been sorted out and removed during the transportation process. As implied above, certain quartz sandstones were formed from large deposits of dune sands in deserts on the continents (See Figure 28.24). Also, some quartz sandstones are formed largely of quartz derived from preexisting sandstones, in which the quartz grains have been recycled.

Lithification of quartz sands to become hard sandstones requires *cementation* by mineral deposition in the interstices between grains. This cementation is accomplished by slowly moving ground water importing the cementing matter as ions in solution. The cementing mineral may be silica ($SiO_2$), in which case the sandstone is called a *sedimentary quartzite,* or *orthoquartzite,* and is an extremely hard rock with great resistance to weathering and erosion. If the cementing material consists of calcium carbonate ($CaCO_3$) a less durable rock results.

A second type of sandstone is called *arkose,* or *feldspathic sandstone.* It is characterized by a large proportion of feldspar, derived from partial weathering of an igneous or metamorphic rock body. Arkose signifies the rapid erosion of a mountainous region of igneous or metamorphic rock and relatively short distance of transportation of the weathering products.

A third type of sandstone may be termed *lithic sandstone.* It contains a large proportion of fine-grained rock particles. This sandstone is generally dark-colored or speckled because of the presence of variously colored rock particles. Some lithic sandstones that are particularly dense and hard contain an admixture of clay minerals. The name *graywacke* has long been used by field geologists for this type of "dirty" sandstone that is gray to almost black.

Lithic sandstones are not restricted to any particular environment of deposition but are derived from complex geologic terrains that have exposures of varied igneous, metamorphic, or older sedimentary rocks. The composition and texture of graywacke suggests that the sediment of which it is formed was poorly sorted, partly unweathered, and was transported in a highly turbulent flow of water. Some varieties show a distinctive structure known as *graded bedding* (Figure 22.10). Upon close examination, a single bed of the rock proves to have a distribution of particle sizes grading from a basal zone of coarse particles (sand or coarse silt) upward to a zone of finer particles (fine silt to clay). One can simulate this form of bedding by placing a mixture of pebbles, sand, silt, and clay in a tall glass cylinder filled with water. The cylinder is shaken vigorously, then allowed to stand upright. The rain of particles reaching the base of the container will be assorted in the same manner as in graded bedding. In Chapter 24, in the discussion of geology of the ocean floor it is explained that graded bedding is found in soft sediments in deep water and can be attributed to tongue-like flows of turbid water traveling from the continental shelves to deep parts of the ocean floor. Sediments of this origin are called *turbidites.* It is quite likely that some forms of graywacke are of this origin.

The compaction and cementation of layers of silt

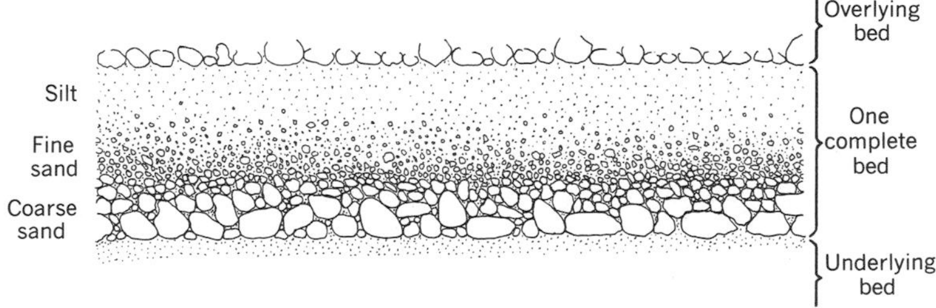


**FIGURE 22.10.** Sketch of a cross section through graded bedding. One complete bed represents the deposits of a single turbidity flow.

gives a compact fine-grained rock known as *siltstone* when largely free of clay particles. Siltstone has the feel of very fine sandpaper and is closely related to fine-grained sandstone, with which there is a complete intergradation. A mixture of silt and clay with water is termed a *mud,* and the sedimentary rock indurated from such a mixture is a *mudstone* (Figure 22.11). Most mudstones also contain minor amounts of sand grains. The compaction and consolidation of clay layers leads to the formation of *claystone.*

Many sedimentary rocks of mud and clay composition are laminated in such a way that they break up easily into small flakes and plates. A rock that breaks apart in this way is described as *fissile* and is generally called a *shale,* a term that serves to distinguish it from *nonfissile* mudstone and claystone. Shale is fissile because clay particles lie in parallel orientation with the bedding and thus form natural surfaces of parting.

The bulk of the claystone and clay shale consists of the clay minerals derived from the alteration of the silicate minerals. Kaolinite, illite, and montmorillonite are the most common of these minerals. Compaction of clay sediments into rock is largely a process of exclusion of water under pressure of the overlying sediments. Because the clay minerals consist of minute flakes and scales, the proportion of water held in the initial sediment is very large. Once thoroughly compacted, claystone and clay shale do not soften appreciably when exposed to water, but under impact they break apart easily.

Shales of mud and clay composition comprise the largest proportion of all sedimentary rocks. They can be subdivided by color into *red shales* and those of gray to black color. The red shales, owing their color to finely disseminated hematite (oxide of iron) are associated with red siltstones and red sandstones in enormously thick accumulations. Collectively known as *red beds,* these strata are interpreted as having been deposited in an environment of abundantly available oxygen, such as would be found on river floodplains and deltas of arid climates. The gray and black shales, also found in great thicknesses, are interpreted as deposited in a marine environment in which oxygen is deficient. The dark color is due to disseminated carbon compounds of organic nature, possibly produced by anaerobic bacteria. Dead organisms produced in shallow water above would rain down to the bottom, furnishing organic matter that would not readily decompose and would be added to the sediment. Petroleum is generally believed to have originated in this way.

A rather unique form of fine-textured clastic sediment is *bentonite,* formed by the alteration of beds of volcanic ash. As explained earlier in this chapter, the glassy shards of silicate mineral composition comprising volcanic ash tend to be altered to montmorillonite. Bentonite layers are found interbedded with claystones and mudstones of detrital origin.

The volcanic ash is in some instances a true volcanic tuff settled out from the atmosphere, or it may be ash that has settled out in standing water or has been transported by streams and redeposited in standing water as *water-laid tuff.* This sedimentary rock has been given an intermediate position between pyroclastic and detrital rocks in Figure 22.6.

**FIGURE 22.11.** Horizontal strata, largely unconsolidated muds and clays, of Cenozoic age, near Price, Oregon. (U.S. Geological Survey.)

## Minerals of the nonclastic rocks

The nonclastic rocks are formed from sediment that may be either directly precipitated from solution (hence inorganic in origin) or secreted by the activity of plants and animals (hence organically derived). Inorganic precipitates have been designated as *hydrogenic sediments* to distinguish them from the second type, or organically derived sediments, which can be designated as *biogenic sediments* (Figure 22.6).

Perhaps the most important class of minerals of the nonclastic sediments are the *carbonates,* compounds of the calcium ion or magnesium ion, or both, with the carbonate ion. Calcium carbonate ($CaCO_3$) is the composition of one of the most abundant and widespread of minerals, *calcite* (Table 22.4). A soft mineral easily scratched with the point of a knife, calcite is most easily recognized in large crystals by the excellent cleavage in three directions, forming rhombohedrons (Figure 22.12). Many common forms of calcite, especially in the sedimentary rocks, show no identifiable crystalline structure to the unaided eye. Application of a drop of dilute hydrochloric acid to the mineral surface results in strong effervescence (frothing) and is a standard test for the presence of calcite.

Of the same composition as calcite but much less abundant is *aragonite,* found in certain invertebrate shells. It makes up the pearly material of the shell.

**FIGURE 22.12.** Rhombohedral cleavage pieces of calcite of a clear variety known as Iceland spar. About half natural size. (Courtesy of Ward's Natural Science Establishment, Inc., Rochester, N.Y.)

Aragonite is a harder mineral than calcite and lacks the good cleavage of calcite.

*Dolomite,* a close relative of calcite, is a carbonate of both calcium and magnesium. Denser and harder than calcite, dolomite effervesces with dilute hydrochloric acid only when in the powdered form. Like calcite, dolomite has excellent rhombohedral cleavage. In the compact form found in rocks, particles with crystal faces are rare.

Sulfate compounds are also important as minerals of the hydrogenic sediments. *Anhydrite,* calcium sulfate, is a fairly soft mineral. It is commonly found in a granular state that gives a sugary appearance to broken surfaces. Derived directly from anhydrite by union with water (hydrolysis) is the mineral *gypsum,* a hydrous calcium sulfate. It can also be precipitated directly from solution. Gypsum is one of the softest of common minerals and defines hardness number 2 on the Mohs scale. It can be scratched with the fingernail. Gypsum has a low specific gravity, 2.2 to 2.4, and is typically fibrous in appearance, often with a silky luster.

*Halite,* or rock salt, was described in Chapter 20. (See Figure 20.11). We are all familiar with the properties of halite, which in the refined pure form constitutes common table salt. Ease of solubility in water is the most obvious property of halite, which belongs to a class of minerals known as *evaporites.* Along with certain other highly soluble salts, halite is deposited from ocean water and the water of salt lakes when evaporation is sustained under aridity of climate. Halite has been widely produced commercially by evaporation of sea water, but by far the greatest deposits are in rock strata.

We turn next to *hematite,* a sesquioxide of iron ($Fe_2O_3$), which is widespread in certain sequences of sedimentary strata (Table 22.4). Notice that hematite represents the *ferric* form of iron oxide, as distinct from the *ferrous* oxide (FeO) found in magnetite. (The composition of magnetite, given in Table 22.2 as $Fe_3O_4$, can also be written as $FeO \cdot Fe_2O_3$, a combination of ferrous and ferric oxides.) In terms of sediments and sedimentary rocks, this distinction is important because hematite contains the greater proportion of oxygen, a consequence of exposure to free oxygen of the atmosphere. We have already noted that the mineral limonite is a hydrous form of sesquioxide of iron and can be derived from hematite by hydrolysis. Hematite occurs in many forms and is particularly important as a sedimentary form of iron ore. We shall refer again to the presence of hematite in very ancient banded iron ores (Chapter 27).

Finally, to this list of common sedimentary minerals we add a form of quartz known as *chalcedony.* It is described as *microcrystalline* or *cryptocrystalline* in structure, because although it is in the crystalline state individual crystals cannot be recognized and the mineral appears as a hard compact substance. Otherwise the mineral properties of quartz apply to chalcedony (Table 22.4). Most persons are familiar with a banded variety of chalcedony known as *agate,* which is ornamental when highly polished.

In sedimentary rocks a rather homely form of chalcedony is widespread and of great importance. This material is *chert,* a hard horn-like substance forming nodules in limestones. It may also occur in layers of relatively pure *bedded chert.* (*Flint* is the popular name for a black variety of chert in which the dark color is due to inclusions of organic matter.) Chert nodules form through replacement of carbonate sediment by silica in sea water trapped in the sediment. This replacement probably occurs before deep burial takes place. However, some chert beds were formed by the cementation of large quantities of siliceous skeletons of *diatoms* (microscopic one-celled plants), *radiolaria* (one-celled animals), or of sponge spicules (small body-supporting parts of certain sponges). The organic origin of silica in sedimentary rocks is indicated in Figure 22.6 by its inclusion under organically-derived mineral matter as well as under the class of chemical precipitates.

## Salts in sea water

If we are to gain an appreciation of the way in which vast quantities of nonclastic sediments have accumulated on the ocean floors throughout the geologic past, it will be necessary to look into the salt content of sea water. It is from dissolved substances in sea water that the carbonate, sulfate, and evaporite minerals have been precipitated, and also from them that organisms have obtained the calcareous and siliceous substances they have secreted as solid mineral matter.

At present the salinity of the oceans is sustained at a fairly constant value by a chemical system in which the amount of matter entering the ocean in each unit of time is balanced by the removal of an equal amount of matter as sedimentary deposits on the ocean floors. This system is thought to be in a *steady state* of action, holding constant the proportions of elements in sea water as well as the total salinity, which averages about 35 parts per thousand by weight, or 3.5% by weight (see Chapter 12). Table 22.5 gives the average composition of salts in sea water in terms of the principal ions in solution.

Whereas the chlorine, sulfate, carbonic acid, and bromine ions and boric acid are among the volatile substances that are postulated to have entered the atmos-

**TABLE 22.4. IMPORTANT HYDROGENIC AND BIOGENIC MINERALS**

| | Mineral Name | Composition | Specific gravity | Hardness, Mohs scale | Crystal system |
|---|---|---|---|---|---|
| CARBONATES | Calcite | Calcium carbonate $CaCO_3$ | 2.72 | 3 | Hexagonal |
| CARBONATES | Aragonite | Calcium carbonate $CaCO_3$ | 2.9–3 | 3.5–4 | Orthorhombic |
| CARBONATES | Dolomite | Calcium-magnesium carbonate $CaMg(CO_3)_2$ | 2.9 | 2.5–4 | Hexagonal |
| EVAPORITES | Anhydrite | Calcium sulfate $CaSO_4$ | 2.7–3 | 3–3.5 | Orthorhombic |
| EVAPORITES | Gypsum | Hydrous calcium sulfate $CaSO_4 \cdot 2H_2O$ | 2 | 2.2–2.4 | Monoclinic |
| EVAPORITES | Halite | Sodium chloride NaCl | 2.1–2.3 | 2–2.5 | Cubic |
| | Hematite | Sesquioxide of iron (ferric) $Fe_2O_3$ | 4.9–5.3 | 5.5–6.5 | Hexagonal |
| | Chalcedony (chert, flint) | Silica $SiO_2$ | 2.6 | 7 | Hexagonal |

phere and hydropshere by outgassing (see Chapter 27), the positive ions of sodium, magnesium, calcium, and potassium (also referred to as *bases*) are believed to have been derived from the alteration of silicate minerals in igneous rocks exposed on the continents. The ions thus released, together with silicon and aluminum in detrital quartz and clay minerals, and many other elements, are carried to the oceans by streams which drain the weathered rock surfaces. Table 22.6 gives representative percentages of the four principal bases dissolved in stream waters.

Notice that the percentage of calcium in stream waters is high, and especially so from basalt rock areas, yet it constitutes only about 1% of the concentration in sea water. Sodium has a higher percentage concentration (31%) in sea water than in stream waters (13% to 27%). Thus it appears that the concentrations of salt constituents in sea water depend not only on how rapidly the constituents enter the ocean, but also on how rapidly they are removed by precipitation as sediments.

The average time that an element remains dissolved in the ocean before removal is known as the *residence time.* Table 22.7 gives the residence times of the four principal bases and silicon, together with their concentrations in sea water. Notice that the concentrations of these constituents are in very nearly the same proportions as their residence times. Sodium, which has a very low rate of chemical reaction in the marine environment, remains much longer in the oceans than the others, and this is reflected in its predominant concentration. Calcium enters the oceans in the largest percentage of the four bases but is relatively easily removed as calcium carbonate to become a sedimentary deposit. Silicon, released in large amounts in the weathering of igneous rocks, has an extremely short residence time, hence it is present in very small amounts in sea water. The same can be said of aluminum (not shown in table), also released in the alteration of aluminosilicate minerals in the igneous rocks.

Judging from the dominance of calcium among the bases of sea water, together with its comparatively short residence time, sediment of calcium carbonate compo-

**TABLE 22.5. MAJOR SALTS IN SEA WATER***

| | | Concentration, g/kg (parts per thousand) | Percent of Total Salt |
|---|---|---|---|
| *Negative ions* | | | |
| Chlorine | $Cl^-$ | 19.0 | 55.0 |
| Sulfate radical | $SO_4^{-2}$ | 2.5 | 7.7 |
| Carbonic acid radical | $HCO_3^-$ | 0.14 (varies) | 0.4 |
| Bromine | $Br^-$ | 0.065 | 0.2 |
| *Positive ions* (bases) | | | |
| Sodium | $Na^+$ | 10.5 | 30.6 |
| Magnesium | $Mg^{+2}$ | 1.3 | 3.7 |
| Calcium | $Ca^{+2}$ | 0.40 | 1.2 |
| Potassium | $K^+$ | 0.38 | 1.1 |
| *Neutral* | | | |
| Boric acid | $H_3BO_3$ | 0.024 | 0.07 |

* Data from D. W. Hood (1966), in R. W. Fairbridge, Ed., *Encyclopedia of Oceanography,* New York, Reinhold, Table 1, p. 793.

**TABLE 22.6. PRINCIPAL BASES IN STREAM WATER***

| | Rock of the Drainage Basin: Igneous, All Varieties | Basalts Only |
|---|---|---|
| Calcium | 52% | 73% |
| Magnesium | 11 | 12 |
| Sodium | 27 | 13 |
| Potassium | 10 | 2 |
| | 100% | 100% |

* Data from W. W. Rubey (1951), *Bull. of Geol. Soc. of Am.,* vol. 62, pp. 1121, 1123.

| Cleavage or Fracture | Luster | Color |
|---|---|---|
| Perfect cleavage in 3 directions at 75° angle. Forms rhombs. | Vitreous to earthy | Colorless, white, or yellowish |
| Cleavage poor. Conchoidal fracture. | Vitreous on crystal surfaces, greasy on fracture surfaces | Colorless, white, or yellow |
| Perfect cleavage in 3 directions at 74° angle. Forms rhombs. | Vitreous to pearly | White; also yellow or brown |
| Cleavage poor in 3 directions. Conchoidal fracture. | Vitreous to pearly | Colorless, white, or grayish |
| Cleavage good in 3 directions. Forms thin sheets. | Pearly to silky | White, gray, or yellow |
| Perfect cleavage in 3 directions. Forms cubes, prisms. | Vitreous | Colorless to white |
| No cleavage. | Metallic or dull | Steel gray, reddish brown, or iron black. Streak cherry red or reddish brown |
| No cleavage. | Waxy to dull | Colorless, white, or any color |

sition will prove to be the dominant nonclastic contribution to sedimentary rocks of the geologic record.

**TABLE 22.7. RESIDENCE TIMES OF PRINCIPAL BASES AND SILICON***

| Element | Residence Time, millions of years | Concentration in Sea Water |
|---|---|---|
| Sodium | 260 | 31 % |
| Magnesium | 45 | 3.7 |
| Calcium | 8 | 1.2 |
| Potassium | 11 | 1.1 |
| Silicon | 0.01 (10,000 years) | 0.003% |

* Data from E. D. Goldberg (1961), in Mary Sears, Ed., *Oceanography,* Washington, D.C., Am. Assoc. Adv. Sci., p. 586.

## The carbonate rocks

*Limestone,* as broadly defined, is a sedimentary rock in which calcite is the predominant mineral. Because either clay minerals or silica (as quartz grains, chalcedony, or chert) can be present in considerable proportions, limestones show a wide variation in chemical and physical properties. No single description is particularly helpful in identifying a specimen of limestone, although the test with dilute hydrochloric acid gives assurance of the presence of calcite. Limestones range in color from white through gray to black, in texture from obviously granular to very fine-grained, and in density from light and porous to very dense. Description of a few common kinds of limestone will serve to accentuate these variations.

The most abundant limestones are of marine origin and are formed by inorganic precipitation, or as the by-product of respiration and photosynthesis of organisms, or by the release of clay-size particles of aragonite upon decay of green algae. Usually dense and fine-grained, with colors ranging from gray to almost black, these marine limestones show well-developed bedding and may contain abundant fossils. Dark color may be due to finely divided carbon. A representative exposure of limestones is seen in Figure 22.13. Many limestones have abundant nodules and inclusions of chert and are described as *cherty limestones.*

An interesting variety of limestone is *chalk,* a soft pure-white rock of low density. Upon microscopic examination, chalk proves to be made up of extremely minute plate-lake particles, called *coccoliths,* derived from the disintegration of *coccolithophores,* a form of algae. Another interesting variety is *lithographic limestone,* a very pure fine-grained crystalline limestone formerly in wide use as an etching surface for reproduction of graphic material.

**FIGURE 22.13.** Dipping limestone strata of the Manlius and Rondout formations, New York State. (Photograph by A. K. Lobeck.)

Important accumulations of limestone consist of the densely compacted skeletons of corals and the secretions of associated algae—they are seen forming today as coral reefs along the coasts of warm oceans (Chapter 24). Rocks formed of these deposits are referred to as *reef limestones.* These limestones are in part fragmental, since the action of waves breaks up the coral formations into small fragments that accumulate among the coral masses or in nearby locations. Limestones composed of broken carbonate particles are recognized in Figure 22.6 as *fragmental limestone.*

In the diagenesis that may accompany the burial of limestone strata under great loads of overlying sediment, the calcite and aragonite may recrystallize into close-fitting grains to produce limestones of granular texture, designated as *crystalline limestones.*

*Dolomite* is a rock composed largely of the mineral of the same name. To avoid confusion, the name *dolostone* has been used to designate the rock as distinct from the mineral. Dolomite rock poses a problem of origin, since the mineral is not excreted by organisms as shell material. Direct precipitation from solution in sea water is not considered adequate to explain the great thicknesses of dolomite rock that are found in the geologic record. The most widely held explanation of the formation of dolomite rock is that it has resulted from the alteration of limestone by a replacement process in which magnesium ions of sea water are substituted for a part of the calcium ions. It is not known whether the replacement, referred to as *dolomitization,* occurs immediately after deposition, or over long periods by the slow movement of salt water through the rock after the limestone has accumulated in thick sequences. As seen in outcrops, dolomite rock is not easily distinguished from limestone, but under the hydrochloric-acid test it is only faintly effervescent. Dolomite is the harder and denser of the two rocks, but these differences may not be appreciable.

## The evaporites

A description of rock strata classified as evaporites would be essentially the same as for the minerals themselves, thus it need not be repeated. Despite the fact that there are many evaporites produced from sea water, the great bulk of these deposits consists of the sulfates of calcium as gypsum and anhydrite and of sodium chloride as halite.

The evaporites occur in association with one another in sedimentary strata, usually with marine sandstones and shales, but in some instances with chemically precipitated limestones and dolomites. Although details differ, most hypotheses of origin of thick sequences of the evaporites of the geologic record require a special set of environmental conditions. First, an arid climate in which evaporation on the average exceeds precipitation is assumed. Such climates are widespread in tropical latitudes today and can be presumed to have been present in the geologic past. Second, a shallow evaporating basin is required, and this may have been a large shallow bay or lagoon cut off from the open sea by a barrier bar. A narrow inlet, through which ocean water could enter to replace water lost by evaporation, is necessary to account for thick beds of evaporites. A slow subsidence of the area of deposition is required to accommodate the accumulating beds.

An entirely different environment of evaporite accumulation is found today in arid intermontane basins within the continents. These evaporating basins, known as *playas,* receive the dissolved products of streams from the surrounding mountains of moist climate. While the continental environment is important as a site of present-day accumulations of evaporites, it is not one conducive to producing strata that would ever become part of the geologic record of the distant future.

When sea water is evaporated under laboratory conditions, there is a definite order of precipitation of salts, that order being in reverse of the solubility of the salts. First, calcium carbonate ($CaCO_3$) is precipitated, followed in order by calcium sulfate ($CaSO_4$), sodium chloride ($NaCl$), complex salts of magnesium, chlorine, and sulfate, and finally by the compounds of potassium. It is interesting to note that chemically precipitated limestone is the first member of the series, hence we might choose to classify this rock as an evaporite. Calcium sulfate is precipitated largely as anhydrite. Most gypsum found in sedimentary rocks is thought to be derived from anhydrite by later union with water. Halite follows anhydrite and is usually the last member of the series to be deposited in any large quantity. The more soluble salts are found in the geologic record in very few occurrences, but they are common in playas.

Huge accumulations of halite have formed at several points in geologic time. A good example is the salt beds and associated layers of red shales and sandstones, gypsum, and anhydrite of the *Permian basin* of Kansas, Oklahoma, and parts of northern Texas and southeastern New Mexico. In the Permian Period dozens of halite beds were deposited here, many being of great thickness. A few individual salt beds 300 to 400 ft (90 to 120 m) in thickness are known. Thick anhydrite beds also occur in the series—one bed over 1300 ft (400 m) is on record. Important salt beds of other geologic ages occur beneath Michigan, Ohio, and western New York.

**Salt plugs and salt domes** In certain areas of very thick sedimentary strata, beds of halite buried at great depth have been forced by the pressure of overlying strata to rise in stalk-like columns. These salt columns slowly penetrate the overlying strata (not unlike the convectional rise of air in a cumulonimbus cloud, Chapter 18) and eventually come to rest with the top of the column at or close to the surface. The *salt plug,* as this odd structure is known, may have a vertical extent of tens of thousands of feet, but a diameter of only a mile or so (Figure 22.14). Typically the salt plug has a cap rock of limestone, gypsum, and anhydrite forced up by the rising salt. At the surface the strata are sometimes arched into an overlying dome, hence the name *salt dome* is given to the surficial portion of the structure. Figure 22.15 shows the distribution of salt domes in the Gulf coastal plain, a region of thick sedimentary strata of relatively young geologic age. Salt rises in such plugs because it has a relatively low mineral specific gravity (2.1) and deforms readily under unequal pressures.

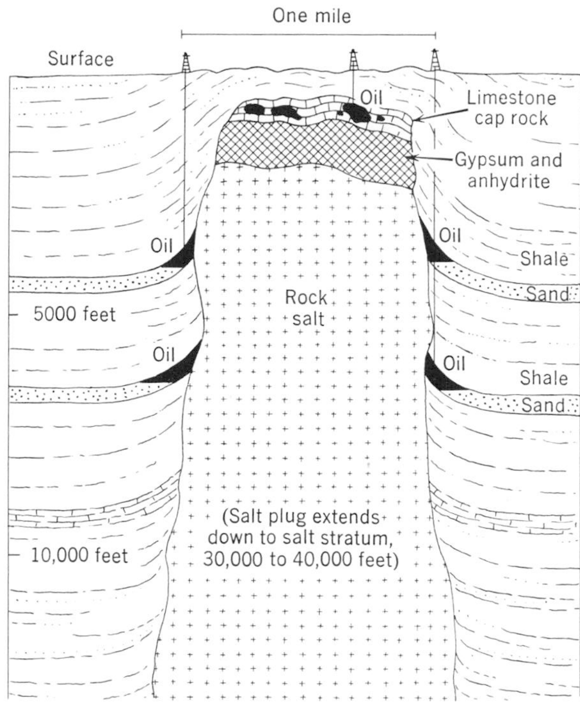


**FIGURE 22.14.** Structure of a salt dome. (© 1960, John Wiley & Sons, New York.)

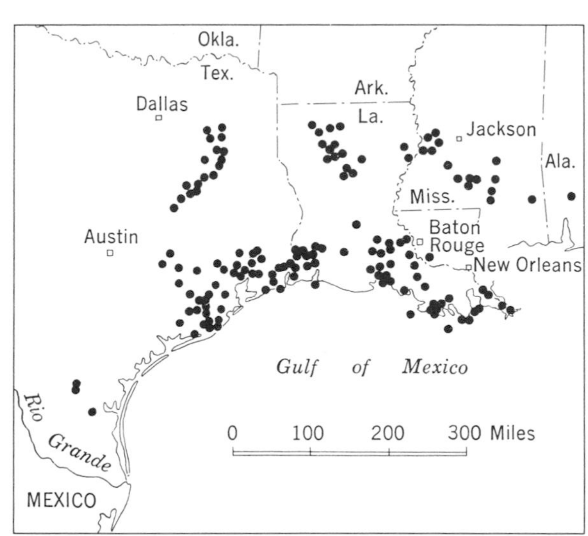


**FIGURE 22.15.** Each black dot represents a salt dome. (© 1960, John Wiley & Sons, New York. Based on a map by K. K. Landes.)

## Peat and coal

In a swamp or bog environment where water saturation persists, plant remains accumulate faster than they can be destroyed by bacterial activity. Only partial decomposition occurs because oxygen is deficient in the stagnant water and the organic acids released by the decay process inhibit further bacterial activity. The product of this environment is *peat,* a soft fibrous material ranging in color from brown to black. Freshwater bogs containing peat deposits occur in vast numbers in those parts of North America and Europe subjected to glaciation (see Chapter 41). Peat from these bogs has been widely used as a low-grade fuel. A second environment of peat formation is salt marshes in tidal waters (see Chapter 38). Because of slowly rising sea level following disappearance of the glacial ice, tidal peat has accumulated in successive layers and in places reaches a thickness of 30 ft (9 m) or more.

Under the load of accumulating sediments, layers of

*A*

*B*

*C*

**FIGURE 22.16.** Specimens of coals. *A.* Lignite from North Dakota. (Photograph by M. E. Strahler.) *B.* Bituminous coal from Virginia. (Photograph by J. B. Eby, U.S. Geological Survey.) *C.* Anthracite from Pennsylvania. (Photograph by M. E. Strahler.)

peat have become compacted into *lignite* or "brown coal," a low-grade fuel intermediate between peat and coal. Lignite is brown and has a woody texture. After being excavated lignite tends to break up spontaneously into small fragments.

Upon further compaction, lignite is transformed into *bituminous coal* or "soft coal," and this in turn has been in places transformed into *anthracite* or "hard coal" where the strata were subjected to intense pressures of folding in the mountain-making process. (See Chapter 37 and Figure 37.19.) Bituminous coal is a dense black substance commonly breaking into cubical or prismatic blocks (Figure 22.16). Anthracite is a hard jet-black substance with a high luster and conchoidal fracture.

Lignite and coal are composed largely of carbon, hydrogen, and oxygen, with minor amounts of ash and sulfur. For convenience in analysis and emphasis upon heat efficiency as a fuel, composition of coal is given in terms of three variable constituents—fixed carbon, volatiles, and water. (Ash and sulfur remain fairly constant.) Figure 22.17 shows the relative proportions of the three variable constituents for representative examples of lignite, bituminous coal, and anthracite. A complete series of intergradations is known. Notice that water is largely driven off in the transition from lignite to bituminous coal. Although the proportion of volatiles undergoes a relative rise from lignite to bituminous coal, the volatiles are almost entirely driven off when anthracite is formed.

Coal occurs in layers, known as *seams,* interbedded with sedimentary strata, which are usually thinly bedded shales, sandstones, and limestones (Figure 22.18). Collectively such accumulations are known as *coal measures.* Individual coal seams range in thickness from a fraction of an inch to several tens of feet. Although coals are found in a wide range of ages in the geologic record,

**FIGURE 22.17.** Composition of representative examples of coals.

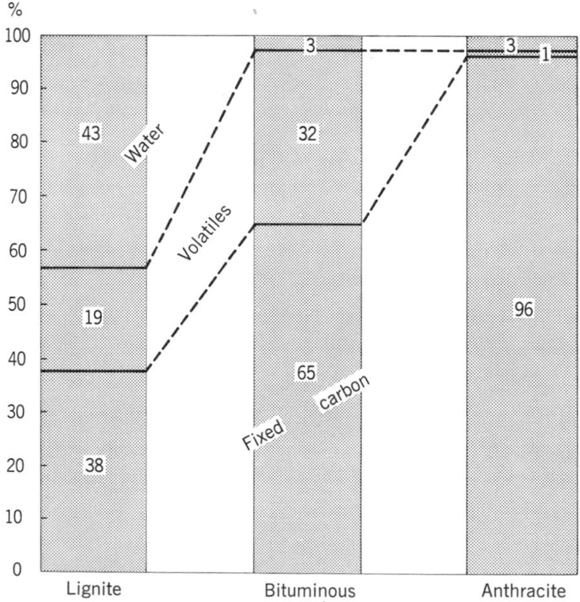

**FIGURE 22.18.** Outcrop of an 8-ft (2.4-m) coal seam, Dawson County, Montana. Large blocks of coal have slumped to the base of the cliff (foreground). (Photograph by M. R. Campbell, U.S. Geological Survey.)

those of the Carboniferous Period between 280 and 345 million years ago, are particularly outstanding (see Chapter 29). Vast expanses of the continents were then featureless plains close to sea level and were covered alternately by swamps bearing forest vegetation and by shallow seas in which sedimentary strata were laid down.

It has been estimated that some 30 ft (9 m) of peat was required to produce 1 ft (0.3 m) of coal. The rate of production of coal has been estimated at 1 ft (0.3 m) per 300 years. On this basis the 50-ft (15-m) Mammoth coal seam of Pennsylvania would have required an initial production of 1500 ft (460 m) of peat in a continuous period of plant growth lasting over 450,000 years. These figures are to a large degree purely speculative, but they give some idea of the extraordinary uniformity of environmental conditions that must have prevailed during the Carboniferous Period.

## Petroleum and natural gas

Petroleum, or "crude oil," is a mixture of several fluid hydrocarbon compounds of organic origin found in localized concentrations in certain sedimentary strata. In composition a typical crude oil might run about as follows: carbon, 82%; hydrogen, 15%; oxygen and nitrogen, 3%. Petroleum is neither a mineral nor a rock, but its close association with the clastic sedimentary rocks justifies inclusion of the subject in this chapter. Natural gas, which is closely linked in origin and occurrence with petroleum, is a mixture of gases, principally *methane* (*marsh gas*) ($CH_4$), and small amounts of *ethane, propane,* and *butane* (all compounds of carbon and hydrogen). In addition there are small amounts of carbon dioxide, nitrogen, oxygen, and sometimes helium.

As found in commercially exploitable accumulations, known as "oil pools," petroleum fills the interconnected pore spaces of a *reservoir rock,* which is usually a sand

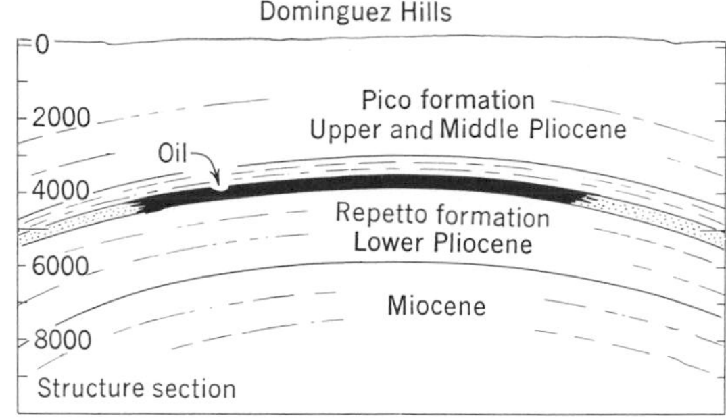


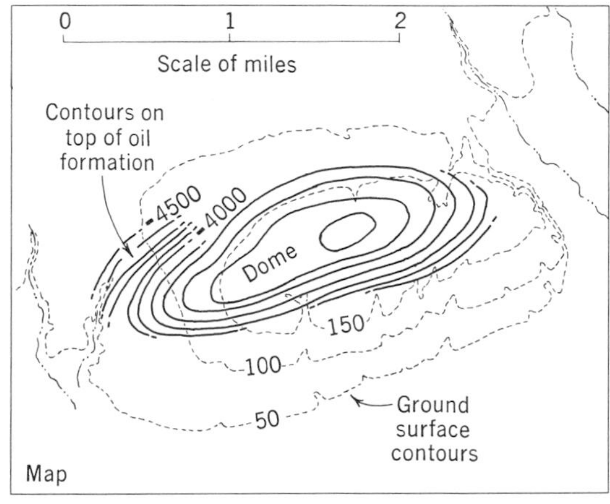


**FIGURE 22.19.** This low dome, the Dominguez Hills, California, provided a trap for an important petroleum pool. (© 1960, John Wiley & Sons, New York. Based on data of H. W. Hoots and U.S. Geological Survey.)

or sandstone, limestone, or dolomite formation. Natural gas accumulates above the oil, while water saturates the zone beneath the oil. It is essential that the reservoir rock be overlain by an impervious cap rock, typically a shale formation, that prevents the upward movement of the petroleum. A favorable structural arrangement of sedimentary rocks is achieved by a number of configurations. The simplest of these is an up-arching of strata in either a *dome* or an *anticline.* (Anticlines are explained in Chapter 26. See Figure 26.11.) Both of the structures trap petroleum and natural gas in the confines of the downwardly concave reservoir rock capped by shale. An example is the small low Dominguez Hills dome of southern California (Figure 22.19). Here a sandstone formation of Pliocene age, lying some 4000 ft (1200 m) beneath the surface, has trapped oil under an impermeable covering layer of shale. Other well-known oil pools formed in dome structures are the Teapot Dome and Rock Springs Dome of Wyoming.

A particularly important sequence of sedimentary strata favorable to petroleum accumulation is found beneath the coastal plain of the Gulf and Atlantic coasts of the United States. Here a great thickness of sedimentary layers takes the form of an enormous wedge tapering from a thin edge on the continent to a thick body under the shallow waters of the continental shelf. Within the wedge individual strata tend to become thinner as they rise in elevation in the inland direction. Where a sandstone layer thins to the point of disappearance, it forms a type of oil trap known as a *pinch out* (Figure 22.20). A large number of oil pools of the coastal plain of Texas are shown in Figure 22.21. Pools occurring in pinch-out traps form two broadly-curved belts paralleling the coast line.

Within the same coastal plain important oil pools occur along the flanks of salt domes (Figure 22.14). Here the oil is trapped in upturned sandstone strata adjacent to the salt plug or in cavernous limestone of the cap rock. Yet another form of trap is that produced by displacement of masses of sedimentary strata along a fault, or plane of slippage. An example is shown in Figure 22.22. Various other types of traps exist.

It is generally agreed that petroleum and natural gas are of organic origin. A major hypothesis of oil origin attributes the oil to microscopic plant forms—for example, diatoms—living in vast numbers in the seas. Upon death of the diatom a very minute particle of oil was released on the ocean floor, becoming incorporated into accumulating sediment. Where this was a dark mud the sediment eventually became a shale formation. Today we find petroleum disseminated through *oil shales,* which can be processed to derive petroleum. Eventually the petroleum must have been forced to migrate from the source rock to the reservoir rock. A number of mechanisms have been proposed for this migration, among them capillary film tension and pressures of compaction and crystallization.

**FIGURE 22.20.** Petroleum trapped by pinch out of sand strata in the updip direction. (© 1960, John Wiley & Sons, New York.)

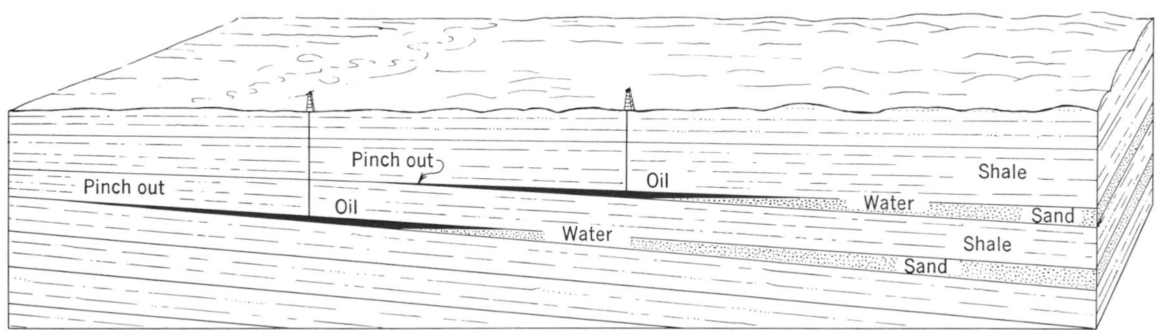

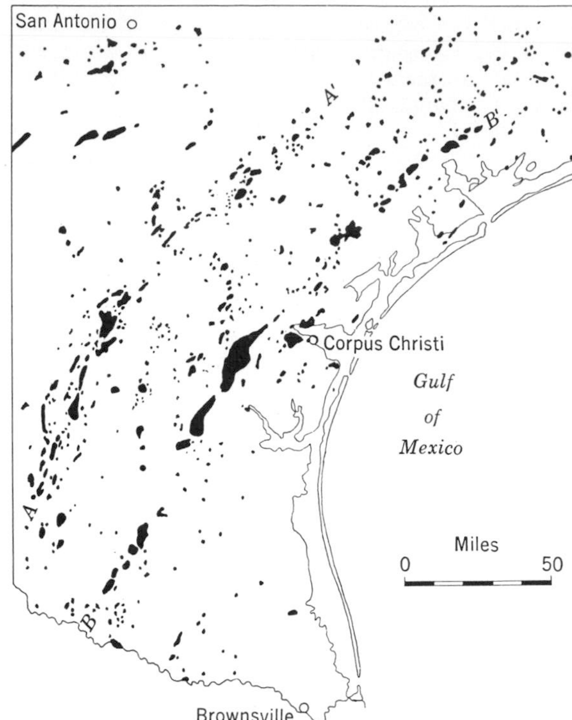


**FIGURE 22.21.** Oil pools, shown in black, form distinct belts along two zones of updip pinch out. Pools of zone *AA'* are in sands of Eocene age, and those of zone *BB'* in sands of Oligocene age. (© 1960, John Wiley & Sons, New York. Based on a map by A. I. Levorsen.)

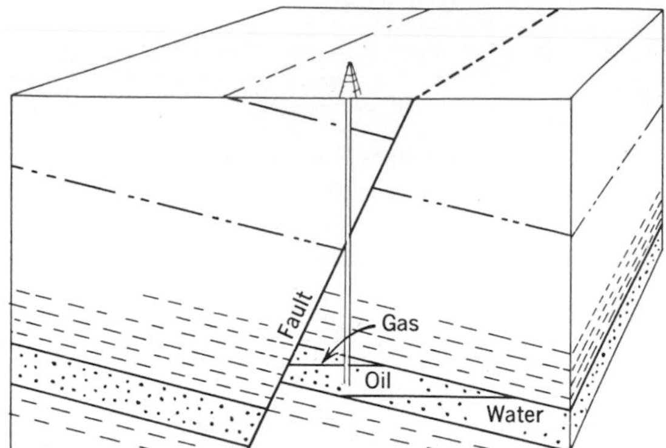


**FIGURE 22.22.** Petroleum accumulation in a fault trap, produced by faulting of impermeable shales against a dipping sandstone layer. (© 1960, John Wiley & Sons, New York.)

## Sediments and sedimentary rocks in review

This chapter has dealt with important basic concepts as well as with many details relating to the manner in which sediment is produced in the atmospheric and marine environments and eventually changed into rock strata by diagenetic processes. Even though the sedimentary rocks of the entire geologic record are trivial in total volume as compared with the igneous rocks of the earth's crust, the quantity of sediment that has been produced throughout recorded geologic time is by itself an enormous amount. We shall find that these widespread thick accumulations of sedimentary strata have had a profound influence upon the development of the continents. The sedimentary rocks have also provided the raw material for several kinds of metamorphic rocks and may also have been melted to form magmas of intrusive igneous rocks. These final portions of the rock transformation cycle will be considered in Chapter 26, where the mountain-making forces and continental evolution are examined.

## References for further study

Dunbar, C. O., and J. Rodgers (1957), *Principles of Stratigraphy,* New York, Wiley, 356 pp.

Weller, J. M. (1960), *Stratigraphic Principles and Practice,* New York, Harper & Row, 725 pp., part II, chaps. 4–9.

Spock, L. E. (1962), *Guide to the Study of Rocks,* 2nd ed., New York, Harper & Row, 298 pp.

Krumbein, W. C., and L. L. Sloss (1963), *Stratigraphy and Sedimentation,* San Francisco, Freeman, 660 pp.

Mason, B. (1966), *Principles of Geochemistry,* 3rd ed., New York, Wiley, 329 pp., chap. 8.

# 23

# The earth's interior

TO DETERMINE THE composition and physical properties of the earth's interior is one of the most difficult problems faced by earth scientists. The deepest mines, such as the Morro Velho Mine in Brazil, give us samples of direct views of rock down to depths of merely 7000 ft (2100 m)—only about 1/3000 of the distance to the earth's center. The deepest bore holes in search of petroleum now penetrate more than 20,000 ft (6 km), but even this depth is trivial in comparison with the earth's radius.

Without direct examinations and tests of the materials in the earth's interior, how can the geologist determine what mineral composition and what conditions of temperature, density, and strength prevail at great depth? Some information comes from examination of rocks that were formerly buried at depths as great as 5–10 mi (8–16 km), but have since become exposed at the surface following crustal uplift and subsequent erosion of the overlying rock. From examination of mineral varieties and structures in what was formerly sedimentary rock but has now been converted to metamorphic rock, some inferences can be made concerning the existence of powerful forces and high temperatures several miles below the surface, but when we consider the earth's radius even this information is only for skin-deep conditions. Volcanoes and lava flows bring magma to the surface from high-temperature pockets within the earth. But there is no reason to believe that the source of most of this magma is more than perhaps 40 mi (64 km) below the surface, which means that volcanic materials are simply representative of rock lying immediately beneath the outermost layers.

Much of this chapter deals with indirect methods used to obtain information about the earth's interior and draws upon a branch of the earth sciences known as *geophysics*. The

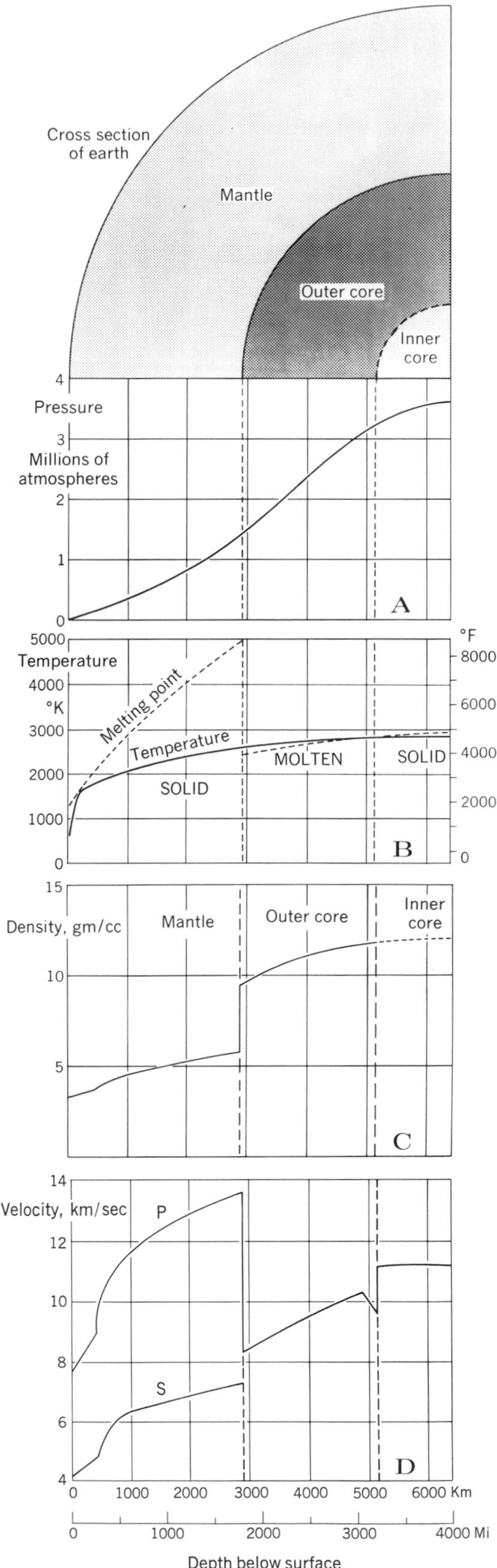


methods of geophysics combine principles of physics and mathematics with the use of sensitive and precise instruments in a scientific method differing strikingly from the direct-observation methods of the earlier naturalists and geologists.

## Pressures and temperatures in the earth's interior

All matter tends to be drawn or held together by gravitational attraction. In the case of the spherical earth gravitational attraction is directed approximately toward the earth's center of mass and gives the quality of weight to all substances. Weight of an object is a product of its mass, or quantity of matter in the object, and the acceleration of gravity, $g$ (Chapter 10). We may say that the weight of an object is equal to the force with which it presses vertically down upon a horizontal surface on which it is resting. At any particular level within the earth the *pressure* (force acting on a surface of given unit area) is equal to the weight of the column of rock lying above it. This force will therefore increase downward to the earth's center.

Because of the presence of surrounding rock, also under similar pressure, the actual pressure on a very small cube of rock is not only downward but also inward from the sides and upward from the bottom and constitutes *confining pressure.* In a gas or liquid yielding readily to change its shape, as the atmosphere and oceans do, the confining pressure is equal and balanced in all directions about a given point and is termed *hydrostatic pressure* (Chapter 12).

As examined at the earth's surface, rock appears to us to be strong and brittle, and we would expect that under great force it would shatter into fragments rather than flow as air or water does. However, under extremely great confining pressures and high temperatures rock can flow slowly like a thick tar and, if given enough time, will come to a state of rest in which the forces within it are perfectly balanced and therefore will be under true hydrostatic pressure.

In Chapter 21, confining pressures to depths of 25 mi (40 km) are given in units of kilobars and atmospheres. At slightly more than one-third of the distance to the earth's center the pressure is 1 million atmospheres, and at the very center it is about 3½ million atmospheres (Figure 23.1*A*). Matter at the earth's center has no weight because it is being attracted outward equally in all directions by the mass of the sphere that surrounds it. Nevertheless, the confining pressure is greatest here because the combined weight of the entire earth mass is directed toward that one point. Notice that rate of pressure increase falls off rapidly as the center is approached, as shown by a flattening of the pressure curve in Figure 23.1*A*.

The enormous confining pressures within the earth

**FIGURE 23.1.** (*A*) Increase in pressure with depth in the earth. (*B*) Increase in temperature with depth. (*C*) Increase in density with depth. (*D*) Velocity of P and S waves. [Data from J. Verhoogen (1960), *American Scientist,* vol. 48; and K. E. Bullen (1963), *An Introduction to the Theory of Seismology,* 3rd ed., Cambridge, Cambridge Univ. Press.]

are of great importance in determining the physical properties of the mineral matter and its behavior when unequal forces are applied.

Temperatures also increase greatly into the earth's interior. Measurements of rock temperature in mines and bore holes show that the rate of temperature rise, or *geothermal gradient,* averages about 1 F° per 50 ft (1 C° per 30 m) of depth. Rate of temperature increase observed near the surface falls off rapidly with depth. Estimates of temperatures from surface to center are shown by graph in Figure 23.1*B* and summarized in Table 23.1. Molten iron from a blast furnace reaches 3500° F (2000° C), and this is not far from representing the earth's interior temperatures. We shall return to the subject of the earth's internal heat at a later point in this chapter.

**TABLE 23.1. TEMPERATURES WITHIN THE EARTH**

| Depth | | Temperature | | |
|---|---|---|---|---|
| miles | kilometers | °F | °C | °K |
| 19 | 30 | 900 | 500 | 775 |
| 62 | 100 | 2000 | 1100 | 1375 |
| 125 | 200 | 2600 | 1400 | 1675 |
| 620 | 1000 | 3200 | 1700 | 1975 |
| 1900 | 3000 | 4200 | 2300 | 2275 |
| 3700 | 6000 | 4600 | 2500 | 2775 |

## The earth's mass and density

One clue to conditions within the earth is given by the astronomer, who has been able to measure the mass of the whole earth by use of Newton's laws of gravitation and mechanics. Mass is quantity of matter and is one of the fundamental properties of the physical universe. We cannot measure mass directly, but only through the force which it exerts owing to gravitational attraction.

Measurement of the earth's mass is relatively simple in principle, although precision determinations require elaborate precautions and refinements of the apparatus used. One simple approach we might consider is through the use of a pendulum of known mass. A second and larger known mass is brought close to one side of the pendulum mass. Mutual attraction between the two masses causes the pendulum mass to be moved slightly toward the larger mass (Figure 23.2*A*). The pendulum now assumes a position at rest, which is the resultant of the force of the earth's gravitational attraction and the force of attraction of the adjacent mass. The masses of earth and adjacent mass are thus in the same ratio as the two forces and could be calculated from measurements of the pendulum length and of the deflection of the pendulum mass. Unfortunately, the actual amount of pendulum deflection is so extremely minute as to be impossible to measure with the necessary degree of accuracy, so this method is not actually used.

One successful method of accurate determination of the earth's mass makes use of a beam balance of basically the same type used in laboratories for precision weighing, but much larger and sturdier in construction than the laboratory type (Figure 23.2*B*). The device is known as the *Poynting balance.* In the original experiment by Poynting a mass, $M_1$, weighing 330 lb (136 kg) was placed on one pan and exactly counterbalanced by weights placed in the other pan. Then a much larger mass, $M_2$, was placed under the plan containing the mass, $M_1$, with their centers of mass separated by a distance, *D*. Mutual attraction of the two masses pulled down their side of the balance, but this imbalance was corrected by the addition of small weights to the opposite pan until exact balance was again achieved. Thus a

**FIGURE 23.2.** (*A*) A simple pendulum theoretically permits the earth's mass to be measured. (*B*) The Poynting balance is a practical instrument for determining the earth's mass. (*C*) The Cavendish torsion balance. [After T. G. Mehlin (1959), *Astronomy,* New York, Wiley.]

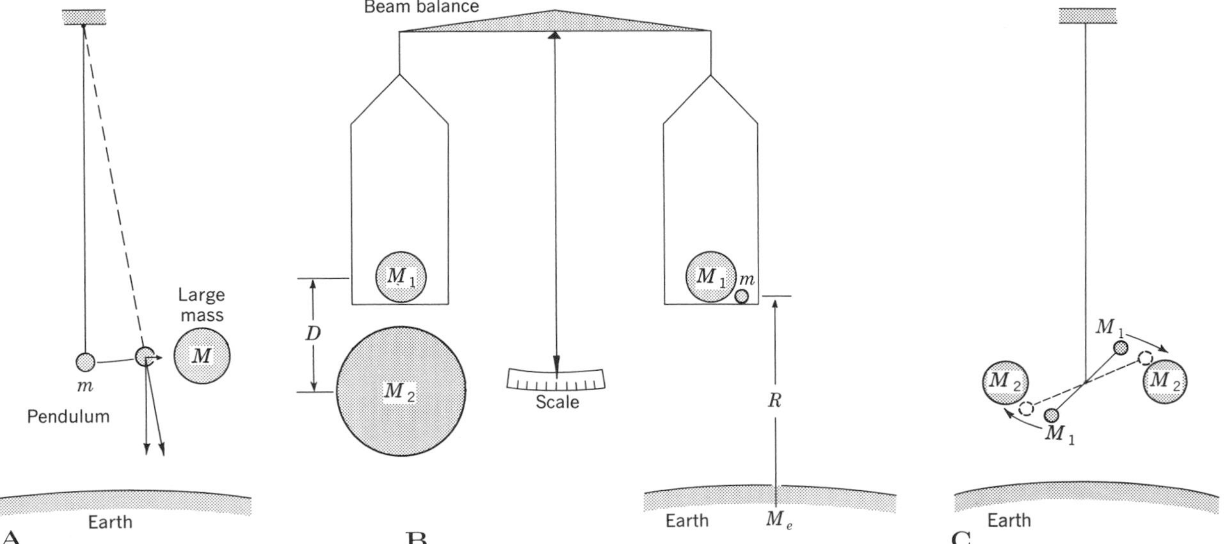

very small mass, *m*, counterbalanced the force of attraction between masses $M_1$ and $M_2$. Actually, it is the attraction between the earth, whose center is at distance *R*, and the small added mass, *m*, that exactly equals the mutual attraction of $M_1$ and $M_2$. Hence, using Newton's law of gravitation, we can write the equation

$$G\,\frac{M_1M_2}{D^2} = G\,\frac{M_em}{R^2}$$

The symbol *G* stands for the *universal gravitational constant*, but since the two *G* terms cancel out, we need not know the value of *G*. All the other terms are known except the earth's mass, $M_e$, thus by solving for $M_e$ we obtain the desired answer. Recent precision determinations give the mass of the earth as about $6.6 \times 10^{21}$ tons. A more nearly exact statement in metric units is $5.975 \times 10^{27}$ g.

Evaluation of the universal gravitational constant was made by Lord Cavendish in 1798, using a device known as the *torsion balance*. This evaluation enabled Cavendish to determine the mass of the earth. The torsion balance illustrated in Figure 23.2*C* consists of a delicate quartz fiber by which is suspended a balanced horizontal rod bearing a small sphere of platinum or gold at each end. From observations of the pendulum-like motion of the bar as it twists back and forth in a horizontal circle it is possible to calculate the force required to turn the bar through a given angular distance. Two large masses are then brought into place close to the two spheres and in the horizontal plane of their centers. Gravitational attraction between each sphere and the large mass adjacent to it causes the bar to be rotated by a very small amount from its initial position at rest. The magnitude of the attractional force can be calculated by the angle of deflection. The force of attraction is given by Newton's equation

$$F = G\,\frac{M_1M_2}{D^2}$$

Having measured the force, *F*, and knowing the masses, $M_1$ and $M_2$, and the separating distance, *D*, the value of *G* can be quickly calculated. When units of centimeters, grams, and seconds are used in the above equation, the value of *G* comes out to $6.€6 \times 10^{-8}$.

Using the known value of *G*, we can now calculate the earth's mass, $M_e$, from the equation

$$M_e = \frac{gR^2}{G}$$

where *g* is the acceleration of gravity (980 cm/sec/sec) and *R* is the earth's radius ($6.37 \times 10^8$ cm). The resulting earth mass is the same as given for the beam balance determination, namely $5.975 \times 10^{27}$ g.

We can compute the volume of the earth from its ellipsoid dimensions (Chapter 10), which comes out to $1.08 \times 10^{27}$ cc. Dividing mass by volume yields the average density of the earth as 5.53 g/cc. This figure is about twice the density of granite (2.6 g/cc). Iron, in comparison, has a density of nearly 8 g/cc. (Mean densities of the planets are given in Table 5.1.)

The geophysicist reasons that because the greater part of known rock of the earth's outermost zone is of the density of granite (2.6 g/cc) or of basalt (3.0 g/cc), which are much less than the average figure of 5.53 g/cc, density must increase greatly toward the earth's center (Figure 23.1*C*). The most reasonable conclusion is that there exists a core of high density, about 11.0 g/cc. The core is usually considered to be composed largely of iron, because if iron were compressed in the earth's center under 2 to 3 million atmospheres of pressure, it would decrease in volume and thereby undergo a density increase from 8.0 to 11.0 g/cc.

Independent supporting evidence for an iron core is found in the composition of meteorites, one class of which is composed of iron. This evidence is discussed in Chapter 31.

Between the outermost layer and the earth's core, density must range somewhere between 4.0 and 6.0 g/cc. A rock that fits this requirement is dunite, an ultra-mafic rock composed largely of olivine (see Chapter 21). Its density is normally about 3.3 g/cc, but would be increased to an acceptable value under the known confining pressures.

## Earthquakes and faults

The most important evidence about the nature of the earth's interior, and particularly about the actual depths at which the composition and properties change, comes from the science of *seismology*, a branch of geophysics dealing with earthquake waves. To understand how earthquake waves give evidence about the earth's interior requires that we first consider how earthquakes are generated and how they are recorded.

The earthquake is known to humans directly as a trembling or shaking of the ground, commonly barely perceptible to the senses, but sometimes so violent as to crack or collapse strong buildings, break water and gas mains, cause gaping cracks in the ground, and thus bring great loss of life and property. The important problem at hand is the nature of the earthquake waves, or *seismic waves*, and their interpretation from the records of the *seismograph*, a sensitive instrument that can record earthquakes thousands of miles distant. A seismograph can detect small vibrations that could not possibly be recognized by the human senses. The records of seismic waves that have passed through the earth's interior regions provide the evidence we seek.

The vast majority of important earthquakes that can be analyzed at long distances from their sources are produced by a type of movement in the earth's crust termed *faulting*. This phenomenon is simply a sudden slippage between two rock masses separated by a fracture surface (Figure 23.3). We see small-scale demonstrations of faulting in common materials such as dry soil, concrete, or rock, which fracture when compressed or when the underlying support is removed—for example, cracks in pavements, sidewalks, or masonry walls. At first the material withstands the forces that tend to bend or twist it, but when the limit of strength is reached, the material suddenly cracks, releasing the strain by a mass displacement in which the mass on one side slips past the other.

Highly indurated rocks of the earth's outermost layers are both strong and brittle, as judged by standards of the materials we see about us. Under great deforming

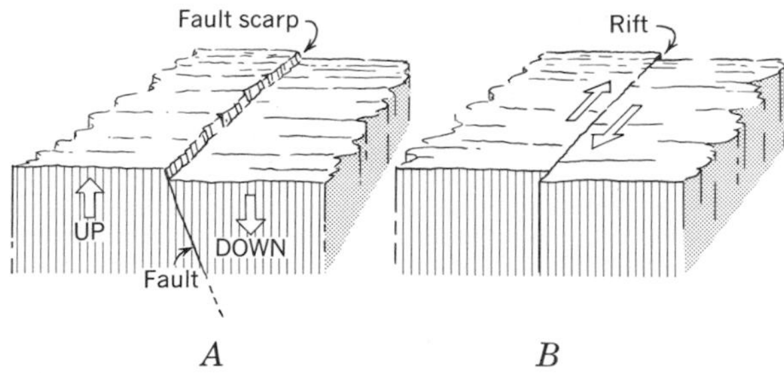


**FIGURE 23.3.** (*A*) Normal fault. (*B*) Transcurrent, or strike-slip fault.

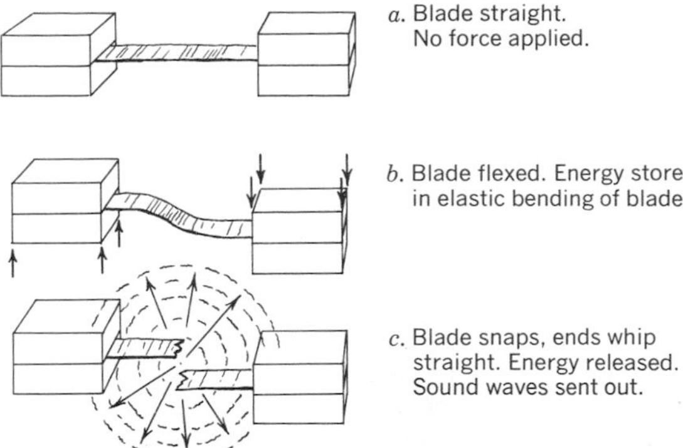


**FIGURE 23.4.** A steel blade, bent until it snaps, illustrates certain basic features of the earthquake mechanism.

stress[1] rock actually bends elastically like steel, but in an amount scarcely detectable in small masses. Despite its ability to withstand great stress with only slight bending, or *strain,* a given rock has an *elastic limit.* If it is strained beyond this limit, a fracture occurs and the bent rock snaps suddenly back to its normal shape.

An earthquake is the disturbance set off by the sudden release of elastic strain. As in a bow slowly bent, the rocks have gradually accumulated energy, only to release it with great suddenness. More will be said in Chapter 26 about the possible origins of forces that produce faulting. It must suffice here to state that there are certain mountain-making belts of the earth's outer layers in which faulting occurs repeatedly as enormous masses of rock are pushed past one another, or over one another, generating countless shocks.

A simple model of a mechanism of earthquakes can be made with a strip of tempered steel, such as a coping saw blade, whose ends are tightly clamped in wooden blocks (Figure 23.4). If the blocks are forced to move parallel with one another to produce an S-bend in the blade, the blade can be bent slowly to the breaking point. When the blade snaps, the broken ends whip back into straight pieces, but the ends are now considerably offset. The twang of the break is equivalent to the earth tremor. This model illustrates the *elastic-rebound theory* of earthquake origin. The theory was proved beyond doubt as the explanation of major earthquakes by actual measurements of bending of the ground on either side of a known line of faulting both before and after the great San Francisco earthquake of 1906. Two scientists of the University of California at Berkeley rechecked, by precise geodetic surveying methods, the exact positions of several triangulation stations (see Chapter 11) on mountain peaks on both sides of the San Andreas fault that runs through San Francisco and on which the slip had taken place (see Figure 23.6). They found that after the earthquake the ground lying close to the fault line had moved most, with a gradually decreasing amount of movement away from the fault (Figure 23.5). The maximum measured displacement along the fault was 21 ft (6.4 m).

The slow bending was accumulating stored energy for hundreds of years before the earthquake occurred, and the rocks were already bent almost to their elastic limit when the first triangulation surveys were made. Slow bending was still in progress between 1851 and 1906, as shown in Figure 23.5. Then in 1906 the rock suddenly snapped to a new position, releasing a tremendous quantity of energy in a series of seismic waves. These spread rapidly away from the fault line, dying out gradually with increasing distance.

**Transcurrent faults and normal faults** Faults of the type that produced the San Francisco earthquake involve a geometry of displacement in which most of the motion of one block with respect to the other is in the horizontal direction. Such a fault is named a *transcurrent fault,* or *strike-slip fault* (Figure 23.3). A fresh break produced in the ground surface by fault motion accompanying the San Francisco earthquake is pictured in Figure 23.6.

Transcurrent faults on a large scale are well represented in the state of California, where they form

**FIGURE 23.5.** An earthquake results from the sudden release of elastic strain that has been accumulated in rock over a long period of time.

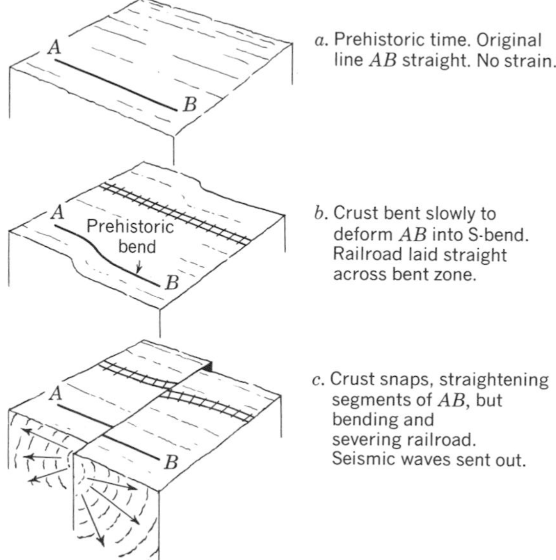


[1] *Stress* is strictly defined as force per unit of surface area. The two words "force" and "stress" can usually be used interchangeably in descriptive statements without regard to a strict difference in meaning.

**FIGURE 23.6.** A fresh scarp produced by horizontal movement during the California earthquake of April 18, 1906. The fault plane cuts a sloping hillside. The area beyond the scarp moved to the right. The main line of the San Andreas fault between Olema and Point Reyes Station, Marin County, California. (Photograph by G. K. Gilbert, U.S. Geological Survey.)

dominant geologic elements. Longest and best known is the San Andreas fault, nearly 600 mi (950 km) long, which can be traced from the Salton Basin, along the foot of San Bernardino Range of southern California, northward continuously to the San Francisco Bay region, where the fault passes out to sea. Movement occurs locally from time to time along the transcurrent faults of California, generating earthquakes of greatly varying intensity. Horizontal movement along these faults is strikingly illustrated by the offsetting of such linear features as roads, fences, pipe lines, and orchard rows (Figure 23.5).

A major transcurrent fault, such as the San Andreas fault, produces a conspicuous *rift zone,* which in places is a straight trench occupied by small lakes or by segments of streams (Figure 23.7). Where a stream has flowed across the fault line for a long period of time during which repeated movements have occurred, the stream may show a marked offset where it has turned to follow the rift for a short distance in order to maintain flow to the displaced downstream portion of its channel. Where a transcurrent fault cuts across hilly or mountainous terrain, imposing *fault scarps* (abrupt steps) may result, because the two parts of a mountain mass are moved past one another, exposing the fault plane (Figure 23.8).

Earthquakes may also be generated by movements on normal faults (Figure 23.3). A particularly good example was the Hebgen earthquake, which occurred in 1959 in Montana. As a result of a single fault displacement, a scarp several feet high was produced instantaneously (see Figure 26.4).

## Earthquake energy

Interpretation of seismograms has made possible a calculation of the quantities of energy released as wave motion by earthquakes of various magnitudes. In 1935

**FIGURE 23.7.** The San Andreas rift zone in the Temblor Range of central California takes the form of a straight valley. View southeast through Palo Prieto Pass with Grant Lake in foreground. (Copyright Spence Air Photograph.)

a leading seismologist, Charles F. Richter, brought forth a scale of earthquake magnitudes describing the quantity of energy released at the earthquake focus. The *Richter scale* consists of numbers ranging from 0 to 8.6. The scale is logarithmic, which is to say that the energy of the shock increases by powers of ten in relation to Richter magnitude numbers. Some data concerning various magnitudes is given below:

| Magnitude, Richter scale | |
|---|---|
| 0 | Smallest detectable quake. Energy release $6.3 \times 10^5$ ergs. |
| 2.5–3 | Quake can be felt if it is nearby. About 100,000 shallow quakes of this magnitude per year. |
| 4.5 | Can cause local damage. |
| 5 | Energy release about equal to first atomic bomb, Alamagordo, New Mexico, 1945. |
| 6 | Destructive in a limited area. About 100 shallow quakes per year of this magnitude. |
| 7 | Rated a major earthquake above this magnitude. Quake can be recorded over whole earth. About 14 per year this great or greater. |
| 7.8 | San Francisco earthquake of 1906. Energy release $3.3 \times 10^{24}$ ergs. |
| 8.4 | Close to maximum known. Energy release $2 \times 10^{25}$ ergs. Examples: Honshu 1933, Assam 1950, Alaska 1964. |
| 8.6 | Maximum observed between 1900 and 1950. Three million times as much energy released as in first atomic bomb. |

Total annual energy release by earthquakes is roughly on the order of $10 \times 10^{26}$ ergs, most of it being from a very few quakes of magnitude greater than 7.

## Earthquake effects

The actual destructiveness of an earthquake also depends upon factors other than the energy release given by Richter magnitude—for example, closeness to the *epicenter* (the surface point directly above the focus of the earthquake) and nature of the subsurface earth materials. *Intensity scales,* designed to measure observed earth-shaking effects, are important in engineering aspects of seismology.

An intensity scale used extensively in the United States is the *modified Mercalli scale* as prepared by C. F. Richter in 1956. Previously, the *Rossi-Forel* intensity scale was in use in this country and remains in use in other parts of the world. The modified Mercalli scale of 1956 recognizes 12 levels of intensity, designated by Roman numerals I through XII. Each intensity is described in terms of phenomena that any person might experience. For example, at intensity IV hanging objects swing, a vibration like that of a passing truck is felt, standing automobiles rock, and windows and dishes rattle. Damage to various classes of masonry is used to establish criteria in the higher numbers of the scale (Figure 23.9). At an intensity of XII, damage to man-made structures is nearly total and large masses of rock are displaced. A detailed listing of phenomena associated with each intensity level is beyond the scope of this discussion.

Many of the destructive effects of a severe earthquake are secondary, in the sense that the earthquake movements set off gravity movements of bodies of rock, soil, and alluvial overburden. An example is the Good Friday Earthquake of March 27, 1964, centered about 75 mi (120 km) from the city of Anchorage, Alaska. Magnitude on the Richter scale was 8.4 to 8.6, which is close to the maximum known. Intensity on the Mercalli scale was probably VII to VIII in Anchorage, but, as most buildings were of frame construction, damage was largely through secondary effects. Of these the most important were landslides of great masses of gravel overlying layers of unstable clay (Figure 23.10). Major snowslides were set off in the adjacent mountains.

**FIGURE 23.8.** Trace of the San Andreas fault across the Indio Hills, Riverside County, southern California. View is northwest. (Copyright Spence Air Photograph.)

**FIGURE 23.9.** Severe masonry damage produced by the San Francisco earthquake and fire of 1906. View is southwest from the corner of Geary and Mason streets. (Photograph by W. C. Mendenhall, U.S. Geological Survey.)

Throughout the region of the Alaskan earthquake sudden changes of land level, both up and down, took place at points as far distant as 300 mi (480 km) from the epicenter and covered a total area of about 80,000 sq mi (200,000 sq km). A belt of uplift reaching a maximum of 30 ft (10 m) runs parallel with the coast and largely offshore, while a broad zone of shallow subsidence, reaching amounts somewhat more than −6 ft (−2 m) lies along the landward side of the uplift zone (Figure 23.11). The epicenter lay between these zones. Sudden rise of the sea floor produced a train of seismic sea waves, a phenomenon described in following paragraphs.

The supposed fault along which slippage occurred to generate the Alaska earthquake is not exposed on land, but presumably lies at depth in the offshore zone in a position between the zone of subsidence and the zone of uplift. The entire zone of seismic activity occupies a position between the Aleutian volcanic arc on the northwest and the deep submarine Aleutian trench on the southeast. The significance of these larger crustal structures is discussed in Chapter 25.

## Seismic sea waves, or tsunamis

An extraordinary kind of ocean wave not related to wind or tide is the *seismic sea wave,* or *tsunami,* produced by a sudden displacement of the sea floor. The

FIGURE 23.10. Slumping and flowage of unconsolidated sediments, resulting in property destruction at Anchorage, Alaska, Good Friday earthquake of March 27, 1964. (U.S. Army Corps of Engineers photograph.)

displacement may be caused by a submarine landslide set off by faulting, a sudden rising or sinking of a rock mass when faulting occurs, or a submarine volcanic eruption. The effect is very much like that of dropping a stone into a very shallow quiet pond. A series of simple oscillatory progressive waves is sent outward in concentric rings (Figure 23.12).

FIGURE 23.11. Map of south-central Alaska showing crustal uplift and subsidence associated with the Good Friday earthquake of March 27, 1964. Contours in meters. Profile and structure section below are drawn through the epicenter along a NW–SE line (AA'). [Redrawn and simplified from G. Plafker (1965), *Science,* vol. 148, p. 1677, Figure 2, and p. 1681, Figure 6.]

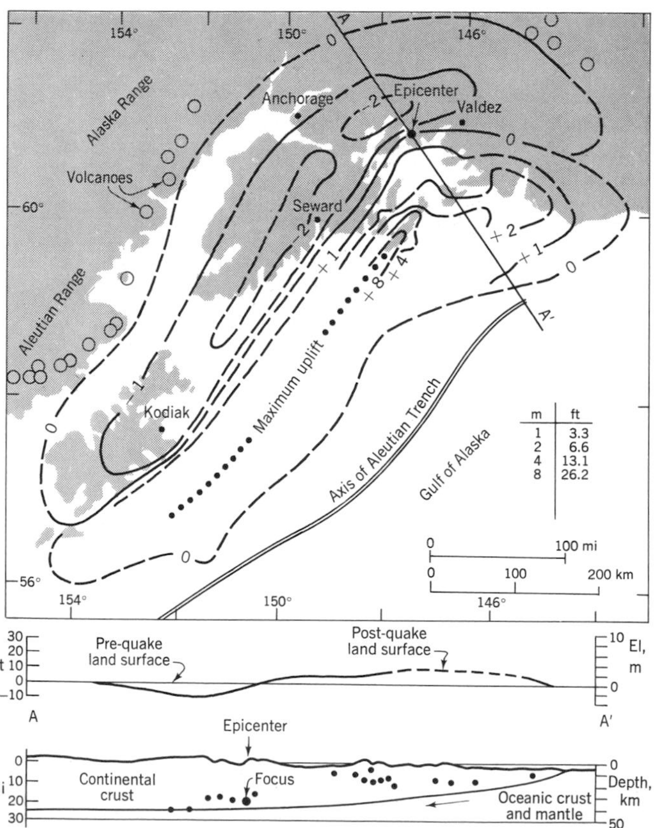


Seismic sea waves are of enormous length, some 60 to 120 mi (100 to 200 km), compared with wind waves and swell, whereas the wave height may be only 1 to 2 ft (0.3 to 0.6 m). Assuming a wave 1 foot high and 100 miles long, the steepness ratio would be 1/528,000, which is extremely low. Such a wave would not be felt by persons on a ship on the open sea.

Seismic sea waves have periods of 10–30 minutes, which is a vastly longer period than even a long swell (20 seconds). To obtain some idea of the velocity of a seismic sea wave, we may imagine it to have a length of 100 miles and a period of 20 minutes. Thus three waves, each 100 miles long, will pass a fixed point each

FIGURE 23.12. Map of the Pacific Ocean showing the locations of a tsunami wave front at one-hour intervals, GMT. The wave originated in the Gulf of Alaska as a result of the Good Friday earthquake of March 27, 1964. [After B. W. Wilson and A. Torum (1968), U.S. Army Corps of Engineers, *Tech Memorandum No. 25,* Washington, D.C., Coastal Engineering Research Center, p. 38, Figure 27.]

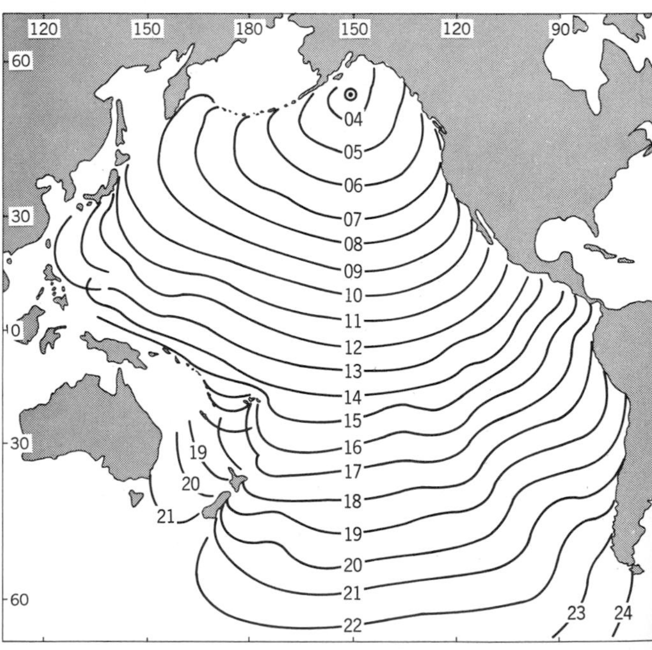

hour. This means a velocity of 300 mi (480 km) per hour.

Seismic sea waves are very long in comparison with the depth of water in which they travel. For example, a 100-mile wave length is roughly 33 times as great as an ocean depth of 3 miles. In such comparatively shallow water the velocity of travel of the simple oscillatory wave varies as the square root of the water depth. Therefore, if we know the time at which the wave was sent out (this information is available from earthquake records) and the time at which the wave arrived at a distant coast, we may calculate roughly the depth of ocean water lying between. Just such a procedure was used in 1856 to estimate the average depth of the Pacific Ocean, long before soundings were available to give direct measurements.

On the other hand seismologists now issue warnings of possible destructive seismic sea waves, using the known depths of the ocean and the known instant of the earthquakes as a basis for computing the time the first waves will reach a given coast (Figure 23.12).

A particularly destructive train of seismic sea waves occurred in the Pacific Ocean on March 3, 1933, providing a good example of the phenomenon. The waves were produced by an earthquake centered beneath the ocean floor at a place 300 mi (480 km) northeast of Tokyo (lat. 39° N., long. 144° E.). The wave train first reached the Japanese shore in ½ hour, Yokohama in 2 hours, Honolulu in 7½ hours, San Francisco in 10⅓ hours, and Iquique, Chile, in 22 hours. On exposed parts of the Japanese coast, where deep water lies close to shore, the waves rose as high as 30 ft (9 m), causing destruction and death in lowlying areas. In May 1960 seismic sea waves generated by an earthquake in Chile spread across the entire Pacific Ocean, causing heavy surf damage and great loss of life at coastal locations in Hawaii, Japan, Okinawa, New Zealand and Alaska.

The individual wave crest takes the form of a slow rise in water level over a period of 10–15 minutes. Superimposed on this are ordinary wind waves. These waves break close to shore, producing a destructive surf which demolishes houses and trees (Figure 23.13).

**FIGURE 23.13.** This great surf was set up by arrival of the second wave of a tsunami on April 1, 1946, at Kawela Bay on the north coast of Oahu, Hawaii. Normally the body of water in this view is a quiet lagoon behind a protecting coral reef. (Photograph by F. P. Shepard, Scripps Institution of Oceanography.)

The first evidence of a seismic wave may, however, be the lowering of water level, causing a seaward withdrawal of the water line and exposing the floors of shallow bays. This is what seems to have happened at Lisbon, Portugal, on November 1, 1755, following an earthquake centered off the Portuguese coast. The sight of the exposed sea floor attracted a large number of townspeople to examine the strange state of affairs. When the following wave crest arrived, the rapid rise of water level drowned many persons.

Several great catastrophes in recorded history seem to have been wrought by seismic sea waves. For example, flooding of the Japanese coast in 1703, with a loss of more than 100,000 lives, may have been of this cause. One should not confuse the seismic sea waves with coastal flooding caused by storm surges.

## The seismograph

In recording an earthquake and analyzing the directions and amounts of the earth motions involved, the mechanical problem is that the instrument itself must be resting on the ground and will therefore also move with the ground. Because the instrument cannot be physically separated from the earth, the seismograph designer must make use of the principle of inertia to overcome the effect of the attachment. *Inertia* is the tendency of any mass to resist a change in a state of rest or of uniform motion in a straight line. The greater the mass of the object, the greater its inertia.

To record an earthquake, then, a very heavy mass, such as an iron ball, might be suspended from a very thin wire or from a flexible coil spring, as shown in Figure 23.14. When the earth moves back and forth or up and down in earthquake wave motion, the large mass will stay almost motionless because the supporting wire or spring flexes easily and does not transmit the motion through to the weight. If a pen is now attached to the mass, so that the point is just touching a sheet of paper wrapped around a moving drum, the pen will produce a wavy line on the paper. Strong shocks will give waves of high *amplitude* (distance from the rest position to a peak or trough), and weak shocks will give waves of low amplitude. When the number of back and forth movements per second (i.e., the *frequency*) is higher, the undulations of the line will be more closely crowded.

The seismograph as thus far described is too simple to be actually workable. In the first place the movement of the ground is so very small that the motion must be greatly magnified if it is to produce a record suitable for study. This magnification may be done by a light ray and a mirror. We know that a small pocket mirror can be used to reflect a spot of sunlight onto the wall of a distant house and that a very slight twist of the hand causes the spot of light to jump many feet. In the seismograph a mirror may be attached to the heavy weight and a very tiny light beam reflected from it onto photographic paper that is attached to the slowly moving drum (Figure 23.15). Of course, either the

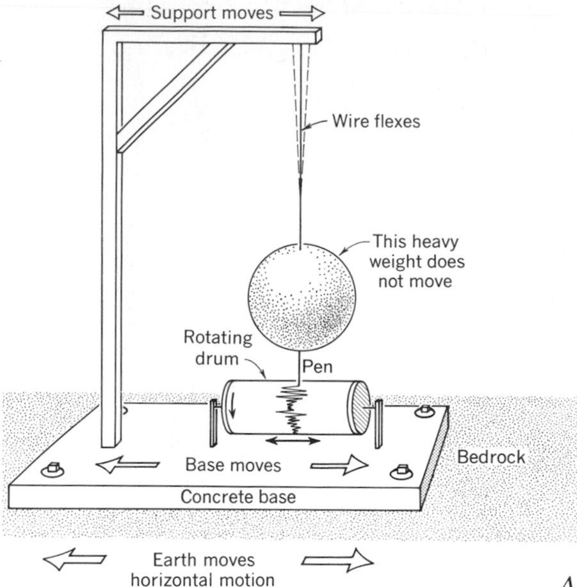


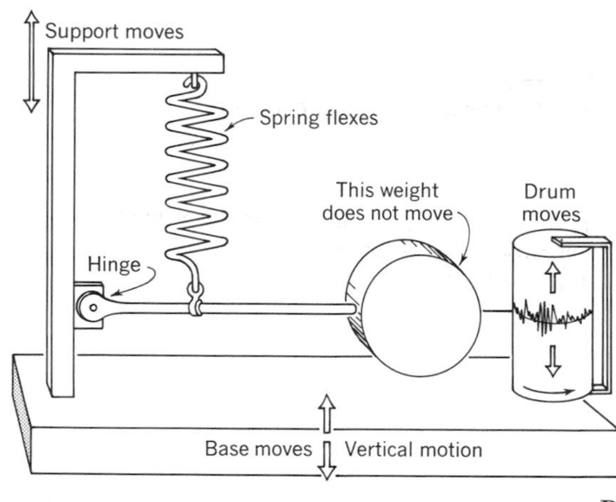


FIGURE 23.14. Inertia of a large mass provides a means of observing seismic waves. Horizontal motions might be detected by the mechanical arrangement shown in *A*, and vertical motions by that shown in *B*. Neither device would actually be useful unless further refined.

room is darkened or the instrument is enclosed, so that the pinpoint of light exposes a line on the photographic paper. Later removed and developed, this paper becomes a record of the earthquake known as a *seismogram.*

A second difficulty with the simple apparatus first described is that the earthquake waves rise and fall very slowly, each back-and-forth movement of the ground taking several seconds. The wire from which the heavy weight is suspended would have to be at least 75 ft (23 m) long, otherwise the weight—acting as a simple pendulum—would be set to swinging at about the same frequency as the waves or faster, and no record would be produced. To make a practical seismograph, the weight can be hung from a support hinged like a gate,

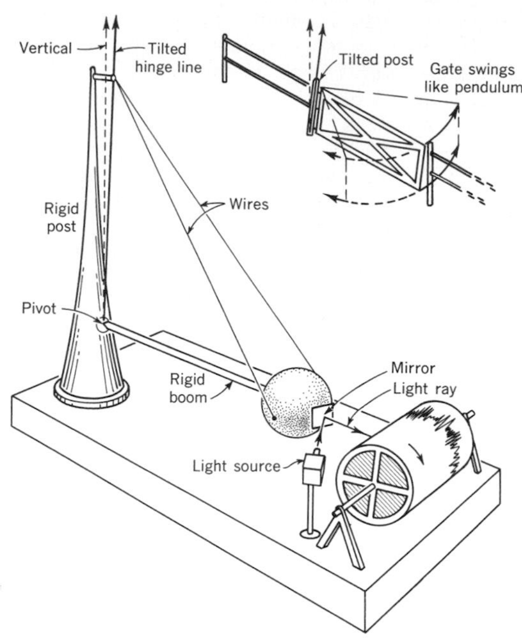


**FIGURE 23.15.** Principle of a horizontal, hinge-type pendulum seismograph. Earth motions are greatly magnified by use of a light ray reflected from a mirror.

as shown in Figure 23.15. When the gatepost is tilted slightly, the gate will swing slowly, like a pendulum with a very long wire.

A third difficulty is that any pendulum tends to continue to swing at a natural frequency depending on its length. Because a record of these pendulum movements would tend to obscure the earthquake movements it is necessary to add a mechanism to *damp* the pendulum, that is, to prevent it from swinging at its own natural frequency.

Modern seismographs make use of magnetic and electronic devices to pick up, amplify, filter, and record the motions of the earth, just as the modern high-fidelity phonograph uses a magnetic pickup, transistorized amplifier, and magnetic loudspeaker instead of the old-style mechanical pickup head and horn.

To analyze earthquakes adequately, a whole battery of seismographs must be operated simultaneously (Figure 23.16), because each instrument records only the wave motion in one particular line of movement, such as east-west, north-south, or vertically. Then too, earthquake waves include a wide range of frequencies superimposed in a complex way. Just as with a radio receiver, each seismograph is tuned to receive a particular frequency band, therefore several are needed to register the full range.

**Interpreting the seismogram** Having now examined the principle of the seismograph, we turn to the interpretation of the wave record, or seismogram (Figure 23.17). Between earthquakes the seismogram shows a continuous record of very small waves called *microseisms*

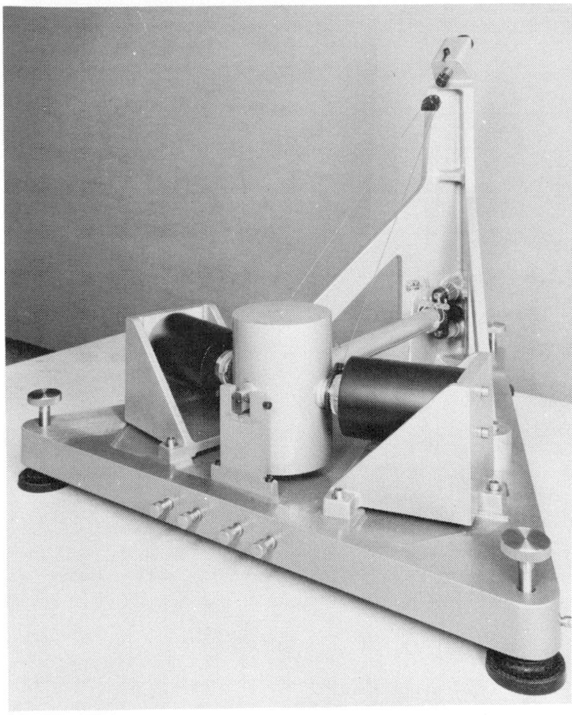

B

A

**FIGURE 23.16.** (*A*) A horizontal seismograph for detecting long-period seismic waves. Mechanism is basically of the design illustrated in Figure 23.15. (*B*) A vertical seismometer for measuring long-period seismic waves. (Courtesy of the Lamont-Doherty Geological Observatory of Columbia University.)

which are made by atmospheric disturbances or causes other than those that generate true earthquakes.

The first indication that a severe earthquake has occurred at a distant point is the sudden beginning of a series of larger-than-average waves called the *primary waves* (P-waves). These waves die down somewhat, then a few minutes later a second burst of activity sets in with the beginning of the *secondary waves* (S-waves). These waves are usually somewhat larger in height than the primary waves. There follow smooth waves that increase greatly in amplitude to a maximum and then slowly die down. These last very high amplitude waves are the *surface waves.* While the primary and secondary waves have traveled through the earth, the surface waves have traveled along the ground surface much as storm swells travel over the sea surface (Figure 23.18).

For an earthquake occurring one quarter of the globe's circumference away (that is, 90 degrees of arc distant, or 10,000 km), the primary waves will take about 13 minutes to reach the receiving station, and the secondary waves will begin to arrive about 11 minutes later.

It was soon apparent to the first students of seis-

**FIGURE 23.17.** This seismogram shows the record of an earthquake whose epicenter was located at a surface distance of 5260 mi (8460 km) from the receiving station, equivalent to 76.4 degrees of arc of the earth's circumference. Figure 23.18 shows the ray paths for this earthquake. [After L. Don Leet (1950), *Earth Waves,* Cambridge, Mass., Harvard Univ. Press.]

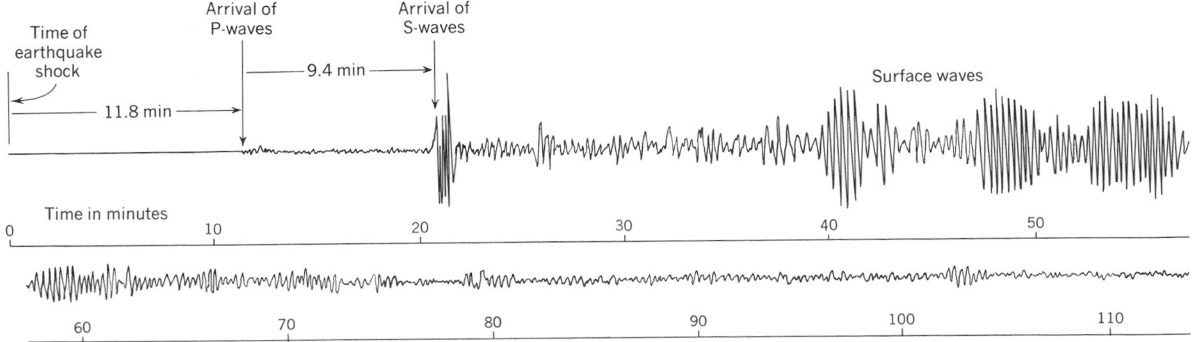

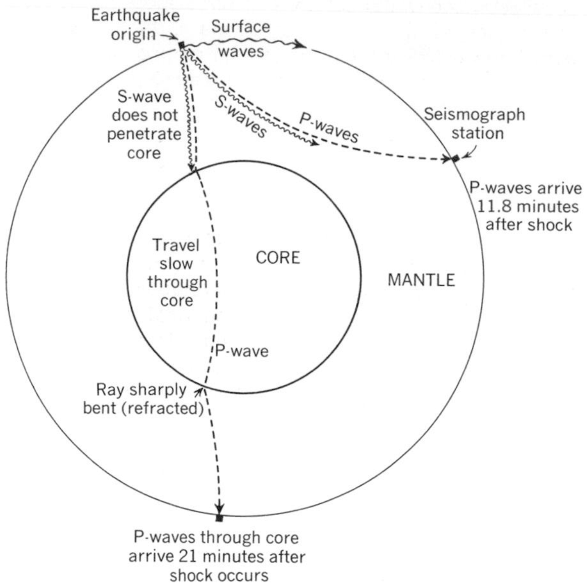

**FIGURE 23.18.** Cross section of the earth showing diagrammatically the paths of P-waves, S-waves, and surface waves. [After L. Don Leet (1950), *Earth Waves,* Cambridge, Mass., Harvard Univ. Press.]

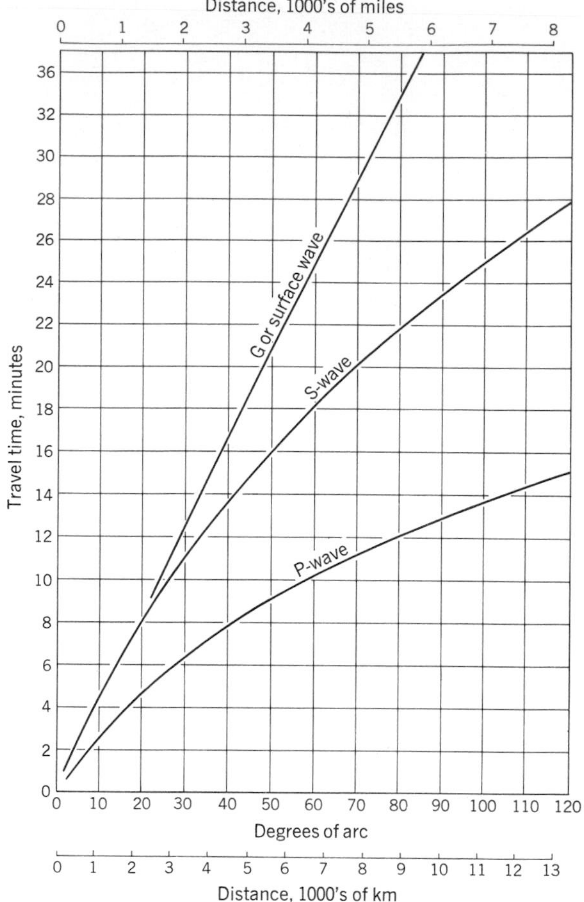


**FIGURE 23.19.** Travel-time curves for earthquakes of 100-km (60-mi) depth of focus. [Based on data of C. F. Richter (1958), *Elementary Seismology,* San Francisco, W. H. Freeman and Co., Appendix VIII.]

mograms that the farther away the earthquake center, or *focus,* the longer the spread of time between the arrival of the primary and secondary wave groups. Both groups start from the focus at the same instant, but the primary group travels faster. Likewise the surface waves travel slowly and come in last. From this discovery, about 1900, came the obvious conclusion that the spread of time between arrival of the wave groups can be used to measure the distance from the focus to the seismograph station.

Figure 23.19 is a graph on which are plotted *travel-time curves* for primary waves and secondary waves. The difference in times of arrival of the primary and secondary waves, read from the graph as the vertical separation of the two curves, corresponds to distance from focus to seismograph, measured along a great circle on the earth's surface. Units of measure are given in both kilometers and degrees of arc.

In the seismogram shown in Figure 23.17, the difference in arrival times of primary and secondary waves in 9.4 minutes. As indicated by a dashed line on Figure 23.18, this time difference corresponds to a distance of 5260 mi (8465 km), or an arc of 76.4°.

Using the figure of distance derived from the travel-time curves, a circle of that radius can be drawn on a globe to show the focus of all possible points of origin of the earthquake. When three such circles are drawn from three widely separated observing stations, the earthquake focus can be located within the limits of a small triangle of error (Figure 23.20).

**Varieties of earthquake waves** When an earthquake shock occurs, several basically different kinds of wave motion are generated. One type, which forms the primary waves, is the same kind of motion as observed in sound waves. As illustrated in Figure 23.21, particles transmitting the primary wave form move only forward and backward in the direction of wave travel. This motion is described as *compression* and *rarefaction* and constitutes a *longitudinal wave,* commonly designated the *P-wave.* We can remember this relation by thinking of the P-wave as a "push" wave. This is easy to keep in mind because the words "primary" and "push" both begin with "P."

In waves of the secondary group, particles transmitting the waves move back and forth at right angles to the direction of wave travel (Figure 23.21). Consequently the secondary wave motion is termed a *transverse wave,* commonly designated the *S-wave.* We may think of these waves as "shake" waves, because like "secondary" the key word begins with "S." In the earth, P-waves travel approximately 1.7 times as rapidly as S-waves.

Surface waves are of a still different type and are analogous to waves on water. They were first analyzed mathematically by the English physicist Lord Rayleigh and are therefore known as *Rayleigh waves.* To visualize the motion in Rayleigh waves, refer to Figure

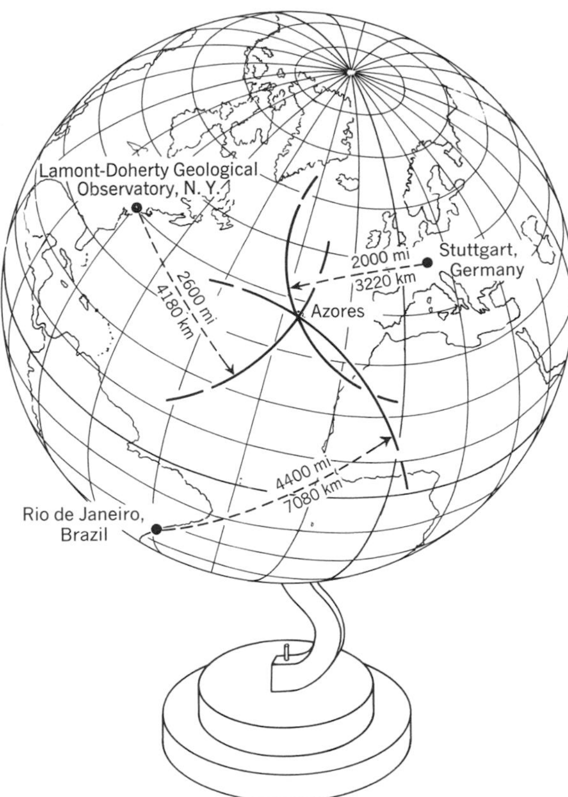


**FIGURE 23.20.** Circles drawn from three seismological observatories yield the location of an earthquake epicenter.

17.2, which shows particle motion in water waves. One difference is that in Rayleigh waves particles move in retrograde orbits. Surface waves of earthquake origin are, of course, extremely low in height in comparison with common ocean waves, but are similar in that they die out very rapidly with depth below the ground surface. More recently a different type of wave, named the *Love wave* after the physicist who discovered it, has been found to make up a part of the surface wave motion. Love waves have a horizontal motion only, rather than the combination of vertical and horizontal motions of the Rayleigh waves.

**FIGURE 23.21.** Diagrammatic representation of particle motions in longitudinal and transverse seismic waves.

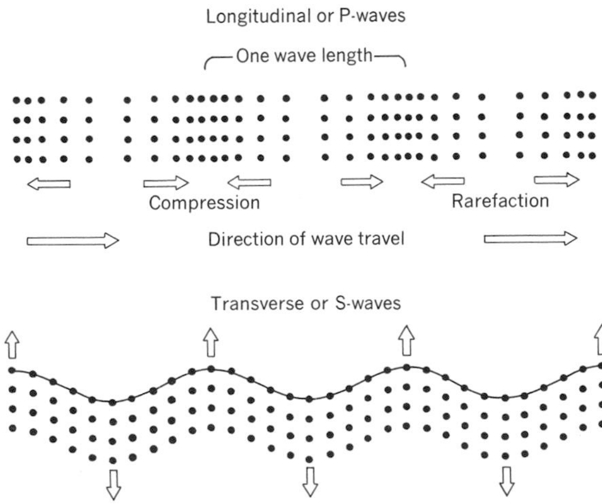


## The earth's core

The main line of thought in this chapter concerns the nature of the earth's interior, far beyond the limits of any direct examination. Study of earthquake waves has confirmed the existence of a spherical *core* at the earth's center and has added insight into its physical nature in the following way: If the earth were in a solid state entirely throughout, the P-waves and S-waves would travel through the center in all possible directions, and the various shock waves of any large earthquake could be recorded by a seismograph located directly opposite on the globe.

It was soon found, however, that there is a large region on the side of the globe opposite the earthquake focus where simple S-waves are not received. Evidently they are prevented from passing through a central region, or core, in the earth (Figures 23.18 and 23.22). Physicists know that transverse waves, or S-waves, cannot be sent through a liquid; hence they have agreed that the earth's core is in a liquid state in contrast to the surrounding *mantle,* which is in a solid state. "Solid" in this case may mean either crystalline or glassy, as defined in Chapter 21. "Solid" also means here that the rock behaves as an elastic solid when subjected to the sudden twists and bends of earthquake waves.

**FIGURE 23.22.** Diagrammatic representation of many possible ray paths from a single earthquake source. [After B. Gutenberg (1951), *Internal Constitution of the Earth,* New York, Dover.]

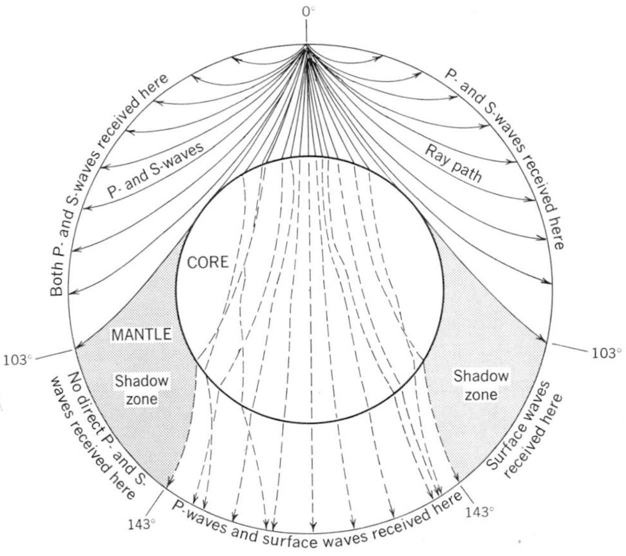

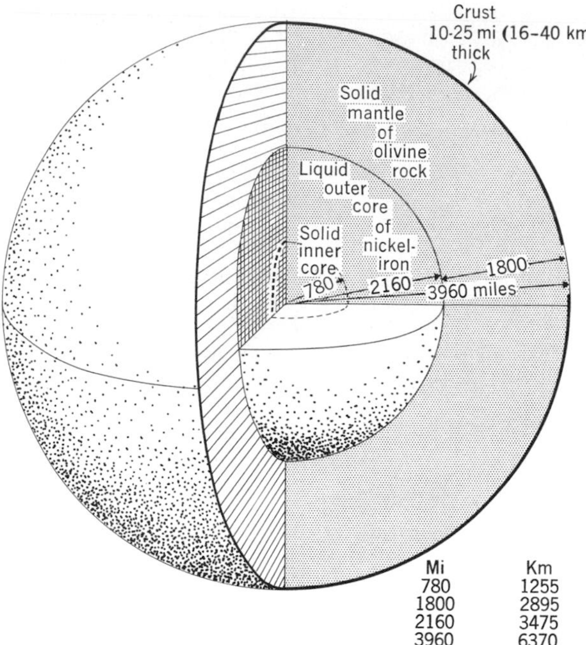


**FIGURE 23.23.** Principal zones of the earth's interior. (© 1960, John Wiley & Sons, New York.)

As shown in Figure 23.22, S-waves are received only within a distance of about 103 degrees of arc from the earthquake source. This arc covers somewhat more than one hemisphere. Because of wave bending as the P-waves travel through the core, there is a zone between 103° and 143° distant from the focus where no direct P-waves or S-waves are received, but only surface waves and complex reflected waves. This is the *shadow zone.* A zone beyond 143° receives only P-waves passing through the core, complex reflected waves, and surface waves.

From the extent of the shadow zone the earth's core is calculated to have a radius of 2160 mi (3475 km), a little more than half of the earth's total radius (Figure 23.23). That the boundary of the core is fairly definite is known because the P-waves are sharply bent at the boundary and their speed drops abruptly to almost half.

Using the density information already discussed, we may conclude that the outer region of the core is composed of liquid iron of great density, under enormous pressure, and at a high temperature. Obviously it is quite impossible for us to imagine what this material is like in terms of our own sensory experiences, principally because the confining pressures of 2 to 3 million atmospheres would give the liquid metal physical properties unlike anything we can examine at the earth's surface. Although laboratory experiments on the rigidity of rock and speed of earthquake waves have used confining pressures up to 12,000 atmospheres, this pressure is equivalent to a depth of only about 25 mi (40 km).

More recently, evidence from earthquake seismology has revealed that the inner part of the core, to a radius of about 780 mi (1255 km), behaves differently from the rest of the core. This behavior suggests a solid state, rather than the liquid state of the outer core.

## The mantle

Another principle of seismology that can be put to use to reveal the nature of the earth's interior is that earthquake waves, both P and S types, travel faster through highly rigid material than through less rigid material. First, however, the meaning of *rigidity* must be made clear.[2] This word applies only to elastic materials—those which bend out of shape when unequal pressures are applied, but which spring back to their original forms when pressures are released. Rigidity is the resistance of an elastic body to a change of shape. Steel and rubber are both elastic, but steel has a much greater rigidity because it bends very much less than rubber under the same deforming stress.

Rocks in general have a high degree of rigidity, whether composed of crystallized or glassy mineral matter, but among the different rocks there is quite a marked variation. Rigidity can be measured by the physicist in the laboratory, not only under the conditions at the earth's surface, but also under great confining pressures and high temperatures such as those which might be expected many miles deep in the earth.

Because the rigidity of rocks determines the velocity of earthquake waves and because the velocity of these waves at various depths can be calculated from seismograms, it is possible to make a good guess concerning the kinds of rock in the earth's mantle.

Figure 23.1*D* shows the changes in velocity of P-waves and S-waves with increasing depth in the earth. Notice that the P-wave curve makes an abrupt drop to lower velocity at the mantle–core boundary, and has a secondary inflection at the boundary between liquid outer core and solid inner core. The S-wave curve terminates at the mantle–core boundary. Both curves are upwardly convex in the mantle, showing that the rate of increase in wave velocity diminishes with depth.

Sand, clay, and silt layers, being made up of loose grains, have low rigidity. Of the various kinds of solid rocks, shale, sandstone, and limestone have moderate rigidity (Figure 23.24). Next in order of increasing rigidity come granite and the other felsic igneous rocks. Diabase and gabbro, basic rocks which have greater density than granite, have about one-third higher rigidity than granite. Next come the ultrabasic rocks, pyroxenite and dunite, with about twice the rigidity of granite and considerably greater density.

The speed of earthquake waves corresponds with this same series: slowest in sand, silt, or clay layers, faster in the sedimentary rocks, higher speed in granite, still faster in basalt and gabbro, and fastest in pyroxenite and dunite. Dolomite, although a sedimentary rock, is exceptional in that it has wave velocities as great as basalt.

[2] "Rigidity" as used here corresponds with the *shear modulus,* a measure of the resistance of an elastic solid to shearing deformation. P-waves are also influenced by the *bulk modulus,* which measures ratio of compressive stress to resulting volume change.

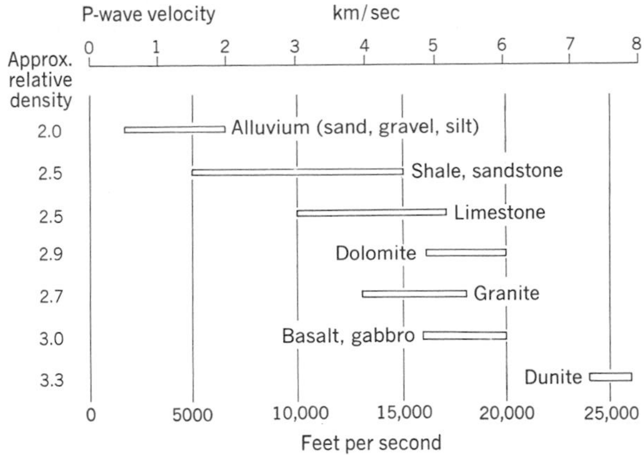


**FIGURE 23.24.** Speed of travel of P-waves in various types of rocks. [Data from M. B. Dobrin (1960), *Introduction to Geophysical Prospecting,* New York, McGraw-Hill.]

In most of the earth's mantle the speed of earthquake waves is so high that only a very rigid and dense rock, such as pyroxenite or dunite, will satisfy the observed conditions. For this reason the mantle is thought to be a zone of solid ultrabasic rock made up of magnesium iron silicate minerals. The mantle is about 1790 mi (2880 km) thick (Figure 23.23). Added to the 2160-mi (3474-km) radius of the iron core, this gives a total radius of 3950 mi (6354 km), which is 99¾ percent of the whole radius of the earth and leaves only a thin shell, known as the *crust,* averaging 10 mi (16 km) in the thickness. (The thickness of the crust at different locations is quite varied.)

## Physical properties of the outer mantle

At first seismologists supposed that earthquakes are set off by fault movements near the earth's surface—at depths down to little more than about 35 mi (55 km). Then further study of seismograms led them to realize that many shocks have a focus very much deeper. Those of intermediate depth occur from 35 to 150 mi (55 to 240 km) down, whereas others, called *deep-focus earthquakes,* originate mostly from 185 to 400 mi (300 to 650 km) down, and a few originate as deep as 450 mi (720 km). Below a depth of 400 to 450 mi the forces that might tend to produce sudden fault slippage are instead relieved by slow plastic flowage of the rock and therefore cannot build up elastic bending to the point of setting off a fault movement.

Thus the earth seems to have an outermost layer which has great strength, but which will break by faulting when unequal stresses are too strong. Below the brittle zone, estimated to be about 40 mi (60 km) thick, and entering the mantle the rock has less strength and brittleness, and an increasingly plastic quality enables it to undergo very slow flowage.

As early as 1914 Joseph Barrell, an American geologist, proposed that the plastic zone of the mantle be called the *asthenosphere* (from a Greek word meaning "weak"), to distinguish it from the overlying rigid zone, or *lithosphere.* The lower limit of the rigid zone represents not a change in rock composition, but instead a change in physical properties. If one end of a cast iron bar is held in a furnace, it becomes white hot and soft, farther out along the bar the iron is red hot and not so soft, and toward the cool end the iron is hard and brittle; in a similar way the behavior of rock changes gradually upward from within the mantle. The rigid zone extends to equal depth under both continents and ocean basins.

In the zone of deep-focus earthquakes, from 185 to 450 mi (300 to 720 km) down, the rock is somewhat plastic, like a very thick tar, but if unequal stresses are suddenly applied it may snap like a brittle solid. Matter possessing these remarkable properties is described as an *elastico-viscous* substance—it can be brittle and plastic at the same time, depending on whether the forces that tend to deform it are applied suddenly and released (as if struck a sharp blow) or

**FIGURE 23.25.** Physical properties of the upper mantle. [Based on data of D. L. Anderson (1962), *Scientific American,* July issue, pp. 58–59.]

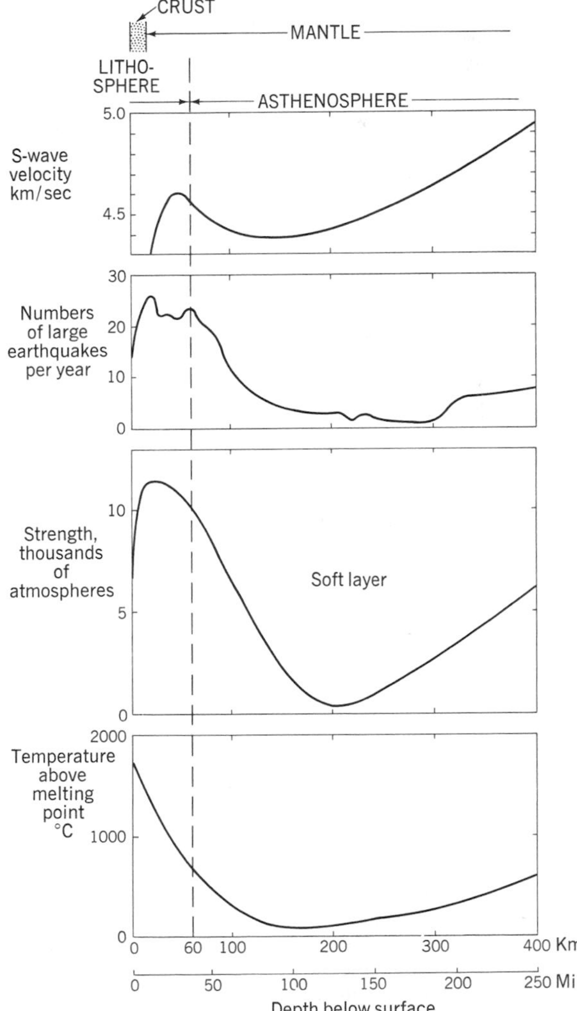

applied steadily (as under the force of gravity). It is said to be possible to make out of cobbler's wax a tuning fork so rigid that it will vibrate with a musical tone when struck, but the same fork left to stand for a long time slowly collapses to a shapeless mass. If the rock below the earth's brittle zone is rigid, as the cobbler's wax is, it can transmit earthquake P-waves (which resemble sound waves), but because it lacks strength it can flow slowly like a thick liquid when steady pressures are applied.

A layer within the upper mantle, in the depth range from 40 to 125 mi (60 to 200 km), is of particular interest because here the mantle rock is at a temperature very close to its melting point. Notice in Figure 23.1*B* that the temperature curve comes close to touching the melting-point curve at a depth of about 100 mi (160 km). The term *plastic layer,* or *soft layer,* has been applied to this part of the mantle, which is within the asthenosphere.

Figure 23.25 shows details of temperature and strength properties of this part of the mantle. The temperature curve gives the difference between the rock temperature and the melting point of that same rock. Notice that this difference declines almost to zero in the depth range 95 to 125 mi (150 to 200 km). The curve of rock strength correspondingly declines, with a minimum approaching zero near the 125-mi (200-km) level. Zero strength would represent a liquid incapable of supporting any load without yielding. Notice that the curve representing numbers of large earthquakes per year declines to very low values (1 or 2 per year) in the depth zone of low strength, then rises again at increasing depth.

The presence of the soft layer in the mantle was suspected as far back as 1926, when the distinguished seismologist Beno Gutenberg presented evidence from wave amplitude studies that earthquake wave velocities are slowed below 40 mi (60 km), after first increasing rapidly from the surface to that depth (Figure 23.25). Reduction in seismic wave velocity can be interpreted as due to a reduction in rigidity of the rock.

We shall refer again to the soft layer of the mantle in attempting to set up hypotheses of evolution of the earth's major crustal features (Chapter 25).

## The earth's crust

The outermost zone of the earth, the *crust,* consists of a layer varying from 5 to 25 mi (3 to 40 km) in thickness. It averages 10 mi (17 km) in thickness when calculated as uniformly spread over the globe. The crust is distinguished from the mantle by the presence of a rather abrupt and clearly defined change in the velocity of seismic waves, indicating that there is a corresponding abrupt change in rigidity of the rock from crust to mantle. A change in rigidity indicates in turn an abrupt change in mineral composition or in physical state of the rocks.

Seismology has provided the means to interpret the thickness and structure of the earth's crust. Where an earthquake has a focus close to the surface and is located only a few hundred miles away from the seismograph station, the seismic waves do not penetrate the earth more than about 100 mi (160 km) before they are gradually turned back toward the surface and reach the seismograph. Interpretation of the complex wave records will reveal the velocities at which the waves traveled at different depths.

Natural earthquakes are unfortunately unpredictable in time and place of occurrence except in a very general way, therefore the best source of information about the shallow zones of the earth come from man-made shocks. One method is to make use of blasts set off at rock quarries and to record them with portable seismographs at various distances from the blasts. In analyzing shallow zones for possible petroleum-bearing structures, small dynamite explosions are used.

Generally speaking, rigidity of crust and mantle rocks increases with depth. Very simply, two possibilities may be considered for the subsurface structure. Figure 23.26*A* shows the case of gradual increase in rock rigidity with depth. As the shock wave penetrates this rock, it encounters regions of progressively faster travel. This change results in a continuous bending, or *refraction,* of the wave path, or ray, in such a way as to turn it toward a path parallel with the surface. Continued bending of the path causes the wave to return eventually to the surface, following a curved path. Continuous refraction of this type might indicate that not only does the rock become more rigid because of increasing confining pressure at depth, but that it also is changing gradually in composition to a rock consisting of denser minerals—that is, from granite (felsic) to basalt (mafic) and then to ultrabasic rock without any abrupt change.

Figure 23.26*B* shows the case in which there exist layers of rock, each of uniform rigidity within itself, but with each successive deeper layer changing

**FIGURE 23.26.** Bending of seismic waves as they travel through rock layers of differing degrees of rigidity. [After M. B. Dobrin (1960), *Introduction to Geophysical Prospecting,* New York, McGraw-Hill.]

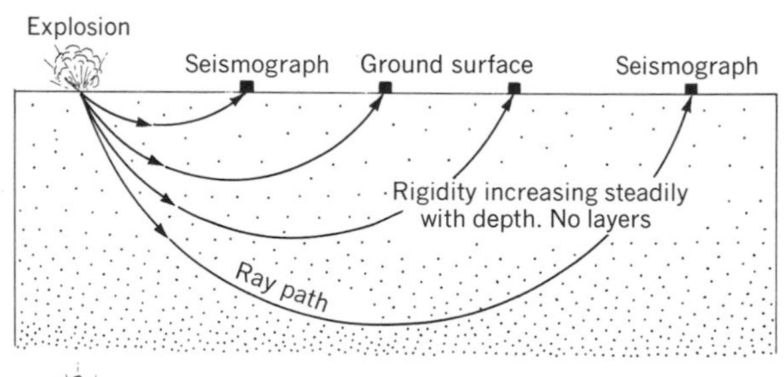


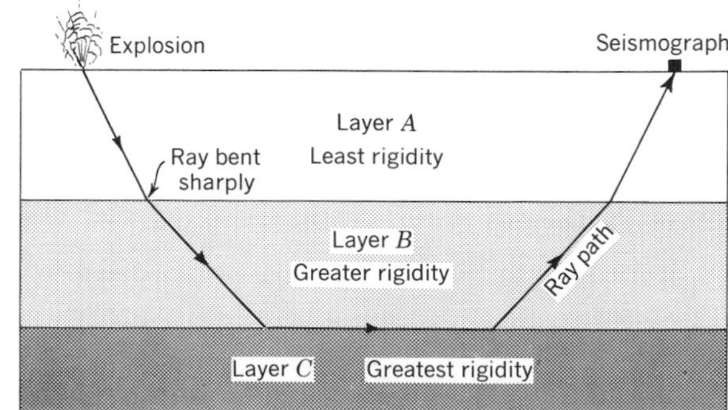

abruptly to higher rigidity. In this case a particular ray of the shock wave travels in a straight line through each layer but is refracted sharply as it enters the next layer. When it strikes a new layer at a certain critical angle, the wave travels along the contact between layers for a certain distance and is then turned upward to return to the surface. When the seismograms of several recording stations are compared, the subsurface paths of the seismic waves can be reconstructed and the velocities of wave travel estimated for different depths. This information in turn makes possible the selection of rock varieties whose physical properties fit the observed wave velocities.

Waves of both shallow earthquakes and surface explosions show quite definitely that the continents consist of a plate-like crust, averaging about 20 mi (33 km) thick, resting upon quite different rock of the mantle. As shown in Figure 23.27, the continental crust consists of largely granitic rock in the upper part and of largely basaltic rock in the lower part.

It is known that the P-waves near the surface travel at about 3.8 mi (6.2 km) per second, which is expected in granitic rock, and that this velocity increases gradually or abruptly to the base of the crust, where it is about 4.3 mi (7 km) per second, a velocity expected in basaltic rock at this depth. At about 20 mi (33 km) depth, on the average, the velocity increases abruptly to more than 5 mi (8 km) per second, a speed to be expected of an ultrabasic rock, such as peridotite. S-waves undergo a corresponding velocity increase with depth. This surface of sudden increase in wave velocity, which separates the crust above from the mantle below, is named the *Mohorovičić discontinuity* after the Yugoslav seismologist who first recognized the discontinuity in 1909 from the records of shallow-focus earthquakes. For obvious reasons, it has become accepted practice to designate this discontinuity as the *Moho,* or simply as the *M-discontinuity.*

At the margins of the continent the crust thins rapidly, and at the same time its base, marked by the M-discontinuity, becomes much shallower, as shown in Figure 23.27. The basaltic rock of the lower part of the continental plate extends out over the ocean-basin floors as a layer 3 to 5 mi (5 to 8 km) thick, but there is no granitic material above it, only a varying thickness of sediment and the overlying water layer averaging 2.5 mi (4 km) depth.

Details of the earth's crust under continents and ocean basins are discussed in Chapters 24 and 25.

**FIGURE 23.27.** Schematic diagram of composition and thickness of crust and mantle under continents and ocean basins.

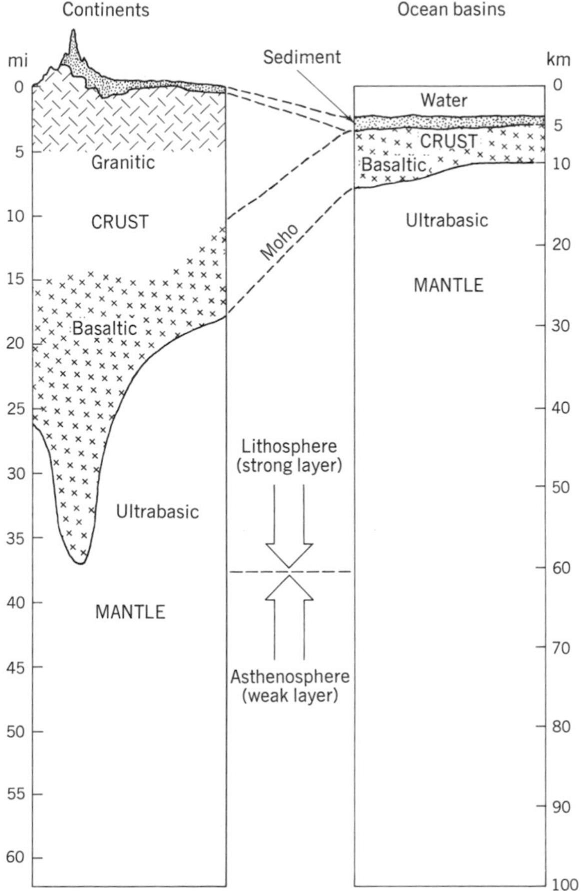


## Composition of the mantle

Returning again to the mantle, we consider briefly the alternative interpretations which have been made as to the chemical compositions and physical states of the matter above and below the M-discontinuity. The more conventional hypothesis considers that the M-discontinuity represents a chemical change from rock of basaltic composition, in the basal part of the crust, to an underlying ultrabasic rock of the composition of dunite or peridotite.

An alternative hypothesis proposes that the rock immediately below the M-discontinuity is of essentially the same chemical composition as the crust above it, but that the minerals exist in a physical state of higher density. *Eclogite,* a rock consisting of garnet and pyroxene, is such a denser rock of essentially the same chemical composition as basalt or gabbro. Eclogite occurs at the earth's surface as a metamorphic rock of possibly igneous origin. It is granular in texture and dark green in color. The density of eclogite is unusually high, 3.4 to 3.6 g/cc, as compared with that of gabbro, about 3.0 g/cc. The hypothesis of a *phase change* suggests that at a certain critical combination of pressure and temperature gabbro changes over to eclogite, and that this phase change causes the M-discontinuity.

Under the hypothesis of a chemical change at the M-discontinuity there are variations in interpretation of the mantle rock. One hypothetical model calls for a transition layer of dunite and peridotite in a heterogeneous mixture immediately below the M-discontinuity. This layer is considered to be of variable thickness—only a few miles under the oceanic crust, but up to 125 mi (200 km) under parts of the continents. Below the dunite-peridotite layer the mantle is said to consist of an ultrabasic rock of a composition about equivalent to a mixture of one part gabbro to three parts dunite (dunite is largely olivine). The resulting mixture is called *pyrolite,* coined from syllables of the words pyroxene and olivine.

At increasing depth, the mantle rock is transformed into mineral matter of increased density. At about 600 mi (1000 km) the rock would have a density of about 3.9 g/cc, if measured at atmospheric pressure. Below this depth, in the lower mantle, the rock is thought to be a highly homogeneous silicate of magnesium and iron. Seismic wave data show a minor discontinuity at about the 600-mi (1000-km) depth, marking the beginning of the lower homogenous layer.

It is an obvious thought that several controversial points concerning the significance of the M-discontinuity and the nature of the mantle rock beneath it might be solved by obtaining samples of rock above and below the discontinuity. The ocean basins would provide localities of least possible depth necessary to attain the goal. A plan to drill a hole passing through the Moho discontinuity (and hence, obviously, resulting in a *Mohole*) was formulated in Washington, D.C., in 1957 by a committee of distinguished representatives of the earth sciences, interested in exploring various aspects of geophysics and geology. Under the name of the American Miscellaneous Society (AMSOC) this committee sought support from the National Science Foundation for preliminary investigations of the feasibility of a Mohole. To drill on the continents would require a hole some 25 mi (40 km) deep, encountering temperatures too high for the operation of drilling equipment. Despite the obvious difficulties of operating a drilling rig in the deep water of the open ocean, a Mohole site there would permit the M-discontinuity to be reached at depths of 6 to 7 mi (10 to 11 km) below sea level. Temperatures at this depth might not be entirely prohibitively high.

Project MOHOLE completed a test phase in which several holes were drilled to depths of several hundred feet into the ocean floor, using modified oil-well drilling equipment mounted on a special floating platform. In 1961 drilling was undertaken near Guadalupe Island in the Pacific Ocean in a water depth of 11,600 ft (3.5 km). After passing through several hundred feet of soft sediment, the drill penetrated only 40 ft (12 m) of basalt. Plans for further drilling were subsequently abandoned when financial support for the project was withdrawn.

## Radiogenic heat

The source of the earth's internal heat is a subject closely tied in with the earth's internal composition and structure. Heat that originates at depth and rises slowly toward the earth's surface is produced from radioactive substances and is referred to as *radiogenic heat.* In order to understand the geologic system of radiogenic heat and its dissipation, a brief discussion of the principles of radioactivity will be helpful for those not already familiar with this area of atomic physics.

It will be recalled that the *nucleus,* or dense core, of an atom consists of two types of particles, *neutrons* and *protons.* For a given element the numbers of neutrons and protons are approximately constant and exist in a specified ratio. Take, for example, the important radioactive form of the element *uranium.* In the nucleus of this form of uranium there are 146 neutrons and 92 protons. The total of neutrons and protons is therefore 238, which quantity is known as the *mass number,* and is designated by a superscript after the symbol for uranium, thus: $U^{238}$. The *atomic number* of an element is equal to the number of protons contained in its nucleus. In the case of uranium the atomic number is 92. Although the atomic number is fixed for each named element, the number of neutrons in the nucleus is subject to some variation. In the case of uranium-238, the number of neutrons is 146, but there exists another form of uranium with 143 neutrons, giving a mass number of 235, and it is designated as *uranium-235.* These differing varieties of the same elements are referred to as *isotopes.* A key to the understanding of radioactivity is that certain isotopes are unstable. This instability can result in the flying off of a small part of the nucleus, reducing the mass number and producing in turn another element. In this spontaneous breakdown, mass is converted into energy, and the release of this energy into the surrounding matter is ultimately in the form of sensible heat.

Let us look further into the nature of the spontaneous radioactive process. Breakdown of the atomic nucleus results in the emission of an *alpha particle,* consisting of two neutrons and two protons. As the alpha particles travel outward through the atoms of the surrounding substance, their energy is transformed into increased activity of the electrons of those atoms, imparting heat to the surrounding substance. Another emission in the radioactive breakdown is the *gamma ray,* an energy form that acts similarly to electromagnetic radiation. Gamma rays are also absorbed by the atoms of the surrounding substance, leading to an increase in heat. A third form of emanation is the *beta particle,* an electron traveling at high velocity. Beta particles also react with surrounding atoms and increase the quantity of heat. The total quantity of heat produced per unit of time in the radioactive process can be exactly calculated for a given quantity of an unstable isotope.

The radioactive disintegration of one parent isotope may lead to the production of yet another unstable isotope, known as a *daughter* product. This product, in turn, may produce yet another unstable isotope, and so forth, until ultimately a stable isotope results and no further radioactivity occurs. Take as an example the system of uranium-238 and its daughter products, leading finally to the stable lead isotope *lead-206* (Figure 23.28). Arrows show the direction of successive changes. Note that each step in the direction of the arrow to the left marks a decrease in the mass number. Uranium-238 decays to produce *thorium-234.* This is followed by a succession of isotopes of six different elements, listed along the bottom of the graph. The disintegration process achieves a steady rate, or equilibrium, with time. In the case of the uranium-238–lead-206 series, each gram of uranium produces 0.71 calories of heat per year.

Other important heat-producing decay sequences in the rocks of the earth are those of *uranium-235,*

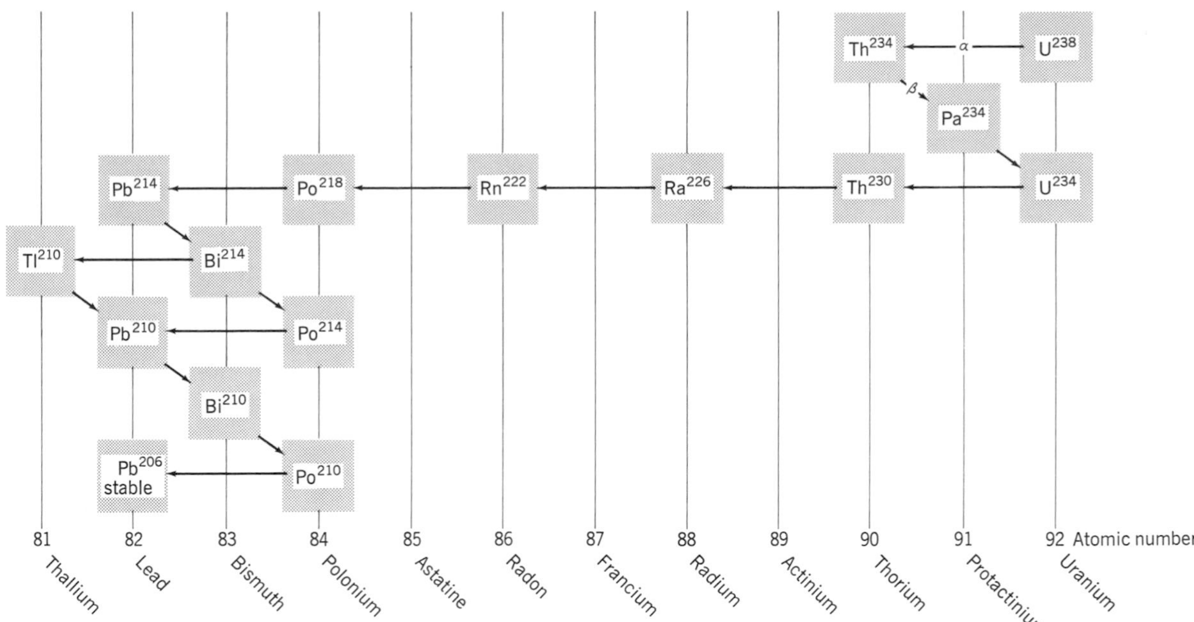


**FIGURE 23.28.** Radioactive decay series of U-238 to Pb-206. [After P. M. Hurley (1959), *How Old Is the Earth?*, Garden City, N.Y., Doubleday, p. 62, Figure 9.]

*thorium-232,* and *potassium-40.* Uranium-235 produces 4.3 calories of heat per gram per year, thorium-232 produces 0.20 calorie, and potassium-40 produces only 0.000027 calorie.

Of great importance in both the thermal history of the earth and the dating of geologic events is a physical law that governs the rate of decay of radioactive isotopes. Once an equilibrium has been reached in the process of radioactive disintegration, the ratio of decrease in the number of atoms of the parent isotope with each unit of time is a constant.

Take for example, potassium-40, which decays to the stable isotopes *calcium-40* and *argon-40.* We can start at any point in time. Let the number of atoms of potassium-40 at time-zero be designated by unity (1.0), as shown at the upper left corner of the graph in Figure 23.29. After 1.31 billion years have elapsed, the number of atoms of potassium-40 will have been reducd to half of the initial number, designated as 0.5 on the vertical scale. The span of time of 1.31 billion years is designated as the *half-life.* In a second elapsed span of 1.31 billion years, the number of atoms of potassium-40 will again be halved, reducing the remaining quantity to 0.25 on the vertical scale. Notice that the ratio of reduction is always the same, e.g. one-half. Such a schedule of decrease in quantity with time is known as an *exponential decay function.* This function applies to all radioactive decay, but the ratio of change, and hence the value of the half-life, is different from one isotope to another.

Figure 23.29 also shows the rate at which the daughter isotopes accumulate. Both are rising curves. Both follow an *exponential increase,* which is the inverse of the exponential decay curve. It should be noted that calcium-40 is produced about 7⅓ times more rapidly than argon-40, hence the curve of calcium-40 rises more steeply. We shall refer to the ratios of parent isotopes to daughter isotopes in the later discussion of methods of rock dating (see Chapter 26).

Table 23.2 gives the half-life of each of the important natural radioisotope series. Notice that there are vast differences in the half-lives of these isotopes. In projecting the production of radiogenic heat back into earliest geologic time, these differences will be highly important. Isotopes with the shorter half-lives were then present in very much larger quantities than today, in contrast with isotopes having extremely long half-lives.

**TABLE 23.2***

| Parent Isotope | Stable Daughter Products | Half-life, billions of years |
|---|---|---|
| Uranium-238 | Lead-206, plus helium | 4.5 |
| Uranium-235 | Lead-207, plus helium | 0.71 |
| Thorium-232 | Lead-208, plus helium | 14 |
| Rubidium-84 | Strontium-87 | 51 |
| Potassium-40 | Argon-40, calcium-40 | 1.3 |

* Data from Brian Mason (1966), *Principles of Geochemistry,* 3rd ed., New York, Wiley. See p. 9.

## Distribution of radiogenic heat

Heat flows continuously upward from depths of the earth toward the surface. We have already noted that the increase in temperature with depth, or geothermal gradient, is well-known from observations in deep mines and in bore holes and has a value of about 1 F° per 50 ft (3 C° per 100 m). The flow of heat because of this thermal gradient averages about 1.4 microcalories

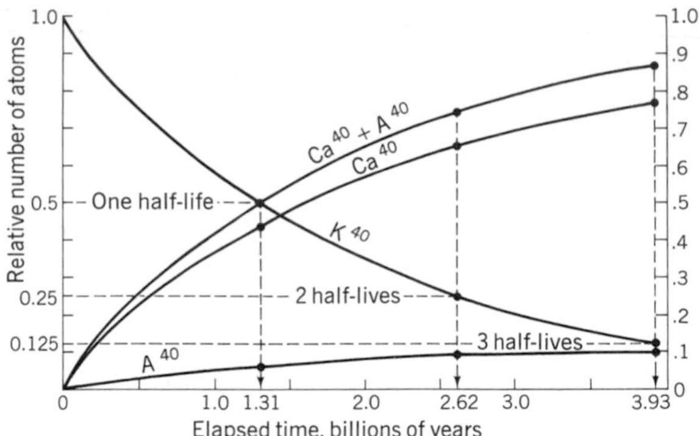


**FIGURE 23.29.** Exponential decay and growth curves for K-40, Ca-40, and A-40. [After P. M. Hurley (1959), *How Old Is the Earth?*, Garden City, N.Y., Doubleday, p. 101, Figure 17.]

(0.0000014 calories) per square centimeter per second. This same figure applies rather well to both continental crust and oceanic crust, despite the marked differences in crustal composition and thickness.

At this rate, the total heat flow in one year is about 50 calories per square centimeter, enough to melt an ice layer 0.2 in. (6 mm) thick. Notice particularly that this quantity of heat is extremely small compared with that received by one square centimeter of the earth's surface from solar radiation (see Chapter 13). Therefore the earth's heat flow from depth is of no significance in the earth's heat balance or in powering the atmospheric and oceanic circulation systems.

Referring to the temperature–depth graph in Figure 23.1, you will notice that the rate of temperature increase with depth falls off very rapidly after the first one hundred miles or so. The flattening of the temperature curve in the lower mantle and core expresses the very low thermal gradient that is postulated to exist within the deep interior. If the thermal gradient decreases rapidly with depth, a logical interpretation is that the rate of production of radiogenic heat is greatest near the earth's surface and decreases rapidly with depth. It has been concluded that the concentration of radioactive isotopes is greatest in the rocks of the crust, but falls off rapidly in the mantle rocks and is very small in the lower mantle and core.

Table 23.3 shows both the concentrations and rates of heat production of the radioactive isotopes of uranium, thorium, and potassium in each of the three

**TABLE 23.3***

| | Concentrations | | | Heat Production, cal/g/yr | | | |
|---|---|---|---|---|---|---|---|
| | U ppm | Th ppm | K % | U | Th | K | Total |
| Granitic | 4 | 14 | 3.5 | 3 | 3 | 1 | 7 |
| Basaltic | 0.6 | 2 | 1.0 | 1.5 | 1.5 | 0.5 | 3.5 |
| Ultrabasic | 0.015 | — | 0.011 | 0.01 | 0.01 | <0.001 | 0.02 |

* Based on data of B. Mason (1966), *Principles of Geochemistry*, 3rd ed., New York, Wiley, Table 11.1; and P. J. Hurley (1959), *How Old Is the Earth?*, New York, Doubleday, p. 64.

classes of rocks. These rates are based upon chemical analyses of samples of igneous rocks collected at the earth's surface. If we project these figures to the assumed corresponding rocks of the crust and mantle, as shown in Figure 23.27, it is seen that the most rapid production of radiogenic heat is by granitic rocks of the upper zone of the continental crust. The ultrabasic mantle rock produces very little heat per unit of weight. It has been estimated that about one-half of all radiogenic heat is produced above a depth of 22 mi (35 km) in the continental crust.

Some support for the conclusion that the iron core of the earth produces almost no radiogenic heat is found in the analysis of iron meteorites. These fragments of matter are thought to represent the disrupted cores of planetary objects of similar origin to the earth (see Chapter 31). Radioactive minerals are present in only very small quantities in iron meteorites.

## Early thermal history of the earth

Modern hypotheses of the earth's origin, discussed in Chapter 27, tend to favor the process of accretion of the earth and other planets through the coming together of cold clouds of dispersed gases and dusts under gravitational attraction. Once formed, such solid masses would grow by the in-fall of solid bodies of many sizes, perhaps including objects similar to the asteroids of the present day Solar System. It is generally supposed that at the time accretion was largely complete the earth's interior temperature had not risen to the melting point, although local areas may have become molten from the energy of impacts. Modern thinking is thus along quite different lines than that of early speculators, such as Laplace, who postulated an earth formed from high-temperature gases and passing from the gaseous state to the molten state in its initial development.

It is interesting to recall that the distinguished nineteenth-century English physicist, Lord Kelvin, had calculated the age of the earth using the premise that the earth cooled from a molten state and that the cooling rate followed simple laws of radiative and conductive heat loss. On this basis he concluded that the earth could not be more than 100 million years old and that an age of 20 to 40 millions of years was a reasonable figure. Present estimates are on the order of 4.6 billion years for the completion of the accretion process. We can excuse Lord Kelvin's gross miscalculation in view of the fact that the phenomenon of radioactivity was not then known.

The discovery of natural radioactivity by Henri Becquerel in 1896, followed by the isolation of radium by Marie and Pierre Curie in 1898, radically altered all scientific thinking about the earth's heat. John Joly in 1909 applied the new knowledge of radioactivity to recalculations of the earth's thermal history. Moreover, Joly brought forward the underlying principle that radiogenic heat provides the prime energy source for vulcanism, intrusion, and deformation of the earth's crust into mountain belts, and perhaps also great horizontal movements of the crust and upper mantle.

It is considered most unlikely that the earth, at the time of its formation as a planet about 4½ billion years ago, contained the same quantity and distribution of radioactive isotopes that we find today. Primarily, there is the consideration that radioactive decay progressively reduces the available supply of radioactive isotopes. Hence we conclude that the total production of radiogenic heat within the earth was at the maximum level at the time of the earth's formation and has diminished ever since. The relative rates of decay of uranium, thorium, and potassium isotopes are not the same, but are well established for each isotope. Figure 23.30 is a graph in which time is plotted on the horizontal axis starting at an arbitrary zero point at the assumed time of formation of the earth. Total planetary radiogenic heat production per year is given on the vertical scale. Curves have been plotted for the major radioactive isotopes of uranium, thorium, and potassium individually, while the total production is shown in a separate curve. Note that uranium-235 and potassium-40 have short half-lives in comparison with these of uranium-238 and thorium-232. Referring to the total curve, it is obvious that total radiogenic heat production was vastly greater when the earth was first formed than it is at present, roughly by a factor of six. The implications of such a history are of great consequence.

First, assume that at the time of the earth's formation by accretion the radioactive isotopes were uniformly distributed throughout the entire earth. There is no reason to think otherwise. Silicate minerals and free iron were also uniformly mixed. Heat would accumulate at great depths, bringing the primary material to the melting point. Melted rock would have tended to rise toward the surface, bringing up with it the radioactive isotopes. Because these latter elements remain in the liquid state at temperatures lower than the transporting minerals, cooling and crystallization of the surrounding minerals would have been accompanied by a sinking of those mineral crystals (which are denser), leaving the liquid fraction closer to the earth's surface. Although such a process of differentiation is speculative, it offers a mechanism for the selective removal of the radioactive isotopes from the inner earth and their eventual concentration near the surface.

**FIGURE 23.30.** Rate of production of radiogenic heat projected back 5 billion years. [Data of A. P. Vinogradov (1961), as shown in B. Mason (1966), *Principles of Geochemistry*, New York, John Wiley & Sons, p. 61, Figure 3.9.]

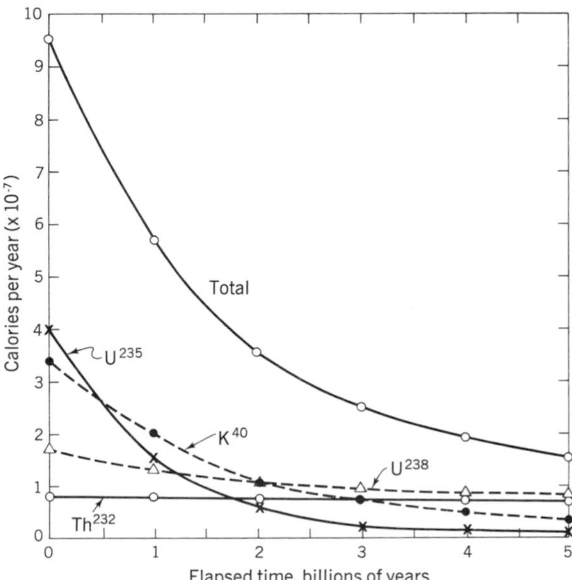


We postulate further that during this same melting process the density layering of the earth came into existence, resulting in the concentration of iron in the core, a less dense ultrabasic rock mantle of olivine above it, and the basaltic crust at the top. During the segregation process the heat production rate was falling. Consequently, along with redistribution of the heat-generating isotopes, the episodes of melting must have become fewer and eventually ceased. Today the earth is thermally stable, in the sense that melting and movement of magma are limited to an extremely shallow layer compared with the earth's total diameter. The inner core and much of the mantle are no longer subject to melting through the accumulation of excess heat.

It is fortunate, indeed, that the chemistry of the radioactive elements is such that they would tend to rise toward the earth's surface throughout its history. If, on the other hand, they had tended to sink and collect near its center, the heat produced by their concentrated activity would have repeatedly melted the earth. Under such conditions no planetary stability would have been possible throughout geologic history. As we find conditions today, radiogenic heat production in the core is negligible, while the rate of surfaceward flow of heat from the upper mantle and crust closely balances the rate of heat production. Consequently the mantle remains for the most part at a temperature lower than its melting point. Only in the soft layer of the mantle is melting on a large scale a likely occurrence.

## The earth's interior in review

In this chapter the science of seismology has been used to interpret the internal structure of the earth and guide the formulation of hypotheses concerning the composition of the matter comprising the earth's spherical shells. We have found that the enormous energy released by earthquakes is itself derived from strains of rock within the crust and upper mantle. Perhaps the basic source of this energy lies in the accumulation of radiogenic heat, produced largely in the crust and upper mantle. The presence of a particularly weak layer in the upper mantle suggests that radiogenic heat has raised rock temperatures close to the melting point in this region. Local occurrences of melting here could provide magmas of ultrabasic rock from which basaltic and granitic magmas might be derived by differentiation.

The crust beneath the ocean basins differs in several

important respects from the crust beneath the continents. In the chapters to follow, these differences will be evaluated. Processes of crustal movement and deformation, as well as of continental evolution, will be examined in the light of various lines of evidence.

## References for further study

Richter, C. F. (1958), *Elementary Seismology,* San Francisco, Freeman, 768 pp.

Howell, B. F., Jr. (1959), *Introduction to Geophysics,* New York, McGraw-Hill, 399 pp., chaps. 5–11.

Hurley, P. M. (1959), *How Old Is the Earth?* Garden City, N.Y., Anchor Books, Doubleday, 160 pp.

Jacobs, J. A., R. D. Russell, and J. T. Wilson (1959), *Physics and Geology,* New York, McGraw-Hill, 424 pp., chaps. 2, 3, 5.

Hodgson, J. H. (1964), *Earthquakes and Earth Structure,* Englewood Cliffs, N.J., Prentice-Hall, 166 pp.

Mason, B. (1966), *Principles of Geochemistry,* New York, Wiley, 329 pp., chap. 3.

# 24

# The ocean basins and their sediments

THE EARTH'S FIRST-ORDER relief features are the continents and ocean basins. Because the elevation and form of these features reflect the composition and structure of the earth's crust, description of the principal surface forms is a necessary preliminary step to the study of the earth's crust.

First, it would be well to reconsider the relative magnitude of the earth's surface relief in terms of the globe as a whole. Human activities are so strongly affected by differences in elevation of the land and by steep ground slopes that in our mind's eye we tend to exaggerate the vertical dimension. Because we can see but a small patch of the earth's surface in one view, even from high in an airplane, we tend to foreshorten the horizontal dimension. If you should draw with chalk a circle 21 feet in diameter, representing the earth's circumference on a scale of 1:2,000,000, all the relief features of the earth's solid surface, from ocean floors to high mountains and plateaus, would fall within the thickness of the chalk line. A line about ⅜-inch wide would take in 12 miles of relief, enough to include Mt. Everest (+29,000 feet) and the deepest known point in the ocean (about −35,000 feet). If you were to trace the profiles of Figure 24.1 on a piece of paper, the trace could be placed over a portion of the chalk line of the 21-foot circle and would show to correct vertical scale the earth's great relief features as they actually are. Thus the topographic features now under discussion can be thought of as scarcely more than minor imperfections on a nearly perfect ellipsoid.

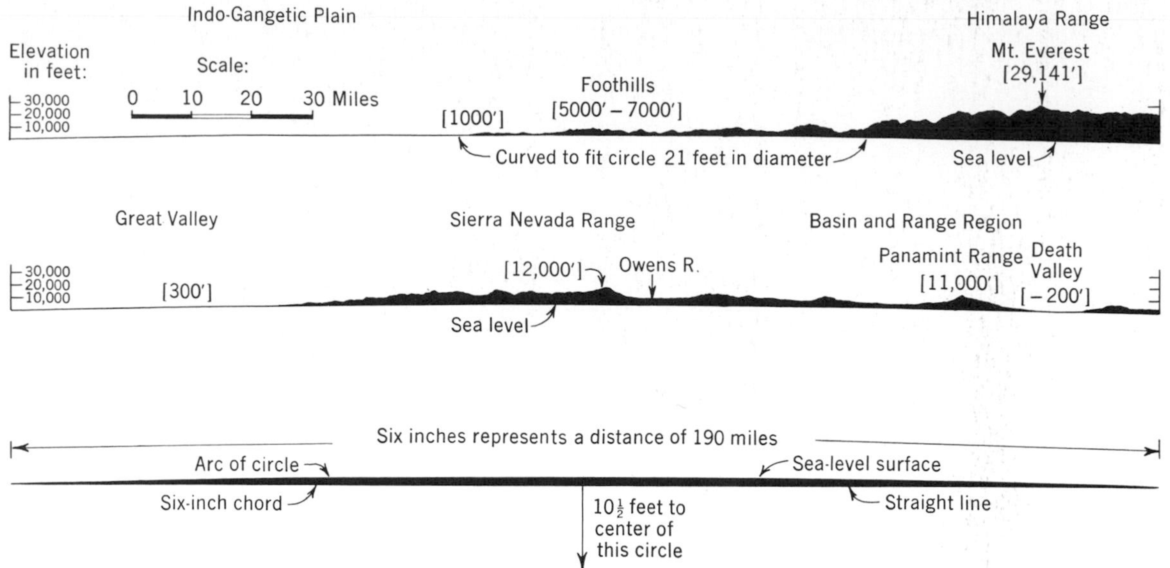


**FIGURE 24.1.** True scale profiles of sections of the earth's surface. Sea-level curvature is scaled to fit a globe 21 ft (6.4 m) in diameter. (© 1960, John Wiley & Sons, New York.)

## Distribution of continents and ocean basins

For this study of the earth's major relief features the waters of the ocean must be imagined to be completely removed, revealing dry land over the entire globe. When this is done, we see that the natural outlines of the continents are larger and more regular than those appearing on the conventional world map or globe based on the shoreline.

To clarify further the general picture of the earth's solid surface form, the proportion of surface lying between equal units of vertical distance is shown graphically in Figure 24.2. The length of each horizontal bar is proportional to the total amount of surface area found within that elevation zone. It is apparent that most of the surface is concentrated in two general zones: (1) on the continents between sea level and 3300 ft (1 km) elevation, and (2) on the floors of the ocean basins from about 10,000 to 20,000 ft (3 to 6 km) below sea level. This graph tells us that in a general way the continents are broad, table-like areas whose edges slope away rapidly to the deep ocean floor. Although the floor does not lie entirely within one elevation zone, vast areas lie at approximately the same depth.

It is important to grasp the idea that the ocean basins are brimful of water, so full that the oceans overlap considerable areas of the continental margins to produce shallow seas bordering the shores. To have a true picture of the continents in relation to the ocean basins, the ocean level must be imagined to be dropped some 500 to 600 ft (150 to 180 m) to uncover these shallow continental shelves and inland seas. The margins of the continents should be studied on a world map or globe

**FIGURE 24.2.** The relative proportion of surface area in each altitude zone of the earth is represented by the length of a bar. (© 1960, John Wiley & Sons, New York.)

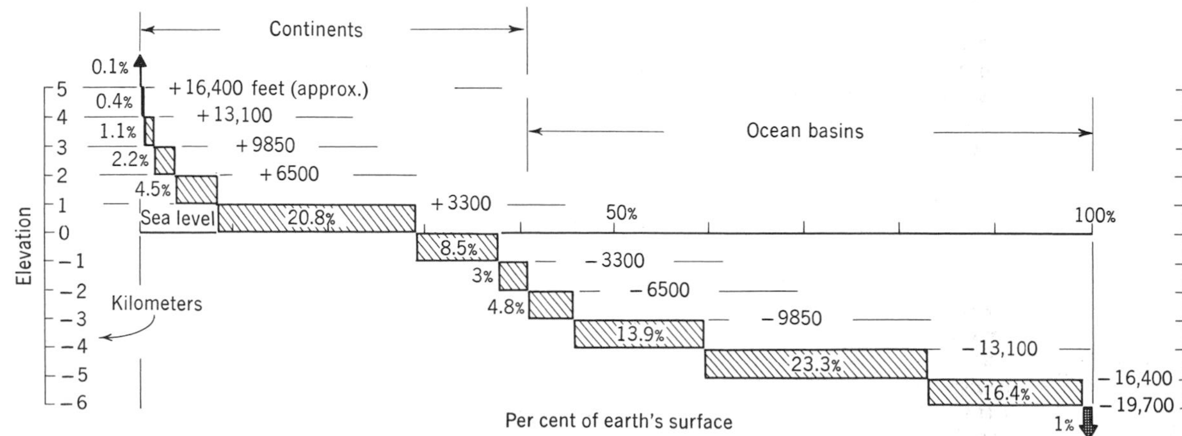

A

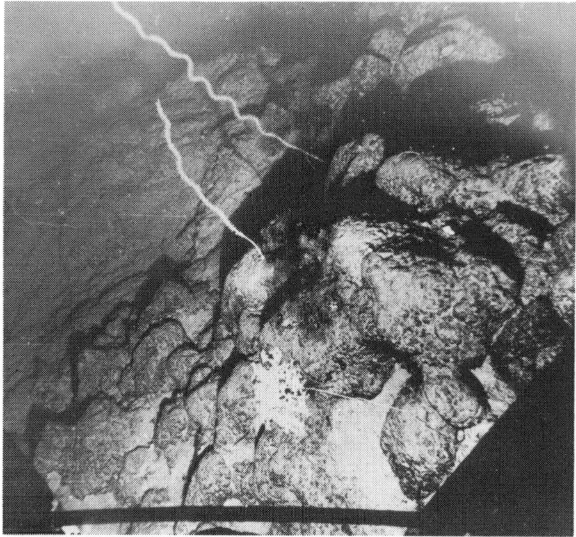

B

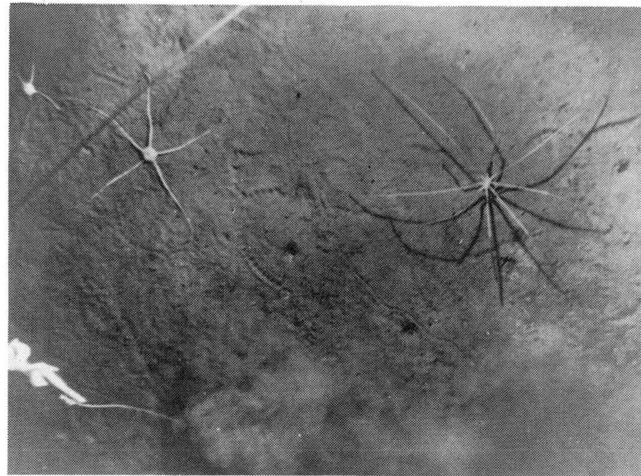

C

**FIGURE 24.3.** Submarine photography. (*A*) A research scientist of the Lamont-Doherty Geological Observatory staff prepares to lower an undersea camera over the side of the Research Vessel *Vema.* (Photograph by courtesy of National Academy of Sciences, IGY.) (*B*) This photograph of the ocean floor at a depth of 6600 ft (2000 m) shows an outcrop of bedrock on the side slopes of Ampere Seamount. Location is lat. 35° N., long. 13° W. (Photograph by courtesy of Maurice Ewing, Director, Lamont-Doherty Geological Observatory of Columbia University.) (*C*) A starfish (left) and a sea spider (right) seen on a mud bottom at a depth of 6000 ft (1800 m) on the continental slope of the eastern United States. (Photograph by D. M. Owen, courtesy of Woods Hole Oceanographic Institution.)

showing the 600-ft (100-fathom, 180-m) submarine contour. If the area lying above that contour is included with the lands, it will be found that the continents make up about 35 percent of the total earth's surface area and the ocean basins about 65 percent.

## Topography of the ocean floor

The general appearance of continental landscape forms is familiar to all, but few persons have seen the deep ocean floor at close range. We now have many undersea photographs taken by a camera lowered to the sea floor from a ship (Figure 24.3), but these give no sense of landscape. Only on specialized types of submarine charts and diagrams made from soundings can the relief forms of the ocean basins be depicted, and most of this is new knowledge acquired since about 1940. Before proceeding to any further discussion of the earth's crust, our knowledge of the earth's larger surface forms must be rounded out by a brief study of the topographic forms beneath the oceans.

In the early decades of oceanographic research, sounding of the ocean bottom had to be done by lowering a heavy weight on a thin steel cable until the weight reached bottom, allowing the depth to be measured by the length of cable let out. Because this was a very slow and costly process, our knowledge of the sea floor was very scanty until the time of World War II, when continuously recording echo-sounding apparatus was put into general use in naval vessels.

The *precision depth recorder* makes use of a sound-emitting device attached to the bottom of the ship. Pulses of sound are sent down through the water from the ship's hull and are reflected from the ocean floor to the ship, where they are picked up by a microphone. An automatic recording device indicates the time required for sound waves to reach the bottom and return. Reflections are plotted continuously by a writing instrument to give a line representing the profile of the ocean bottom (Figure 24.4).

By allowing the precision depth recorder to operate continuously while the ship travels, a profile across the sea floor is obtained. This information can be used to make maps of the sea floor only if the exact position of the ship is known at all times. Fortunately, precise positioning of a vessel is no longer a problem. Echo sounding has enormously increased our knowledge of the configuration of the ocean floors within a span of only two decades, and the mid-twentieth century

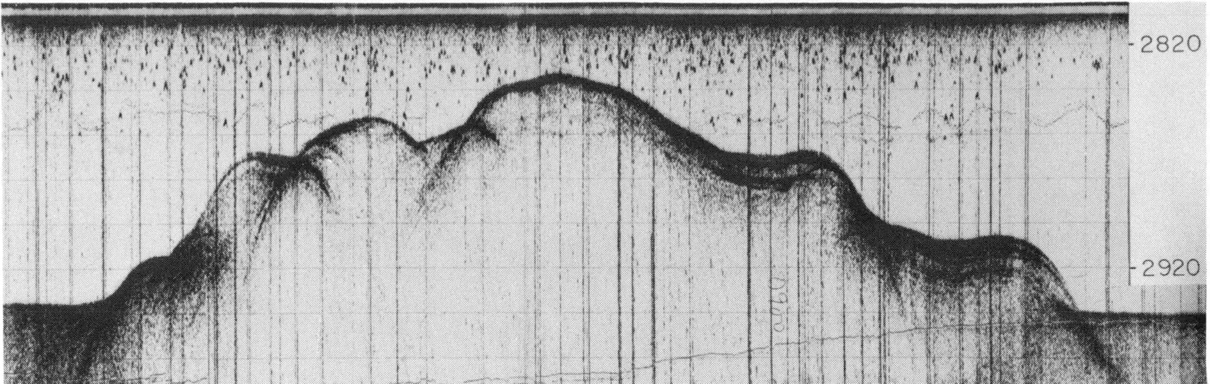


**FIGURE 24.4.** Photograph of the actual trace made by a precision depth recorder aboard the Research Vessel *Vema*. Depth in fathoms is given by figures at the right. The entire profile spans about 10 mi (16 km). An abyssal hill is shown flanked by the very flat surface of the Pernambuco Abyssal Plain. Location is about lat. 13° S., long. 28° W. (Courtesy of Maurice Ewing, Director, Lamont-Doherty Geological Observatory of Columbia University.)

can truly be called a golden age of undersea exploration.

According to a system of submarine landform classification set up in 1959 by Professor Bruce C. Heezen and co-workers of the Lamont-Doherty Geological Observatory of Columbia University, the topographic features of the ocean basins fall into three major divisions: (1) the continental margins, (2) the ocean-basin floors, and (3) the Mid-Oceanic Ridge. As is obvious from the terms themselves, the continental margins lie in belts directly adjacent to the continent, and the Mid-Oceanic Ridge divides the basin roughly in half, thus the floor of an ocean basin lies in two parts, one on either side of that ridge. Figure 24.5 and the accompanying profile show these major topographic divisions as they apply to the North Atlantic basin. Let us consider the various features characteristically found in each of the major divisions.

**The continental margins** Perhaps the best known and most easily studied of the units within the continental margins are the *continental shelves,* which fringe the continents in widths from a few miles to more than 200 mi (320 km). Generally having very smooth and gently sloping floors, the continental shelves are for the most part less than 600 ft (180 m) deep. A particularly fine example is the continental shelf of the eastern coast of the United States (Figure 24.6).

Also constituting a true segment of the continents are the *epicontinental marginal seas,* shallow bodies of water lying well within the continental blocks. Generally of depths greater than 600 ft (180 m) the epicontinental seas not only are deeper than the continental shelves, but have appreciably greater relief as well. Examples are the Gulf of Maine and the Gulf of St. Lawrence.

Along their seaward margins the continental shelves give away to the *continental slopes* (Figure 24.6). Although the actual inclination of the slope with respect to the horizontal is only 3 to 6 degrees, this is exceptionally steep for submarine relief features and appears quite precipitous on the highly exaggerated profiles (Figure 24.7). The continental slope drops from the sharply defined brink of the shelf to depths of 4500 to 10,500 ft (1370 to 3200 m). Here the slope lessens rapidly, though not abruptly, and is replaced by the *continental rise,* a surface of much gentler slope decreasing in steepness toward the ocean-basin floor (Figures 24.6 and 24.7). Ranging in width from perhaps a hundred to several hundred miles, the continental rise has generally moderate to low relief. At its outer margin the continental rise reaches depths of 17,000 ft (5100 m) where it may be in direct contact with the deep floor of the ocean basin.

Notching the continental slope are *submarine canyons,* which may be visualized as resembling gullies cut by water erosion in the side of a hill, but on a huge scale (Figure 24.6). It seems likely that they have been scoured by currents of muddy water that slide in snakelike tongues down the slope to the deep parts of the basins. Such flows of denser muddy water are termed *turbidity flows,* or *turbidity currents.* They have been produced experimentally in the laboratory and are known to occur in lakes and reservoirs where muddy river water enters a still body of clear water. On continental shelves and deltas of large rivers mud is continually accumulating and may form precariously situated deposits that are easily disturbed and sent sliding by storm waves or earthquake shocks.

**The ocean-basin floor** Second of the major topographic divisions of the ocean basins is the extensive region of basin floor, generally lying in the depth range of 15,000 to 18,000 ft (4600 to 5500 m). The ocean-basin floor comprises three categories of forms: abyssal plains and hills, oceanic rises, and seamounts.

An *abyssal plain* is an area of the deep ocean floor having a flat bottom with the very faint slope of less than 1 part in 1000 (Figure 24.6). Characteristically situated at the foot of the continental rise, the abyssal plain is represented in all the oceans. Examples are the Hatteras and Nares Abyssal Plains at depths of roughly 18,000 ft (5500 m) (Figure 24.7). The only reasonable explanation for such nearly perfect flatness is that the abyssal plains are surfaces formed by long-

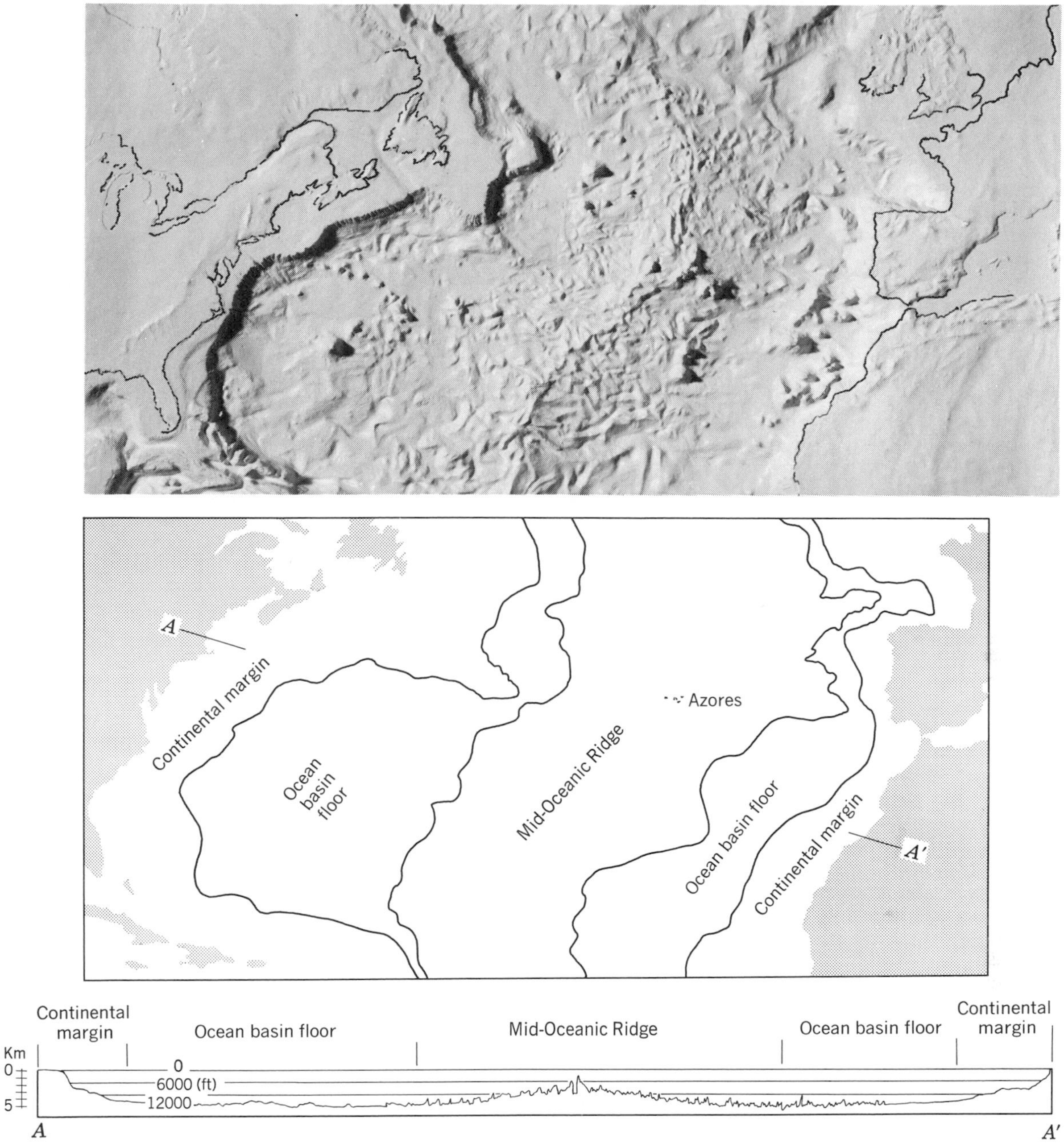

**FIGURE 24.5.** (*Above*) Terrain model of the North Atlantic Ocean basin. Vertical exaggeration about 25 times. (Official U.S. Navy photograph, courtesy of U.S. Naval Training Device Center.) (*Below*) Outline map of the major divisions of the North Atlantic Ocean basin, with representative profile from New England to the Sahara coast of Africa. Vertical exaggeration about 40 times. [After B. C. Heezen, M. Tharp, and M. Ewing (1959), *The Floors of the Oceans,* Geol. Soc. Amer. Spec. Paper 65, p. 16, Figure 9.]

continued deposition from turbidity flows which have spread out into thin sheets upon reaching the ocean floor. Previously existing irregularities of the ocean floor have thus been almost entirely buried over large areas.

Those submarine canyons already referred to as scoring the continental slope and rise are relatively deep steep-walled forms, carved as they are into the face of a great escarpment. Of very different nature are *mid-ocean canyons,* found on the abyssal plains of the ocean-basin floors. First to be charted in some detail was the Northwest Atlantic Mid-Ocean Canyon (Figure 24.8), which runs southward along the abyssal plain and is thought to have a system of branching tributary channels, much as a river system on land. Profiles across the Mid-Ocean Canyon have been made in 48 places and show that it consists of a linear flat-

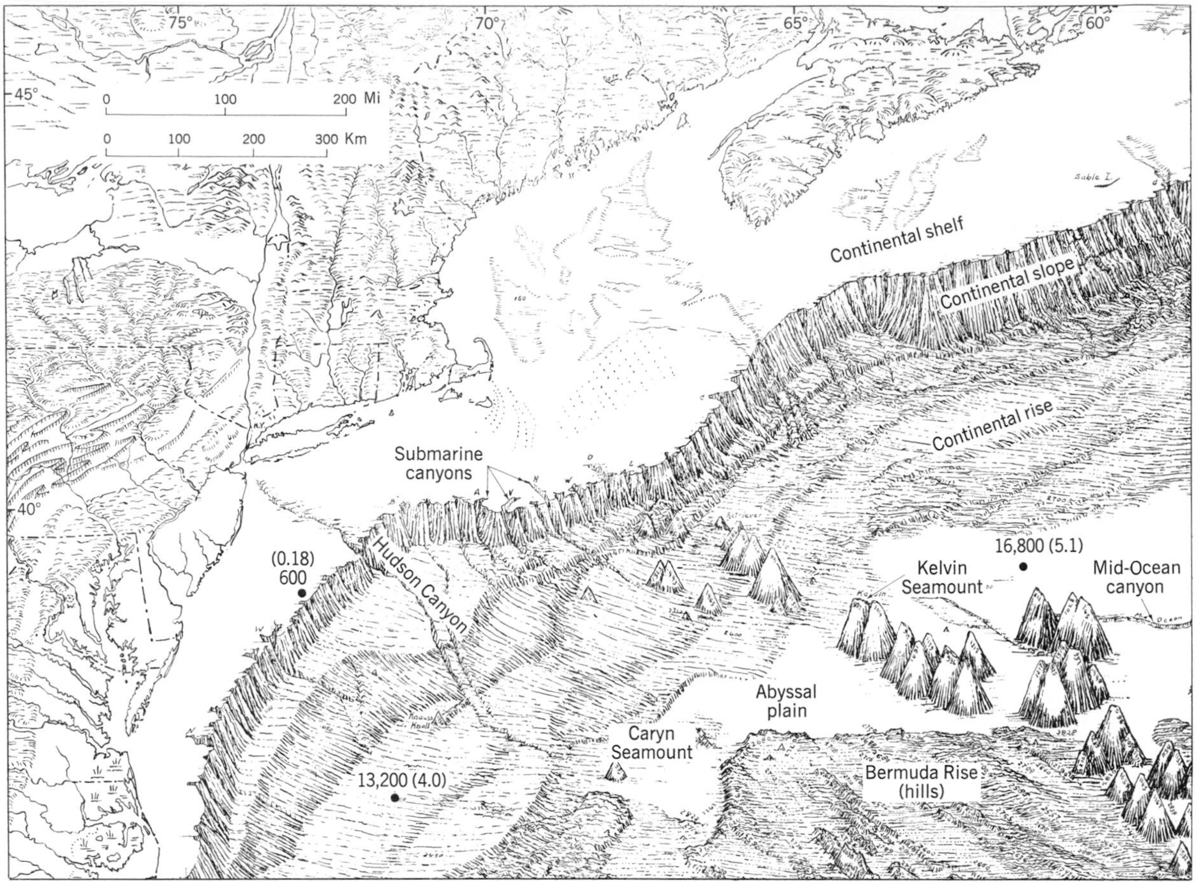

**FIGURE 24.6.** Features of the continental margin and ocean-basin floor off the coast of the northeastern United States. Depth in ft; km in parentheses. [Portion of *Physiographic Diagram of the North Atlantic Ocean* (1968), revised, by B. C. Heezen and M. Tharp, Boulder, Colo., Geol. Soc. of Amer., reproduced by permission.]

floored depression from 1 to 5 mi (1.5 to 8 km) wide and from a few tens to a few hundreds of feet deep. Elevation of the canyon floor decreases steadily southward along its course, but its trend runs parallel with the slope of the abyssal plain rather than down that slope. This and other known mid-ocean canyons lie parallel to the continental margin.

Although the origin of the mid-ocean canyons is not fully understood, they are postulated to be produced by the flow of turbidity currents, much as in the case of many of the submarine canyons, except that the flow takes place on much lower gradients. It is entirely out of the question that such abyssal forms could have ever been carved by terrestrial streams, and therefore

**FIGURE 24.7.** Two profiles across parts of the North Atlantic Ocean basin show several characteristic features of the ocean floors. (© 1960, John Wiley & Sons, New York. Data by B. C. Heezen, Lamont-Doherty Geological Observatory of Columbia University.)

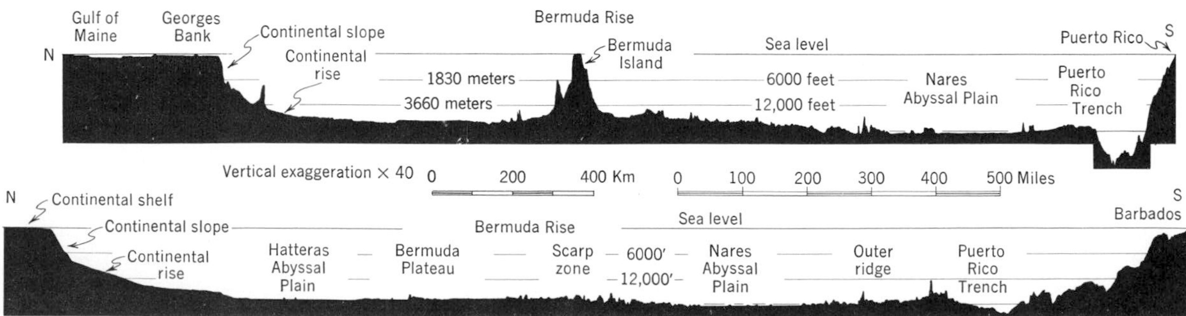

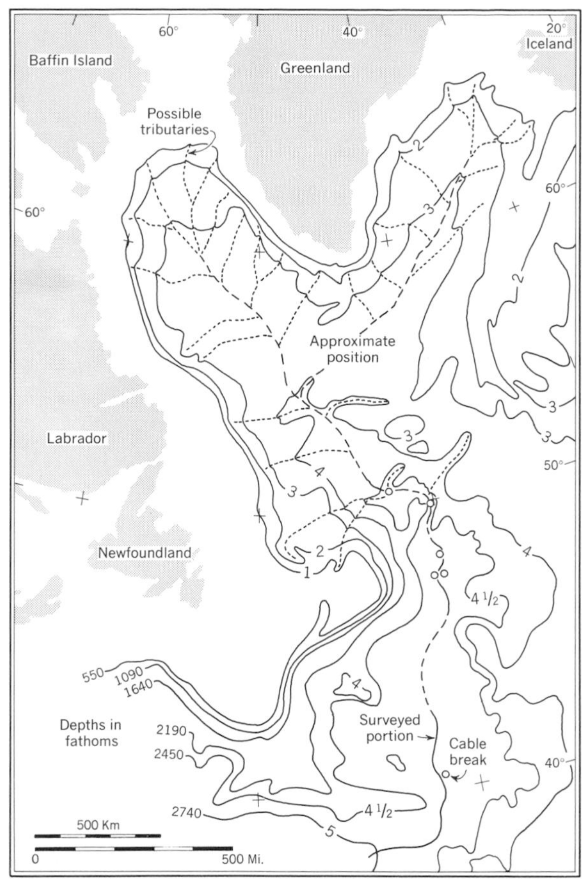


FIGURE 24.8. Map of the Northwest Atlantic Mid-Ocean Canyon. Submarine contours in kilometers of depth, with fathom equivalents. [After B. C. Heezen, M. Tharp, and M. Ewing (1959), *The Floors of the Oceans,* Geol. Soc. Amer. Spec. Paper 65, p. 67, Figure 29.]

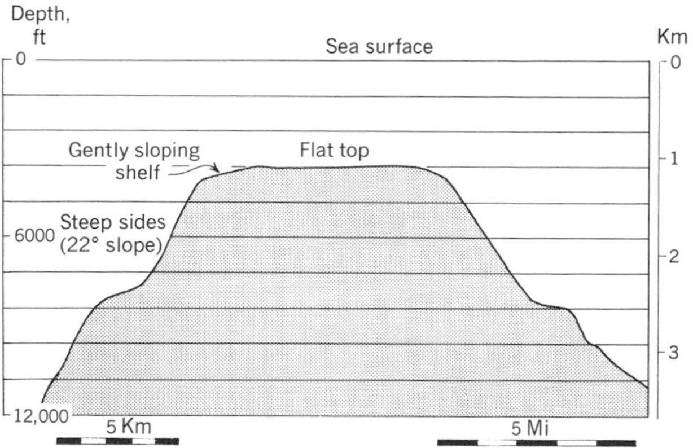


FIGURE 24.10. Profile of the first guyot to be discovered in the Pacific Ocean basin (1944). The location of this flat-topped seamount is about lat. 9° N., long. 163° E. [After H. H. Hess (1946), *Amer. Jour. Sci.,* vol. 244.]

any explanation relies on processes taking place within the oceans.

*Abyssal hills* are small hills rising to heights of a few tens to a few hundreds of feet above the ocean-basin floor and may be so numerous as to occupy nearly all the floor. Isolated abyssal hills also occur on the abyssal plains. Zones of abyssal hills are well developed in the North Atlantic basin along the mid-ocean side of the great abyssal plains.

Still another characteristic topographic unit of the ocean-basin floor is the *oceanic rise,* an area hundreds of miles in breadth over which the surface rises several hundred feet above the surrounding abyssal plains. Within the rise, relief may range from gentle to very rugged. An example is the Bermuda Rise, shown in both profiles of Figure 24.7 and in the lower right corner of Figure 24.6. In places this rise consists of hills 120 to 300 ft (35 to 90 m) high and 2 to 10 mi (3 to 16 km) wide. Along the eastern edge the rise is broken by a series of scarps 1800 to 5400 ft (550 to 1600 m) high. Located near the center of the Bermuda Rise is a pedestal 50 by 80 mi (80 by 130 km) at its base, upon which the islands of Bermuda are situated. This pedestal appears to have been formed by the accumulation of reef limestones upon a volcanic deposit.

Perhaps the most fascinating of the strange features of the ocean basins are the *seamounts,* isolated peaks rising 3000 ft (900 m) or more above the sea floor. Although seamounts also occur on the continental rises they are most conspicuous on the ocean-basin floors. A good example from the Atlantic basin is the Kelvin Seamount Group, forming a row of conical peaks extending across the continental rise for 600 mi (1000 km) southeastward toward the Bermuda Rise (Figure 24.6). Shown in natural-scale profile (Figure 24.9), even the most striking seamount of this group may not appear particularly impressive (few mountains do when thus presented), but its bulk is apparent when we note that the seamount rises almost 11,000 ft (3350 m) above the abyssal plain and is 25 mi (40 km) wide at the base.

Altogether several hundred seamounts have been found in the Pacific Ocean, a number vastly greater than those occurring in the Atlantic. Many of the Pacific seamounts are conspicuously flat topped and extremely steep sided (Figure 24.10) and were given the name of *guyots,* in honor of a geologist of the nineteenth

FIGURE 24.9. Kelvin Seamount shown in true-scale profile. [After B. C. Heezen, M. Tharp, and M. Ewing (1959), *The Floors of the Oceans,* Geol. Soc. Amer. Spec. Paper 65, p. 77, Figure 34.]

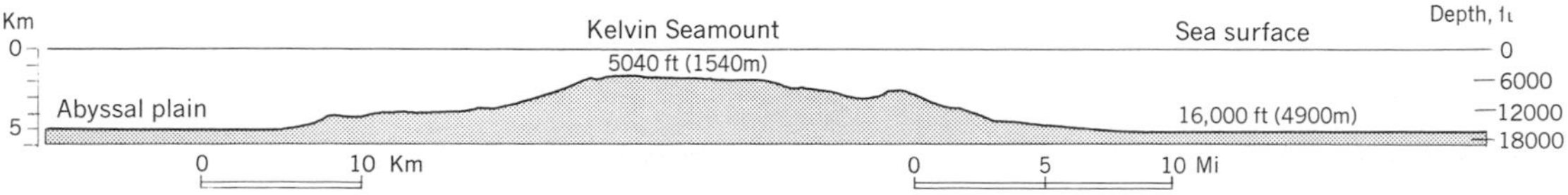

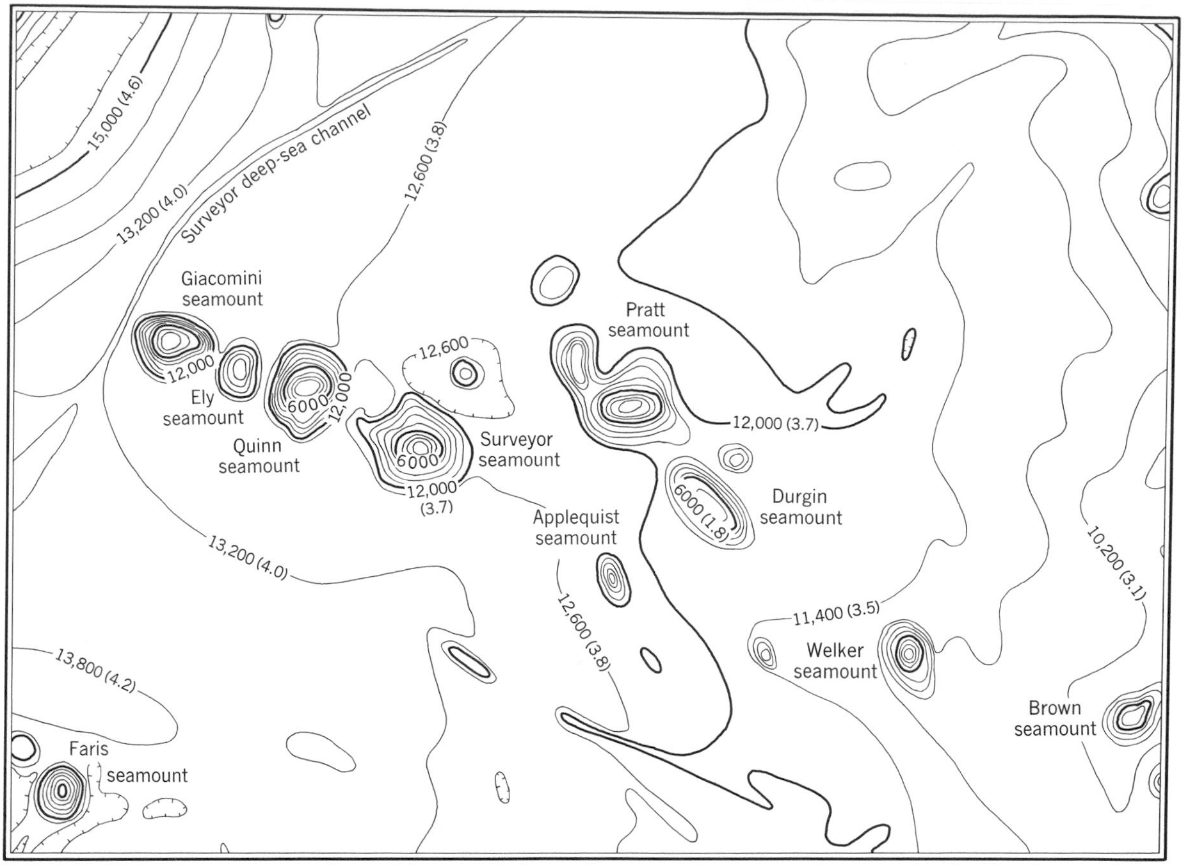

**FIGURE 24.11.** This portion of a bathymetric chart of the Gulf of Alaska shows ten seamounts rising above an abyssal plain. Contours labeled in ft, with km in parentheses. [After W. M. Gibson (1960), *Geol. Soc. Amer. Bull.*, vol. 71.]

century. A widely held explanation of the guyot is that it represents a volcanic cone formerly rising above sea level. Erosion by waves planed off the top, after which the earth's crust in that locality subsided, carrying the truncated volcano to its present depth far below the sea surface. A map of the submarine topography of the Gulf of Alaska shows many guyots rising above the Alaskan Abyssal Plain, which slopes gradually from a depth of 10,800 ft (3300 m) on the east to 16,800 ft (5100 m) on the west (Figure 24.11).

In the basin floor of the eastern Pacific Ocean is a network of submarine escarpments trending almost east–west in a series of nearly straight parallel lines (Figure 24.12). Actually these features are in part better described as narrow straight fractures, for in places they are moatlike in form, up to 30 mi (50 km) wide and as much as 10,000 ft (3000 m) deep. Their lengths are from 1500 to 3000 mi (2400 to 4800 km). There seems to be little doubt that these scarps and moats are produced by faulting and that each line represents a fracture zone extending deep into the crust.

Many other straight, narrow fault zones have been found over the ocean-basin floors. A striking example is the Ninetyeast Ridge of the Indian Ocean. This straight wall-like submarine ridge runs north–south for 3000 mi (4800 km) and rises some 11,000 ft (3400 m) above the adjacent floor.

**The Mid-Oceanic Ridge** We turn now to the third of the major divisions of the ocean basins, the *Mid-Oceanic Ridge* (Figure 24.5). One of the most remarkable of the major discoveries coming out of oceanographic explorations of the mid-twentieth century has been the charting of a great submarine mountain chain extending for a total length of some 40,000 mi (64,000 km) (Figure 24.13). The ridge runs down the middle of the North and South Atlantic ocean basins, into the Indian Ocean basin, then passes between Australia and Antarctica to enter the South Pacific basin. Turning north along the eastern side of the Pacific basin, where it is named the East Pacific Rise, the ridge contacts the North American continent along the coast of Mexico. The Mid-Oceanic Ridge also extends across the Arctic Ocean basin.

Of the great Mid-Oceanic Ridge the part best known from detailed studies is the *Mid-Atlantic Ridge,* seen in the profile of Figure 24.14. The ridge in its entirety is a belt, some 1200 to 1500 mi (1900 to 2400 km) wide, in which the surface rises through a series of steps from abyssal plains on both sides toward the central, or

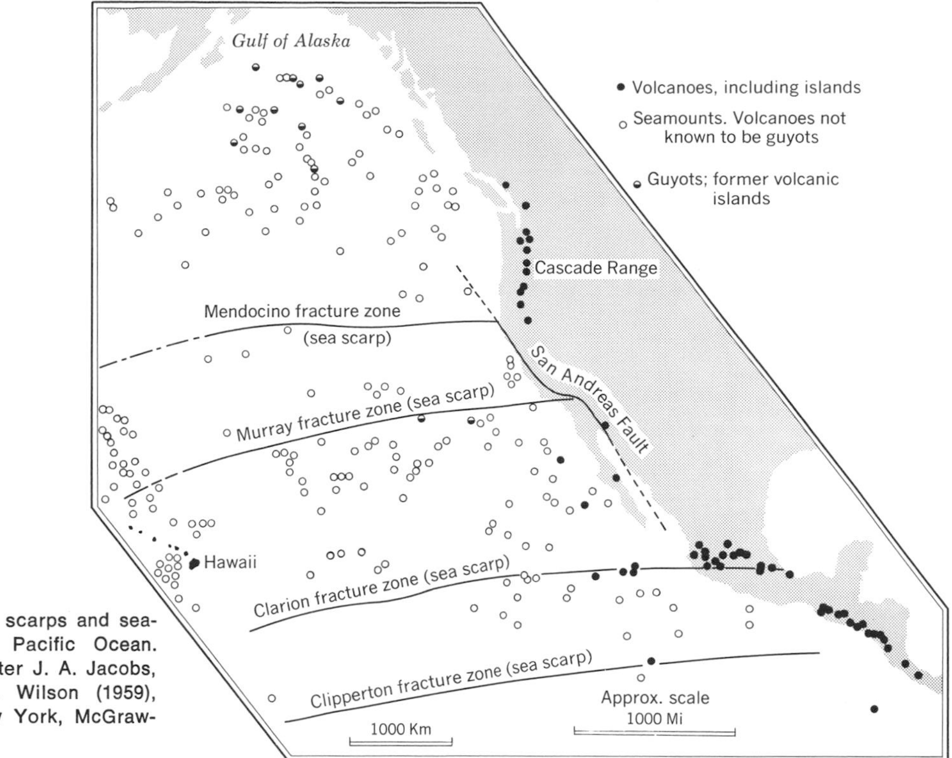


**FIGURE 24.12.** Map of sea scarps and seamounts of the northeast Pacific Ocean. [Data by H. W. Menard. After J. A. Jacobs, R. D. Russell, and J. T. Wilson (1959), *Physics and Geology,* New York, McGraw-Hill, p. 273, Figure 12-18.]

median, line where the ridge assumes mountainous proportions. The higher points lie at depths of 6000 to 9000 ft (1800 to 2700 m). With reference to the adjoining abyssal plains, then, the Mid-Atlantic Ridge has a height of roughly 12,000 ft (3700 m).

A distinctive feature of the principal continuous ridge is that instead of having a single high crest line, as many narrow mountain chains of the continents have, there is a characteristic trenchlike depression, or *rift valley,* running precisely down the mid-line of the highest part of the ridge. This rift shows well on the upper profile of Figure 24.14. Along with other parallel scarps and steplike rises on both sides, the rift strongly suggests that the crust has been pulled apart along the central zone. A particularly significant feature of the axial rift is that it is broken into many segments, the ends of which appear to be offset along transverse fractures (Figure 24.13). This arrangement of offset segments is particularly striking in the equatorial zone of the Atlantic Ocean, where a single offset displaces the main axial rift by as much as 400 mi (640 km). Figure 24.15 is a detailed outline map of a similar zone of offsetting south of Africa. It seems obvious by inspection that the transverse fracture zones are transcurrent faults (Chapter 23). More will be said of this problem of ridge origin in the discussion of structure and evolution of the continents and ocean basins.

**Trenches and island arcs** The deepest points on the ocean floors occur in long narrow *trenches,* also referred to as *foredeeps,* commonly with maximum depths of 24,000 to 30,000 ft (7300 to 9000 m). Almost invariably the trenches lie immediately adjacent to and on the oceanward side of long narrow submarine ridges, the *island arcs* (Figure 24.16), or coastal ranges of the continental margins, known as the *mountain arcs.*

An example of a deep trench of the North Atlantic Ocean is the Puerto Rico Trench, running along the north side of that island, and its extension to the west in the Cayman Trench, lying south of Cuba (Figure 24.17). A cross-profile of the Puerto Rico Trench is shown in the right-hand side of the upper profile of Figure 24.7. The deepest point in this trench is more than 27,000 ft (8400 m) below sea level.

Trenches of the western North Pacific Ocean are particularly striking (Figure 24.16). Deepest of all may be the Marianas Trench, where a record depth of 36,152 ft (11,022 m) has been measured. At least four other Pacific trenches have depths over 32,800 ft (10,000 m).

Trenches have widths of 25 to 75 mi (40 to 120 km) and lengths of 300 to over 2800 mi (500 to over 4500 km). Longest of all is the Peru-Chile Trench off the west coast of South America, running for 3660 mi (5900 km) (Figure 24.18). This trench is particularly striking because of the proximity and great elevation of the Andes range, which lies only a short distance to the east.

At this point it must suffice to note that the oceanic trenches are zones along which the earth's crust has been forced downward and that this activity is closely tied in with the elevation of the adjacent island and mountain arcs. Even though they are partially filled by soft sediment from turbidity currents, so that the floors are locally abyssal plains, the filling process is so slow

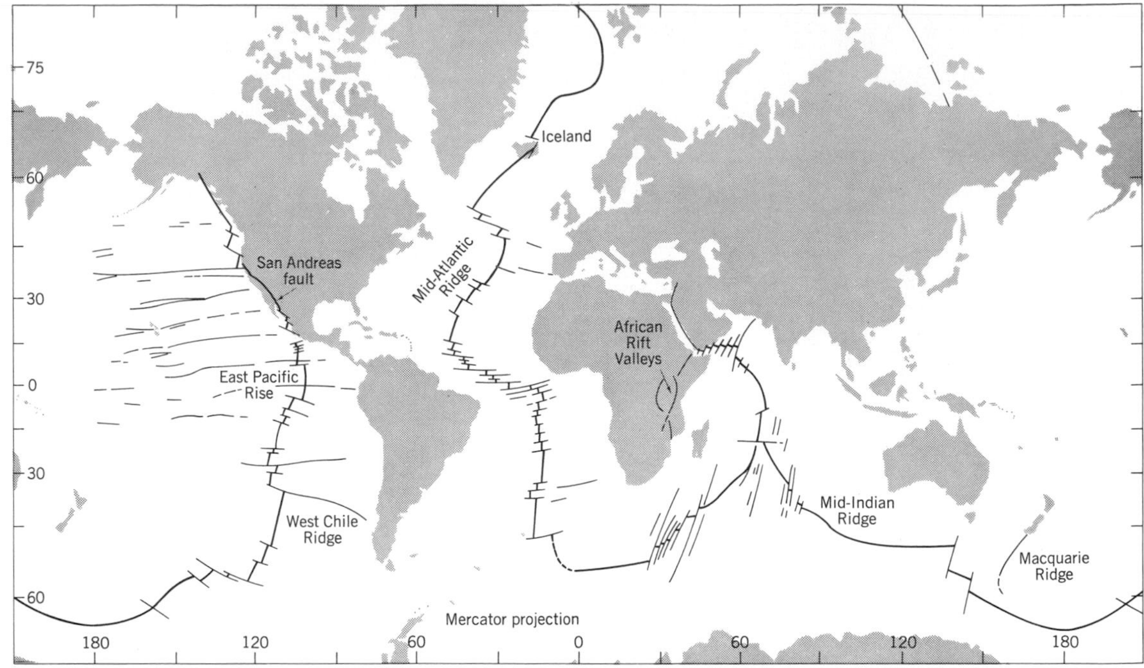


**FIGURE 24.13.** Mid-oceanic ridge system (heavy lines) and related fracture zones (light lines). [After L. R. Sykes (1969), in *The Earth's Crust and Upper Mantle,* Geophysical Monograph 13, Washington, D.C., Amer. Geophys. Union, p. 149, Figure 1. Based on data of B. C. Heezen, M. Tharp, H. W. Menard, and other sources.]

that the trenches maintain their great depth. Should a similar trench be produced within the limits of a continent, it would be kept filled with sedimentary deposits brought by debris-ladened streams issuing from adjacent mountain ranges, as in the case of the Indo-Gangetic plain bordering the Himalaya Range.

## Sediment accumulations on the ocean floor

Beginning with the voyage of *H.M.S. Challenger,* in the 1870s, oceanographers have systematically taken samples of materials of the ocean floors. At first this could be done only by means of dredges that scraped off a thin layer and brought it to the surface for examination. Dredge samples taken in the deep ocean basins by the *Challenger* expedition proved to be highly misleading, for they were found to consist almost entirely of soft, very fine-textured clays.

By the 1930's information about the sediment layer itself began to be obtained by the process of *coring,* which is simply vertical penetration by a long section of pipe that cuts a cylindrical sample, or *core.* Brought

**FIGURE 24.14.** These two profiles across the Mid-Atlantic Ridge show two somewhat different sets of features associated with the ridge. The profiles are based upon soundings continuously recorded by echo sounder on the Research Vessel *Atlantis.* [After B. C. Heezen, M. Tharp, and M. Ewing (1959), *The Floors of the Oceans,* Geol. Soc. Amer. Spec. Paper 65, Plate 22.]

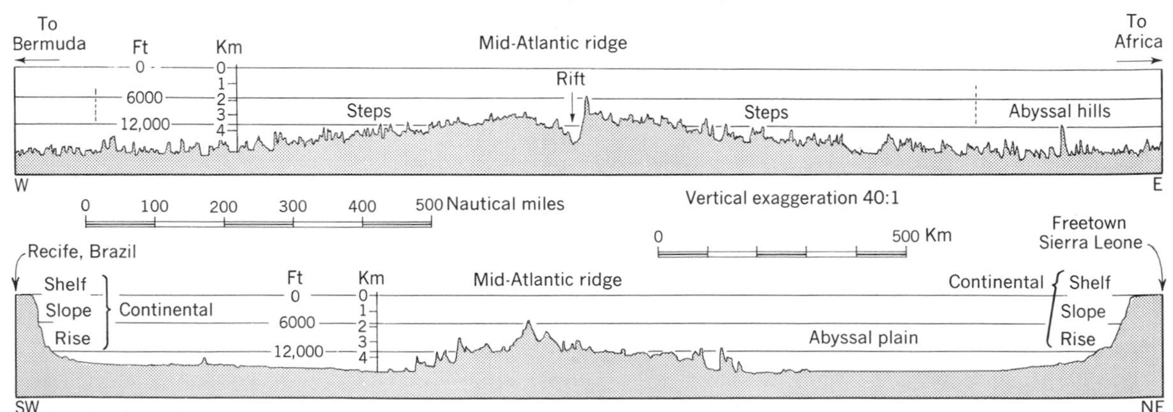

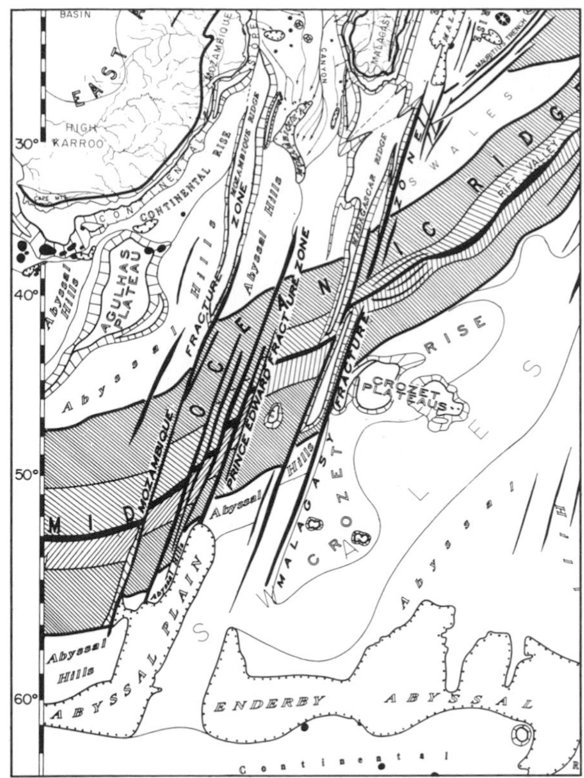


FIGURE 24.15. Fracture zones oblique to the axis of the Mid-Oceanic Ridge southeast of Africa. [Portion of map of physiographic provinces to accompany *Physiographic Diagram of the Indian Ocean* by B. C. Heezen and M. Tharp (1964), Boulder, Colo., Geol. Soc. of Amer., reproduced by permission.]

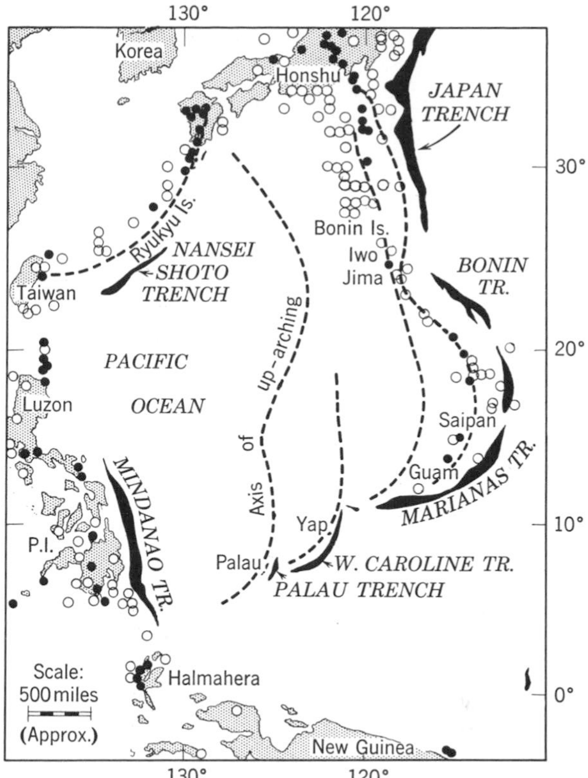


FIGURE 24.16. Map of the western Pacific Ocean showing trenches (black), island arcs (dashed lines), active volcanoes (black dots), and epicenters of deep-focus earthquakes (open circles). (© 1960, John Wiley & Sons, New York. Based on a map by H. H. Hess.)

to the surface, the core is extruded, giving a complete cross section of the layer. In the 1940's the core sampler was improved in design to include an internal piston, which helps to hold the core intact as it is thrust upward into the tube. Tube lengths were gradually increased until cores over 50 ft (15 m) were readily obtained (Figure 24.19). The cores are cut in half longitudinally, revealing the bedded structure and permitting small interior samples to be taken for microscopic examination and chemical and physical analysis.

The most recent advance in deep sampling of the sediment of the ocean floor has been through the use of oil-well drilling methods. Following the demise of project MOHOLE (Chapter 23), oceanographers formed a program named the National Ocean Sediment Coring Project. Under support of the National Science Foundation, a specially designed 10,000-ton vessel, the *Glomar Challenger,* was built with the capability of drilling into the ocean floor to a depth of 2500 ft (750 m) in water depths as great as 25,000 ft (7600 m). Not only can the drill pass through a sediment layer, but also it can obtain cores of the bedrock beneath. In 1968 the *Glomar Challenger,* with teams of scientists aboard to direct the research, embarked upon a cruise that by the end of 1969 had drilled 80 holes and logged over 40,000 mi (64,000 km) of traverse of the Atlantic and Pacific Oceans. In terms of new findings concerning the sediment and bedrock of the ocean floors, this cruise has been hailed as the most successful oceanographic mission of all time.

A different type of information concerning the sediments of the ocean floors comes from application of the *seismic reflection* principle. In a manner somewhat like that of the precision depth recorder, the impulse from a small explosion is sent to the ocean bottom and reflected from the bottom and from layered structures below the bottom. As in the case of the echo sounder, the returning waves are picked up by a hydrophone and recorded on paper. In a *seismic profiler traverse* explosions or other forms of sudden energy release are made at 10-second intervals along the line of the ship's course and there results a profile showing the contact of sediment with bedrock, as well as profiles of certain reflecting horizons within the sediment. As applied by Professor Maurice Ewing, John E. Ewing, and co-workers of the staff of the Lamont-Doherty Geological Observatory, seismic reflection profiling has yielded a remarkably clear picture of the distribution and thickness of the sediment layer over the ocean floors.

One type of sediment accumulation, seen in the Mid-Oceanic Ridge with its strong relief, is *ponding* of sediment in isolated topographic basins (Figure 24.20).

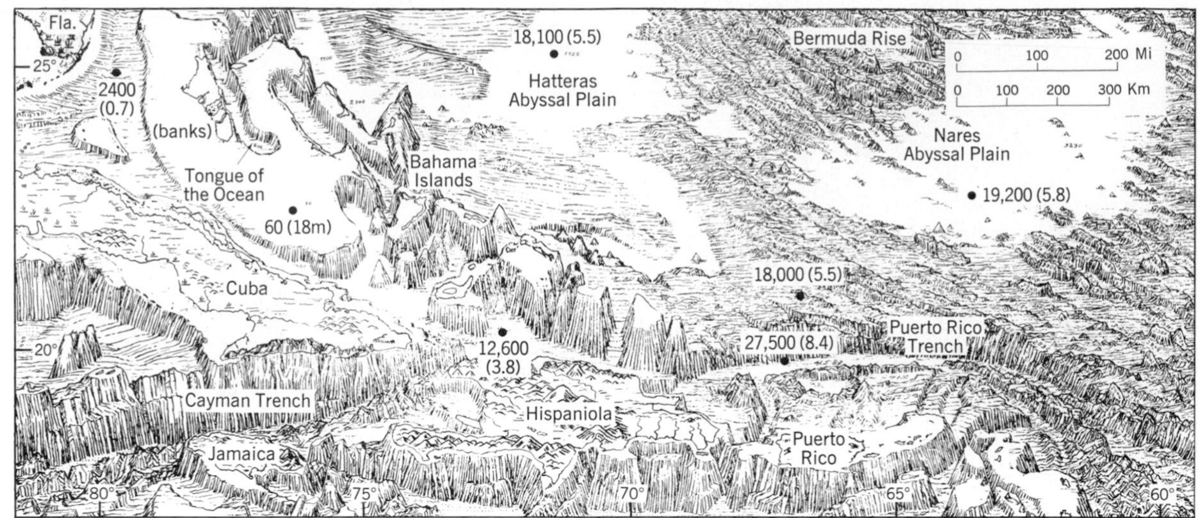


**FIGURE 24.17.** Puerto Rico and Cayman trenches. Depths in ft; km in parentheses. [Portion of *Physiographic Diagram of the North Atlantic Ocean* (1968), revised, by B. C. Heezen and M. Tharp, Boulder, Colo., Geol. Soc. of Amer., reproduced by permission.]

Notice that sediment is lacking near the ridge axis but thickens outward toward the flanks, where sediment thickness up to 1600 to 2000 ft (500 to 600 m) are encountered.

A different type of sediment accumulation is shown in Figure 24.21. Here the ocean floor is a smooth abyssal plain at a depth of over 6000 ft (5000 m), grading eastward into the rising flank of the Mid-Atlantic Ridge. The sediment accumulation, over 10,000 ft (3000 m) thick in places, forms a continuous blanket. Two reflecting horizons are revealed by the seismic profiler traverse. The upper of these, designated *Horizon A,* represents a marked physical change in the sediment type.

Partial filling of the Peru-Chile trench by sediment is shown in Figure 24.22. Whereas in the upper seismic reflection profile the trench is barren of sediment, the lower profile shows about 5000 ft (1500 m) of sediment producing a flat floor. Many reflective layers give a strongly bedded appearance to this deposit.

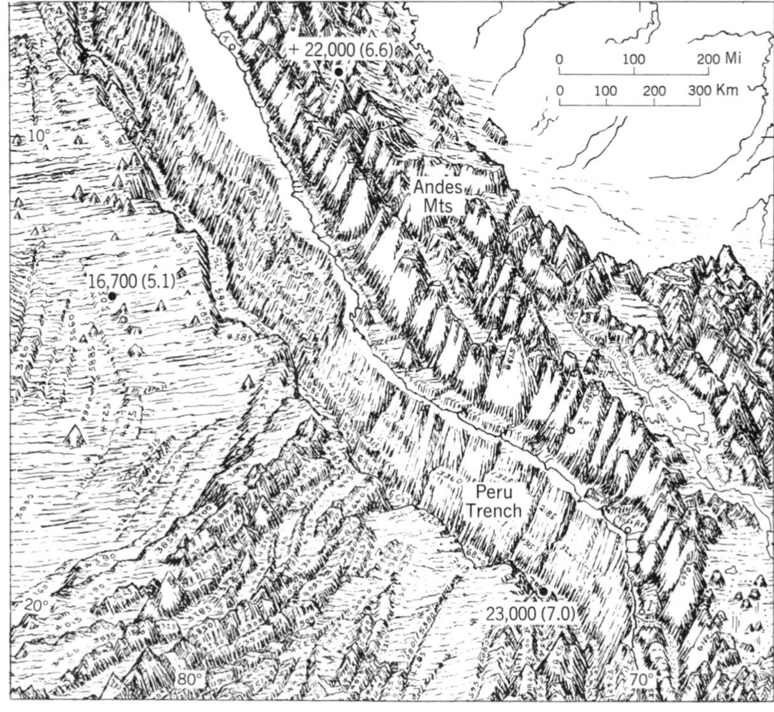


**FIGURE 24.18.** The Peru-Chile Trench, off the west coast of South America. [Portion of *Physiographic Diagram of the South Atlantic Ocean* (1961), By B. C. Heezen and M. Tharp, Boulder, Colo., Geol Soc. of Amer., reproduced by permission.]

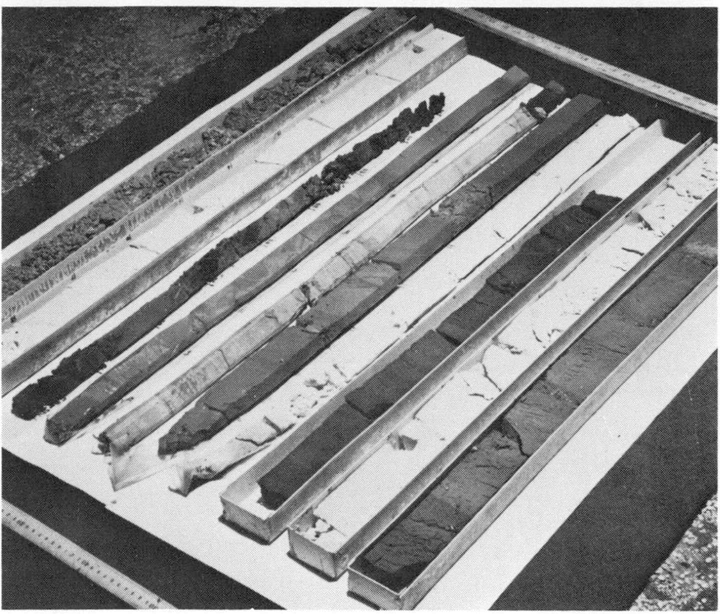

**FIGURE 24.19.** Obtaining deep-sea cores aboard the Research Vessel *Vema*. On the left a piston coring tube with its heavy driving weight is prepared for lowering. On the right members of the ship's company bring a 50 ft (12 m) core aboard. Below are shown cores that have been extruded into plastic tubes, then sliced through the center to reveal composition and layering for study. Core segments shown here are about 3 ft (1 m) long. (Courtesy of Lamont-Doherty Geological Observatory of Columbia University, and National Academy of Sciences, IGY.)

**Terrestrial sources of deep ocean sediment** Setting aside for the moment the thick accumulations of marine sediments found at shallow depths on the continental margins and obviously derived from the continents through direct transportation by streams, waves, and currents, let us consider the possible terrestrial sources of sediment on the deep ocean floors far from land.

Atmospheric circulation provides an important transport mechanism for the movement of extremely fine particles from lands to the oceans. Mineral particles are raised high into the atmosphere by dust storms of the tropical deserts in latitudes 10° to 30° north and south. Tropical easterlies carry these particles far westward over the adjacent oceans, where they may settle to the ocean surface or may be carried down in raindrops. Other important sources of atmospheric dusts are volcanic eruptions, emitting minute shards of volcanic glass (Chapter 21), and the vaporization of meteors in the upper atmosphere (Chapter 5).

Transport by surface ocean currents is an obvious means for the wide distribution of very fine suspended particles derived from sources close to the continental

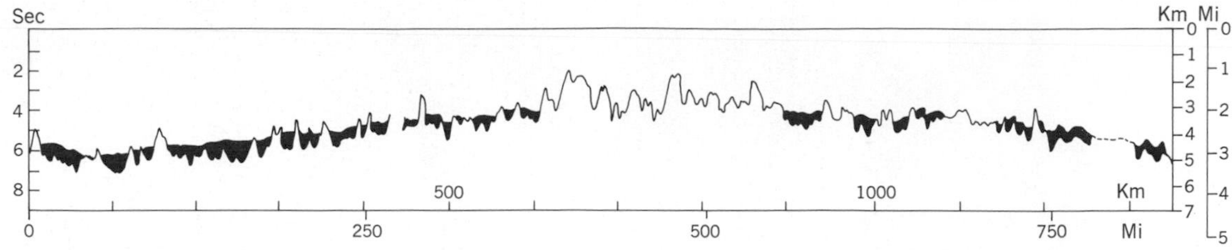


**FIGURE 24.20.** Tracing of seismic reflection profile obliquely crossing the Mid-Atlantic Ridge at about 40° N. Sediment deposits shown in solid black. Basement rock (bedrock) lies beneath. [After J. Ewing and M. Ewing (1967), *Science*, vol. 156, p. 1591, Figure 2.]

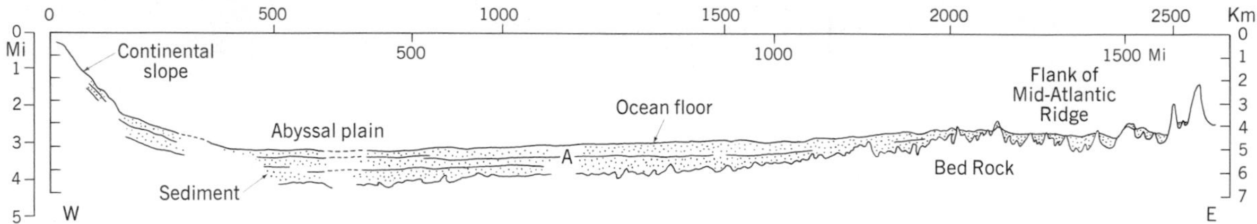


**FIGURE 24.21.** Sketch of seismic reflection profile of the Argentine Basin of the South Atlantic, off Buenos Aires at latitude 36°–38° S. [After M. Ewing, W. J. Ludwig, and J. I. Ewing (1964), *Jour. Geophys. Res.*, vol. 69, p. 2011, Figure 6.]

margins. The patterns of oceanic circulation, particularly the great gyres and the Antarctic circumpolar current system, are described in Chapter 16.

A related mechanism is transport by icebergs, which float far out to sea and melt, dropping mineral fragments of many sizes. By this means even huge boulders may reach positions hundreds of miles from the nearest land.

The great bulk of the thick sediment layers found beneath abyssal plains and in trenches requires transport mechanisms of far greater capability than those described in the paragraphs above. *Bottom currents* capable of moving large quantities of sediment close to the ocean bed are thought to be of major importance, although their extent is not well known. Bottom photographs show various markings indicative of scour by rapid flow. For example, *ripple marks* of a type produced by currents have been photographed at depths as great as 16,000 ft (5000 m) (Figure 24.23). Structure of the sediments themselves in some instances shows that the grains have been sorted and redeposited by current action. The presence of deep countercurrents, referred to in Chapter 16, has been confirmed by direct measurement. There is now abundant evidence that bottom currents with speeds of 0.3 to 0.6 ft (10 to 20 cm) per second, capable of moving sand of medium and coarse grades, operate at depths as great as 10,000 to 20,000 ft (3000 to 6000 m). It should be noted that bottom currents can move sediment on horizontal surfaces, or even up-grade, but they usually flow along the contour of sloping surfaces.

**FIGURE 24.22.** Sketches of seismic reflection profiles of barren (*above*) and partially-filled (*below*) sections of the Peru-Chile Trench. [After D. W. Scholl, R. von Huene, and J. B. Ridlon (1968), *Science*, vol. 159, p. 870, Figure 2.]

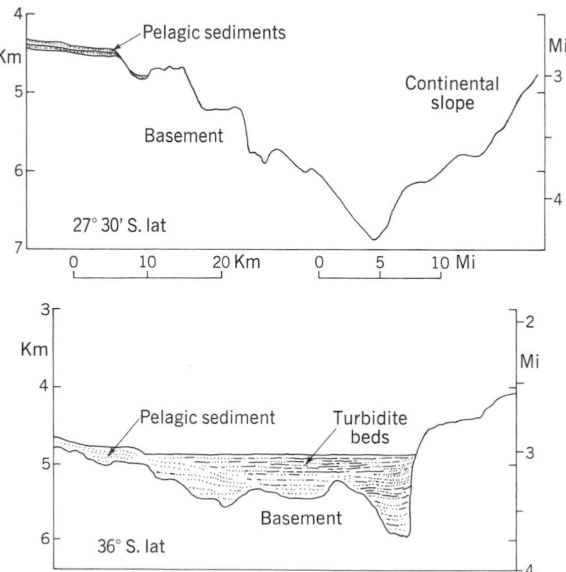


Finally, the action of turbidity currents in transporting sediment from relatively high positions of accumulation to the deepest parts of the ocean floor is now recognized as probably responsible for most thick accumulations of sediment consisting of silts and fine sands as well as of finer particles.

A turbidity current crossing the continental slope and rise off the Grand Banks of Newfoundland in 1929 was sufficiently powerful to break in succession several transatlantic cables lying across its path. From a knowledge of the exact time of each cable break the velocity of the turbidity current was determined and found to have decreased from 63 mi (100 km) per hour, where the bottom gradient was 1 in 170, to 14 mi (23 km) per hour, where the gradient was only 1 in 2000. In this case the turbidity current was set off by an earthquake shock, causing unconsolidated sediments of the continental slope to slump and to mix with sea water to produce a highly turbid suspension. The turbid tongue

**FIGURE 24.23.** Short-crested ripples on the floor of the Scotia Sea (lat. 56°S, long. 63°W) at a depth of about 13,000 ft (4000 m). (Photograph by courtesy of Charles D. Hollister, Woods Hole Oceanographic Institution.)

ultimately spread out upon the abyssal plain, forming a layer of sediment averaging 3 ft (1 m) thickness over an area of perhaps 80,000 sq mi (200,000 sq km).

An interesting feature of the deposits of turbidity currents is the gradation of particle sizes within each layer resulting from varying rates of settlement of sizes from suspension, as explained in Chapter 22. Turbidity-current deposits show graded bedding throughout, each graded layer being the result of a single turbidity flow (Figure 22.10).

Total thickness of sediments of turbidity-current origin varies greatly from place to place on the ocean-basin floor. As the seismic reflection profiles show, this type of sediment is thickest on the sides of basins and the continental rise, within reach of the continental shelves from which the sediment is derived. In addition to continental sources, turbidity currents can be derived from sediment accumulation on seamounts and on the steep upland slopes within the Mid-Oceanic Ridge.

## Classification and composition of deep-sea sediments

Our knowledge of the nature and distribution of sediments of the deep ocean floor is far from complete at this time, but new information is being obtained at a rapid rate. Despite the complexity of the sediment distribution patterns, significant facts are known and serve as the basis for classifying the sediments and specifying the environments of their accumulation.

Four main classes of deep-sea sediments are shown in Table 24.1. We can begin with the *biogenic-pelagic sediments,* which consist principally of calcareous or siliceous mineral matter secreted by organisms. The word biogenic is used in the same sense as in Chapter 22. The word pelagic (from the Greek word *pelagikos,* for "sea") simply means "originating in, or derived from, the ocean." The pelagic organisms of most importance in furnishing deep-sea sediment are *plankton,* the very small floating plants and animals growing in vast numbers in the shallow well-oxygenated surface layer of the ocean. These organisms secrete hard structures, referred to as *tests.* Upon death of the organism the organic matter is destroyed, but the tests sink down to great depths and, if not dissolved in passage, reach the ocean floor.

**TABLE 24.1. CLASSIFICATION OF DEEP-SEA SEDIMENTS***

| | |
|---|---|
| I | Biogenic-Pelagic Sediments |
| | Oozes |
| | Calcareous ooze |
| | Siliceous ooze |
| | Organic compounds |
| II | Pelagic-Detrital Sediments |
| | Brown clay (Red clay) |
| | Glacial-marine sediment |
| | Volcanic ash |
| III | Bottom-Transported Detrital Sediments |
| | Turbidites |
| | Contourites |
| | Terrigenous muds |
| IV | Hydrogenic Sediments |
| | Montmorillonite |
| | Zeolites (Phillipsite) |
| | Manganese nodules |

* Based in part on a classification by K. Turekian (1968), *Oceans,* Englewood Cliffs, N.J., Prentice-Hall, p. 34, Table 3-1.

Accumulated sediment formed of 30 percent or more of tests is classified as deep-sea *ooze* and is further subdivided according to whether the tests are of calcareous or siliceous composition. *Calcareous ooze* is composed of the tests of foraminifera, or pteropods, or of coccoliths, all of calcareous composition. Foramini-

A

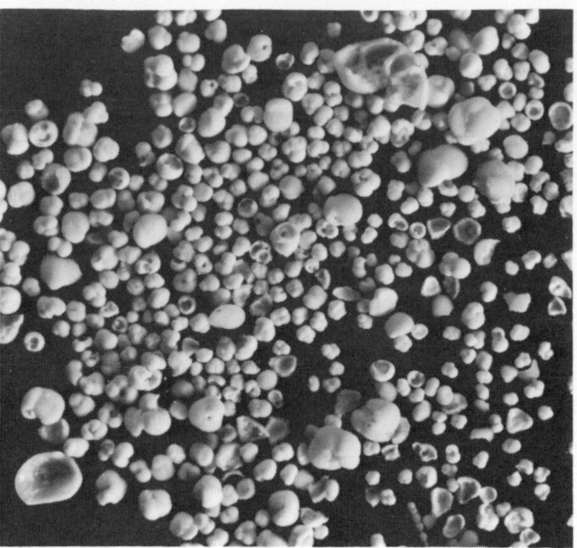

B

**FIGURE 24.24** Calcareous ooze of the ocean floor. (*A*) Photograph of the deep-sea floor showing calcareous ooze at a depth of 15,000 ft (4510 m) in the east equatorial Pacific Ocean. The photograph shows an area of about 50 sq ft (5 sq m). The small mounds in the right foreground are probably formed by the burrowing action of worms. Several spongelike animals and small echinoids are visible. (Photograph by Carl J. Shipek, U.S. Navy Electronics Laboratory, San Diego, California.) (*B*) Calcareous shells and shell fragments separated by sieving a sample of Globigerina ooze, the bulk of which is composed of fine clay material. This sample is from a core obtained by scientists of the Research Vessel *Vema* from a depth of 10,000 ft (3000 m) in the South Atlantic Ocean. Enlargement about 12 times. (Photograph by A. McIntyre, courtesy of Lamont-Doherty Geological Observatory of Columbia University.)

fera are one-celled animals, of which the genus *Globigerina* is particularly important (Figure 24.24). Commonly present along with foraminifera are tiny molluscs, known as *pteropods,* which secrete tests of aragonite. The term *globigerina ooze* is applied to sediment rich in tests of both foraminifera and pteropods. Coccoliths are fragile calcite tests of a type of algae (microscopic plants) and are an abundant constituent of the very fine-grained calcareous oozes.

Because the calcareous tests are dissolved in sea water as they sink, calcareous oozes accumulate only on floors in water depths less than about 15,000 ft (4500 m). Consequently bottom areas with high proportions of calcium carbonate are quite closely correlated with topographically high areas of the ocean basins. In the Atlantic Ocean concentration of calcium carbonate is high along the axis of the Mid-Atlantic Ridge but is relatively low on the abyssal basins on either side. Rate of biological productivity, which tends to be high in areas of warm ocean currents and in zones of upwelling, also influences the richness of calcium carbonate in bottom sediments.

*Siliceous ooze,* consisting of 30 percent or more of siliceous tests, is derived from a number of organisms, of which the diatoms and radiolaria are most important. *Diatoms* are one-celled plants, and *radiolaria* are microscopic animals. Both secrete ornate siliceous tests with radial symmetry (Figure 24.25). Siliceous oozes are found largely in two oceanic zones—between latitudes 45°–60° in both hemispheres, and in limited portions of the equatorial Pacific Ocean.

Rate of accumulation of oozes has been estimated as from 0.4 to 2 in. (1 to 5 cm) per 1000 years. The oozes, both calcareous and siliceous, usually contain substantial amounts of inorganic clays.

Under the heading of biogenic pelagic sediments we can also include organic matter that escapes decomposition and becomes incorporated into muds on the floors of deep basins, where anaerobic conditions prevail. This environment, which is comparatively rare today, is described in Chapter 22 in connection with the origin of petroleum. An example of such a basin is the Black Sea, over 7250 ft (2200 m) deep and almost completely cut off from the Mediterranean Sea. Here, under stagnant bottom conditions, oxygen is depleted and a black mud rich in organic matter is deposited. Over the oceans generally, water circulation is adequate to bring oxygen to even the deepest places, allowing destruction of organic matter as it sinks or upon arrival at the bottom.

*Pelagic-detrital sediments* are particles of nonbiogenic matter that have settled to the bottom from the near-surface layer above. As we have already stated, such particles may be brought from continental locations as suspended matter in surface ocean currents or in icebergs drifting with those currents. Volcanic and terrestrial dusts carried by winds also furnish detrital matter to the ocean surface, as does the vaporization of meteors in the overlying outer atmosphere. It is obvious that the mineral composition of these detrital sediments can be quite complex, with the proportions of the components depending upon geologic nature of the sources and distances from those sources.

The most widespread of pelagic-detrital sediments is *brown clay,* which is a soft plastic material with a greasy feel. This clay typically is low in calcium carbonate (less than 30 percent) and consists for the most part of clay minerals, among them illite, chlorite, and kaolinite derived from continental sources. (These minerals are described in Chapter 22.) Montmorillonite may be present but is believed to have been derived by alteration of volcanic materials after their deposition. Quartz in minute grains is abundant in some brown clays, and there may be minor amounts of feldspars and micas, all derived from continental surfaces. Rate of accumulation of brown clay is extremely slow and has been estimated at 0.004 to 0.04 in. (0.1 to 1 mm) per 1000 years.

The relative abundances of kaolinite and chlorite in brown clay change with geographical position in a manner that reflects conditions of origin of those minerals. Kaolinite, which is produced by silicate rock weathering in warm humid climates of low latitudes, is 5 to 15 times more abundant than chlorite in the Atlantic Ocean in the latitude range 20° N. to 20° S. Chlorite, which is easily destroyed in a warm climate, becomes two to four times more abundant than kaolinite in latitudes poleward of about 45°. Illite, produced from the alteration of micas, shows its greatest abundances near the continents, from which it is derived. Quartz shows concentrations in the lee of tropical deserts, from which it is brought by easterly winds. Quartz concentration also occurs in middle to high latitude locations, where it can be attributed to an abundance of freshly pulverized rock produced by Pleistocene continental glaciation.

On deep ocean floors in both Arctic and Antarctic waters sediments have been found that appear to have been brought by icebergs from continental glaciers. Designated as *glacial-marine,* these sediments consist of silt with some clay and are formed of finely ground fresh rock. Consequently they show little oxidation or mineral alteration. Glacial-marine sediments were evidently far more widespread in area of deposition during stages of glaciation, for they have been found buried beneath globigerina ooze forming today.

Fine volcanic ash travels widely as dust in the atmosphere, as already stated. Dust from a single great volcanic explosion achieves global distribution and can be expected to produce a very thin pelagic sediment layer simultaneously in many parts of the world ocean. Horizons of volcanic ash have been found in many sediment cores and there is no doubt that a definable layer up to several hundreds of miles in extent can be associated with a single volcanic eruption. Ash horizons are represented in deep-sea sediment by concentrations of glass shards. This glass is highly susceptible to mineral alteration, as explained in later paragraphs.

*Bottom-transported detrital sediments* have been mentioned earlier. These include thick accumulations of turbidity-current deposits, or *turbidites,* which are sands and coarse silts showing graded bedding. Other stratified sands and silts, the *contourites,* show sorting and stratification by contour-following bottom currents. Bordering the continents, in a zone at or near the base of the continental slopes, are found *terrigenous muds,* apparently brought to the deep ocean floor by bottom currents. Finer-grained than the sand and coarse silt of turbidites, the terrigenous muds are silty clays. The presence of silt and the lack of complete oxidation set the terrigenous muds apart from brown clay. Colors of the terrigenous muds may be blue, green, black, or red. Blue and green colors result from the presence of ferrous iron oxide and reflect a deficiency of oxygen, or a lack of time for oxidation to have occurred. Red muds, colored by ferric iron oxide, show complete oxidation of iron, but this probably occurred during transport on the lands. Black muds, as we have already noted, have a relatively high organic content and show a depositional environment of stagnant water with little oxygen present.

*Hydrogenic sediments* of the deep ocean floors include minerals formed by alteration in place or reformed from other minerals.[1] Perhaps the most important alteration product is the clay mineral montmorillonite, described in Chapter 22. This mineral is derived from volcanic materials, including volcanic ash and basaltic rock exposed on the ocean floor. A second alteration product is *phillipsite,* a silicate mineral of the *zeolite group,* also derived from volcanic materials of basaltic composition. Phillipsite is a hydrous aluminosilicate of calcium, sodium, and potassium. It forms in minute needle-like crystals that may constitute as much as 50 percent or more of the bottom sediment in parts of the central Pacific Ocean basin, where basaltic volcanic rocks are abundant. This mineral is rare near the bordering continents and is not found in the other oceans.

A great deal of interest centers around the finding of abundant nodules of hydrous manganese and iron oxides exposed on the surface of the deep ocean floors in many places. Referred to as *manganese nodules,* these objects often prove to be thick mineral coatings surrounding nuclei of volcanic rock (Figure 24.26). Manganese nodules are believed to be formed from manganese and iron derived either from detrital sediments of continental origin or from volcanic rocks of the ocean floor. Although widely distributed over the deep ocean floors, manganese nodules seem not to be present in areas where sediment rich in calcium carbonate is accumulating in abundance.

The deep-sea sediments have been described here in some detail because of their great importance for the interpretation of global environmental conditions. Cores of these deposits show alternations of various types of sediment, each reflecting certain physical and chemical conditions of the ocean waters or a certain set of climatic conditions prevailing in the atmosphere. For example, a thick accumulation of turbidites reflects a glacial stage in which vast amounts of sediment were being brought to the brink of the continental shelf. Particular species of foraminifera are associated with water temperature of a given range. By studying species variations in layers of calcareous ooze a record of changing atmospheric temperatures can be derived. (See Chapter 41.)

[1] Alternatively, the term *indigenous sediments* is used. The minerals of which they are formed are also described as *authigenic,* meaning "formed in place."

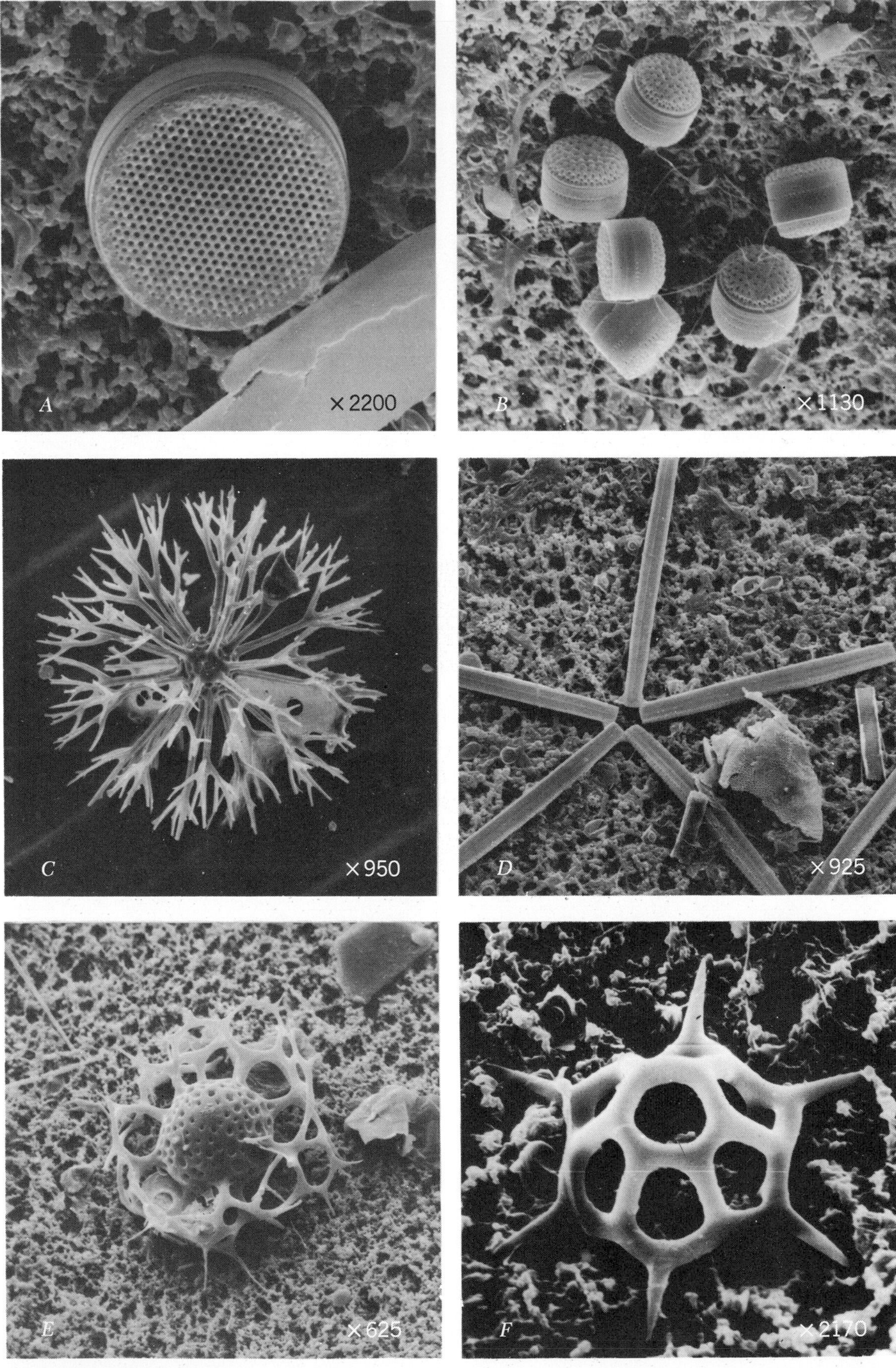
A
×2200
B
×1130
C
×950
D
×925
E
×625
F
×2170

**FIGURE 24.26.** A manganese nodule, about 4 in. (11 cm) high, dredged from the floor of the Atlantic Ocean. Cross section reveals a nucleus of volcanic rock (light color) surrounded by a layer of manganese and iron oxides. (Karl K. Turekian, *Oceans,* © 1968. By permission of the author and Prentice-Hall, Inc.)

## Coral reefs and the reef deposits

Coral reefs are massive rock structures of biogenic origin built close to sea level along coasts situated in warm waters of low latitudes. It is appropriate that we inquire into this subject as a part of an examination of the ocean basins because coral reefs form on the shores of many volcanic islands rising sharply from the deep ocean floor. Here detrital fragments of coral rock contribute sediment to the adjacent ocean floor. Because coral reefs form only in very shallow water, they are important indicators of changes in sea level. Rising or sinking of the crust beneath the ocean floor can be interpreted from reef deposits found today far above or below the level at which they were formed.

The framework of reefs is built by the secretions of both corals and algae growing vigorously in the surf zone. The living animals and plants build new structures upon old, extending reefs seaward into deeper water or upward to the surface. Wave attack pulverizes exposed coral structures to form a calcareous sediment, which may be deposited in cavities in the reef or spread out on the seaward slope.

Coral reefs are largely limited to the latitude zone between 30° N. and 25° S., where water temperatures are at least as high as 68° F (20° C) and usually between 77° and 86° F (25° and 30° C). Global distribution of waters above these temperatures can be found on the world maps of sea-surface temperatures, Figure 14.13. Vigorous growth of reef-building corals is limited to the surface-water zone, less than 150 ft (45 m) in depth. Corals thrive where the water is highly agitated as well as free of suspended sediment. As a result, reef growth is most rapid along exposed coastal positions—as off headlands—and along sides of islands facing into the prevailing direction of wave approach. Turbid water issuing from the mouths of streams inhibits or prevents reef development.

**FIGURE 24.25.** Plankton seen in high magnification under the electron scanning microscope. Magnifications indicated on individual photographs. These specimens were collected in plankton nets from within the uppermost 650 ft (200 m) in the western North Atlantic Ocean. *A, B,* and *D:* Diatoms. *C* and *E:* Radiolaria. *F:* Silicoflagellate. (Photographs by courtesy of Allan W. H. Bé, Lamont-Doherty Geological Observatory of Columbia University.)

**Forms of coral reefs** Coral reefs take three basic forms. First and simplest is the *fringing reef,* a shelf-like attachment to the land varying in width from 0.25 to 0.5 mi (0.4 to 0.8 km) or more when well developed (Figure 24.27). As noted above, fringing reefs are best developed along exposed headlands and may be absent in bays into which fresh water is being brought by streams (Figure 24.28). The reef surface is remarkably flat and lies at a level about one-third of the tide range below mean high water. The reef surface is thus exposed at low tide, but covered by surf at high tide.

A second form is the *barrier reef,* a long narrow coral embankment lying offshore and enclosing a lagoon between reef and mainland (Figure 24.29). The lagoon may be up to 10 mi (16 km) wide or wider, and the barrier reef up to 3000 ft (900 m) wide. The lagoon is normally 120 to 240 ft (35 to 75 m) deep and is flat-floored, but it has numerous stalk-like columns of coral that may reach up to the water surface. On the seaward side of the barrier the submarine surface slopes steeply away into deep water. Coral fragments are spread upon this slope. At intervals along the barrier reef there are gaps, termed *passes,* through which excess water brought into the lagoon by breaking waves is returned to the sea.

A third reef form is the *atoll,* a ring-like reef of coral enclosing only a lagoon of open water (Figure 24.30). In general, the reef and lagoon of an atoll are similar in form and development to the barrier reef and its lagoon. Here and there on the atoll are low islands of coral sand sufficiently large and high to be habitable but vulnerable to inundation in tropical storms. Atolls appear in isolated groups far from any islands of non-coralline rock in the vast expanses of the western Pacific Ocean.

**Theories of coral-reef development** Several plausible but divergent theories of origin of coral reefs, particularly of the fringing reefs and atolls, have been proposed and debated in the last 12 decades. Two are discussed here. Earliest and one of the most successful is the *subsidence theory* proposed by Charles Darwin in 1842 as a result of that great naturalist's observations during the voyage of *H.M.S. Beagle.* Darwin's theory was again taken up and strongly supported by the geomorphologist W. M. Davis in the 1920s.

According to Darwin and Davis a fringing reef is first formed during the slow subsidence of a volcanic island (Figure 24.31). Coral growth, continuing uninterruptedly during subsidence, builds the reef upward, maintaining the reef surface at or close to sea level. Because the reef is built directly upward while

**FIGURE 24.27.** A small island near the coast of Java, showing a fringing coral reef, best developed on the side facing the direction of wave approach. The white band is a beach of coral sand, bordering the central area of tropical rainforest. (Photograph by Luchtvaart-Afdeeling, Ned. Ind. Leger, Bandoeng.)

the island shore is gradually being inundated, a lagoon is formed and becomes wider as subsidence continues. Note that in the barrier-reef stage, shown in sector *B* of Figure 24.31, the island possesses the characteristic embayed coast to be expected from submergence of a fluvially dissected landmass. With continued subsidence the volcanic island is diminished to a small remnant, then it finally disappears, leaving an atoll lagoon in its place.

More recently, additional support of the subsidence theory has come from the Bikini Atoll in connection with seismic refraction studies carried out there after World War II. As shown in Figure 24.32, there is strong indication of the presence of more than 5000 ft (1500 m) of calcareous deposits beneath the atoll. A drill hole penetrated 2500 ft (760 m) of reef materials identified as formed in shallow water. Beneath the calcareous deposits is a possible volcanic core. If the seismic data are being correctly interpreted, there is no escape from the conclusion that reef growth kept pace with slow subsidence over a long period. If they had been rapidly brought down to depths below 200 ft (60 m) or so, the reef corals would have died and continued subsidence would have resulted in a flat-topped seamount, or guyot.

**FIGURE 24.28.** A fringing coral reef. (© 1960, John Wiley & Sons, New York. After a drawing by W. M. Davis.)

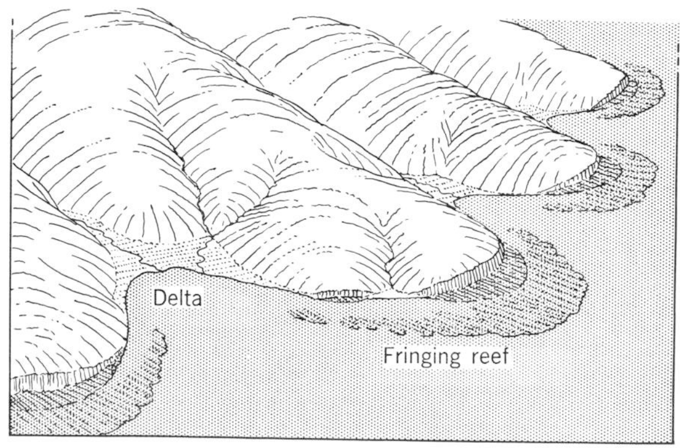


Holes drilled in 1952 into Eniwetok Atoll penetrated over 4000 ft (1200 m) of reef rock to reach a basement of basalt. All of the reef rock is identified as a shallow-water deposit and clearly represents the upbuilding of a submerging reef. Age of the reef rock was found to be progressively older with depth. That below 2800 ft (850 m) was of Eocene age, 36 million years old or more. Sinking of the oceanic crust of this magnitude and duration is of great importance in interpreting the development of the ocean basins (Chapter 25).

A second explanation of major importance is the *glacial-control theory* of reefs developed largely by the geologist R. A. Daly in the 1930s and 1940s. The theory is based upon an observation, made in 1894 by the European physical geographer Albrecht Penck, to the effect that the surprising uniformity of water depth in coral lagoons (approximately 250 ft; 75 m) might be explained by a low stand of ocean level during glaciations. Daly added to this point the postulate

**FIGURE 24.29.** Barrier coral reef, reef islands, and lagoon. Tahaa Island, Society Islands. (Official U.S. Navy Photograph.)

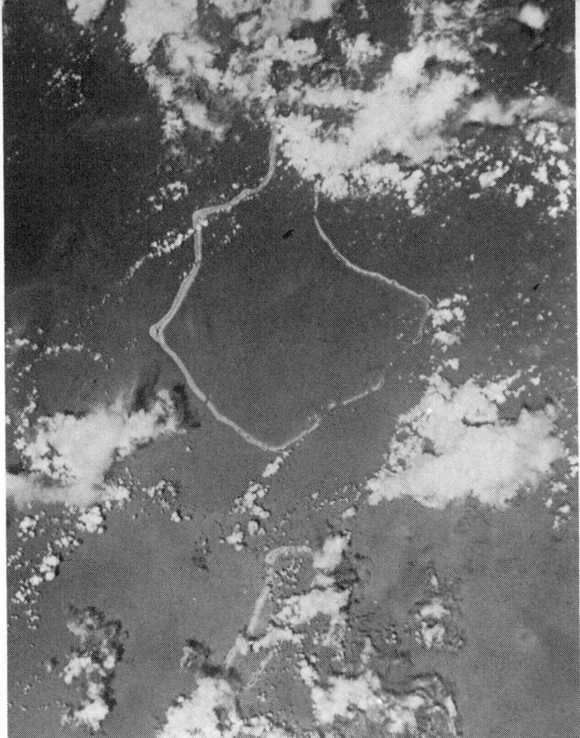

FIGURE 24.30. Rongelap Atoll, Marshall Islands, Pacific Ocean, photographed by astronauts aboard *Gemini V* spacecraft at an altitude of about 150 mi (240 km). (NASA photograph.)

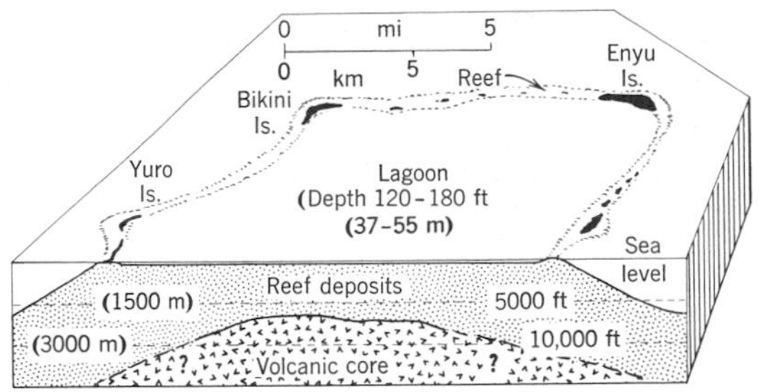


FIGURE 24.32. Block diagram of Bikini Atoll, Pacific Ocean. (© 1960, John Wiley & Sons, New York. Based on data of M. Dobrin and others.)

that the lowering of water temperature greatly reduced, or entirely stopped, coral-reef growth during these low-level stages, permitting wave action to abrade broad rock platforms along the coasts and in some cases to bevel small islands completely. Then, as the oceans rapidly warmed, coral growth set in at the margins of the eroded platforms. Reef upbuilding was maintained during the postglacial rise in sea level to reach the present level.

That the world-wide lowering of sea level and reduction of water temperatures occurred during Pleistocene glaciations is inescapable in the light of independent evidence. Whether wave erosion was sufficiently rapid to produce the broad rock platforms required by the glacial-control theory is, however, subject to serious question. Platforms as broad as those required for the larger atolls could not have been eroded in basaltic rock in the short spans of time available. The mechanisms of slow crustal subsidence and glacially controlled changes of sea level must both be taken into account and applied to the degree that evidence dictates in explaining the outward form and internal structure of coral reefs in any given locality.

FIGURE 24.31. Stages in the development of an atoll, according to the subsidence theory. (© 1960, John Wiley & Sons, New York. Based on a drawing by W. M. Davis.)

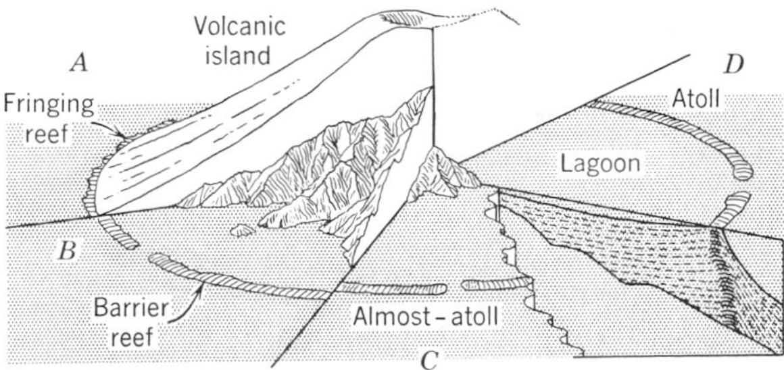


## Ocean basins and continents compared

The major relief forms and sedimentary accumulations of the continents are basically different from those of the ocean basins. We should expect these differences to exist for two reasons: (1) the mineral and rock composition, internal structure, and past history of the continents are radically different from those of the ocean basins, and (2) the processes of erosion of bedrock and the transportation and deposition of sediment operate far more intensively on land under the atmosphere than on the deep ocean floors.

Consider a few points of comparison between relief elements of the second order of magnitude of the continents and those of ocean basins, already treated:

Similarities in large features are largely in the mountain chains, which have the same arcuate patterns seen in the island arcs and submarine ridges, and are similarly produced by an upbending or upthrusting of the crust or by the growth of volcanoes. A significant feature of the form of mountain and island arcs is that the arc is usually bowed convexly outward from the main body of the continent. How this fits into a theory of the development of continents is treated in later pages.

Like the volcanic islands and seamounts of the oceans, some of the terrestrial volcanoes form isolated peaks rising from vast lowlands. More abundantly, however, volcanoes of the continents are superimposed on mountain arcs, and in this respect they are analogous to the volcanic islands built upon the island arcs.

As in the ocean basins, major parts of the continental surfaces are in vast plains, plateaus, or hill regions of only moderate relief. One basic difference is that whereas the abyssal plains are of extremely low slope and of extremely low relief, the continental surfaces slope relatively more steeply toward the sea because they are adjusted to the forms of river systems which drain the lands. Although there is extensive bottom transport of sediment beneath the oceans, most of this activity occurs close to the bordering continents where large terrestrial sources of sediment are available. Pelagic sediment accumulation is extremely slow in comparison with continental accumulation rates.

Erosion of bedrock masses of the ocean basins is trivial compared with that which occurs on the continents. Consequently, although great thickness of highly indurated rock upon the continents have been removed by erosion processes to produce low-lying plains of erosion, no such features have yet been formed in the ocean basins. Even the flattening of seamounts to produce guyots is probably the work of wave erosion at the sea surface. Erosional forms beneath the sea are probably largely limited to submarine canyons and landslide scars carved into the more steeply sloping surfaces underlain by poorly consolidated sediments of the continental slopes.

To understand why the ocean basins are so strikingly different in so many ways from the continents requires further study of the crust. Composition, thickness, and large-scale movements of the crust are examined in the two chapters to follow. In this examination lines of evidence provided by several scientific disciplines converge and reinforce one another to yield a consistent pattern of geological change.

## References for further study

Kuenen, P. H. (1950), *Marine Geology,* New York, Wiley, 568 pp.

Guilcher, A. (1958), *Coastal and Submarine Morphology,* New York, Wiley, 274 pp.

Heezen, B. C., M. Tharp, and M. Ewing (1959), *The Floors of the Oceans,* Geol. Soc. Amer., Special Paper 65, 122 pp.

Shepard, F. P. (1963), *Submarine Geology,* 2nd ed., New York, Harper & Row, 557 pp.

Fairbridge, R. W., Ed. (1966), *Encyclopedia of Oceanography,* New York, Reinhold, 1021 pp.

Turekian, K. K. (1968), *Oceans,* Englewood Cliffs, N.J., Prentice-Hall, 120 pp., chaps. 1, 2, 3.

# 25

# The crust of the continents and ocean basins

IN THIS CHAPTER we continue to inquire into the nature of the earth's crust, with particular attention to the differences between the oceanic crust and the continental crust. Once these differences are established, it is possible to draw inferences concerning the origins of the continents and ocean basins and to reconstruct the larger events of geologic history that have shaped the crust into the arrangements we find today.

A first step is to review the geologic evidence based upon analysis of rocks exposed at the surface or available through samples taken by drilling. As this evidence is very limited in terms of determining deep crustal structure, we must turn quickly to indirect methods of geophysics in which the data of seismic wave refraction and variations in the acceleration of gravity are combined to yield models of the crust and upper mantle in which the outlines of layers or irregular masses are drawn. The picture of crustal structure derived from these methods is essentially one of a static configuration of masses, whereas the complete picture is one of crustal change.

There is good reason to believe that the crust is now in motion—the occurrence of earthquakes and accompanying fault movements is ample proof—and that the accumulated movements of the geologic past have been of enormous scale. To develop the concept of a dynamic crust it is necessary to use other geophysical methods of investigation. These include a global analysis of the zones of seismic activity and vulcanism, a study of place-to-place variations in upward heat flow in the crust, and an interpretation of the regional patterns of minor variations in the external magnetic field.

## The geologic evidence

Many samples of the bedrock of the ocean floors have been obtained by dredging and by drilling. Dredge samples bring up rock fragments from submarine rock outcrops situated on high points of abyssal hills, seamounts, and the summits of ridges and peaks within the Mid-Oceanic Ridge system. Core samples of rock beneath the sediment layer have been obtained by drilling, initially by the MOHOLE project (Chapter 23) and subsequently by the National Ocean Sediment Coring Project (Chapter 24). In addition, volcanic islands built upon the deep ocean floors in mid-Atlantic and mid-Pacific regions bring to view samples of magmas coming from within the oceanic crust.

Almost without exception, the bedrock of samples from the ocean floors has proved to be basalt. Some basic intrusive rocks have also been found. Geologists recognize some regional differences between basalts of the various ocean basins. Basalts of the Atlantic Ocean basin are of a variety rich in olivine, whereas those of the Pacific Ocean basin contain little or no olivine. The latter variety is designated as *tholeiitic basalt.* The Mid-Oceanic Ridge seems to consist largely of basalt flows which have erupted from fissures and spread out upon the floor. Pillow lavas, indicative of cooling of magma upon contact with sea water, have been photographed and brought to the surface in samples. In later paragraphs, the basalt lava flows of the Mid-Oceanic Ridge will be discussed in further detail.

Basalts of the Pacific Ocean basin are found in a large

**FIGURE 25.1.** Continental shields of the Northern Hemisphere and their bordering mountain arcs. (© 1960, John Wiley & Sons, New York. Based on a map by A. J. Eardley.)

central region surrounded by a volcanic belt in which andesite lavas predominate. As early as 1911 a line was drawn in the southwest Pacific marking the division between andesitic and basaltic rocks. The *andesite line,* as this boundary is known, is often taken as marking the outer limit of the Pacific Ocean basin as a geologic unit (see Figure 25.23). Although large ocean areas—such as the Philippine Sea, Sea of Japan, Sea of Okhotsk, and Bering Sea—lie beween the andesite line and the Asiatic mainland, those seas with their island arcs and trenches are considered as lying within the continental margins. Along the eastern side of the Pacific, the andesite line is drawn close to the continents. Here island arcs are missing. Consequently there is a fundamental difference in this respect between the two sides of the Pacific Ocean basin. Note that the Atlantic Ocean basin lacks island arcs and has no surrounding belt of andesitic volcanoes, hence no line for the Atlantic comparable to the andesite line of the Pacific can be drawn.

Sedimenatry strata cover vast areas of the continents. From the fragments of rock brought up from oil wells and from examinations of the edges of rock strata exposed by erosion in cliffs and canyon walls, the geologist has developed a fairly good knowledge of the thickness of the sedimentary strata in North America and Europe. If all the sedimentary rock of the United States mainland were spread uniformly over the 48 contiguous states (about one-third of this surface now has no sedimentary strata), it would produce a layer about 0.75 mi (1.2 km) thick. For all of North America a similar average would be about 0.5 mi (0.8 km), a figure less than for the 48 United States alone because much of Canada consists of exposed igneous and metamorphic rock. If we consider the continental crust to be roughly 25 mi (40 km) thick, the sedimentary rocks obviously make up only a small percent and can be thought of as a mere paper-thin layer. Even when those metamorphic rocks that were once sedimentary layers are added to the sedimentary strata, the percentage is still trivial in comparison with igneous rock, which makes up the remainder of the crust.

Granitic igneous rocks are found over vast areas of the continents where there is no sedimentary cover to obscure them. Furthermore, from well borings and exposures at the bottoms of deep canyons it is known that granitic rocks are widely present under the sedimentary strata.

Geologists have applied the term *continental shield* to the vast area of extremely ancient rock forming the stable heartland of a continent. Shields consist partly of plutonic igneous rocks and partly of metamorphosed sedimentary and volcanic rocks. The average composition is that of a felsic igneous rock, and we are justified in using the adjective "granitic" for shield rock as a whole.[1] Rock age ranges from one billion to 3½ billions of years and includes the oldest known rocks of the earth's crust (Figure 25.1). Although the continental shields include some areas of highlands and some isolated mountains, they are for the most part undulating plains of relatively low elevation and have had a history of erosional removal of many thousands of feet of rock in the last billion years. Further details of the structure, composition, age, and history of the continental shields, and a description of the metamorphic rocks are given in Chapter 26.

To the geologist, one of the most striking points of difference between continental crust and oceanic crust is in the measured ages of rock samples. The oldest known oceanic basalts are only 50 million years old and we have no reason as yet to suspect that any of the oceanic basalt is very much older than 150 million years. Yet the ages of most continental shield rocks exceed one billion years—they are older by a factor of from 20 to 60 times. We should not, however, leap to the conclusion that the oceanic crust is very much younger than the continental crust. Ages of oceanic basalts are based upon samples taken from the upper surface of the oceanic crust. Since these basalts are volcanic extrusives, they may represent only a thin veneer of comparatively young lava flows coating and concealing a very much older crust below. Consider that processes of denudation are extremely slow over the bedrock of the deep ocean floors. Whereas on continents denudation uncovers the oldest rock, extrusion of submarine lavas and the deposition of sediments would tend to bury and conceal the oldest oceanic crustal rock.

## Evidence from plateau basalts

Unlike the ocean basins, over which the crust is almost entirely of basaltic composition, the continents show thick basalt only in the form of a few plateaus built of basaltic lava layers. Two excellent examples of *plateau basalts,* as geologists call these occurrences, are the Columbia Plateau of Oregon, Washington, and Idaho and the Deccan Plateau of peninsular India (Figures 25.2 and 25.3). Here layer upon layer of highly fluid basalt lava welled up from cracks, or *fissures,* to spread in thin sheets, one on top of another. Many of the individual basalt layers are separated by layers of volcanic ash and by sedimentary strata representing deposition in shallow lakes or in stream-valley floors that existed between periods of outpouring. The Columbia River plateau basalts cover about 50,000 sq mi (130,000 sq km), an area about the size of the state of New York. Basalt thickness totals several thousands of feet. This is a considerable body of basalt to account for.

A reasonable explanation of plateau basalts is that this rock represents a sample of a basaltic layer lying beneath the granitic layer. Although in a solid condition generally, this basalt has become molten here and there in great pockets at various intervals throughout geologic time. The magma has been forced surfaceward through fissures in the granitic layer. Both because of the increasing weight of successive lava flows and because of loss of magma from the molten pocket, the granitic layer beneath the plateau has fractured and collapsed, producing a shallow basin (Figure 25.4). Although the occurrence of plateau basalts does not by any means prove that a basaltic layer exists everywhere under the granitic layer of the continents, it is in agreement with such a hypothesis. Plateau basalts

[1] Rock of felsic or granitic composition of the continental crust is also described as *sialic rock,* or simply *sial.* This word is coined from syllables of silica and alumina. The corresponding term for mafic rock of basaltic or ultrabasic composition is *sima,* coined from syllables of silica and magnesium.

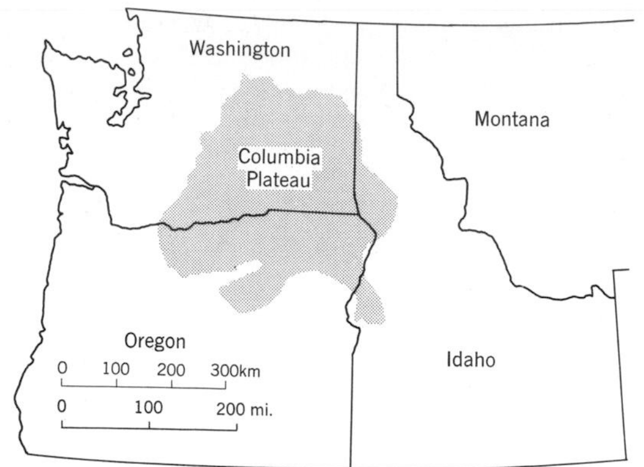


**FIGURE 25.2.** Approximate present surface extent of the Columbia Plateau basalts.

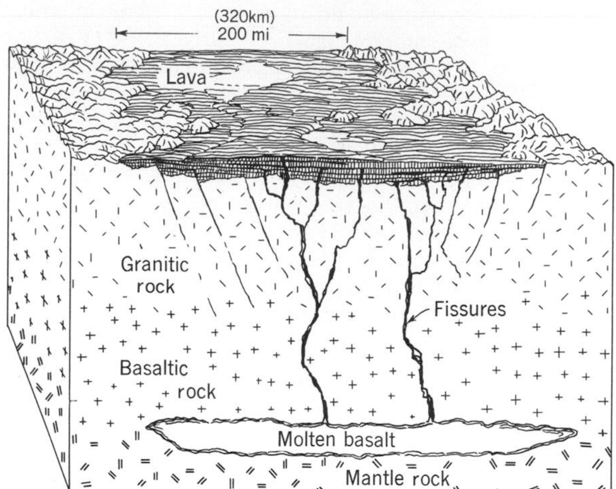


**FIGURE 25.4.** Schematic drawing suggesting the relation of plateau basalts to crustal zones beneath.

are olivine-rich and differ as a group from tholeiitic basalts of the ocean basin.

## Evidence of seismic refraction

The principle of seismic refraction as a means of detecting layered structure within the crust and mantle is treated in Chapter 23. This discussion adds a number of details.

Generalizing with respect to the oceanic crust as a whole, changes in seismic wave velocities show two well-defined layers of consolidated rock below the sediment layer but above the M-discontinuity (Moho). Table 25.1 gives details of layer thicknesses, wave velocities, densities, and probable composition.

The first layer, unconsolidated sediments, has been described in Chapter 24. The second layer, designated the *basement layer,* shows P-wave velocities more than double that of the sediment above, indicating a considerable degree of consolidation associated with a density of 2.7 g/cc. Interpretation of the composition of this layer has been twofold: that it is (a) consolidated sediments of greater age than the unconsolidated sediments above it, or (b) volcanic rock of basaltic composition. Where reached by drilling, the second layer has proved to be of basaltic rock, and this interpretation is now strongly favored. The third layer, almost certainly composed of basalt, is named the *oceanic layer.* It is the main crustal layer of the ocean floors, with an average thickness of about 3 mi (5 km) and a density of about 3 g/cc. The M-discontinuity is encountered at an average depth of about 7.5 mi (12 km).

**FIGURE 25.3.** Approximate present surface extent of the Deccan Plateau basalts of India.

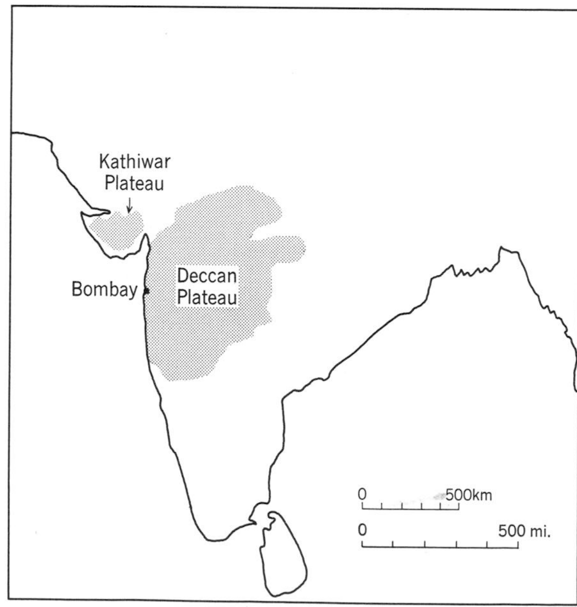


Layered structure of the oceanic crust is by no means uniform. Differences of particular interest are found over the Mid-Oceanic Ridge, as shown in Figure 25.5. The oceanic layer thins and rises on the ridge flanks. Near the ridge axis the M-discontinuity disappears and the basaltic layer grades downward gradually into rock of mantle characteristics. P-wave velocities characteristic of the mantle are found here at depth as shallow as 5 to 6 mi (9 to 10 km). Obviously, the Mid-Oceanic Ridge is a crustal zone of unusual development as compared with zones on either side and will warrant our further attention. An immediate interpretation is that mantle rock is rising beneath the ridge axis.

We have already taken note, in Chapter 23, of the fact that the continental crust shows a gradation from an upper region of P-wave velocities of about 6.2 km/sec to a lower region in which velocities reach 7 km/sec. These velocities are interpreted as representing the change from granitic rock to basaltic rock from top to bottom of the continental crust. The M-discontinuity lies at an average depth of 20 mi (33 km) but in places extends down to 40 mi (65 km) (Figure 23.27).

In summary, the continental crust differs from the oceanic crust in three important respects: (1) The continental crust is much thicker. (2) The continental crust

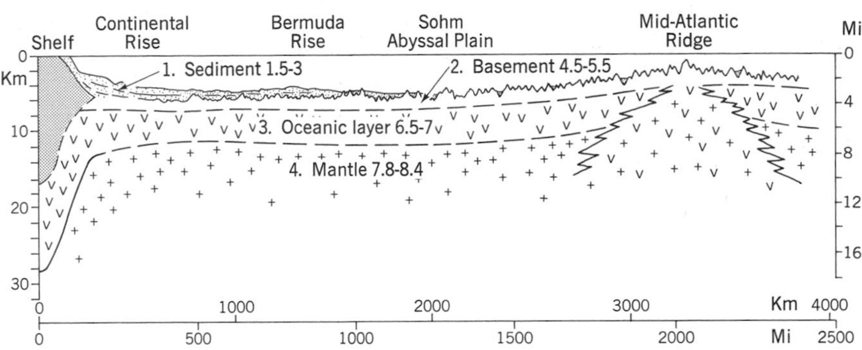


**FIGURE 25.5.** Generalized west-to-east cross section of the oceanic crust of the western North Atlantic. Figures after layer names give P-wave velocities in km/sec. [After J. Ewing (1969), In *The Earth's Crust and Upper Mantle*, Geophysical Monograph 13, Washington, D.C., Amer. Geophys. Union, p. 221, Figure 1.]

lacks the clearly defined two-layer structure of the oceanic crust. (3) The continental crust varies much more widely in thickness from place to place.

The zone of transition from continental crust to oceanic crust is one of particular scientific interest. No single description can apply on a global basis to this transition zone. Figure 25.6 shows a cross section along the stable eastern margin of North America, where volcanic activity is lacking and seismic activity is at a low level. Seismic refraction studies show a thickening of a layer of consolidated sediments over the continental shelf. This layer may correspond in seismic properties with the second layer of the typical oceanic crust. This layer and layers of unconsolidated and semiconsolidated sediment above it thicken and descend under the continental slope. The M-discontinuity, which has a depth of about 19 mi (30 km) under the continent, rises rapidly beneath the continental slope. A hypothetical correlation with the typical oceanic layers is shown by dashed lines. The pinching out of the upper granitic crustal zone, accompanied by a steep rise in both the basaltic zone and the M-discontinuity beneath it, are believed to be generally applicable characteristics of the stable continental margins.

Seismic refraction studies have steadily built up a clearer picture of the continental crust, particularly that

**TABLE 25.1. LAYERS OF THE OCEAN FLOOR***

| Layer | Thickness, km | Velocity of P-waves, km/sec | Density, g/cc | Composition |
|---|---|---|---|---|
| Sea Water | 4.5 | 1.5 | 1.0 | Sea water |
| Layer 1 | 0.45 | 1.5–3.0 | 2.3 | Unconsolidated sediments |
| Layer 2 — Basement layer | 1.5 | 4.5–5.5 | 2.7 | Volcanic rocks or consolidated sediments |
| Layer 3 — Oceanic layer | 5.0 | 6.5–7.1 | 3.0 | Basalt |
| *M-Discontinuity (Depth 12 km)* | | | | |
| Layer 4 — Mantle | | 7.7–8.3 | 3.4 | Ultrabasic rock |

* Data from J. Ewing (1969), in *The Earth's Crust and Upper Mantle*, Geophysical Monograph 13, Washington, Amer. Geophys. Union, pp. 220–225; and K. K. Turekian (1968), *Oceans*, Englewood Cliffs, N.J., Prentice-Hall, Table 1–1, p. 11.

of North America and Eurasia (Figure 25.7). An example of recent work in explosion seismology in North America is *Project Early Rise,* conducted in 1964, in which 38

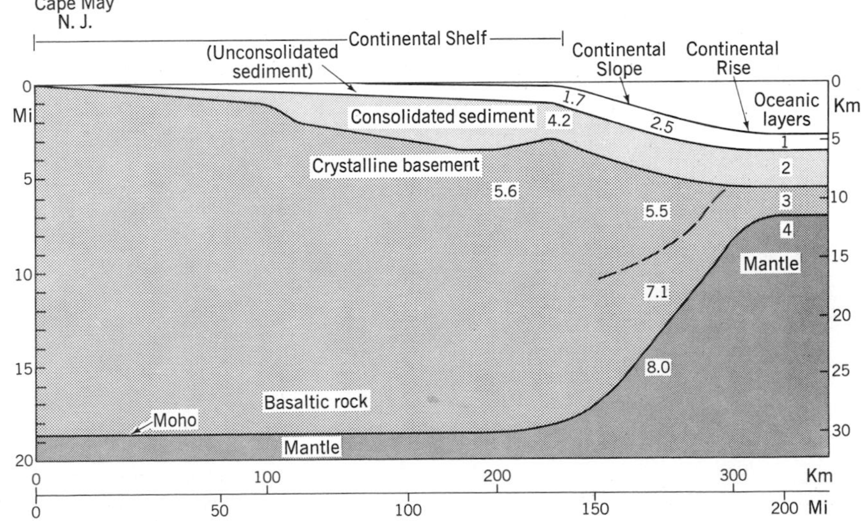


**FIGURE 25.6.** Structure section of the continental margin of eastern North America. Interpretation is based in part on seismic refraction studies. [Data from M. Ewing, J. L. Worzel, N. Steenland, and F. Press (1950), *Geol. Soc. Amer. Bull.*, vol. 61; J. Ewing and M. Ewing (1959), *Geol. Soc. Amer. Bull.*, vol. 70.]

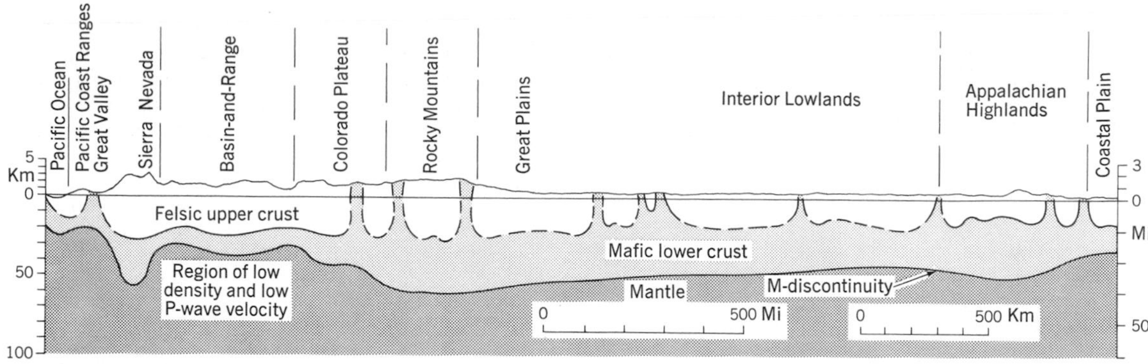


**FIGURE 25.7.** Transcontinental profile and crustal cross section based on seismic refraction data. Topographic profile is on a larger scale than crustal section. Contact between upper and lower crust is schematic only. [After L. C. Pakiser and I. Zietz (1965), *Rev. of Geophys.*, vol. 3, No. 4, p. 513, Figure 5.]

detonations of five-ton explosive charges were made in Lake Superior. Seismic recorders were situated at intervals along about a dozen lines, two of which were of transcontinental orientation and about ten in a radial-line pattern covering much of the United States and Canada.

Analysis of these and other explosion seismic data have confirmed the existence of an upper crustal zone of granitic rock with P-wave velocities between 5.9 and 6.2 km/sec. Beneath this upper zone is a lower crustal zone of mafic composition with P-wave velocities of 6.6 to 7.1 km/sec. No persistent discontinuity has been confirmed between these two zones, and for this reason they should not be designated as layers comparable to those of the oceanic crust. The well-defined M-discontinuity ranges in depth from 19 to 31 mi (30 to 50 km). P-wave velocities in the uppermost mantle range from 7.8 to 8.3 km/sec, which is essentially the same range as under the oceanic crust.

Figure 25.8 is a map of the United States showing the depth in kilometers to the M-discontinuity—note that on both the profile and the map depth is greatest under mountain ranges. A conspicuously deep *mountain root*

**FIGURE 25.8.** Crustal thickness in kilometers beneath the 48 contiguous United States. Profile and cross section line of Figure 25.7 shown by the dashed line. [After L. C. Pakiser and I. Zietz (1965), *Rev. of Geophys.*, vol. 3, No. 4, p. 507, Figure 2.]

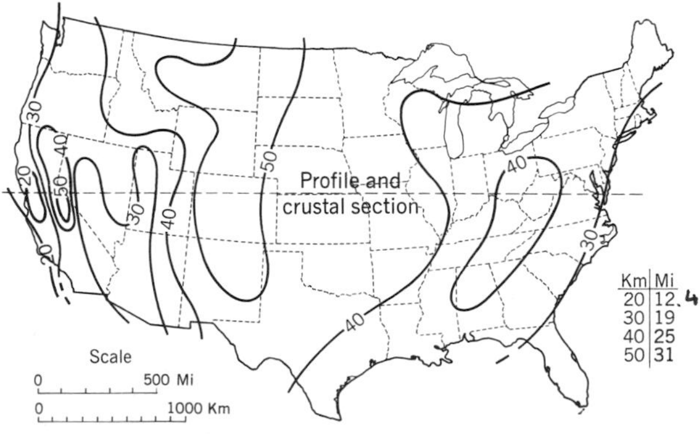


is shown under the Sierra Nevada range, reaching to 30 mi (50 km). A marked increase in depth occurs under both the Rocky Mountain belt and the Appalachian Highlands. Unusually shallow depths beneath the Basin-and-Range region indicate that this is an anomalous crustal region requiring special explanation.

Seismic refraction studies of Eurasia show its crust to have many similarities with the North American crust. Over vast expanses of northern Russia the continental crust has a nearly uniform depth of 22 to 25 mi (35 to 40 km), which is about the same as in the North American interior lowlands. However, much greater thicknesses are associated with the great mountain chains and high plateaus of south-central Asia, where depths as great as 40 mi (65 km) are widely recorded. A possible maximum depth of 46 mi (75 km) has been found beneath the Pamirs, a great mountain mass with elevations exceeding 24,000 ft (7 km).

Of particular interest is the crustal structure of the western continental margin of Asia, where great island arcs and trenches lie off the mainland. Figure 25.9 shows cross sections and a map of crustal configuration based on seismic refraction data obtained by Soviet scientists. The cross sections begin at the right with the Kurile-Kamchatka Trench and the adjoining Kurile island arc. Notice that beneath the contact line of trench with island arc the M-discontinuity projects down in a deep root structure, interpreted by these scientists as continental crust. Under the Sea of Okhotsk the crust thins greatly and is designated as *suboceanic crust,* intermediate in classification between true oceanic and continental crusts. Thick sediments are found here. Farther westward, as the Asiatic mainland is reached, the crust again thickens and is identified as continental crust. These cross sections suggest the interpretation that the island arc region is one in which continental crust is in process of formation. We shall follow up this suggestion on later pages.

## Regional variations in the upper mantle

Seismic refraction studies have revealed increasingly detailed information on the upper mantle as well as of

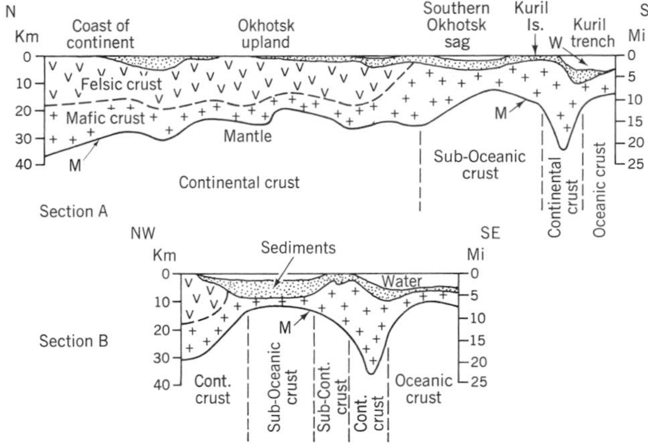


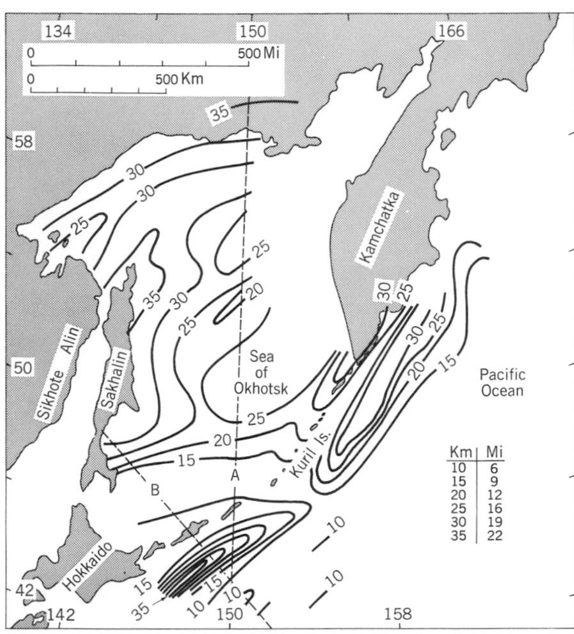


**FIGURE 25.9** Map and crustal cross sections of the Kurile-Kamchatka-Okhotsk region of eastern Asia. Map contours show depth in km to the M-discontinuity. Cross sections show classification of crust into continental and oceanic types. [After I. P. Kosminskaya and Y. V. Riznichenko (1964), in *Research in Geophys.*, vol. 2, H. Odishaw, Ed., Cambridge, Mass., M.I.T. Press, p. 110, Figure 22, and p. 111, Figure 23.]

the crust. It has become apparent that the mantle is not horizontally uniform in properties. Because, as we shall find, movements on a large scale within the plastic mantle are responsible for crustal deformation, geophysicists and geochemists have concentrated a major effort upon this zone. Under the title of the *Upper Mantle Project* a program of international scientific cooperation was begun in 1962 to continue until 1971. Research contributed to this project by scientists of many nationalities has greatly advanced our knowledge of the mantle.

Seismic observations have shown that the velocity of P-waves beneath the M-discontinuity has definite regional variations over the United States. Figure 25.10 shows lines of equal P-wave velocity as estimated from the seismic data of various sources, including surface explosions, underground nuclear explosions, and earthquakes. The central and eastern part of the country has mantle velocities above 8.0 km/sec, whereas a broad zone lying between the Rocky Mountain chain and the Pacific coast has velocities lower than 7.8 km/sec. Velocities rise again to over 8 km/sec westward into the oceanic subcrustal zone of the Pacific. The belt of lower velocities includes the Basin-and-Range region and the Sierra Nevada as well as the Columbia Plateau and the Cascade Range. Recall that the Basin-and-Range region is one in which the M-discontinuity is at unusually shallow depth (Figure 25.7). We have also seen that this region lies on the line of northward projection of the Mid-Oceanic Ridge from the point at which it makes contact with the North American continent in the Gulf of California (see Figure 24.13). The Basin-and-Range region is one of intensive recent crustal activity involving large-scale faulting of the crust. Volcanic activity is also strongly developed in the Columbia Plateau and the Cascade Range to the north and west of the faulted zone. These facts point to the possibility that the Basin-and-Range region may indeed be a part of the Mid-Oceanic Ridge system and may be more closely allied with oceanic structure than with continental structure.

## Evidence from gravity measurements

One of the most important concepts concerning the state of the earth's crust has been developed by precision gravity measurements at different places on the earth's surface. As explained in Chapter 10, the plumb bob hangs normal to the surface of the geoid, the equilibrium surface that would be defined by the level of still water in an imaginary system of sea-level canals or tunnels cut through the continents. It was discovered early in the history of geodetic measurements of the length of a degree of latitude that the plumb bob is attracted slightly toward the mass of material within mountains so that it does not hang in a true vertical line reckoned according to the zenith position among the stars.

If the earth consisted of perfectly uniform concentric layers of rock of the same density in each layer and of a surface which was a perfectly smooth ellipsoid, the plumb bob would hang precisely true at all points. That is, the upward projection of the plumb line would point exactly to the celestial zenith after corrections are made for earth rotation. Suppose that on such an ideal earth there has been built a great pyramid of rock (Figure 25.11) and that a plumb bob has been set up for study on the plain near the foot of the pyramid. Knowing the density of the rock of which the pyramid is built, as well as its dimensions and hence its volume, we can easily and accurately compute the mass. From the law of gravitation, which states that the attractive force between the plumb bob and the mountain varies directly as the product of their masses and inversely as the

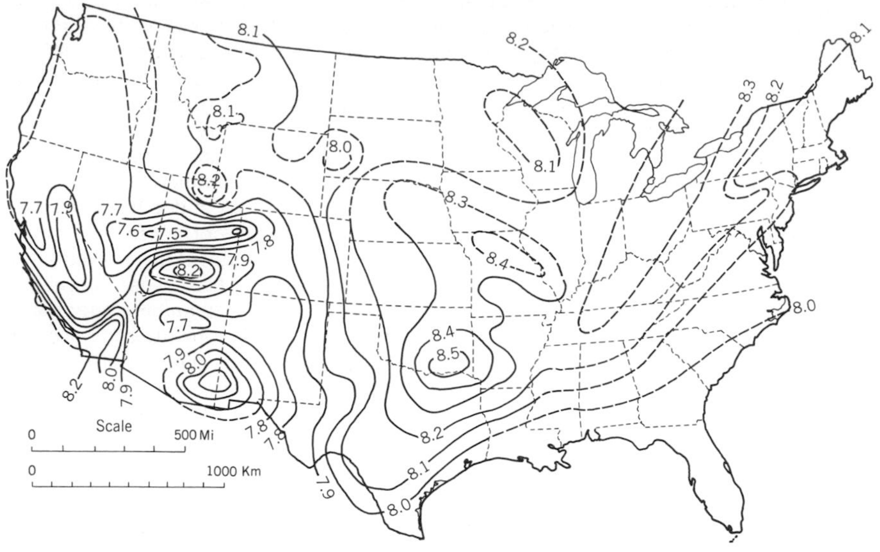


FIGURE 25.10. Map of the United States showing lines of equal P-wave velocity (km/sec) in the upper mantle. [After E. Herrin and J. Taggart (1962), *Bull. Seis. Soc. Amer.,* vol. 52, p. 1037.]

square of the distance between them, the force pulling the plumb bob from the vertical is determined. This fact in turn allows us to predict the deflection of the plumb line, which is the angle between the two possible plumb lines: one with the pyramid present; the other without any objects on the surrounding surface.

More than a century ago the British geodesist Sir George Everest was engaged in triangulation surveys and precise measurements of the lengths of degrees of latitude on the Indo-Gangetic Plain in north India. To the north rises the greatest of continental mountain ranges, The Himalaya, culminating in many peaks over 25,000 ft (7.6 km) above sea level. Knowing the dimensions of the range and the average density of rocks exposed in it, Everest computed the amount by which the plumb bob should be drawn toward the range from a given distance away. To his surprise the plumb bob was attracted far less than the calculated attraction (Figure 25.12).

The importance of Everest's discovery was soon realized by two fellow Englishmen, Sir George Airy, Astronomer Royal of England, and J. H. Pratt, Archdeacon of Calcutta, who proposed an explanation that has since been one of the most powerful influences in the development of geologic theories. It was immediately obvious to both of these men that if the plumb bob is not drawn toward the mountains in the amount expected, it is because the material lying beneath the mountains is less dense than elsewhere and that this lack of density largely makes up for the additional mass of the mountains. Although Airy and Pratt were in agreement on this principle, each man developed a somewhat different concept of the structure of the earth's crust to describe the arrangement of less dense material under mountains.

Although the deflection of the plumb bob provided impetus for the investigation of mountain roots, it has been through gravity surveys that the theory of crustal structure has been developed. In Chapter 10, under the subject of correction of gravity readings, the *Bouguer correction* was explained as a correction taking into account the presence of a rock mass lying above the ellipsoid of reference (as in the case of a plateau) or for a deficiency of mass (as in the case of a part of the ocean basins). In making the Bouguer correction a single density value (2.67 g/cc) was assigned to all rock, another value (1.03 g/cc) to sea water. (A mean rock density value of about 2.9 g/cc is now considered a better estimate on which to base a Bouguer-type correction.)

FIGURE 25.11. Deflection of a plumb bob by a pyramid on a plain.

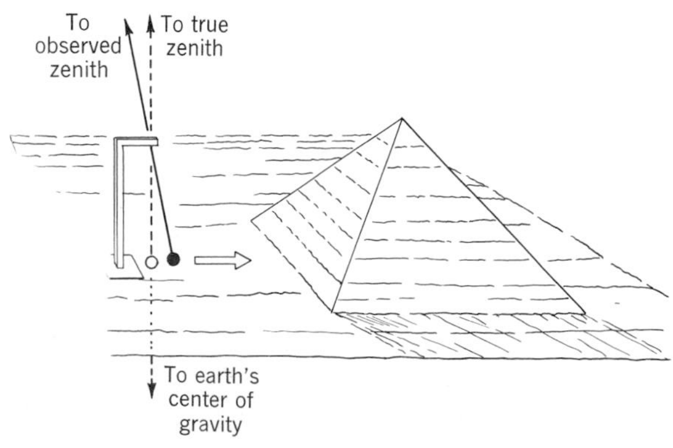


FIGURE 25.12. Attraction of The Himalaya for a plumb bob on the Gangetic plain is not as great as might be expected for so large a mountain mass.

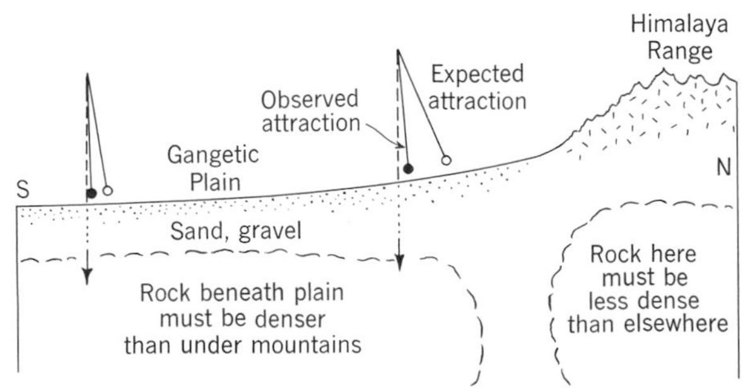

Where the earth's surface departs from a level surface to an appreciable degree, an additional correction must be made for the influence of mountain masses rising above the level of the gravity station and for valleys dropping below that level. This *topographic correction* is combined with the Bouguer correction and added to the *free-air anomaly,* which is the difference between observed gravity and the ideal sea-level value after the free-air correction has been made (see Chapter 10). When the appropriate subtraction has been made, any difference remaining with respect to theoretical sea-level gravity is known as the *Bouguer anomaly.* Quite substantial Bouguer anomalies exist over various parts of the continents. Bouguer anomalies of negative sign and amounts exceeding 200 milligals are found in mountain and plateau regions of the western United States. The anomaly decreases to zero over large areas of low plains of the central and southeastern United States and becomes positive over the continental shelf. Over the ocean basins positive anomalies exceed 250 miligals. When the Bouguer anomaly is examined on a global basis the same relationship between altitude and anomaly is found to exist over most areas. Gravity, including the Bouguer correction, is less than average (negative Bouguer anomaly) over high areas but greater than average (positive Bouguer anomaly) over the ocean basins. As in the case of the smaller-than-anticipated deflection of the plumb bob, the negative Bouguer anomaly over high regions represents a deficiency of mass at depth in the crust because the rock there is less dense than average. The positive Bouguer anomaly suggests that denser-than-average matter underlies the ocean basins. Let us return, then, to the interpretations advanced by Airy and Pratt.

## Isostasy

Airy's hypothesis, proposed in 1855, is illustrated by a simple model using floating blocks (Figure 25.13). Suppose that we take several blocks, or prisms, of a metal such as copper. Although all prisms have the same dimensions of cross section, they are cut to varying lengths. Because copper is less dense than mercury, the prisms will float in a dish of that liquid metal. If all blocks are floated side by side in the same orientation, the longest block will float with the greatest amount rising above the level of the mercury surface, and the shortest block has its upper surface lowest. With all blocks now floating at rest, it is obvious that the block rising highest also extends to greatest depth.

Airy supposed that the material of which the mountains are composed extends far down into the earth to form roots composed of lighter (less dense) material. This lighter material, which may be granitic rock, protrudes downward into a location normally occupied by denser basaltic or ultrabasic rock. Under a plains region the root of less dense rock will be very shallow, and under the floors of the ocean basins it will be shallowest of all.

Pratt's alternative hypothesis, proposed in 1859, is illustrated by a similar model (Figure 25.14), but the model is complicated by the need to use prisms of different kinds of metals, each with a different density. These prisms, although of the same cross-sectional size, are cut in lengths such that all prisms have the same weight. The dense metals silver and lead have short prisms, while the less dense metals iron and zinc have long prisms. If we now float these in a pan of mercury, they will all sink to such a depth that their bases are at the same level. The force with which each prism presses down upon the mercury at its base is the same for all prisms. According to Pratt this level represents the lower limit of the earth's strength as a rigid substance and is located about 60 mi (100 km) deep, whether beneath mountains, plains, or ocean basins. The material is less dense under mountains than under low plains and is most dense under ocean floors.

The condition of floating at rest, whether as visualized by Airy or by Pratt, has since been given the name *isostasy,* from Greek words *isos,* equal, and *stasis,* a

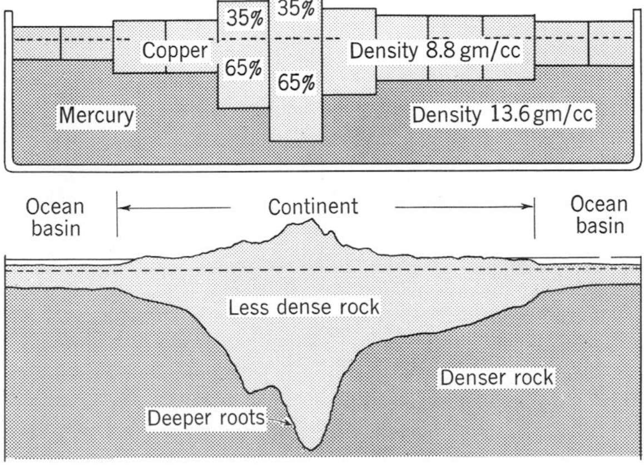


**FIGURE 25.13.** The Airy hypothesis of mountain roots is suggested by the equilibrium positions of blocks of the same density.

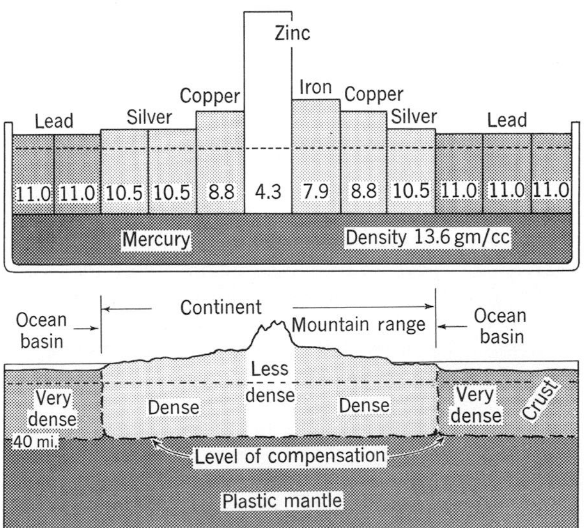


**FIGURE 25.14.** According to the Pratt hypothesis, crustal elements have different densities.

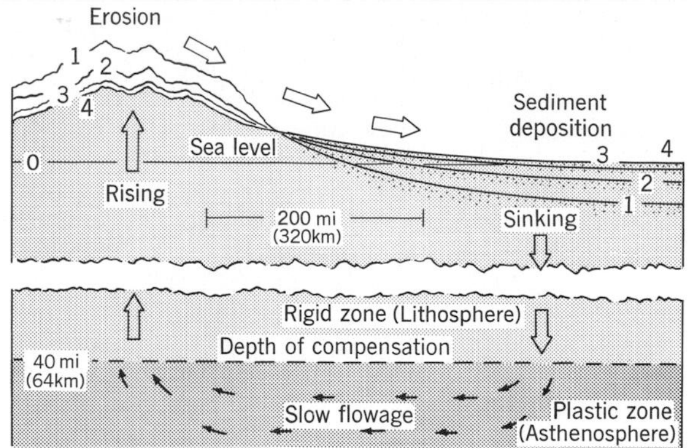


**FIGURE 25.15.** Schematic diagram of isostatic compensation for erosion and sediment deposition.

standing still. Isostasy is merely a state of equilibrium.

According to the theory of isostasy the brittle zone floats at rest on the plastic mantle beneath. We have assigned the name *lithosphere* to the brittle zone, the term *asthenosphere* to the soft layer beneath (Chapter 24). Suppose that in the metal-block model used to illustrate Pratt's hypothesis we take a thin slice off the zinc block and add it to the adjoining iron block. The shortened zinc block will rise, but not quite to its former height. The combined iron-and-zinc block will sink, but its upper surface will not fall to quite as low a level as the iron block had previously.

Much the same effect is felt on the earth when erosion processes transport rock particles from mountains to adjacent plains or shallow seas where they are deposited as layers of sediment (Figure 25.15). The mountains rise a bit and the adjacent plain sinks a bit, but in each interval of time the mountain does not rise quite as high as formerly, nor does the surface of the plain sink to quite as low a level as formerly. After vastly long spans of time the mountain and plain will reach nearly the same level. Underneath the mountains the plastic material of the asthenosphere will flow in slowly to occupy the space vacated by the rising block, just as the mercury in the model flows in beneath the rising zinc bolck. Of course, as this newly introduced plastic material rises it comes into a region of reduced temperature and cools to become a strong, brittle rock—that is, it becomes a part of the lithosphere. Similarly, under the sinking plain the brittle rock mass is forced down into the region of the asthenosphere, but here it is heated and becomes plastic itself, forming a part of the plastic zone. This excess material at depth must slowly flow horizontally to escape. It seems only logical that it will move toward the region under the rising mountains. The level of the base of the lithosphere is therefore referred to as the *depth of compensation,* for it is below this depth that changes in load on the earth's surface are equalized, or compensated for, by slow flowage of the asthenosphere. The depth of compensation is variously estimated to be from as shallow a depth as 35 mi (55 km) to as deep as 75 mi (120 km). We have selected 40 mi (60 km) as a working figure, although Pratt used 60 mi (100 km) in his explanation.

The Airy model of isostasy has been used with various assumptions of average density of the crust and mantle rock and depth of the M-discontinuity. The first step is to make assumptions about a column whose surface coincides with sea level. For example, we might choose to assume that this crustal column has a depth of 30 km and an average density of 2.9 g/cc (Figure 25.16). An assumed value for density of the mantle rock beneath is 3.3 g/cc. Next, it is assumed that for each increase of 1 km in surface elevation with respect to sea level the base of the column is lengthened by 7.5 km. Figure 25.16 shows such columns for elevations of 1, 2, and 3 km. A model of oceanic crust is also shown for comparison. Depth of compensation is double the crustal column length and exceeds 100 km under the longest column.

Selection of column length and rock densities is governed by seismic refraction data on depth to the M-discontinuity and on density of crust and mantle. Thus the fields of seismology and gravity provide mutual support in design of the crustal model.

Having set up the isostatic crustal model, the next step is to compute a gravity correction based upon the masses of the columns computed according to surface elevation. This *isostatic correction* is subtracted from the Bouguer correction, leaving a much smaller value known as the *isostatic anomaly.* If the crustal model is a true one and the condition of isostasy prevails, this anomaly should have zero value. In actual fact, computed isostatic anomalies ranging from −30 to +30 miligals characterize most of the surface of the continents. These anomalies take the form of small "hills" and "depressions," reflecting place-to-place differences in rock density caused by the presence of superficial rock masses of various dimensions, compositions, and struc-

**FIGURE 25.16.** Simplified Airy isostatic model of crust. [Based on parameters suggested by G. P. Woollard (1966), *The Earth Beneath the Continents, Geophysical Monograph 10,* Washington, D.C., Amer. Geophys. Union, p. 563.]

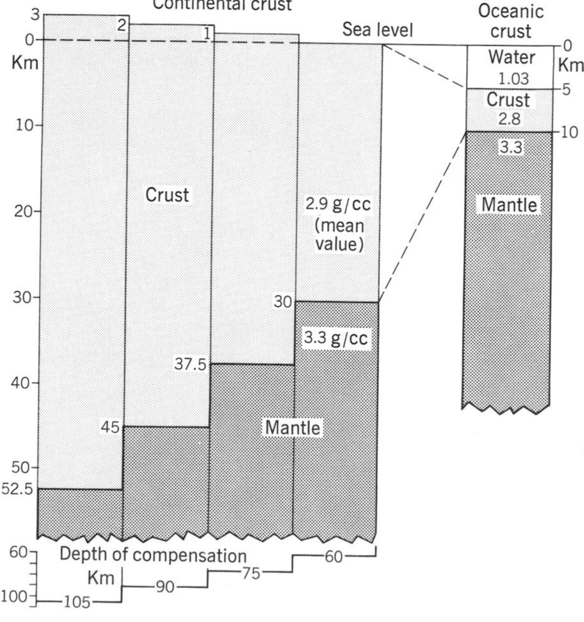

tures. On the whole, however, much of the earth's crust, both continental and oceanic, is judged to be near isostatic equilibrium. We shall find, however, that certain narrow belts associated with mountain arcs and trenches have very large isostatic anomalies in both positive and negative directions. In these places the crust is far from being in isostatic equilibrium.

**Geosynclines and isostasy** The principle of isostasy may be applied to explain—in part, at least—one of the most remarkable qualities of thick deposits of sedimentary rock layers. In certain belts on the continents the geologist has measured truly enormous thicknesses of sedimentary strata that from their appearance, relation to one another, and content of fossil animal forms must have been deposited with only short interruptions within periods of perhaps 25–60 million years—that is, within a single geologic period. In Newfoundland, for example, measurements show that almost 5 mi (8 km) of sedimentary layers—mostly shales, sandstones, and conglomerates—were laid down in one continuous 50-million year period of deposition. Moreover the strata of several successive periods are found, one overlying the other, in such belts. Examples are found for each era in the geologic past.

The important point about such great thicknesses of strata is that all the layers in the series may be of a kind of sediment found today in shallow epicontinental seas or continental shelves. From this observation comes the conclusion that certain of these ancient seas must have been shallow during the entire geologic period of deposition and therefore that the floor of the sea must have been sinking at about the same rate as the sediment layers were added.

The principle of isostasy provides part of the explanation. The sinking is partly a response to the sediment load as it is added. Plastic flowage of mantle rock in the asthenosphere below the depth of compensation may occur rapidly enough to preserve a condition of isostasy, approximately in effect at all times. If the rate of addition of sediment should increase greatly, the rate of sinking will also increase.

However, the compacted sediment would have a density only about five-sixths as great as the rock it displaces downward. Therefore the addition of 6000 ft of sediment should cause subsidence of only 5000 ft. If the crust were affected only by isostatic adjustments, the shallow sea would be gradually filled and deposition would change from marine sediments to continental sediments. It seems, then, that crustal downwarping must be initiated and maintained by forces other than those of isostatic adjustment. The broad-scale crustal warpings, independent of isostasy, are referred to as *epeirogenic* movements. They appear to provide the primary control of crustal subsidence, whereas isostasy can account for the great thickness of the sediment body.

A cross section through the Atlantic continental shelf (Figure 25.6) shows a thickening of the wedge of consolidated sediment to a maximum thickness of about 2.5 mi (4 km). We see here a case of crustal subsidence accompanied by sedimentation.

The name *geosyncline* is applied to the sediment accumulation in a subsiding trough in which strata are being laid down in a shallow sea. When the period of deposition is completed, the form of the body of strata constituting the geosyncline will be much longer than wide because it lies in a long crustal downfold between higher crustal masses, and it will have a flat top surface but a curved convex-down bottom surface.

**Ice sheets and isostasy** Another remarkable geologic event is the rising of ground level going on today over parts of North America and Europe where the great Pleistocene ice sheets stood some 25,000–50,000 years ago. It is known, from the rising elevation of surveying reference points and from ancient beaches now high above sea level, that the region of the Scandinavian countries and the Baltic Sea is rising at a rate of from 15 to 30 ft (5 to 10 m) per 1000 years. It is more than a remarkable coincidence that the center of most rapid crustal rise was also the center of the Pleistocene ice sheet (Figure 25.17).

Again the principle of isostasy is involved in the explanation. When the weight of an ice sheet several thousands of feet thick at the center is added to the crust, the crust must sag a bit, forcing plastic mantle rock to move away from beneath. When the ice melts away, the load is removed, and the crust must begin to rise in order to restore isostasy. Because of the very slow rate of flow of the plastic rock, isostasy cannot be restored fast enough to keep pace with rapid melting of

**FIGURE 25.17.** Present rate of uplift of the Baltic region is shown here by lines of equal uplift in centimeters per century, with equivalent values in inches per century. [Based on data by B. Gutenberg. After J. A. Jacobs, R. D. Russell, and J. T. Wilson (1959), *Physics and Geology,* New York, McGraw-Hill, p. 98, Figure 4–5.]

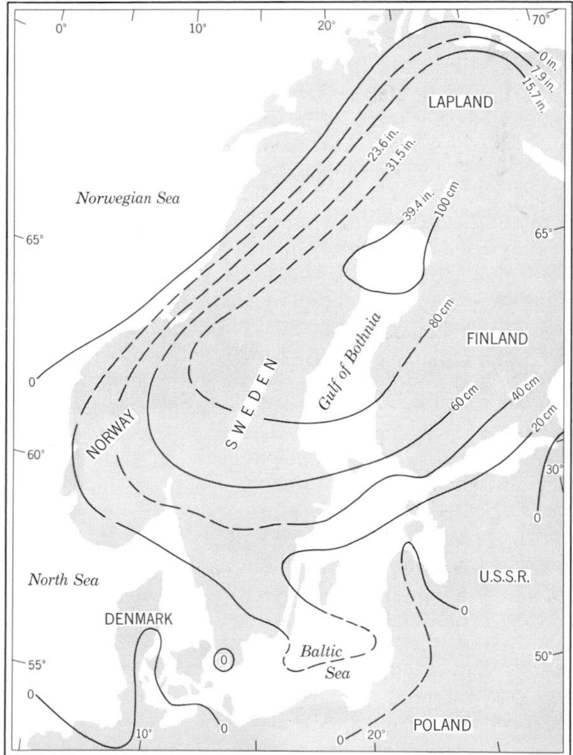

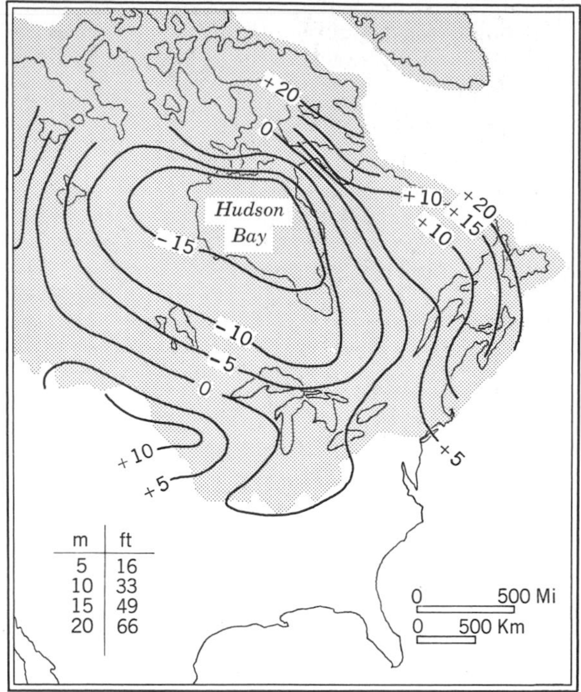


**FIGURE 25.18.** Geoid contours superimposed upon the area covered by Pleistocene ice sheets in eastern North America (*shaded area*). Contours, in meters, are for the best-fitting ellipsoid. [Data after Irene Fischer, (1959), *Jour. Geophys. Research*, vol. 64, p. 75.]

the ice. The rise of the crust therefore continues today.

Geodesy now enters the picture. It will be recalled from Chapter 10 that the surface of the geoid is depressed (that is, lies below the ellipsoid of reference) in those areas where there is a deficiency of mass in the earth's crust. Where a region formerly beneath a great ice sheet has not yet been restored to isostatic adjustment and remains depressed, as in the case of the Baltic region of Europe and the Hudson Bay region of North America, we may expect that the geoidal contours will show a corresponding depression. In Figure 25.18 are shown geoidal contours superimposed upon the area of the Laurentide Ice Sheet. Note the remarkable degree of correspondence of the center of geoidal depression with the center of the former ice sheet. This is a striking illustration of the complementary relation between two fields of the earth sciences, geodesy and glaciology.

We turn next to those zones of the earth's crust where isostatic equilibrium is greatly disturbed today—the trenches and island arcs.

**The primary island and mountain arcs** If we should plot on a world map the locations of those zones of the earth where most of the active and recently active volcanoes lie and where the intermediate- and deep-focus earthquakes originate, they would be found to be heavily concentrated along certain chains of great mountain ranges of the continents, designated as *alpine ranges,* and along those submarine ridges whose higher points emerge here and there to form the *island arcs* (Figure 25.19). Alpine ranges and island arcs are formed into curved segments, termed *primary arcs,* in which each arc is bowed convexly outward from the continental interior toward the ocean basins.

The world distribution of the primary arcs was pointed out in the nineteenth century by the geologist E. Suess and others, who noted that the geologic evidence shows the alpine mountain ranges of the arcs to be comparatively young—indeed, to be among the most recently formed of the larger relief features of the earth.

The primary arcs form two *great-circle belts,* as shown in Figure 25.19. One is the *circum-Pacific belt,* rimming the Pacific continental margins of the Americas and Asia. The second, the *Eurasian-Melanesian belt,* runs from the Mediterranean region across southern Asia to the Celebes, where it meets the circum-Pacific belt in a T-junction.

The modern primary arcs are the sites of great recent disturbances of the earth's crust, included under the general term *orogeny* (from the Greek *oros,* mountain, and *geneia,* origin), or simply the event of mountain making. The process is termed *orogenesis.*

As noted in Chapter 24, deep trenches are situated in close proximity on the oceanic side of the Pacific island arcs. In the case of the Alaskan and Andean alpine ranges, deep trenches lie immediately offshore. The Himalayan Range is bounded on the south by the Indo-Gangetic Plain, which can be thought of as a crustal trench completely filled with sediment derived by erosion from the adjacent mountains. It is therefore an important generalization that linear depressions of the crust are found adjacent to the linear zones of uplift, and therefore that these two crustal elements must be treated together as genetically related forms.

Strong negative gravity anomalies exist over the oceanic trenches. Figure 25.20 is a map on which lines of equal isostatic anomaly have been drawn for a part of the East Indies. Note the strong negative anomaly over the Sunda Trench. Along with the deficiency of gravitational attraction over the trenches there is also found a positive isostatic gravity anomaly over the adjoining island arc. Note in Figure 25.20 that strong positive anomalies exist on the mountainous island of Java, immediately north of the negative anomaly of the Sunda Trench.

Strong negative anomalies of the trenches are interpreted to mean that here the crust has been forced down and is being held down against the forces of buoyancy. Strong positive anomalies can mean that the island arc is being pushed up and held up by forces within the crust.

Imagine that three large cakes of ice are floating in a tub of water as shown in Figure 25.21. The middle cake is floating at rest with about seven-eighths of its bulk submerged. This case corresponds to isostatic balance with no gravity anomaly. The ice on the left cake is being pushed by an additional force from beneath and is projecting much farther out of the water than it would be if it were floating at rest. This case represents a positive gravity anomaly. On the right is a negative gravity anomaly, represented by the ice block being held down by an outside force.

We can speculate that the trenches represent zones in which the brittle crust and upper mantle (lithosphere) are being forced to buckle downwards, whereas under

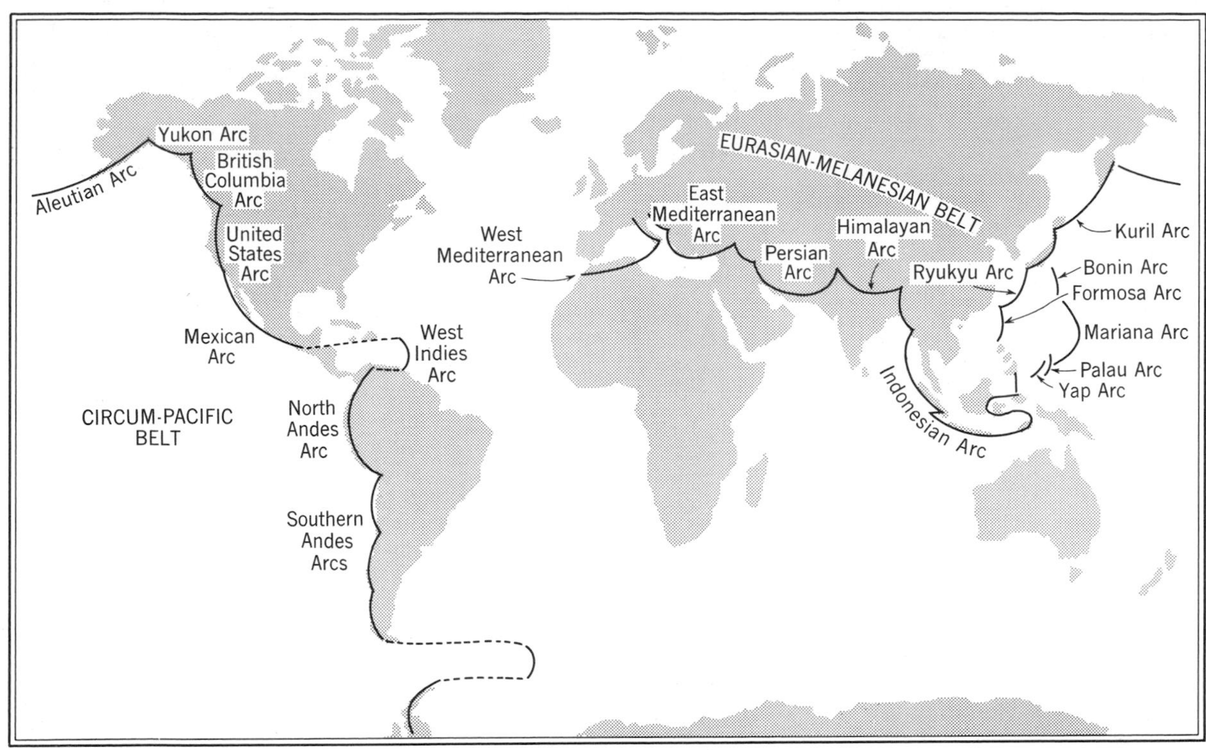


**FIGURE 25.19.** Generalized world map of the primary arcs. [After a map by J. A. Jacobs, R. D. Russell, and J. T. Wilson (1959), *Physics and Geology,* New York, McGraw-Hill, p. 291, Figure 14-1.]

the island arcs the lithosphere is being forced to bend up. Lateral compression under horizontal forces appears to be presently occurring in these zones.

Alpine mountain belts typically show only small isostatic gravity anomalies and are thought to be close to isostatic adjustment, suggesting that orogenic forces are no longer in action and that sufficient time has elapsed for isostatic balance to be achieved.

**FIGURE 25.20.** Isostatic anomaly map of the Indonesian Archipelago. Contours in milligals. Positive and negative areas are indicated by plus and minus signs. [After W. A. Heiskanen and F. A. Vening Meinesz (1958), *The Earth and Its Gravity Field,* New York, McGraw-Hill, Map 10C-2.]

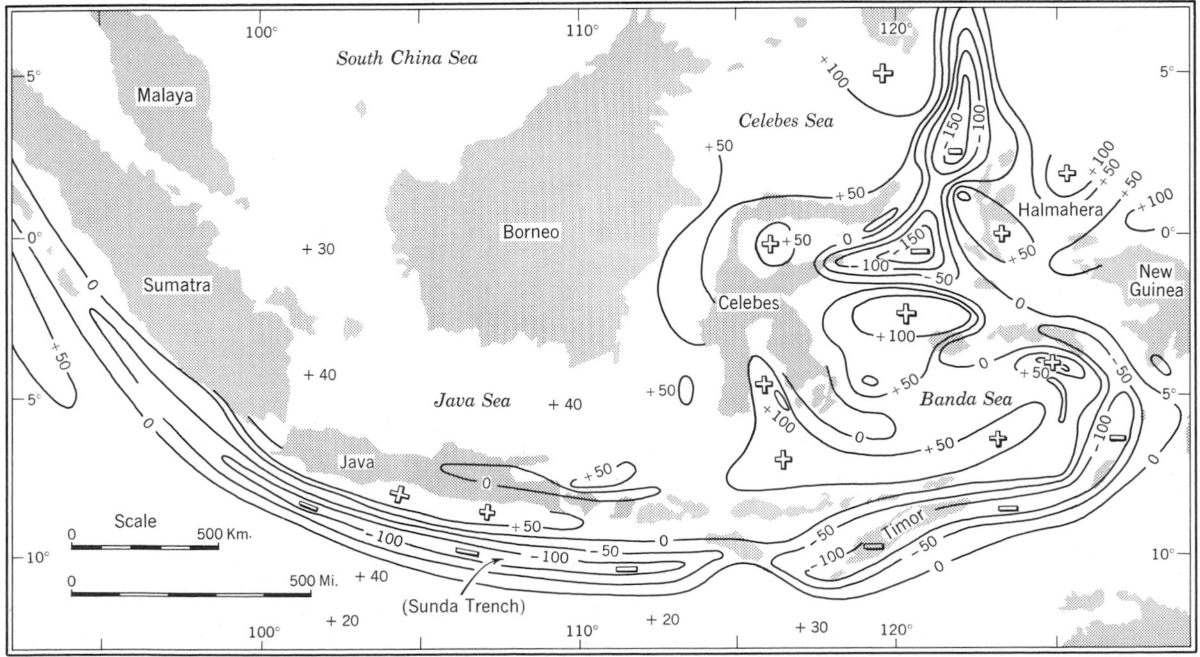

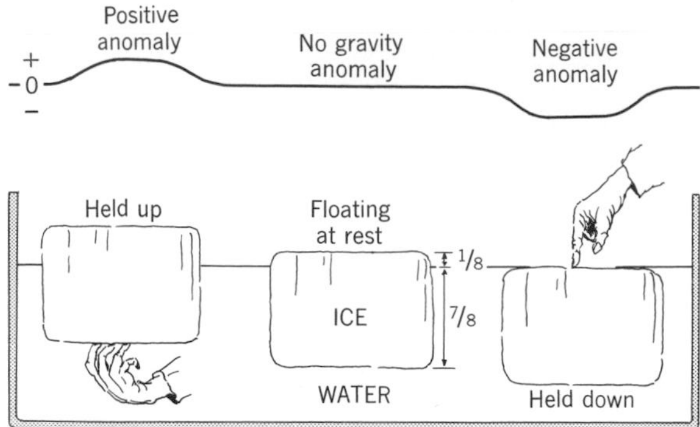


**FIGURE 25.21.** The principle of an isostatic gravity anomaly can be illustrated by a floating cake of ice.

## Evidence from deep-focus earthquakes

If it is agreed that the earth's crust is being forced to buckle into island arcs and deep oceanic trenches, we shall next want to know if the crust is merely folded in the process or if it is actually shattered along fault planes extending through the crust. Evidence that movement is by slippage along a great slanting fault plane is provided by earthquakes whose foci range from shallow to extremely deep.

To understand the nature of this evidence, consider the case of the island arc made up of northern Japan and the Kuril Islands (Figure 25.22). Adjoining this arc on the east is the Japan Trench. To the west lies the relatively shallow Sea of Japan and Sea of Okhotsk. The Japan Trench shows a strong negative isostatic gravity anomaly, whereas the island belt has a positive anomaly.

Earthquakes are frequent in this region, and their centers have been plotted in considerable numbers. Shallow quakes are abundant over the Japan Trench, those of intermediate depth occur under the island belt, while those of deep focus are centered under the margin of the Asiatic mainland. When we plot these centers on a vertical cross section, as is done on the face of the block diagram in Figure 25.22, it is obvious that they define a slanting zone where sudden slippage has been occurring. This zone is a great fault breaking through the crust and penetrating far down into the mantle. As pointed out in Chapter 22, the mantle is plastic when stresses are very slowly and steadily applied, but when stresses are intense and are suddenly applied, it is possible for the mantle rock to fracture by faulting, thus generating the deep-focus earthquake. A map of the Pacific Ocean (Figure 25.23) shows the systematic relations between earthquake epicenters and the circum-Pacific belt of primary arcs.

We can now reconstruct a general model of mountain-making deformation, as shown in Figure 25.24. In Block *A* great lateral pressures (shown by large arrows in the crust) have forced the crust to buckle upward in a great upfold, or *welt.* Upon the welt are great masses of volcanic rock forming the summit of the island arc. Immediately in front of the island arc the crust has been forced down to produce the trench. The crust and rigid part of the outermost mantle have broken in a major thrust fault, permitting the island arc to slip past the trench. Although most of the deformation in the mantle is by plastic flowage, sudden slips do occur along the fault zone, generating deep-focus earthquakes.

What we see pictured in Block *A* of Figure 25.24 is the first stage in orogeny along a primary arc. Between the island arc and the continental mainland lies a shallow sea in which are accumulating thick sedimentary strata (a geosyncline) formed of debris shed from the volcanic mountains. The volcanoes themselves are formed of andesite lava, which, as explained in Chapter 21, is of much the same composition as diorite, a granitic igneous rock.

In Block *B* the orogeny has advanced to a later stage in which the sedimentary strata of the geosyncline have been compressed into folds, the deeper portions being changed into metamorphic rocks. In the succeeding chapter we shall examine the details of geosynclinal evolution and mountain building.

**FIGURE 25.22.** Block diagram of the Japan-Kuril arc showing how earthquake foci are distributed in the crust and mantle beneath. [Based on data of B. Gutenberg and C. F. Richter (1949), *Seismicity of the Earth,* Princeton, N.J., Princeton Univ. Press.]

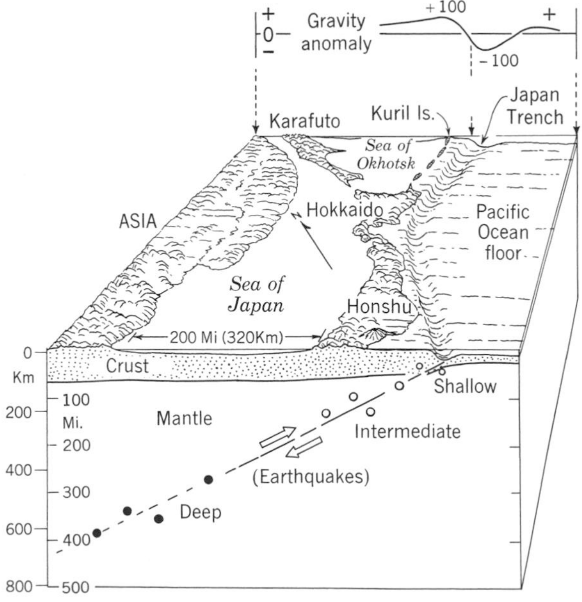


## Heat flow through the crust

Chapter 23 introduced the subject of upward flow of heat through the upper mantle and crust. Much scientific interest lies in place-to-place variations in the upward heat flow. One might, for example, reason that a rapid rate of heat flow is associated with nearness to a magma chamber, or perhaps that a general rise of mantle rock is bringing the hotter deeper part of the mantle closer to the surface. Correspondingly, a low rate of heat flow might be interpreted to mean that the crust is sinking and that the source of heat is correspondingly depressed to greater depths. If this reasoning is car-

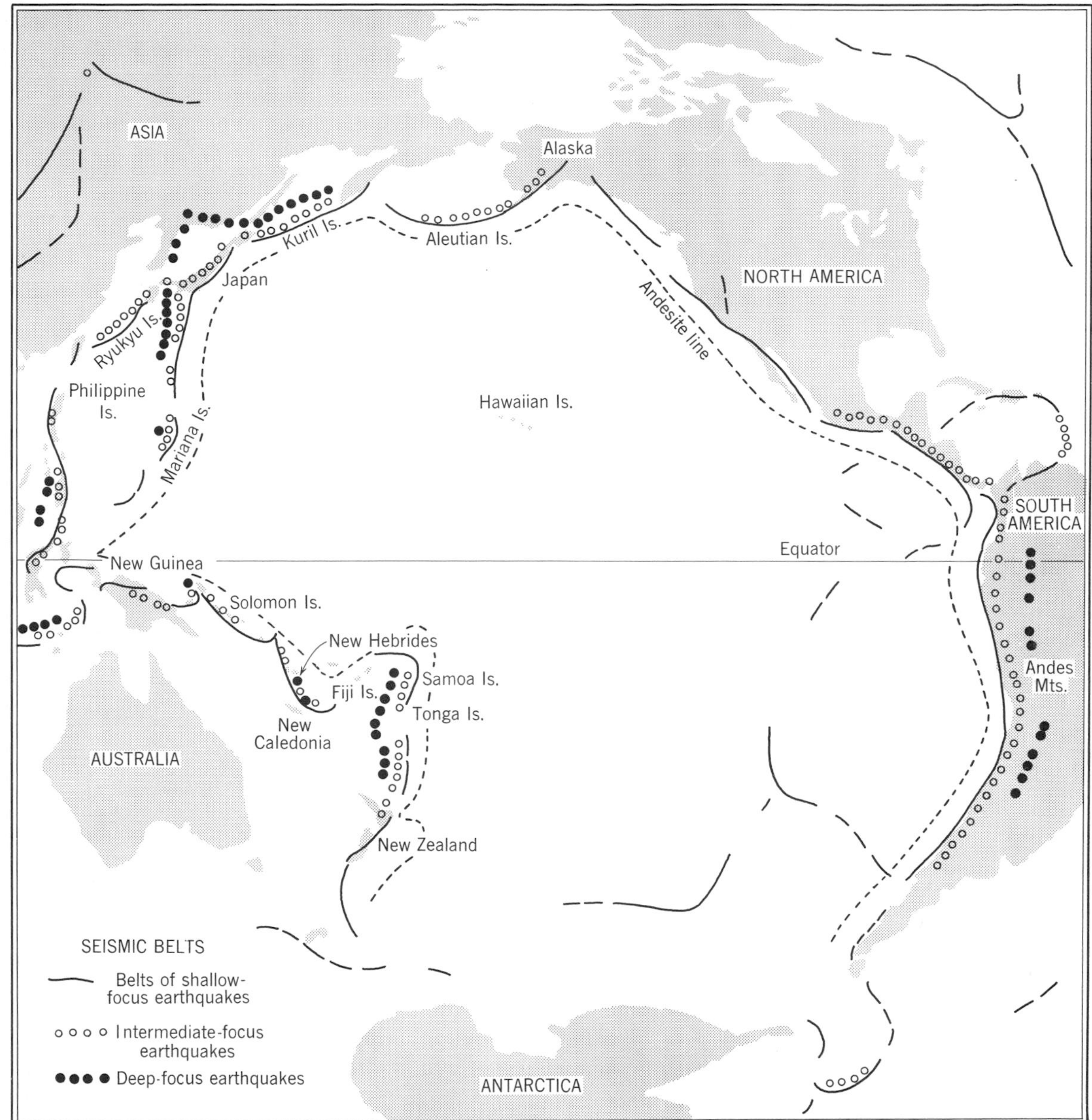


**FIGURE 25.23.** Map of the Pacific Ocean showing the relation of earthquake epicenters to island and mountain arcs. [After B. Gutenberg and C. F. Richter (1949), *Seismicity of the Earth,* Princeton, N.J., Princeton Univ. Press.]

ried further, it might be expected that heat flow would be rapid along the axis of the Mid-Oceanic Ridge, if this is in fact a zone of rising mantle rock, whereas heat flow would show low values under an oceanic trench or a geosyncline, if these are zones of crustal sinking.

Heat flow measurements are made over the ocean bottom by a *thermal probe,* consisting essentially of two thermal sensors spaced a few meters apart in a hollow tube. The tube is thrust into the bottom sediment. After a suitable lapse of time, the lower sensor will register a higher temperature than the upper sensor. The temperature difference permits the thermal gradient to be calculated, and from this information the rate of heat flow is derived. A newer technique developed by Professor Maurice Ewing uses thermal sensors attached to the outside of the piston corer and enables the thermal gradient to be measured in as little as four minutes to a depth of 60 ft (18 m).

Heat flow is stated in units of microcalories per square centimeter per second. Values of 0.7 to 0.8 are considered as low rates. Values over 2.0 are considered high, while extreme values reach 8.0.

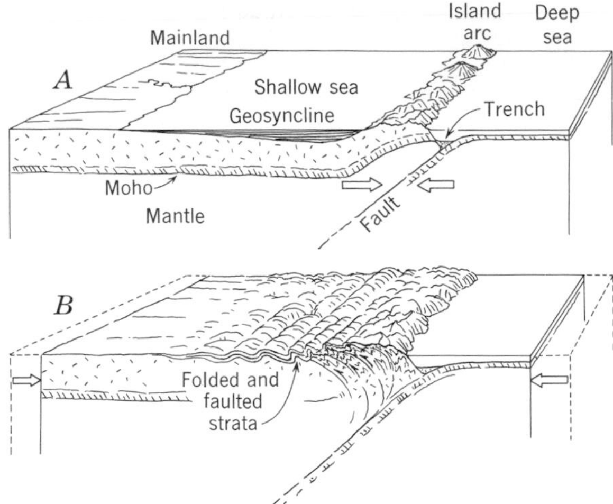


**FIGURE 25.24.** Block diagrams suggesting the evolution of a volcanic island arc into a belt of intensely deformed rocks of the continental crust.

Heat flow averages about the same for both oceanic and continental areas—about 1.2 microcalories/sq cm/sec—but there are important differences within both oceanic and continental crusts. The central axis of the Mid-Oceanic Ridge system in a zone about 100 mi (160 km) wide shows exceptionally high values. Along the ridge flanks heat flow is 1½ to 2 times as great as the average for oceans. Continental shields show low values. (See Table 25.2.)

## Crustal types

Before attempting to draw up a general theory of global tectonics[2] we shall pull together the various lines of geological and geophysical data into a classification of crustal types. In Table 25.2 nine crustal classes are assigned characteristic values of thickness, mantle P-wave velocity, and heat flow. A stability rating is included.

[2] *Tectonics* is the study of the structural features of the earth's crust and their origin. The adjective *tectonic* refers to large-scale movements of the crust and mantle resulting in rock deformation.

*A. Continental shield* crust has the highest mantle velocities, a comparatively low rate of heat flow, and small isostatic gravity anomalies. Continental shields are stable areas of ancient largely granitic rock now lacking in volcanic activity and showing little seismic activity.

*B. Covered shield* crust is found in midcontinental locations and is often included with continental shield, which it resembles in most characteristics. Granitic shield rocks are covered by moderate thicknesses of sedimentary strata.

*C. Marginal geosyncline* crust is topped by great thicknesses of sedimentary strata accumulated on the continental shelf and undeformed except for downwarping on a broad scale. The Gulf Coast geosyncline, with sediment thicknesses up to 10 mi (16 km), provides an outstanding example. This crust is stable and is essentially in isostatic equilibrium.

*D. Basin-and-range* crust is noteworthy for the shallower depth to M-discontinuity and the abnormally low P-wave velocities in the mantle. Geologically this type of unstable crust is strongly faulted into blocks that are displaced upwards and downwards. Crustal extension, or pulling apart, is suggested by this type of structure. Average elevations are high. Movement along normal faults is active. Heat flow is high.

*E. Alpine* crust is found in the mountain arcs of geologically recent or presently active crustal compression and elevation. Intrusions of plutonic rock and extrusions of andesitic lavas are characteristic. Tectonic activity in these zones was preceded by thick deposition of sediments in geosynclines. These sediments have been severely folded and faulted, then raised to high elevation. Isostatic gravity anomalies are small, indicating prevailing isostatic equilibrium. The crust is thick, forming deep mountain roots.

*F. Island arc* crust is found under extremely unstable linear belts with intensive seismic and volcanic activity.

**TABLE 25.2. CRUSTAL TYPES***

| | Crustal Thickness, km | P-wave Velocity in Mantle, km/sec | Heat Flow, microcal/ $cm^2$/sec | Tectonic Characteristics |
|---|---|---|---|---|
| *A.* Continental shield | 35 | 8.3 | 0.7–0.9 | Very stable |
| *B.* Covered shield | 38 | 8.2 | 0.8–1.2 | Stable |
| *C.* Marginal geosyncline | 20–30 | 8.1 | ----- | Stable |
| *D.* Basin-and-range | 30 | 7.8 | 1.7–2.5 | Very unstable |
| *E.* Alpine | 55 | 8.0 | Variable 0.7–2.0 | Very unstable |
| *F.* Island arc | 30 | 7.4–7.8 | Variable 0.7–4.0 | Very unstable |
| *G.* Oceanic trench | ? | ? | Low (?) | Very unstable |
| *H.* Deep ocean | 11 | 8.1–8.2 | 1.3 | Very stable |
| *I.* Mid-Oceanic Ridge | 10 | 7.4–7.6 | High, variable, 1.0–8.0 | Unstable |

* Based in part on data of J. N. Brune (1969), in *The Earth's Crust and Upper Mantle,* Geophysical Monograph 13, Washington, D.C., Amer. Geophysical Union, pp. 230–242.

Andesitic volcanoes are numerous. Locally large positive isostatic anomalies occur, while heat flow varies locally from very high to very low. Variations in crustal thickness are large. P-wave velocities in the upper mantle are abnormally low.

*G. Oceanic trench* crust occurs in a narrow belt adjacent to the island arc crust, but little is known of its physical characteristics. Strong negative isostatic anomalies are present, in contrast to the strong positive anomalies in the adjacent island arc. Low values of heat flow have been observed, but are not well substantiated.

*H. Deep ocean* crust is of small but fairly uniform thickness. Mantle velocity is about the same as under shield crust. Heat flow is close to the world average value. This is very stable crust and shows very little seismic activity.

*I. Mid-Oceanic Ridge* crust is comparatively thin on ridge flanks and lacks an M-discontinuity under the axial region. P-wave velocity in the shallow mantle rock is abnormally low. Heat flow is variable and can be very high. Basaltic volcanic eruptions are abundant and small earthquakes are common in this unstable crust. Crustal extension with intensive fracturing is characteristic.

We return now to a major item of unfinished business—the interpretation of crustal processes taking place beneath the Mid-Oceanic Ridge. This belt of intensive crustal activity differs strikingly from the belts of island arcs and mountain arcs. Whereas the latter are zones of crustal compression, the Mid-Oceanic Ridge is a zone of crustal *extension,* or pulling-apart. The outward form of the axial rift suggests that extension is taking place. However, our explanation must account for the fact that the zone of rifting is also one of comparatively high elevation and that there exists no huge gaping trench at the line of separation. First, however, we must seek independent proof that crustal extension is in progress. Search for this evidence leads back to a topic of earlier consideration—the earth's magnetic field and its variations at the earth's surface.

## Paleomagnetism and reversals of the earth's magnetic field

Basaltic lavas contain, in addition to the abundant silicate minerals, minor amounts of oxides of iron and titanium—magnetite, the mineral of which lodestone is a naturally magnetic variety, is an example. At the high temperatures of the magma, these minerals have no natural magnetism. However, as cooling sets in each crystallized mineral passes a critical temperature, known as the *Curie point,* below which the mineral is magnetized by lines of force of the earth's field. At first this magnetization is not permanent, but rather of the type known as *soft magnetization,* similar to that acquired by soft iron. With further cooling, however, the soft magnetism abruptly becomes permanent, a state known as *hard magnetization,* resembling the permanent magnetic condition of the alnico magnet. Thus a permanent record of the earth's magnetic field is locked into the solidified lava.

In the study of rock magnetism, a sample of rock is removed from the surrounding bedrock. Orientation of the specimen core is carefully documented in terms of geographic north and horizontality. The specimen is then placed in a sensitive magnetometer, which measures the direction and intensity of the permanent magnetism within the rock, and as for a magnetic needle, the angles of declination and dip are determined. After a number of samples have been obtained from a single lava flow and the magnetic parameters compared for consistency and averaged, the direction and inclination of the "fossilized" magnetism, or *paleomagnetism,* can be compared with present conditions and with the magnetic field at other locations and different times in the geologic past.

As early as 1906, Bernard Brunhes, a French physicist, had observed that the magnetic polarity of some samples of lavas is exactly the reverse of present conditions. He concluded that the earth's magnetic poles must have been reversed at the time the lava solidified. One might wish to propose as an alternative hypothesis that the rock magnetism itself has undergone a change in polarity, but in recent years there has been general agreement among members of the scientific community that the rock magnetism is permanent and a reliable indicator of the former states of the earth's magnetic field.

In addition to the magnetic data of the lava, there is needed a determination of the age of the rock—e.g., the date of solidification of the magma. Such information is available through dating methods based on radioactive mineral decay and is described in Chapter 26. Extensive determinations of both magnetic parameters and rock age have revealed that there have been at least nine reversals of the earth's magnetic field in the last 3½ million years of geologic time. Figure 25.25 shows the time scale of magnetic events. Polarity such

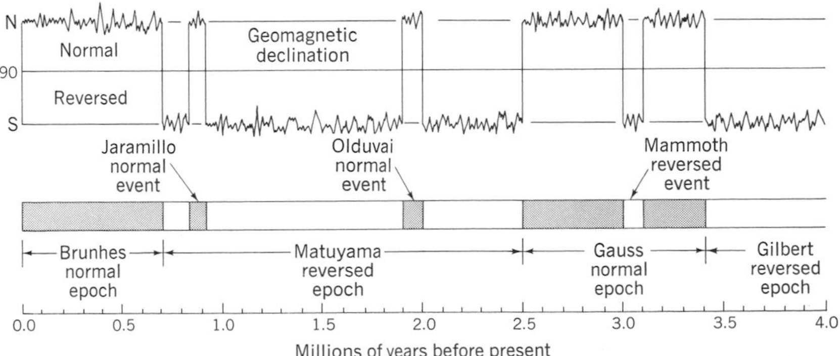


**FIGURE 25.25.** Time scale of magnetic polarity reversals. The graph of geomagnetic declination fluctuations is schematic. [After A. Cox, R. R. Doell, and G. B. Dalrymple (1964), *Science,* vol. 144, p. 1541, Figure 3, and other sources.]

as that existing today is referred to as a *normal epoch*, opposite polarity as a *reversed epoch*. Each epoch is named for an individual or a locality. For example, the pioneer work of Bernard Bruhnes is recognized in assigning his name to the present normal epoch, which began about 700,000 years ago. An epoch of reversal, named for the Japanese scientist Motonori Matuyama, extends to 2½ million years before the present and includes shorter periods of normal polarity classified as *events*. A still older normal epoch, named in honor of the mathematician Karl Gauss (1777–1855), carries back the paleomagnetic record to about 3½ million years and contains one brief reversed event. Oldest of the reversed epochs thus far dated is named after Sir William Gilbert, whose early work on terrestrial magnetism was discussed in Chapter 7.

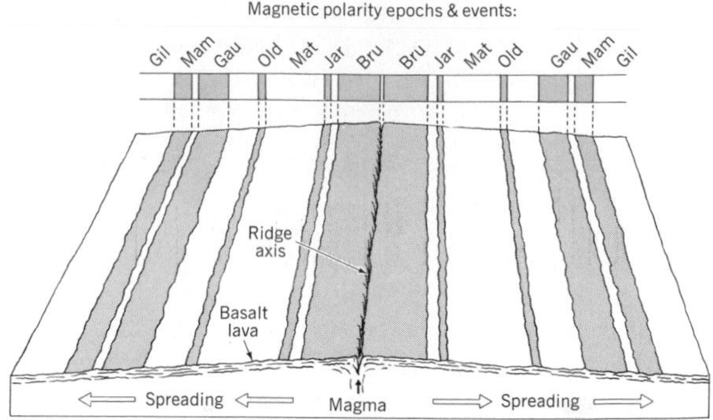


**FIGURE 25.26.** Schematic diagram of development of symmetrical pattern of magnetic polarity belts in oceanic basalts during crustal spreading. (See Figure 25.25 for time scale.)

## Rock magnetism and crustal spreading

We are now prepared to return to the subject of crustal spreading along the Mid-Oceanic Ridge suggested in Chapter 24. If the axial rift valley of the Mid-Oceanic Ridge is a line of upwelling of basaltic lavas, and if crustal spreading is a continuing process, the lava flows that have poured out in the vicinity of the rift valley will be slowly moved away from the rift. Lavas of a given geologic age will thus divide into two narrow strips, one on each side of the rift. As time passes these strips will increase in distance of separation, as shown in Figure 25.26. If lavas are identified and classified in terms of the epochs of normal and reversed magnetic field, these epochs will be represented by symmetrical strip-patterns, as shown in Figure 25.26.

Confirmation of the symmetrical magnetic strips has been found in the interpretation of magnetic information gained in the course of oceanographic surveys. We cannot, of course, take oriented core samples of lavas from the ocean floors. However, it is possible to operate a sensitive magnetometer during a ship's traverse across the Mid-Oceanic Ridge. When this is done, it is found that the value of magnetic inclination fluctuates with a range of about 1000 gammas (Figure 25.27). These departures from a constant normal value are referred to as *magnetic anomalies*. When several parallel cross-lines of magnetometer survey have been run across the Mid-Oceanic Ridge, the magnetic anomalies can be resolved into a pattern, such as that shown in Figure 25.28. Notice the mirror symmetry of the striped pattern with respect to the axial line. From a study of the anomaly pattern, it is possible to identify the normal and reversed epochs.

Recently it has been found possible to identify the normal and reversed magnetic epochs in samples of soft sediment obtained from the ocean floor by piston-coring. Here epochs are encountered in sequence from top to bottom within the core.

Core orientation is not known in terms of north and south, since they are turned frequently during extraction and handling. However, top and bottom are known. Therefore paleomagnetic analysis can be based upon magnetic inclination, but not upon declination. (Refer to Chapter 7 for any needed background information.) At high latitudes, inclination is a high angle with respect to the horizontal. Small specimens are cut from the core and subjected to measurement of magnetic inclination.

Figure 25.29 shows actual data from a core taken from North Pacific waters. Each dot represents a sample from the core. Depth in core is given on the vertical axis, and inclination in degrees on the horizontal axis. A negative sign means that the north-seeking end of a dip needle would point down (normal field) a positive sign

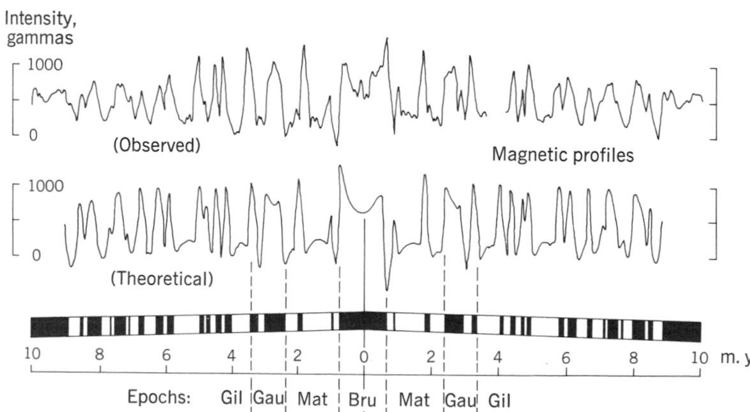


**FIGURE 25.27.** Observed profile of magnetic intensity (*above*) along a traverse of the Mid-Oceanic Ridge at about lat. 60° S. in the South Pacific. Theoretical magnetic profile and time-scale of magnetic polarity reversals are shown (*below*). [After W. C. Pitman and J. R. Heirtzler (1966), *Science*, vol. 154, p. 1166, Figure 3.]

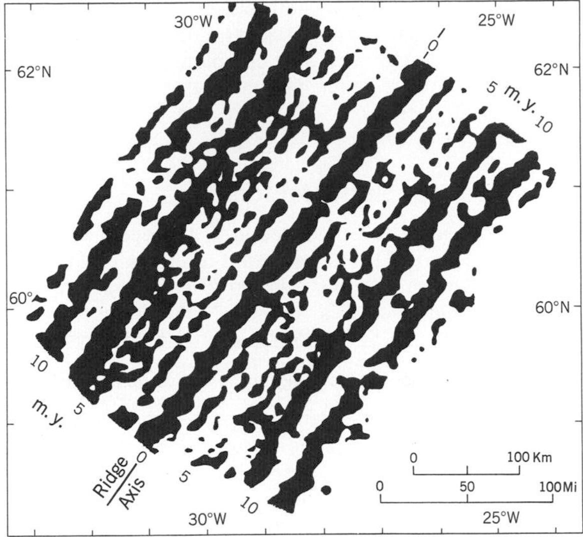


**FIGURE 25.28.** Magnetic anomaly pattern for Reykjanes Ridge, located on the Mid-Atlantic Ridge southwest of Iceland, with approximate rock ages in millions of years. [After J. R. Heirtzler, X. Le Pichon, and J. G. Baron (1966), *Deep-Sea Research,* vol. 13, p. 427.]

means that the same end of the needle would point up into the air (reversed field). Along the right of the graphs is the history of polarity reversals, with time in millions of years before the present.

Because of the established time scale of polarity reversals, it is possible to establish the rate of accumulation of deep sediment at the locations sampled by the cores. For North Pacific cores, this rate was found to differ from core to core and ranged between 0.1 and 0.4 in. (0.3 and 1.1 cm) per year. Sediment cores reveal older (as yet unnamed) epochs of polarity reversals dating back to 5 million years or so.

**FIGURE 25.29.** Changes in magnetic inclination with depth in sediments of a core taken at about lat. 45° N. in the Pacific Ocean by the Research Vessel *Vema.* [After N. Opdyke (1968), in *The History of the Earth's Crust: A Symposium,* R. A. Phinney, Ed., Princeton, N.J., Princeton Univ. Press, p. 64, Figure 3.]

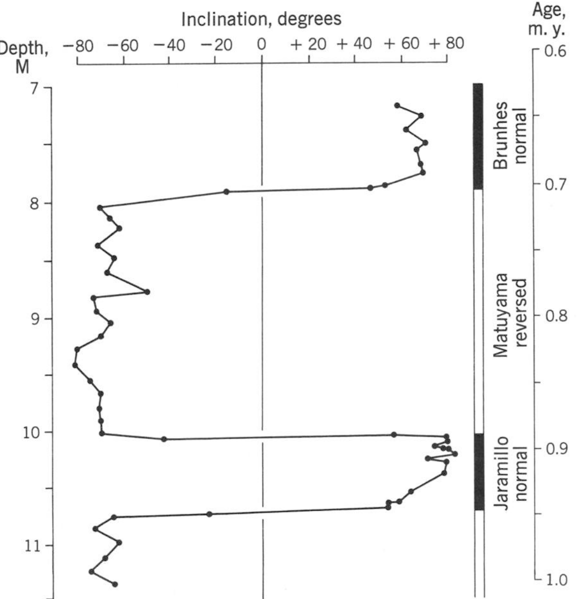


It is apparent that the evidence of rock magnetism not only makes a virtual certainty of crustal spreading, but also allows the rates and total distances to be estimated as well. Take for example the case of the anomaly pattern shown in Figure 25.28, which is part of the Mid-Atlantic ridge south of Iceland in the North Atlantic. Here the width of the anomaly zone is 750 mi (1200 km), which represents the total distance of crustal separation in about 4 million years. The average rate of horizontal motion of the crust during this time has been about 0.4 in. (1 cm) per year, which means that the rate of separation is double this value, or 0.8 in. (2 cm) per year. Elsewhere the rate of spreading are found to be higher, up to 1.8 in. (4.5 cm) per year.

Using rates of spreading as a basis of estimate, reversals of polarity found in magnetic anomaly patterns have been extrapolated back as far as 80 million years, which falls in the Cretaceous era of geologic time.

In Chapter 26, we shall return to the subject of crustal spreading as it applies to geologic history and the possible separation of the continents from a single parent mass. At this point there remains the need to fit crustal spreading into a workable system of crustal movements that will combine orogeny along continental margins with rifting of the Mid-Oceanic Ridge.

## Faulting accompanying oceanic crustal spreading

In Chapter 24, under the description of the Mid-Oceanic Ridge system, attention was called to numerous faults cutting at more-or-less right angles across the central rift and accompanied by very large offsets of that rift. (See Figures 24.13 and 24.15.) These faults were tentatively identified as transcurrent (strike-slip) faults in which one crustal block as a unit slides past another in horizontal motion. Figure 25.30*A* illustrates a transcurrent fault offsetting the axial rift line. When one walks toward the line of the fault (approaching from either direction) the block on the opposite side has moved toward the left. This case is designated a *left-lateral* (*sinistral*) transcurrent fault. Figure 25.30*B* illustrates the opposite sense of motion, a *right-lateral* (*dextral*) transcurrent fault.

One might suppose that by merely observing the direction of offsetting of the central rift line of the Mid-

**FIGURE 25.30.** Transcurrent faults: *A* left-lateral (sinistral); *B*, right-lateral (dextral).

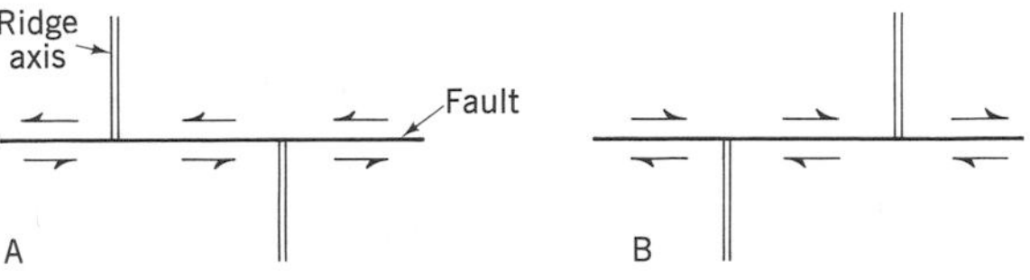

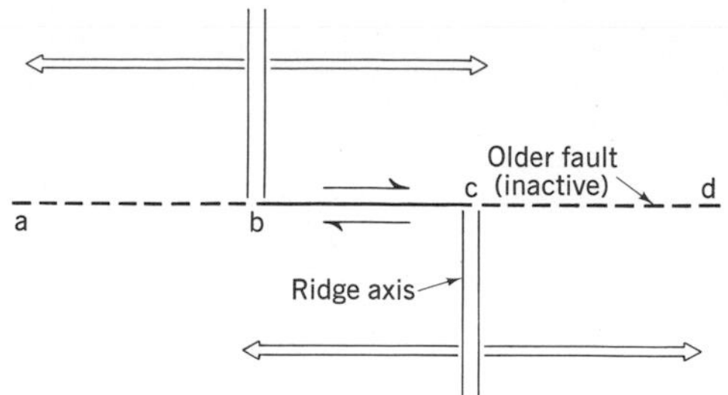


**FIGURE 25.31.** Transform fault of dextral type.

Oceanic Ridge that the transverse faults could easily be labeled left-lateral or right-lateral. However, if crustal spreading is in progress, a new set of differential motions comes into play.

Figure 25.31 shows an offset of the ridge axis. If crustal spreading is in progress, as indicated by the broad arrows, horizontal movement between blocks in the segment *b–c* will be of right-lateral sense, as the small arrows show. Such a fault has been named by J. Tuzo Wilson a *transform fault,* and is opposite in relative motion to the transcurrent fault shown in Figure 25.30*A,* even though the ridge axis has the identical plan of offset in both cases. Note further that if spreading is at equal rate along the axial rift, there will be no faulting in progress on either of lines *a–b* or *c–d.* Thus the transform fault is limited to the segment between the offset ends. Of course, there may exist older transcurrent faults along the lines *a–b* and *c–d,* and such is apparently the case for much of the Mid-Oceanic Ridge, as a glance at the map will show (Figure 24.13).

Existence of transform faulting was predicted in 1965 as a consequence of crustal spreading. Confirmation came in 1967, when a seismologist, Lynn R. Sykes, examining the records of earthquakes originating along the faults between offset ends of the Mid-Oceanic Ridge, was able to show that the first motions of the earthquakes along the fracture zones indicated faulting in the transform sense, while those along the axis indicated normal faulting. (Direction of fault motion can now be ascertained by study of the initial wave of the P-wave group.) Thus seismology has given independent evidence of crustal spreading. In combination with evidence of magnetic anomalies and the ages of sediments and basalts on both sides of the central rift, the seismic evidence has demonstrated crustal spreading to the extent of virtually complete acceptance by members of the scientific community.

## Plate theory of global tectonics

Rapid advances in our knowledge of the oceanic crust, and in particular of the wide extent of crustal spreading in the Mid-Oceanic Ridge, has led to a general hypothesis of global tectonics meeting with rather widespread acceptance among geologists and geophysicists as an effective working model. The term *plate tectonics* has been applied to the hypothesis, which features the largely horizontal movements of plate-like elements of the strong, brittle lithosphere over a readily-yielding asthenosphere having essentially no strength. The characteristics of the soft layer of the mantle were reviewed in Chapter 23. The lithospheric plates consist of both crust and upper mantle and include both oceanic and continental crust.

Many scientists have made valuable contributions leading to our present model of plate tectonics. The roster of contributors includes many names of distinction and covers many branches of the earth sciences. The particular model of plate tectonics selected for presentation here was described in a paper published in 1968. Its author based his hypothesis upon discussions with more than 20 research scientists of the Lamont-Doherty Geological Observatory of Columbia University and drew upon the work of these and many other persons. In this respect, the model reflects the collective efforts of many individuals and integrates an enormous accumulation of information gathered by many research programs and institutions.

Six principal rigid plates are defined in the total system of global tectonics. Each plate moves horizontally as a unit and may also rotate as it moves over the asthenosphere. Obviously, two major possibilities are that adjacent plates may move apart, creating a widening gap between them, or they may move together, causing crustal rupture of the edges of the plates. A third possibility is that they may slide along each other.

Figure 25.32 is a three-dimensional schematic dia-

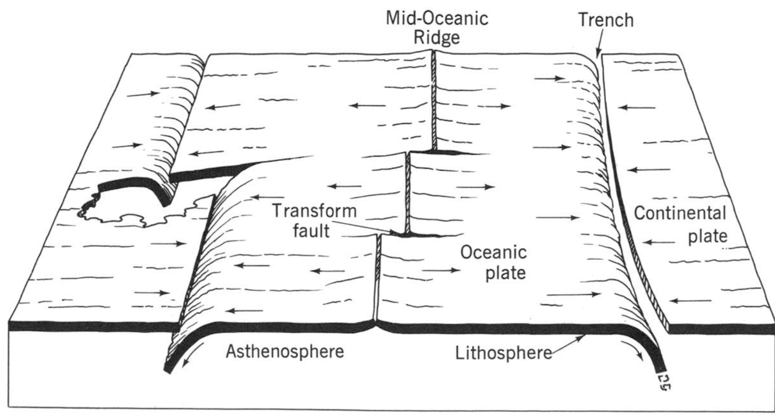


**FIGURE 25.32.** Schematic block diagram of plate tectonics. Earth-curvature removed. (Based on data of X. Le Pichon, L. R. Sykes, B. Isacks and others.)

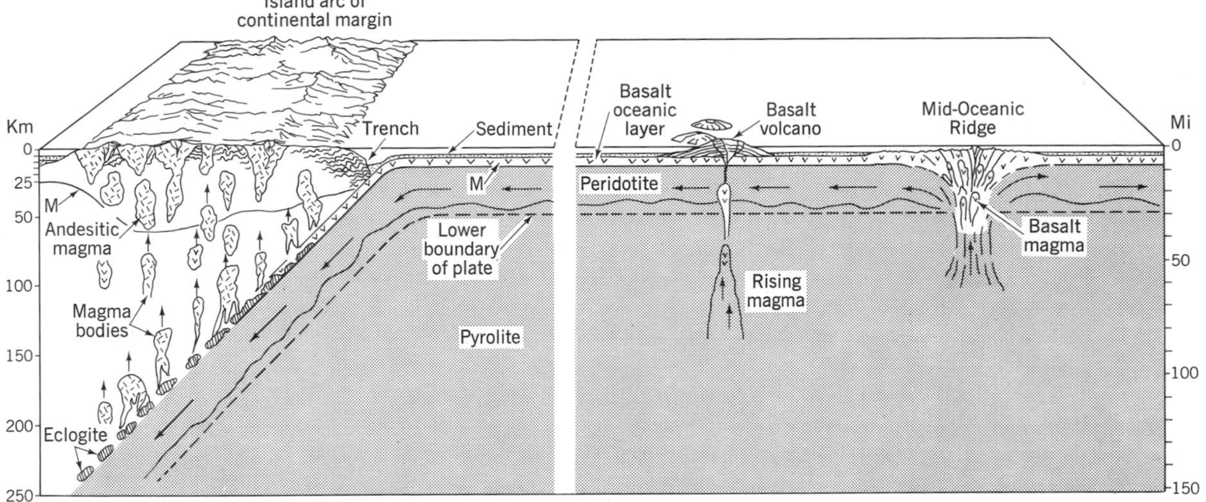


**FIGURE 25.33.** Block diagram illustrating hypothetical details of plate tectonics at island-arc or continental margin. [Modified from H. H. Hess' 1962 model, as given by A. E. Ringwood (1969), in *The Earth's Crust and Upper Mantle, Geophysical Monograph 13,* Washington, D.C., Amer. Geophys. Union, p. 12, Figure 5.]

gram showing relationships among lithospheric plates. Plates pulling apart beneath the oceans produce the Mid-Oceanic Ridge system with its axial rift and transcurrent and transform faults. Where plates converge, the edge of one plate is bent down and forced to descend into the asthenosphere, where it is heated and absorbed into the mantle rock at great depth.

Figure 25.33 shows details of the crust and mantle in a hypothetical cross-section from Mid-Oceanic Ridge to island arc. Notice the postulated rising of the mantle rock under the Mid-Oceanic Ridge to provide new oceanic crust as spreading occurs. Rising motions tend to elevate the axis of the Mid-Oceanic Ridge. Ultrabasic rock of the mantle must be differentiated into basaltic magma and it is inferred here that the denser magma fractions sink back into the mantle. Notice that isolated basaltic volcanoes form over the oceanic crust by eruption through the plate. Where the plate descends into the mantle, oceanic sediments are crumpled and accumulated against the adjacent plate. Melting of the descending crust produces magmas, which are differentiated to yield andesitic magma, leaving behind ultrabasic magma (eclogite). Rising andesitic magmas produce volcanoes and thus build the island arc. As a result, the crust thickens and becomes felsic (sialic) in composition, taking on characteristics of the continental crust.

Returning to the global plan of plate tectonics, it has been postulated that there are six enormous plates (Figure 25.34). The *America plate* includes North American and South American continental crust and all of the oceanic crust of the western Atlantic extending eastward to the Mid-Atlantic Ridge. This America plate has a relative westward motion as a single unit and consequently there is no important tectonic activity along the eastern margins of the American continents. The western edge of the America plate lies along the western continental margins.

The *Pacific plate,* the only unit bearing only oceanic crust, occupies all of the Pacific region west of the East Pacific Rise. It is forced down under the America plate along the compressional zone of the Alaskan–British Columbia coastal region. The *Antarctica plate* occupies the globe south of the Mid-Oceanic Ridge system. An extension of this plate, lying between the East Pacific Rise and South America, moves eastward against the west margin of South America, meeting in the compressional zone of the Peru-Chile Trench and the Andes range. The *Africa plate* consists of the African continental crust and a zone of surrounding oceanic crust limited by the Mid-Oceanic Ridge.

A single *Eurasia plate,* which consists largely of continental crust, is bounded on east and south by compressional zones of the great alpine mountain chains and island arcs, but also extends into the North Atlantic as oceanic crust lying east of the Mid-Atlantic ridge. An *India block,* consisting of continental crust of India and Australia as well as of oceanic crust of the Indian Ocean and a part of the southwestern Pacific, is separated from the Pacific plate by a compressional belt passing through New Zealand. Other smaller lithospheric blocks may be required to complete the picture.

Because of its vast extent the Pacific plate can be expected to possess, at its westernmost portion, the oldest oceanic crust on earth. In 1970 deep-sea cores obtained on Leg 6 of the voyage of the *Glomar Challenger* provided confirmation of this inference. Sediments as old as early Cretaceous age or upper Jurassic age, in the range of 125 to 150 million years, were identified in cores from nine drill sites in the vicinity of longitude 156° to 158° E. Figure 25.34 includes a sketch-map of age zones of the Pacific plate. (See Tables 26.2 and 30.1 for geologic periods and epochs.)

While the six-plate hypothesis of global tectonics appears to offer a unifying explanation of most of the major crustal phenomena, it should be regarded as only one of a number of possible models of its kind. Discrepancies are known. We may anticipate modifica-

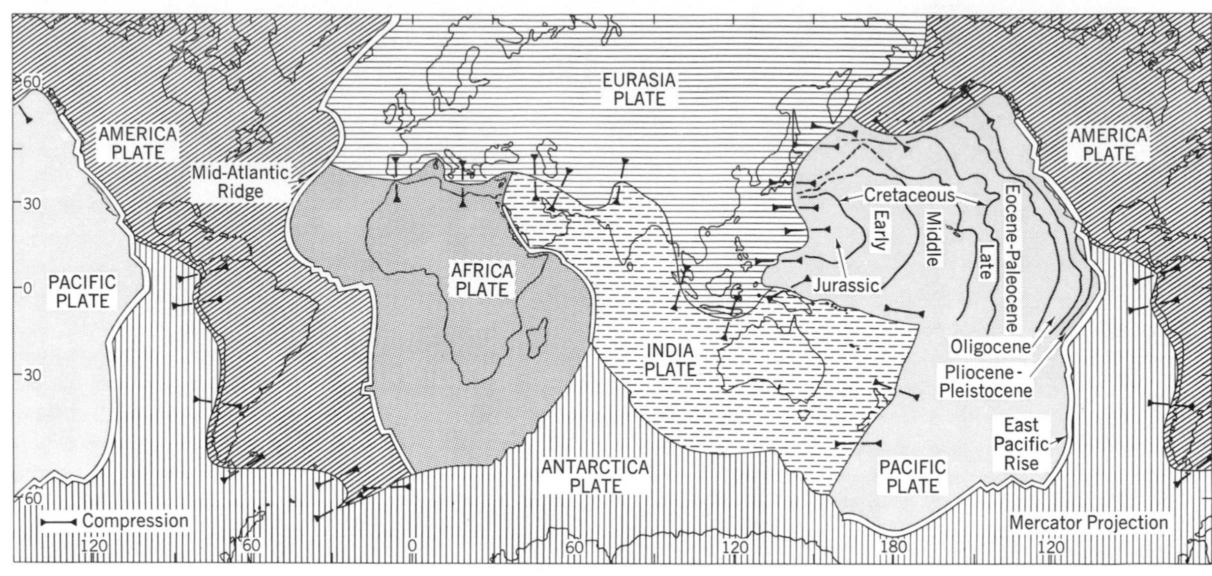


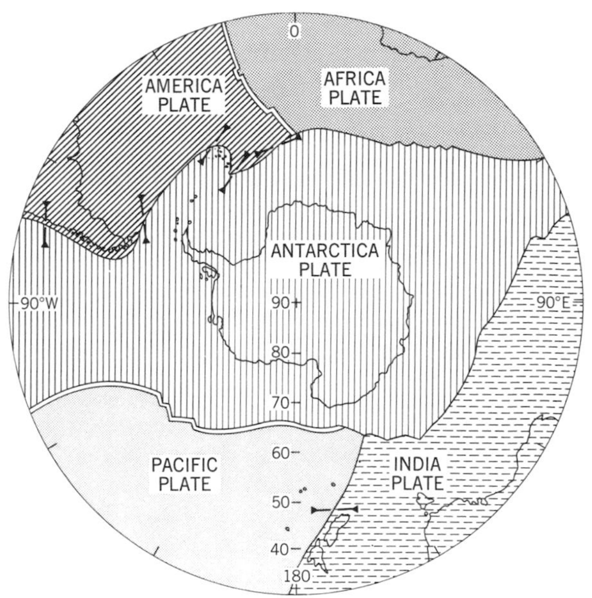


**FIGURE 25.34.** World and polar maps of a system of six lithospheric plates. Double-line plate boundary shows Mid-Oceanic Ridge rift zone on which spreading is active. Other plate boundaries in solid lines. Double arrow symbol shows zones of active compression. [Modified and simplified from a map by X. Le Pichon (1968), *Jour. Geophys. Res.*, vol. 73, p. 3675, Figure 6. Pacific plate ages from A. G. Fischer, B. C. Heezen, and others (1970), *Science,* vol. 168, p. 1211, Figure 1.]

tions of the model from time to time as new data are brought to light.

## Convection currents in the mantle

Crustal spreading and plate tectonics require a driving mechanism. Little is known of actual mass movements within the mantle, but most models of global tectonics have been referred to systems of very slow mantle circulation under the general heading of *convection currents.*

One of the leading proponents of mantle convection currents was F. A. Vening Meinesz, a Dutch geophysicist who developed methods of measuring the acceleration of gravity by means of instruments carried in a submarine. In his gravity studies of the East Indies, Vening Meinesz mapped the great negative gravity anomalies over the trenches adjacent to those island arcs. Partly as a means of explaining these anomalies, he proposed that the downward-acting forces needed to maintain the negative values of gravity are part of a convection current system.

Figure 25.35*A* shows a model of convection involving the entire thickness of the mantle, as conceived by several scientists whose speculations both preceded and followed the work of Vening Meinesz. Rising of less dense mantle rock under the Mid-Oceanic Ridge and corresponding sinking beneath the compressional zones of the trenches and island arcs are key activities

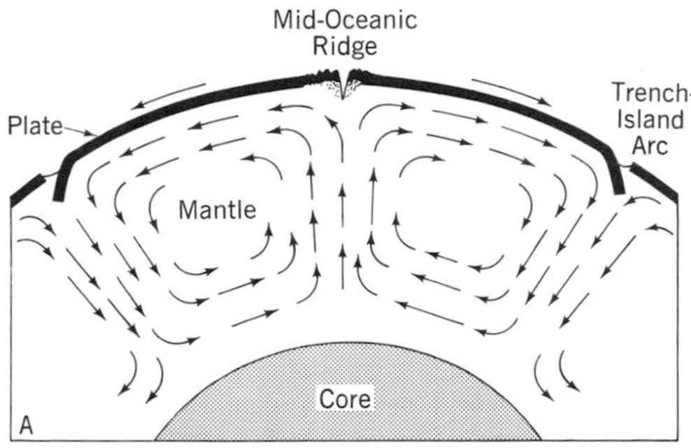


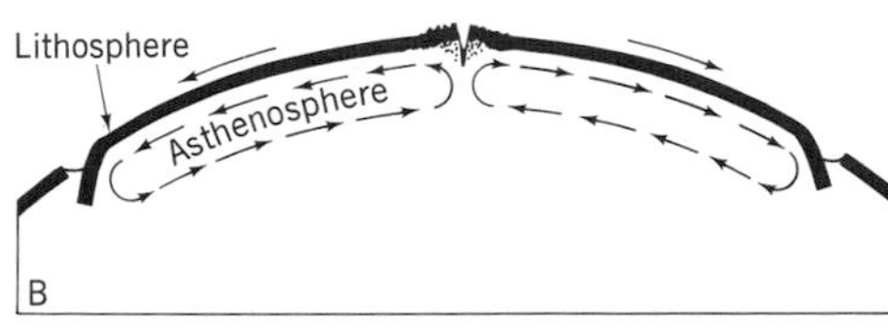


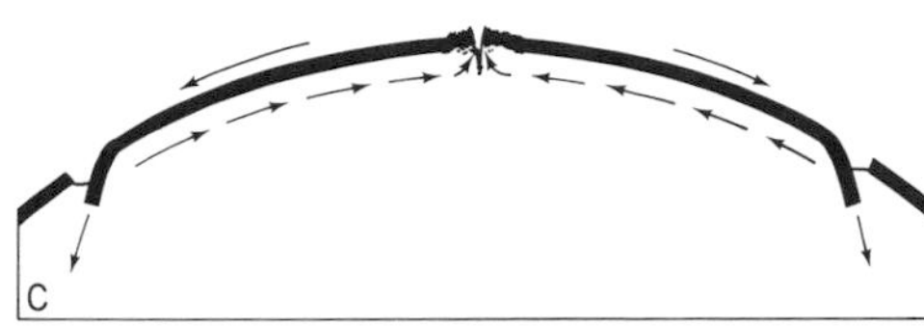


**FIGURE 25.35.** Schematic diagrams of convection hypotheses. (*A*) Large, deep convection cells. (*B*) Shallow convection layer. (*C*) Opposite flow beneath lithospheric plate.

within the convection system. Dominantly horizontal motion under the lithospheric plate would exert a drag, causing the plate to move away from the Mid-Oceanic Ridge and toward the compressional belt. Rates of flow of mantle rock were originally postulated to be on the order of magnitude of 0.04 in. (1 mm) per year throughout most of the system, but this rate is only one-tenth that required by crustal spreading.

More recently a model has been proposed in which convection occurs within a very shallow zone of the upper mantle (Figure 25.35*B*). All motion takes place within the asthenosphere, or soft layer. The lithosphere is moved by drag force of the flow beneath. Advocates of the plate theory of tectonics have devised a totally different model in which the asthenosphere moves in the opposite direction to the lithospheric plate (Figure 25.35*C*). In this case the drag force would tend to oppose the plate motion and we would have to look for some other force to cause the plate to move. It has been suggested that the sinking of the down-turned edge of the plate is capable of exerting a pull on the rest of the plate. Objections have been voiced against all of the above models of lithosphere-moving mechanisms, while at the same time other models of quite different sorts have been proposed.

The energy source for convectional or other large-scale motions of the mantle may lie in the uneven accumulation of radiogenic heat, or it may consist of kinetic energy of motions persisting from much earlier time in the earth's history. Earth rotation has been invoked as a driving mechanism. Another hypothesis requires energy input from an asteroid impact.

## Crustal spreading and compression and geologic history

The cumulative effects of crustal spreading and corresponding orogenic and volcanic activities along zones of crustal compression take us far back into the realm of geologic history of the earth. Obviously, if crustal spreading has been in progress for significantly long periods of time, entire continents have moved over large aggregate distances. One problem is to put them back into their original places. If volcanic and orogenic processes have been in progress over significantly long periods of time, continental crust has been produced in large volumes. In the next chapter we examine the origin and growth of the continents, as well as their past movements with respect to one another on a global scale.

## References for further study

Poldervaart, A., Ed. (1955), *Crust of the Earth,* Boulder, Colo., Geol. Soc. Amer., Special Paper No. 62, 676 pp.

Richter, C. F. (1958), *Elementary Seismology,* San Francisco, Freeman, 768 pp., chaps. 25, 26.

Howell, B. F., Jr. (1959), *Introduction to Geophysics,* New York, McGraw-Hill, 399 pp., chaps. 15, 19, 20, 21.

Jacobs, J. A., R. D. Russell, and J. T. Wilson (1959), *Physics and Geology,* New York, McGraw-Hill, 424 pp., chaps. 4, 14, 16.

Phinney, R. A., Ed. (1968), *The History of the Earth's Crust; a Symposium,* Princeton, N.J., Princeton Univ. Press, 244 pp.

Nat. Acad. Sci.-Nat. Res. Council (1969), *The Earth's Crust and Upper Mantle,* Geophysical Monograph 13, Washington, D.C., Am. Geophys. Union, 735 pp.

# 26

# Tectonic forms and continental evolution

IN THIS CHAPTER we attempt to piece together a tentative sequence of events continental crust with a view to interpreting the characteristic sequences of events, throughout geologic time, which have led to the evolution of the continents as we find them today. From geophysical evidence relating to rock properties and forces at depths far too great to yield direct knowledge, we return to inferences based upon observations by geologists working upon the surfaces of the continents.

## Evidences of crustal deformation

As the geologist examines exposed rocks, he finds unmistakable evidence that certain parts of the earth's crust have been crumpled and fractured on a scale so enormous as to be difficult to comprehend and still more difficult to explain satisfactorily in terms of natural forces and rock properties as we observe them at the earth's surface. Here the rock may be of sedimentary composition—a series of sandstone, shale or limestone beds—but instead of lying horizontally the strata are wrinkled into a series of folds (Figure 26.1). It might seem as if the rock had been plastic, like clay, at the time crumpling took place.

Evidence that such contorted strata were once flat-lying and that they were deposited beneath the sea is often undeniable. For example, the surfaces of the sandstone layers often show ripple markings identical in form to those commonly seen in loose sand on the bottom under shallow water near a beach (Figure 26.2).

Shale and limestone strata frequently contain great numbers of fossil shells. These could not have clung to a steeply sloping sea bottom, for many are half shells or broken shell fragments like those one sees lying loose on beaches.

Folded strata are often broken by faults, providing evidence that the rock behaved as a brittle solid, yielding with a sudden movement when its elastic limit was exceeded. The strata are sheared off cleanly along the fault, and if a particularly distinctive layer is present on one side its continuation may perhaps be found by searching higher or lower among the strata on the other side of the fault.

A most important question facing the geologist is to explain how these strata could be crumpled into folds, like a soft clay, but also have sharp breaks, like a brittle solid. It is possible that the rock was plastic at one time and later became brittle, but in some localities there are indications that both the folding and faulting occurred at about the same time, with the rock in the same physical state.

Other difficult questions present themselves. At what depth did this deformation occur? What was the nature of the forces involved? How long did the process take? Why did deformation occur at this place, but not affect similar sedimentary strata of the same geologic age 200 miles distant? Is any crustal contortion of this kind in progress today? If so, where can we go to observe it?

## Catastrophism and uniformitarianism

Early in the nineteenth century, before modern geological science was fully established along the lines that it is today, one group of naturalists explained folding and faulting as the result of one or more sudden catastrophes. Leader of this school was an able French student of fossil life forms, Baron Cuvier, who wrote: "The dislocation and overturning of older strata show without any doubt that the causes which brought them into the position which they now occupy, were sudden and violent. . . . the evidences of those great and terrible events are everywhere to be clearly seen by anyone who knows how to read the record of the rocks." Those who supported this view were known as *catastrophists*. They held that not only were our present mountains, cliffs, and canyons formed by violent catastrophe, but all the animals whose shells and bones we now find as fossils in the strata were suddenly killed in the cataclysm. This theory was tenable only as long as evidence consisted of a few observations in only one region, but it gradually became clear that no single world-wide catastrophe can explain all known relations among strata and their fossil content. Furthermore, the length of time needed for the various events of geologic history was grossly underestimated by the catastrophists.

**FIGURE 26.1.** Folded and faulted strata, Glacier National Park, Montana. (Photograph by Douglas Johnson.)

**FIGURE 26.2.** These ripple marks were formed on a nearly horizontal sea floor, but have since been tilted by mountain-making movements to an almost vertical attitude. Precambrian quartzite strata in the Baraboo Range, Wisconsin. (Photograph by A. N. Strahler.)

A sound basis for reconstructing geologic events is provided by the principle that processes acting in the past have been essentially the same as those seen in action over the face of the earth today. This principle, which was strongly maintained by a Scottish geologist, James Hutton (1726–1797), was termed *uniformitarianism.* It is often summarized in the statement that "the present holds the key to the past." The geologist believes that if he can watch a volcano in eruption and see the molten lava pour down the side of the mountain into the sea he will learn the explanation for similar kinds of lava forms now found enclosed in ancient rocks. If he studies the manner in which sediments are being laid down around the mouth of the Mississippi River today he can learn how to interpret similar layers of shale and siltstone, which he finds exposed in the walls of canyons far inland from present-day shores. Uniformitarianism signifies the belief in similar processes acting to cause similar resultant products

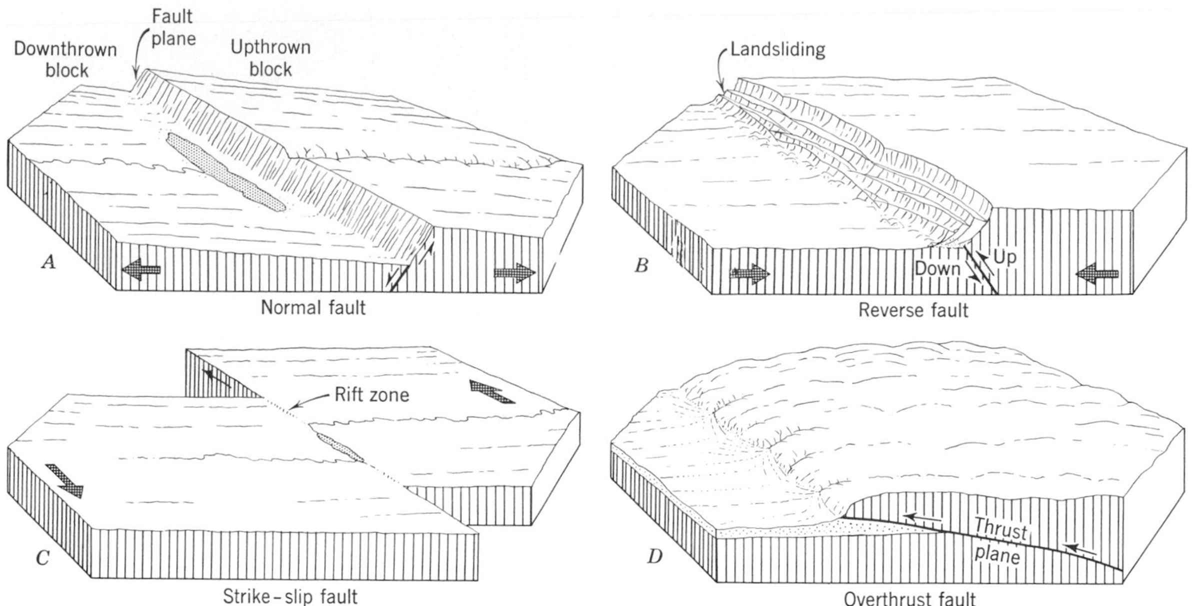


**FIGURE 26.3.** Four basic forms of faults and their surface expression. (© 1960, John Wiley & Sons, New York.)

throughout all geologic time, as distinct from successive violent cataclysms.

## Fault structures and surface forms

The general principle of faulting, as related to earthquakes, was discussed in Chapter 23. Strike-slip, or transcurrent faults, were introduced in Chapter 24 as unique features of the Mid-Oceanic Ridges undergoing crustal spreading. We now continue the study of faults as observed over the continental surfaces.

The *fault plane,* or fracture surface upon which slippage occurs, may take any orientation with respect to the horizontal, and the displacement of corresponding points on two sides of the fault may range from a few inches, in very small faults, to several tens of miles in certain great faults. Movement occurs by a series of slips, each involving but a few inches to a few feet of displacement and occurring almost instantaneously, thus generating an earthquake shock. Over spans of thousands of years the slippage along a large fault may total thousands of feet, if movement continues in the same relative directions. It is by such long-continued faulting that small and large blocks of the earth's crust are displaced with respect to one another, bringing major landscape features into existence.

Figure 26.3 illustrates four basic types of faults, classified according to the inclination and relative directions of movement along the fault plane. In the *normal fault* the fault plane is steeply inclined in the direction of the downthrown block. Normal faulting produces a cliff-like *fault scarp* (Figure 26.4).

The *reverse fault* also involves dominantly vertical motion, but the fault plane is inclined downward toward the upthrown side. A fault scarp is thus produced, but it would tend to form an overhanging cliff. As rock cannot support its own weight in large overhanging masses, the scarp produced by reverse faulting will undergo repeated landsliding of the slump-block type (Figure 32.28). As the large arrows in Diagram *A* suggest, movement on a normal fault must be accompanied by a horizontal separation of reference points on the downthrown and upthrown blocks, showing that crustal extension, at least locally, is associated with normal faulting. In contrast (Diagram *B*) movement on a reverse fault brings the blocks closer together and suggests that a compressional stress is acting locally.

**FIGURE 26.4.** Red Canyon fault scarp, produced during the Hebgen Lake, Montana, earthquake of August 17, 1959. (Photograph by Irving J. Whitkind, U.S. Geological Survey.)

**FIGURE 26.5.** An overthrust fault (slanting line marked by arrows) along which folded cherty limestones have been thrust over similar rocks beneath. Locality is near Atoka, Oklahoma. (Photograph by Lofman; courtesy of Standard Oil Company, New Jersey.)

The *strike-slip fault* (Diagram *C*) is characterized by displacement only in the horizontal direction, along a near-vertical fault plane. Thus one block slides past the other. If strike-slip faulting occurs on a plain of very low relief, as the diagram suggests, no topographic scarp will result. In undulating terrain a discontinuous narrow trench, or *rift,* marks the line of the fault (see Figure 23.7).

The *low-angle overthust fault* (Diagram *D*) involves movement of a plate-like body of rock on a fault plane that is very gently inclined (Figure 26.5). Points that were formerly separated by distances of many miles may thus become superimposed. Overthrusts are associated with strong crustal compression in orogenic belts.

Normal faulting produces scarps of various heights and lengths and in various combinations. Because the movement proceeds by a series of small slips separated by long periods of time, the upper part of a major scarp will usually be considerably worn back by erosion processes. Not only will the original fault plane have been destroyed, but the scarp will have been reduced to a lower average angle of slope and may be deeply

**FIGURE 26.6.** Graben and horst. (© 1960, John Wiley & Sons, New York.)

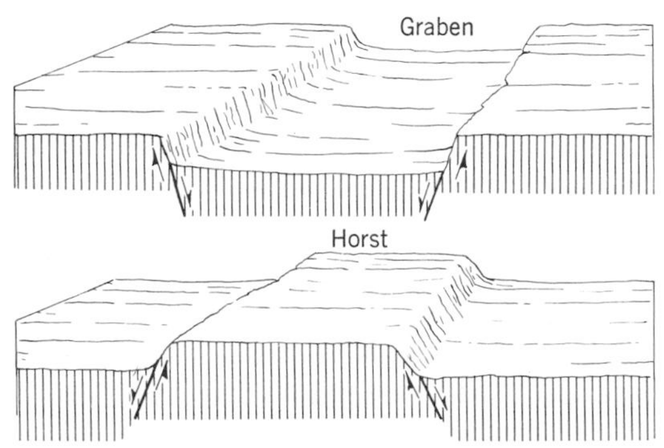


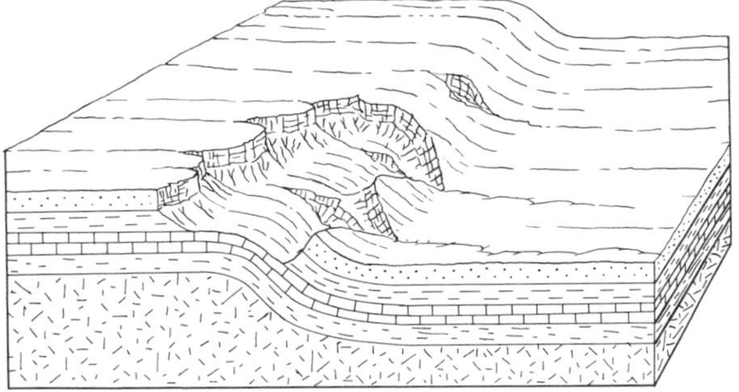

**FIGURE 26.7.** A monocline, partially eroded. (© 1960, John Wiley & Sons, New York.)

**FIGURE 26.8.** Tilted and lifted mountain blocks. (© 1960, John Wiley & Sons, New York.)

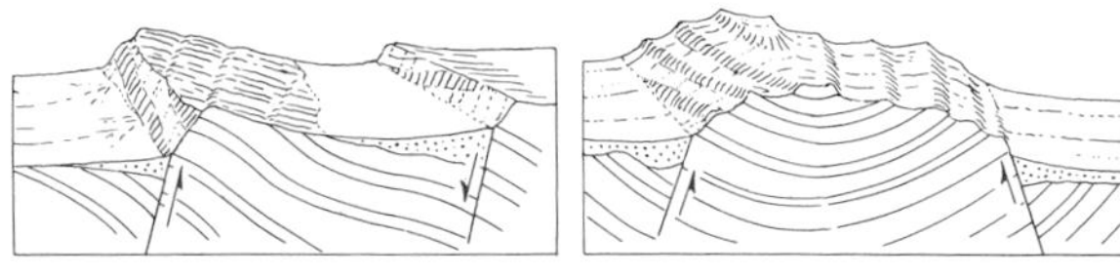

**FIGURE 26.9.** View southeast up Death Valley and the valley of the Amargosa River, California. (Copyrighted Spence Air Photos.)

notched by ravines and canyons. Nevertheless, the scarp maintains a generally straight base for many miles, representing the line along which the fault plane emerges.

Scarp erosion is accompanied by deposition of alluvium as a sheet of overburden burying the fault line. Consequently, when renewed fault movements occur a small scarp is formed in the alluvial materials (Figure 23.8). The formation of a number of such *alluvial scarps,* accompanied by earthquakes, has occurred in historic time along various active major fault lines in Nevada, Utah, Montana, and Idaho.

Normal faults commonly are arranged in pairs, running parallel with one another, but with opposite sides downthrown or upthrown. The result is a down-dropped fault block, or *graben,* lying between the faults, or an uplifted block, a *horst,* between them (Figure 26.6). Grabens can form broad flat-floored valleys, many miles wide and tens of miles long, bounded by bold straight scarps. An example is the Rhine graben of western Germany, some 20 mi (32 km) wide and 150 mi (240 km) long, bounded on the west by the Vosges Mountains and on the east by the Black Forest Mountains. In the United States the Klamath Lake basin of Oregon provides an excellent illustration of a graben 6 to 10 mi (10 to 16 km) wide and bounded by fault scarps up to 1000 ft (300 m) high.

An interesting variation of the normal fault is the *monocline,* a downbend, or flexure, in layered rocks separating plateaus of differing elevation (Figure 26.7). In the monocline strata of such rocks as limestone and shale have yielded by bending, rather than by fracturing, where one crustal block has moved down with relation to another. Monoclines may turn into faults at greater depth or may give way to normal faults when traced along their length.

Normal faulting affecting large masses of the upper continental crust has in certain regions involved such large vertical displacements that *fault block mountains* have resulted (Figure 26.8). Individual uplifted blocks,

**FIGURE 26.10.** Block diagram of anticlinal ridges of the Jura Mountains, France and Switzerland. (Drawn by Erwin Raisz; © 1960, John Wiley & Sons, New York.)

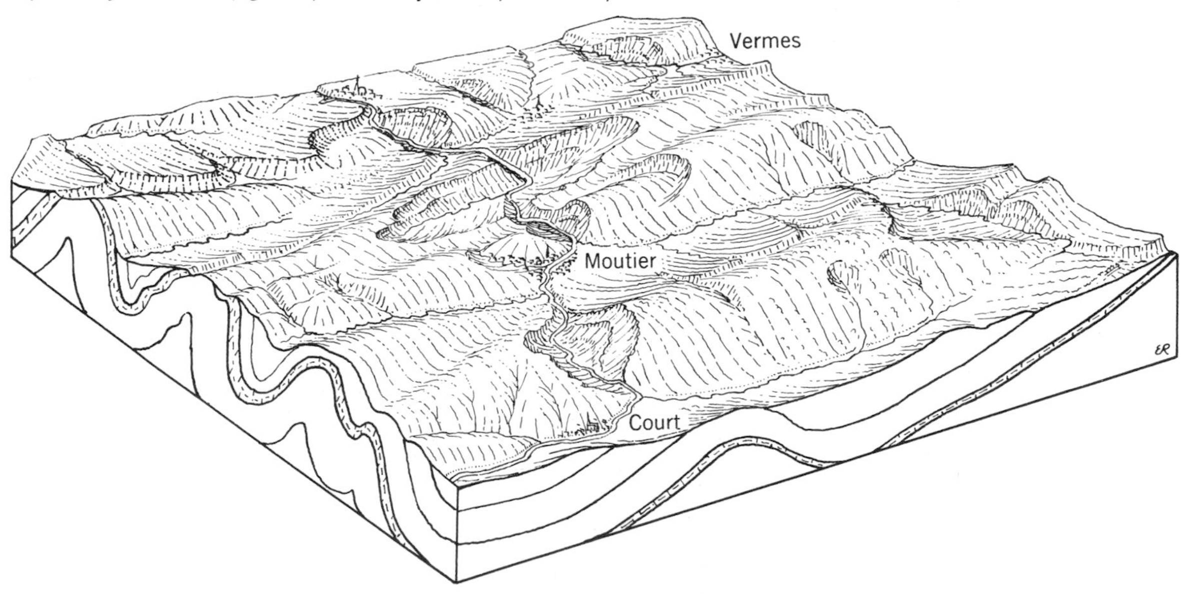

commonly tilted during uplift, may be several miles wide and several tens of miles long. Between the upfaulted blocks are downfaulted blocks which form topographic basins. Although partly filled by alluvium eroded from the adjacent uplifted blocks, these basins form major open valleys. Topographic relief in a region of fault blocks is often on the order of several thousands of feet.

One of the most extensive regions of fault block mountains and fault basins is the Basin-and-Range region of Nevada, Arizona, western Utah, southeastern California, southern Oregon, and parts of New Mexico (Figure 26.9). Reference was made in Chapter 25 to this region as having distinctive crustal properties. Extension, or pulling apart, on a large scale has apparently been in progress here in fairly recent geologic time, with tectonic activity continuing to the present.

## Open folds of sedimentary strata

Compressional forces acting upon sedimentary strata have produced many belts of open wave-like folds, typically located in positions on the continental-interior side of belts of more intensive orogenic activity. The geologist refers to a trough-like downfold as a *syncline,* and to a crest-like upfold as an *anticline.* Figure 26.10 is a block-diagram of a geologically famous region of simple open folds, the Jura Mountains bordering the European Alps along the northwest side. Notice that anticlines of limestone form ridge crests, while synclines form the intervening valleys.

Typically, the crest line of an anticlinal fold is not horizontal but descends or rises along the length of the fold axis. Descent of the fold axis is referred to as *plunge* (Figure 26.11). Figure 26.12 shows an eroded anticline which plunges toward the observer. Upturned strata on the flanks of the anticline form lines of sharp-crested ridges. Notice that these ridges change direction sharply as they cross the axial line of the fold. Figure 26.13 shows a deeply-eroded plunging syncline of sedimentary strata in which the direction of plunge is away from the observer.

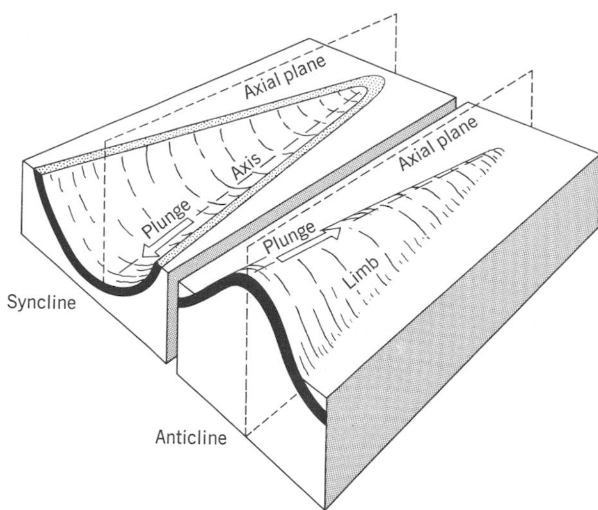


**FIGURE 26.11.** Plunging folds.

## Complexly folded and faulted belts

Highly complex combinations of intense folding and low-angle overthrust faulting have been produced in narrow orogenic belts (Chapter 25). Marine sedimentary strata of a geosyncline have been crumpled into tightly compressed folds in which the axial planes of the anticlines were first rotated forward, or *overturned* (Figure 26.14). Overturning of anticlines continued until the axial planes were nearly horizontal, producing *recumbent folds.* The recumbent folds then developed low-angle overthrust faults upon which they slid forward as *thrust sheets,* or *nappes*[1]. A single nappe may have a width of many miles in the direction of movement. In some places, one nappe slid over another until several were superimposed, giving *imbricate structure.*

The European Alps have long been the object of intensive geologic study because of the extreme com-

[1] The term "nappe" is of French origin—its German equivalent is *decke* (plural, *decken*).

**FIGURE 26.12.** Sheep Mountain, an elongated dome near Greybull, Wyoming. (Photograph by Barnum Brown, American Museum of Natural History.)

**FIGURE 26.13.** Oblique air view of the Belcher Islands, Hudson Bay, Canada. These are partially submerged ridges eroded from folded strata. A syncline forms the upper part of the view. (Royal Canadian Air Force official photograph.)

plexity of their folded and thrust-faulted structures, revealed in striking exposures in the steep mountain walls. The nappe structure is illustrated in Figure 26.15, and its relation to the landforms is shown. Despite their geologic complexity, nappes may have little topographic expression and may escape notice unless a detailed examination is made of the strata above and below the thrust plane. If fossils in the overlying rock are of an older geologic period than those below, an overthrust is clearly indicated.

Erosion of a thrust sheet has resulted in development of a bold escarpment in those places where the overthrust rocks are more resistant to erosion than the rocks beneath. A fine example is the Lewis overthrust in Montana, in which rocks of Precambrian age were thrust eastward many miles over weak shales of Cretaceous age (Figure 26.16).

Erosion of a wide nappe may result in the isolation of a fragment of the sheet from the main part (Figure 26.17). The isolated erosion remnant of a nappe is termed a *klippe* (plural, *klippen*). An example is seen in Chief Mountain, a klippe of the Lewis overthrust sheet referred to above.

Erosion of a nappe may also result in removal of the sheet at one or more points, revealing the underlying rock as a patch entirely surrounded by the thrust sheet (Figure 26.17). Such an exposure is termed a *window* (German: *fenster*).

## Rock metamorphism

Consideration of the third major class of rocks, the metamorphic rocks, has been deferred to this point in order that some understanding might first be gained of the nature of rock deformation and intrusion and of the broad patterns of crustal types and their relationships to tectonic activity. The metamorphic rocks are by-products of orogeny and intrusion.

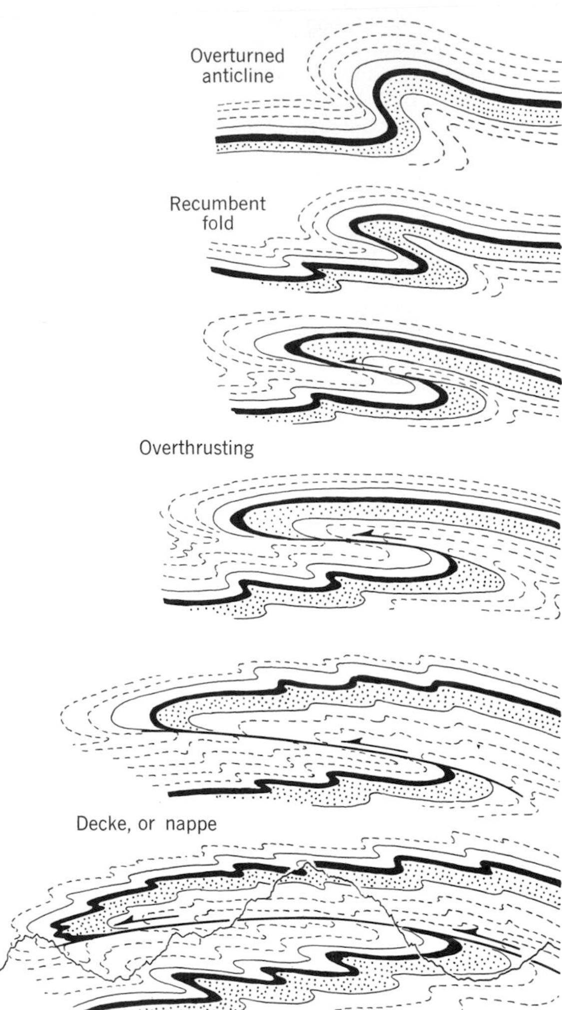


**FIGURE 26.14.** Development of overturned, recumbent, and overthrust folds and nappes. [Suggested by drawings of A. Heim (1922), *Geologie der Schweiz,* vol. II-1, Leipzig, Tauschnitz.]

Metamorphism may affect rocks of both igneous and sedimentary origins. Changes may be effected by application of unequal stresses during the orogenic process under conditions of high confining pressure and high temperature. Such changes constitute *dynamothermal metamorphism* and most often take place deep within thick sedimentary strata of geosynclines. The effect of dynamothermal metamorphism is felt in two ways. First, original minerals recrystallize and new minerals are formed. Second, a new set of structures is imposed on the rock and may replace or obliterate original bedding structures. Dynamothermal metamorphism has affected enormous bodies of rock within the root zones of mountain chains of the alpine type. Consequently the effects are seen over large areas and are often described as *regional metamorphism.*

Application of high temperatures alone can also cause

**FIGURE 26.15.** Structure section through a portion of the Helvetian Alps, Switzerland, showing nappes. Horizontal and vertical scales are the same. [Simplified from A. Heim (1922), *Geologie der Schweiz,* vol. II-1, Leipzig, Tauschnitz.]

metamorphism. Such effects are often conspicuous in country rock close to an igneous intrusion. The changes are essentially those of baking in a high-temperature oven. A shale rock close to an igneous contact may experience a hardening and color change not unlike that caused by baking of brick or tile. However, most large igneous intrusions cause *contact metamorphism* by emanations of hot watery solutions containing ions of many kinds. These are highly active solutions and cause mineral alteration of the country rock. The process of mineral replacement is known as *metasomatism* and may leave original structures, such as bedding in sedimentary rocks, essentially intact.

## Metamorphic minerals

Metamorphism is a change of mineral state in response to a change in environment. Minerals unsuited to the environment of deformation under stress at high pressures and high temperatures will be altered to form minerals capable of attaining equilibrium under those environments. There will often be changes in grain size and shape as well.

Many of the most common and abundant minerals of metamorphic rocks are also abundant constituents of igneous and sedimentary rocks and have been described in Chapters 20 and 22. Quartz, one of the most abundant of minerals in rocks of all classes, persists unaltered in metamorphic rocks, or is recrystallized or introduced by invading solutions. The feldspars are commonly produced by contact metamorphism. Hornblende, olivine, biotite, and muscovite are commonly formed during metamorphism from the constituents of clay-rich sediments. Chlorite, serpentine, and talc are also formed by silicate mineral alteration. Calcite usually persists from the original carbonate rock but easily recrystallizes under pressure. Dolomite also tends to persist from original sedimentary rocks.

Among the more important new minerals distinctive of dynamothermal metamorphism are the following (Table 26.1): *kyanite, andalusite, staurolite,* and *garnet* (variety *almandite*). All four are aluminosilicates. As a group they are hard minerals with specific gravities comparable to those of the mafic minerals. Crystals of distinctive form grow in the metamorphic rock and are often easily recognized (Figure 26.18). *Wollastonite,* a silicate of calcium, is derived from carbonate rocks by contact metamorphism. *Tremolite,* a magnesium silicate, is derived from recrystallization of dolomite. *Graphite,* consisting of carbon, comes from carbonaceous matter in sedimentary rocks.

## Metamorphic rocks

It has been a common practice to subdivide the metamorphic rocks into two groups: First are rocks with obvious parallel structures which appear as lines on the rock surface—these structures are *foliation,* a crude layering along which the rock easily separates, and *banding,* a layered arrangement of strongly knit crystals forming a massive rock. Second are metamorphic rocks lacking in obvious parallel structures and characterized by granular texture.

*Slate* is a very fine-grained (aphanitic) rock that splits readily into smooth-surfaced sheets along cleavage surfaces. Slate is largely derived from fine-grained clay-rich sedimentary sediments (shale). The cleavage of slate is a new structure imposed by metamorphism and usually cuts across the original bedding. Slate colors range from gray to green to red.

*Schist* is a foliated rock and comes in many varieties. Foliation results from the parallel alignment of easily cleavable minerals, usually micas, chlorite, or talc. The

**FIGURE 26.16.** The Lewis overthrust fault is marked by the light-colored slanting line about midway up the mountain side (arrow). The rock mass above the thrust moved from left to right. Northern Rocky Mountains, Montana. (Photograph by Douglas Johnson.)

**TABLE 26.1. REPRESENTATIVE METAMORPHIC MINERALS**

| Mineral name | Composition | Specific Gravity | Hardness, Mohs scale | Crystal System and Habit | Color | Occurrence in Rocks |
|---|---|---|---|---|---|---|
| Kyanite | Aluminum silicate $Al_2SiO_5$ | 3.6 | 7 | Triclinic system Bladed crystals | Blue, bluish gray, green, white | Schists, gneisses |
| Andalusite | Aluminum silicate $Al_2SiO_5$ | 3.2 | 7½ | Orthorhombic system Prismatic crystals, nearly square | Gray, whitish | Schists, slates |
| Staurolite | Hydrous alumino-silicate with iron $FeAl_5(OH)(SiO_6)_2$ | 3.7 | 7–7½ | Orthorhombic system Prisms, esp. penetration twins | Brown | Schists, gneisses |
| Garnet (var. Almandite) | Aluminosilicate of iron $Fe_3Al_2(SiO_4)_3$ | 4.2 | 7 | Isometric system Dodecahedrons, trapezohedrons | Deep red, brownish red | Schists, gneisses |
| Wollastonite | Calcium silicate $CaSiO_3$ | 2.8 | 4½–5 | Triclinic system Fibrous or columnar | White or gray | Crystalline limestones |
| Tremolite (an amphibole) | Hydrous magnesium silicate $H_2Mg_7(SiO_3)_8$ | 3.1 | 5–6 | Monoclinic system Prismatic, fibrous | White, gray, green | Crystalline dolomites and limestones, schists |
| Graphite | Carbon C | 3.1 | 1–2 | Hexagonal system | Dark gray, black, Metallic luster Gray streak Sectile | Schists, gneisses, marbles |

reflecting surfaces of these minerals give a characteristic glistening sheen to the foliation surfaces (Figure 26.19). Other minerals with well-developed external crystal forms and larger grain size are scattered through most schists. These grains are known as *porphyroblasts* and may consist of garnet or staurolite. Schists have undergone a high degree of metamorphism and their origin is not always clear. Most schists are interpreted as altered clastic sedimentary strata rich in aluminosilicate minerals. It is commonly inferred that slates represent an intermediate grade of metamorphism between shale and schist, and this sequence is borne out in various localities by tracing the changes continuously from one region to another.

Basaltic lava flows subjected to dynamothermal metamorphism yield a foliated rock of dark greenish color that has long been known to geologists as *greenstone.* It is perhaps more properly referred to as *greenschist.*

*Gneiss,* a general term for a metamorphic rock showing banding or lineation, requires subdivision into gneisses of different origins. Certain granite bodies show an elongation of crystals into streak-like or pencil-like forms, suggestive of flowage of the granite in its

**FIGURE 26.17.** Block diagram of a deeply eroded thrust sheet with erosional outlier (klippe) and window (fenster.)

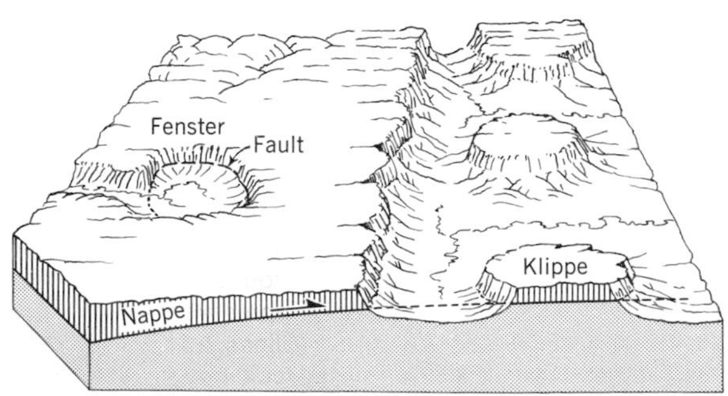


**FIGURE 26.18.** Garnet crystals in schist. The larger crystal is 0.8 in. (2 cm) across. (Photograph by A. N. Strahler.)

**FIGURE 26.19.** Mica schist. This fragment, about 6 in. (15 cm) long, shows a glistening, undulating surface of natural parting (above). An edgewise view (below) shows the thin foliation planes. (Photograph by A. N. Strahler.)

final stages of solidification or later under tectonic stresses. Such a rock is often termed a *granite gneiss.*

Certain banded gneisses consist of alternate layers of foliated rock and granular rock. The latter may be granitic or composed of quartz and feldspar (Figure 26.20). Where the rock clearly consists both of schist layers and igneous-like layers, the rock is presumed to have resulted from the injection of igneous components by solutions penetrating the schist layers. Such rocks are described as *injection gneisses.* The bands may be contorted into small folds (Figure 26.21). Injection gneisses can often be traced into masses of pure granite, suggesting that the invading granite magma has *assimilated* the country rock. Thus there arises the possibility that granite magmas and the batholiths that result from them are derived by melting of metamorphosed sedimentary rocks. The process is known as *granitization.* Controversy has been intense between those who consider granite to have its origin as a true igneous magma differentiated from a primary magma of more basaltic composition and those who espouse granitization.

**FIGURE 26.20.** A banded gneiss of Precambrian age. (Photograph by A. N. Strahler.)

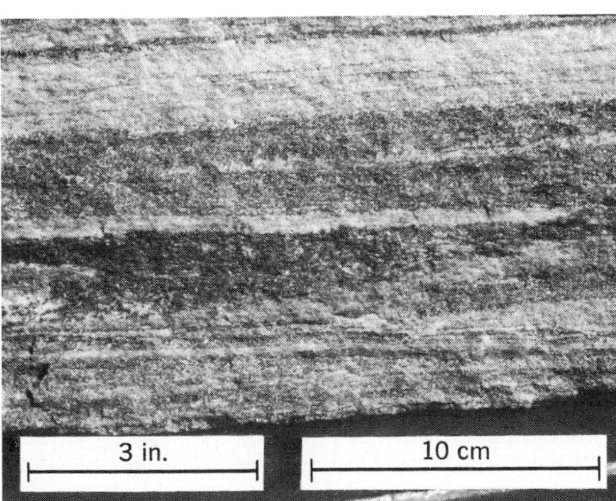

**FIGURE 26.21.** Outcrop of banded gneiss of Precambrian age, east coast of Hudson Bay, south of Povungnituk, Quebec. (Photograph G.S.C. No. 125221 by F. C. Taylor, Geological Survey of Canada, Ottawa.)

Of the granular metamorphic rocks, the most widespread are metamorphosed from sedimentary rocks. Pure quartz sandstone undergoes minor physical change and virtually no chemical change when subjected to the same orogenic process that produces slates and schists. Under extreme pressure, the quartz grains are crushed and forced into closer contact. Strongly cemented by silica, this process results in a *metaquartzite,* one of the hardest and most durable rocks known. When forced to break, this rock gives a conchoidal fracture.

Limestone and dolomite are metamorphosed into *marble,* which is typically a light-colored granular rock exhibiting a sugary texture on a freshly broken surface. Although white when pure, marbles come in many colors, depending upon the presence of impurities. Some marbles contain substantial amounts of silicate minerals—such as silica (as chert or chalcedony), olivine, and serpentine—or graphite, producing ornamental stone of great beauty when polished. Where metamorphism of a siliceous limestone results from heating, the mineral wollastonite is formed.

Various other granular or nonfoliated metamorphic rocks exist in minor quantities. *Serpentinite,* composed largely of serpentine, is sometimes found in large masses believed to have been derived from ultramafic rocks such as peridotite or dunite. *Eclogite,* which was mentioned in the discussion of composition of the mantle (Chapter 23), is a rare rock consisting of garnet and pyroxene and is thought to have been metamorphosed from basalt.

Metamorphic rocks are found today over wide areas of the continental shields. They represent the root structures of intensely folded geosynclines from which many thousands of feet of overlying rock have been uncovered. Lineation and foliation of these rocks, along with the orientation of folds within them, can be interpreted to delineate ancient orogenic belts and thus give a means for reconstructing the growth of the continental shields.

## Tectonic events in the scale of geologic time

We have arrived at a point in this study of the earth's history where a geologic time scale in the sense of epoch (Chapter 3) is required. It becomes necessary to refer the events of intrusion, extrusion, folding, faulting, and sedimentation to an established time scale to synchronize the history of these events from place to place over the earth and also to correlate with events which have occurred on the moon and the nearer terrestrial planets.

The search for a means by which to establish the *absolute age* in years of an event in the earth's past history was for decades frustrating and, in retrospect, misleading. Geological estimates were based upon two lines of calculation—salinity of the oceans and thickness of accumulated sediments. It was thought that the total amount of salt in the oceans, a figure subject to rather close estimate, could be divided by the annual increment of salt to give the age of the oceans. The annual increment of salt was estimated from chemical analyses of stream waters and estimated annual stream discharges. Toward the end of the nineteenth century the calculation was made that the total weight of sodium in the oceans is about $1.6 \times 10^{16}$ tons, and that the annual increment of sodium is about $1.6 \times 10^{8}$ tons. Division yields a figure of roughly 100 million ($10^8$) years. Two major sources of error come immediately to mind. We know now that the salts of the ocean enter sediments and that a given element has a certain residence time, that of sodium being 230 millions of years (Table 22.7). As a result, the salinity of the oceans has probably remained close to its present value for a large part of geologic time. Proof that enormous quantities of sodium have been removed from the oceans lies in the known occurrence of thick salt beds (Chapter 22). A second major source of error lies in the extrapolation of present rates of sodium contribution far into the past. We have good reason to believe that continents stand high today, in comparison with average elevations in much of the past, so that present rates are probably much too high.

The second approach was to total the measured thicknesses of sedimentary strata, taking the thickest known deposit of each age unit of the geologic column. These totaled somewhere in the amount of 100 mi, or about 500,000 ft. Using a value of one foot per 200 years as an average rate of accumulation, an age of about 100 million years was obtained for the start of sedimentation. Allowing for periods of nondeposition by introducing a correction factor of 15 times, the age would come to 1½ billion years. Between uncertainties as to rates of deposition and lengths of periods of nondeposition, this method is scarcely better than a blind guess. A dozen or more estimates made between 1860 and 1909 range from roughly 20 million to 1½ billion years.

Recall that Lord Kelvin, late in the nineteenth century, had made a calculation of the earth's age based upon rates of cooling of both earth and sun (Chapter 6). Kelvin's estimate was for a time span of 20 to 40 millions of years for all of earth history. This figure was disappointingly short to the geologists and also to Darwin and his followers, whose theory of organic evolution by natural selection seemed to require much longer spans of time. Darwin originally estimated that 300 million years were needed for only the later stages of evolution. Kelvin had moved his estimate far in the wrong direction, but it was difficult to find any flaw in his application of what were believed to be correct laws of physics.

Dramatically, the dilemma over the age of the earth and the duration of periods of geologic time was solved with the discovery of radioactivity, an event we have referred to in Chapter 23. Using these principles, the first reliable age determinations of rocks were made in 1907 by B. B. Boltwood, a chemist. His figures have required only minor adjustments to the present day. The oldest rock age found by Boltwood was about 1.6 billion years.

## Radiometric age determination

Basic principles of radioactivity and production of heat by spontaneous decay of radioactive isotopes are discussed in Chapter 23. These principles provide us with the basis of a method of determining the age in years of an igneous rock, a procedure of science known as *geochronometry.* Ages thus determined are referred to as *radiometric* ages.

At the time of solidification of an igneous rock from its liquid state, minute amounts of minerals containing radioactive isotopes are entrapped within the crystal lattices of the common rock-forming minerals and in some cases comprise distinctive radioactive minerals. At this initial point in time there are present none of the stable daughter products that comprise the end of the decay series. However, as time passes the stable end member of each series is produced at a constant rate and accumulates in place. Knowing the half-life of the decay system (see Table 23.2) it is possible to estimate closely the time elapsed since mineral crystallization occurred. An accurate chemical determination of the ratio between the radioactive isotope and the stable daughter product must be made. A fairly simple mathematical equation is used to derive the age in years of the mineral under analysis. Take for example, the uranium–lead series $U^{238}$–$Pb^{206}$, which has a half-life of 4½ billion years. Quantities of both uranium-238 and lead-206 are measured from a sample of uranium-bearing minerals (e.g. *uraninite* or *pitchblende*) or from a common mineral (*zircon*) enclosing the radioactive isotopes. The instrument used for such determinations is the *mass spectrometer.* The ratio of lead to uranium is then entered into the following equation:

$$\text{Age (millions of years)} = 6.50 \times 10^{9} \text{ logarithm } (1 + Pb^{206}/U^{238})$$

(The "logarithm" referred to in the equation is the *natural logarithm* of the number within the parentheses and may be found in a set of mathematical tables.)

Similar age determinations can be made using the

series $U^{235}$–$Pb^{207}$. Because both series of uranium–lead isotopes are normally present in the same mineral sample, analysis of one series can serve as a cross-check upon the other. Accuracy of the method depends upon the accuracy with which the half-life of the series is known. In this case, accuracy of the half-life of the $U^{238}$–$Pb^{206}$ series is known to within 1%, and that of the $U^{235}$–$Pb^{207}$ series to within 2%. It is therefore possible to determine the absolute age of a sample of uranium-bearing mineral to within about 2% of the true value, and in some cases as closely as 1%. But this level of accuracy also assumes that none of the components in the decay series have been lost from the sample. Use of the uranium–lead systems for age determination can be applied to the oldest rocks known, as well as to meteorites. As noted in Chapter 31, age of meteorites is close to 4.6 billion years, about one billion years older than the oldest rocks of the earth's crust that have thus far been dated.

It may be mentioned in passing that the radioactive thorium–lead decay series, $Th^{232}$–$Pb^{207}$, listed in Table 23.2 as an important heat-producing system, is in disfavor for age determination because loss of the lead tends to occur and to give erroneously low ages.

Of great importance in age determination is the potassium–argon series $K^{40}$–$Ar^{40}$, with a half-life of 1.3 billion years. It is particularly adaptable to use with the micas, specifically muscovite and biotite, and hornblende, all of which are widely present in igneous rocks. The potassium–argon series gives reliable minimum ages for fine-grained volcanic rocks (lavas) which cannot be dated by other methods. Moreover, the method can be used for relatively young rocks (as young as one million years), as well as the most ancient rocks. It has been a highly important tool for the geologist, particularly in deciding which of two rock groups is the older.

The rubidium–strontium decay series, $Rb^{87}$–$Sr^{87}$, with an extremely long half-life of 47 billion years, is of great value in dating both individual minerals and whole rock samples. It has proved successful in dating metamorphic rocks and thus in dating the orogenies that produced the metamorphism.

Ideally, the above three dating systems—uranium to lead, potassium to argon, and strontium to rubidium—should serve as cross-checks upon one another when all three are applied to mineral samples from the same rock body. In some instances the ages check out as closely similar, but there are instances in which moderate discrepancies are evident. Despite existing uncertainties, the radiometric ages given for various events in the time-table of the earth's history are now accepted by geologists as valid within small percentages of error. Success of the radiometric age determinations of rocks stands as a striking scientific achievement based upon the application of principles of physical chemistry to geology.

## The geologic time scale

The continuum of geologic time for which we have fragmentary rock records going back to about 3½ billion years (abbreviated to b.y.) has been subdivided into blocks of time on the basis of episodes of more-or-less continuous sedimentary deposition. These periods of widespread quiescence are interspersed with episodes of widespread tectonic activity during which geosynclinal sediments were typically subjected to disturbances, including faulting and folding, intrusion, and crustal uplift. The procedures followed in establishing these time blocks and the geological activities that took place within or between them are discussed in more detail in Chapter 28. For our present purposes, which include a study of the broad outlines of continental evolution, it will suffice to name the major time divisions of the record and assign radiometric ages to them.

Table 26.2 shows the durations and radiometric ages of the larger divisions of geologic time. Perhaps the most significant transitional point in the geologic time scale occurs where *Precambrian time* gives way to the three eras of abundant life: *Paleozoic, Mesozoic,* and *Cenozoic.* The rocks of Precambrian time contain evidences of only primitive life forms, and these are not of much help in interpreting and correlating the rocks in which they occur. Instead, Precambrian time is divided on the basis of lithologies (rock types) and their structures. In contrast, the eras of abundant life contain advanced life forms preserved as fossils, enabling time divisions to be established and correlated on a world-wide basis according to the specific life forms present in each stratum. Table 26.2 names 12 periods of geologic time within the three eras. Durations of the periods and ages of the time boundaries that separate the periods are established by radiometric means, largely from age determinations of igneous rocks that have intruded the sedimentary strata or extrusives (lavas) that interfinger those strata. Chapter 28 deals with the methods of stratigraphic geology and the basis for establishing and correlating the periods beginning with the Cambrian period.

Precambrian time, while enduring five to six times as long as the Paleozoic, Mesozoic, and Cenozoic eras combined, has proved extremely difficult to subdivide on any basis that has global continuity. Almost all the Precambrian rocks are igneous or metamorphic. Great thicknesses of sedimentary and volcanic rock were intensely folded and faulted, then intruded by granites, and these complexes in turn were metamorphosed into schists and gneisses. Erosion has removed enormous volumes of this rock. Fortunately, radiometric dating of the Precambrian rocks in combination with detailed field studies of rock relationships has made it possible to organize a generalized sequence of major events. Even so, the Precambrian rocks of one part of a continent cannot be satisfactorily correlated with those of another part, let alone correlated from one continent to another.

Table 26.2 names several orogenies. For the Precambrian three major orogenies are listed, with approximate ages of occurrence. These orogenies serve to subdivide Precambrian time into three blocks of time, which, for lack of any widely accepted nomenclature, we have designated simply as "upper," "middle," and "lower" divisions. Crude as this tripartite subdivision may be, it serves the purpose of allowing us to set up a succession of events to explain the evolution of the continental crust.

**TABLE 26.2. THE GEOLOGIC TIME SCALE***

| Era | Period | | Duration m.y. | Age m.y. | Orogenies |
|---|---|---|---|---|---|
| CENOZOIC | Quaternary | | 2.5 | | |
| | | | | 2.5 | Cascadian |
| | Tertiary | | 62.5 | | |
| | | | | 65 | |
| MESOZOIC | Cretaceous | | 71 | | Laramian |
| | | | | 136 | |
| | Jurassic | | 54 | | Nevadian |
| | | | | 190 | |
| | Triassic | | 35 | | |
| | | | | 225 | |
| PALEOZOIC | Permian | | 55 | | Appalachian (Hercynian) |
| | | | | 280 | |
| | Carboniferous | Pennsylvanian | 45 | | |
| | | | | 325 | |
| | | Mississippian | 20 | | |
| | | | | 345 | Acadian |
| | Devonian | | 50 | | |
| | | | | 395 | (Caledonian) |
| | Silurian | | 35 | | |
| | | | | 430 | Taconian |
| | Ordovician | | 70 | | |
| | | | | 500 | |
| | Cambrian | | 70 | | |
| | | | | 570 | |
| | | | Duration b.y. | Age b.y. | |
| PRECAMBRIAN or PROTOZOIC | Upper Precambrian | | 0.3–0.4 | | |
| | | | | 0.9–1.0 | Grenville |
| | Middle Precambrian | | 0.6–0.8 | | |
| | | | | 1.6–1.7 | Hudsonian |
| | | | 0.7–0.9 | | |
| | | | | 2.4–2.5 | Kenoran |
| | Lower Precambrian | | 0.9–1.0 | | |
| | Oldest dated rocks | | | 3.4±0.1 | |
| | Earth accretion completed | | | 4.6–4.7 | |
| | Age of universe | | | 7–9? | |

* Data sources: D. Eicher (1968), *Geologic Time,* Englewood Clfffs, N.J., Prentice-Hall, end paper; M. Kay and E. H. Colbert (1965), *Stratigraphy and Earth History,* New York, Wiley, p. 74.

## Life history of the Appalachians

The general pattern of orogeny has been repeated in different places on the continents in a number of occurrences since the early Precambrian. Much can be learned about mountain building by selecting a single example and tracing its development from beginning to end.

Our Appalachian Range, that great mountain belt running from Georgia and Alabama northeastward through New England and beyond, is a fine example for study, not only because it is familiar to so many North Americans, but also because it is a fairly old system now so deeply eroded as to expose its structure and roots. In contrast, new alpine ranges of the primary arcs—the Alps, Atlas, Himalaya, Cascade, and Andes ranges—have been recently completed or are still rising and the greater part of the mountain mass has not yet been removed by erosion processes.

Development of the Appalachian Mountains had its beginnings early in the Paleozoic Era, about 600 million years before the present.

**Geosynclinal deposition** Figure 26.22 shows the eastern margin of North America as it probably was early in the Paleozoic Era. In what is now the Appalachian mountain belt there existed a shallow epicontinental sea separated from the deep ocean basin on the eastern side by chains of rugged islands forming island arcs quite similar to those of the western Pacific Ocean today. Figure 25.22 shows a similar modern case, the shallow East China Sea and Yellow Sea bordered on the east by the narrow mountain zone of Korea and the Ryukyu island arc. Here the great Hwang Ho and Yangtse River bring sediment from the interior of Asia to be spread by currents over the shallow sea floor.

Similarly, an examination of the strata of early Paleozoic age in the Appalachian region shows that limy and sandy sediment was being desposited in a zone close to the continent. Of the two island arcs the inner one is

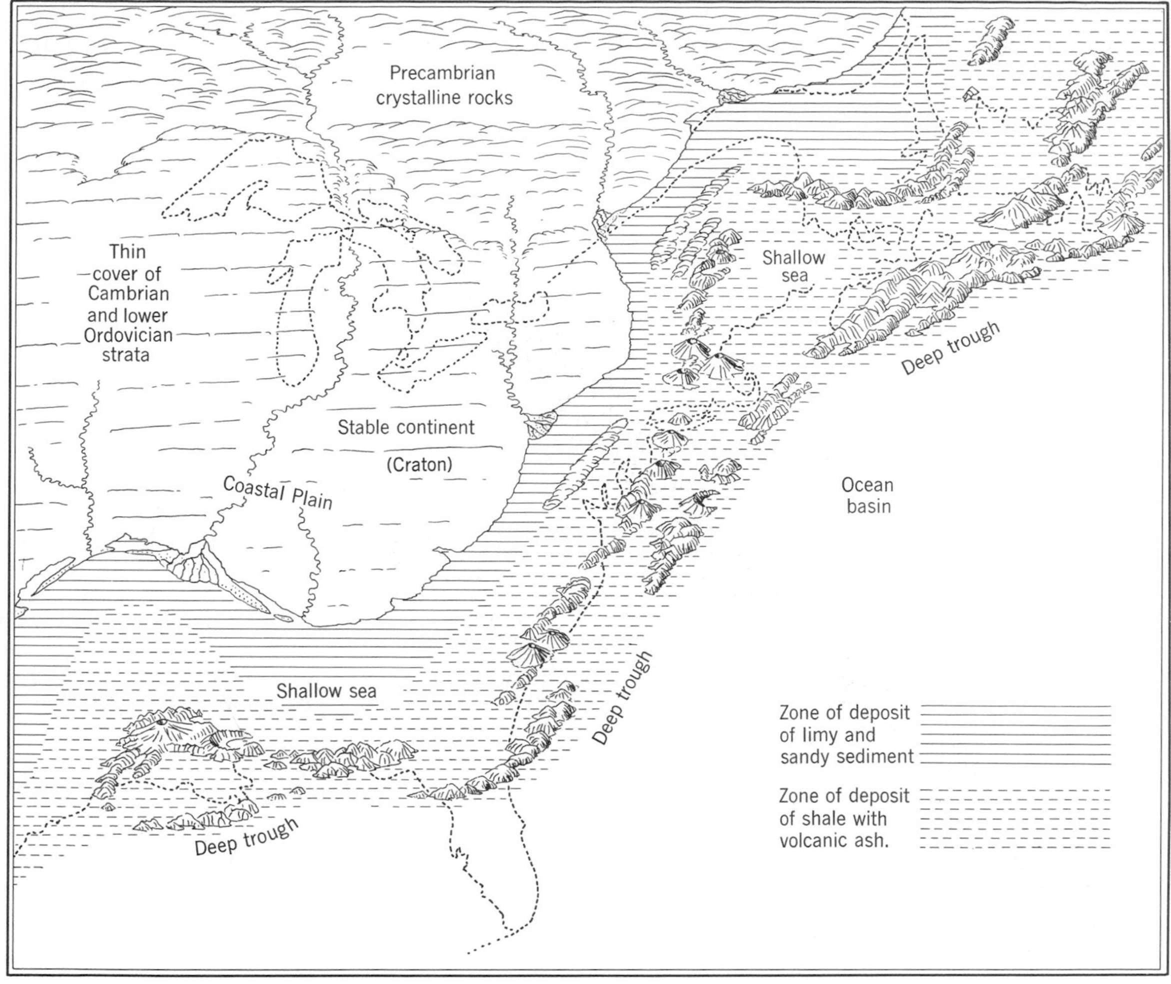


**FIGURE 26.22.** Paleogeography of eastern North America during the Middle Ordovician Period. [Modified and simplified after a map by Erwin Raisz from M. Kay (1951), *Geol. Soc. Amer. Memoir* 48, Plate I.]

shown as largely a chain of volcanoes and the outer as a narrow rugged land belt formed by sharp unbuckling of the crust. A cross section of these features is shown in Figure 26.23. Adjacent to the volcanic island chain subsidence was relatively more rapid. Here ash and mud layers were being laid down in greater quantities than in the region of limy and sandy sediments. Consequently, in the cross-sectional diagram of the shallow sea from continent to outer island arc the sedimentary deposit is thickest close to the volcanic islands. Here existed a deepening geosyncline in which great thicknesses of sediment accumulated, at all times keeping the trough filled to shallow-sea depths.

The outer island arc represented a rapidly rising upfold in the crust. Consequently these islands were rugged and high. From their steep slopes vast quantities of rock debris were swept into the seas on either side. Continued rise of the crustal upfold maintained the source of supply of coarse clastic sediment. In contrast, the North American continent had been reduced by long-continued erosion to a low plain. With respect to the geosyncline the stable continental mass is referred to as a *craton.* Streams and rivers draining this land were sluggish and brought only a small supply of sediment into the geosyncline from the craton to the west. Once depressed by large-scale crustal buckling in response to deep-seated orogenic forces, the sea floor nearest the island arcs was able to receive by far the greater weight of sediment. By the requirement of isostasy the trough continued to subside at a more rapid rate, the amount of sinking regulated in part by the amount of load added.

Altogether, throughout the Paleozoic Era, a total thickness of several miles of strata accumulated in the geosyncline. When we consider, however, that the entire trough was from 300 to 600 mi (500 to 1000 km) wide, the strata were not appreciably tilted from the horizontal even where most deeply bowed down.

**Appalachian orogeny** Geosynclinal deposition is finally terminated by orogeny. Rather suddenly, and for reasons not understood, intensified movement is renewed on the great descending fault zone, crowding the volcanic island chains against the geosynclinal accumulations and causing the strata to be crumpled and thrust against the edge of the continental crust as shown in Figure

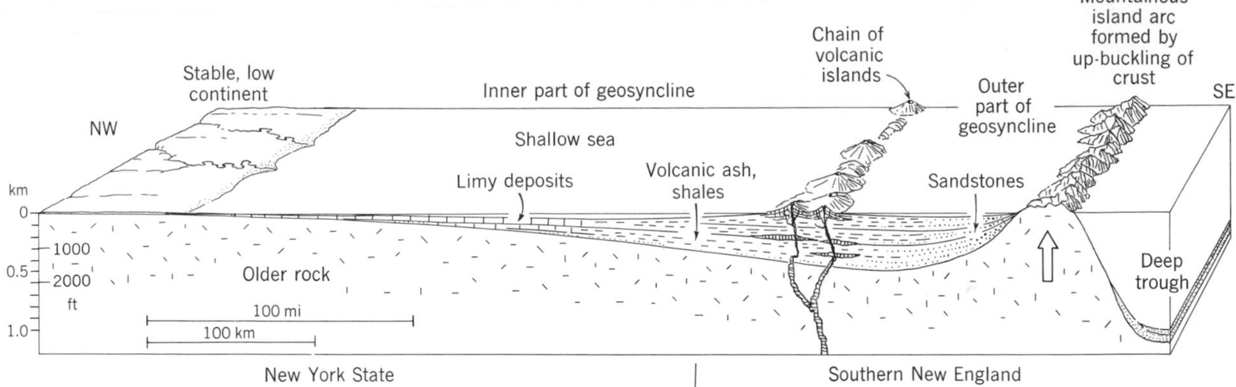


**FIGURE 26.23.** Schematic cross section of Ordovician geosyncline with volcanic and island arcs in northeastern North America. [Suggested by an illustration from M. Kay (1951), *Geol. Soc. Amer. Memoir* 48, Plate 9.]

26.24. The more deeply buried sediment layers, subjected to dynamothermal metamorphism, have been altered into schists and gneisses. Local melting of these rocks has formed a pocket of felsic magma in the root zone of the intense folding. The magma has invaded the overlying rocks to become a batholith.

Although the folds in sedimentary strata of the geosyncline lie in the brittle outer zone of the earth, it is obvious that these rocks have not shattered, except along the faults, but instead have behaved more as a plastic clay. This is because the thick shale layers actually have plastic properties and are readily squeezed out of shape if unequal forces are applied for long periods of time. Limestone, too, exhibits a plastic property under great pressure because the layers of atoms within mineral crystals can slip internally like a pack of playing cards and thus continually rearrange themselves. Sandstone layers remain brittle, even under high confining pressures, but slippage occurs along countless tiny faults and tensional cracks, giving the over-all appearance that the layer has been bent.

Orogeny is generally considered to take much less time than the preceding period of deposition of strata in the geosyncline. In some of the youngest mountain ranges, such as the Coast Ranges of California or the Atlas Mountains of North Africa, sedimentary layers about 2 million years old are now folded strongly. This means that mountain making can be accomplished in periods of time roughly on the order of 1 to 5 million years, whereas the preceding period of accumulation of sedimentary strata may be from 25 to 100 million years long, or longer.

To continue with the study of Appalachian tectonic development, we shall reduce our scope of examination to a small part of the entire geosyncline's width. The series of block diagrams in Figure 26.25 shows what may have taken place in the Hudson Valley and Hudson Highlands region of southern New York State. The belt of ground shown here is about 50 mi (80 km) long and perhaps 5 mi (8 km) wide. The long dimension of the block runs from northwest to southeast, or about at right angles to the length of the geosyncline.

Block *A* shows the shallow sea of the geosyncline with the uppermost strata still approximately horizontal.

**FIGURE 26.24.** Schematic block diagram of an orogenic belt after folding and intrusion have occurred.

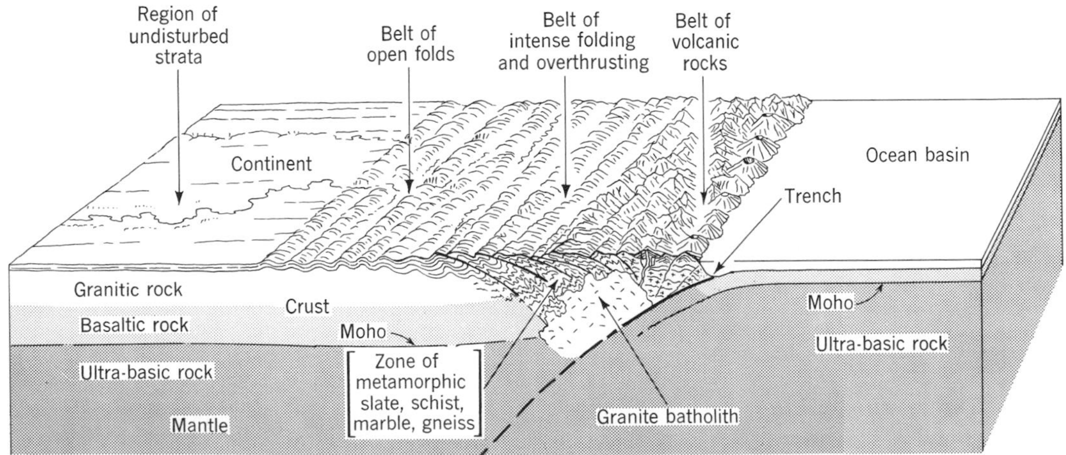

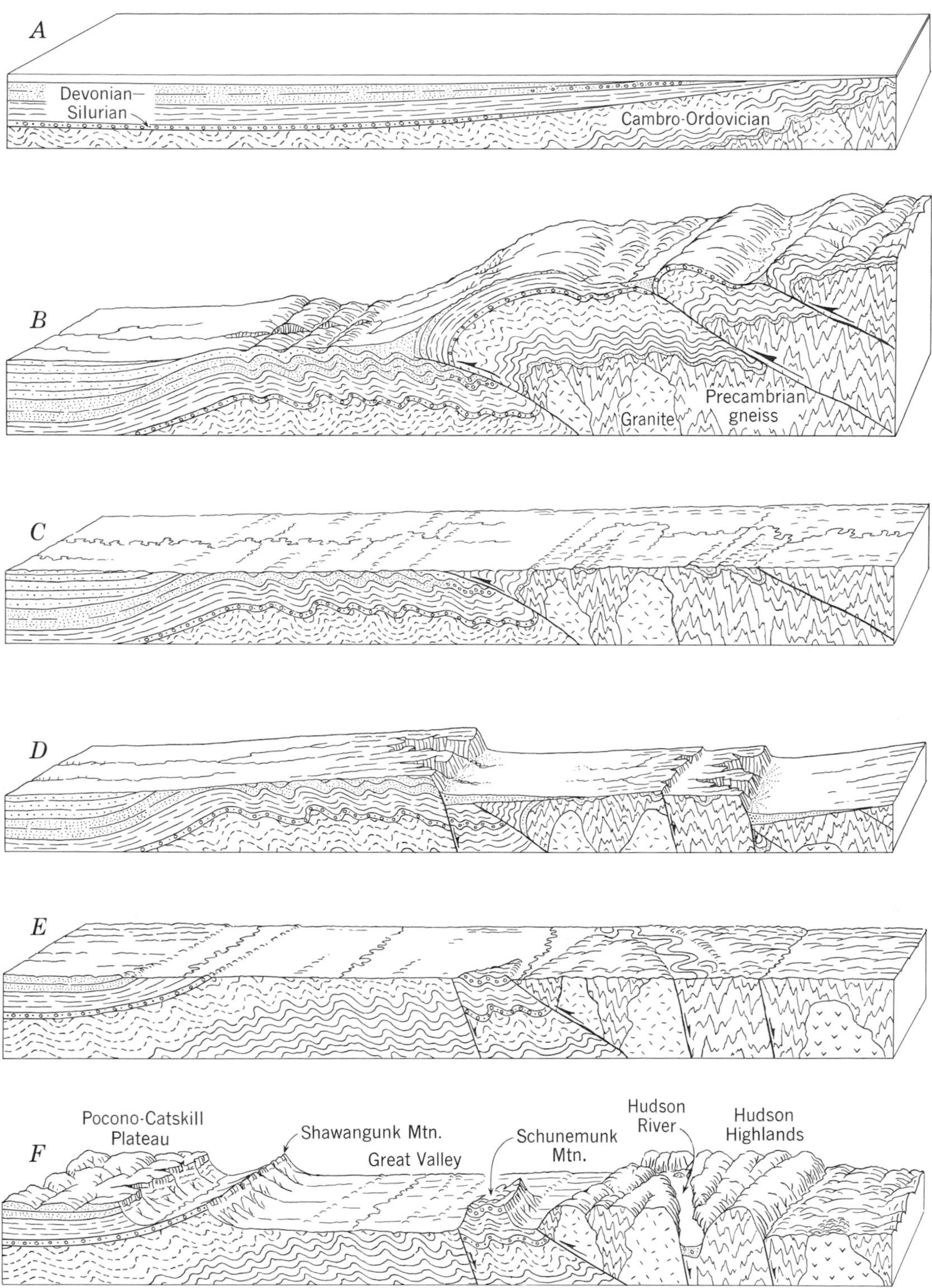


**FIGURE 26.25.** This series of block diagrams shows the geologic development of the Hudson Valley region in New York State. The long dimension of the block runs northwest-southeast, across the grain of the geologic structure. (*A*) Strata accumulated in a shallow Devonian seaway. (*B*) Folding and thrusting occurred during the Appalachian revolution at the close of the Paleozoic Era. (*C*) Folds were largely beveled and mountain roots exposed in the development of a peneplain in the Triassic Period. (*D*) Block faulting at the close of the Triassic Period raised tabular mountain masses separated by steep escarpments. (*E*) By the middle of the Cenozoic Era a much later peneplanation had reduced the region to an undulating plain. (*F*) The modern landscape owes its relief features to different degrees of resistance of the rock bodies to erosion.

Previously, in the early Paleozoic Era, the *Taconian orogeny* had occurred (Table 26.2), folding the strata of earlier Paleozoic age, but after extensive erosion the geosyncline persisted, receiving the newer strata during middle Paleozoic time. In the Permian Period, which closed the Paleozoic Era, another orogeny set in, bringing about the folding and faulting of all strata and the older underlying metamorphic rocks to produce the structures shown in Block *B.* Low-angle overthrust faults are shown by lines sloping down toward the right on Block *B.* Several miles of crustal shortening has occurred.

**Continental erosion** Processes of denudation were, of course, in action from the time that the new mountains first began to be elevated above the sea. These processes include fluvial erosion, the wearing down of a continental surface by the scouring action of streams, combined with the wear of rain water flowing over the sloping ground. Erosion is greatly aided by rock weathering. Weathering and fluvial erosion are discussed in detail in Chapters 32 through 36. In high mountains erosion is also performed by glaciers, while in deserts wind scour is an important erosion process.

Although erosion and weathering begin as soon as a new land surface appears, it is not until long after the folding and rapid uplift have ceased that denudation can reduce the mountain mass. From the appearance of the world's youngest mountain ranges it can be concluded that rivers and glaciers will have cut deep canyons with intervening sharp divides and peaks long before mountain-making movements cease. As the divides and peaks become lower the ruggedness of the mountains gradually disappears. Removal of rock mass by erosion is, of course, accompanied by isostatic rise of the crust, but this does not entirely restore the mass lost, thus after millions of years a gently undulating plain of erosion, termed a *peneplain,* occupies the place where the mountains once stood.

Block *C* of Figure 26.25 shows the peneplain produced over the Appalachian belt following the orogeny at the close of the Paleozoic Era. Rocks at the surface of the peneplain are the exposed mountain roots. Paleozoic sediments were in places changed into metamorphic rocks—marble, slate, and quartzite. Granite intrusives shown in this section were emplaced in a previous orogeny, probably the *Acadian orogeny* (Table 26.2), which caused much intrusion and metamorphism in what is now New England and the Maritime Provinces of Canada.

The peneplain shown in Block *C* was completed in the Appalachian region about 200 million years ago, during the Mesozoic Era. The peneplain sloped gently eastward.

**Block faulting** In the Triassic Period of the Mesozoic Era the Appalachian region experienced a different kind of crustal disturbance. Block *D* (Figure 26.25) shows that the crust has broken into several blocks separated by normal faults, and that at each fault the edge of the block on the western side has risen, whereas that next to it on the east has sunk. Block faulting is interpreted as representing a pulling apart of the crust and is the opposite of the compression that produced folds and overthrust faults in the earlier orogeny. As Block *D* shows, erosion carved the higher edges of the blocks into canyons, eventually producing mountainous belts of considerable ruggedness. The detrital sediment was swept down into the downtilted margins of the fault blocks and there accumulated as layers of alluvium, which were subsequently buried and indurated to become sedimentary rock. In this manner certain areas of the Appalachian region came to have thick strata of reddish shales and sandstones, but these were wedge-like patches in contrast to the extensive strata deposited in the broad shallow seas of the great geosyncline of the Paleozoic Era. Moreover, the Triassic strata in this region were deposited on land, and hence contain structures typical of stream action, along with remains of plants and air-breathing animals—such sediments are described as *terrestrial* to distinguish them from marine sediments of the geosyncline. (Block faulting like that in the Appalachians should not be regarded as an essential event in the evolution of orogenic belts. It is included here for the sake of completing a history of the Appalachian region.)

**Epeirogenic uplift and erosion** After the block faulting and deposition of sediment of the early part of the Mesozoic Era, the Appalachian region again underwent a period of erosion lasting for much of the balance of that era and again resulting in the production of a peneplain. Then, in the early Cenozoic Era, the entire eastern part of the continent was broadly uparched, and this event was followed by still more prolonged erosion to produce the peneplain shown in Block *E* of Figure 26.25. By then the Appalachian mountain roots were deeply exposed, revealing Precambrian and early Paleozoic slates, schists, gneisses, and intrusives in the eastern part of the belt shown in the diagram.

Elsewhere in the world, orogenies (Nevadian, Laramian) took place in the latter part of the Mesozoic Era, but the crust under the Appalachian region had long since ceased to have much activity. There were in progress, however, slow rising and sinking movements of the crust, termed *epeirogenic movements.* During the Cenozoic Era an epeirogenic movement gradually raised the entire Appalachian region by some 1000 to 2000 ft (300 to 600 m) in a broad arch or dome, thus the rivers flowing toward the Atlantic shore were increased in steepness of gradient and again carved deep valleys into the mountain roots. As a result the softest and weakest rocks (shales and limestones) were carved out quickly to form broad valleys and the hard rocks (sandstone, quartzite, granite, and gneiss) were left standing to form mountain ridges and plateaus. The results of this selective erosion are shown in Block *F,* which is a roughly diagrammatic sketch of the present-day topography including the Catskill and Pocono Plateaus, the Hudson Valley, and the Hudson Highlands.

Although selective erosion following epeirogenic uplift rarely produces as bold relief as that found in such young ranges as the Alps, The Himalaya, or Andes, it can result in mountains of considerable majesty—as witnessed by the Great Smoky Mountains of the southern Appalachians and the White and Green Mountains of New England. These last-mentioned ranges are believed to owe their relief almost entirely to erosion following epeirogenic uplift of a crustal mass which had been reduced at least once before to a peneplain.

## Evolution of the continental crust

Origin of the continents has long been a major problem of geology. Most modern thought on this problem favors the supposition that the continental crust was not present when the accretion of the earth was completed, some 4.6 billions of years ago. Instead, the continents were formed later of rock of felsic mineral composition gradually segregated from an original crustal rock of mafic composition, perhaps similar to basalt of the present oceanic and sub-continental crust. Some support for this inference lies in the fact that among the oldest known rocks of the continental shields there is found an abundance of greenstone, already described as metamorphosed volcanic rock of basaltic composition.

A mechanism of segregation of felsic mineral matter from rock of average mafic composition perhaps can be found in the processes of igneous mineral alteration by hydrolysis, yielding silica and aluminosilicate clay minerals which were then deposited as geosynclial sediments and subsequently melted into granitic magmas during orogeny. There are, of course, various problems and uncertainties connected with the selective removal of mafic components—iron, magnesium, and calcium. Another mechanism that might be invoked is that of magmatic segregation described in Chapter 21. A rising magma of mafic composition could, after fractionation of the earlier-crystallizing mafic minerals, yield a granitic magma, which would solidify as a batholith in the upper part of the crust. Again, we are brought back to the problem of origin of granites and granite magmas. In any case, the hypothesis of continental evolution requires that initially small elevated masses of granitic rock were added to by repetitions of the sedimentation–orogeny sequence described for the Appalachians.

If the continents developed by growth throughout Precambrian time, we should look to the distributions of rock ages in the continental shields. Perhaps through this study a pattern suggestive of growth stages will emerge. The oldest rocks of the shields, older than about 2.5 b.y., comprise relatively small patches of shield and are designated as *continental nuclei.*

Figure 26.26 shows the world distribution of continental nuclei. These areas have yielded rocks with radiometric ages older than 2.7 b.y., although most determinations are in the somewhat younger range of 2.3 to 2.7 b.y. In addition to the areas shown on the map, there is an area of very old rock, dated in the 2.3–2.7 b.y. range, in the region of the Baltic Sea (see Figure 26.29). This *Baltic Shield* may also be considered a continental nucleus. Perhaps significantly, the *Angara Shield* (see Figure 26.29) of Siberia has not yielded extremely great ages.

The continental nuclei are surrounded by or are contiguous with larger areas of shield rock with maximum ages falling in middle and upper Precambrian time. Figure 26.27 is a map of North America showing the crustal rocks zoned into provinces according to ages of the oldest intrusives. Nuclei consist of the Superior (Keewatin), Wyoming, and Slave provinces. The Churchill province (1.3 to 2.3 b.y.) surrounds the nuclei, except on the southwest side, where the Central province (1.3 to 1.7 b.y.) and Grenville province (0.8 to 1.3 b.y.) are contiguous. A great Cordilleran province runs down the west side of the continent with intrusives not older than 440 m.y. The Appalachian province is dominated by intrusives under 440 m.y., but some Precambrian ages of the range 0.8 to 1.3 b.y. are scattered throughout. A Greenland province containing rocks older than 1.3 b.y. is perhaps essentially contemporaneous with the Central province.

Figure 26.28 is a geologic map of portions of Ontario, Manitoba, and Quebec lying north of Lake Superior and between Hudson Bay and Lake Winnipeg, Canada, showing the *Superior geologic province,* one of the continental nuclei. The patterns on the geologic

**FIGURE 26.26.** World distribution of exposed nuclei of the continents. Areas outlined contain rocks having radiometric ages greater than 2.7 billion years. [Based on data of P. M. Hurley and J. R. Rand (1969), *Science,* vol. 164, pp. 1229–1242.]

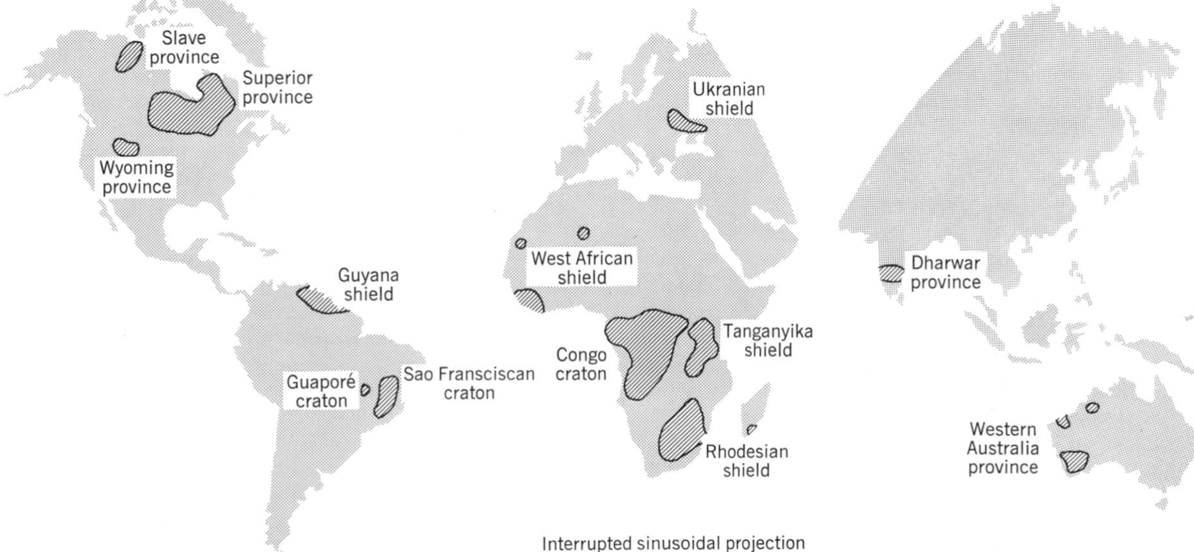

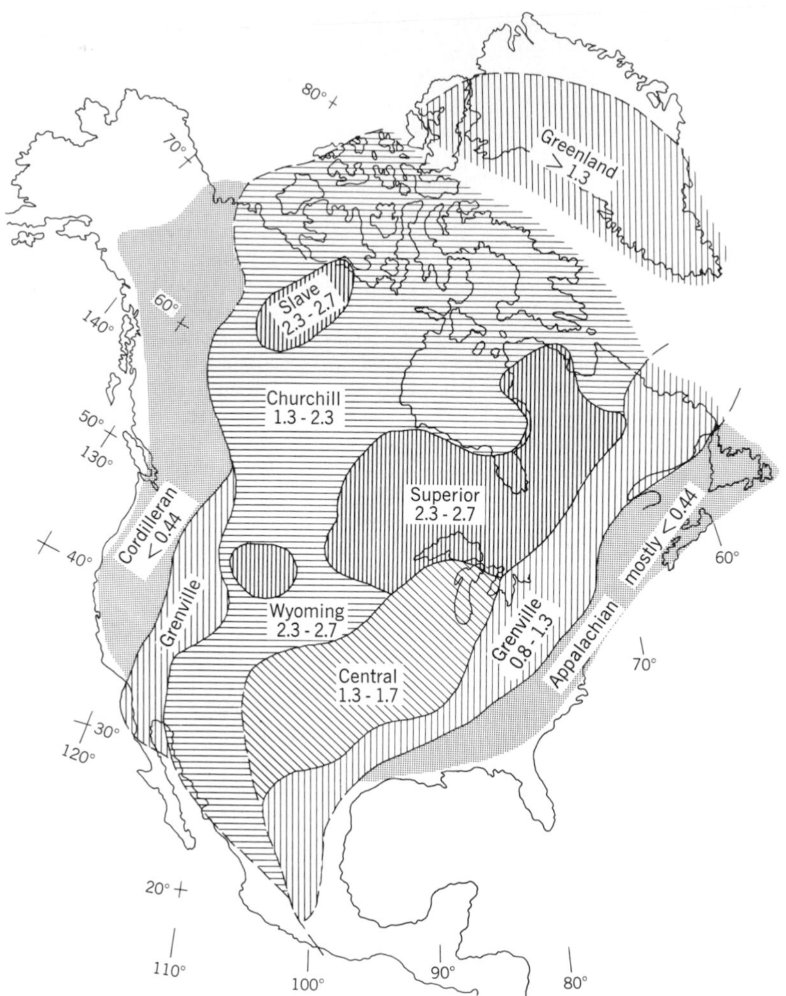


**FIGURE 26.27.** Geologic provinces of the North American shield. Radiometric ages of oldest granite-forming events in billions of years. Boundaries should be considered largely provisional. [Based on map data of A. E. J. Engel (1963), *Science*, vol. 140, pp. 143–152; and P. M. Hurley and J. R. Rand (1969), *Science*, vol. 164, p. 1231, Figure 2.]

map represent the several ages and varieties of rocks as they are exposed at the surface. Oldest of these are the Keewatin lavas, over 2.7 billion years old, which may once have been the volcanic rocks of an ancient island arc. Closely associated with the Keewatin lavas are some sedimentary strata, now greatly metamorphosed, known as the Timiskaming series. These are of clastic sediments—conglomerates and sandstones—such as those that may have been laid down in a geosyncline immediately adjacent to the ancient island arc. Other patches of somewhat younger but nevertheless extremely ancient rocks are also found in this province, but most of the area is underlain by intrusive rocks (now gneisses) which invaded later in the Precambrian, largely engulfing the older rocks.

The age distribution of Precambrian rocks suggests that the continents originated with relatively small nuclei and that they have grown throughout geologic time by the formation of new marginal sets of island arcs and geosynclines, which through orogeny were converted into granitic continental crust.

Continued growth of continents by accretion through post-Precambrian time should lead to recognizable patterns of orogenic belts, representing former primary arcs, and these should surround the continental shields.

The gross tectonic patterns of continental structure are illustrated by the Eurasian continent (Figure 26.29). The vast shield areas are shown in their entireties, even though throughout large areas they are actually covered by flat-lying sedimentary strata. The *Russian-Baltic Shield* and the *Angara Shield* are surrounded by the mountain arcs of Paleozoic and Mesozoic orogenies. The present-day primary arcs of Cenozoic age lie south and east of the older arcs, close to the border of the continent. Note that the shield area of peninsular India seems completely isolated by the Indian Ocean basin on the south, a point we shall refer to again.

## Continental drift

For over half a century a highly controversial issue in geological circles was the possible validity of a remarkable suggestion concerning the origin of continents: the hypothesis of *continental drift.* Briefly, it was proposed that originally one single continental plate of granitic composition existed, lasted intact through the Paleozoic Era, but then split into parts which slowly drifted over the remainder of the globe to become the individual continents we know today. Figure 26.30 is a

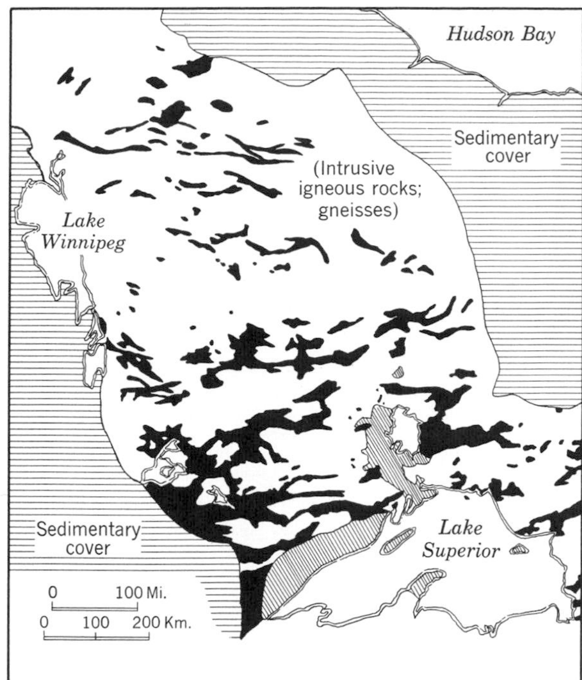


**FIGURE 26.28.** Simplified geologic map of the western portion of the Keewatin geologic province of Canada. Black patches are underlain by Keewatin metamorphic rocks; and white areas by intrusive igneous rock and gneisses. Diagonally ruled areas are of younger Precambrian rocks. [After J. A. Jacobs, R. D. Russell, and J. T. Wilson (1959), *Physics and Geology,* New York, McGraw-Hill, p. 325, Figure 15.6.]

map showing one interpretation of the supposed original parent continent, known as *Gondwanaland.*[2] The heart of this continent was the combined shield masses of South America, peninsular India, South Africa, Antarctica, and Australia, whose rocks are in many respects strikingly similar.

Criticism was effectively leveled against the original concept that drifting apart of the continents was accomplished by extremely slow movement of the brittle continental plates floating like great rafts pushing through the mantle. It was postulated that South America and Africa were originally joined together in the parent continent. This postulate seemed reasonable not only because of the remarkable fit of their coast lines, but also because of certain similarities in rock types and enclosed fossil forms at corresponding positions in the margins of the two continents. The great Andes mountain chain on the western edge of South America was explained as the deformation produced by impacts upon the leading edge of the drifting continent as it "plowed" across the basaltic layer of the Pacific floor.

Until the middle 1960s opposition to continental drift remained strong in the scientific community, but the recognition of the true extent and rate of crustal spreading along the Mid-Oceanic Ridge almost overnight swung the large body of opinion in favor of continental drift. Intensive search for new evidence was undertaken on a larger scale than before and seems to have met with a high level of success.

Figure 26.31 shows a recent interpretation of the continents assembled before drift began. Shaded areas are those continental nuclei already discussed (Figure 26.26). Although shown nested into one continent, the arrangement of nuclei into two groups suggests that there were originally two centers of continental crust accumulation: *Laurasia* in the Northern Hemisphere and *Gondwanaland* in the Southern Hemisphere. Notice the absence of Asia in this reconstruction, although it was included in the earlier version (Figure 26.30). Central America, with its younger mountain arcs, is interpreted as having formed following separation of the continents. Peninsular India, western Australia, Madagascar, and Antarctica are closely clustered beside the southern African continent.

Recent studies suggest that continental separation may have begun along the western northern margin of Africa in mid-Triassic time about 200 m.y. before the present, and that South America was finally separated from southern Africa in the Cretaceous Period, about −130 m.y. As the Americas drew away from Africa and Europe, new oceanic crust was formed by rise of mantle rock in the Mid-Oceanic Ridge axis. Thus the Atlantic Ocean crust has formed since about early Cretaceous time and may not be much older than about −130 to −140 m.y. This inference as to the young age of the Atlantic Ocean floor is in line with radiometric ages of oceanic basalts and sediments, which have not been found much older than Cretaceous. Similarly, separation of Antarctica, Australia, and peninsular India from southern Africa is postulated to have taken place to the accompaniment of crustal spreading along the Mid-Oceanic Ridge in the Indian Ocean.

Evidence for the former unity of the continental shields takes a variety of forms. Matching of similar rock types and rock ages from the margin of one continent to another provides one line of evidence. The case of South America and Africa is particularly interesting. As Figure 26.31 shows, small fragments of continental nuclei in South America seem to fit with larger nuclei in Africa. Moreover, the trends of orogenic structures in the area between these nuceli are continuous from one continent to another, whereas today these structures project directly out toward the ocean basin and appear to have been abruptly truncated. In the North Atlantic, tectonic structures of the Appalachian belt, passing through Nova Scotia and Newfoundland, appear to line up with corresponding structures of the same geologic age in the British Isles and Norway.

Matching of fragments of the Gondwanaland nuclei in a single continental mass has been based in part on similarities of sedimentary rocks and their contained fossils of Paleozoic age. In the Permian Period, beginning about −280 m.y., the Southern Hemisphere landmasses underwent a continental glaciation. Glacial rubble dragged by the ice over older rock surfaces has become lithified into a distinctive rock known as a *tillite.* Tillite of this age found today in South America, southern Africa, India, Antarctica, Austrialia, and Tas-

[2] When first suggested by E. Suess near the end of the nineteenth century the single continent was named Gondwanaland, but a leading German exponent of the theory, Alfred A. Wegener, in 1910 named the original continent *Pangaea.*

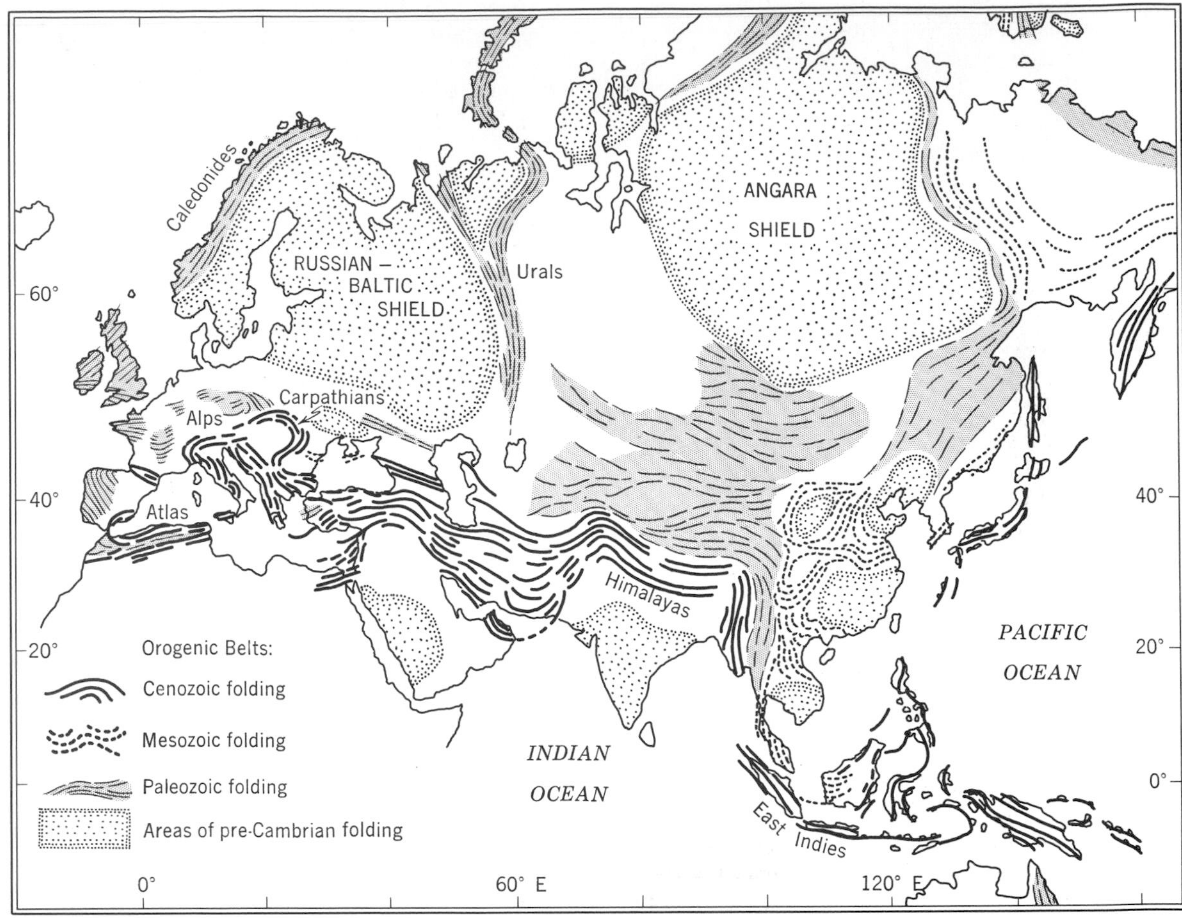


**FIGURE 26.29.** Ancient and modern mountain arcs of Eurasia, shown schematically by bands of curved lines. (© 1960, John Wiley & Sons, New York. Based on a map by Umbgrove.)

mania is interpreted as the deposit of a single continental ice sheet developed at the time these crustal masses were yet in one piece and occupying a south polar position. Overlying the tillite are sedimentary strata, including coal-bearing formations. Distinctive and specialized plants of genus *Glossopteris* and genus *Gangamopteris* are found as fossils in these sedimentary strata. According to those who support the hypothesis of continental drift, the simultaneous development of these plants on widely separated continents would have been an impossibility. A similar argument for Gondwanaland has been based on distribution of animals supposed to be incapable of migrating from one continent to another over deep ocean water. (Refer to Chapters 29 and 30 for further details, evidences, and inferred events of continental drift.)

## Polar wandering and continental drift

Some highly important independent evidence favoring drift is based upon paleomagnetism, making use of principles of rock magnetism already explained in Chapter 25 in connection with the subject of reversals of magnetic polarity.

Recall that lavas, upon cooling, retain permanent residual magnetism with respect to the lines of force of the earth's magnetic field prevailing at the time of cooling. If undisturbed rocks are subject to analysis of magnetic declination and inclination, the position of the earth's magnetic pole at the time of rock formation can be ascertained within a small radius of error (on the order of a circle with radius 5 degrees of latitude arc). The method can also be used on sedimentary rocks, such as sandstones and shales. Pole positions have now been determined at many places and for all major divisions of geologic time from Precambrian through Cenozoic.

For a given continent, the successive pole positions throughout geologic time form a curved line, or *pole path,* that travels over the scope of an entire hemisphere. Figure 26.32 shows two such paths, one for Europe, as determined from rocks of the British Isles, and one for North America. Geologic dates are given for points on the paths, starting with the Precambrian.

Now, it is generally agreed that the earth's dipolar magnetic field has always been closely related to the earth's axis of rotation (Chapter 7), hence that the magnetic north pole throughout the geologic past has been approximately equivalent to a geographic pole of rota-

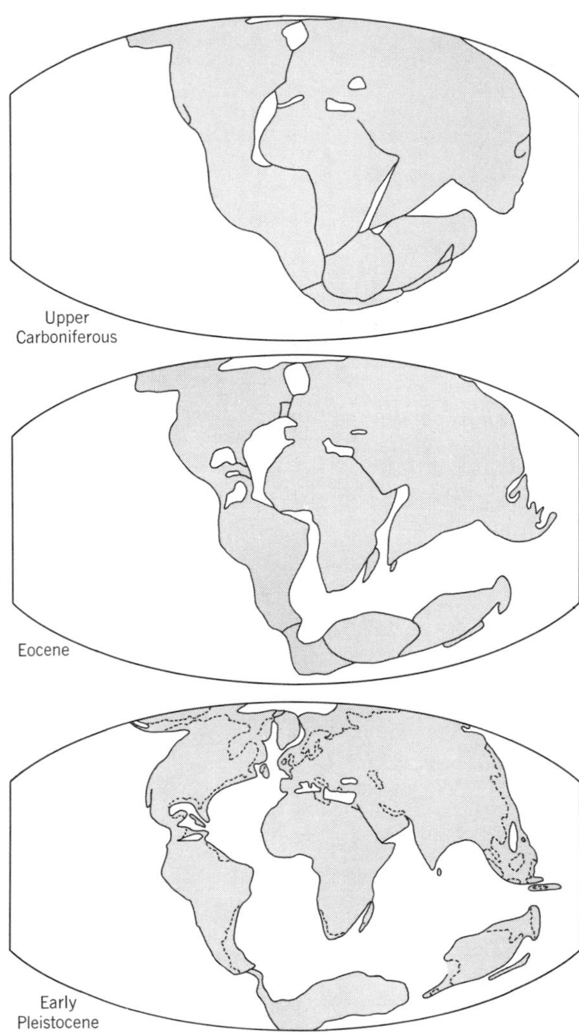


**FIGURE 26.30.** Original concept of the nested continents of Pangea (Gondwanaland) and their gradual separation by continental drift. Exact latitudes and longitudes are not specified. [After A. Wegener (1924), *The Origin of Continents and Oceans,* 3rd ed., New York, Dutton, p. 6, Figure 1.]

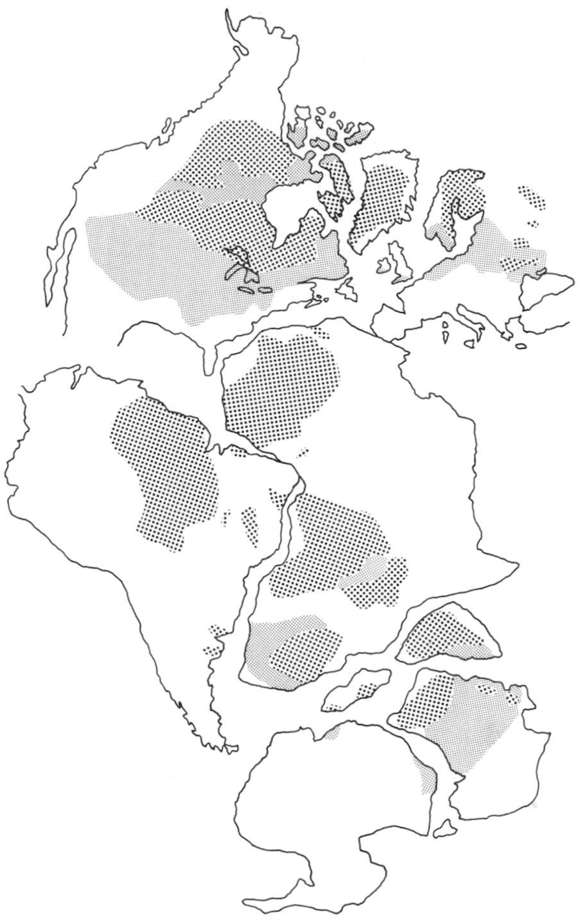

**FIGURE 26.31.** Reassembled continents, prior to start of continental drift. Dark pattern: areas of oldest shield rocks (older than −1.7 b.y.). Light pattern: rocks in the age range −0.8 to −1.7 b.y. [Map redrawn from P. M. Hurley and J. R. Rand (1969), *Science,* vol. 164, p. 1237, Figure 8.]

tion. We can assume that the earth's axis of rotation has remained fixed in space, subject, of course, to its processional motion (Chapter 2). Therefore we should not consider the pole as wandering, but rather that the continent moves over the rotating globe, changing its latitude and longitude with respect to the axis of earth rotation. Figure 26.33 is a Southern Hemisphere map, centered upon the south pole. Past positions of Australia are plotted, based upon paleomagnetism in rocks of ages from Precambrian to Cenozoic. (Names of epochs within the Cenozoic Era are given in Table 30.1.)

One interpretation of a pole path such as that shown in Figure 26.32, or of the moving continent as depicted in Figure 26.33, is that the entire rigid lithosphere of the earth has slowly rotated over the asthenosphere beneath. This motion, known as *polar wandering,* must affect all surface points over the globe in exactly the same manner. Polar wandering can be attributed to changes in distribution of mass over the earth's surface. For example, the formation of a large icecap upon a continent would upset the equilibrium of rotation and might set off polar wandering to a new position of equilibrium.

As an alternative possibility, consider that a single pole path results from drifting of an individual continent. If several continents are separating as they drift, the pole paths will diverge, as traced back from the present pole to earlier eras. Divergent pole paths can serve as evidence in favor of continental drift. In particular, if the divergence ceases to increase beyond Triassic time, remaining constant thereafter back to the Precambrian, we have some measure of proof that the separation of those continents began in the Triassic. The amount of separation between North America and Europe averages about 30 degrees of arc, which amounts to about 2100 mi (3400 km). This is approximately the present amount of separation of Newfoundland from England on a great-circle arc.

Comparing the two polar paths in Figure 26.32, we see that the divergence increases rapidly back to the Triassic period, then, despite various irregularities, re-

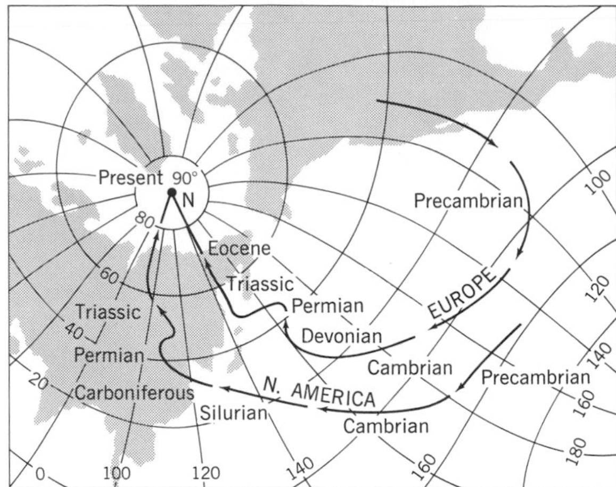


**FIGURE 26.32.** Generalized paths of polar wandering based on paleomagnetic data from Europe and North America. Data are plotted on oblique Mercator projection (conformal). [Simplified from a map by S. K. Runcorn (1963), in *Polar Wandering and Continental Drift,* A. C. Munyan, Ed., Tulsa, Okla., Soc. of Econ. Paleon. & Mineral., p. 51, Figure 2.]

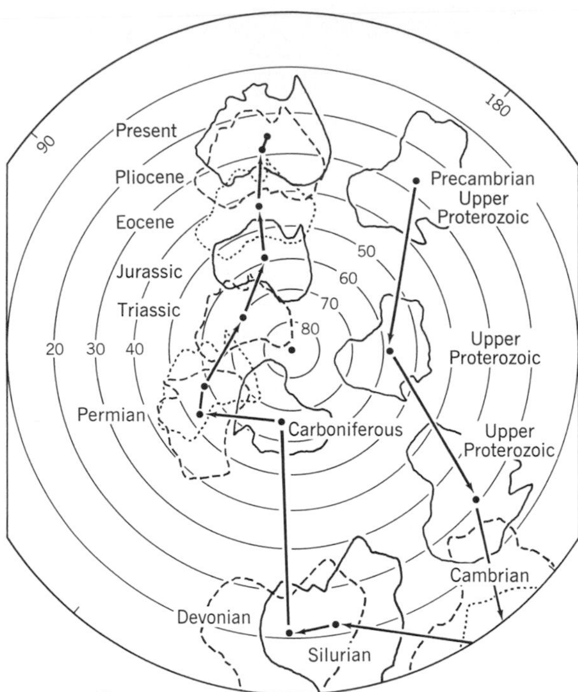


**FIGURE 26.33.** Position of Australia relative to the pole throughout geologic time, as interpreted from paleomagnetic data. Stereographic polar projection (conformal). [Modified from a map by S. K. Runcorn (1959), *Science,* vol. 129, p. 1007, Figure 6.]

mains about constant back into the Cambrian period. When we plot pole paths for India, Australia, and Antarctica essentially the same relationships result, suggesting separation among those continents. Polar wandering by rotation of the entire global lithosphere as a unit is not required, whereas continental separation is indicated.

While the revival of the hypothesis of continental drift has aroused enthusiastic support, a substantial division of opinion exists among those scientists best qualified to judge the evidence. Many of the arguments, pro and con, deal with matters of extreme specialization and complexity. Those who hear the debate as interested bystanders are cautioned to hold their decision in abeyance and to be prepared for many new findings that will most surely come to illuminate the issues.

## Crustal tectonics in review

In this chapter and the previous one we have reviewed a chain of remarkable scientific discoveries. In less than one decade these discoveries have revolutionized our thinking about the behavior of the earth's crust. Convergent lines of evidence derived from the methods of geophysics, geochemistry, geology, and biology have made a virtual certainty of horizontal lithospheric motions on a scale and at a rate that would have seemed to border on fantasy if they had been suggested little more than a decade earlier.

The geologic record of orogeny, vulcanism, and intrusion had been accurately interpreted for more than a century before the discoveries of the last decade added a new dimension to the earth's history. It is to the record of the rocks that we return in the next three chapters as we look into the meaning of the stratigraphic sequences preserved from early Precambrian time to the recent. First, however, we shall attempt to reconstruct the origin and early history of the earth as a planet.

## References for further study

Billings, M. P. (1954), *Structural Geology,* 2nd ed., Englewood Cliffs, N.J., Prentice-Hall, 514 pp.

Hurley, P. M. (1959), *How Old Is the Earth?,* Garden City, N.Y., Doubleday, 160 pp.

Jacobs, J. A., R. D. Russell, and J. T. Wilson (1959), *Physics and Geology,* New York, McGraw-Hill, 424 pp., chap. 15.

Spock, L. E. (1962), *Guide to the Study of Rocks,* 2nd ed., New York, Harper & Row, 298 pp., chap. 9.

Eicher, D. L. (1968), *Geologic Time, Englewood* Cliffs, N.J., Prentice-Hall, 149 pp., chaps. 1, 4, 6.

Phinney, R. A., Ed. (1968), *The History of the Earth's Crust; A Symposium,* Princeton, N.J., Princeton Univ. Press, 244 pp.

# 27

# Origin and early history of the earth

IN THIS CHAPTER we attempt to piece together a tentative sequence of events comprising the origin of the solar system and the early geologic history of planet Earth. Awareness that evidence is fragmentary and sometimes misleading, and that highly divergent and often contradictory hypotheses continue to be discussed and modified by the best qualified scientists of our time, should not prevent us from trying to set up a tentative calendar of possible events.

This chapter relates a history of great changes in the evolution and operation of natural systems. Changes that occurred throughout early history of the earth stand in marked contrast to the orderly and uniform operation of natural systems within the past one-half to one billion years. Whereas this late geologic history is dominated by repetitious cycles of processes and forms within the limits of over-all uniformity, the early history is a progression from one profoundly unique state to another in an irreversible order of change. Early history also differs in character from late history in the time scale used. Whereas early history is described in billion-year units of time, late geologic time is discussed in million-year units of time—a thousand-fold difference in the magnitude of time units. If we were to pick out any single 100-million-year time interval in early history, we should perhaps find that no significant changes in operation of natural systems could be discerned from the beginning to the end of that period. It is only when we encompass the total time range of perhaps five billion years that the radical nature of the changes is striking.

This chapter therefore deals with profound and sweeping changes in the states and structural arrangements of matter within the solar system, and more particularly, within and upon planet Earth.

## Conditions which a solar-system hypothesis must satisfy

Any hypothesis of solar-system origin and planetary development must provide an explanation or solution for several basic facts. Certain of these points have been discussed in previous chapters.

1. The hypothesis must account for the uniformity of direction of revolution and rotation of almost all planets and their satellites, as well as the fact that the orbital planes of almost all of these bodies are in approximate parallelism. The approximately constant ratios of the distances of successive planets from the sun, demonstrated empirically by Bode's law, must be justified. (See Chapter 5.)

2. An explanation must be given for the fact that whereas the sun contains most of the mass of the solar system, its rate of rotation is very slow and most of the angular momentum of the system is concentrated in the planets, especially in the outer planets. (See Chapter 5.)

3. It will need to account for the fact that although the chemical composition of the sun is very similar to the average composition of the entire solar system, the composition of the earth is strikingly different from either of these. These differences are discussed in detail in later paragraphs of this chapter. There is also a significant difference in chemical composition between the four inner or terrestrial planets, as a group, and the four great outer planets as a group.

4. The moon's low specific gravity and probable lack of a dense iron core must be explained. (See Chapter 31.)

## Chemical compositions of sun, solar system, and earth compared

Let us compare the chemical composition of our sun with the average composition of the entire solar system, and contrast these compositions with that of our earth. We shall then compare the average composition of the four inner planets with that of the four great outer planets. The differences and similarities are highly significant in terms of origin of the solar system.

The chemical composition of the sun's atmosphere is determined by spectroscopic analysis of solar rays. No information is directly available for the sun's interior, and it must be assumed that the solar atmospheric analysis applies equally to the entire sun. Of the 92 naturally occurring elements, 66 have been recognized on the sun. All remaining elements may exist there as well, some in quantities too small to permit identification. Table 27.1 gives the abundances of the twenty most abundant elements in the sun's atmosphere, as determined by spectroscopic analysis, in order of decreasing quantity. The numbers given are ratios of atoms of

**TABLE 27.1. ABUNDANCES OF ELEMENTS IN SUN AND SOLAR SYSTEM***

| Sun's Atmosphere | | | | Solar System | | | |
|---|---|---|---|---|---|---|---|
| Rank | Element | Symbol | Abundance (atoms per atom of Si) | Rank | Element | Symbol | Abundance (atoms per atom of Si) |
| 1 | Hydrogen | H | 32,000 | 1 | Hydrogen | H | 26,000 |
| 2 | Helium | He | 5,000 | 2 | Helium | He | 2,100 |
| 3 | Oxygen | O | 29 | 3 | Oxygen | O | 23.6 |
| 4 | Carbon | C | 17 | 4 | Carbon | C | 13.5 |
| 5 | Nitrogen | N | 3 | 5 | Nitrogen | N | 2.44 |
| (6) | (Neon) | (Ne) | — | 6 | Neon | Ne | 2.36 |
| 7 | Silicon | Si | 1.00 | 7 | Magnesium | Mg | 1.05 |
| 8 | Magnesium | Mg | 0.79 | 8 | Silicon | Si | 1.00 |
| 9 | Sulfur | S | 0.63 | 9 | Iron | Fe | 0.89 |
| 10 | Iron | Fe | 0.12 | 10 | Sulfur | S | 0.56 |
| (11) | (Argon) | (Ar) | — | 11 | Argon | A | 0.23 |
| 12 | Sodium | Na | 0.063 | 12 | Aluminum | Al | 0.85 |
| 13 | Aluminum | Al | 0.050 | 13 | Calcium | Ca | 0.074 |
| 14 | Calcium | Ca | 0.045 | 14 | Sodium | Na | 0.063 |
| 15 | Nickel | Ni | 0.026 | 15 | Nickel | Ni | 0.046 |
| 16 | Copper | Cu | 0.0035 | 16 | Phosphorus | P | 0.013 |
| 17 | Chromium | Cr | 0.0033 | 17 | Chromium | Cr | 0.012 |
| 18 | Manganese | Mn | 0.0025 | 18 | Manganese | Mn | 0.0088 |
| 19 | Potassium | K | 0.0016 | 19 | Fluorine | F | 0.0036 |
| 20 | Titanium | Ti | 0.0015 | 20 | Potassium | K | 0.0032 |
| 21 | Cobalt | Co | 0.0014 | 21 | Titanium | Ti | 0.0023 |
| 22 | Zinc | Zn | 0.0008 | 22 | Cobalt | Co | 0.0023 |
| | | | | 23 | Chlorine | Cl | 0.0020 |
| | | | | 24 | Zinc | Zn | 0.0015 |
| | | | | 25 | Copper | Cu | 0.00092 |
| | | | | 26 | Vanadium | V | 0.00090 |

* Data sources: Sun's atmosphere—after Aller (1961). Solar system—from A. G. W. Cameron (1968), in *Origin and Distribution of the Elements*, L. H. Ahrens, ed., Pergamon Press, New York. See p. 127.

each element relative to the abundance of the silicon atom. (Note that the number for silicon is unity.) Although neither neon nor argon has been spectroscopically identified on the sun, both are probably present in important quantities—the quantity of neon is thought to be about equal to that of nitrogen, and argon may have an abundance about equal to that of sulfur or iron. Changes are to be expected in the quantities and orders listed as more accurate analyses are made.

Hydrogen and helium together account for practically all of the sun's mass. These elements, with atomic weights of 1 and 4 respectively, are the lightest of the elements and the most volatile. Following far behind in abundance are oxygen and carbon, in roughly equal amounts. A third group of elements consists of nitrogen, silicon, magnesium, and sulfur. Neon and argon would also fall into this group. The remaining 12 elements are metals, most of which occur in mere traces in comparison with hydrogen and helium.

Average composition of the solar system is given in the second column of Table 27.1. Abundances of elements have been estimated from a combination of sources, including the solar spectrum, solar cosmic rays, and meteorites of the chondrite type. Abundances of the 26 most abundant elements are given in the table. As in the sun's atmosphere, hydrogen and helium are the preponderant elements, in roughly the same proportions as in the sun. Oxygen comes third, in about the same amount as in the sun, while the abundances of carbon, nitrogen, magnesium, silicon, iron, and sulfur are much the same as in the sun. Values assigned to neon and argon give them important places in the ranking scale. Altogether, the elemental abundances in the sun's atmosphere are very much like those of the entire solar system.

Next examine the table of abundances of elements of the entire earth (Table 27.2). Because the units used here are those of percentage by weight, this table cannot be combined with the first. The most striking difference is in the order of the elements themselves. Hydrogen and helium do not even appear among the first 15 elements on earth. Iron is most abundant, comprising about one-third of the weight of the earth, whereas it constitutes only 1/80 of 1 percent of the sun's mass. Oxygen, about 30% in the earth, is third-ranking in both sun and solar system. Amounts of silicon and magnesium are about equal in the earth, together with iron and oxygen comprising 92% of the earth's mass. The remainder of elements on the list are essentially those found in a comparable ranking in the sun. It should be emphasized that the composition of the earth as shown in Table 27.2 is not established with a high degree of certainty and the figures should be treated as estimates only.

In summary, the virtual absence in the earth of the highly volatile light gases hydrogen and helium, as well as of neon and argon, forms a glaring contrast with the abundances of those elements in the sun and solar system. Clearly, any hypothesis of solar system origin must account for this contrast in abundances of elements.

**TABLE 27.2. COMPOSITION OF THE EARTH AND CHONDRITE METEORITES***

| Rank | Element | Symbol | Earth Average (% by wt.) | | Average of Chondrites (% by wt.) | |
|---|---|---|---|---|---|---|
| 1 | Iron | Fe | 34.6 | 92.0 | 27.2 | 91.8 |
| 2 | Oxygen | O | 29.5 | | 33.2 | |
| 3 | Silicon | Si | 15.2 | | 17.1 | |
| 4 | Magnesium | Mg | 12.7 | | 14.3 | |
| 5 | Nickel | Ni | 2.4 | | 1.6 | |
| 6 | Sulfur | S | 1.9 | | 1.9 | |
| 7 | Calcium | Ca | 1.1 | | 1.3 | |
| 8 | Aluminum | Al | 1.1 | | 1.2 | |
| 9 | Sodium | Na | 0.57 | | 0.64 | |
| 10 | Chromium | Cr | 0.26 | | 0.29 | |
| 11 | Manganese | Mn | 0.22 | | 0.25 | |
| 12 | Cobalt | Co | 0.13 | | 0.09 | |
| 13 | Phosphorus | P | 0.10 | | 0.11 | |
| 14 | Potassium | K | 0.07 | | 0.08 | |
| 15 | Titanium | Ti | 0.05 | | 0.06 | |

* Data from Brian Mason (1966), *Principles of Geochemistry,* 3rd ed., New York, Wiley, Tables 3.7 and 2.4.

## Chemical compositions of the inner and outer planets compared

The four inner or terrestrial planets (Mercury, Venus, Earth, and Mars) from a closely related group with respect to both their small size and high average density. The four great outer planets (Jupiter, Saturn, Uranus, and Neptune) form a group related by their large size and low average density. Table 27.3 gives comparative figures on mass and density.

High densities of the inner planets suggest that all are composed largely of silicate minerals with abundant iron. Whether iron cores and silicate mantles exist in all four is not known. In terms of chemical composition, all four of these planets probably have abundances of elements similar to that of the earth, as given in Table 27.2.

The four great outer planets (Pluto is largely an unknown planet) have low densities—not greatly different from the density of water at the earth's surface (Table 27.3). It is likely that Jupiter and Saturn, the larger pair of the four, have compositions quite like that of the sun (Table 27.1), about ¾ of the mass being hydrogen and

**TABLE 27.3. MASSES AND DENSITIES OF THE PLANETS**

| | Mass, relative to earth | Mean Density, g/cc |
|---|---|---|
| Inner Planets (Terrestrial) | | |
| Mercury | 0.06 | 5.0 |
| Venus | 0.81 | 5.1 |
| Earth | 1.00 | 5.5 |
| Mars | 1.08 | 3.9 |
| Outer Planets | | |
| Jupiter | 318 | 1.3 |
| Saturn | 95 | 0.7 |
| Uranus | 15 | 1.7 |
| Neptune | 17 | 1.6 |
| (Pluto) | 0.9 | ? |

about ¼ helium. Most of the remainder (about 2% of the mass) consists of the elements carbon, nitrogen, and oxygen, which are thought to be in the form of the compounds methane ($CH_4$), ammonia ($NH_3$), and water ($H_2O$). Rock-forming elements, such as iron, silicon, and magnesium, which with oxygen constitute the bulk of the inner planets, may comprise only a very small fraction of the masses of the outer planets.

It has been suggested recently that Jupiter has no rocky or metallic iron core, but has, instead, a core of extremely dense gases, largely hydrogen and helium. Under enormous gravitational pressures—in excess of 7000 tons per square inch (10,000 kg per sq mm)—these gases would attain densities more than 30 times that of water and would behave physically like metallic solids.

Uranus and Neptune, the smaller pair of the four outer planets, are thought to have very much less free (molecular) hydrogen than Jupiter and Saturn. Most of the volatiles consist of water, methane, and ammonia. Of these, water as ice may constitute about half of each planet's mass.

Comparatively low atmospheric temperatures, combined with the extremely powerful gravitational attraction that the great planetary masses exert, seem to have effectively prevented the escape of the dominant volatile elements into outer space. Uranus and Neptune may have originally possessed much larger proportions of hydrogen and helium, but if so these gases have been greatly depleted in comparison with Jupiter and Saturn.

Using the reasonable assumption that the original substance of all planets was of a composition essentially similar to that of the sun, any hypothesis of solar system origin must explain how the inner planets lost or were separated from most of the hydrogen, helium, and other highly volatile elements originally present.

## Hypotheses of solar system origin

Seen in broad-scale historical review, hypotheses of the origin of the solar system have fallen into two major divisions, or schools of thought. One school attempted to find an explanation of the planets through an external force acting upon the sun to cause that star to yield forth the substance from which the planets and all other objects of the solar system are derived. Typically, the external force evoked was either a direct impact or a tidal force exerted by another stellar object in close proximity to the sun. The second school postulates an ancestral *nebula,* which is simply a cloud of gas containing highly dispersed small particles, from which, by some process of condensation or agglomeration, the discrete bodies of the solar system were ultimately formed. While the first-named category of explanations requires a single catastrophic event of short duration, the second or nebular category postulates a continuum of changes over a vast span of time.

We shall review a number of the hypotheses in chronological order of their statement. In 1749, the French philosopher Buffon proposed that during a collision with a passing comet, the substance of the planets was torn from the sun. Only a few years later (1755) the German philosopher Immanuel Kant, following an earlier proposal by Descartes, suggested that the solar system originated as a cloud of gas and dust, with a high concentration in the central region, which eventually became the sun. Thus the two major schools of thought were born and came into direct conflict.

**The nebular hypothesis** Kant's suggestion was taken up by the French astronomer Laplace, who in 1796 published the *nebular hypothesis,* according to which the sun was thought to be originally a hot rotating mass of gas and dust larger than the largest of the present planetary orbits. The nebula through its own gravitational attraction contracted into a smaller volume and at the same time greatly increased the velocity of its rotation. At a certain critical point the centrifugal force of rotation at the equator of the nebula exactly balanced the gravitational force. Then, as the nebula continued to contract, the matter in the equatorial belt was left behind in the form of a ring, which split off, providing the substance out of which the outermost planet was formed (Figure 27.1). The same process, repeated, produced nebular rings for each planet, the entire system thus superficially resembling Saturn and its rings.

Laplace supposed that the diffuse matter in each ring then condensed to form a single planet and moreover that the planet in turn shrank and left behind rings which became its satellites.

The nebular hypothesis enjoyed widespread popularity for more than a century, but serious objections to it were presented by astronomers and geologists at the beginning of the twentieth century, with the result that the hypothesis was quickly discarded as impossible. One serious objection, raised many years earlier by the Scottish physicist Clerk Maxwell and discussed in Chapter 5, relates to the distribution of angular momentum in the solar system. It was argued that if the nebular hypothesis of Laplace were correct, the sun should have enormously greater angular momentum than it does and should rotate about 200 times faster than it now does. As a further objection to the nebular hypothesis it was difficult to find any reason for the intermittent contraction of the sun to produce rings, rather than a continuous contraction into a single mass. Also, if the rings were composed of highly heated gases, the gas molecules would readily escape the sun's gravitational field and the rings would disintegrate.

**The planetesimal hypothesis** The sudden demise of Laplace's nebular hypothesis led quickly to the formulation in 1905 of a radically different explanation by two professors at the University of Chicago, T. C. Chamberlin, a geologist, and F. R. Moulton, an astronomer. They took up the suggestion made first by Buffon. The *planetesimal hypothesis,* as it was known, requires that a rapidly moving star once passed close to our sun, the mutual gravitational attraction of the two bodies raising two great tidal bulges on the sun. As a result there were ejected from opposite sides of the sun's surface a pair of curved arms of gaseous matter somewhat like the known solar prominences of today, but much larger. The total mass thus ejected was much greater than that of the present planets, but most of it fell back to the sun's surface. That which remained in highly elliptical orbits about the sun condensed from the gas-

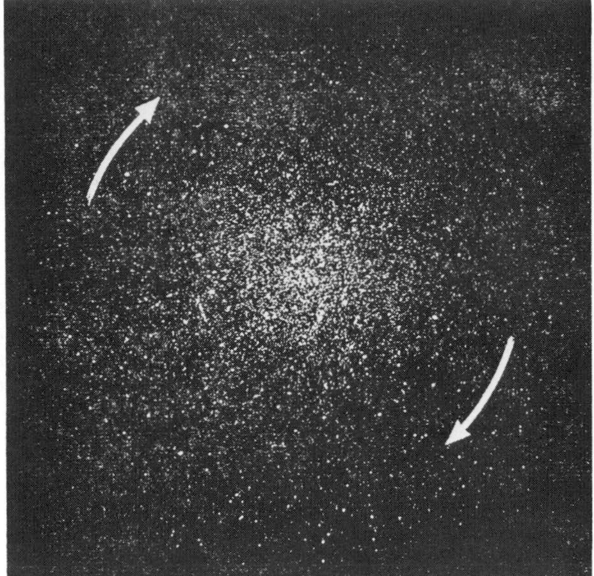
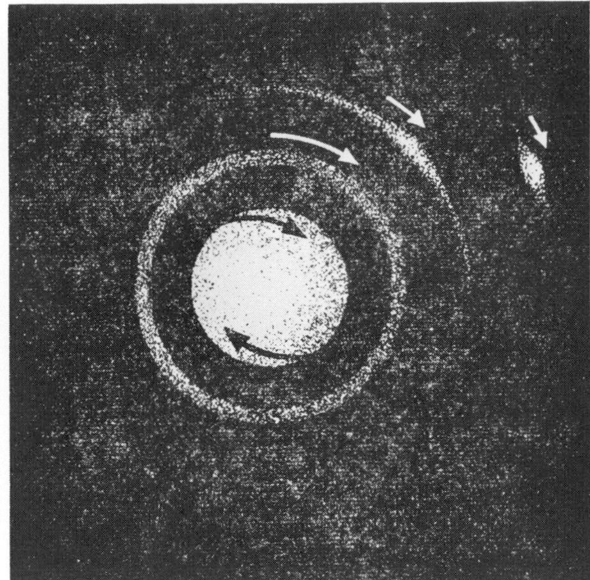

**FIGURE 27.1.** Diagrammatic representation of Laplace's nebular hypothesis of origin of the solar system. On the left is a rotating nebula of hot gas. On the right the nebula is shrinking and leaving behind rings of gas that will condense to form the planets. (Yerkes Observatory.)

eous state into small solid particles, known as *planetesimals*. These in turn joined by collisions, the larger absorbing the smaller, to produce the planets. Gradually the space of the planetary orbits was swept clean of most of the planetesimals.

Chamberlin and Moulton supposed that the planets thus grew by accretion of masses of many sizes. Although receiving the impacts of the planetesimals, the planets remained in the solid state throughout. A modification of the hypothesis by the geologist Joseph Barrell, of Yale University, included a phase in which the earth, under the impacts of large planetesimals, became molten for a time.

The planetesimal hypothesis relies upon the rapid motion of the passing star to have provided the angular momentum of the planets and to have been responsible for the uniformity in direction of rotation and revolution of the planets and satellites. A serious objection to the planetesimal hypotheses is that for matter to be drawn out, the passing star must have come within a distance of the sun not more than the diameters of the two stars themselves, an extremely unlikely event, while their closing velocity must have been some 3000 mi (5000 km) per second, a figure considered unreasonable because it exceeds the escape velocity of the galaxy.

Since this hypothesis calls for a rare, or special event in nature, having many of the aspects of an extraordinary accident, it does not tend to be strong. Nevertheless, the concept of formation of planetesimals from a gaseous mass and their gathering together to form planets by gradual accretion is a valuable concept that has much to recommend it.

**The tidal hypothesis** Closely related in mechanism to the planetesimal hypothesis was an alternative proposal made shortly thereafter by the English astronomers Sir James Jeans and Sir Harold Jeffreys. They also supposed that a passing star had exerted a tidal pull upon the sun, but that the effect was to cause a long filament of gases to be drawn from the sun. The outer part of the filament escaped into space, the inner part fell back into the sun, and the middle part formed itself into a string of bead-like masses which condensed to form the planets (Figure 27.2).

The tidal hypothesis is subject to much the same objections as the planetesimal hypothesis. Jeffreys later revised the hypothesis to require the approaching star to collide with the sun, plowing through the sun to a depth of about one-quarter its diameter. The collision dragged away from the sun sufficient matter to form the planets. It is now thought that any gaseous matter, could it be drawn from the sun, would be of such high temperatures that the rapidly moving gas molecules would quickly escape into space, dissipating the cloud entirely.

New chemical evidence has now virtually ruled out the possibility that the planets were derived of matter from the sun's interior. Thermonuclear reactions within the sun's interior would have destroyed all *deuterium* (heavy hydrogen—an isotope of hydrogen) at an early stage in its history as a star. Hence our earth and meteorites would not now possess deuterium in their compositions. On the contrary, deuterium is found in the gases enclosed in meteorites as well as in earth matter. This finding provides proof that planetary matter originated outside of the limits of a dense high-temperature stellar interior, whether it be that of the sun or of a passing star.

**The double-star hypothesis** In the 1930s the English astronomer R. A. Lyttleton presented yet another hypothesis requiring a great catastrophe of nature. He postulated that the sun formerly had a companion much larger than itself, and that the two formed what is called

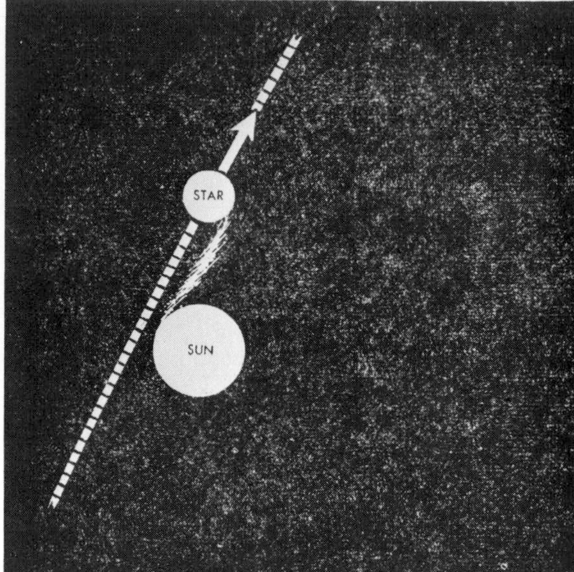


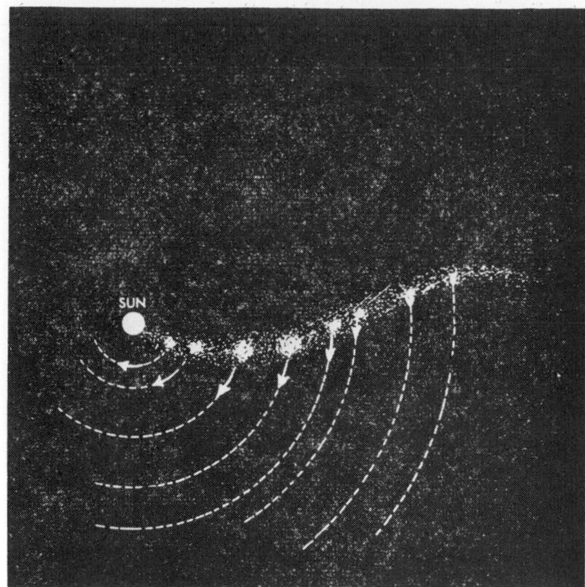


**FIGURE 27.2.** According to the Jeans-Jeffreys hypothesis of 1917 a passing star draws out a long filament from the sun (left). The gas then cools and condenses into planets (right). (Yerkes Observatory.)

in astronomy a *binary system,* or *double star* (Chapter 6). Such pairs are well-known in our galaxy. In this case the sun was very much the smaller of the pair. The larger star is considered to have undergone a violent explosion, flaring up into a brilliant star of a type known as a *supernova.* The violent explosion that results in a supernova occurs about once every two or three centuries in our galaxy.

Lyttleton postulated that the violence of the explosion of the sun's companion caused the larger body to move rapidly away from the sun and to escape altogether into space. Material ejected at high velocities from the exploding star also largely escaped, but a very small fraction of one percent of the exploded matter remained behind, captured by the gravitational field of the sun, to form the planets.

Initially extremely hot, the captured matter would have been in a gaseous state and would have spread out into a great flat disk surrounding the sun, much as Saturn's rings surround that planet. The ring then cooled into small discrete particles, much like the planetesimals of the earlier theories, and these began to collect into small aggregates of various sizes. The larger ones would have intercepted and absorbed the smaller ones until they formed a few large ancestral planets moving in orbits about the sun at distances about comparable to those of the present great planets.

As the early planets grew their rotational velocities increased enormously, until each was finally torn apart into two bodies with several smaller bodies, like droplets, isolated between (Figure 27.3). The larger bodies became the great planets, while the small droplets became the terrestrial planets, and these, through changes in orbits, moved closer to the sun.

Lyttleton's hypothesis is intriguing in that the matter of the planets and their satellites is derived not from the sun, but from another star. Nevertheless, the explanation is vulnerable to the same objections as its predecessors, including the likelihood that gases so greatly heated as those produced by explosion of a star would rapidly escape into space.

**Condensation hypotheses** In recent years scholarly thought about the origin of the solar system has returned in one respect to the basic concept of Kant and Laplace, that the solar system developed in an orderly series of stages beginning with a primeval cloud of gas and dust—the solar nebula—which contracted to a rotating disk-like body with the sun occupying a central position. Through a condensation process the substance of the nebula ultimately formed into the existing solid bodies of the solar system. Strikingly different from Laplace's nebular hypothesis, however, is the newer postulate that the original cloud of gas and dust was very cold, rather than being highly heated, as Laplace imagined it to be.

**FIGURE 27.3.** The astronomer R. A. Lyttleton has conjectured that a rapidly rotating large planet (*left*) became unstable and broke up into two large parts, with a number of small "droplets" between them (*right*). [After R. A. Lyttleton (1956), *The Modern Universe,* New York, Harper & Row, p. 172.]

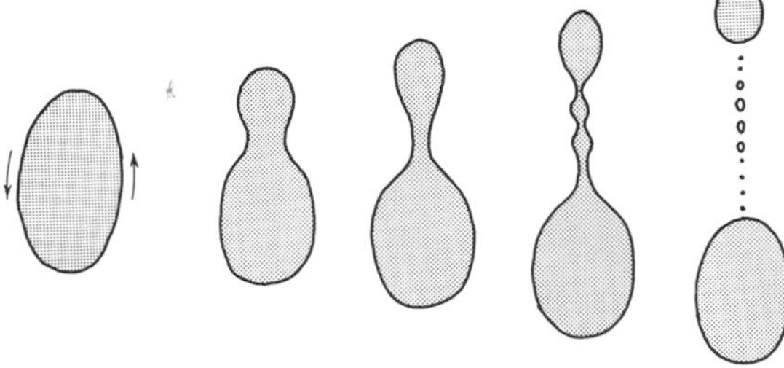

The newer concepts of evolution of a solar nebula we shall group together for convenience under the general heading of *condensation hypotheses.* Any modern condensation hypothesis must conform with an acceptable model of evolution of the sun as a star (see Chapter 6). Stars begin their development from large clouds of cold interstellar gas composed mostly of hydrogen. When such a cloud is compressed to a density of about 1000 hydrogen atoms per cubic centimeter, it begins to collapse under gravitational attraction. As a result of compression, the contracting mass ultimately becomes highly heated and a series of internal thermonuclear reactions begins. During a highly luminous phase that lasts about 10 million ($10^7$) years, the star shrinks in size. When this early contraction phase is complete, the star joins the main sequence of stars and thereafter remains essentially constant in diameter and temperature for a very long time.

At some stage during our sun's contraction phase, the planets and other objects of the solar system were formed. It is precisely with this rather trivial event (as judged from the standpoint of the total evolutionary history of a star) that the various versions of the condensation hypotheses are concerned. In their larger perspective, the planets are as insignificant to the origin of the sun as are tiny spattered droplets of molten metal produced in the pouring of an ingot.

An early version of the condensation hypothesis of planetary formation was introduced about 1944 by the German astronomer Karl von Weizsäcker. In reviving Kant's suggestion, von Weizsäcker proposed that as the sun was formed it was surrounded by a cloud of gas and dust having a mass about one-tenth that of the sun. The cloud was of approximately cosmic composition, which is essentially similar to the composition of the sun as well. Gradually the cloud of gas and dust became concentrated into a greatly flattened disk in what is now the plane of the ecliptic. Composed largely of hydrogen and helium, the cloud was in a complex state of motion, with regular eddies (vortices) of various sizes (Figure 27.4). The eddies, arranged in concentric zones of increasing size outward within the cloud, were regarded by von Weizsäcker as providing a mechanism whereby angular momentum could be transferred from the sun outward into the material of the disk, at the same time slowing the sun's rate of rotation.

According to von Weizsäcker, local increases in density of spacing of the particles would have occurred in the zones between adjacent eddies, causing aggregation to begin by mutual gravitational attraction. Small solid objects, essentially similar to the planetesimals of the Chamberlin-Moulton hypothesis, would have formed and grown by accretion and collision into larger bodies, eventually forming the planets.

Under von Weizsäcker's hypothesis, temperatures within the disk of gas and dust would have been very high close to the sun, but decreasing rapidly toward the outer periphery. Under high temperatures in the inner zone only the least volatile elements would have been able to condense into a solid state, and the rate of planetary accumulation was slow. At the same time, the volatiles, including almost all hydrogen and helium, would have been driven out and lost. Thus the small size and silicate-iron composition of the inner planets is explained. Because of the low temperatures in the outer zone of the disk the volatile elements were easily and quickly condensed, along with the less volatile elements, resulting in the growth of the great planets with their thick shells of ice, ammonia, and methane, and their atmospheres of hydrogen and helium.

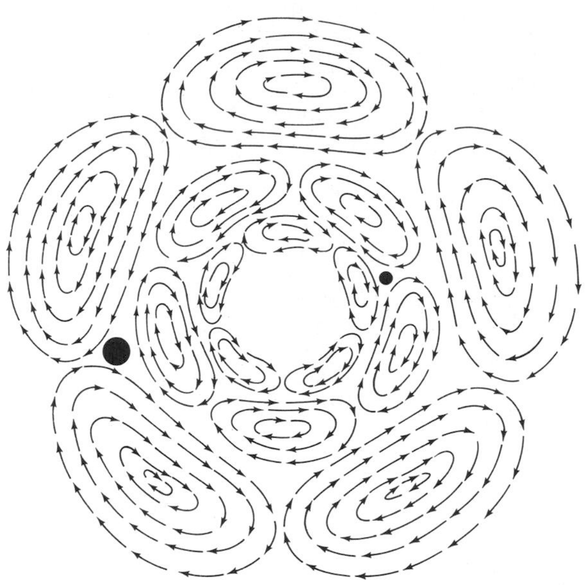

**FIGURE 27.4.** Schematic diagram of the formation of planetary bodies (black disks) in zones between eddies in a nebula of dust and gas, as conceived by von Weizsäcker. Denser concentration of matter at the center of the nebula is not shown.

In 1951 Gerald P. Kuiper, an astronomer then at the University of Chicago, proposed modifications in von Weizsäcker's hypothesis. Instead of regular eddies arranged in concentric zones, he postulated a highly irregular, or chaotic, type of turbulent motion within the nebular disk. Where local concentrations of matter were sufficiently dense, condensation by gravitational attraction occurred, producing bodies which Kuiper referred to as *protoplanets.* Composition of the protoplanet was essentially the same as that of the sun. In addition to one large protoplanet for each major planet, there were many smaller protoplanets. While the centers of the protoplanets were relatively dense, the outer zones were composed of the volatile gases extending to contacts with adjacent protoplanets.

At about this point in time, after the protoplanets had swept up most of the material in the nebular disk in complete darkness and at very low temperatures, contraction of the central mass formed the sun. As soon as the sun began to shine, its radiation heated the atmospheres of the nearer protoplanets and drove off most of the lighter gases, leaving only the very small fraction of the original mass in the condensed core of heavier elements to become the planets as we know them today. The outer planets were too far from the sun to be strongly heated and were thus able to retain a much larger fraction of their gaseous constituents. Eventually the excess gases, largely hydrogen and helium, were dissipated into space, leaving only the condensed protoplanet cores.

**Urey's hypothesis** At about the same time that Kuiper was presenting his version of planetary development, the distinguished chemist and Nobel laureate Harold C. Urey was applying principles of chemistry to problems of the solar system, particularly through the investigation of the compositions of meteorites. These studies led Urey to attempt to formulate a unified hypothesis of origin of the planets, moon, asteroids, and meteorites to account for the observed chemical and physical phenomena. The following paragraphs are based largely on Urey's interpretations of events in the evolution of the solar system.

As contraction of the solar nebula began, any original turbulent motions which its various parts might have had were smoothed out by internal friction and transformed into a slow rotation of the entire mass. With contraction continuing, the conservation of angular momentum caused the angular velocity to increase as the diameter of the nebula became smaller.

Transfer of angular momentum from the central region, or solar mass, to the outer parts of the nebula that later formed the planets posed a vexing problem. It was then suggested that angular momentum might have been transferred outward through the nebula through the action of magnetic fields. This process has now achieved wide acceptance in the scientific community.

As contraction of the nebula continued and its rotational rate increased, the nebula took the form of a greatly flattened ellipsoid. The degree of flattening progressed until the nebula came to resemble a rather thin plate-like disk, with a solar mass concentrated at the center (Figure 27.5). It is estimated that about one-third of the nebular mass was in the disk, about two-thirds in the central condensation.

During contraction those particles near the periphery whose centripetal acceleration exactly matched the gravitational acceleration of the total nebular mass were left behind in orbits of fixed size in the equatorial plane of the nebula. There was thus formed a thin nebular disk outside of the contracting mass. This disk comprised the matter from which planets were later formed.

In a manner not fully explained or understood, the cold gas and dust of the nebular disk apparently became separated into gravitationally bound bodies. Perhaps this clustering resulted from chance groupings of the particles. The resulting bodies would have been subjected to the disruptive tidal forces of the sun, hence they would necessarily have had to be of sufficient mass that the mutual forces of gravitational attraction holding the particles together would have exceeded the disruptive tidal forces. Because of the large quantities of hydrogen and helium then present in the solar nebula, the mass of a body that could retain its identity would have been large enough that, after most of the hydrogen and helium had escaped, the remaining heavier elements would have a mass roughly equal to the present mass of the moon. This would imply that the initial condensation would have had a mass 300–400 times that of the moon today. Thus the term *lunar-sized body* was applied by Urey to describe the individual nebular bodies.

The cold finely divided substance of the lunar-sized nebular bodies accumulated by collisions to form solid objects roughly on the order of size of the moon. Such bodies, called *protoplanets* by Urey, would have been too small to hold atmospheres of hydrogen and helium, which largely escaped into space. Many of the protoplanets became unstable as they grew, ultimately exploding into vast numbers of minute solid particles. Protoplanets and vast swarms of smaller particles were now moving about the sun in planetary orbits. Collisions of these objects occurred in great number, so that in about 10 million years time they formed by accretion into the planets as we know them.

Smaller particles falling into the earth lost their excess energy into a primitive atmosphere and reacted chemically with it. Larger objects—the meteorites—arrived at the ground surface only slightly warmed. Still larger masses tens or hundreds of miles in diameter and moving at high speeds, penetrated the earth's atmosphere without appreciable loss of energy and were largely volatilized on impact. It may be that such impacts caused local melting of the rock to produce lava pools, but for the earth as a whole the temperature remained below the melting point. The rate of accumulation of a planet would have increased as the planet's mass increased because of its stronger gravitational field and larger intercepting cross section. Periods of rotation of the planets were determined during the process of growth. When completed, the terrestrial planets consisted largely of a mixture of iron and silicates throughout. In earth, separation of these substances into a core and a mantle are considered to have occurred throughout ensuing geologic time by internal processes. The great planets were able to hold the methane, ammonia, hydrogen, and water, which they now possess in abundance, because of their strong gravitational fields and their colder temperatures.

In recent years, the transfer of angular momentum from sun to planets and a consequent slowing of the sun's rotation have been attributed in part to the action of the solar wind (see Chapter 7). Matter streaming from the sun and intercepted by the planets is considered to be a process adequate to remove angular momentum from the sun to the extent observed. It is estimated that in the last 5 billion years rotation of the sun has been slowed by about 50% through action of the solar wind.

**Loss of volatiles from earth** We have placed a great deal of emphasis upon the striking difference between

**FIGURE 27.5.** According to the modern condensation hypothesis, contraction of the solar nebula produces a thin disk of cold dust and gas that rotates about a central solar mass.

bulk chemical composition of the earth and the compositions of both sun and solar system (Tables 27.1 and 27.2). Von Weizsäcker's hypothesis of solar system formation explained the loss of volatiles from the inner planets as related to nearness to the sun and high temperatures during accretion. However, the more recent developments in detailing the condensation hypothesis as developed by Urey and others require that the first condensations into solid lunar-sized bodies (protoplanets) and smaller particles took place at temperatures too low to permit melting of rock material, most of which was silicate and iron. This solid matter was probably in a highly oxidized state—in other words, oxygen existed in combination with other elements. Iron was in an oxide form. Loss of the highly volatile hydrogen and helium is explained, for these elements remain in the gaseous state at temperatures very close to absolute zero. Argon, neon, krypton, and zenon are also gases of extremely low freezing points and would remain in the gaseous state. Velocities of molecules of hydrogen and helium would have exceeded the escape velocities of the protoplanets. Once the central mass of the nebula had condensed enough to form the sun and it began to radiate, force of the solar wind (Chapter 7) would perhaps have swept large quantities of these gases into interstellar space, beyond the limits of the solar system.

At temperatures far below freezing of water much of the matter of the primeval dust–gas cloud of the nebula was in the solid or liquid state. Water, which would have been ice, with methane and ammonia would have formed a slush of mixed ice and liquid particles. Had the entire nebula at any time been subjected to very high temperatures, these volatiles would have been driven off, whereas they exist today in large quantities in the four great outer planets. Yet these and many other substances were in some way driven off from the inner planets. When and how did this depletion of volatiles occur?

Most qualified scientists who engage in serious discussions of planetary origin agree that no episode of high temperatures and melting of silicates and iron occurred during the nebular phase. Instead, a subsequent high-temperature episode is required. This high-temperature episode also was one of chemical reduction—that is, the liberation of free oxygen from its chemical bonds with other elements, particularly iron. Essentially the same process goes on in a blast furnace, causing the oxygen to be driven off from iron-oxide ore to produce free iron in the molten state. It is estimated that the temperatures during the heating episode exceeded 1800° F (1000° C).

The source of heat for a high-temperature episode is readily found in the process of gravitational collapse. As dispersed matter of the nebula became concentrated into discrete masses, gravitational attraction increased. As the matter moved more rapidly toward these centers of gravity, kinetic energy was converted into heat. The larger the mass of the accumulating planetesimal became, the higher its temperature rose.

At a certain point in the episode of heating, methane ($CH_4$), ammonia ($NH_3$), and water ($H_2O$) were vaporized and became gaseous atmospheres surrounding the growing bodies of planetary material. As temperatures

**TABLE 27.4. VOLATILE AND NONVOLATILE ELEMENTS UNDER REDUCING CONDITIONS AT HIGH TEMPERATURES***

| Volatile (listed in order of cosmic abundance) | | Nonvolatile (listed in order of bulk earth composition) | |
|---|---|---|---|
| Hydrogen | H (as $H_2O$) | Iron | Fe |
| Helium | He | Silicon | Si |
| Neon | Ne | Magnesium | Mg |
| Nitrogen | N (as $N_2$) | Nickel | Ni |
| Carbon | C (as $CO_2$) | Calcium | Ca |
| Sulfur | S | Aluminum | Al |
| Argon | A | Chromium | Cr |
| Sodium | Na | Manganese | Mn |
| Chlorine | Cl | Cobalt | Co |
| Potassium | K | Phosphorus | P |
| Zinc | Zn | Titanium | Ti |
| Fluorine | F | Copper | Cu |

* Data in part from A. E. Ringwood (1966), in *Advances in Earth Science,* P. M. Hurley, Ed., Cambridge, Mass., M.I.T. Press, Table 3, p. 293.

rose above 1800° F (1000° C) all of the remaining matter melted. At very high temperatures many of the elements became volatile and were driven off from the melt as gaseous emanations. On the other hand, another group of elements is not volatile at these same temperatures. Table 27.4 lists selected examples of elements in both volatile and nonvolatile categories under a high-temperature reducing environment. Temperatures of 2400° to 2700° F (1300° to 1500° C) are assumed. The elements listed here will be found within the lists of abundances of elements in the sun, solar system, and earth (Tables 27.1 and 27.2).

As temperatures rose in the dense molten bodies during the high-temperature reducing phase of planetary history, a depletion of volatile elements occurred. However, this does not mean that all volatile elements were lost, for we know that important quantities exist today in the earth. Although the chemical environment was one of reduction, vast quantities of oxygen were retained in the melt in combination with silicon. However, much of the iron was reduced to the free metallic state, eventually to become the planetary cores.

Time of occurrence of the high-temperature reducing phase is subject to much discussion and difference of opinion. Under the Urey hypothesis the larger protoplanets underwent a high temperature stage and may have attained temperatures of about 3600° F (2000° C). Loss of volatiles occurred at that time. The protoplanets then cooled to a temperature near 32° F (0° C). Subsequent break-up of these bodies provided the cold solid particles from which the planets were formed at low temperatures by accretion. Under this hypothesis, the growth of the earth to its present size involved no large-scale melting, although later melting through accumulation of radiogenic heat remains a possibility, as we noted in Chapter 23.

It has recently been suggested that the early solar wind was possibly far more powerful than today, and was capable of heating protoplanets to temperatures sufficiently high to melt their interiors. A process of eddy-current heating resulting from interaction of turbulent magnetic fields surrounding the bodies has been suggested as a means of internal heating. Further development of the theory of these processes may lead to an explanation of a high-temperature phase alternative to the hypothesis of heating by gravitational collapse.

More recently (early 1960s) A. E. Ringwood has argued from a minority standpoint that Urey's multi-stage hypothesis is unnecessarily complicated, and that a single-stage hypothesis can be defended. Ringwood postulates that the planets grew by accretion of cold highly oxidized substances of the primordial nebula. As the growing planets became heated by gravitational collapse, ultimately the temperatures reached a level at which the outer layer melted, followed by complete melting of the planet and depletion of the volatiles. The differentiation (separation) of metallic core from silicate mantle within the earth took place during this process of accretion and heating. When the earth was completely melted the primitive atmosphere was blown off.

As a final observation concerning the chemical evolution of the earth from a primordial nebula of solar composition, the disproportionate increase of iron and nickel as compared with other nonvolatiles on the list is a fact that must be explained by the condensation hyptheses. Referring to Tables 27.1 and 27.2, note that iron rose from ninth place (below magnesium) in the sun's list to take first place on the earth's list. Nickel correspondingly rose from thirteenth place to fifth place. Other nonvolatiles on the list—notably silicon, magnesium, and aluminum—retained their positions relative to each other in both lists, but because of their higher percentages of the total material in the earth and meteorites they moved upward several places in the second tabulation.

It may be informative to look at the average composition of chondrite (stony) meteorites, for which percentages are listed in the second column of Table 27.2. The values are strikingly similar to those for the earth, although reversals of order occur. Again, iron and nickel are high on the list. If, as Urey proposed, these meteorites represent fragments of the protoplanets that were formed in the first stage of accretion, the loss of volatiles and rise in proportion of iron and nickel occurred in those bodies during a high-temperature phase preceding their disruption.

**Cameron's hypothesis**[1] The hypotheses of von Weizsäcker, Kuiper, Urey, Ringwood, and others have been under continual analysis and criticism by astronomers and geochemists under research stimulation provided by the explosive growth of the space sciences in the 1960s. It is not possible to cover these developments in a brief chapter. However, we take note of important contributions in the 1960s by Professor A. G. W. Cameron, an astronomer, while conducting research in cooperation with Dr. Robert Jastrow at the NASA Goddard Institute for Space Studies in New York City.

Cameron's concept of the collapsing interstellar cloud is quite different from that of scientists mentioned above, in that his picture of a rotating nebular disk at first contains no central solar body. Instead, the sun is formed at a later stage by secondary processes. Planetary bodies first accumulated within the flattened rotating disk, which at this time consisted largely of hot ionized gases entrapping a magnetic field. As more and more energy was built up in the magnetic field, matter of the nebula was caused to flow inwards toward the center of the nebula. This centripetal flow of nebular gas is described as a streaming motion.

Thus in Cameron's interpretation the planets were formed before the sun. Gases streamed past the planets to accumulate in the center of the nebula, forming the sun. At the same time, outward flow of gas was taking place at the outer edges of the nebula. Under Cameron's hypothesis, the inner planets captured substantial primordial atmospheres from gas which was streaming past them, but all subsequently lost these primordial atmospheres.

## Early history of the earth[2]

At a point in time about 4.7 billion years ago (−4.7 b.y.) aggregation of the planets was essentially complete, although infall of objects was to continue throughout all ensuing time, as the moon's surface shows. However, the completed earth was then very different in many respects from its present form. Its internal structure had yet to be reorganized. Lacking a fluid metallic core, the earth would have had no magnetic field and no magnetosphere to protect its surface from the sweeping action of the solar wind. Continents and ocean basins were probably not then differentiated. Furthermore, there probably existed no significant atmosphere and no oceans. We shall now attempt to reconstruct a schedule of events of profound change in various aspects of the earth's physical systems. These changes form an irreversible sequence leading to the relatively stable physical and chemical conditions that have prevailed in approximately the last 0.6 b.y.

The first aeon[3] of the earth's history spans the time from the earth's accretion, about −4.5 to −4.7 b.y. before the present, up to the time recorded by the oldest known rocks, metamorphic in type, about −3.6 b.y. This first aeon is a period of no tangible record, hence it is one of inference guided only by indirect lines of evidence. As we noted in Chapter 23 in discussing the early thermal history of the earth, the first aeon was probably a time of vast internal earth changes. From a uniformly distributed original mixture composed largely of silicates and iron, the process of differentiation and gravity separation was carried out by episodes of melting under the accumulated heat of radioactivity. The layered structure of the earth—with its basaltic crust, mantle, and core—developed. The magnetic field and magnetosphere came into existence. Continental masses of less dense granitic rock began to appear, constituting

[1] A. G. W. Cameron (1968), "Origin of the Solar System," Chapter 15, pp. 611–642 of *Introduction to Space Science,* 2nd ed., W. N. Hess and G. D. Mead, Eds. New York, Gordon and Breach, 1056 pp.

[2] The remainder of this chapter and Table 27.6 are based in large part on data by Professor Preston E. Cloud, Jr.: (1968), "Atmospheric and Hydrospheric Evolution on the Primitive Earth," *Science,* vol. 160, pp. 729–736; and (1968), "Pre-Metazoan Evolution and the Origins of the Metazoa," pp. 1–72 in *Evolution and Environment,* E. T. Drake, Ed., New Haven, Yale Univ. Press.

[3] The term *aeon* is used here to denote one billion years.

the continental nuclei that today occupy central positions within the continental shields.

**Origin of atmosphere and hydrosphere** Let us look first into the question of the earth's early atmosphere and hydrosphere. The term *hydrosphere* is convenient to apply not only to the oceans, but to all surface and ground water readily available for circulation over the earth. When and how did the earth's atmosphere and hydrosphere originate? The history of scientific thought on this subject offers two quite different lines of hypotheses, one of which has been generally rejected. Consider the rejected possibility first. Could the earth's atmosphere and hydrosphere have been present continuously from the time of the earth's accretion, constituting a large primitive (primordial) reservoir of matter? We are referring now to a collection of substances that can be referred to as *volatiles,* because they are elements in a gaseous molecular state at fairly low temperatures, or easily attain that state in combination with oxygen or hydrogen. First and foremost is water ($H_2O$), which comprises close to 93% by weight of the total quantity of excess volatiles within the atmosphere and hydrosphere, including water entrapped in sedimentary rocks (Table 27.5). Next in importance is carbon (C) in combination with oxygen as carbon dioxide ($CO_2$) comprising about 5% of the total. Chlorine ($Cl_2$) is also important (1.7%), followed by molecular nitrogen ($N_2$, 0.24%) and sulfur (S, 0.13%). Molecular hydrogen ($H_2$) follows with 0.07%, and there are also traces of argon (A), fluorine ($F_2$) and many other elements.

**TABLE 27.5. COMPOSITION OF GASES FROM INTERNAL EARTH SOURCES COMPARED WITH TOTAL EARTH VOLATILES***

| | Excess Volatiles of Earth's Hydrosphere and Atmosphere | Gases in Hot Springs, Fumaroles, and Geysers | Volcanic Gases from Basaltic Lava of Mauna Loa and Kilauea |
|---|---|---|---|
| Water, $H_2O$ | 92.8 | 99.4 | 57.8 |
| Total carbon, as $CO_2$ | 5.1 | 0.33 | 23.5 |
| Sulfur, $S_2$ | 0.13 | 0.03 | 12.6 |
| Nitrogen, $N_2$ | 0.24 | 0.05 | 5.7 |
| Argon, A | trace | trace | 0.3 |
| Chlorine, $Cl_2$ | 1.7 | 0.12 | 0.1 |
| Fluorine, $F_2$ | trace | 0.03 | — |
| Hydrogen, $H_2$ | 0.07 | 0.05 | 0.04 |

* Data from W. W. Rubey (1952), Geol. Soc. Amer., Bull. vol. 62, p. 1137, Table 6. Figures in table represent percentages by weight.

The hypothesis of a dense primitive atmosphere is based on the supposition that the earth, at the time of its formation, was in a molten condition or, if not originally molten, at least passed through a molten phase. The hypothesis states that the volatile constituents, largely water and carbon dioxide, were entirely in a vapor state and surrounded the hot earth as a dense atmosphere. As the earth cooled and became solid, temperatures ultimately dropped to a sufficiently low level that most of the water condensed to form the primitive oceans.

The hypothesis of a primitive dense atmosphere surrounding a molten earth has been disqualified by various lines of evidence. If the earth had been molten, most of the water (perhaps as much as 99%) known to be present today would have been contained in solution in the melt, rather than being free in the gaseous envelope. Condensation of atmospheric water vapor upon cooling could have furnished only a fraction of the quantity of water existing in the present atmosphere and hydrosphere. A second line of reasoning concerns the chemical nature of the supposed primitive atmosphere and ocean water. It is reasonable to conclude that the water formed by condensation would have been highly acid because of the presence of dissolved chlorine, bromine, fluorine, and other volatiles now found in sedimentary rocks. Such a highly acid ocean would have reacted vigorously with the rock-forming minerals, eventually neutralizing the solution by combination of the acid radicals with the common bases—namely, calcium, magnesium, sodium, and potassium. It has been estimated that the total quantity of rock required to be weathered to accomplish this neutralization would be considerably greater than the total quantity of igneous rock known to have been altered by weathering in all of geologic time.

We therefore conclude that the earth, early in the first aeon of its life, had a very small and relatively unimportant original atmosphere. The present atmosphere and hydrosphere are now generally thought to have evolved slowly by emanation from sources deep within the solid earth, a process referred to as *outgassing.* This hypothesis holds that practically all of the excess volatile constituents came from within the earth. The new atmosphere would have consisted largely of carbon dioxide ($CO_2$), nitrogen ($N_2$), hydrogen ($H_2$), and water ($H_2O$).

It has been suggested that the dense atmosphere of Venus has developed largely by outgassing. Note that Venus' atmosphere, composed largely of carbon dioxide and almost entirely lacking in oxygen and water, is quite unlike that of the earth. Water in quantities comparable to the earth's hydrosphere may have been produced by outgassing from Venus, but the hydrogen may have largely escaped into space and the oxygen may have combined with mineral matter exposed at the planetary surface.

As we shall see in the remainder of this chapter, the abundant oxygen of the earth's atmosphere has developed and is maintained through biological activity. That neither Venus nor Mars have significant amounts of oxygen can be explained by the absence of life on those planets, and as yet there have been found no signs of life.

The extremely rarified atmosphere of Mars may be due to a combination of factors unfavorable to outgassing and to holding of an atmosphere. First, Mars is a small planet, only one-tenth of the mass of earth, with an escape velocity one-third that of the earth. A liquid iron core probably does not exist in Mars and the planet seems to have no magnetic field. Consequently Mars would easily lose its atmospheric gases under force of the solar wind. The cratered surface of

Mars suggests that little igneous activity has occurred on that planet, hence outgassing would not have been aided by rise of magma and volcanic extrusion such as that which has characterized the earth's history.

That the process of outgassing is going on today is evident from chemical analysis of gases emitted from hot springs, fumaroles, and geysers (see Chapter 33)—a *fumarole* is a hole which emits superheated steam, and a *geyser* is a type of hot spring that intermittently discharges steam and water under high pressure. Hot springs, fumaroles, and geysers are associated with volcanic activity. Their heat is derived from recently intruded igneous rocks at depth. Much of the water that is emitted is recirculated ground water, but part of the water may be *juvenile water*—e.g., water that is derived from the earth's interior and which has not previously existed above the earth's surface.

Table 27.5 shows the results of chemical analysis of samples of volatiles from hot springs, fumaroles, and geysers. Averaged together, these analyses show over 99% water by weight, about 0.3% carbon dioxide, and lesser amounts of chlorine, sulfur, hydrogen, fluorine, and argon. Compare these percentages with those of the excess volatiles of the earth's atmosphere and hydrosphere. The degree of agreement is quite high. The higher proportion of water in the hot springs can be explained through the addition of atmospheric water that has entered the ground water reservoir and is being recirculated. Geologists have calculated that if only 0.8% of the water emerging from hot springs and related phenomena is truly juvenile water, the total quantity of juvenile water produced by the world's hot springs would be fully adequate to account for the entire volume of the world ocean, assuming this production to have gone on at the same rate for three billion years.

Another source of volatiles is lava of erupting volcanoes. Analyses of gases contained in fluid basalt from craters of the Hawaiian volcanoes Kilauea and Mauna Loa show a general correspondence in proportions with those of the earth's volatiles, as shown in Table 27.5. The proportions are not, however, as closely matched as for hot springs. Gases trapped in solid igneous rocks have also been analyzed. For granite samples, particularly, the percentages are quite closely matched with those of the earth's volatiles. On the basis of these observed proportions of gases derived from igneous rocks, some geologists have concluded that the excess volatiles of the hydrosphere and atmosphere are essentially of internal earth origin.

While outgassing was probably a continued activity throughout the first aeon of earth history, there is a possibility that the rate of outgassing was substantially speeded up about at −3.6 b.y. Professor Preston E. Cloud has proposed as a hypothesis that the moon was captured by the earth at this point in time. He argues that the intense tidal flexing set up by close proximity of the moon would have generated additional heat within the earth and would have promoted both rapid outgassing and the rise of igneous magmas to form intrusive bodies in the crust. This *thermal episode,* if it occurred, might well have increased the rate of production of the atmosphere and hydrosphere, raising greatly the total quantity of excess volatiles.

During the first aeon the salts of the sea were accumulating in a growing ocean from weathering products of rocks at the surface in island arcs and continental nuclei. To attempt to reconstruct the changes in composition of sea water as the oceans developed is highly speculative. It is reasonable to suppose that initially, and perhaps through some part of the first aeon, ocean salinity was low and the water was highly acid because of the predominance of the volatile constituents. The total volume of the oceans was probably increasing rapidly. As acids in rainwater reacted with igneous rocks (which may have at first been mostly basaltic types), the proportions of bases in sea water perhaps increased rapidly and the acidity was greatly reduced.

**The second aeon** Pausing for a review of conditions at about −3.5 b.y., it is inferred that both atmosphere and oceans then existed in substantial proportions, but that the atmosphere contained almost no free oxygen.

Very small quantities of free oxygen were continually produced by photochemical action in which the water molecule ($H_2O$) is dissociated into hydrogen and free oxygen by action of ultraviolet light. It is estimated that before −3.0 b.y. the free oxygen content of the atmosphere was less than 0.01% of its present atmospheric concentration, because the oxygen produced by this process was immediately withdrawn by oxidation of minerals.

Ocean water may have reached a salinity comparable to that which exists today. Continents were well developed, though smaller than today. Substantial quantities of sedimentary rock were being produced by the accumulation of detrital materials released by weathering and transported by running water and currents to continental margins and into shallow epicontinental seas. Essentially, then, the processes of vulcanism, erosion, geosynclinal sedimentation, orogeny, and intrusion were well established by this time. Sedimentary rocks probably as old as −3.2 b.y. have been identified, along with what seem to be fossil remains of the most primitive life forms. We therefore turn to the consideration of the conditions surrounding the origin and development of that earliest life.

**Beginnings of life on earth** In the almost complete absence of free oxygen in the atmosphere, there would have been no ozone layer to absorb the ultraviolet rays of the sun's spectrum. As noted in Chapter 12, the existing ozone layer protects most forms of life on earth from extinction by ultraviolet radiation. The earliest forms of life must therefore have been without dependence upon oxygen (e.g., *anaerobic*) and either capable of surviving under ultraviolet radiation or able to develop in places protected from such radiation. It is beyond the scope of this treatment of earth history to attempt to explain the biochemical processes that may have bridged the gap from nonliving to living matter. The event of life origin, or simply *biogenesis,* probably occurred in shallow ocean water exposed to solar radiation sometime in the period between −3.8 and −3.5 b.y. There is, of course, no record of this event.

The oldest known materials that can be speculatively interpreted as remains of life forms come from sedimentary rocks whose age is in the range from −3.2 to −3.0 b.y. These rocks are exposed in the Swaziland region of South Africa and are the oldest known sedimentary rocks that are largely unaltered by metamorphism. The life-like forms are found embedded in layers of chert, a rock composed largely of silica. As shown in the photographs in Figure 27.6, the objects in question are spheroidal in form and range in diameter from 0.0002 to 0.001 in. (5 to 25 microns). Also found are filament-like wisps of carbonaceous matter. If truly organic in origin, these earliest life forms were organisms that manufacture their own substance.

What are generally accepted as the oldest undoubted fossils occur in sedimentary rocks dated as at least −2.7 b.y., and perhaps as old as the Swaziland rocks.

**FIGURE 27.6.** Contenders for distinction as the oldest fossils on earth. Forms seen through a microscope in thin rock slices. Length of the bar is 10 microns (0.0004 in.; 0.01 mm).

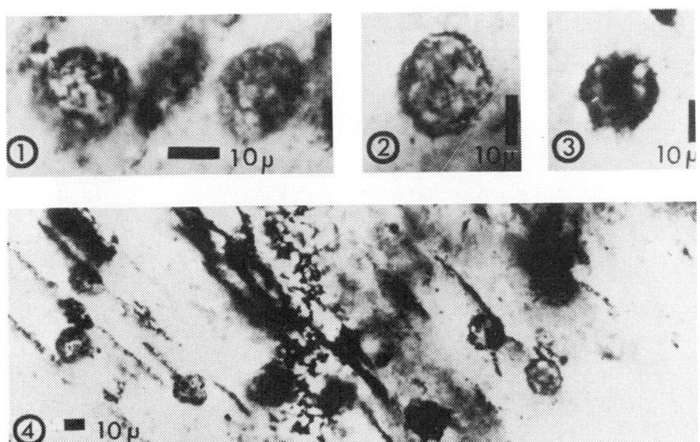


*A.* Microstructures possibly representing primitive alga-like life forms, from the Onerwacht Series, Eastern Transvaal, South Africa. Rock age is greater than 3.2 billion years. [Photograph by B. Nagy and L. A. Nagy (1969), *Nature*, vol. 223, p. 1227, Figure 1.]

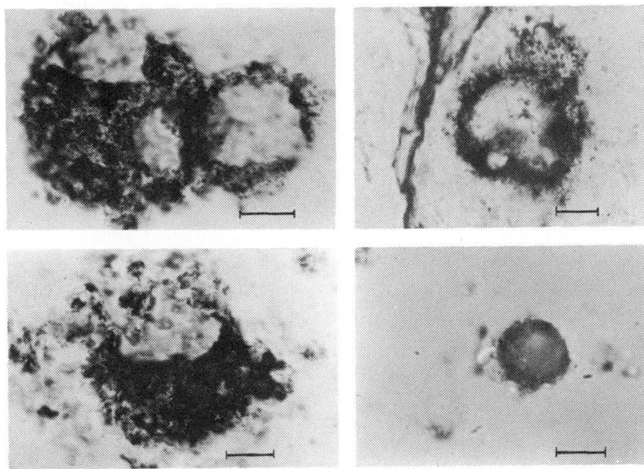

*B.* Spheroidal microstructures considered to be possible alga-like fossils, found in black chert of the Fig Tree Series, near Barberton, South Africa. Rock age is greater than 3.1 billion years. (Photograph by courtesy of Elso S. Barghoorn; see J. W. Schopf and E. S. Barghoorn (1967), *Science*, vol. 156, p. 509, Figure 1–4.)

**FIGURE 27.7.** Polished limestone surface showing laminated structure of a stromatolite of the Bulawayan Series, Southern Rhodesia. The specimen is 6 in. (13 cm) long. (Photograph by courtesy of Preston Cloud.)

Spheroidal objects 0.0002 to 0.0004 in. (4 to 10 microns) in diameter have been found in Minnesota in the Soudan Iron Formation, older than −2.7 b.y. and possibly exceeding −3.0 b.y. These structures may be remnants of bacteria or blue-green algae (Figure 27.8). In carbonate strata of the Bulayawan Series in southern Rhodesia there have been found spheroidal bodies, 0.0004 to 0.0008 in. (10 to 20 microns) in diameter, interpreted as primitive algae of a type that precipitate and bind mineral matter in layers, building up laminated structures (Figure 27.7). Such algal structures, well preserved in the late Precambrian and younger geologic record, are referred to as *stromatolites* and take the form of layers, crusts, and domes. Stromatolites are known to form in the intertidal and subtidal range of the marine environment. The intertidal forms are built up from tidal mud flats and attain heights approximating the level of high tide. The structures in the ancient South African rocks are a primitive form of algal stromatolite, thus they are built as a result of the life processes of a class of life-form known as *procaryotes,* which are organisms having no nuclear wall within the cell and no well-defined chromosome structure. These organisms therefore do not undergo cell division by mitosis or display sexual reproduction in the usual sense.

The next important step in life history seems to have been the development of a type of photosynthesis in which oxygen is released in the chemical reaction, as in green plants of today. Development of the first oxygen-releasing organisms, a form of blue-green algae, was the first step in a major change in composition of the earth's atmosphere and evidently occurred in the period −3.0 to −2.0 b.y. But unless the atmospheric oxygen thus produced was also simultaneously removed from the atmosphere, it would have been a hazard to the organisms themselves. A likely acceptor of free oxygen is the ferrous form of iron oxide (FeO) derived from rock weathering taking place on the land surfaces. Brought to the oceans by stream transport, this ferrous iron oxide would combine with additional oxygen, producing ferric iron oxide ($Fe_2O_3$), which could be deposited on the sea floor in accumulating layers of sedimentary rocks.

In fact, there exist banded iron formations whose age ranges from more than −3.0 to about −2.0 or −1.8 b.y. These rocks consist of thin layers of silica in which alternating bands are rich in ferric iron oxide in the mineral forms of hematite and magnetite. The banding suggests that there existed a fluctuating rhythm of precipitation and nonprecipitation of iron related to oxygen production. While the primitive procaryotes were the dominant life form, oxygen produced by photosynthesis was locked up in the sedimentary iron formations as fast as it was produced, thus oxygen could not accumulate in appreciable quantities in the atmosphere.

What seem to be the oldest fossils accepted without reservation as true remains of organisms are known as the *Gunflint microflora* and occur in cherty layers in banded iron formations in Ontario and Minnesota (Figure 27.8). These rocks are dated at more than −1.7 b.y. and possibly as old as −1.9 b.y. These forms are undoubted blue-green algae that have formed stromatolite mounds or reef-like masses (Figure 27.9).

During the period from −3.0 to −2.0 b.y. changes were slowly taking place in the oceans and ocean basins. Outgassing continued to supply volatiles, largely water, which steadily increased the volume of ocean water. Unless the capacity of the ocean basins increased concomitantly to accommodate the larger water volume, the oceans would have inundated the continents and created a world ocean. To explain why this ultimate drowning did not occur, we can draw upon the principle of isostasy in conjunction with the program of continental evolution explained in Chapter 26. As granite magmas continued to rise and invade the continental crust, and as more igneous rock was converted by weathering, transportation, and deposition into less dense sedimentary rock, the continental crust was thickened as well as expanded in area. It has been estimated that the continental crust has increased in volume at an average rate of 0.3 cu mi (1.3 cu km) per year throughout geologic time.

**FIGURE 27.9.** Stromatolites of the late Precambrian. *Upper:* Stromatolite dome, about 10 ft (3 m) in amplitude, from Paradise Island limestone formation, Northwest Queensland. Age about −1.6 b.y. *Lower:* Cross sections of small stromatolite domes from Dolomite Series, Boetsap, Southwest Africa, age about −2.0 b.y. (Photographs by courtesy of Preston Cloud.)

**FIGURE 27.8.** Fossils of the Gunflint microflora, north shore of Lake Superior, Ontario. (*A*) Filaments interpreted as a radiating algal colony. (*B, C,* and *D*) Sketches of modern one-celled blue-green alga, showing cell division and single cell. (*E* and *F*) Living form of dinoflagellate showing single cell and cell division. (*G* and *H*) Microfossils interpreted as algal cells undergoing division. (Photographs by courtesy of Preston Cloud.)

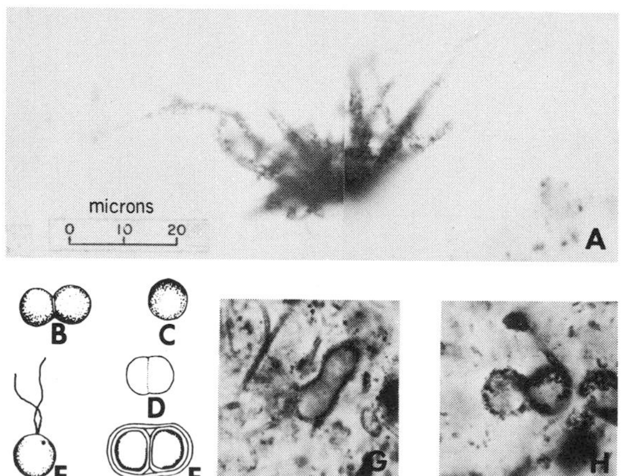


In response to the requirements of isostasy, the thickened continents would have risen higher with respect to the basaltic oceanic floors, thereby deepening the ocean basins and increasing their total capacity. Obviously, it is not to be expected that the increase of sea water volume would at all times exactly balance the increase of basin volume, so that episodes of greater emergence and partial inundation of continents would be an expectable part of the geologic record.

**Development of atmospheric oxygen** A significant turning point in atmospheric composition may have come about at −2.0 to −1.8 b.y., as increased plant activity raised the atmospheric oxygen level to approximately 0.1% of the present-day value. The change is attributed to the development of more advanced oxygen-producing enzymes. One consequence of increased oxygen would have been the accumulation on land of much ferric iron oxide, which would form thin coatings upon sediment grains. Sedimentary strata produced by accumulation of such stained particles have a red color, and are known as *red beds*. Extensive deposition of red beds did occur following −1.8 b.y., for these beds are an important part of the Precambrian sedimentary record.

**Carbon dioxide and carbonate rocks** During the time following −2.0 or −1.8 b.y., the carbon dioxide content of the atmosphere is thought to have decreased greatly. Whereas earlier carbon dioxide may have constituted a substantial percentage of the atmosphere (as contrasted with the present value of 0.03% by volume), it was subsequently withdrawn from the atmosphere to be stored in carbonate rocks. Enormous quantities of carbon and oxygen exist in combination with the bases calcium and magnesium derived from rock weathering and converted into limestones and dolomites. It is estimated that at present some $73 \times 10^{15}$ tons ($67 \times 10^{21}$g) of carbon dioxide is stored in sedimentary rocks, a quantity about 600 times as great as the present quantity of carbon dioxide in circulation in the atmosphere, hydrosphere, and biosphere. Great amounts of organic carbon were also entrapped in sedimentary rocks and have added to the total amount of carbon removed from circulation.

**The late Precambrian** At some point in time, which may have been earlier than −1.0 b.y., the carbon dioxide content of the atmosphere and hydrosphere appears to have been established at a value close to that existing today, namely 0.03% by volume. Once established, this low value has been maintained by a withdrawal of carbon dioxide at a rate equal to the rate at which it has been added by outgassing. It can be deduced that if significant releases of the stored carbon dioxide were to occur, raising the amount of carbon dioxide available for circulation, profound changes would occur in the life environment of the oceans. Many forms of marine life cannot tolerate marked changes in the acidity (pH) of the ocean water. That these same life forms have been maintained continuously throughout the entire geologic record since the time of their first appearance suggests that the oceanic environment has held to remarkably uniform properties of temperature and acidity since at least the late Precambrian, commencing about one aeon before present.

Atmospheric free oxygen in the late Precambrian has been estimated as about 1% of its present-day value. This is sufficient oxygen to screen much of the lethal ultraviolet radiation from the ocean surface. Below a depth of a few centimeters of sea water, which would have absorbed the remaining incoming ultraviolet radiation, complex life could evolve.

One consequence of this environmental change was the development of a more advanced form of marine life, the *eucaryotic cell.* This cell possesses a nuclear wall and well-developed chromosomes, and it is capable of mitotic cell division and sexual reproduction. Development of the eucaryotic cell in the late Precambrian made possible the development of all advanced forms of life to follow.

In the time span −0.7 to −0.6 b.y., which represents the end of the Precambrian and the beginning of the Paleozoic Era, there evolved the *Metazoa*—the multicelled animal life forms that make up most of the animal world with which we are familiar. A metazoan organism can be described as one having a mouth and a digestive system, a circulatory system for oxygen distribution, and a nervous system for control. These animal forms diversified rapidly and became extremely complex in a relatively short period. Consequently early in the Paleozoic Era animal life was represented by a highly diverse fauna, including most of the invertebrates.

**Early earth history in review** Approximately four aeons of earth history span the interval from the completion of earth accumulation to the end of the Precambrian time. Many profound and irreversible changes occurred during this early period, including internal reorganization of the earth, development of continents and ocean basins, and production of the atmosphere and hydrosphere by outgassing. Composition of the atmosphere reached its present proportions only near the very end of this four-aeon time span. Consequently the attainment of an oxygen-rich atmosphere, needed for development of advanced forms of life, represents only a terminal episode. Table 27.6 recapitulates the major events of early earth history in outline form.

The first four aeons of earth history were dominated by physical and chemical systems in transient states—that is, in rapidly changing states. However, the changes must have declined greatly in rate, tending finally to reach the steady state that has characterized the earth's surface environment ever since. So now we turn to the final stage in earth history, consisting of the three great geologic eras of abundant life under essentially uniform physical and chemical conditions.

**TABLE 27.6. A TIMETABLE FOR EARLY EARTH HISTORY***

| Billions of Years before the Present | Events (Largely Inferred or Hypothetical) |
|---|---|
| −7.0 | Formation of our galaxy. |
| −5.0 | Nebular contraction in process. |
| −4.8 to −4.5 | Accretion of planets completed. No primordial atmosphere remaining on earth. No magnetic field or magnetosphere. Solar wind sweeps earth. |
| −4.5 to −3.5 (First aeon) | Internal differentiation of earth in progress. Possible melting on large scale. Core and mantle segregated, magnetic field and magnetosphere formed. Outgassing in progress. Volatiles forming atmosphere and hydrosphere. No free oxygen (concentration 0.01% of present level); U-V (ultraviolet) radiation intense. No ozone layer. Continents begin to develop. Sedimentation begins. Ocean basins deepen. Ocean volume and salinity increasing. |
| −3.7 to −3.6 | Possible lunar capture. Possible episode of accelerated outgassing and magma rise. |
| −3.6 to −3.5 | Oldest known rocks (igneous and metamorphic) formed in continental crust. |
| <−3.5 | Evolution of pre-living compounds (amino acids) under U-V radiation.<br>Biogenesis occurs (anaerobic forms). |

**TABLE 27.6. A TIMETABLE FOR EARLY EARTH HISTORY* (Continued)**

| | |
|---|---|
| −3.4 to −3.2 | Oldest possibly-living forms (autotrophs) preserved in Swaziland System, South Africa; algal forms and carbonaceous filaments in chert. (Ocean volume increasing. Continents growing. Ocean basins deepening.) |
| >−2.7 | Possible oldest fossils: spheroidal objects in Soudan Iron Formation, Minnesota; algal stromatolites in Bulawayan Series, Southern Rhodesia. |
| −2.7 to −2.0 | Procaryotes develop. Rise of oxygen-releasing photosynthesizers in blue-green algae. Release of biological oxygen increases. Ferric iron compounds formed; banded iron formations deposited. Oxygen in atmosphere remains very low. $CO_2$ level high. |
| −2.0 to −1.8 | Advanced oxygen-mediating enzymes developed. Rate of free oxygen production rises. Oxygen approaches 0.1% of present value. Gunflint microflora, blue-green algae, forming stromatolite mounds. |
| −1.8 to −1.0 | Red beds formed in thick accumulations. $CO_2$ content of atmosphere decreasing. Carbonate rocks deposited in abundance. Eucaryotic cell develops. |
| −1.0 to −0.7 | Oxygen level rises rapidly; approaches 1% of present value. Ozone layer begins to form, shielding earth surface from part of U-V radiation. |
| −0.7 to −0.6 | Precambrian-Paleozoic transition. Ocean salinity and pH at present level. |
| −0.57 | Start of the Paleozoic Era. Metazoa evolve. Rapid diversification of multicelled animal life in seas. Oxygen above 1% of present level. $CO_2$ at present level. |
| −0.57 to 0.0 | Paleozoic, Mesozoic, and Cenozoic Eras of abundant life. Uniformity of atmospheric and oceanic environments prevails (except oxygen value). Rate of production of $CO_2$ by outgassing balanced by storage in carbonate rock and buried organic matter. |

* See footnote 2 on p. 484.

## References for further study

Mehlin, T. G. (1959), *Astronomy,* New York, Wiley, 392 pp., chap. 14.

Brancazio, P. J., and A. G. W. Cameron, eds. (1964), *The Origin and Evolution of Atmospheres and Oceans,* New York, Wiley, 314 pp., chaps. 1, 6.

Mason, B. (1966), *Principles of Geochemistry,* New York, Wiley, 329 pp., chaps. 2, 3, 7, 8.

Fairbridge, R. W., ed. (1967), *Encyclopedia of Atmospheric Sciences and Astrogeology,* New York, Reinhold, 1200 pp. See: Planetary evolution; Planet earth—origin and evolution; Solar system—origin; Solar system—review of theories.

Jastrow, R. (1967), *Red Giants and White Dwarfs; The Evolution of Stars, Planets and Life,* New York, Harper & Row, 176 pp.

Lyttleton, R. A. (1968), *Mysteries of the Solar System,* Oxford, Clarendon Press, 261 pp.

Whipple, F. L. (1968), *Earth, Moon, and Planets,* 3rd ed., Cambridge, Mass., Harvard Univ. Press, 297 pp., chap. 14.

# 28

# Principles of stratigraphic interpretation

STRATIGRAPHY IS THAT branch of historical geology dealing with the sequence of events in the earth's history as they can be interpreted from evidence found in sedimentary rocks. Included in stratigraphy are the records of deposition of sedimentary strata, of the geographical distributions of land and sea, and of the conditions of climate and terrain.

Indispensable to the pursuit of stratigraphy is *paleontology,* the science of fossil remains of animals and plants. The paleontologist identifies, names, and classifies fossils, and determines their evolutionary development. The stratigrapher uses fossils both to correlate strata in age of deposition and to establish the physical and chemical environments of deposition. *Paleoecology* is a science linking stratigraphy and paleontology by relating the ancient organisms to their environments.

Stratigraphic geology uses many of the same methods and has many of the same objectives as the study of civilized man's history. In both fields there must be an intensive search for evidence of what happened. From the actual record, whether it be in rock strata or in a written document, certain interpretations and inferences can be made by the historian skilled in guessing at the hidden meanings of seemingly trivial details. In both fields a major problem is the fragmentary nature of the record, where either an event left no records or the record has been destroyed by some catastrophe in subsequent times. Naturally, the problem of inadequate records generally becomes more serious as older and older periods of history are considered. A period well documented in one region is often not documented at all in another.

C

KAIBAB
KAIBAB
TOROWEAP
COCONINO
HERMIT
SUPAI
COCONINO

D

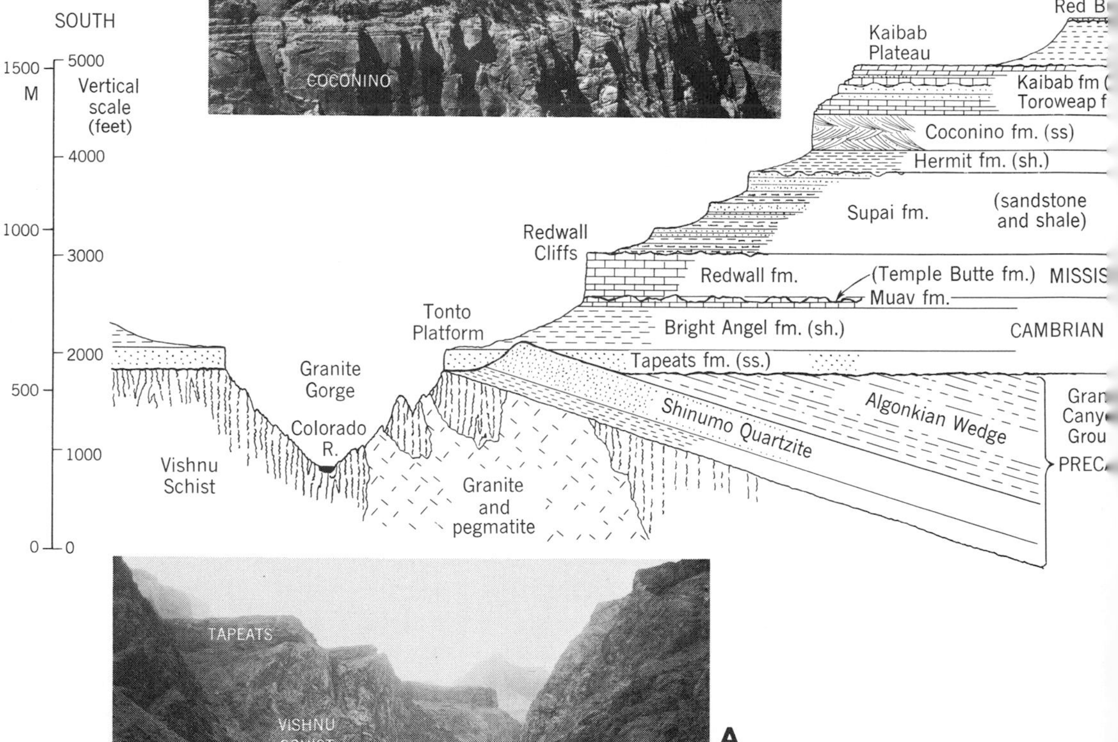

SOUTH

Vertical scale (feet)

1500 M — 5000
4000
1000 — 3000
2000
500 — 1000
0 — 0

Red B
Kaibab Plateau
Kaibab fm (
Toroweap f
Coconino fm. (ss)
Hermit fm. (sh.)
Supai fm.
(sandstone and shale)
Redwall Cliffs
Redwall fm.
(Temple Butte fm.)
MISSIS
Muav fm.
Tonto Platform
Bright Angel fm. (sh.)
CAMBRIAN
Tapeats fm. (ss.)
Granite Gorge
Colorado R.
Shinumo Quartzite
Algonkian Wedge
Gran Cany Grou
PRECA
Vishnu Schist
Granite and pegmatite

TAPEATS
VISHNU SCHIST

A

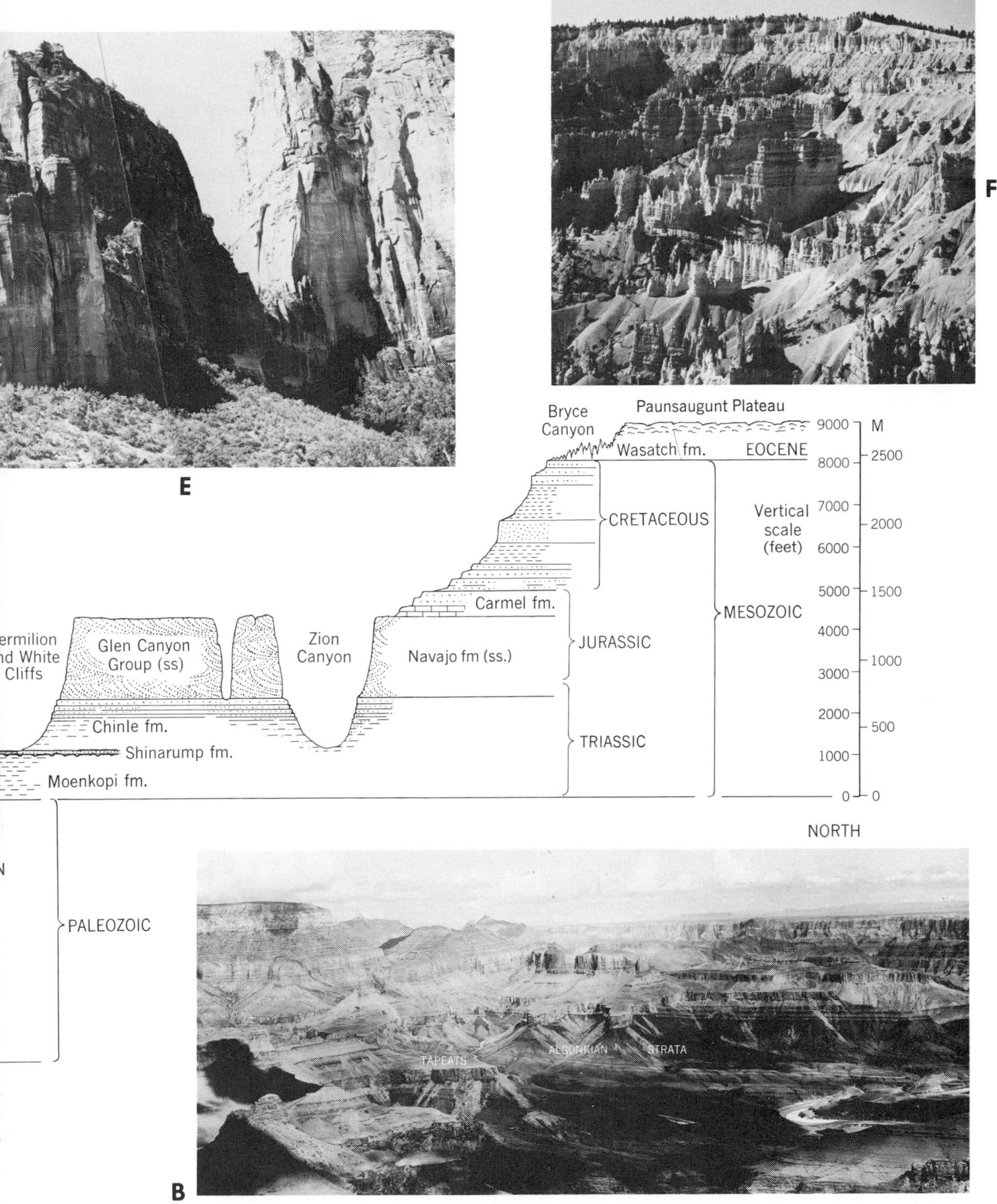


**FIGURE 28.1.** The geologic record of rock strata from Grand Canyon, Arizona, through progressively younger formations of Zion Canyon and Bryce Canyon, Utah. (Refer to Figure 28.21 for a map.) (*A*) Archean schists of the Inner Gorge at the foot of the Bright Angel Trail. These metamorphic rocks, of Precambrian age, are the oldest rocks of the entire sequence. (Photograph by Douglas Johnson.) (*B*) Precambrian sedimentary strata comprising the Algonkian wedge, in the eastern part of Grand Canyon. (Photograph by Carkhuff, U.S. Geological Survey.) (*C*) General view of sedimentary sequence of Grand Canyon from Point Sublime. (Photograph by A. N. Strahler.) (*D*) Uppermost strata of the rim of Grand Canyon. (Photograph by Douglas Johnson.) (*E*) The walls of Zion Canyon, Utah. These great cliffs are of Jurassic sandstone. (Photograph by A. N. Strahler.) (*F*) Bryce Canyon, Utah. Erosional forms in the Wasatch formation of Eocene age. (Photograph by D. L. Babenroth.)

In this chapter we inquire into the basic principles and methods of historical geology in order to obtain an appreciation of the type of problem that the geologist has faced and solved repeatedly. For illustration, a classic geologic region, familiar to many Americans, will be referred to repeatedly: the Colorado Plateau region in northern Arizona and southern Utah. Here lie three of our most famous national parks—Grand Canyon, Zion, and Bryce—whose rocks span all the eras of geologic time and are beautifully displayed in cliffs and canyon walls.

The over-all view of Grand Canyon, Zion Canyon, and Bryce Canyon shown in Figure 28.1 makes apparent the way in which the whole panorama of geologic time is exposed. Each of the three canyons is cut into a different sequence of strata, each sequence having been stripped back by erosion processes to expose the sequence beneath. In the bottom of Grand Canyon are the most ancient rocks, those of Precambrian age. From these we ascend to deposits of successively younger eras of geologic time by a set of great rock stairs. Actually the stair treads are broad platforms, but the risers between are clearly marked in great lines of cliffs. The traveler can conveniently make this ascent through geologic time beginning at Grand Canyon National Park, then driving north to Zion National Park, and last to Bryce National Park. (See Figure 28.21.)

## Relative age of strata

A geologic principle so simple as to seem self-evident is that among a series of sedimentary strata whose attitude is approximately horizontal, each bed is younger than the bed beneath, but older than the bed above it. This age relationship could not be otherwise in the case of sediment layers deposited from suspension in water or air. Thus the first inference to be made concerning the strata exposed in the walls of Grand Canyon (Figure 28.1) is that they are arranged in order of decreasing age of deposit from bottom to top. The same can be said of the layers seen in the walls of Zion Canyon and of Bryce Canyon. We cannot, using this principle alone, say which of the three canyons displays the oldest series of strata because the three localities are separated by many miles of intervening ground.

Despite the simplicity of the *principle of superposition,* as this age-layering principle is termed, there are two possible causes for concern. First, it might be objected that the strata have been bodily overturned during orogeny, as may happen in close folding of strata, and that the uppermost beds are therefore actually the oldest. The geologist routinely checks against this possibility of error by examining closely certain details of the sedimentary rock. Features such as ripple marking, curvature of fine layers (cross-bedding) in certain sandstones, and orientation of fossil shells give evidence of whether the strata are overturned from their original attitude. A second objection could be that the principle of superposition does not tell whether the successive strata differ greatly in age or only by very small intervals of time.

Looking at the upper walls of Grand Canyon in Figure 28.1, the eye spans about 3000 ft (900 m) of thickness of strata in almost perfectly horizontal, parallel arrangement. The entire sequence of strata consists of several major layers, each with a distinctive appearance and composition. Each of these layers is referred to as a geologic *formation* and has been given a name. At the base, forming the edge of the Tonto Platform, is the *Tapeats* formation, a sandstone layer about 200 ft (60 m) thick. Above this is a soft, gray, sandy shale layer, about 500 ft (150 m) thick, named the *Bright Angel* formation, which forms smooth, gentle slopes. Above this, forming a great sheer wall 500 ft (150 m) high, are three formations of limestone: the *Muav, Temple Butte,* and *Redwall* formations. Still higher are layers of red sandstone and shale, totaling about 1000 ft (300 m) in thickness, making up the *Supai* and *Hermit* formations. These are overlain by a pure creamy-white sandstone layer, the *Coconino* formation, whose sheer 300-ft (90-m) cliff is easily seen in the upper canyon walls. Forming the canyon rim are the *Toroweap* and *Kaibab* formations of limestone, together about 500 ft (150 m) thick.

## Disconformities

The type of question not answered by the principle of superposition is this: Were all the sandstone, shale, and limestone strata of the Grand Canyon walls deposited in quick succession, so that in terms of available geologic time since the start of the Mesozoic Era (600 m.y.) we may consider them all as being of approximately the same age? Or do they represent widely different periods of geologic time, so that the lowest formation, the Tapeats sandstone, is extremely ancient, but the rim formation, the Kaibab limestone, is very recent? In this case there might conceivably be a difference in age of as much as 600 m.y. in the two formations. Assuming such an age difference to exist, we are faced with the further possibility that the entire sequence of rocks, 3000 ft (900 m) thick, represents slow, continuous deposition of sediment without interruption of any consequence throughout the entire span of time.

A quite different possibility is that each formation was deposited in a short period, but that the records of periods of deposition are themselves separated by long intervals of time when no deposition took place. It is likely that for long periods of time, each tens of millions of years long, there would be no deposition or erosion of sediment.

We must therefore complicate the interpretation still further, as illustrated in Figure 28.2. Perhaps the bottommost three formations, Tapeats sandstone, Bright Angel shale, and Muav limestone, were deposited in rather rapid succession in a shallow sea, as shown in diagram *A*. Additional formations of which we have no record were possibly added to these three (diagram *B*). Then a broad rise of the earth's crust brought these formations above sea level, where fluvial erosion removed great quantities of rock (diagrams *C* and *D*). With only the Tapeats, Bright Angel, and Muav formations remaining, a downsinking of the crust occurred, depressing them below sea level and producing a

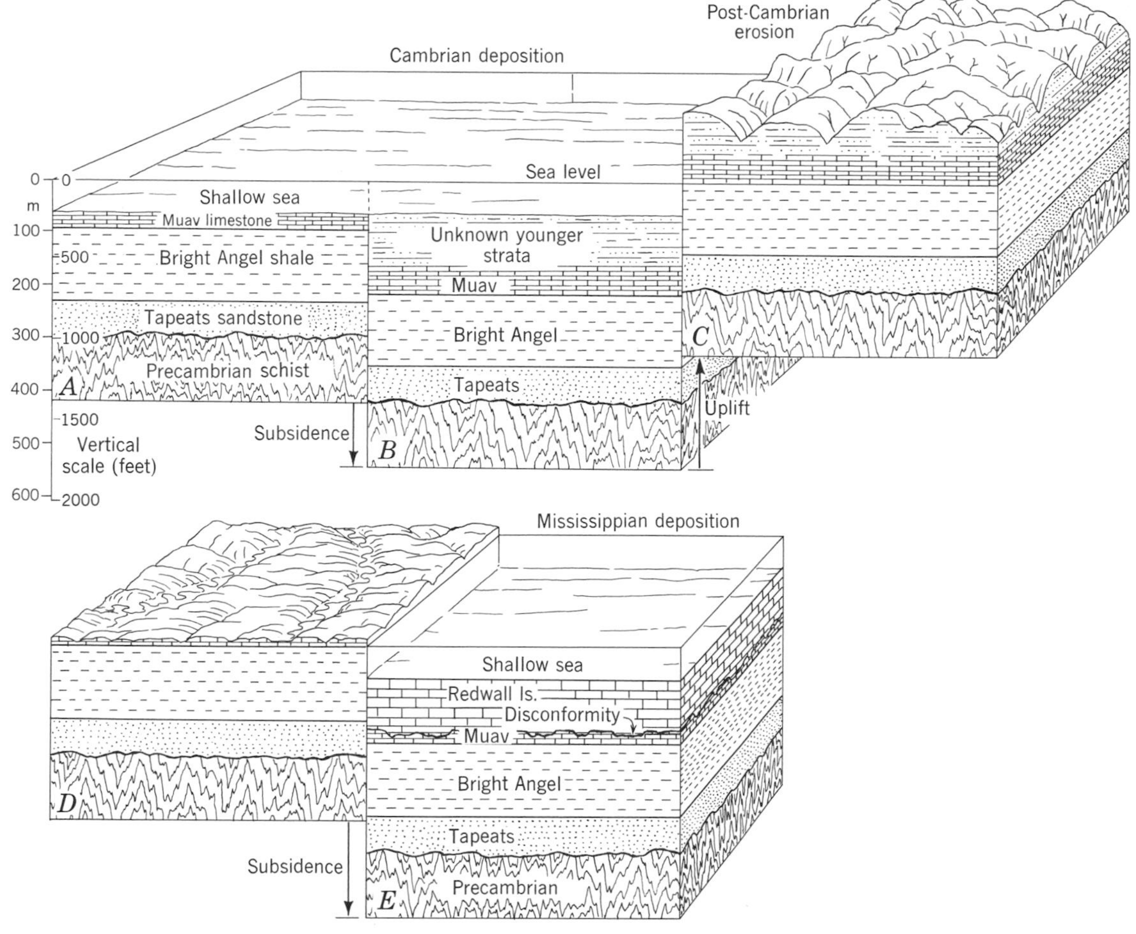


**FIGURE 28.2.** Sequence of events leading to the development of a disconformity in the walls of Grand Canyon.

shallow sea in which a new period of deposition began (diagram *E*). This submergence would have allowed deposition of the Redwall limestone formation directly upon the older Muav formation.

Thus the thin line that we now see between the Muav and Redwall formations is the sole indicator of a vast period of lost record, that is, of a time period for which no rock has been retained here. A surface of separation between two formations, representing a great gap of time, is termed a *disconformity.* The history of events just described above for the Grand Canyon formations of lower Paleozoic ages is the actual history as worked out by stratigraphers.

## Continuity of strata

The strata of the walls of Zion Canyon do not resemble most of those in Grand Canyon. In Zion the most striking feature is the sheer sandstone wall, 1000 to 2000 ft (300 to 600 m) high, with scarcely a foothold. Step-like forms such as those in Grand Canyon occur only in the lower part of the walls. It seems certain that the strata of the two canyons were deposited under different conditions. Although it is possible that both series were deposited at the same time in unlike environments, this situation is not likely because the two regions are only a few tens of miles apart. It is more likely that the strata of Zion Canyon differ in age from those in Grand Canyon. Which sequence is the younger?

One means of ascertaining whether strata in two localities are of the same or different age is to travel the ground from one locality to the other, observing the strata continuously along the line of march. If one can actually walk upon the same rock layer throughout the entire distance, the similarity of age is proved by the *principle of continuity.* A simple case is shown in Figure 28.3, where the same layer can be followed for miles in the rim of a series of canyons and cliffs. Where strata have been partly removed from a region by erosion, a combination of continuity and superposition (Figure 28.4) can be used, in traveling across country, to determine relative ages of rock strata in widely separated places. It is this combination method that is required to prove that the rocks of Grand Canyon are all of older age than those of Zion Canyon and that these in turn are all older than the strata of Bryce Canyon.

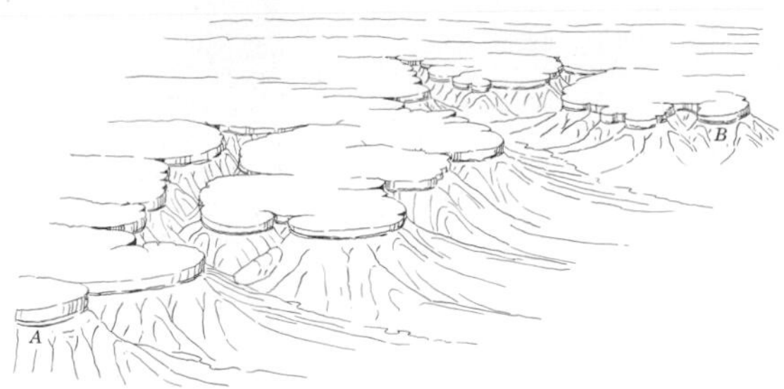


**FIGURE 28.3.** Principle of correlation of strata by direct continuity. The bed at *A* can be traced without interruption to a distant location, *B*.

## Fossils

Of all sources of information, perhaps the most helpful to the stratigrapher are *fossils,* those ancient plant and animal remains or impressions preserved by burial in sedimentary strata. About the year 1800 an English civil engineer and geologist, William Smith, observed that the fossils in strata exposed in canal excavations were of like species in all parts of a formation that could be proved to be one and the same bed by direct continuity. Fossil species in strata above or below were found to be distinctively different, but to occur consistently in the same order in widely separate localities. Once the order was established by direct observation, the fossils themselves became the evidence for age of strata elsewhere in the world. For example, the fossils in certain strata in Wales were studied early in the nineteenth century, and these rocks became established as the original standard for the *Cambrian Period* of geologic time (*Cambria* is the Latin name for Wales). One distinctive fossil animal, the *trilobite,* was abundant in the Cambrian seas, and consequently some of its various species serve as guide fossils for the Cambrian Period throughout the world.

The value of fossils in telling us the age of rock strata arises from the fact that all forms of plant and animal life have continually and systematically undergone changes with passage of time, a process termed *organic evolution.* If we have before us a complete, or nearly complete, description of past life forms as determined from fossils, and if we know the geologic age to which each fossil form belongs, it is often a simple matter to give the age of any sedimentary layer merely by extracting a few fossils from the rock and comparing them with the reference forms. A fossil species particularly well suited to determination of age of strata is known as an *index fossil.* Although this practice works well in many cases, there are frequent difficulties. For one thing, many strata contain no fossils, usually because the conditions under which the sediment was being deposited were unsuitable for maintenance or preservation of plant or animal life. A second problem is that some fossil organisms showed such slow changes that almost identical forms survived over a long span of geologic time.

The determination of age is much more convincing when an entire natural assemblage of animal forms, or *fauna,* is studied, because a distinctive combination of animal types is far less likely to be duplicated by chance than similarity of single types. Establishment of a working sequence of ages of index fossils and faunas had to be made in the first instance from observations of the positions of those fossils in the stratigraphic column. The principle of *succession of faunas*—which is simply that each formation has a different fauna (or flora) from that in the formations above it and below it—

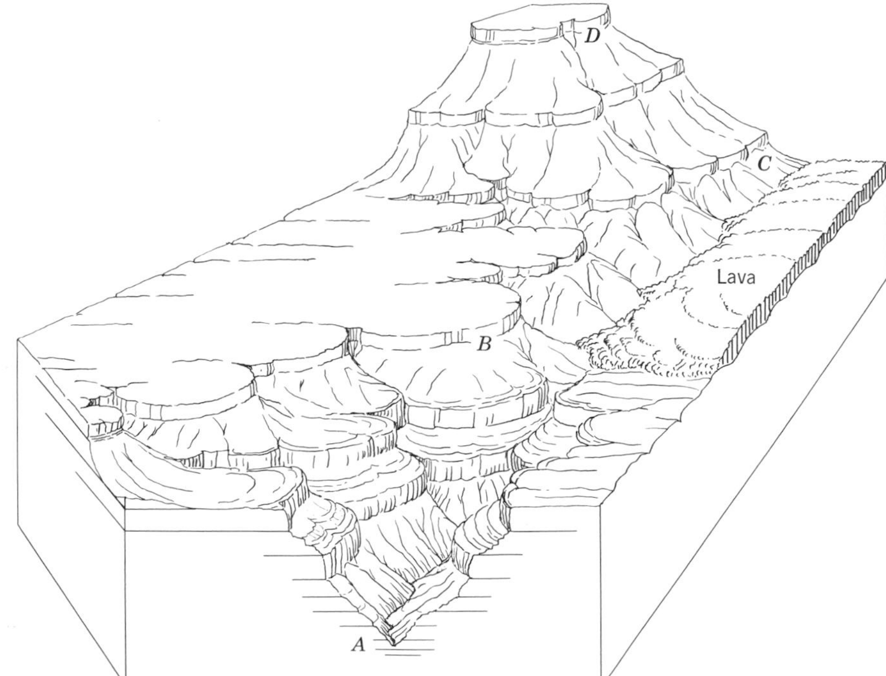


**FIGURE 28.4.** Combination of the principles of continuity and superposition in stratigraphic correlation. The order of succession from *A* to *B* is evident from direct superposition, from *B* to *C* by continuity, and from *C* to *D* by superposition.

**FIGURE 28.5.** This fossil trilobite from the Bright Angel shale of Grand Canyon establishes the formation as being of Cambrian age. The head is to the left. About 1½ times natural size. (Photograph by courtesy of the Department of the Interior, Grand Canyon National Park.)

**FIGURE 28.7.** This impression of a fern leaf was found on a bedding plane of fine-grained red shale of the Hermit formation in the walls of Grand Canyon. About natural size. (Photograph by courtesy of the Department of the Interior, Grand Canyon National Park.)

was proved by use of the principles of superposition and continuity.

In the Bright Angel formation of Grand Canyon many fossil trilobites have been found (Figure 28.5). Specimens can be seen in displays provided by the National Park Service at Grand Canyon. Because these trilobites belong to particular varieties resembling those found in the original Cambrian strata of Wales, the geologist can state that the two sets of strata are of almost the same age. Thus a jump of thousands of miles with no direct connection between the strata was bridged through the use of particular index fossils.

Examples of distinctive fossils of Grand Canyon strata include ancient representatives of the *gastropods* (snails) and *pelecypods* (clams) from the Kaibab limestone formation, comprising the canyon rim rocks (Figure 28.6). These fossils are now composed of silica, which replaced the original shells of carbonate matter. They were released from the enclosing rock by use of an acid bath, which dissolved the carbonate matrix and left the silica intact. Extremely minute shell details are preserved in these fossils, even though no original shell matter remains.

Figure 28.7 illustrates a Grand Canyon fossil of a different kind. This object is easily recognizable as a plant leaf, resembling that of a modern fern. What we see here is merely an impression of the leaf on the bedding plane of a fine-grained red shale, the *Hermit* formation, in the upper walls of the canyon. Many plant fossils consist of a thin layer of carbon representing the altered plant tissue. Some fossils consist only of the cavity in which the shell formerly existed, but from which the shell has been removed by action of circulating ground water.

World-wide studies by stratigraphers and paleontologists over the last 150 years have yielded an extremely

**FIGURE 28.6.** Fossils of the Kaibab strata of Permian age in the Grand Canyon. Left, a gastropod, whose shell had a coiled form somewhat resembling that of a modern snail. Right, a simple clam shell, not greatly unlike certain forms seen today. (Photographs by courtesy of N. D. Newell, American Museum of Natural History.)

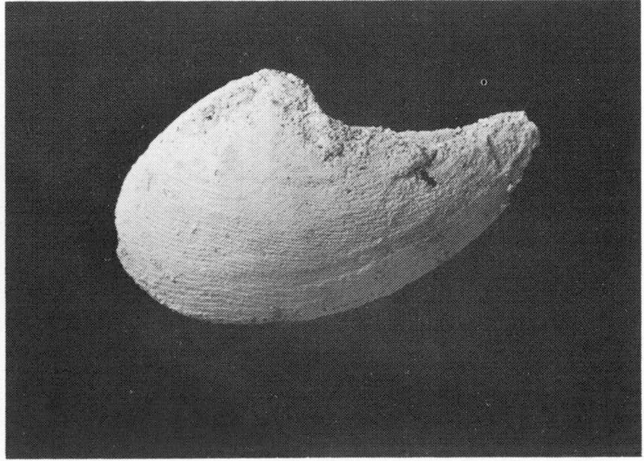

detailed and nearly complete reference table of the divisions and subdivisions of geologic time, together with index fossils for all ages from the Cambrian to the present.

## Unconformities in the Grand Canyon

Although the strata of Grand Canyon, Zion Canyon, and Bryce Canyon illustrate all major divisions of geologic time, the record is by no means complete. We know of many important gaps, and these can only be filled by going to other localities. Nevertheless, this region is a good one on which to base a preliminary review of the major divisions of geologic time.

Eras and periods have been introduced in Chapter 26. (Refer to Table 26.2 for names and radiometric ages.) The subdivisions of Precambrian time based on physical rock relationship and radiometric ages, have been reviewed in Chapter 26. We shall begin by examination of the Precambrian rocks of Grand Canyon. The inner lower gorge of Grand Canyon provides the geologist with a now-classic example of Precambrian rocks far from the Canadian Shield. Because of their unusual structure and arrangement these rocks allow us to develop further concepts in stratigraphic interpretation.

Precambrian rocks in Grand Canyon lie beneath the Cambrian Tapeats sandstone, the rim rock of the Tonto Platform which forms the brink of the Inner Gorge (Figure 28.1*A*). Looking down into the narrow Inner Gorge, one notices that the walls are here completely lacking in horizontal bedding planes, but instead have an extremely rough surface with sets of nearly vertical partings giving a grooved appearance to the rock walls. This rock, the *Vishnu schist,* is a metamorphosed sedimentary rock rich in quartz, mica, and hornblende. Here and there bands of coarse-grained diorite and granite cut through the schist. No fossils or indications of life have been found in the Vishnu schist, although this is not surprising for a highly metamorphosed rock of thls type. The Vishnu schist is dated as of early Precambrian age, older than 2.4 b.y. (Table 26.2). In the Grand Canyon region this lower Precambrian division is named *Archean.* The orogeny in which the Vishnu schist was altered and intruded is perhaps equivalent to the Kenoran orogeny.

If we follow along the rim of the Tonto Platform, continuing to study the walls of the Inner Gorge below us, a new geologic feature enters the picture (Figure 28.1*B*). A sloping wedge of tilted sedimentary strata appears between the Tapeats sandstone and the Vishnu schist. The wedge continues to thicken until several thousand feet of strata are exposed. This tilted sedimentary series, consisting of shales and sandstones and belonging to the *Grand Canyon Group,* includes several individual formations whose names are not important here. In this area the Grand Canyon Group is assigned to the *Algonkian* time division of the Precambrian, and is correlated with the late Precambrian rocks of the Canadian Shield. The age would perhaps be 1.7 b.y. or younger.

From the principle of superposition it is evident that the Algonkian sedimentary strata are younger than the Archean Vishnu schist, upon which they rest, but they are older than the Cambrian Tapeats formation, beneath which they lie. Thus, even without knowing their exact position in geologic time, it is fairly certain that the Algonkian rocks belong to the late or middle Precambrian. Some hemispherical masses (stromatolites) found in limy layers of the Algonkian strata represent deposits made by lime-secreting algae.

An explanation of the Algonkian rock wedge in Grand Canyon is given in the series of block diagrams of Figure 28.8. Geosynclinal sedimentary strata of early Precambrian age were crumpled and metamorphosed into the Vishnu schist by one of the earliest orogenies (Kenoran?) of which we have any record. Next, these mountains were reduced by erosion to a peneplain (*B*).

**FIGURE 28.8.** This set of block diagrams shows the manner in which the great wedges of Algonkian strata came into existence in the lower Grand Canyon. [After C. O. Dunbar (1960), *Historical Geology,* New York, John Wiley & Sons, p. 96, Figure 53.]

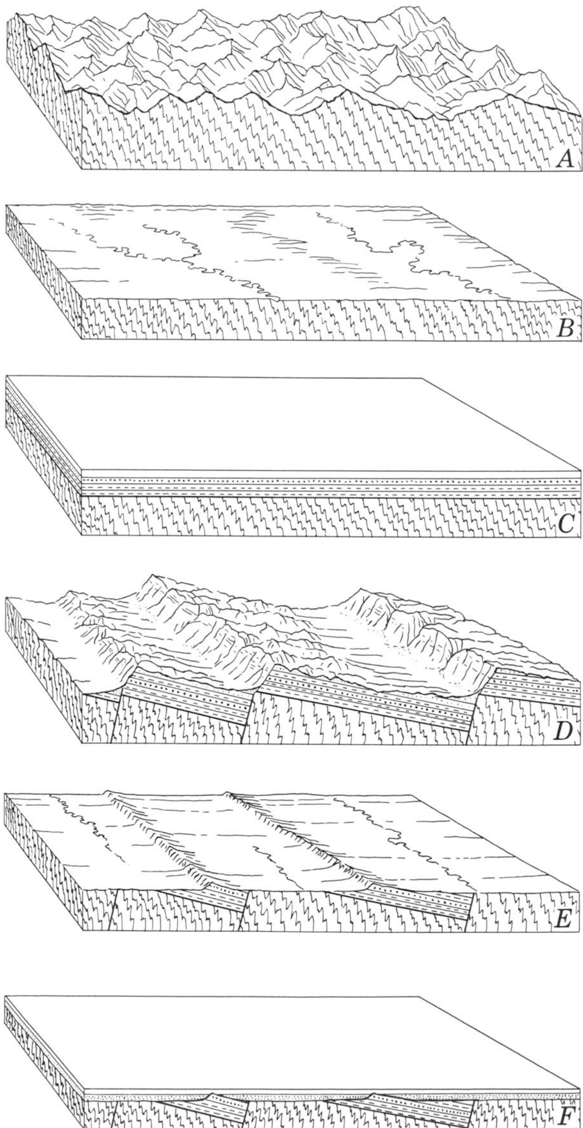

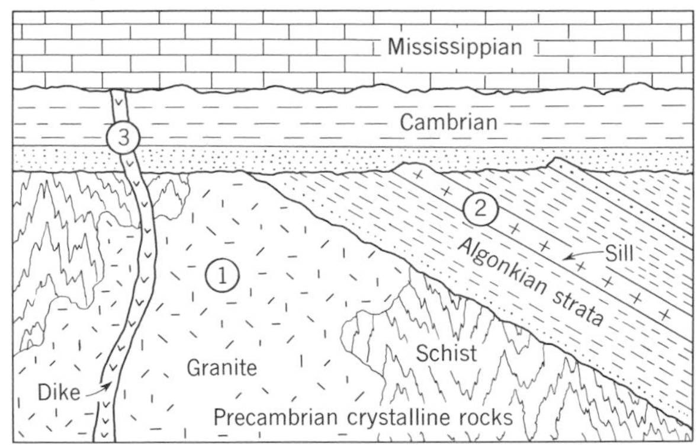


**FIGURE 28.9.** Radiometric dating of igneous bodies allows limiting ages to be established for the enclosing and overlying sedimentary strata.

After epeirogenic crustal sinking, a great thickness of Algonkian sediments was deposited in horizontal layers (*C*), but these layers were later tilted in great fault blocks (*D*). Again prolonged erosion removed the mountains, creating a second peneplain above which a few of the harder sandstone masses projected as ridges (*E*). This topography existed at the close of the Precambrian time. Again crustal sinking took place, causing the region to become a shallow sea, which received the Cambrian sediments (*F*). Hence in places the Cambrian layers rest directly upon the Vishnu schist, but in other places they rest upon a thick wedge of Algonkian strata.

The line of separation seen between the Algonkian beds and the Vishnu schist in the canyon wall is referred to as an *angular unconformity,* since the layers of one group are not parallel with but at an angle to the layers of the other group. The line is evidence not only of a vast erosion period that intervened between the formation of the two rock groups, but also of an orogeny that followed the development of the older rock group. A second unconformity exists in the line of separation between the Cambrian Tapeats sandstone and all of the Precambrian. This unconformity is shown in detail in Figure 28.1. Notice that a highly resistant formation, the Shinumo Quartzite, stood as a residual mass above the general level of the late Precambrian peneplain. It protrudes through the Tapeats sandstone, which was deposited around the high mass but did not cover it.

In few places on earth are unconformities displayed so clearly and on so grand a scale as in the bottom of Grand Canyon. The term *disconformity,* explained in connection with the line of separation of the Muav limestone and the Redwall limestone, refers to an erosion interval produced merely by simple vertical rising and sinking of the crust (epeirogenic movement) with no tilting or faulting intervening, only erosion. Thus in a disconformity the strata above and below the line are horizontal and parallel, whereas in an angular unconformity the rocks are discordant in attitude along the separation line.

Radiometric age determinations on intrusive and extrusive igneous bodies within a complex arrangement of sedimentary strata can be of great assistance in assigning dates to the rock groups lying above and below unconformities. Figure 28.9 shows a hypothetical example as it might be applied to a case resembling that of rocks of the inner Grand Canyon.

Suppose that radiometric ages are found for each of the three different igneous rock bodies, labeled 1, 2, and 3 in the diagram. If the igneous rock No. 1 has an age of 2.4 b.y., we can say that the adjacent schist, into which the igneous rock was intruded, is more than 2.4 b.y. old. We can also say that the tilted strata on the right are younger than 2.4 b.y. because they were deposited after igneous body No. 1 was leveled off by erosion.

Igneous body No. 2 is a sill which was intruded into the tilted strata, but whether before or after they were tilted can only be pure conjecture from the evidence shown. If the age of igneous rock No. 2 turned out to be 1.8 b.y., it would mean that the tilted strata are a least that old, perhaps much more, but not exceeding the 2.4 b.y. limit set by igneous rock No. 1.

If igneous rock No. 3, a thin vertical dike, yielded an age of 400 m.y., we would know that the Cambrian Period is older than 400 m.y., but that the Mississippian Period is younger than 400 m.y.

## Interpretation of sedimentary sequences

The stratigrapher is faced with the problem of interpreting the circumstances of deposition of sequences of strata. A student examining an exposure of strata might be prompted to ask a number of pertinent questions about the rocks before him: Were the sediments deposited on land, under exposure to the atmosphere, or were they deposited on the ocean floor? These alternatives present further questions: If the sediments are terrestrial, were they transported and deposited by streams or by wind? If marine, are they part of the body of a river delta or were they deposited in the shallow quiet water of a lagoon or in the moderately deep water of a subsiding geosynclinal basin? The answers to such questions come from the nature of the rock and its structures (lithologic information) and from the contained fossils, when any are present (paleontological information). We shall first take up some stratigraphic principles, then apply them to interpretation of strata of the Colorado Plateau region as seen in Grand Canyon, Zion Canyon, and Bryce Canyon.

## Environments of sediment deposition

It has been found meaningful to assign environments of sediment deposition to three major groups: marine, terrestrial, and littoral. Figure 28.10 is a schematic cross section to illustrate the relationships and subdivisions of these environments.

The *marine environment* includes all ocean water and bottom lying below the level of low tide. The *terrestrial environment* includes all land surfaces lying above high-tide level, but we can assume that inland basins below sea level and cut off from ocean waters would be also terrestrial. The *littoral environment* lies in the *intertidal zone* between high and low tide levels and is thus al-

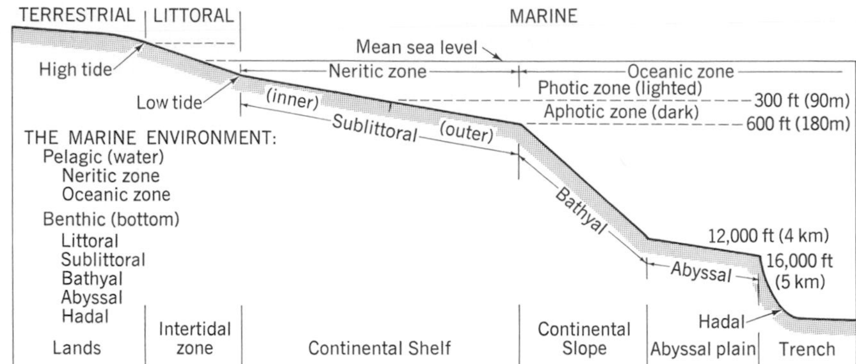


ternately exposed to the atmosphere and covered by sea water.

The marine environment is further broken down into the mass of water itself (*pelagic* body) and the bottom (*benthic* layer). We have encountered the term "pelagic" in the discussion of deep-sea sediments in Chapter 24. Obviously, sediments do not accumulate in the pelagic body, but it is the living space of floating organisms (plankton) and swimming animals (nekton) which settle to the bottom to become part of the sediment. We have seen that detrital mineral particles can also settle through the water to form bottom sediment. In terms of the pelagic body, or water mass, there are two environmental divisions: the *neritic zone,* shallower than 600 ft (180 m), and the *oceanic zone,* deeper than that level.

The benthic layer, which is the site of sediment accumulation, as well as the home of organisms dwelling on the bottom (*benthos*), is subdivided into depth zones as follows (Figure 28.11):

*Littoral:* Intertidal zone (Littoral environment)
*Sublittoral:* Low tide to —600 ft (—180 m); continental shelf and shallow epicontinental sea.
*Inner sublittoral:* Low tide to about —300 ft (—90 m); in the photic (lighted) zone.
*Outer sublittoral:* From —300 ft (—90 m) to —600 ft (—180 m); in the aphotic (dark) zone.
*Bathyal:* Continental slope and continental rise from —600 ft (—180 m) to about —12,000 ft (—4 km).
*Abyssal:* Abyssal plains and abyssal hills in the range from —12,000 ft (—4 km) to —16,000 ft (—5 km).
*Hadal:* Trenches below —16,000 ft (—5 km).

We shall not discuss further the sedimentation in the bathyal, abyssal, and hadal bottom environments, as these were covered in Chapter 24. It is with the shallower zones, sublittoral and littoral, that continental stratigraphy is principally concerned in the interpretation of the marine sediments of the continents. While the geosynclines subsided to great depths during the process of sediment accumulation, their bottom environments generally remained in the sublittoral depth range.

Terrestrial environments are of a wide variety of types. First, there are *aquatic* environments, consisting of lakes and ponds (*lacustrine* environment), streams (*fluvial* environments), and fresh-water marshes and swamps.

**FIGURE 28.11.** The Redwall cliffs in Grand Canyon, showing characteristic alcove forms. The sheer wall is 600 ft (180 m) high. The Bright Angel formation forms the lower slopes. [Drawing by H. H. Nichols, from C. E. Dutton (1882), *Tertiary History of the Grand Canyon District,* Washington, D.C., U.S. Govt. Printing Office, Plate 41.]

Many forms of stream deposits are aqueous environments only at the time of deposition, but are exposed to the atmosphere most of the time—for example, floodplains, alluvial fans, and parts of deltas. Nonaquatic environments of sediment deposition are defined in terms of processes of transportation other than flowing water. These include the subglacial zone of deposition and surfaces of accumulation of wind transported sand and silt. A unique terrestrial environment of deposition is the playa (Chapter 22) in which evaporites accumulate. This zone is alternately flooded by water and exposed to evaporation. The nature of terrestrial environments will be fully appreciated only by a study of the geomorphic and hydrologic processes (Chapters 32 through 41).

## Rock units

In earlier pages the distinctive rock units of Paleozoic age in Grand Canyon were designated as *formations.* We shall now inquire further into the matter of designating rock units in sequences of sedimentary strata. We have seen that the rock unit designated as a *formation* has a distinctive set of physical properties maintained fairly uniformly from bottom to top and is clearly set off from higher and lower formations exhibiting different sets of physical properties. By physical properties are meant *lithologic* properties, which encompass the variety or varieties of sedimentary rock along with their bedding structures.

Grand Canyon offers at least four good examples of formations that consist essentially of a single rock type throughout the unit. The Tapeats formation of Cambrian age consists for the most part of a hard massive sandstone of chocolate color and with a thickness of about 300 ft (90 m) (Figure 28.1*A*). Although there are minor departures from this lithology, the Tapeats formation is clearly identifiable and is sharply set off from the overlying Bright Angel formation, which is largely a soft shale. A second example is the Redwall formation, a single massive layer of dense bluish-gray crystalline limestone about 650 ft (200 m) thick (Figure 28.11). This formation, of Mississippian age, makes a sheer wall wherever it is exposed and can be crossed by foot trail at very few places in the entire Grand Canyon. A third example is the Hermit formation, exposed high in the canyon sequence (Figure 28.1). This rock unit consists of soft red shale and shaly sandstone and is about 400 ft (120 m) thick. True, close examination of the Hermit formation will reveal alternate layerings of shale and sandstone, but the over-all appearance is one of lithologic uniformity. A fourth example is the Coconino formation, a striking creamy-white sandstone in an apparently unbroken layer 330 ft (100 m) thick, forming a sheer wall a short distance below the rim of Grand Canyon. (Figure 28.1*D* and Figure 28.19).

Some formations consist of two, three, or four distinctively different rock types in relatively thin beds arranged in alternate or irregular succession throughout the formation. In Grand Canyon an example is the Bright Angel formation of Cambrian age exposed in gentle slopes rising from the Tonto platform (Figure 28.12). Throughout its 350-ft (105-m) thickness, this formation is mostly a soft mica-rich greenish shale, but there are a number of sandstone beds from 1 to 3 ft (0.3 to 0.9 m) thick spaced at intervals throughout the shale. Near the middle of the formation are three 10-ft (3-m) beds of rusty-brown dolomite separated by shale. Here is a formation containing three lithologies, one making up the bulk of the formation, the other two interspersed in thin layers. Yet, in contrast to the massive sandstone and limestone formations below and above, the Bright Angel formation is distinctive and unambiguous.

Within a formation it is often desirable to single out a rock unit of distinctive properties as a *member.* For example, the three dolomite beds in the middle of the Bright Angel formation are so distinctive as to warrant designation as a member (Figure 28.12).

Two or more formations together can be recognized as a *group.* An example is the *Tonto group* consisting of three Cambrian formations, the Tapeats, Bright Angel, and Muav (Figure 28.1). Notice that this group is bounded below by an unconformity and above by a disconformity. The Tonto group, as we have shown in Figure 28.2, is a more-or-less continuous succession of marine deposits representing one unbroken time

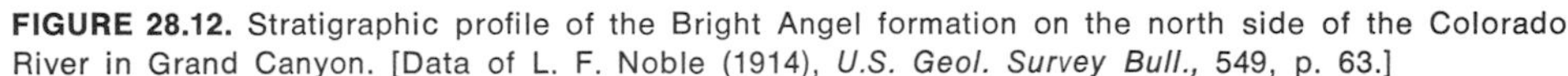
**FIGURE 28.12.** Stratigraphic profile of the Bright Angel formation on the north side of the Colorado River in Grand Canyon. [Data of L. F. Noble (1914), *U.S. Geol. Survey Bull.,* 549, p. 63.]

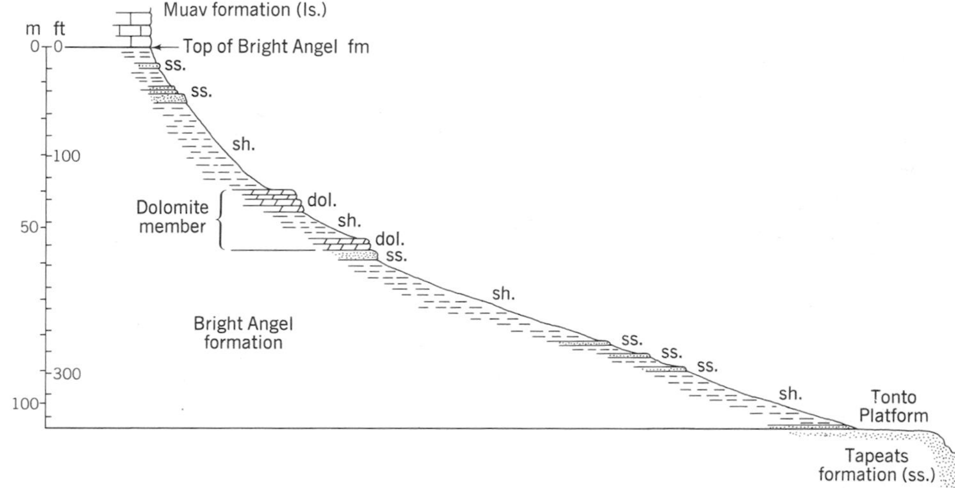

period and set off by important episodes of crustal activity.

## Biostratigraphic units

We have seen that a fauna, which is a distinctive assemblage of fossil species, is useful in correlating strata from place to place. It is therefore desirable in some instances to define a unit of strata in terms of the fossils alone, and without regard to the lithologic characteristics of those strata. So defined, the strata comprise a *biostratigraphic unit.* A biostratigraphic unit distinguished by a particular fossil species or a particular fossil fauna is referred to as a *zone.*

The Cambrian Bright Angel formation of Grand Canyon provides a fine example of a *faunal zone.* It can be seen on the Bright Angel Trail about one-quarter of a mile north of Indian Gardens in Bright Angel Canyon. This distinctive faunal zone is so narrow in vertical extent that it is essentially restricted to a single *horizon.* Two distinctive fossils in this horizon are trilobite species named *Glossopleura mckeei* and *Alokistocare althea* (Figure 28.13 *A* and *B*)—the first name refers to the genus, the second name to the species. In addition, the fauna consists of a third trilobite, *Anoria tontoensis,* a cystid (similar to a "sea lily") named *Eocrinus multibrachiatus,* a conical-shelled gastropod (snail), *Hyolithes sp.* ("sp." means "no specific name assigned"), and a brachiopod, *Lingulella mckeei.* Brachiopods, now largely extinct, somewhat resembled modern clams. The last three fossils are illustrated in Figure 28.13 *C, D,* and *E.* The names and photographs of these fossils are given here to provide a real example

**FIGURE 28.13.** Representative specimens of fossils of the *Glossopleura-Alokistocare* fauna of the Cambrian strata of Grand Canyon. Length of bar is 1 cm (0.4 in.). (A) *Glossopleura mckeei,* a trilobite. (B) *Alokistocare althea,* a trilobite. (C) *Eocrinus multibrachiatus,* a crinoid. (D) *Lingulella mckeei,* a brachiopod. (*E*) *Hyolithes sp.,* a gastropod. [Photographs from C. E. Resser (1945), Washington, D.C., Carnegie Inst. of Washington, Publication 563, Part II, Plates 16, 18, 19, 21, and 22.]

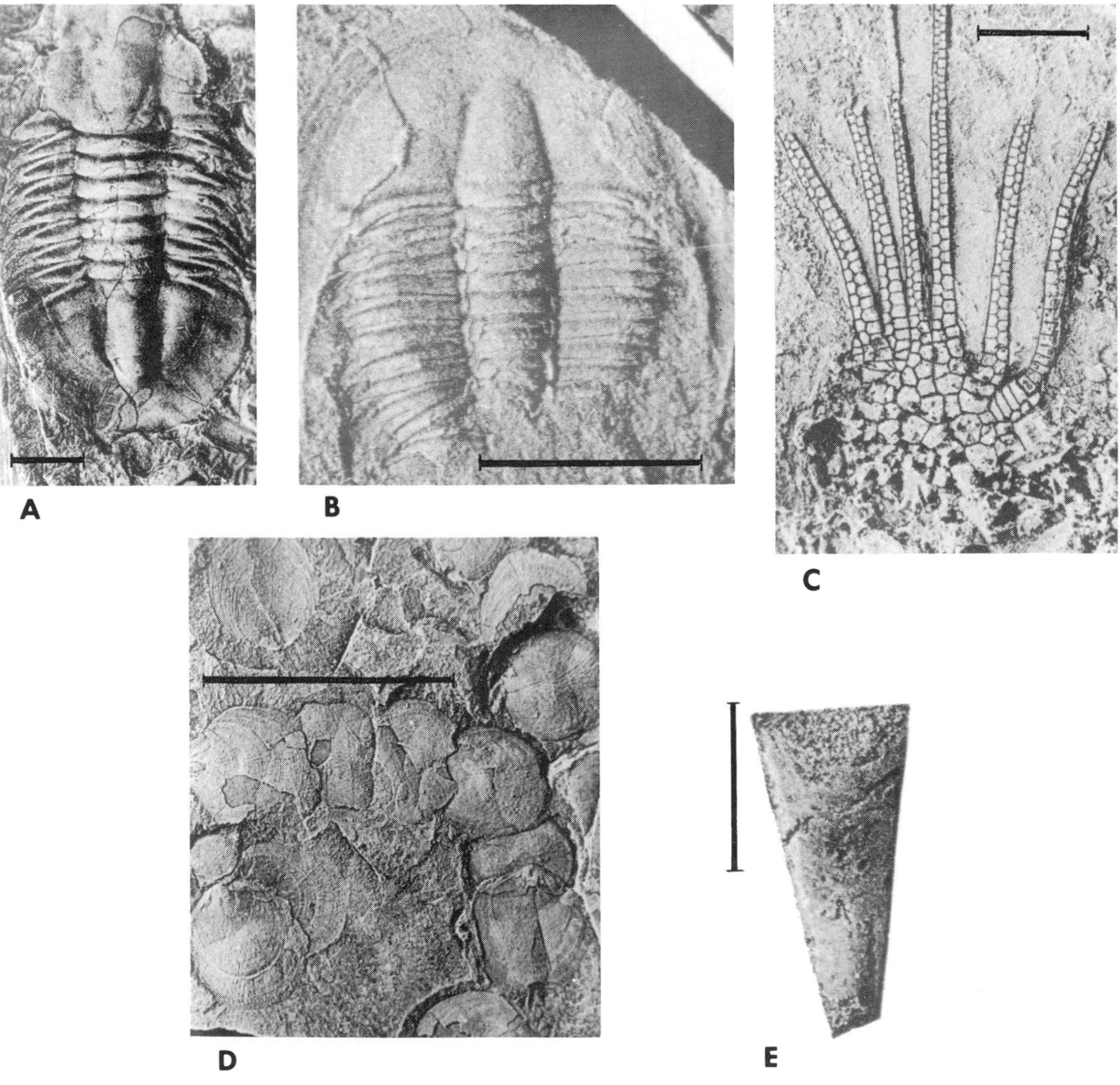

of the working procedures of the stratigrapher. The *Glossopleura-Alokistocare* faunal zone can be traced in exposures of the Bright Angel formation for a horizontal distance of almost 180 mi (290 km) across northern Arizona. Wherever this zone is located it will be found to contain the same species. The same fauna is not, however, duplicated above or below this zone.

The thin faunal zone we have examined in detail is interpreted as having been deposited at very nearly the same time throughout its 180-mi extent. If this interpretation is valid, the horizon serves to synchronize the sequence of deposition over a large area. One might describe this horizon as a "time line" or, in formal terms, an *isochron* ("iso," same, plus "chron," time). In three dimensions, the faunal horizon would define a "time plane," or an *isochronous surface.*

## Regional variations in lithology and thickness

So far, we have limited our interpretation of a sedimentary sequence to the column of beds exposed at one locality. The stratigrapher conducts his investigation by moving about from place to place, examining the column of strata of a given age group wherever it is well exposed. Each lithologic unit is carefully measured and described. Fossils, if present, are collected and identified. Samples of rock may be taken for laboratory study, including microscopic examination and chemical analysis. Data are plotted to scale in a narrow vertical column, known as a *stratigraphic column.* A number of such columns obtained on a line of cross-country traverse are placed side by side, spaced to horizontal scale. Connecting lines are drawn to correlate lithologic units (formations and members) and faunal zones.

Figure 28.14 is an assemblage of stratigraphic columns for the Cambrian of northern Arizona from the Grand Wash Cliffs on the west to the Little Colorado River on the east. Localities follow the winding course of Grand Canyon, since the Cambrian is not exposed elsewhere. Lithologic units are shown by conventional patterns, explained in the accompanying key. Dashed lines connect corresponding lithologic contacts. Because present-day elevation of the land has no particular

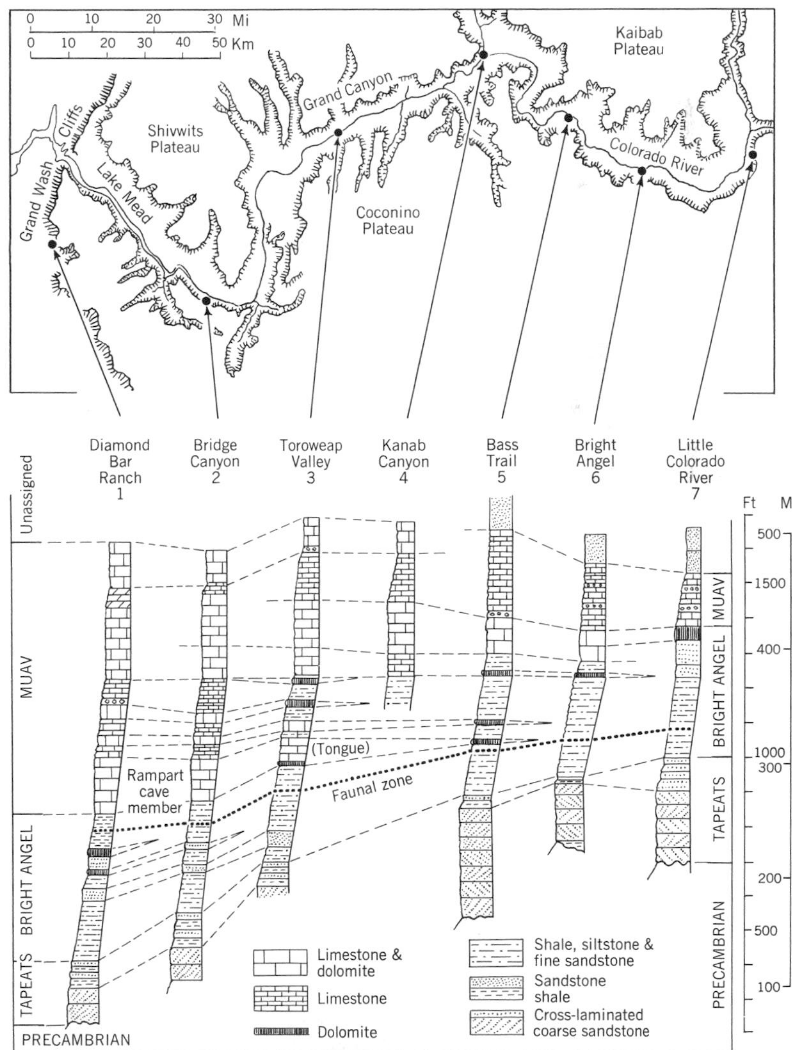


**FIGURE 28.14.** Columnar stratigraphic sections and index map of Cambrian formations of the Grand Canyon. [Modified and simplified from E. D. McKee (1945), *Cambrian History of the Grand Canyon Region,* Washington, D.C., Carnegie Inst. of Washington, Publication 563, Part I, p. 18, Figure 2A, and p. 19, Figure 2B.]

significance so far as Cambrian time is concerned, an arbitrary horizon line has been established at a point in the middle of the Muav formation. The sections are then scaled up and down from this arbitrary zero reference line. It would be equally feasible to use the top of the Muav formation as the zero reference line, except that an erosional disconformity exists there and we do not know what thicknesses of Cambrian strata were formerly present above that surface.

In interpreting the stratigraphic sections of Figure 28.14, we notice several points of interest. First, the total thickness of the Cambrian increases toward the west. Thickening westward is brought about in a rather complex manner. We do not find that each lithologic unit found at Grand Canyon merely thickens proportionately toward the west while maintaining its lithologic identity. To give one exception, new lithologic units appear in the section, and these tend to thicken westward. An example is the Rampart Cave member. In the Bass Trail section this member is represented by only a thin dolomite bed in the middle of the Bright Angel shale. It is absent in the Bright Angel section, about 10 mi (16 km) to the east. Toward the west this dolomite bed thickens and changes in composition from a rusty-brown dolomite to a mottled limestone with dolomite beds. Along the Grand Wash Cliffs still farther west the Rampart Cave member is a massive unit about 180 ft (85 m) thick. This unit is described as a *tongue.* It is interpreted to mean that accumulation of carbonate sediment was abundant in the western part of the region, diminished progressively eastward, and ceased at a point near what is now the eastern part of Grand Canyon. It is also obvious that shale strata assigned to the upper half of the Bright Angel formation in the eastern part of the traverse are correlated in time with carbonate strata assigned to the Muav formation in the western end of the traverse. Evidently the formations defined on the basis of lithology are not everywhere of the same age. Notice that the line representing the Glossopleura-Alokistocare faunal zone starts at the west near the top of the Bright Angel formation, but ends up at the east near the bottom of that formation.

## Time units and the concept of facies change

Stratigraphic interpretation proves to be a far more complex process than one might have gathered from reading William Smith's account of lower Paleozoic strata in England. Yet this very complexity, if it can be unraveled satisfactorily, yields a meaningful history of changes in depositional sites and in sediment types and thicknesses. Let us pursue the Cambrian stratigraphy of Northern Arizona by a change of approach. The measured sections of Cambrian strata shown in Figure 28.14 can be reconstituted into a schematic diagram in which horizontal lines represent planes of equal time or isochronous surfaces (Figure 28.15). Actual thickness of units is disregarded in this representation. Cover the diagram with a sheet of paper. Now move the paper gradually up, keeping the edge horizontal and uncovering the diagram from the bottom upwards. As this is done, the sequence of deposition emerges to view. A series of connected dots and triangles on the diagram represents the formation boundaries.

Starting with the base of the Tapeats sandstone, notice that deposition begins in the west and spreads eastward up the undulating slope of the erosional surface on the Precambrian rocks beneath. Here we see *transgression* of strata, caused by a rising sea level encroaching upon a landmass (or sinking landmass gradually becoming submerged beneath an ocean of fixed sea level). At certain points during the transgression the formation boundary makes an abrupt reverse inflection, showing a temporary reversal of the transgression. The reverse trend is known as *regression.* Notice, also, that as deposition of Tapeats sandstone progresses eastward it is accompanied in the west by deposition of shale of the lower Bright Angel formation.

Progressing further up the diagram, carbonate deposition begins first at the west end of the section, transgressing eastward for a time, then regressing to the west to leave a tongue of limestone and dolomite. Several such tongues are recorded. Tongues of shale extend westward between the dolomite tongues. The gross pattern is known as *intertonguing.* Finally, however, the transgression brought a continuous environmen of carbonate deposition to this region and the remainder of the accumulation is solidly limestone and dolomite.

In summary, the Grand Canyon region in the first part of the Cambrian period was a landmass exposed to erosion. Gradually the landmass subsided, beginning first in the west. The sea invaded from the west, gradually submerging the land. Starting in early Cambrian time the shoreline thus crossed the region from west to east and by late middle Cambrian time lay somewhere far to the east of this region. As the shoreline encroached upon the land sand deposition accompanied it, followed to seaward by clay and silt deposition, and still farther out by carbonate sediment deposition. Evidently three depositional environments are represented in the time sequence at any given geographical location. We can assume that the environment was controlled by water depth and by distance from land.

The stratigrapher has developed a method of expressing the general appearance, composition, and depositional environment of a rock unit by means of a single designation, known as *facies.* As defined in a dictionary, the word "facies" means "general appearance" (it comes from the Latin word for "face"). To the stratigrapher, facies takes on a more specialized meaning and must be narrowed down to one of a number of reference frames. For example, facies relating to the gross physical qualities of rocks within a unit is known as *lithofacies.* In the case of the Cambrian strata of Grand Canyon, there are at least three distinct lithofacies: (1) a near-shore sand facies of the Tapeats formation, (2) an offshore silt-clay facies represented by the Bright Angel shales, and (3) a carbonate facies represented by the Muav formation and its tongues. *Biofacies* is a general description of the fauna assemblage within strata and can be independent of lithology.

Above the time-section in Figure 28.15 are three maps showing three stages in the Cambrian sedimentation. The three principal facies are shown by line

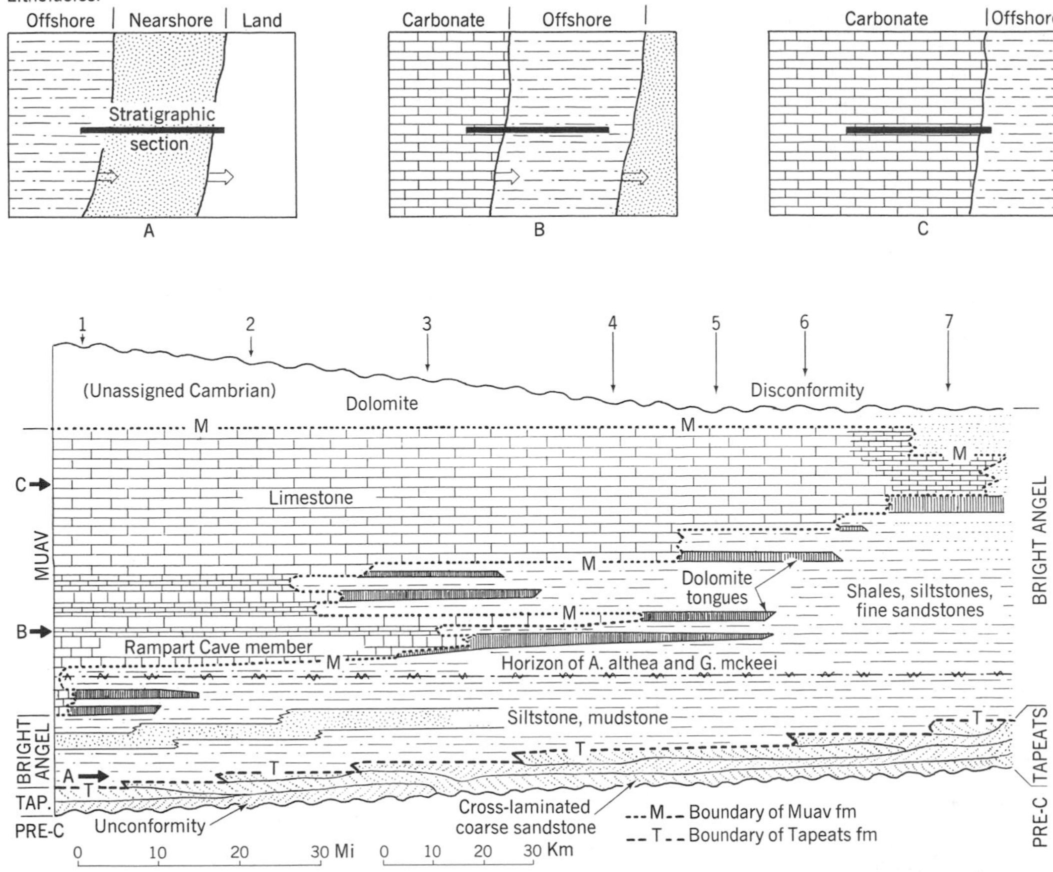


**FIGURE 28.15.** Lithofacies–time diagram of the same Cambrian stratigraphic sequence shown in Figure 28.14. Numbers refer to locations of stratigraphic sections shown in Figure 28.14. Horizontal lines represent isochrones. Schematic lithofacies maps above apply to time lines marked *A, B,* and *C* on lower diagram. [Lower diagram modified from E. D. McKee (1945), *Cambrian History of the Grand Canyon Region,* Washington, D.C., Carnegie Inst. of Washington, Publication 563, Part I, p. 14, Figure 1.]

patterns. Reconstructions of this kind are known as *paleogeographic maps.* They supplement the stratigraphic cross-sections by giving area relationships, including shorelines, lands, shallow seas, and troughs. (See Figure 30.19.)

## Paleozoic environments in the Grand Canyon region

Continuing up the walls of Grand Canyon, let us try to interpret certain of the prominent lithologic units in terms of environments of deposition.

Ordovician and Silurian strata are missing from the eastern Grand Canyon region and it is supposed that a low stable land mass existed here throughout those two periods. Events of great geological importance, including geosynclinal deposition and orogeny, occurred in both eastern and western North America during the Ordovician and Silurian periods, but left no record in the Grand Canyon region. The Devonian Period is represented by the Temple Butte Formation, a dolomite rock (Figure 28.1). It is about 100 ft (30 m) thick in eastern Grand Canyon but thickens greatly westward. We can interpret this dolomite as a carbonate deposit in shallow water of a sea that invaded from the west, then retreated to expose the land and permit partial removal of the formation by erosion.

The Redwall formation of Mississippian age appears to be a single massive unit, but upon close study it has proved to consist of four members. The lower half of the Redwall in eastern Grand Canyon is composed of dolomite, the upper half of limestone. During Mississippian time the sea invaded the Grand Canyon region three times. Probably additional limestones were deposited, above what is now the top of the formation, but were removed by later erosion. The Redwall formation has yielded many fossils of marine origin, including shellfish and corals.

Moving up to a position above the Redwall cliff in Grand Canyon we come to a series of red sandstones with red shale beds intervening, forming a series of steps in the canyon wall (Figure 28.16). These rocks comprise the Supai formation, of Pennsylvanian and

**FIGURE 28.16.** Panoramic drawing, by the artist W. H. Holmes, looking south across Grand Canyon from Point Sublime. *S,* Supai; *R,* Redwall; *B,* Bright Angel; *T,* Tapeats; *V,* Vishnu. [From C. E. Dutton (1882), *Tertiary History of the Grand Canyon District,* Washington, D.C., U.S. Govt. Printing Office, Plate 29.]

Permian age. Obviously, we are encountering a quite different environment of sedimentation from any recorded in older Paleozoic strata of the canyon. These strata are *red beds* and were particularly widespread near the close of the Paleozoic Era. In the total thickness of about 700 ft (210 m), the Supai formation includes three major cliffs of sandstone. Although buff-colored on a freshly broken surface, these sandstones are stained red by iron oxides washed down from red shales above. A particularly interesting sedimentary structure within the sandstones is represented by innumerable sloping laminations, constituting *crossbedding* (Figure 28.17). Various types of crossbedding exist, each caused by a different mechanism of deposition (Figure 28.18). The particular types of crossbedding in the Supai sandstones indicate sand transport by flowing water in stream channels crossing a low delta surface and depositing the sediment in shallow water at the outer delta margins. (The formation and structure of a delta are shown in Figures 35.28 and 35.30.) From the directions of down-slope (dip) of the laminations within the crossbedding it has been ascertained that streams coming from a landmass in southern Utah carried sediment southward and westward to form a large delta in the Grand Canyon region. At times a deepening of the water allowed deposition of red muds instead of stream-bed sands, accounting for the red shale layers found today between the crossbedded

**FIGURE 28.17.** Large-scale tabular planar cross-bedding in the Supai formation. Walapai trail to Havasu Canyon, Arizona. (Photograph by Edwin D. McKee.)

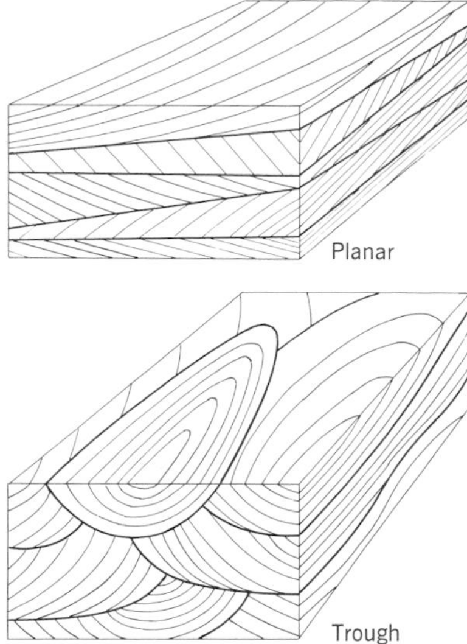


**FIGURE 28.18.** Two varieties of cross-lamination. The heavy line at the base of each set of laminations represents a surface of erosion truncating older sets of laminations beneath. Upper block shows planar lamination, seen in dune deposits. Lower block shows trough variety typical of streambed deposits. [After E. D. McKee, and G. W. Weir (1953), *Geol. Soc. Amer., Bull.*, 64, p. 387, Figure 2.]

**FIGURE 28.19.** Large-scale cross-laminations in the Coconino formation of Grand Canyon. *Above:* Cliff of Coconino sandstone, about 300 ft (90 m) high. West wall of Hermit Basin in Grand Canyon. *Below:* Detail of wedge-planar cross laminations, Kaibab Trail, Grand Canyon. (Photographs by Edwin D. McKee.)

sandstone layers. The red color of the muds is considered by some investigators to indicate an arid climate prevailing over the source area. Another point of evidence favoring interpretation of the Supai formation as an ancient delta lies in the almost complete absence of any fossils in the red beds. Organisms would not be expected to live in turbid water on a bottom constantly receiving muddy sediment or thick sands.

Above the Supai formation lies the Hermit shale, mentioned in earlier paragraphs. This formation is also of early Permian age and was probably deposited shortly after the upper part of the Supai formation under much the same conditions, although the Hermit formation lacks sandstones. Throughout the red shales and siltstones of the Hermit formation are found impressions of ferns (Figure 28.7). These land plants were probably carried from nearby areas as fragments in streams bringing the sediment to the delta.

A sharp change in depositional environment is signaled by the Coconino formation, of Permian age, which overlies the Supai and Hermit red beds. A pure, well-sorted, almost white sandstone makes up the entire Coconino formation, which appears as a sheer wall about 300 ft (90 m) high (Figure 28.1*D*). The Coconino formation exhibits crossbedding throughout, but in contrast to the small size of the laminations in the Supai sandstones those of the Coconino formation are on a huge scale (Figure 28.19). Individual laminations are up to 60 or 70 ft (18 to 20 m) in length and are inclined at angles up to 34° from the horizontal. Clearly, these laminations indicate that the Coconino formation consists of lithified sand dunes. These dunes must have accumulated on land under desert conditions. Analysis of directions of dip of the laminations shows that winds blew from north to south. On some of the sloping lamination surfaces have been found tracks of vertebrate animals, probably reptiles, giving further evidence of a terrestrial environment. Similar tracks will be found in large numbers today on the steep lee slopes of modern dunes. In early Permian time winds blowing over exposed sand deposits in an area of what is now Utah carried large quantities of sand southward into a low flat basin which existed in the Grand Canyon region. However, this terrestrial sedimentation was terminated by a crustal subsidence and the sea again invaded the region.

Rim rocks of the Grand Canyon are of Permian age and consist of two carbonate units, the Toroweap formation and the Kaibab formation (Figure 28.1). We shall treat the two formations together, as they are quite similar and represent similar environments of deposition. Beds of limestone, chert, sandy limestone, dolomitic limestone, and sandstone make up much of these formations. There are also some red beds and gypsum layers. The calcium carbonate layers contain many marine fossils, including brachiopods, corals, sponges, and bryozoans. These rocks represent many transgressions and regressions in which environments changed repeatedly from shallow marine water to shallow coastal lagoons with high salt concentrations. Silica was probably brought in solution to the coastal

**FIGURE 28.20.** This butte of Moenkopi shale, capped by Shinarump conglomerate, is an erosional outlier of the Chocolate Cliffs near the Arizona-Utah border. North is to the left. [Drawing by W. H. Holmes, from C. E. Dutton (1882), *Tertiary History of the Grand Canyon District,* Washington, D.C., U.S. Govt. Printing Office, Plate 12.]

waters by streams, which also carried muds and sands. Fossils are of brackish-water types (Figure 28.6) as well as normal marine types.

## Mesozoic environments of the Grand Canyon region

Leaving the rim of Grand Canyon, one finds a vast undulating plateau representing the exposed upper surface of the Kaibab formation. In this semiarid climate limestone is a highly resistant rock and forms elevated plateaus and mesas. A small remnant of younger strata (escaping erosional removal by merest chance) is found close to the South Rim of Grand Canyon. Named Red Butte, this remnant takes us into the Triassic Period, which is the oldest of the three Mesozoic periods (Figure 28.1). Many miles back from the rim of Grand Canyon, the Triassic rocks form a continuous low cliff line, particularly conspicuous to the north of the canyon, where it is known as the Chocolate Cliffs (Figure 28.20). Exposures of the complete Triassic section are crossed by the main highway connecting Grand Canyon with Zion Canyon, in the vicinity of the Utah-Arizona boundary. The relationship of Mesozoic rocks to Paleozoic rocks is shown in Figure 28.21.

The Chocolate cliffs consist of two Triassic formations: lowermost is the Moenkopi formation, largely of reddish-brown shales, siltstones, and thin sandstones, with a total thickness of about 800 ft (240 m). This weak rock, which forms a slope, is topped by the Shinarump formation, a thin hard conglomerate layer standing out as a sharp rim. The Moenkopi formation contains a variety of interesting features. Siltstones in thin slabs are in many places beautifully ripplemarked (Figure 28.22). This kind of ripple mark is made by water currents and suggests the action of shallow tidal waters. The same slab has *shrinkage cracks,* suggesting exposure to the air, perhaps at low tide. Other slabs show *rain*

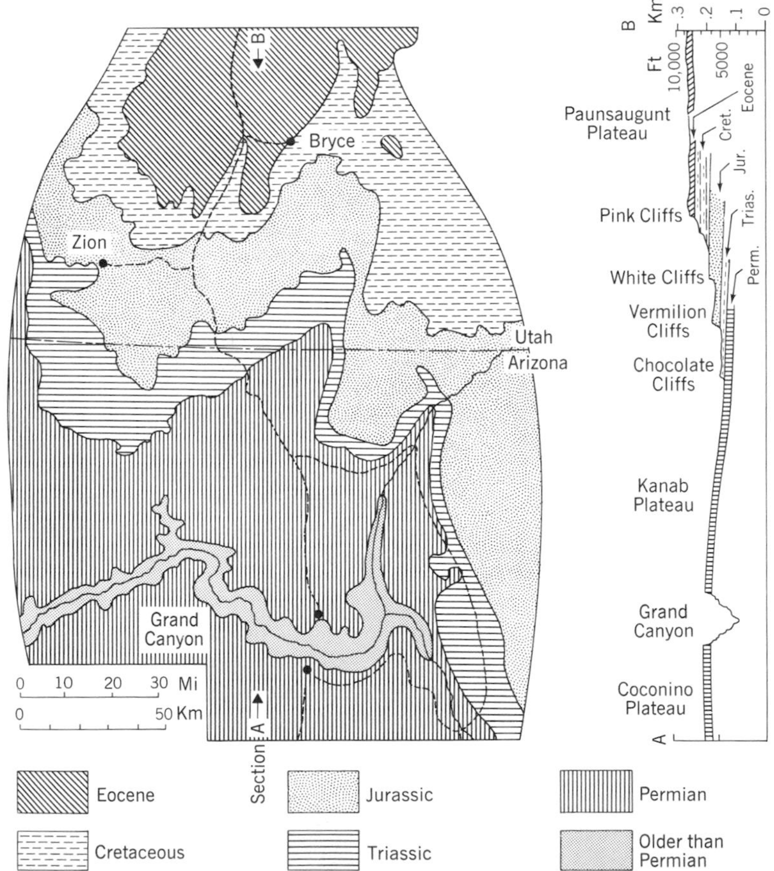


**FIGURE 28.21.** Simplified geologic map and structure section of the Grand Canyon–Zion Canyon–Bryce Canyon region of Arizona and Utah.

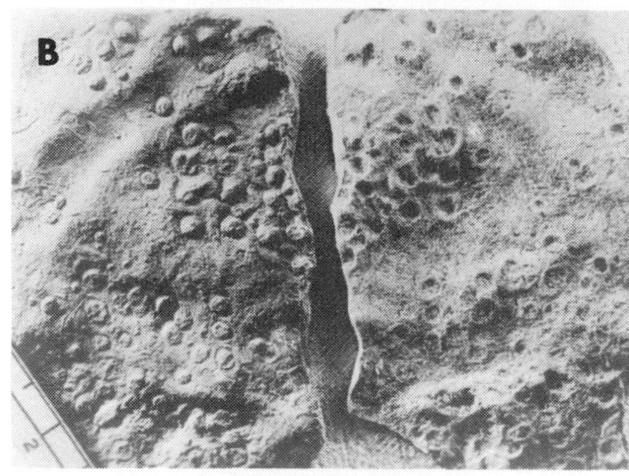

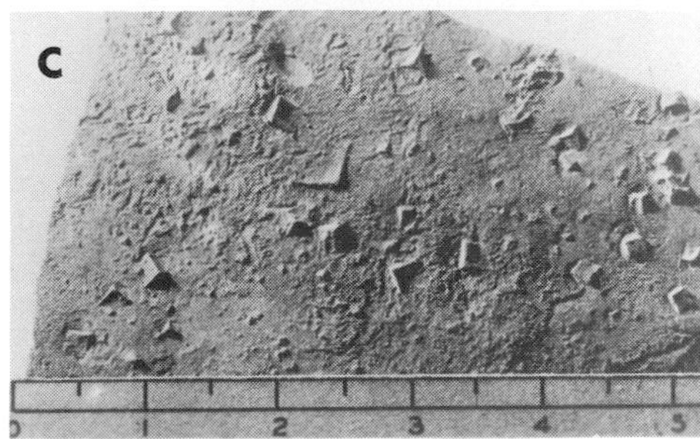

**FIGURE 28.22.** Sedimentary bedding-plane structures of the Moenkopi formation. Scales in inches. (A) Ripple marks. (B) Rain pits and casts. Slab on left is upside down. (C) Casts of halite crystals. [Photographs by E. D. McKee (1954), *Geol. Soc. Amer. Memoir,* 61, Plates 6 and 10.]

*pits,* the fossilized impressions of rain drops (Figure 28.22 *B*). There are also slabs with casts of salt crystals, suggesting evaporation of concentrated brine in shallow tidal lagoons. It is evident that at least some parts of the Moenkopi formation were deposited in an intertidal zone (littoral environment) on mudflats alternately covered by shallow water and exposed to a dry atmosphere. Skulls and bones of amphibians are found in these rocks, as well as reptile tracks. These fossil evidences also support the interpretation of partial exposure of mudflats at low water. Perhaps some of the deposits are actually those of broad river floodplains. All of the red mud and sand is considered to have been brought to the coastal belt of deposition from highland sources to the east in what is now Colorado and New Mexico. Some beds of marine limestone extend as a tongue into the Moenkopi red beds from the west, indicating a temporary transgression of a carbonate facies from a deeper sea to the west. Many gypsum beds are also present, suggestive of times of evaporation in broad shallow playas. Evidences thus point to aridity of climate, or at least to a climate having an alternate dry and wet season.

The Shinarump conglomerate, which is the basal part of the Chinle formation, is a hard conglomerate capping the weak Moenkopi beds. It is an interesting bed to interpret—from less than a foot to 40-ft (12-m) thick, it contains well-rounded gravels, obviously transported a long distance in turbulent streams, and it rests upon an erosion surface scored by channels carved in the Moenkopi red beds. Evidently there was an important crustal uplift, causing an episode of rapid stream erosion, and this was followed by a flood of stream gravels brought from rapidly rising highlands to the east and south. In other words, this conglomerate gives evidence of tectonic events in a distant area. Rise of a mountain block by faulting is one type of uplift that is rapid and can provide a source of coarse detritus. Detailed study of the Shinarump gravels has shown that they occupy the courses of sinuous channels. Logs from distant forests were carried by the swift streams in flood and became lodged among the stream gravels. Today we find these logs petrified in the Shinarump conglomerate and in the overlying Chinle beds (Figure 28.23). The original wood of the trees has been replaced by silica in the forms of chalcedony, jasper, and opal. Despite replacement, the growth rings and radial structures of the wood are preserved in many specimens to varying degrees. Following World War II, as the search for uranium ores reached high intensity in the Colorado Plateau region, it was found that *carnotite,* a uranium-oxide ore, was concentrated in the conglomerate of the fossil stream channels.

Terrestrial deposition following the spreading out of the Shinarump gravels quickly changed from gravels to very fine-grained silts and clays with interbedded sands which accumulated to thicknesses of several hundred feet north and east of the Grand Canyon as

**FIGURE 28.23.** Fragments of fossil (silicified) tree trunks from the Chinle formation of Triassic age, Petrified Forest National Monument, Arizona. These logs are about 2 ft (0.6 m) in diameter. (Photograph by U.S. Geological Survey.)

**FIGURE 28.24.** Planar cross-lamination in ancient dune sands of the Navajo sandstone, Zion Canyon, Utah. (Photograph by Douglas Johnson.)

the overlying portion of the Chinle formation. Never indurated, these sediments remain soft and easily erodible today, forming the *Painted Desert,* a landscape in variegated pastel shades. The rounded hills and innumerable V-shaped valleys of this landscape are best described as miniature mountains or *badlands* (see Figure 36.11). Some beds of volcanic ash are interspersed with the mudstones, which may represent floodplain deposits. Fossils of land animals and plants demonstrate that these deposits are terrestrial. Skeletons of primitive dinosaurs have been found in the Chinle formation.

As the Triassic period drew to a close, terrestrial sedimentation in northern Arizona and southern Utah changed to coarser-grained materials, resulting in a series of massive sandstone beds interbedded with soft siltstones.

As Triassic time merged into Jurassic time, the facies of deposition underwent a striking change over northern Arizona and southern Utah. Zion Canyon derives its character from a sheer cliff of sandstone rising unbroken through 2000 ft (600 m) (Figure 28.1*E*). This unit is the Navajo formation. Upon close examination at places where weathering has etched the surface we find the key to interpretation of this enormous accumulation of sand. Like the Coconino formation of Grand Canyon, the Navajo formation consists of large-scale cross bedding throughout its entire extent and can best be interpreted as composed of lithified dune sands (Figure 28.24).

We shall pass over the remaining strata of Jurassic age and those of Cretaceous age in the Plateau region, but not because they are lacking in importance. As the traveler proceeds from Zion Canyon northward toward Bryce Canyon, these upper Jurassic and Cretaceous strata will be crossed in succession. They are largely clastic sediments, some of marine facies, others of terrestrial facies. Altogether a total thickness of over 3000 ft (900 m) of strata was deposited before the close of the Mesozoic Era.

After a long period of crustal stability—nearly a half billion years spanning the entire Paleozoic and Mesozoic Eras—the Colorado Plateau region experienced some of the effects of a major tectonic event, the Laramian orogeny. Although causing uplift and orogeny primarily in the Rocky Mountains to the east, activity in the Colorado Plateau was limited to breaking of the strata into large blocks moved slightly upward or downward with respect to their neighbors along a series of north-south faults and monoclinal flexures (see Figure 26.7). The whole region experienced uplift and a great deal of erosion, which removed some of the Mesozoic rock from the Grand Canyon region.

## Record of the Cenozoic Era at Bryce Canyon

As the traveler approaches Bryce Canyon, he rises to a high plateau over 8000 ft (2400 m) in elevation. On the eastern rim of this plateau lies Bryce Canyon, eroded by streams that are in the process of undermining the capping formation of the plateau. The plateau is locally named the Paunsaugunt Plateau and the escarpment which forms its rim is known as the Pink Cliffs. Here we find intricately sculptured forms including innumerable pinnacles and walls carved in a soft rock of variegated shades of pink, red, and cream (Figure 28.1*F*). Rocks of the plateau are of Eocene age and comprise the Wasatch formation, about 1000 ft (300 m) thick. The Eocene Epoch is a subdivision of the Tertiary Period. (See Table 30.1.)

The Wasatch formation proves upon examination to be largely of carbonate composition. In places there are dense limestone layers, elsewhere the rock is soft calcareous mudstone. Fossils scattered through the formation indicate that the carbonate sediment accumulated in a shallow fresh-water lake. Here we have an illustration of a *lacustrine* sediment.

The Eocene lake in which the Wasatch beds accumulated occupied a large basin covering much of central and eastern Utah and extending north into Wyoming and east into Colorado (Figure 28.25). It has been named Green River Lake. In the Bryce Canyon area calcareous sediment was precipitated in the lake, whereas farther north the accumulations were of muds of detrital minerals brought from nearby highlands. We do not know the elevation of Green River Lake, but it was probably low in comparison with the high elevations of the region today.

Other than volcanic rocks, in this part of the Colorado Plateau region no record remains of rocks younger than the Eocene Epoch of the Tertiary Period. Late in the Tertiary the Colorado Plateau region was subjected to renewed faulting, which raised large blocks to the high elevations we find there today. Erosion was greatly intensified following this uplift. The Colorado River and its tributaries carved deep canyons into the strata.

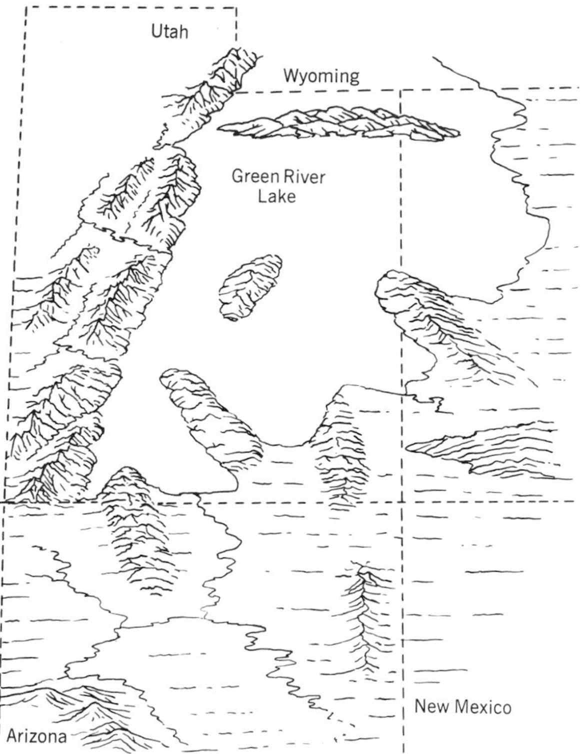


**FIGURE 28.25.** Physiographic diagram of Green River Lake and surrounding areas in middle Eocene time. [After M. Kay and E. H. Colbert (1965), *Stratigraphy and Life History,* New York, John Wiley & Sons, p. 521, Figure 21-15.]

Within the past million years or so the Colorado River has succeeded in excavating its mile-deep canyon into the Precambrian shield rocks beneath.

## A stratigraphic column in review

The Colorado Plateau region has provided us with a succession of strata excellent for historical interpretation. This is a region of spectacular scenery seen by millions of persons each year and explained to many of them by educational programs at three National Parks and a number of National Monuments. We have interpreted a number of distinctive depositional environments ranging from marine through littoral to terrestrial. The primary purpose of following up the entire stratigraphic column from the Inner Gorge of Grand Canyon to the brink of the Pink Cliffs at Bryce Canyon has been to illustrate principles of stratigraphy and the working methods of the stratigrapher.

In one respect, the choice of the Colorado Plateau as a region of stratigraphic interpretation has been a very poor one. For since the beginning of the Paleozoic Era, this region has been a part of the North American Precambrian shield, and to the stratigrapher this represents a highly stable crustal region, or craton, receiving only comparatively thin sedimentary sequences as compared with the enormous thicknesses of strata accumulating in geosynclines along the continental margins.

## References for further study

Dunbar, C., and J. Rodgers (1957), *Principles of Stratigraphy,* New York, Wiley, 356 pp.

Weller, J. M. (1960), *Stratigraphic Principles and Practice,* New York, Harper & Row, 725 pp.

Maxson, J. H. (1961), *Geologic Map of the Bright Angel Quadrangle, Grand Canyon National Park,* Grand Canyon Natural Hist. Assoc.

Kay, M., and E. H. Colbert (1965), *Stratigraphy and Life History,* New York, Wiley, 736 pp.

Laporte, L. F. (1968), *Ancient Environments,* Englewood Cliffs, N.J., Prentice-Hall, 115 pp.

# 29

# Changing life forms in a changing environment: 1. The Paleozoic Era[1]

TO THE GEOLOGIST an inquiry into the evolution of plants and animals through the eras of abundant life has far more than biological significance. Organisms have made essential contributions to the compositions of the atmosphere and oceans and to the accumulations of sedimentary rocks—to put the point more strongly, plants and animals have made the atmosphere what it is today. That this assertion is valid is apparent when the composition of the homosphere is compared with the compositions of gases released by the earth from volcanoes or entrapped in igneous rocks (Chapter 27). Our modern atmosphere consists of about one-fifth free oxygen and only a tiny fraction of carbon dioxide, while the primitive atmosphere postulated by inference from outgassing in progress today probably had almost no free oxygen, but instead a larger proportion of carbon dioxide. We have only to look at the stratigraphic record to gain an appreciation of the enormous quantities of calcium carbonate that have been secreted by organisms and of the large amounts of organically produced hydrocarbons embedded in the sediments.

So far as we know, only planet Earth of all objects of the solar system has abundant life in advanced forms. Only Earth has a plethora of both atmospheric gases and liquid water. Add to these valuable assets a moderate temperature regime through the accident of favorable placement in the succession of planetary orbits. We are neither too hot, as is Mercury, nor too cold, as are the outer planets. Most of the free water on our planet remains in the liquid state because surface temperatures remain largely between those very narrow limits of the freezing point and the boiling point. It is almost a certainty

[1] Data used in this chapter and in Chapter 30 are drawn in large part from A. L. McAlester (1968), *The History of Life,* Englewood Cliffs, N.J., Prentice-Hall, 151 pp.; M. Kay and E. H. Colbert (1965), *Stratigraphy and Life History,* New York, Wiley, 736 pp.; and C. O. Dunbar and K. M. Waage (1969), *Historical Geology,* 3rd ed., New York, Wiley, 556 pp.

that life began in the oceans and that the primary phases of evolution of complex life forms took place in the oceans. In this chapter we shall trace the broad outlines of this organic evolution with particular attention to the interaction of organisms with their environment.

## Mechanisms of organic evolution

With the passage of time, as generation upon generation of individuals of a species of plant or animal are reproduced, the average set of physical characteristics of the population of individuals undergoes change. This change is termed *organic evolution.* While any one individual of a species can, by reaction with his environment, develop some physical attributes different from those of other individuals, such *acquired characteristics* cannot be passed on to another generation.

Evolution can proceed only through changes which can be inherited—that is, transmitted from one generation to the next through genetic materials contained in the reproductive cells of the organism. The *gene* is the unit of genetic material, and each gene is responsible for the replication of a particular characteristic of the organism. No adult individual of a species is identical in all respects to either parent, to any sibling (except in the case of identical twins), or to any offspring. The reason that such differences exist is that genes of two individuals are exchanged in the process of sexual reproduction. In this way each new individual receives a unique combination of thousands of characteristics. This process of production of individual differences is known as *recombination.*

A second mechanism of inherited change occurs through a sudden change in a gene, or groups of genes, and is known as a *mutation.* This form of change is permanent in the sense that it will be transmitted to succeeding generations. Mutations occur in only a very small fraction of genes. Causes of mutations are not well understood, but it is thought that some mutations are caused by exposure to radiation or to certain chemical substances, or by temperature changes. In the broad sense, then, mutations are brought about by environmental forces over which the organism exerts no control.

Individuals of one species, differing from one another because of recombination of genetic materials or by mutations that are inherited, comprise a *population.* Since the processes of inheritance operate in a random fashion within the population, all physical variations due to recombination within the populations would be retained and there would be no net change from generation to generation. Mutations, while capable of causing population change, are not only rare events but offer no consistent direction of change. The fact that evolutionary changes are in one direction—for example, a progressive increase in size of a particular organ—points to a guiding mechanism of forced change of population characteristics.

Charles Darwin is credited with formulating and demonstrating the principle of *natural selection* as the control of change in populations of species. He reasoned from intensive studies of populations of various living animals that the struggle for survival against the unfavorable pressures of the physical environment and the competition of other animals tends to eliminate those lines of inheritance that produce the least fit individuals. On the other hand, individuals better equipped to survive tend to propagate a disproportionately larger number of the individuals of succeeding populations. For example, a predatory animal possessing better legs would be more successful in catching his prey. In times of scarcity of victims, the better-endowed animal would be more likely to survive and propagate a new generation than an animal with weak legs. The characteristics of populations would on the average trend in the direction of improvements of function. Hereditary changes introduced by recombination and mutations would eventually be eliminated if they contributed to failure to survive, but would be retained if they contributed to success in survival.

We have used the word "species" without definition. Most persons have a good empirical concept of species based upon obvious physical differences and similarities among individuals in the animal world. We unhesitatingly assign a domestic cat to a different species from a bobcat, but we may not be so sure if the domestic dog is of a different species from the wolf. In the latter case, the dog (*Canis familiaris*) is of a different species from the wolf (*Canis lupus*), but the two species can interbreed, as witness certain dog varieties that resemble wolves in many features.

Assuming that the biologist has a satisfactory definition of species, let us go on to consider how a species evolves, or, more to the point, how a single species can give rise to two species. It is supposed that the change occurs because of geographical isolation of a segment of the species population. For example, a rising mountain chain might form a physical barrier between two regions, or the breakup and drifting of continents might place an impassable oceanic barrier between two landmasses formerly united. Isolation permits the progressive changes in the two populations to drift independently to the point that they can no longer be considered alike. Eventually the changes proceed to the point that interbreeding can no longer take place, and if brought together again the two populations would not have the genetic capability of reuniting. Various other kinds of barriers exist that effectively prevent interbreeding of similar species. When interbreeding does occur, leading to hybridization, a new species may result, although the survival of hybrids is generally an event of low probability.

Although this brief account of the evolutionary process is both incomplete and inadequate, it permits us to try to make some order out of the development of life in response to the changing environments throughout geological history.

## Classification of life forms

To proceed further, it is necessary to have some knowledge of the system of classification of plants and animals into a hierarchy of levels of grouping. The first basis of subdivision is into two groups, the plant kingdom and the animal kingdom. Plants more advanced than single-celled forms are organisms characterized by growth through the process of *photosynthesis,* in which atmospheric carbon dioxide and water are combined with solar energy in the presence of chlorophyll to produce carbohydrate, at the same time liberating free oxygen. Plants lack mechanisms of locomotion and either remain stationary and anchored in place or are transported by other mechanisms. There are, of course, exceptions to the last two statements—some plants (fungi, bacteria) lack chlorophyll and do not carry on photosynthesis, and some microscopic plants, particularly certain algae, can swim freely.

Animals are characterized by the need to ingest food manufactured by other animals or plants and to digest this food in order to provide growth materials and energy. Animals engage in respiration, in which oxygen is taken into the cell to burn food and release energy. Oxidation is accompanied by the release of carbon dioxide. Many forms of animals are capable of locomotion, but others are fixed in place and require that food be brought to them.

The first level of subdivision of both plants and animals is into *phyla.* Our interest here is primarily in organisms that are abundant as fossils or have played important roles in forming sediments.

For our purposes it will suffice to know that several plant phyla make up the aquatic plants. These include bacteria, blue-green algae, green algae, brown algae, red algae, and a phylum containing diatoms and coccolith-producing organisms. Another plant phylum includes the fungi (yeasts, molds, mushrooms). The green land plants are encompassed by two phyla, the *bryophytes* (mosses and liverworts) and the *vascular plants.* The term "vascular" refers to the presence of a *vascular system* of roots and conducting tubes by means of which water and nutrients are carried from one part of the plant to another. The vascular plants include all terrestrial herbs, shrubs, and trees and will be the main objects of our study of plant evolution in this chapter.

Ten animal phyla important in the fossil record are named in Table 29.1. The Latin name is given, along with a common name and some names of important animal groups within the phylum. Phyla which have few fossil representatives are not included.

The *Protozoa,* or one-celled animals, are set apart from all remaining phyla, which are *Metazoa.* We have already referred to the Metazoa in Chapter 27 as animals with many cells differentiated into various tissues and organs for the purposes of carrying out such functions as ingestion, digestion, respiration, control, and so forth. All animals except the vertebrates, which are a subphylum of the *Chordata,* are referred to as *invertebrates.* Whereas the vertebrates have an internal bony skeleton, the invertebrates have no internal skeleton but can have shells of mineral matter or external skeletons (*exoskeletons*) of hardened organic matter (*chitin*).

Other taxonomic units of diminishing level below the phyla in the hierarchy of classification are the *class, order, family, genus,* and *species.* A number of these units will be mentioned specifically throughout this chapter, but in most cases their common names will be used rather than the scientific Latin names. We shall also be interested in the numbers of classes, orders, or families as rough measures of the degree of diversity of plant and animal life.

**TABLE 29.1. PRINCIPAL ANIMAL PHYLA IMPORTANT AS FOSSILS**

| | Phylum | Common Name | Representative Groups |
|---|---|---|---|
| Invertebrates | Protozoa | | Foraminifera, radiolaria |
| | METAZOA | | |
| | Porifera | Sponges | |
| | Coelenterata | Coelenterates | Corals, jellyfish, sea anemone |
| | Bryozoa | Bryozoans | "Moss animals," "sea mats" |
| | Brachiopoda | Brachiopods | |
| | Mollusca | Molluscs | Pelecypods or bivalves (clam, mussel, oyster, scallop)<br>Gastropods (snail, slug, conch)<br>Cephalopods (Squid, octopus, nautilus, ammonite) |
| | Annelida | Annelids | Segmented worms, earthworms, leeches |
| | Arthropoda | Arthropods | Crustaceans (crab, lobster, shrimp)<br>Trilobites<br>Ostracodes<br>Insects<br>Arachnids (spiders) |
| | Echinodermata | Echinoderms | Crinoids (sea lilies)<br>Sea cucumbers, sea urchins, starfishes |
| Vertebrates | Chordata | Vertebrates (a subphylum) | Fishes<br>Amphibians<br>Reptiles<br>Birds<br>Mammals |

## Life of early Cambrian time

Chapter 27 closed the review of earth history through the Precambrian time with the sudden appearance upon the scene of the Metazoa, a surprisingly diverse and complex animal assemblage. Somehow, in what seems to have been a very short interval of geologic time, the simple plant forms—bacteria and blue-green algae—had given rise to highly advanced animal forms.

There are, however, a few fossils considered to be of latest Precambrian time that resemble primitive animals. These fossils are impressions on the bedding planes of sandstone outcropping in the Ediacara Hills of southern Australia. Collected and studied by an Australian paleontologist M. F. Glaessner, the *Ediacara fauna,* as it is known, is represented by about 1500 specimens. Many of these fossils are of rounded outline with various concentric, radial, or bilaterally symmetrical patterns (Figure 29.1). They may be the impressions of soft-bodied animals. Certain of these forms have been interpreted as animals like the modern jelly-

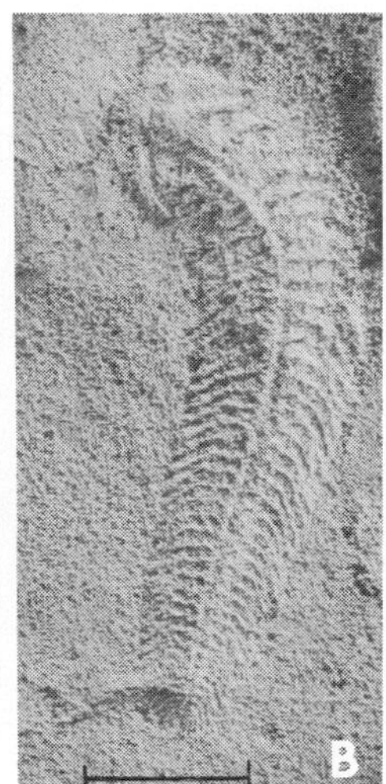

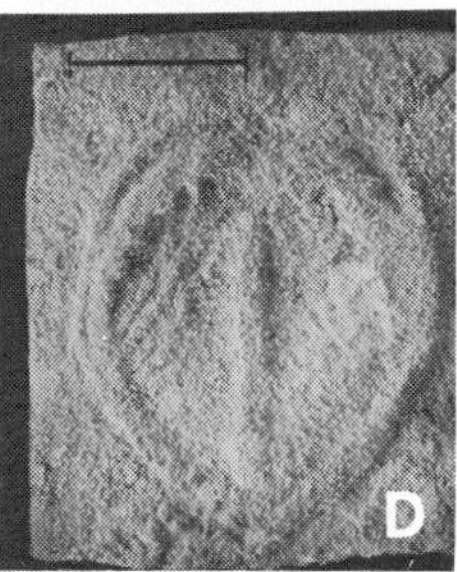


**FIGURE 29.1.** Representative fossils of the Ediacara fauna from the Pound Sandstone, of Late Precambrian age, South Australia. (*A*) Circular organism with possible coiled arms. (*B*) Worm-like form. (*C*) Jellyfish-like form. (*D*) Shield-shaped form, possibly a crustacean. (Photographs by courtesy of Professor M. F. Glaessner, University of Adelaide.)

fish. The fauna also include a long narrow form with many lateral indentations and a central groove, resembling certain segmented worms. If these forms have been correctly interpreted, they represent two animal phyla in existence today. Other forms in this fauna seem to have no modern equivalents.

Fossilized remains of invertebrate animals with hard shells or external skeletal parts are found in wide variety and great abundance in the lowest strata of the Cambrian Period. A typical Cambrian fauna was described in Chapter 28 from the Bright Angel formation of Grand Canyon. Evidently most of the animal phyla present today were in existence then, yet there is no earlier fossil record by which we can trace the organic evolution of these forms.

One hypothesis, generally favored today, is that the evolutionary process operated so rapidly as the Paleozoic Era began that no earlier succession would have existed in Precambrian rocks. Others have argued that invertebrates gradually evolving in the later Precambrian time had no hard parts that could be preserved, hence that the fossil record begins only with the development of shells or skeletons. This second hypothesis seems difficult to accept because there are abundant Precambrian shales in which the impressions of soft-bodied animals could be preserved. Yet, with the exception of the possible case of the Ediacara fauna, no impressions have been found of the invertebrate phyla known only from lower Cambrian time. It is also suggested that the Metazoa may have evolved over a long span of the late Precambrian but were physically limited to small isolated pockets in the sea where algae were concentrated and provided an oxygen supply. Only in Cambrian time, when atmospheric oxygen became abundantly available, were these animals able to spread widely and increase to large populations.

## Evolution of invertebrates in the lower Paleozoic

While marine life in the Cambrian Period included representatives of the major invertebrate phyla, the abundance of forms was by no means uniformly distributed among them. Trilobites were probably the most abundant animals, judging by the fact that about 60% of Cambrian fossils are trilobites. These arthropods, enclosed in segmented outer skeletons of chitin, were bottom-living animals (benthos). Figure 29.2 is a restoration of a group of animals of the Cambrian sea floor showing several trilobites. Now extinct, these crustaceans can be thought of as outwardly resembling a modern "horseshoe crab."

Brachiopods comprised a second important group of Cambrian invertebrates. It is estimated that about 30% of Cambrian fossils are of this phylum. At first glance, a brachiopod would seem to be a clam (pelecypod), but there is an important difference in the two forms of shellfish. The brachiopod is bilaterally symmetrical on either side of a plane cutting both shells in half in a direction perpendicular to their meeting edges (Figure 29.3). In the clam, the plane of symmetry runs between the shells, one of which is on the left, the other on the right. Brachiopods are thought to have been attached to the bottom in such a way that the upper shell could be raised to admit food. In some brachiopods the lower shell is greatly enlarged at the expense of the upper shell, which serves as a lid.

The remaining invertebrates of the early Cambrian time included sponges, arthropods besides trilobites, annelids (segmented worms), and jellyfish, all shown in Figure 29.2. A remarkable fossil assemblage of middle Cambrian age, the *Walcott fauna,* was discovered in 1910 in British Columbia by a distinguished paleontologist, Charles D. Walcott. From a quarry in the Burgess shale Walcott obtained over 35,000 specimens, including large numbers of impressions of soft-bodied animals. Among these are impressions of arthropods and annelids such as those pictured in Figure 29.2.

It is particularly noteworthy that the Cambrian record has a scarcity of coelenterates (corals), bryozoans, gastropods, pelecypods (bivalves), cephalopods, crinoids (sea lilies), starfish, and echinoids (sea urchins). This deficiency is brought out by an abundance chart of invertebrates (Figure 29.4). However, as the Ordovician Period began these same animals increased greatly in abundance. Notice particularly that the trilobites expanded rapidly in abundance of genera and species in early Cambrian, reached their maximum in middle and late Cambrian, then declined steadily throughout the remainder of the Paleozoic Era. There is also the case

**FIGURE 29.2.** Restoration of the middle Cambrian sea floor of eastern British Columbia, showing conditions at the time of deposition of the Burgess shale formation. Sponges are shown at far left and right, trilobites and arthropods in the center and at left, segmented worms on the bottom, and a jellyfish at upper left. (Photograph by courtesy of the Smithsonian Institution.)

of some curious Cambrian invertebrate animals of a phylum not listed in Table 29.1. These are the *archaeocyathids,* elongate conical fossils resembling small cornucopias. Although found widely distributed in Cambrian strata of the world, these animals became extinct before that period closed, thus they serve as excellent guide fossils for the Cambrian Period.

**FIGURE 29.3.** Brachiopods attached in various positions to the sea bottom. Forms *A, B, C,* and *E* are attached by a stalk (pedicle), whereas form *D* is held by a long point on the lower shell embedded in the mud bottom. [Redrawn from W. H. Twenhofel and R. R. Schrock (1935), *Invertebrate Paleontology,* New York, McGraw-Hill, p. 260, Figure 93.]

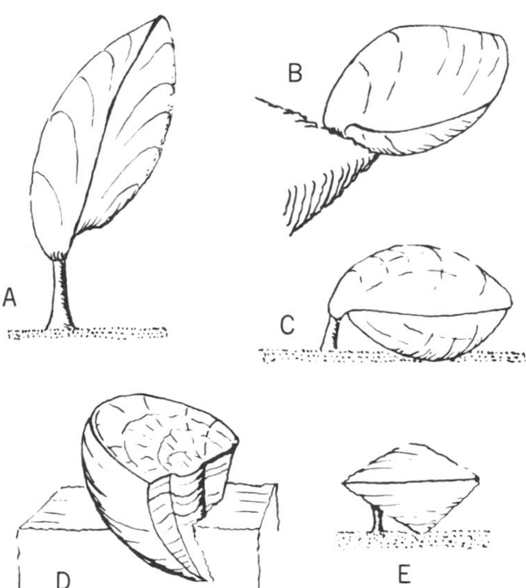


The important point about evolution in the Cambrian Period is that it seems to have "gotten off to a false start" with respect to the Paleozoic Era as a whole. We shall need to look into this development in terms of evolutionary principles.

## Evolutionary radiations and extinctions

The fossil record shows that numbers of new groups of animals (that is to say, new classes, orders, families, and genera) increase rapidly in abundance in certain limited spans of time, rather than showing a steady increase. This rapid diversification of groups constitutes *evolutionary radiation.* A period of radiation is followed by a much longer span of time in which the new groups persist with little change. The causes of evolutionary radiation are complex and not well understood, but it can be reasoned that the onset of a particularly favorable set of environmental conditions is partly responsible.

In the case of the almost explosive radiation of the earliest Cambrian faunas, the rapid increase in free atmospheric oxygen was perhaps a major factor, along with the crustal stability and presence of large expanses of shallow inland (epicontinental) seas. Whatever the reasons, early Cambrian time was especially favorable to the diversification of trilobites, brachiopods, and archaeocyathids.

Evolution tends to proceed on a series of one-way branching tracks. New groups form readily and proceed on parallel or diverging tracks, but the reverse trend,

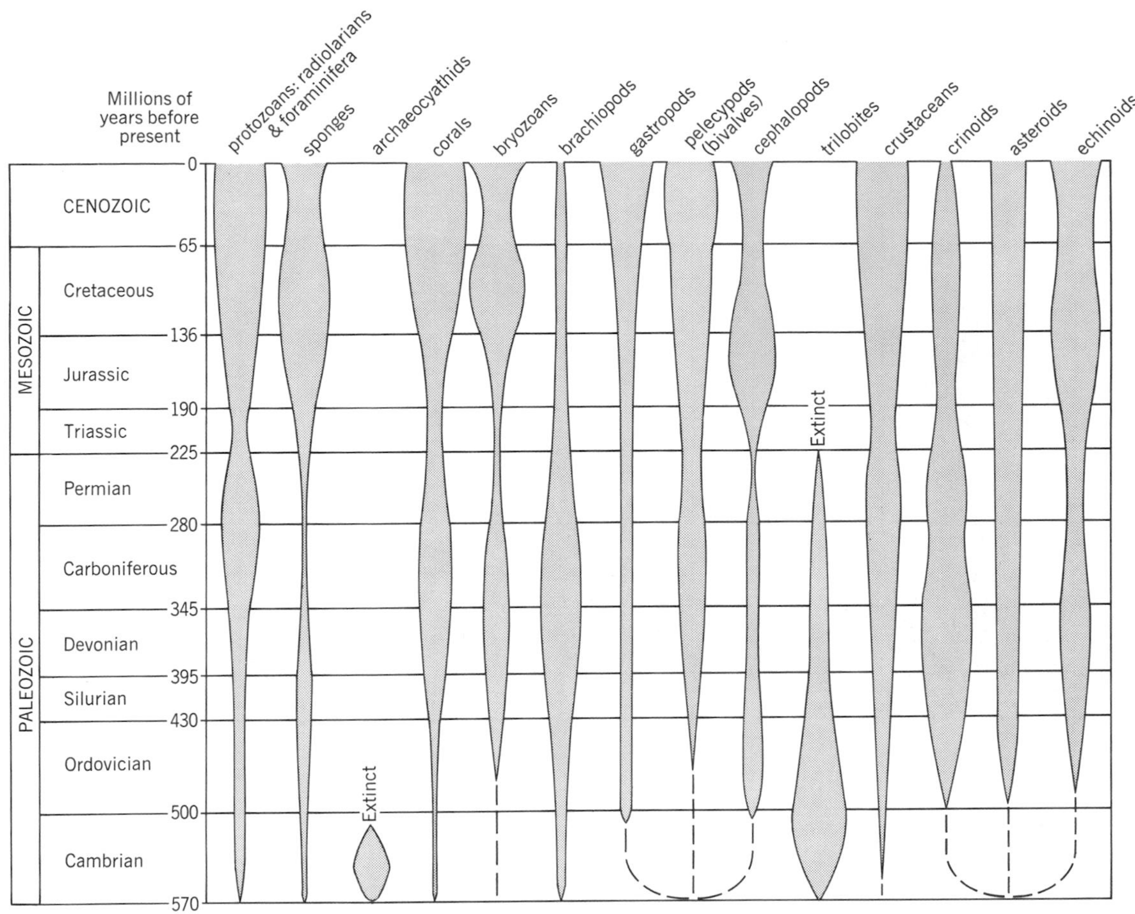


**FIGURE 29.4.** Evolution of the major groups of invertebrate marine animals. Width of band shows relative abundance of groups. [Data from A. L. McAlester (1968), *The History of Life,* Englewood Cliffs, N.J., Prentice-Hall, pp. 60–61, Figure 3-7.]

to have those tracks rejoin and unite with other groups into a common line, is forbidden by the impossibility of interbreeding and exchange of genetic materials. For many groups the evolutionary track simply ends by failure to propagate, and the result is *extinction.*

Extinctions of large numbers of animal groups seem to have occurred rapidly at certain points in the geologic column. Again, environmental changes of one sort or another are assumed to have been responsible for large-scale extinctions. Widespread volcanic and orogenic activity, accompanied by changes in atmospheric and oceanic temperatures, may be expected to place severe stresses upon faunas. Widespread emergence of continental shields and mountain belts has at times sharply reduced the areas of shallow seas, isolating one sea from another. Major extinctions have coincided with such conditions.

Rapid extinctions of large groups of organisms lead to vacant environments, and these are rapidly filled by adaptive radiation of other groups of organisms. We shall see that major episodes of extinction and subsequent rapid evolutionary radiation mark the transitions from one geologic era to the next.

## Life of the Ordovician and Silurian seas

By the end of the Cambrian Period trilobites had been reduced greatly by extinctions while the archaeocyathids became completely extinct. On the other hand, brachiopods, sponges, and crustaceans held their own and increased gradually in abundance (Figure 29.4). With the coming of the Ordovician Period, about 500 m.y. before present, a rapid evolutionary radiation took place among several phyla. Within the phylum of coelenterates the class of corals expanded rapidly. The bryozoans, which are not known from the Cambrian, entered the record in the Ordovician and expanded rapidly. Shell-bearing gastropods, pelecypods (bivalves), and cephalopods showed rapid divergence, as did crinoids, starfish, and echinoids (Figure 29.4). Thus during the Ordovician period the important lines of invertebrate evolution were reestablished in a way that was to persist with only moderate changes through the remainder of the Paleozoic.

Figure 29.5 is a restoration of the sea floor of Silurian time showing the abundance of corals, brachipods, cephalopods, and crinoids. Corals had become in-

**FIGURE 29.5.** Reconstruction of a reef environment on the sea floor of Silurian time in Illinois. The large, head-like masses are corals. Crinoids rise in flower-like fashion. Trilobites, brachiopods, clams, and cephalopods are on the bottom at right. (Photograph by courtesy of Field Museum of Natural History.)

creasingly important and grew in such abundance in the Silurian as to produce important reef deposits of limestone. It is such a reef environment that is pictured in Figure 29.5.

## Spread of life to the lands

Until late Silurian time the lands were totally devoid of plant and animal life. The landscape would have presented everywhere the barren appearance of what are now our driest deserts—the Sahara, Namib, and Kalahari. Yet much of the early Paleozoic lands must have lain in regions of abundant rainfall, for persistent deserts would be expected only under the subtropical high pressure cells, and in the lee of such high mountain ranges as may have existed. Erosion by running water must have been intense, as judged by present-day standards, since today high-rainfall areas are also regions where dense forest vegetation strongly inhibits erosion. Large volumes of detrital sediment were available in the early Paleozoic wherever elevation of the land furnished strong gradients for the flow of water.

Lack of sufficient atmospheric oxygen was probably the major single deterrent to occupation of the terrestrial environment by plants and animals. For all organisms, the lethal effect of ultraviolet radiation was a barrier to life that could only be removed when sufficient oxygen was present to absorb this radiation and generate an ozone layer (see Chapter 12). For animals adequate oxygen was also a requirement for sustaining life processes. Recall that the oxygen level at the Precambrian-Paleozoic transition stood perhaps at about 1% of its present atmospheric level (PAL). According to the estimates of two atmospheric scientists, L. V. Berkner and L. C. Marshall, the oxygen level rose quite steadily throughout the Cambrian, Ordovician, and Silurian periods, as shown in the graph of Figure 29.6. By late Silurian time the level had reached 10% PAL, effectively shielding the ground from lethal ultraviolet radiation. Land pants appear in the fossil record at this time.

Transition from the water environment to the land environment posed serious difficulties to both plants and animals, requiring profound changes in structure and function. One difficulty for animals was to emerge from a salt solution to which the body fluids were matched and enter fresh water, which could rapidly dilute those fluids. A second difficulty for animals was posed by leaving the aqueous environment, from which oxygen in solution is absorbed by specialized tissues, to enter the atmospheric environment in which oxygen must be absorbed directly from a gaseous medium.

For all organisms, exposure to air would result in fatal desiccation (drying-out) and required development of a protective coating to retain vital fluids or the means to replace them as fast as they were lost. Desiccation also constituted a barrier to sexual reproduction, for water-dwelling organisms release their reproductive cells (gametes) into fluid surroundings where fertilization takes place. New means of protecting these cells had to be developed.

The transition from salt water to land seems logically to have been a two-stage process: salt water to fresh water, then fresh water to atmosphere. Difficult as the transition was, an environment with abundant oxygen for animals and intense sunlight for plant photosynthesis was awaiting occupation. An almost explosive evolutionary radiation took place, first among the plants.

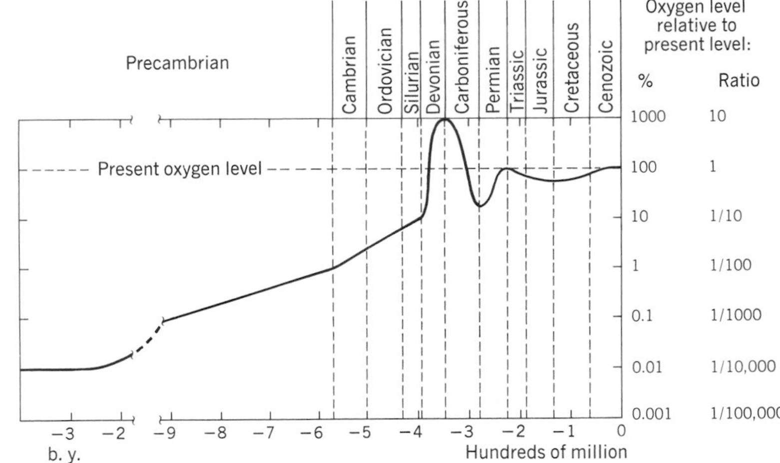


**FIGURE 29.6.** Postulated changes in the level of atmospheric oxygen throughout geologic time. [After L. V. Berkner and L. C. Marshall (1964), in *The Origin and Evolution of the Atmosphere and Oceans,* P. J. Brancazio and A. G. W. Cameron, Eds., New York, Wiley, p. 120, Figure 6.15.]

## Land plants of the Devonian Period

The vascular land plants are believed to have evolved from the green algae, which are the only phylum of algae using chlorophyll in photosynthesis in the same way as do the higher plants. The green algae were successful in making a transition to fresh water, as witness the familiar green "scum" seen on small fresh-water ponds. There is no fossil record of the supposed evolution from green algae to the vascular plants, but some measure of support for this relationship is found in the bryophytes, a plant phylum that includes the mosses and liverworts. These plants now live in wet well-shaded environments on land but are limited to small

**FIGURE 29.7.** Evolution of the vascular plants. Width of band shows relative abundance of groups. [Data from A. L. McAlester (1968), *The History of Life,* Englewood Cliffs, N.J., Prentice-Hall, pp. 86–87, Figure 5-2.]

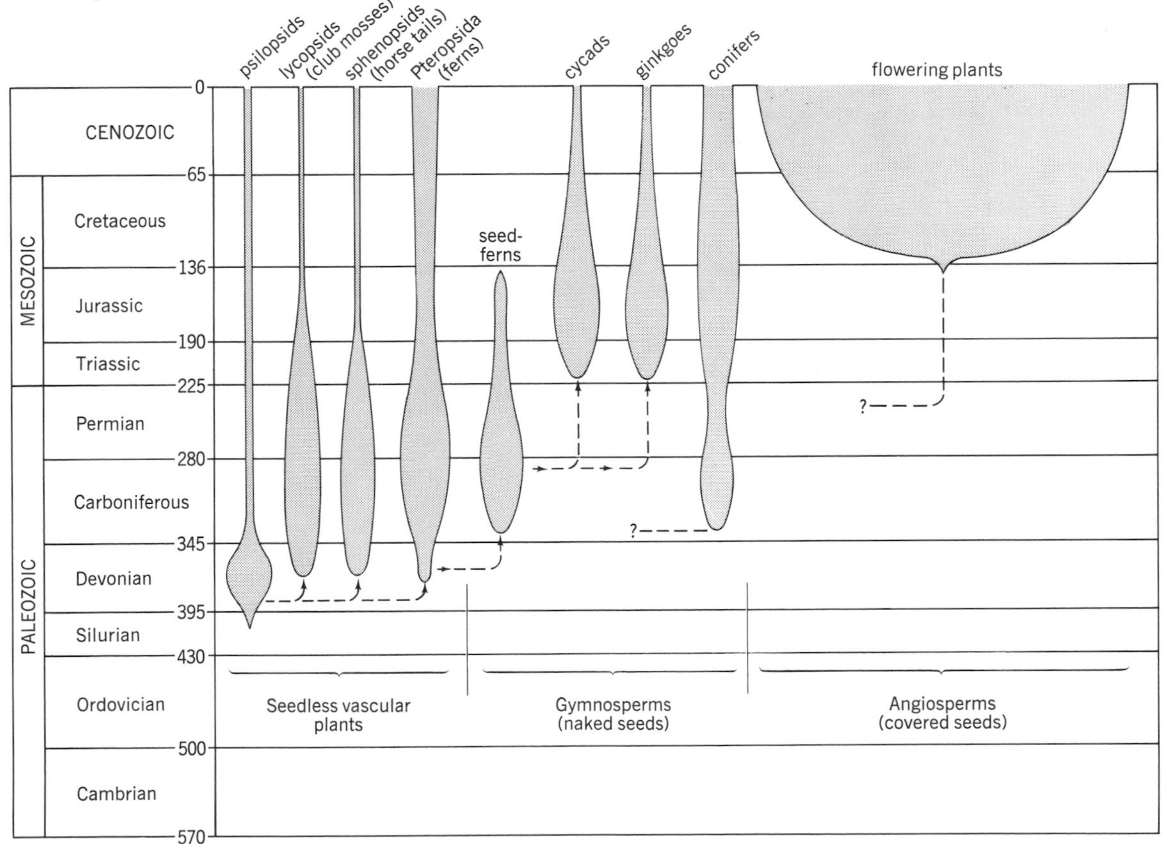

size because they lack structures for transferring fluids from one part to another within the individual and, moreover, have no means of protecting the reproductive cells from drying out after they are separated from the parent plant. It seems possible that the vascular plants evolved through plants related to the bryophytes, but there is no fossil record of such an evolutionary chain.

The vascular plants met the needs of the land environment by developing roots for intake of soil moisture, leaves for photosynthesis, and stems containing a *vascular system* of specialized conductive tissue for transporting fluids between roots and leaves. In addition, plants have developed on their leaves a specialized outer cell layer covered by a protective layer, the *cuticle,* capable of preventing evaporative water loss, but also containing openings (*stomata*) through which the release of transpired water can be regulated.

The vascular plants are subdivided into two groups: those which are seedless, designated as *pteridophytes,* and those which are seed-bearing, designated the *spermatophytes.* The pteridophytes are ferns or fern-like plants and include the modern club mosses and horse-tails. The reproductive process of the seedless plants is quite elaborate and cannot be detailed here. It must suffice to know that the adult pteridophyte releases *spores.* The spore produces a small specialized asexual plant that releases both eggs and sperm, and these unite to produce the embryonic spore-producing plant.

The evolution of the vascular plants is shown in Figure 29.7. First to evolve were the seedless plants. One group appears first in the rocks of upper Silurian age. These were the *psilopsids,* simple plants lacking in roots or leaves. They diversified rapidly in the Devonian Period, but then rapidly subsided to minor importance. In Devonian time the remaining three groups evolved with great rapidity. These are the *lycopsids,* represented today by the club mosses, the *sphenopsids* seen today in the horse-tails, and the *pteropsids* or ferns (Figure 29.8). All three plant groups included species of tall trees, although today only the ferns attain tree size.

**FIGURE 29.8.** Reconstruction of a tree-fern, *Eospermatopteris,* from the upper Devonian of the Catskill Mountains. [W. Goldring (1924), New York State Museum Bull. 251, plate 1. Courtesy of New York State Museum and Science Service.]

By the middle of Devonian time, some 420 m.y. ago, rich forests of seedless vascular plants covered the lands. You will notice that in Figure 29.6 the oxygen level shows a sharp increase in the Devonian Period, rising to a postulated level on the order of ten times the present level. This rise is inferred from the great expansion of plant growth, resulting in the liberation of great amounts of oxygen that could not be used by animals or in mineral oxidation.

## Fishes to amphibians

Origin of the vertebrates is obscure—there is no fossil record preceding the occurrence of fishes in the late Ordovician time. From that point on, the record is clear for the evolutionary succession from fishes to amphibians, then to reptiles, birds, and finally mammals. By Silurian time fishes with thick bony armor were well developed and included both bottom-scavengers and carnivorous types. Both the sharks and the bony fishes evolved from these early armored fishes before the close of the Devonian Period (see Figure 29.16).

Transition from fishes to land animals began with fishes having lobe-like fins containing muscles and articulated bones outside the body. These fishes must have entered the fresh-water environment and developed the capacity to breathe air by means of lungs. The modern lungfish retains this capacity and by resorting to air breathing survives the drying up of streams and lakes in the wet-dry tropical climate. The fossil record shows that a group of lobe-finned fishes, the *crossopterygians,* developed the capacity to move about on land through the modification of fins into stubby legs (Figure 29.9). Thus there emerged in late Devonian time an amphibian, the *labyrinthodont,* which became the dominant land vertebrate in the ensuing Carboniferous Period. These animals, which resembled a modern alligator, had representatives up to several feet in length. They probably spent much of their time in or near water and were inhabitants of the great swamp forests. The labyrinthodonts declined rapidly in the Permian Period and became extinct early in the Mesozoic Era.

## Life of the Carboniferous Period

The Carboniferous Period, starting about −345 m.y. and ending about −280 m.y., includes two subperiods, the Mississippian and Pennsylvanian, often treated as separate periods. As with the Devonian, the Mississippian Period was a time of extensive shallow inland seas providing a favorable environment for marine life. For the most part the marine invertebrates held their own in terms of abundances, except for the trilobites, which were steadily declining (Figure 29.4). The Pennsylvanian Period, or upper Carboniferous, saw a world-wide trend toward extensive areas of low-lying fresh-water swamps repeatedly inundated by shallow seas. The terrestrial environment, with its great swamp forest and rich insect

**FIGURE 29.9.** Transition to the land. *Left:* Lobe-finned fish, crossoptygerians of Devonian time, try the terrestrial environment. *Right:* Labyrinthodont amphibians have made the transition. (Painted by F. L. Jaques under direction of William K. Gregory. Photographs by courtesy of American Museum of Natural History.)

life, is thus an outstanding feature of the upper Carboniferous.

In addition to the three groups of seedless vascular plants which had arisen in Devonian time, there evolved in the Carboniferous Period the first of the seed-bearing plants. These were the *seed-ferns,* one of four classes of seed-bearing plants comprising the *gymnosperms.* As Figure 29.7 shows, the seed-ferns later gave

**FIGURE 29.10.** Restoration of a Carboniferous forest. Seedless trees and seed-ferns dominate. *F,* Seed-fern. *L,* Lycopsid. *S,* Sphenopsid. (Photograph by courtesy of Illinois State Museum.)

rise to two of the four gymnosperm classes, the cycads and ginkgoes, but these became prominent only in the Mesozoic Era. The fourth class consisted of the *conifers,* or cone-bearing, needle-leaf gymnosperms. These also arose in lower Carboniferous time and had many representatives throughout the period, but they were primitive forms now largely extinct.

Figure 29.10 is a restoration of a Carboniferous forest showing seedless trees as well as seed-ferns. Forests such as this must have grown in great luxuriance over long periods of time, judging from the thickness of coal seams derived from compaction of the partially decayed vegetative mass that was produced. The conversion of Carboniferous peat to coal, with estimates of the thicknesses and time spans required, has been discussed in Chapter 22.

A decline in atmospheric oxygen to near present levels in Carboniferous time is postulated on the supposition that the decay of great quantities of plant matter would have used substantial amounts of oxygen. The oxygen curve in Figure 29.6 is therefore shown as dropping sharply in Carboniferous time.

Climate of the Carboniferous Period has been interpreted as exceptionally mild and equable over large areas of North America and Europe. The structure and succulent foliage of forest plants suggest a moist frost-free climate, while the existence of swamps is in itself proof of ample rainfall.

A most interesting feature of deposition of Pennsylvanian coal-bearing strata is a distinctive repetition of a sequence of sedimentary layers of both marine and terrestrial sources. The phenomenon is known as *cyclic sedimentation,* and the sequence itself constitutes a *cyclothem* (Figure 29.11). The cyclothem begins with a sandstone layer, followed in turn by shale and fresh-water limestone. Above the limestone is a clay layer upon which rests the coal seam. Following the coal are some layers of marine shale and limestone. Each cyclothem is separated from the next by a disconformity. In other words, an episode of emergence and erosion followed the cyclothem. Interpretation of the cyclothem strata rests upon a cyclic rise and fall of sea level. The succession of terrestrial sedimentation occurred while sea level was in its lower position and was replaced by the fresh-water swamp as sea level gradually rose, impeding land drainage. The swamp was then inundated by the sea and became a marine environment. A very gradual crustal subsidence, superimposed upon the cycles of sea level fluctuation, permitted the cyclothem sediments to be preserved.

Among the invertebrates, two phyla invaded the terrestrial environment to become abundant in Carboniferous time. One of these is the gastropod, which was able to develop air-breathing apparatus and to emerge from the water as a land snail. These animals were not abundant, however, until much later in the geologic column. By far the more striking evolutionary development was that of the insects and arachnids (spiders and scorpions), which became very abundant in the Carboniferous Period.

Insects are a class of the phylum *Arthropoda,* which includes the crustaceans. Like the crustaceans, the insects have a tough waterproof outer covering of organic matter. This covering was very likely an important factor in successful emergence from a water environment into the air. The development of wings for flight was an enormous advantage to the insects both in obtaining food and in evading predators. As a result the evolutionary radiation of the insects was spectacular. Some 400 kinds of insects are known from the Pennsylvanian Period. Although most were unlike modern insects, an exception was the cockroach, some species of which attained a length of several inches (Figure 29.12). A dragonfly-like insect was perhaps the largest—a fossil specimen with wingspread of 29 in. (74 cm) has been found. Evolutionary radiation of insects continued throughout geologic time, and there are today about 500,000 insect species known.

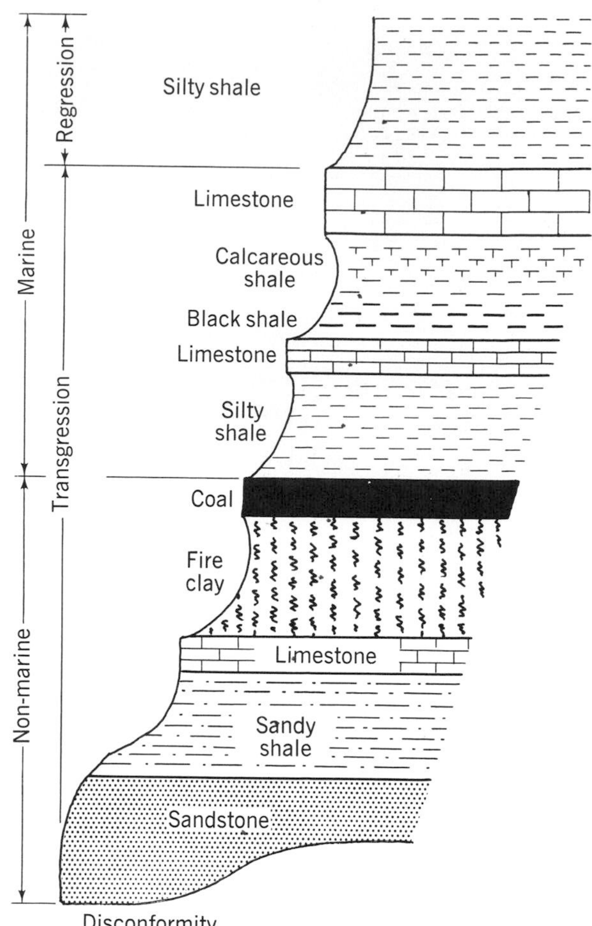


**FIGURE 29.11.** Stratigraphic section of an idealized, completely developed Pennsylvanian cyclothem in Illinois. [After J. M. Weller (1960), *Stratigraphic Principles and Practice,* New York, Harper & Row, p. 372, Figure 145.]

The first reptiles had evolved from amphibians during the Carboniferous Period, and by late in that period were competing strongly with the amphibians for the terrestrial environment. Reptiles had developed the capacity to lay eggs with protective shells which could be hatched on dry land. Thus freed from dependence upon water bodies, the reptiles enjoyed an expanded environment and were soon to undergo a great evolutionary radiation.

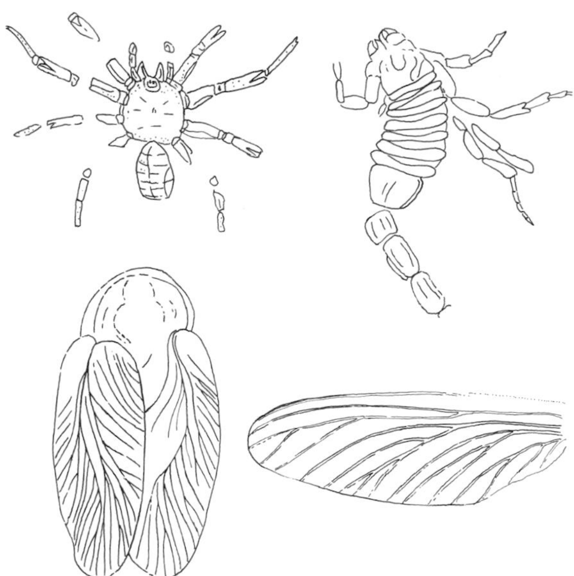

**FIGURE 29.12.** Sketches of fossil arachnids (*above*) and insects (*below*) from Carboniferous strata of Illinois and Germany. *Upper left:* a spider-like arachnid. *Upper right: Eoscorpius,* a primitive scorpion. *Lower left:* a cockroach. *Lower right:* wing of a dragonfly-like insect of order *Orthoptera.* All about natural size. [Redrawn from K. A. von Zittel, (1900), *Text-Book of Paleontology,* vol. 1, London, Macmillan and Co., pp. 679–684.]

## Changing environments at the close of an era: the Permian Period

For decades a favorite theory held by geologists was that orogeny should be world-wide and synchronous, occurring at the end of each era. Thus the Appalachian orogeny (described in Chapter 26) which deformed Paleozoic strata of the Appalachian region is usually assigned the position of a terminal event in the Paleozoic Era.

Because the strata involved in that deformation are no older than of lower Permian age, orogeny may well have begun by the middle of that period. In unconformities elsewhere in North America there is indisputable evidence that orogeny occurred in late Carboniferous time. Intense folding and overthrusting of geosynclinal strata occurred in the western and southcentral United States, and block faulting in the Maritime Provinces of Canada. Thus we find that crustal unrest in one place or another extended over all of the closing 70 to 80 m.y. of the Paleozoic Era. Environments of sediment deposition in the Permian Period reflect this crustal unrest, for the continents stood comparatively high and terrestrial sediments are widespread, as noted in the case of the Permian rocks of Grand Canyon (Chapter 28).

If we are to give tentative acceptance to the hypothesis of continental drift, as increasing evidence seems to warrant, it will be necessary to treat Permian environments in terms of a single continent—Gondwanaland—uniting the shields of South America, Africa, peninsular India, Australia, and Antarctica, as shown in Figure 26.31. North America and Europe must also be regarded as fused together, possibly with a continental nucleus, Laurasia, separate from that of Gondwanaland. We should not forget that the hypothesis requires that this state of continental fusion existed throughout the entire Paleozoic Era and far back into the Precambrian as well, but it is only in late Carboniferous time that the hypothesis becomes particularly significant in interpreting the environment of life on the lands.

Recall that the paleomagnetic evidence of polar wandering places Australia close to the south pole in late Paleozoic time (Figure 26.33), although it had been in low latitudes from Cambrian time through the Devonian Period. Figure 29.13 shows the Gondwana shield cluster of Figure 26.31 placed in a pole-centered position, as perhaps it might have been in late Carboniferous time. A large, pole-centered landmass is, of course, ideally situated for the development of an ice sheet, as exemplified in modern Antarctica. We have noted in Chapter 26 that there are unmistakable evidences of glaciation in late Carboniferous time in South America, southern Africa, India, and Australia. Grooved and scored rock surfaces underlie thick *tillites,* which are lithified glacial deposits of unsorted bouldery debris. Other sediments associated with glaciation are also found in conjunction with the tillites. Part of the geological evidence for a single continent rests upon the need for a much larger landmass than presently exists in the widely separated continental shield fragments. The glacial deposits range in age from late Carboniferous into early Permian time. In Brazil and southern Africa the glacial deposits are overlain by strata containing marine faunas, showing an important episode of submergence of parts of Gondwanaland, but the remainder of the Permian strata of southern Africa are continental.

Returning to the question of atmospheric evolution, Figure 29.6 shows the oxygen level as falling to a low point in late Carboniferous and early Permian time. This

**FIGURE 29.13.** Hypothetical restoration of the nested continents of Gondwanaland. Location of tillites and other glacial deposits of upper Carboniferous time, together with inferred directions of ice motion and limit of a single great ice sheet, are as postulated by A. L. Du Toit in 1937. [Outlines of continents from A. G. Smith and A. Hallam (1970), *Nature,* vol. 224; path of pole wandering from M. W. McElhinny and G. R. Luck (1970), *Science,* vol. 168, p. 831, Figure 1.]

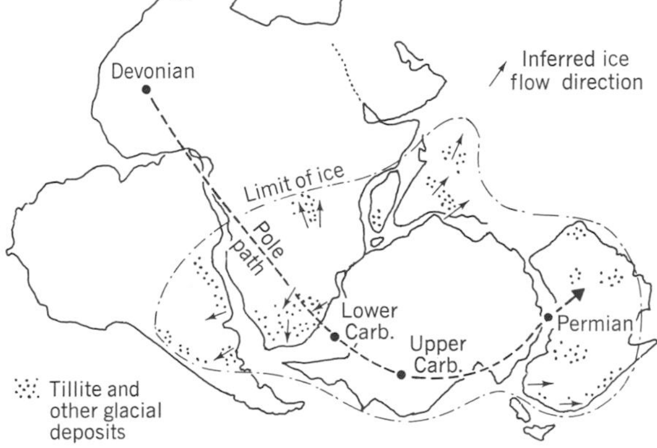

drop is postulated on the assumption that during the glaciation of that time the cold temperatures would have inhibited plant growth, at least in large areas of the continents, and would have resulted in reduced oxygen production by photosynthesis. After glaciation, the oxygen level is considered to have returned to a value close to that of the present.

Permian strata are also widespread over North America, Europe, and Asia. Two distinctly different environments are represented by these strata. Red beds with thick evaporites in the Central United States, Russia, and other localities suggest that there were large areas of arid climate. Occurrence of coal beds in the Appalachians, Siberia, and Manchuria indicate that other regions had warm moist climates. On the whole, however, there was an abundance of terrestrial environments in the Permian Period. Southern Africa and other Gondwana shield fragments are interpreted as having elevated plateau-like terrain. Red beds containing fossils of land animals and plants were probably deposited on low deltaic plains and flood plains. While these land environments fostered an almost explosive evolutionary radiation of the reptiles, the restriction of seas must have been highly unfavorable for many forms of marine life, for one of the great animal extinctions of geologic time occurred during the Permian.

Among the invertebrates a decline in abundances of groups can be seen in the narrowing widths of a number of the graphs of Figure 29.4. However, these graphs do not show the extent to which extinctions and replacements occurred. Approximately half of the invertebrate families present in the Permian Period became extinct and failed to make the transition into the Triassic Period which followed. The trilobites underwent total extinction along with several orders of corals, crinoids, bryozoans, and brachiopods. New groups which expanded in the early Mesozoic make up most of the modern invertebrates.

Permian time saw the extinction of the armored fishes and a sharp decline in the sharks. In contrast, the bony fishes underwent an expansion as Permian time gave way to Triassic time.

## Reptiles of the Permian Period

An almost explosive evolutionary radiation of reptiles is a particularly outstanding feature of the Permian Period. These earliest reptiles were *cotylosaurs* (Figure 29.14), descended from the labyrinthodont amphibians. Because all other reptiles arose from them, the cotylosaurs have been designated as the *stem reptiles.* They were heavy-limbed alligator-like creatures and attained lengths of several feet. Early in their history the stem reptiles gave rise to a half-dozen reptile groups. Of these only one group, the *mammal-like reptiles,* achieved dominance in the Permian. They made the transition into the Mesozoic Era, although with serious depletions, and declined rapidly in the Triassic Period. We shall have more to say about these reptiles in the chapter to follow.

**FIGURE 29.14.** Reconstruction of the skeleton of *Diadectes,* a representative cotylosaur from the Permian of Texas. Length about 6 ft (2 m). [From E. H. Colbert (1955), *Evolution of the Vertebrates,* New York, John Wiley & Sons, p. 113, Figure 36D.]

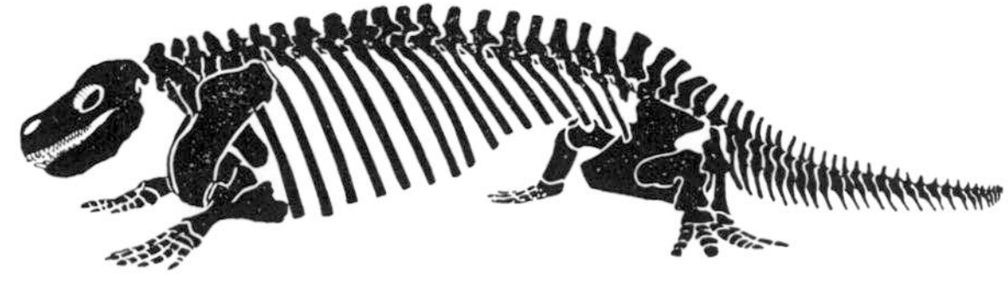

**FIGURE 29.15.** Reconstruction of a mammal-like reptile, *Lycaenops,* of late Permian time. (Painting by John C. Germann, courtesy of American Museum of Natural History.)

A mammal-like reptile from southern Africa, similar to that pictured in Figure 29.15, has been found in the Permian strata of northern Russia, showing that routes of land migration existed between Africa and Eurasia. Under the hypothesis of united continents of Laurasia and Gondwanaland, this migration would be expected, and a free interchange of reptile faunas could continue well into the Mesozoic Era.

Data on reptilian abundances in Permian and Triassic periods shows what might appear to be a contradiction in trends. Whereas the number of reptilian genera fell from 199 in the upper Permian to 56 in the lower Triassic, the number of orders rose from 4 in the upper Permian to 7 in the lower Triassic.[2] Actually, the rising trend of orders is the more informative statistic in expressing the evolutionary radiation of the reptiles in an environment that was especially favorable to land animals. Most of the reduction in genera results from extinctions in the mammal-like reptiles and thus conceals the true trend.

The same continuum from Permian time into Triassic time of terrestrial environments favoring land animals also favored land plants. As a consequence the evolutionary trends of the land plants do not seem to reflect the crisis that was so strongly felt by the marine invertebrates (Figure 29.7).

[2] Data from M. Kay and E. H. Colbert (1965), *Stratigraphy and Life History,* New York, Wiley, p. 351.

## An era in review

The word *Paleozoic* comes from the Greek words for "ancient" and "animal life." Ancient as this life may seem, it is significant that most of the animal phyla of the modern world had developed at or near the start of the Paleozoic Era. In that sense, ancient and modern life are one. However, within those phyla most of the early groups became extinct and were replaced with new ones at one time or another in the geologic record. In that sense, Paleozoic life is truly ancient. The evolutionary process led to many mistakes in terms of long-term survival, yet an environment vacated by extinction of one group seems never to have remained vacant for long and evolutionary radiation has never lagged far behind.

This chapter has attempted to provide only a glimpse of the processes and forms of organic evolution in a changing environment. Among the many details of historical geology left untold are the ever-changing paleogeographical distributions of lands and seas, geosynclines, and mountain belts. Nor have the orogenies within the Paleozoic been documented in sequence in time and place. Figure 29.16 summarizes the evolution of plants and animals through the three areas of abundant life.

The next chapter will take us through the Mesozoic Era, the middle time of animal life, and the Cenozoic Era, the time of new or recent life. Although the life forms changed significantly throughout these eras, the basic evolutionary mechanisms acted as they did throughout the Paleozoic Era. However, the study of new life forms will give opportunity to look into further details of the evolutionary process.

## References for further study

Colbert, E. H. (1955), *Evolution of the Vertebrates,* New York, Wiley, 479 pp.

Savage, J. M. (1963), *Evolution,* New York, Holt, Rinehart and Winston, 160 pp.

Colbert, E. H. (1965), *The Age of Reptiles,* New York, Norton, 228 pp.

Kay, M., and E. H. Colbert (1965), *Stratigraphy and Life History,* New York, Wiley, 736 pp.

Laporte, L. F. (1968), *Ancient Environments,* Englewood Cliffs, N.J., Prentice-Hall, 115 pp., chaps. 3, 6.

McAlester, A. L. (1968), *The History of Life,* Englewood Cliffs, N.J., Prentice-Hall, 151 pp.

Dunbar, C. O., and K. M. Waage (1969), *Historical Geology,* 3rd ed., New York, Wiley, 556 pp.

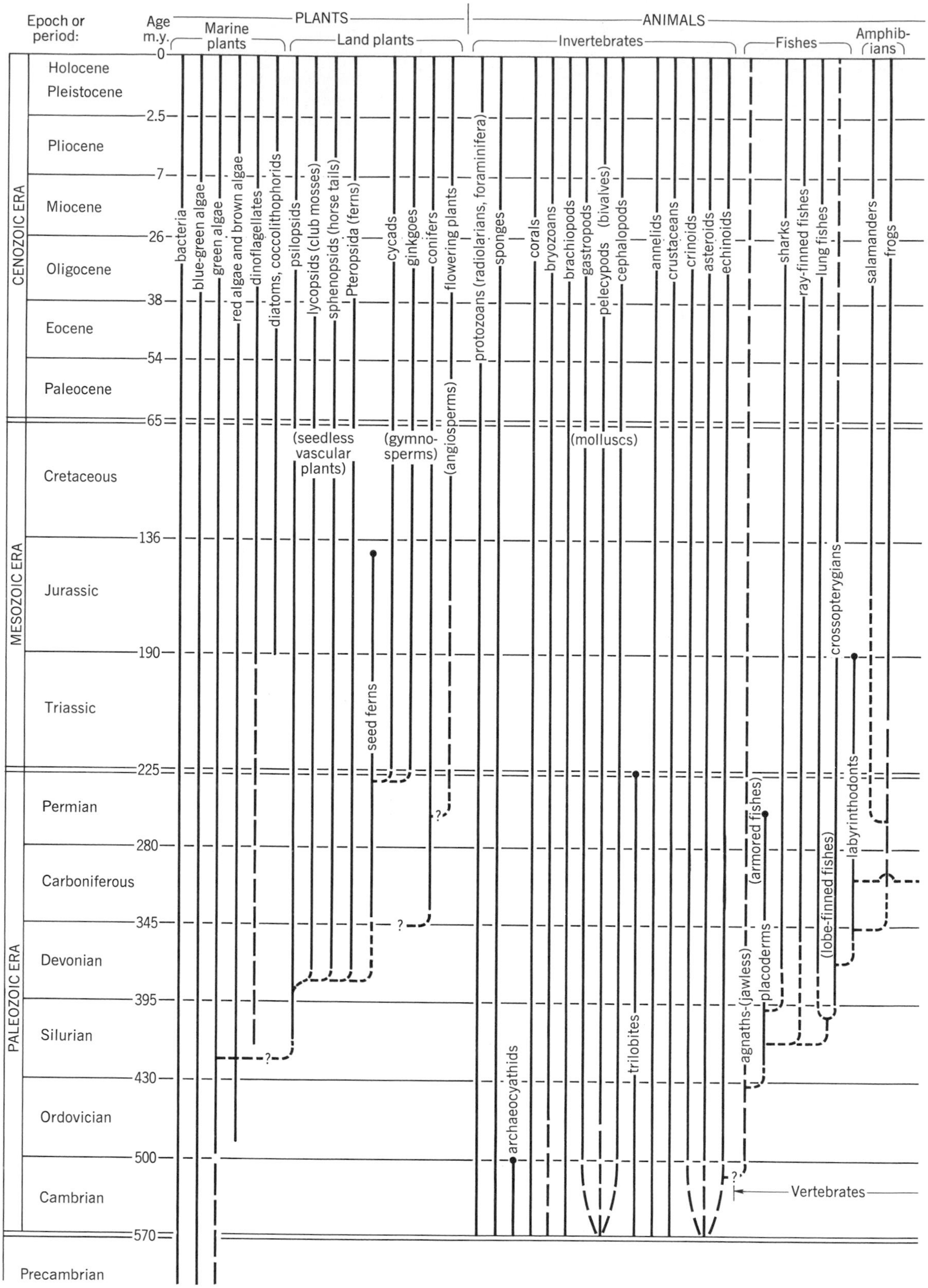

| Era | Epoch or period: | Age m.y. |
|---|---|---|
| CENOZOIC ERA | Holocene | 0 |
| | Pleistocene | |
| | | 2.5 |
| | Pliocene | |
| | | 7 |
| | Miocene | |
| | | 26 |
| | Oligocene | |
| | | 38 |
| | Eocene | |
| | | 54 |
| | Paleocene | |
| | | 65 |
| MESOZOIC ERA | Cretaceous | |
| | | 136 |
| | Jurassic | |
| | | 190 |
| | Triassic | |
| | | 225 |
| PALEOZOIC ERA | Permian | |
| | | 280 |
| | Carboniferous | |
| | | 345 |
| | Devonian | |
| | | 395 |
| | Silurian | |
| | | 430 |
| | Ordovician | |
| | | 500 |
| | Cambrian | |
| | | 570 |
| | Precambrian | |

PLANTS

Marine plants: bacteria, blue-green algae, green algae, red algae and brown algae, dinoflagellates, diatoms, coccolithophorids

Land plants: psilopsids, lycopsids (club mosses), sphenopsids (horse tails), Pteropsida (ferns) (seedless vascular plants); seed ferns; cycads, ginkgoes, conifers (gymno-sperms); flowering plants (angiosperms)

ANIMALS

Invertebrates: protozoans (radiolarians, foraminifera), sponges, archaeocyathids, corals, bryozoans, brachiopods, gastropods, pelecypods (bivalves), cephalopods (molluscs), trilobites, annelids, crustaceans, crinoids, asteroids, echinoids

Vertebrates

Fishes: agnaths-(jawless) (armored fishes), placoderms, sharks, ray-finned fishes, lung fishes, crossopterygians (lobe-finned fishes)

Amphibians: labyrinthodonts, salamanders, frogs

**FIGURE 29.16.** Summary chart of the evolution of major plant and animal groups from Cambrian time to the present. [Based on data of A. L. McAlester (1968), *The History of Life,* Englewood Cliffs, N.J., Prentice-Hall, 151 pp.]

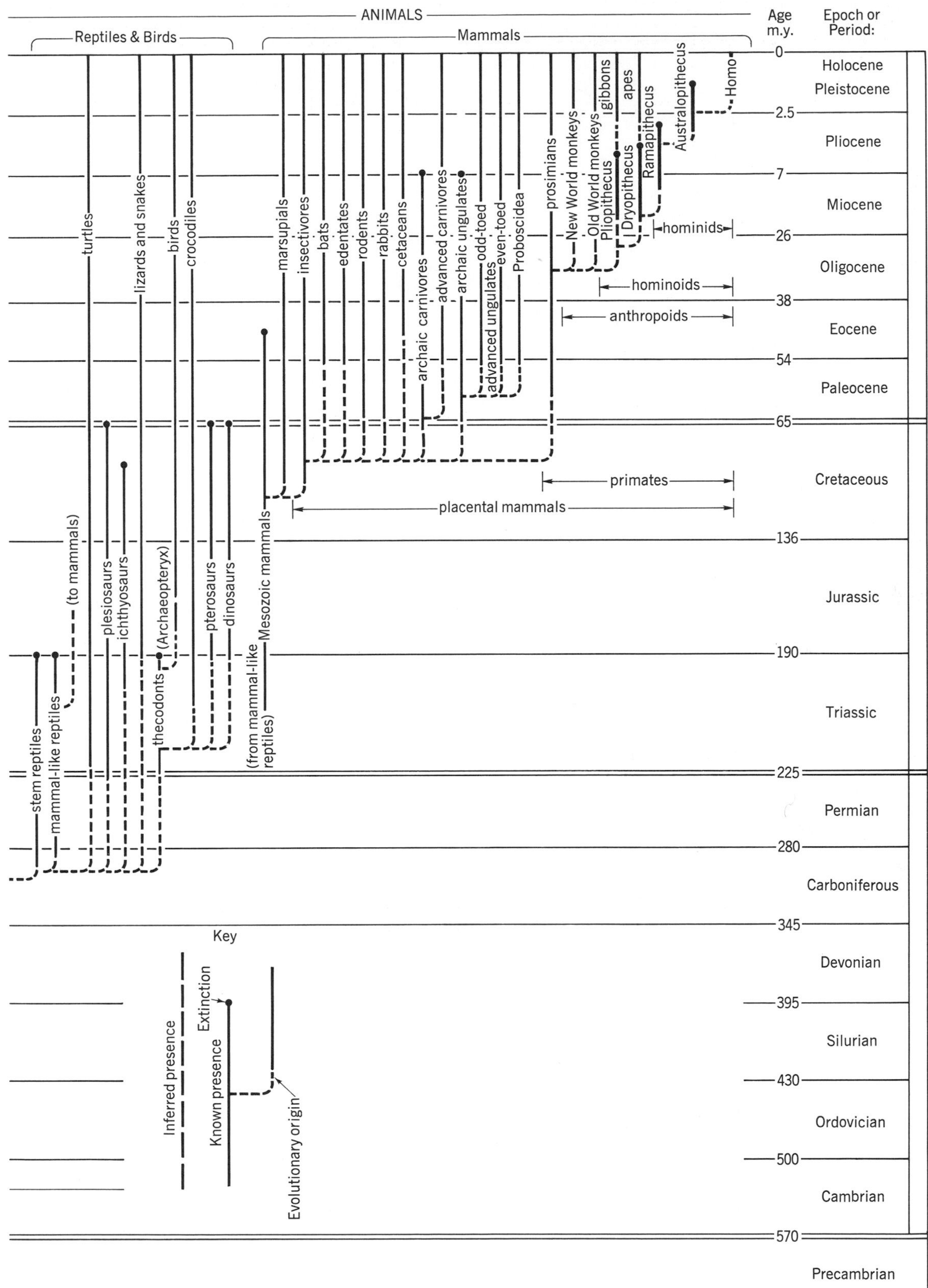
ANIMALS
Reptiles & Birds
Mammals
Age m.y.
Epoch or Period:
turtles
lizards and snakes
birds
crocodiles
marsupials
insectivores
bats
edentates
rodents
rabbits
cetaceans
archaic carnivores
advanced carnivores
archaic ungulates
advanced ungulates
odd-toed
even-toed
Proboscidea
prosimians
New World monkeys
Old World monkeys
Pliopithecus
gibbons
Dryopithecus
apes
Ramapithecus
Australopithecus
Homo
hominids
hominoids
anthropoids
primates
placental mammals
stem reptiles
mammal-like reptiles
(to mammals)
plesiosaurs
ichthyosaurs
thecodonts
(Archaeopteryx)
pterosaurs
dinosaurs
Mesozoic mammals
(from mammal-like reptiles)
0
Holocene
Pleistocene
2.5
Pliocene
7
Miocene
26
Oligocene
38
Eocene
54
Paleocene
65
Cretaceous
136
Jurassic
190
Triassic
225
Permian
280
Carboniferous
345
Devonian
395
Silurian
430
Ordovician
500
Cambrian
570
Precambrian
Key
Inferred presence
Known presence
Extinction
Evolutionary origin

# 30

# Changing life forms in a changing environment: 2. The Mesozoic and Cenozoic Eras

THE ERA OF middle life, the Mesozoic Era, offers many lessons of life adaptation to environmental opportunities as well as of survival failures. Because the Mesozoic Era saw both the rise and fall of several reptilian groups, including species of enormous individuals with almost unbelievable conformations, this era has been aptly subtitled the *Age of Reptiles*. Yet, almost equally dramatic evolutionary radiations and extinctions are to be found among the land plants and the marine invertebrates. If we are to give tentative acceptance to the hypothesis of continental drift, the Mesozoic Era represents the time of fragmentation of the continents. We must therefore look for effects of that event upon organisms incapable of crossing deep ocean basins.

## World environments of the Triassic Period

Interpretation of strata and their fossils leaves little doubt that the continents (or a single continent) stood high in average elevation as Permian time yielded to Triassic time, a condition reflecting the lingering effects of late Paleozoic orogenies. In both southern Africa and Brazil the continental deposits of the upper Permian were continued in thick sequences of sandstones, siltstones, and shales, including red beds, and also containing coal seams and the abundant remains of reptiles and land plants. Toward the end of the Triassic Period both of these regions were the sites of great outpourings of plateau basalts covering about 300,000 sq mi (800,000 sq km) in each region. In eastern North America Triassic time was also one of red-bed deposition accompanied by basaltic volcanic activity. (Refer to Chapter 26 and Figure 26.25.) Recall also that continental sediments, in large part red beds, were deposited in the Grand Canyon region in the Triassic Period (Chapter 28).

Although widespread aridity is easily inferred by the presence of red beds, their climatic significance is not really well understood. Ample precipitation for rich forest vegetation, shown by occurrence of coals, is at odds with an interpretation of aridity. Possibly extensive areas of alternately wet and dry climate existed then, as they do today over large tropical areas of the world. Absence of glacial deposits within the Triassic stratigraphic column suggests a prevailingly mild-to-warm climate.

## Evolution in the Triassic Period

As stated in the preceding chapter, the important mammal-like reptiles that dominated reptilian life of Permian time sustained heavy losses by extinctions at the close of that period. Nevertheless, many of these reptile forms persisted into the Triassic. Among the most interesting of the mammal-like reptiles was the genus *Lystrosaurus*, a small animal, somewhat resembling a hippopotamus, with massive wide-set legs (Figure 30.1). Fossil remains of *Lystrosaurus* are abundant in Triassic strata of southern Africa and are also found in India, Russia, and China. Search for *Lystrosaurus* fossils in Triassic rocks of Antarctica was intensified in view of increasing support for continental drift, since it is considered almost an impossibility for this animal to have migrated to

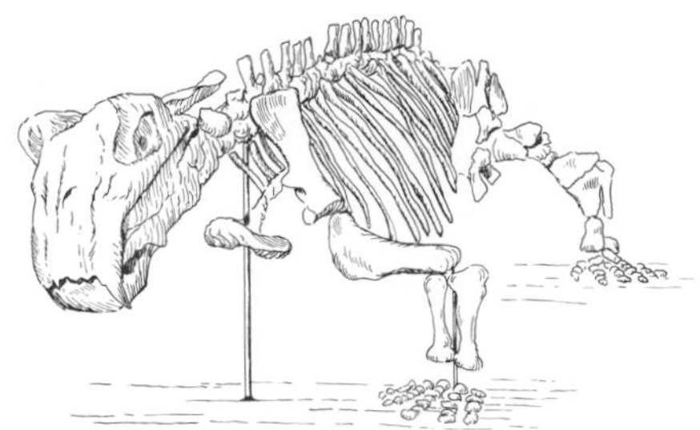

**FIGURE 30.1.** Mounted partial skeleton of *Lystrosaurus*, a mammal-like reptile of Triassic age, about 3 ft (1 m) long. (Sketched from a photograph by A. W. Crompton.)

Antarctica across the broad and deep ocean basin that now separates Antarctica from all other continents. The search met with success in December of 1969 when remains of *Lystrosaurus* were found in the Transantarctic Mountains, about 400 mi (640 km) from the South Pole. The fossil find was hailed as one of the most significant in modern times, for it throws paleontologic evidence strongly in favor of the existence of a unified single continent of Gondwanaland as late as the Triassic Period.

More important from the standpoint of evolutionary radiation was the emergence in Triassic time of several important reptile groups that were to dominate the Mesozoic Era. Evolving from the stem-reptiles of the Permian Period (see Chapter 29), were turtles, lizards and snakes, and two groups of marine reptiles now extinct, the *plesiosaurs* and the *ichthyosaurs* (Figure 30.2). Turtles, quite similar to those of today, entered

**FIGURE 30.2.** Evolution of the reptiles. Width of band shows relative abundance of groups. [Data from A. L. McAlester (1968), *The History of Life*, Englewood Cliffs, N.J., Prentice-Hall, pp. 104–105, Figure 6-1.]

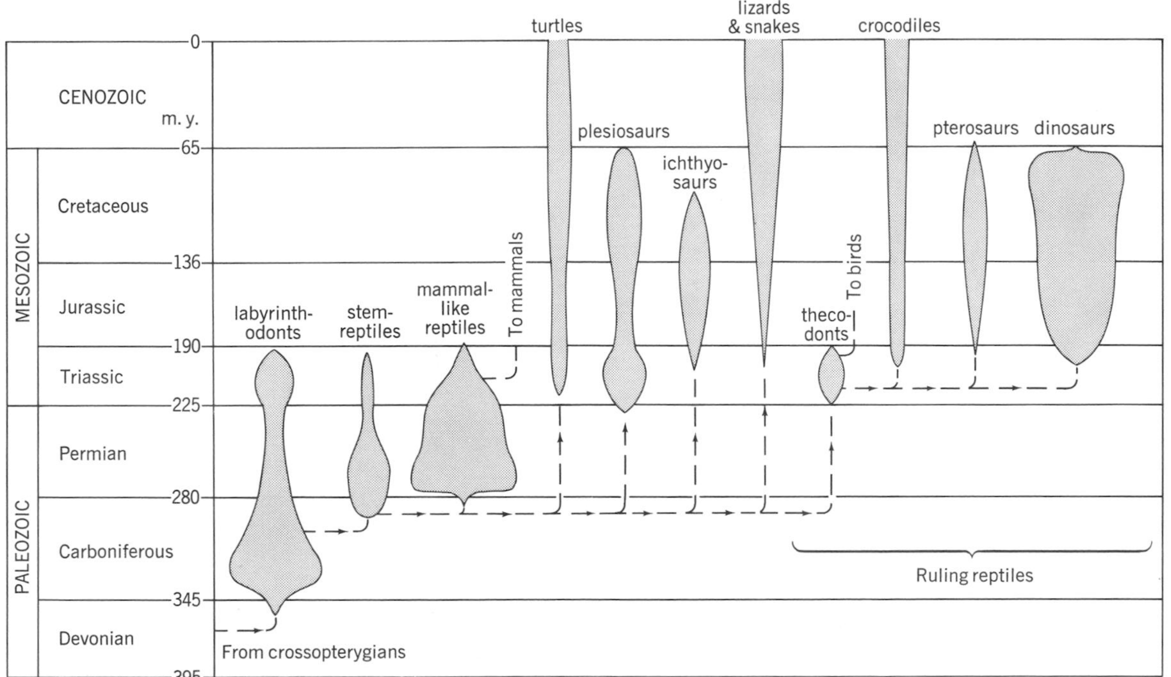

**FIGURE 30.3.** Reconstruction of plesiosaurs and ichthyosaurs. (From a painting by C. R. Knight; photograph by courtesy of American Museum of Natural History.)

the scene in the Triassic Period and persisted steadily through all succeeding time. Their success is attributed to an effective protective shell, to aquatic habits, and to being omnivorous. Lizards do not appear until the upper Triassic, and they are rarely preserved as fossils. The snakes are believed to have evolved from the lizards, but are not found as fossils until late in Mesozoic time.

The large carnivorous marine reptiles are particularly interesting, since they bear some superficial resemblance to whales (which are mammals) and can be thought of as having occupied an equivalent evolutionary niche. Like the whales of much later time, the plesiosaurs and ichthyosaurs returned from the land to the sea. Both were predatory animals living mostly on fish. They were descended from the cotylosaurs, mentioned in Chapter 29 as alligator-like stem-reptiles. The plesiosaurs were long-necked creatures with bulbous bodies and paddle-like fins (Figure 30.3). These animals reached lengths up to 50 ft (15 m). The ichthyosaurs outwardly resembled whales or dolphins, but with narrow sharply pointed jaws (Figure 30.3).

Lastly, of the reptile groups that arose from the stem-reptiles, we come to the *thecodonts,* which had evolved as small animals in the Triassic Period. The thecodonts had achieved a major evolutionary advantage by acquiring good running legs. Their limbs, instead of spreading outward, projected down, directly beneath the body. In some thecodonts the hind legs took over the running function, becoming greatly enlarged. Simultaneously the forelegs became smaller and could easily be held off the ground, developing new functions such as grasping, clawing, and holding (Figure 30.4). These bipeds were to become the ancestors of the *ruling reptiles* (dinosaurs, flying reptiles, crocodiles) and birds. By late Triassic time there had evolved small predatory bipedal dinosaurs whose agility enabled with to prey upon more sluggish reptiles and other animals.

Plant life underwent major evolutionary changes in the Triassic Period, setting the pattern for all of the remaining Mesozoic Era (Figure 29.7). Among the gymnosperms, the *cycads* and *ginkgoes* had arisen from the seed-ferns and showed rapid evolutionary radiation in Triassic time. The cycads were palm-like in appearance, although they are not related to true palms. The ginkgoes were straight-trunked trees with fan-like leaves (Figure 30.5). Representatives of both cycads and ginkgoes survived through to the present, although most became extinct at the close of the Mesozoic Era (Figure 29.7). Logs of petrified wood found in the Chinle formation of Arizona have been identified as conifers (see Chapter 28 and Figure 28.23). Specimens up to 100 ft (30 m) long and 10 ft (3 m) in basal diameter have been found, attesting to the noble stature of these conifers of Triassic forests.

Turning next to marine invertebrate animals, we find that most groups showed evolutionary expansions throughout the Mesozoic Era (Figure 29.4). An exception was the brachiopod group, which never regained importance after the extinctions of the Permian crisis.

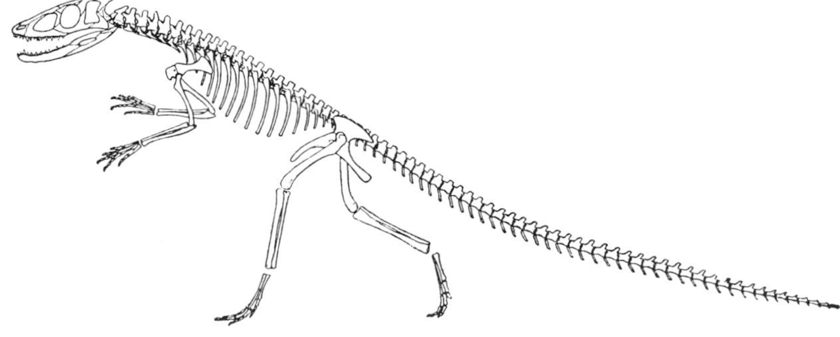

**FIGURE 30.4.** Skeleton of a thecodont reptile, about 4 ft (1.2 m) long. [From E. H. Colbert (1955), *Evolution of the Vertebrates,* New York, John Wiley & Sons, p. 149, Figure 48.]

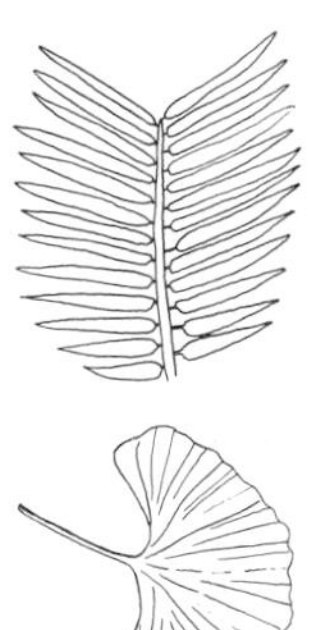

**FIGURE 30.5.** Gymnosperms of the Mesozoic Era. (*A*) Reconstruction of cycads of the Jurassic Period. Scene includes bipedal reptiles (lower left), primitive birds (center), and flying reptiles (upper part). (Painting by C. R. Knight; courtesy of the Field Museum of Natural History.) (*B*) Sketch of a fossil leaf of a Mesozoic cycad (*above*), and of a modern ginkgo leaf (*below*).

Rather than attempt to detail the Mesozoic history of the invertebrates, we shall concentrate upon the single case of the *ammonites,* which are a subclass of the cephalopods. The ammonite shell with its flaring coil is familiar to many persons through the modern "chambered nautilus" (Figure 30.6). The squid-like animal occupies the outermost chamber of the shell. Successive chambers are separated by partitions secreted at intervals during growth. On the interior of the shell, the partition forms a line known as a *suture.* In many cephalopods the suture is a simple smooth line girdling the shell. In the ammonites, however, the suture is convoluted into *saddles* and *lobes* (Figure 30.7). Patterns of sutures showing varying degrees of complexity of involution permit the ammonites to be classified. Triassic ammonites in particular had a typical suture pattern in which the saddles are smoothly rounded, while the lobes are serrated (Figure 30.7).

**FIGURE 30.6.** Cross section of a modern chambered nautilus. [Simplified from W. H. Twenhofel and R. R. Schrock (1935), *Invertebrate Paleontology,* New York, McGraw-Hill, p. 365, Figure 137.]

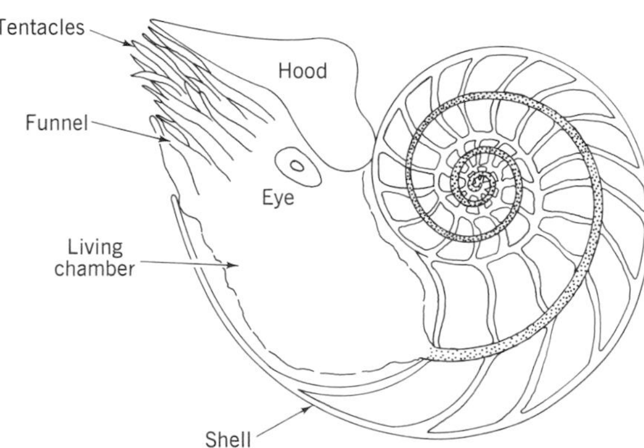


**FIGURE 30.7.** A Triassic ammonite, *Ceratites nodosus,* showing rounded saddles and serrate lobes of the suture line. [From K. von Zittel (1900), *Textbook of Paleontology,* vol. 1, London, Macmillan, p. 559, Figure 1143.]

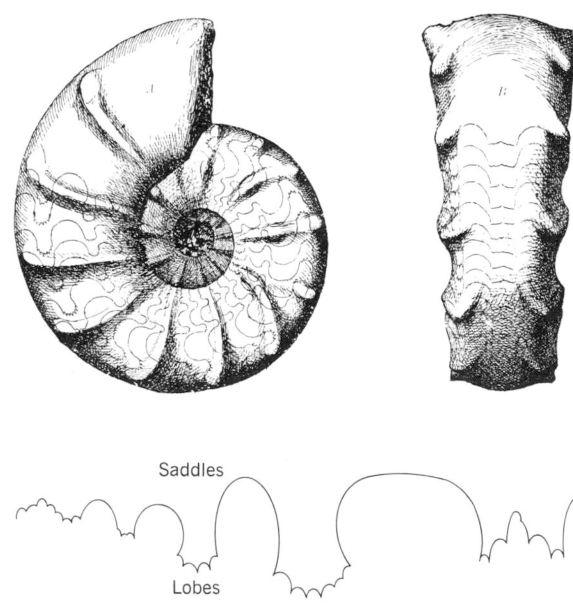

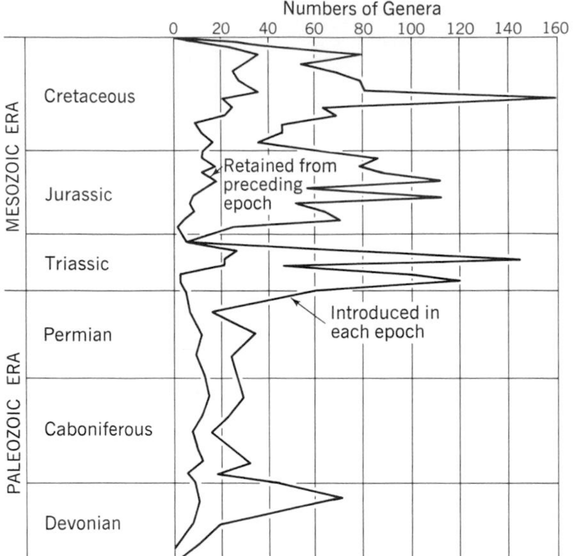


**FIGURE 30.8.** Graph of abundances of ammonite genera from Devonian through Cretaceous periods. (Data of B. Kummel.)

What is interesting about the ammonites is the manner in which extremes of evolutionary radiation followed near-extinction a number of times in the history of the group. Figure 30.8 is a graph showing numbers of genera retained from the preceding epoch of time and the numbers of new genera introduced in each epoch. Although ammonites were abundant from Devonian time to the close of the Paleozoic Era, few of these genera were retained in the early Triassic time. Instead, a large number of new genera arose in the Triassic Period, but almost all of these in turn suffered extinction at the close of that period. In fact, only one genus survived into the Jurassic, but from that single source a great evolutionary radiation occurred. A secondary decline marked the close of the Jurassic, followed by sharp radiation in the Cretaceous. The close of the Cretaceous Period, which is also the close of the Mesozoic Era, saw an almost total extinction of the Mesozoic genera. It is easy to see why the many varieties of fossil ammonites provide excellent means of distinguishing among strata of the three periods of the Mesozoic Era.

The Triassic Period also saw the evolution of modern reef-building corals and a great diversification of bivalved molluscs (pelecypods).

Our emphasis upon continental sediments and terrestrial plants and animals in the Triassic Period should not obscure the fact that important geosynclines existed in the Cordilleran, arctic, and Rocky Mountain regions of North America, as well as in Eurasia. Consequently there are thick sections of marine sediments of Triassic age, as well as continental sediments and volcanics.

## The Jurassic Period

The Jurassic Period seems to have had an abundance of favorable marine and terrestrial environments. As a consequence there developed a richly diversified fauna in shallow marine waters as well as an evolutionary radiation of reptiles, particularly the dinosaurs, on the lands. Rich forests of this period have already been referred to. Important coal seams occur in the Jurassic strata at a number of widely separated localities of the world. Occurrence of coal in the island of Spitzbergen, now situated between latitudes 75° and 80° N., has been cited in many textbooks as evidence of a mild climate of global extent. Under the hypothesis of continental drift, however, continental separation had just begun and those coal deposits which today are found at high latitudes in both hemispheres may well have been concentrated in lower latitudes at the time they were formed. But, on the other hand, the widespread occurrence of coral reef deposits and the lack of glacial deposits suggest that mildness of climate was of wide latitudinal extent. We have already seen that areas of desert existed in the Jurassic, as evidenced by the thick dune deposits of the Navajo sandstone formation in the Zion Canyon area and surrounding region (Chapter 28).

## The dinosaurs

Every child is familiar with the appearance of several varieties of the great dinosaurs of Jurassic and Cretaceous times. Even such names as *Tyrannosaurus* and *Brontosaurus* are widely known. The word *dinosaur,* a popular term, means "terrible lizard." It includes two orders distinguished according to an anatomical difference that is not readily apparent to anyone but a specialist. One order, the *Ornithischia,* had a birdlike pelvis, while a second, the *Saurischia,* had a pelvis of a type normal to reptiles. Both orders arose in the Triassic from common ancestors, the thecodonts, and gave rise to five groups of herbivorous dinosaurs and one group of carnivorous dinosaurs (Figure 30.9). By late Jurassic time all six groups had evolved into the large animals with which we are familiar.

Of those dinosaurs with a reptile-like pelvis there developed one carnivorous branch, the *theropods,* and one herbivorous branch, the *sauropods.* The theropods were three-toed bipedal animals with a high degree of mobility. They had huge heads and fiercly armed jaws. *Allosaurus,* a Jurassic theropod, attained a length of 35 ft (11 m), while *Tyrannosaurus,* the largest terrestrial predator in any time, reached a length of 50 ft (15 m) and stood 18 ft (5.5 m) high (Figure 30.10). The sauropods reverted to the quadripedal stance and a herbivorous diet. They became huge animals, perhaps sluggish in moving about, and may have had to seek safety in rivers and lakes. Largest of the sauropods, and also largest of all dinosaurs, was *Brontosaurus* of Cretaceous time, reaching a length of 65 ft (20 m) (Figure 30.11). Longer, but not as heavy, was *Diplodocus,* with a length of almost 85 ft (26 m).

Of the four groups of dinosaurs with a birdlike pelvis, two became important in the Jurassic Period. The *ornithopods* were bipedal herbivores. They culminated in Cretaceous time in the familiar *duckbill* dinosaur, *Trachodon* (Figure 30.12). These animals were bipeds and probably swift runners, as they had no armor to

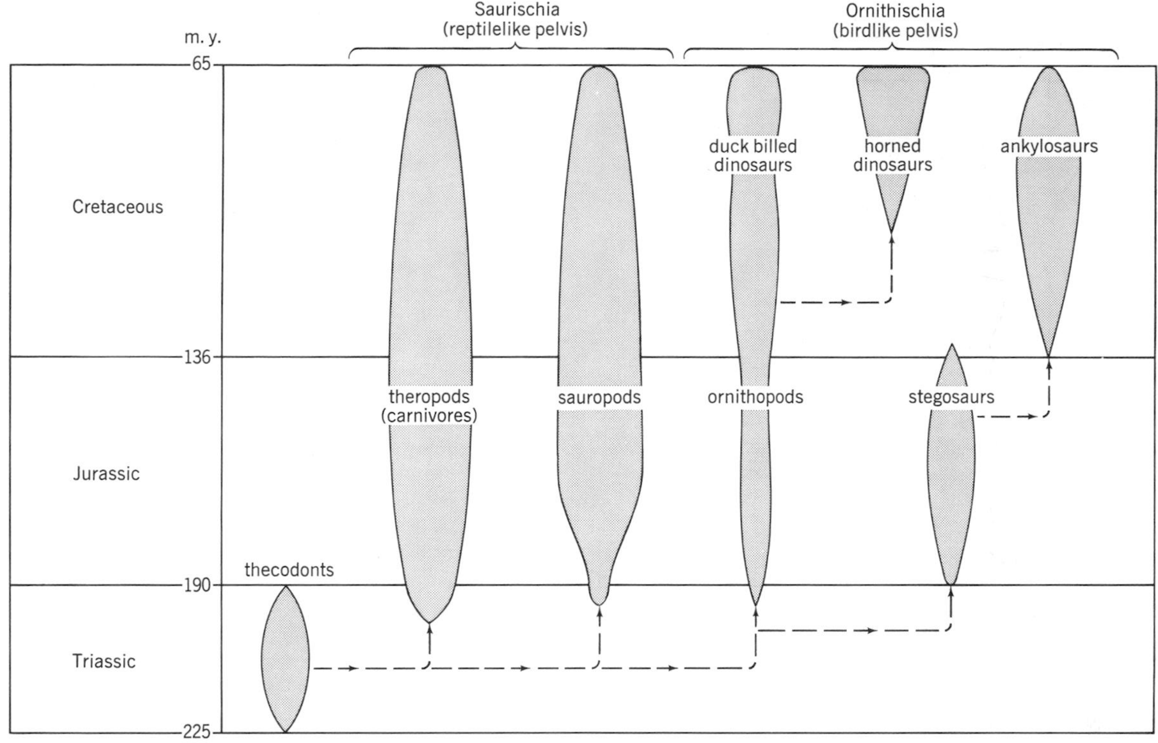


**FIGURE 30.9.** Evolution of the dinosaurs. Width of band shows relative abundance of groups. [Data from A. L. McAlester (1968), *The History of Life,* Englewood Cliffs, N.J., Prentice-Hall, p. 112, Figure 6-9.]

protect them. Also from the ornithopods there developed in the Cretaceous Period the *Ceratopsia,* or horned dinosaurs. Figure 30.13 shows the heavily armored *Triceratops* confronted by *Tyrannosaurus.*

The *stegosaurs,* protected with a bony armor, arose in late Triassic time and were important dinosaurs throughout the Jurassic Period. Paired bony plates running down the spine and a spiked tail, used as a weapon, characterize *Stegosaurus* (Figure 30.14). From the stegosaurs there evolved in the Cretaceous Period the *ankylosaurs,* heavily armored with bony plates (Figure 30.15).

## Other animals of Jurassic time

While the dinosaurs have drawn first attention among the reptiles of the Mesozoic, other groups are equally interesting. The marine reptiles have been discussed in earlier paragraphs. Another reptile group of much

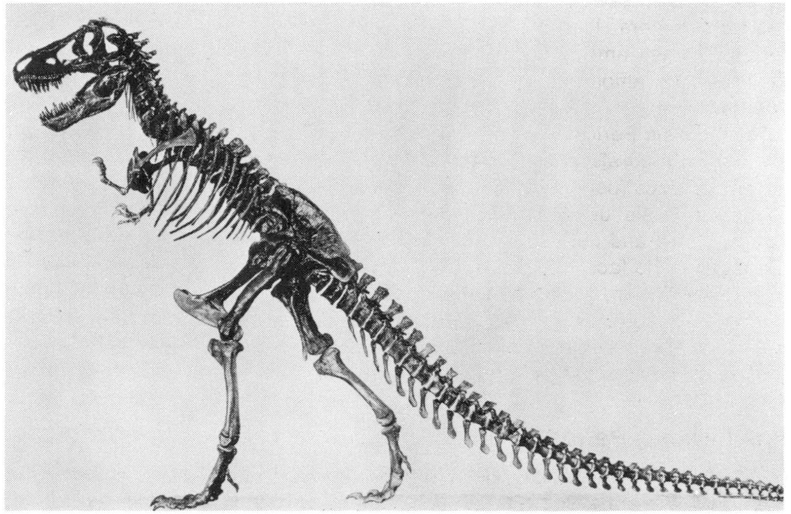

**FIGURE 30.10.** Skeleton of *Tyrannosaurus rex* of Cretaceous age. The skeleton is about 50 ft (15 m) in overall length, and about 18 ft (5.5 m) high. (Courtesy of American Museum of Natural History.)

**FIGURE 30.11.** Reconstruction of *Brontosaurus,* a herbivorous dinosaur of Jurassic age. Its over-all length reached about 65 ft (20 m). (From a painting by C. R. Knight, courtesy of Field Museum of Natural History.)

interest is the *pterosaurs,* winged bat-like animals of the Jurassic and Cretaceous periods. The example shown in Figure 30.16 had a wingspread of 20 ft (6 m) and was probably a gliding and soaring animal. The wings were formed of a thin membrane of skin supported by bones of a single elongated finger.

Probably the most celebrated of all fossil finds is the remarkably preserved skeleton and feathers of the first known bird, *Archaeopteryx* (Figure 30.17). This animal was found in Bavaria enclosed in fine-grained lithographic limestone of Jurassic age. Predecessors of this highly developed animal are unknown, since the preservation of a bird as a fossil is an unlikely event. These first birds are thought to have evolved from the thecodonts and retain many of the characteristics of those reptiles. The Jurassic birds have teeth and their skeletal structure is like that of the small reptiles. Unlike reptiles, however, birds today are warm-blooded animals. When the transition to the warm-blooded state was made is not known, but it must have been a great advantage in adapting to life in cold climates.

## Appearance of the mammals

An evolutionary event of great significance is the appearance in the Jurassic Period of the primitive mammals. These had arisen from the mammal-like reptiles, which were abundant in the Triassic Period. Mammals are distinct from reptiles in several respects. First, the young of mammals are born live—the mammalian egg is fertilized within the female body and there attains an advanced state of development before entering a hostile environment. Along with this form of reproduction, the mammal possesses milk glands to provide food for the young after birth. Second, the mammals are warm-blooded. They can not only generate heat, but can also reduce body temperatures below that of the surrounding air by means of evaporation. When provided with an insulating coat of hair, mammals can adapt to life under extremely cold conditions, as can the birds. Reptiles are cold-blooded animals, which is to say that they lack a body-heating mechanism and take on the temperatures of the surrounding air or water. Consequently reptiles require warm climates, or climates with a warm season. Reptile growth continues throughout the life of the individual, whereas a mammal quickly matures to a fixed size, which it maintains.

**FIGURE 30.12.** Reconstruction of an ornithopod dinosaur, *Trachodon mirabilis* of late Cretaceous age. Erect individual stands about 15 ft (4.5 m) high. (From a painting by C. R. Knight, courtesy of American Museum of Natural History.)

Paleontologists distinguish the early mammals from the mammal-like reptiles on the basis of jaw and tooth structures. Mammal teeth developed specialized functions, including sharp incisors at the front and massive molars for grinding at the back (Figure 30.18*A*). On the basis of teeth, the primitive mammals of the Jurassic Period are grouped into four orders, but only one of these, the *Pantotheres,* gave rise to all later mammals. By late Cretaceous time two new orders of mammals had arisen: the marsupials and the insectivores. *Marsupials* are pouch-bearing mammals, of which the kangaroo and opossum are modern survivors. *Insectivores,* represented today by the moles and shrews, were later to give rise to the placental mammals which underwent a phenomenal evolutionary radiation in the Cenozoic Era (Figure 30.18*B*). The Mesozoic Era was, however, the initial period of evolutionary experimentation for the mammals, just as the Cambrian was the period of experimentation for the marine invertebrates.

## The Cretaceous Period—close of an era

Throughout the Cretaceous Period there prevailed much the same conditions of extensive shallow epi-

**FIGURE 30.13.** *Tyrannosaurus* (*right*) confronting *Triceratops* (*left*). (Restoration of a late Cretaceous landscape by C. R. Knight, courtesy of Field Museum of Natural History.)

continental seas as in the Jurassic Period. Limestones were deposited in these seas in both Europe and North America. It is interesting to note that the name "Cretaceous" comes from the word "chalk" and was first used to designate the chalk formation that makes the white cliffs of Dover and the opposing French coast of the English Channel. Lands continued to provide favorable thermal environments for the great reptiles as well as ample supplies of plant food.

We can use the upper part of the Cretaceous Period in North America as a representative example of geosynclinal development and paleographic interpretation. Figure 30.19 is a paleogeographic map of the upper Cretaceous showing the extent of existing strata drawn upon a map of the modern continent. The most striking feature is the great Rocky Mountain Seaway extending from Alberta to Mexico. In this seaway lay the Rocky Mountain Geosyncline, shown in cross section in Figure 30.20. Great thicknesses of detrital sediments were brought into the geosyncline from Cordilleran highlands to the west. These mountains had been produced by folding and thrusting in the Nevadian orogeny which closed the Jurassic Period in this part of the continent. Farther to the west, along what is now the Pacific coast, lay another belt of marine deposition consisting of a series of deep basins. Sediments deposited in these basins were derived both from the Cordilleran highlands and from volcanic islands that are postulated to have lain to the west.

**FIGURE 30.14.** Reconstruction of *Stegosaurus,* an armor-plated dinosaur of Jurassic age. Distinctive are the small head, double row of backbone plates, and the spiked tail. This animal was about 17 ft (5 m) long and 9 ft (3 m) high. (Courtesy of American Museum of Natural History.)

While the western part of the continent was experiencing a crustal evolution of geosynclinal deposition and orogeny, the eastern half was a stable continental platform, as it had been throughout Jurassic time as well. Denudation of the exposed Canadian shield and its southern extension into the United States, continuing through both Jurassic and Cretaceous Periods, had reduced this region to a peneplain (refer to Chapter 26 and Figure 26.25). But in lower Cretaceous time the continental margins began to subside and to become submerged by shallow seas of a widening continental shelf. Submergence began in the Gulf Coast area and Florida, then spread along the eastern seaboard states until an inner limit was reached, as shown in Figure 30.19. These Cretaceous strata, with the Cenozoic strata which now rest upon them, today comprise the *Coastal Plain* geologic province of the United States. We can

**FIGURE 30.15.** Model reconstruction of *Ankylosaurus,* an armored dinosaur of the Cretaceous period. This specimen was about 15 ft (4.6 m) long. (Courtesy of American Museum of Natural History.)

**FIGURE 30.16.** Pterosaurs, gliding and soaring from marine cliffs, are shown in this restoration of a scene from the Cretaceous period. (Mural painting by Constantin Astori, courtesy of American Museum of Natural History.)

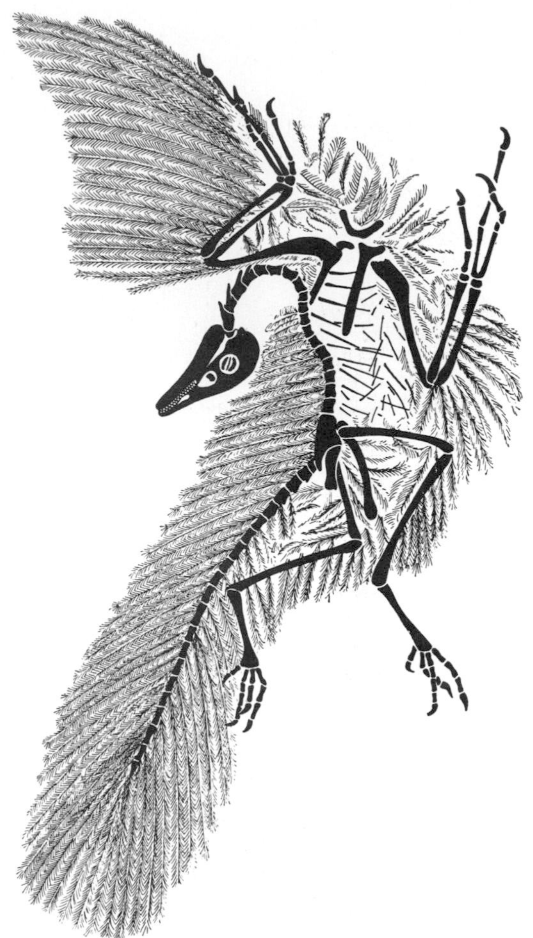

**FIGURE 30.17.** Drawing of a fossil of the earliest known bird, *Archaeopteryx.* A skeleton and impressions of the feathers were preserved in this rare specimen from the Solenhofen limestone of Jurassic age in Bavaria. The drawing is somewhat less than one-third natural size. Figure 30.5*A* shows reconstructions of this bird in its natural habitat. [From E. H. Colbert (1955), *Evolution of the Vertebrates,* New York, John Wiley & Sons, p. 177, Figure 57.]

say, then, that the architecture of the eastern half of the North American continent was largely completed by the close of the Cretaceous Period.

Late in Cretaceous time, the thick geosynclinal sediments of the Rocky Mountain geosyncline, shown in Figure 30.20, began to be raised into a chain of great anticlinal ranges. Today, these up-arched structures constitute the Rocky Mountains. This orogenic development, along with other Cretaceous orogenic movements in the western United States, is usually designated the *Laramian orogeny.* As in the case of the Appalachian orogeny that closed the Paleozoic Era, the Laramian orogeny was not a single terminal event, but was spread over a large part of the Cretaceous Period. Accompanying orogeny was intrusion of a number of great batholiths of the western United States. These are outlined in Figure 30.21.

## Rise of the flowering plants

Equally significant to the development of early mammals in the late Cretaceous time was the sudden and explosive evolutionary radiation of the *angiosperms,* those flowering plants with covered seeds (Figure 29.7). They succeeded the *gymnosperms,* or plants with naked seeds, which were the dominant vascular plants of the Mesozoic Era. The reproduction of the gymnosperms takes place through the dispersion by wind of embryonic seeds and pollen grains carrying the sperm. Union of a pollen grain with an embryonic seed allows fertilization to take place at some place on the ground far removed from the parent plant. Obviously, this mechanism has the disadvantage that the fertilization process takes place in unprotected surroundings, while the dispersal and union of spores and embryonic seeds depends upon the random actions of the wind.

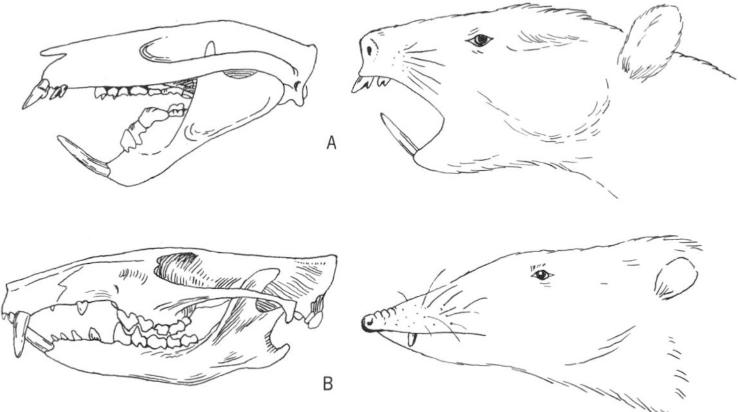


**FIGURE 30.18.** Mesozoic mammals—skulls and restorations of heads, about natural size. (*A*) A multituberculate mammal of the Jurassic period. (*B*) A shrew-like insectivore of Cretaceous age. [After C. O. Dunbar and K. M. Waage (1969), *Historical Geology,* 3rd ed., New York, John Wiley & Sons, p. 365, Figure 15-20, and p. 395, Figure 16-24.]

In the angiosperms, pollen fertilizes an embryonic seed held within the base of the flower, producing a mature seed attached to the parent plant until it is ready to be dropped to the ground. Birds or insects, attracted to the flower, carry out the pollination process, which thus has a higher degree of reliability than in the case of the wind-transport of pollen. Enclosure of the angiosperm seed in a fleshy fruit attractive to birds as food further aids in the dispersal of the seeds over long distances.

Perhaps as a result of these advances in seed fertilization and dispersal, the angiosperms underwent a phenomenal evolutionary radiation at the very end of the Mesozoic Era, so that when the Cenozoic Era began the angiosperms had already replaced the gymnosperms as the dominant vascular land plants. As the

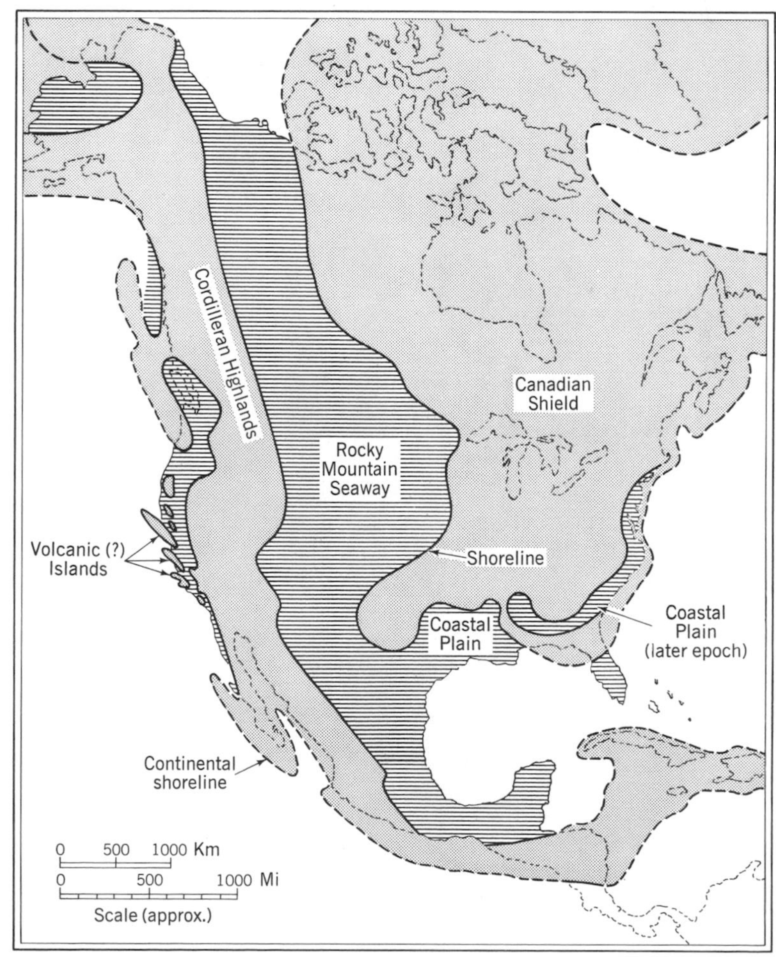


**FIGURE 30.19.** Paleogeographic map of North America in upper Cretaceous time, specifically, the *Turonian Epoch.* Extensive parts of the map are conjectural. The dark pattern shows areas receiving marine sedimentary deposits. The light pattern shows hypothetical continental limits. [Redrawn and simplified from a map by Charles Schuchert (1955), *Atlas of Paleogeographical Maps of North America,* New York, John Wiley & Sons, Map No. 73.]

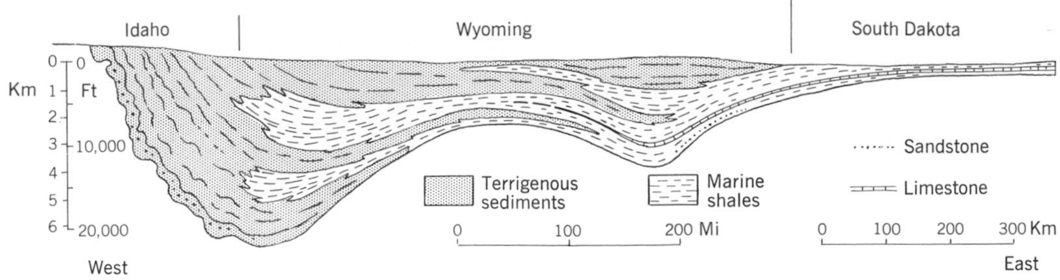


**FIGURE 30.20.** Restored stratigraphic cross section of the Rocky Mountain geosyncline, showing conditions at the close of the Cretaceous Period. Tongues of terrestrial sediments derived from sources to the west interfinger with tongues of marine sediments dominant on the east. [Redrawn and simplified from M. Kay and E. H. Colbert (1965), *Stratigraphy and Life History,* New York, John Wiley & Sons, p. 442, Figure 18-25.]

Cretaceous Period drew to a close, the cycads and ginkgoes suffered a great decline. Of the gymnosperms, only the conifers persisted into the Cenozoic Era in abundance. The ferns also made this transition in abundance (Figure 29.7).

**FIGURE 30.21.** Map of Cretaceous batholiths of western North America. The word "Batholith" has been omitted from each label. [After C. O. Dunbar and K. M. Waage (1969), *Historical Geology,* 3rd ed., New York, John Wiley & Sons, p. 376, Figure 16-7.]

## Extinctions at the close of the Cretaceous Period

The Cretaceous Period saw the culmination of the dinosaurs, along with marine reptiles, crocodiles, turtles, lizards, snakes, and flying reptiles. Dinosaurs were evidently able to migrate freely from one continent to the other. Under the hypothesis of continental drift, the continents were already separated, but may have retained points of contact. Those who do not favor continental drift call upon *land bridges* to provide migration routes. For example, migrations between Eurasia and the American continents are postulated to have taken place over a land bridge located at what is now the Bering Strait. Africa lies close to Eurasia and migratory routes pose no special problem. Australia may well have had land bridges with southwestern Asia. Antarctica, however, has an isolation that severely strains the hypothesis of land bridges in preference to continental unity preceding continental drift.

The close of the Cretaceous Period is marked by great extinctions, of which the total disappearance of all dinosaurs is the most celebrated. The large marine reptiles (not including the turtles) and flying reptiles also suffered total extinction. Recall, also, that the ammonites became almost totally extinct at this point in time. Extinctions also affected certain groups of pelecypods and cephalopods other than the ammonites. Yet other animal groups successfully made the transition into the Cenozoic Era and some reflect no special evolutionary crisis at this time.

Cause or causes of the great extinctions continue to be a matter of scientific speculation. Onset of unfavorable heat and moisture environments on land through orogeny and the reduction in areas of shallow seas offer no specific causes that might act selectively upon one animal group but not upon another. Bursts of high-energy radiation from the sun or a passing star, disease epidemics, and disruption of the food chain by destruction of one-celled planktonic organisms are mechanisms of extinction that have been suggested for consideration. The fossil record itself has yielded no direct evidence bearing on the cause of extinction of a given species or genus. Perhaps new findings of geochemistry and geophysics will shed some light on this problem.

## The Cenozoic Era

The Cenozoic Era, or era of "recent life," consists of only 65 million years of geologic time, whereas the Cretaceous Period which preceded it had a duration of 70 m.y. (see Table 26.2). The combined nine periods of Mesozoic and Paleozoic Eras average about 62 m.y. each, which is close to the total duration of the entire Cenozoic Era. Yet, because the geologic record is present in more completeness of detail as time approaches the present, the Cenozoic Era does not lack for a rich history. Much of the record of life of the Cenozoic Era is a familiar one, dominated as it is by mammals, seed-bearing plants, and invertebrate animals similar to those living today. At the same time, there were many animals, Cenozoic mammals in particular, that would seem quite bizarre if we were to encounter them on the modern landscape.

Subdivision of the Cenozoic Era into subordinate time units brings us immediately into conflicts of usage. While of minor importance in understanding the events of Cenozoic history, the alternative systems of time subdivision need to be stated at least briefly. In the older or classical tradition of geology, the Cenozoic Era contains two periods, the *Tertiary Period* and the *Quaternary Period* (Table 30.1*A*). Of these the first is

**TABLE 30.1. SUBDIVISIONS OF THE CENOZOIC ERA***

| *A* | | *B* | | Epoch | Duration | Age | |
|---|---|---|---|---|---|---|---|
| | | | | | | 0 | |
| CENOZOIC ERA | Quaternary Period | CENOZOIC ERA | Tertiary Period | Holocene (Recent) | | 11,000 yr | |
| | | | | | m.y. | m.y. | |
| CENOZOIC ERA | Quaternary Period | CENOZOIC ERA | Tertiary Period | Pleistocene | 2 | 2 | (2.5) |
| CENOZOIC ERA | Tertiary Period | CENOZOIC ERA | Tertiary Period | Pliocene | 11 | 13 | (7) |
| CENOZOIC ERA | Tertiary Period | CENOZOIC ERA | Tertiary Period | Miocene | 12 | 25 | (26) |
| CENOZOIC ERA | Tertiary Period | CENOZOIC ERA | Tertiary Period | Oligocene | 11 | 36 | (38) |
| CENOZOIC ERA | Tertiary Period | CENOZOIC ERA | Tertiary Period | Eocene | 22 | 58 | (54) |
| CENOZOIC ERA | Tertiary Period | CENOZOIC ERA | Tertiary Period | Paleocene | 7 | 65 | (65) |

* Ages from C. O. Dunbar and K. M. Waage (1969), *Historical Geology,* New York, Wiley, Figure 17-2. Figures in parentheses from A. L. McAlester (1968), *The History of Life,* Englewood Cliffs, N.J., Prentice-Hall, back end paper.

dominant in duration, spanning all but about two million years of the total duration of the era. The Quaternary Period includes the *Pleistocene Epoch* and the *Recent Epoch,* and the Tertiary Period includes the *Paleocene, Eocene, Oligocene, Miocene,* and *Pliocene Epochs.*

The newer terminology, shown in Table 30.1*B,* equates the Tertiary Period with the entire Cenozoic Era, thereby eliminating the necessity of using the name "Tertiary." In other words, we can jump directly from the era of time to the epoch of time. The epochs remain the same under the newer terminology, except that *Holocene* has been substituted for Recent, a change that has now been generally accepted. The syllable "cene," found in all epoch names and also in the first syllable of Cenozoic, comes from the Greek *kainos,* meaning "recent."

The history of the Cenozoic Era was first deciphered from fossil assemblages within a series of superimposed strata in the regions surrounding London and Paris. The English Channel cuts through what would otherwise be a single geological province. It was soon recognized that among the invertebrate faunas of this stratigraphic column the percentages of species living today increased from low values near the base to a high proportion near the top. A French paleontologist had made detailed studies of the faunas and had identified about 5000 species in the column, of which about 3000 species are now extinct. Based upon this information, the English geologist Sir Charles Lyell proposed in 1839 the following names and definitions for three epochs:

| Epoch | Percentage of Species Now Living |
|---|---|
| Pliocene ("more recent") | 30–50 |
| Miocene ("less recent") | about 16 |
| Eocene ("dawn of recent") | about 3½ |

Subsequent study led to the insertion of the Oligocene Epoch into this sequence and the addition of a Paleocene Epoch at the base to replace a part of the original Eocene. The Pleistocene Epoch, replacing what was originally the upper part of the Pliocene, is essentially equivalent to the time of widespread glaciations, the last of which ended about 10,000 to 12,000 years ago. Considerable difference of opinion exists as to the placing of a date upon the Pliocene-Pleistocene time boundary; arbitrary figures range from 1 m.y. to 2.5 m.y. for this boundary. The Holocene Epoch is, by definition, the brief interval from the end of the Pleistocene Epoch to the present.

## North America in Cenozoic time

As the Cenozoic Era began, most of the present continent of North America was land, and was to remain so throughout the entire era. Two zones of marine sedimentation were, however, of major importance from the beginning of the era. Largest of these was the continental margin from Yucatan to Florida, almost surrounding the Gulf of Mexico. Here a geosyncline persisted and deepened. Later, marine sedimentation was extended north along the Atlantic coast and reached at least as far as southern New England. Today the uplifted Cenozoic and Cretaceous strata of the Gulf Coast and Atlantic Coast constitute the Coastal Plain geologic province. (See Figures 37.31 and 37.32.)

A second zone of important marine deposition lay along the western coast of the continent. Deep but narrow basins in California received great thicknesses of detrital sediment throughout the Cenozoic Era. For example, in what is now the Great Valley of California a thickness of over 16,000 ft (5 km) of shales and sandstones was deposited in a narrow geosyncline.

Over much of the Rocky Mountain region and Great Plains the mountains raised in the Laramian orogeny were furnishing detritus to streams that flowed into intermontane basins and also eastward over the Great

Plains, depositing continental sediments during much of Cenozoic time. These strata are of particular interest because they contain the fossil remains of land animals and plants of the era.

In what is now the Alps region of southern Europe, thick accumulations of detrital sediment were being laid down close to mountain arcs raised in early Cenozoic time. Similar developments were taking place in the sites of the present Himalayan and Andean ranges and elsewhere along the zone of primary mountain arcs (see Chapter 25).

Under the hypothesis of continental drift, the Cenozoic zones of orogenic and volcanic activity, with associated basins of thick detrital sedimentation, represent the margins of lithospheric plates being crumpled against down-moving plates of oceanic crust. We have seen that the plate hypothesis explains why the eastern continental margins of the Americas were relatively stable throughout the Cenozoic Era, whereas the western margins, comprising arcs of the circumpacific belt, were zones of almost continuous volcanic and orogenic activity during the same era.

## The age of mammals

While the marine invertebrates have provided us with the means of subdividing the Cenozoic Era into epochs and lesser units of time, it is the phenomenal rise of the mammals on land that makes the era unique.

The mammals which began this spectacular evolutionary radiation were not particularly prepossessing in any sense. They were small long-tailed creatures with short legs and five-toed feet on which they walked flat-footed. The modern hedgehog has been cited as giving us a good example of the body shape and walking gait of these early mammals. Their brains were correspondingly small. Like the primitive mammals of the Jurassic and Cretaceous Periods, from which they evolved, the early Cenozoic mammals had long pointed jaws.

Evolution among the groups of mammals showed certain trends in common. Increase of size is very marked, along with a disproportionately large increase in brain size and hence in intelligence of several of the groups. Teeth have showed a high degree of specialization, the changes depending upon function. The principal divergence in tooth development has been into the high-crowned deeply involuted teeth of the grazing herbivores, as contrasted with the sharply pointed or sharpened teeth of the carnivores, adapted to tearing and cutting of flesh. One of the most striking changes setting apart one mammal group from another has been in the feet and limbs. Grazing animals of the plains regions developed the capacity to rise up on one or two toes, which became elongated and strengthened, while the remaining digits disappeared. Thus equipped, these animals would run swifty to escape from predators. Carnivores developed powerful sharp claws for slashing and holding their prey, while another mammal group developed long digits suited to tree climbing.

In this very limited review of the evolution of life forms we cannot begin to give a full picture of the Cenozoic history of mammals. Even the classification of mammals poses a formidable problem in itself. But by focusing attention upon a few evolutionary principles and trends we can at least gain some perspective about Man's place among his fellow mammals.

First, it is important to make a distinction between two groups of mammals, the *marsupials* and the *placental mammals.* Marsupials, or pouch-bearing mammals, give birth to very small immature young which must enter a pouch on the mother's abdomen. Here the offspring are suckled and grow to sufficient size to survive in the outside environment. Placental mammals retain the embryonic young in a fluid-filled membrane within the uterus where it can be nourished, until it attains an advanced state of development, through an umbilical tube receiving nutrients from a highly developed part, the *placenta,* of the membrane. This mechanism would seem to offer advantages in better protection of the young, although the marsupials have managed very well, as witness the kangaroo and opossum. Under competition, the placental mammals

**TABLE 30.2. PRINCIPAL ORDERS OF PLACENTAL MAMMALS***

| Order | Common name | Representatives |
|---|---|---|
| Insectivora | Insectivores | Shrews, moles, hedgehogs |
| Chiroptera | | Bats |
| Edentata | Edentates | Anteaters, sloths, armadillos |
| Primates | Primates | Lemurs, tarsiers, monkeys, apes, Man |
| Rodentia | Rodents | Squirrels, beavers, mice and rats, porcupines, chinchillas |
| Lagomorpha | | Rabbits, hares |
| Cetacea | Cetaceans | Whales, porpoises, dolphins |
| Carnivora | Archaic carnivores (extinct) | Credodonts |
| Carnivora | Advanced carnivores | Dogs and wolves, foxes, bears, pandas, raccoons, weasels, mink, otters, wolverines, badgers, skunks, civets, cats, sea lions, seals, walruses |
| Archaic ungulates, mostly hoof-bearing herbivores (extinct) | | |
| Perisodactyla | Odd-toed hoofed ungulates | Horses, titanotheres, tapirs, rhinoceroses |
| Artiodactyla | Even-toed hoofed ungulates | Pigs, peccaries, hippopotamuses, oreodonts, camels, deer, giraffes, pronghorns, antelopes, goats, sheep, muskoxen, cattle |
| Proboscidea | Proboscideans | Mastodons, mammoths, elephants |

* Based on data of E. H. Colbert (1955), *Evolution of the Vertebrates,* New York, Wiley, pp. 254–255.

were the more successful in terms of evolutionary radiation and came to dominate the mammal world in all continents except Australia.

The placental mammals show an extreme diversification in terms of anatomical structure and adaptation to varied environments. Altogether 28 orders evolved during the Cenozoic Era, but 12 are now extinct. Table 30.2 lists eleven of the living orders with common names and representative animals. The remaining five orders, not listed, included rather rare and bizarre creatures, such as the sea cows, aardvarks, pangolins, and conies. Several extinct orders are grouped together under the title of the *archaic ungulates.* The carnivores have been broken into two groups, the *advanced carnivores,* which include all living groups, and the *archaic carnivores,* all of which are extinct.

## Archaic mammals

As the Paleocene Epoch opened, the marsupials and insectivores, both of which were important in the Cretaceous Period, were the two most important orders on the scene (Figure 30.22). Their predecessors, the pantotheres, survived through the Paleocene Epoch but became extinct shortly thereafter. The insectivores, which were the original order of placental mammals, gave rise to all other placental mammals. Among the first to appear were two now-extinct groups, the archaic carnivores and the archaic ungulates.

The archaic carnivores, known as *creodonts,* were at first small animals with slender bodies, long tails, and short legs. Many remained small, but some became large animals, outwardly resembling bears, during the Paleocene Epoch. Most of the creodonts were extinct by Oligocene time and none remained by Pliocene time. However, in Paleocene time the creodonts had given rise to the advanced carnivores, which subsequently underwent a rapid evolutionary radiation (Figure 30.22).

The archaic ungulates were hoofed animals that quickly became the dominant herbivores in Paleocene time. No single description will fit these animals. They ranged in size from animals as small as a modern sheep to huge creatures as large as a rhinoceros (Figure 30.23). An important characteristic of these early ungulates was specialization of the teeth. The front teeth were set chisel-like across the front of the mouth, facilitating the cropping of vegetation. The rear teeth were massive, high-crowned, and with more or less square or rectangular upper surfaces adapted to grinding grasses and leaves. These dentition characteristics persisted through all later ungulates and are seen today in the modern horse, camel, and cattle. In the larger ungulates the feet were broad and short, somewhat like those of the modern elephant.

A very interesting story lies in the occupation of South America by archaic ungulates early in the Cenozoic Era. Evidently a land connection existed between North and South America in Paleocene time, enabling these animals to migrate from North America, Eurasia, and Africa, which retained land connections generally throughout the entire Cenozoic Era. From the standpoint

**FIGURE 30.22.** Evolution of the mammals. Width of band shows relative abundance of groups. [Data from A. L. McAlester (1968), *The History of Life,* Englewood Cliffs, N.J., Prentice-Hall, pp. 122–123, Figure 6-19.]

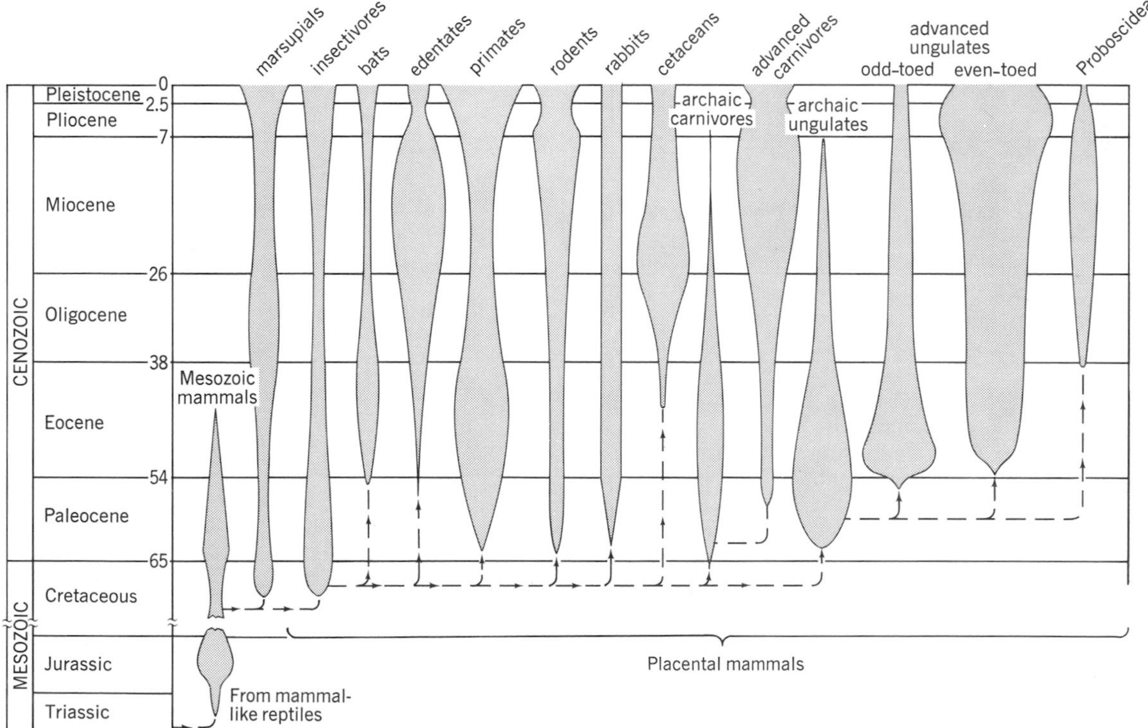

**FIGURE 30.23.** Reconstruction of *Uintatherium,* a hoofed mammal of Eocene age. This archaic ungulate attained the size of the modern African white rhinoceras. [From E. H. Colbert (1955), *Evolution of the Vertebrates,* New York, John Wiley & Sons, p. 333, Figure 93.]

of evolution of land animals, these connected continents can be designated as the World Continent. In Eocene time the connection with South America was severed and that continent became isolated. Evolutionary radiation of the ungulates continued independently in South America and led to the development of five new orders. A number of marsupials had also reached South America in Paleocene time and continued their evolution independently thereafter. Late in the Cenozoic Era, toward the end of Pliocene time, connection was reestablished with the World Continent and migrations into South America were resumed. The mixing of very diverse faunas resulted in the extinction of many of the earlier South American mammal groups, including all five primitive ungulate orders. Extinction is attributed in part to the onslaught of intelligent, cunning carnivores, and to competition from more efficient advanced ungulates, all of which invaded from the World Continent.

Along the same lines is the even stranger case of Australia, which was populated largely by marsupials in the early Cenozoic time, when a land connection existed with Eurasia. Placental mammals, on the other hand, did not establish a foothold on Australia, with the exception of bats and rodents. The connecting bridge was then broken and Australia remained isolated thereafter. In isolation free of competition from the placental mammals, the marsupials of Australia evolved into a bizarre mammalian fauna seen today in the kangaroo, wallaby, wombat, koala "bear," and Tasmanian wolf.

Evolution in isolation, seen in the examples of South America and Australia, illustrates the principle of *parallelism*[1] in evolution. The primitive ungulates performed the functions of herbivores in South America in much the same manner as the advanced ungulates served as herbivores in the World Continent. The carnivorous marsupials of South America functioned in the same manner as the advanced carnivores of the World Continent. Under parallelism of evolution, unlike animal groups perform like functions, adapting to similar environments and developing analogous structures (such as grinding teeth) of quite similar forms.

[1] Parallelism in evolution is also designated by the term *convergence,* although as strictly defined the two terms have somewhat different meanings.

## Evolution of the advanced ungulates

The advanced ungulates consist of two orders, one of which we can simply designate as *odd-toed,* the other as *even-toed* (Table 30.2). These herbivores were browsing or grazing animals and many groups were forced to develop unusual leg and foot structures to secure the speed needed to escape from the carnivores. The ability to stand on the toes favored strengthening of the middle digits at the expense of those on the sides. Thus the five toes of the ancestral ungulates were reduced to three, two, or one. The odd-toed ungulates may have three toes, with the center line of the foot running down the center toe, or a single toe equipped with a solid hoof. The three-toed foot is seen in the tapirs and rhinoceroses, and the single-toed foot in the modern horse.

Evolution of the horse throughout Cenozoic time is a particularly fine example of adaptation to the need to run swiftly (Figure 30.24). As the animal increased in size, the legs and feet were lengthened and the lateral toes were lost. Ultimately there remained only a single

**FIGURE 30.24.** Evolution of the horse forelimb, skull, and molar teeth, beginning with *Eohippus* in the Eocene Epoch and ending with modern *Equus.* Skull of *Equus* is shown as cut away to expose the molars. [Forelimbs redrawn from W. D. Matthew, courtesy of American Museum of Natural History; teeth sketched from photographs prepared by Carl O. Dunbar from collections of the Yale Peabody Museum; skulls redrawn from E. H. Colbert (1955), *Evolution of the Vertebrates,* New York, John Wiley & Sons, p. 362, Figure 103.]

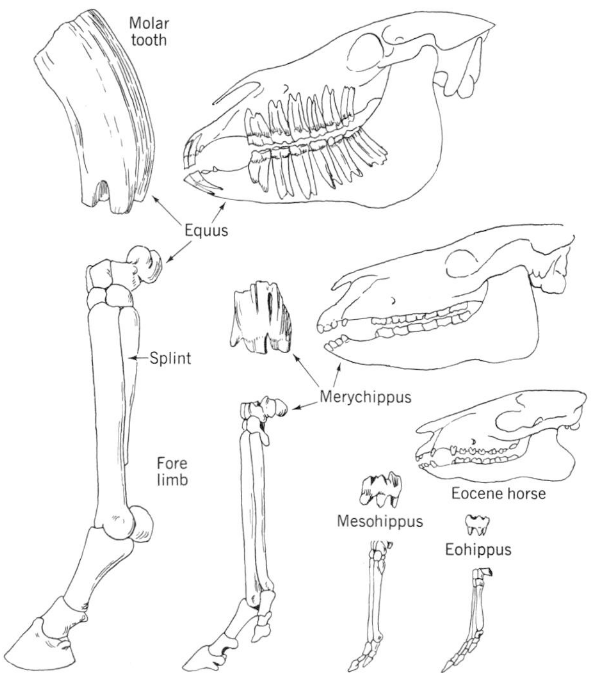

**FIGURE 30.25.** Restoration of a landscape in Nebraska during late Miocene time. *Left:* Short-legged rhinoceros. *Right:* Four-tusked mastodon. (Painting by C. R. Knight, courtesy of Field Musem of Natural History.)

toe equipped with a solid hoof. At the same time important changes took place in the skull. The sharp incisor teeth were moved forward and separated from the molars, which moved to the sides and developed higher and flatter crowns. The jaws became heavier and deeper to accommodate the larger teeth, causing the face to project farther forward beyond the eyes.

In the even-toed ungulates three digits were lost, while the remaining two developed hooves. These cloven-hoofed animals are exemplified today by the camel, giraffe, goat, sheep, and cattle.

While some ungulates were developing improved facilities for running to escape predators, others were developing enormous bulk and tough hides. An example is seen in the formidable African rhinoceros, which has a sharp horn and an armor-like hide. In Oligocene

**FIGURE 30.26.** Evolution of the primates. [Data from A. L. McAlester (1968), *The History of Life,* Englewood Cliffs, N.J., Prentice-Hall, pp. 130–131, Figure 7-1.]

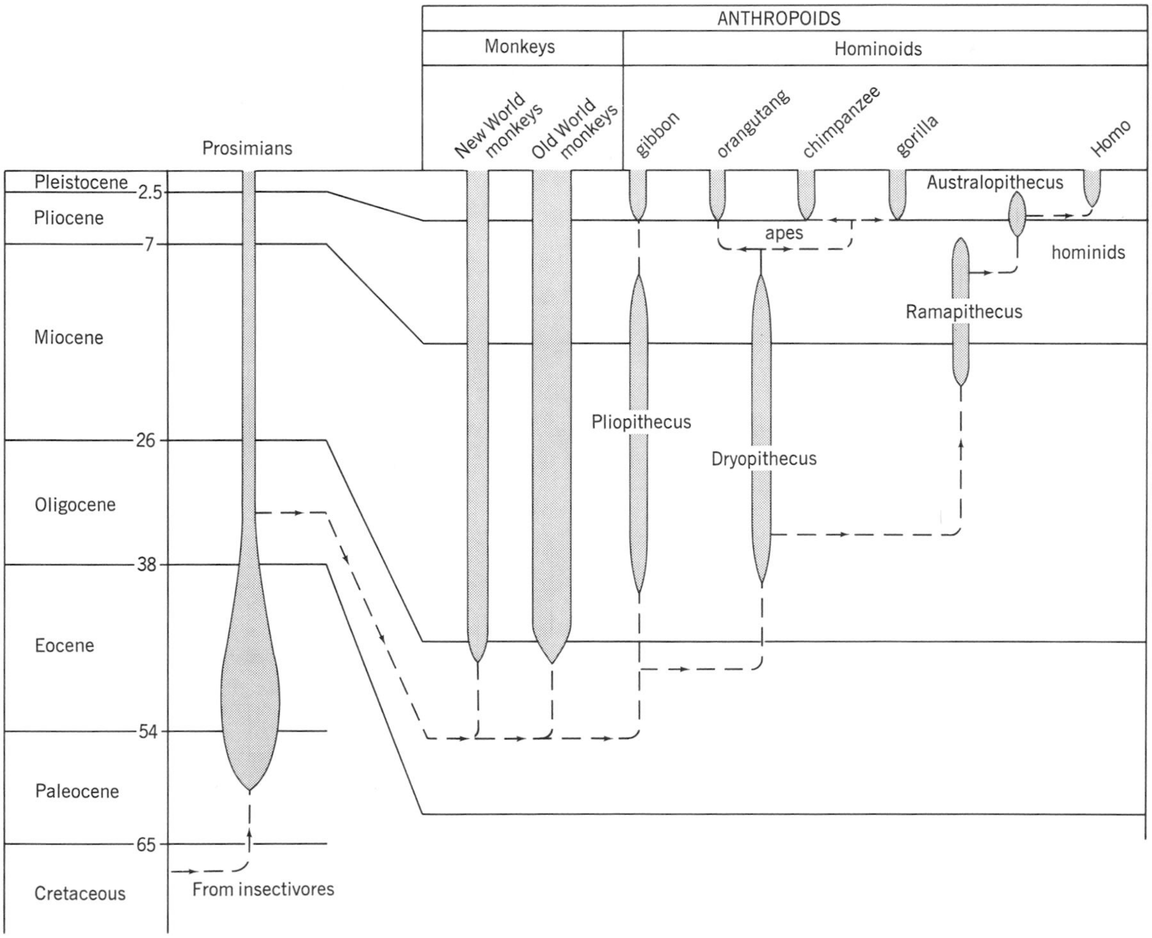

time there lived a member of the rhinoceros family known as *Baluchitherium,* which was 25 ft (7.5 m) long and had a shoulder height of 18 ft (5.5 m). This animal was the largest land mammal ever to exist. Interesting also were the *titanotheres,* a now-extinct group of the odd-toed ungulates. In Oligocene time a representative of this group reached a height of 8 ft (2.4 m).

The elephants, constituting a separate order of mammals, arose early in the Cenozoic Era from the primitive ungulates. Evolution of the long trunk and tusks seen in the modern elephant and in the extinct mastodons and mammoths of the Pleistocene Epoch was slow in coming. A four-tusked mastodon with comparatively short trunk is shown in a reconstructed landscape of late Miocene time, together with rhinoceroses, in Figure 30.25. Notice the grasses and deciduous trees, lending a modern look to the scene.

## Evolution of the primates

Leaving aside the evolutionary development of other important orders, such as the modern carnivores and the cetaceans (whales and porpoises), we turn finally to the evolution of the primates, which gave rise to men very late in the Cenozoic Era.

The order of primates consists of two suborders. The older of these, and the stem from which the remaining primates evolved, consists of the *prosimians* ("prosimian" means simply "premonkey"). The second suborder consists of the *anthropoids,* which includes monkeys, apes, and men (Figure 30.26).

Like all other orders of placental mammals, the prosimians arose early in the Cenozoic Era from the insectivores, small animals resembling the tree shrews of today. Prosimians are represented today by the lemurs, lorises, and tarsiers, which are small tree-dwelling mammals of Africa and Asia. Lemur-like prosimians entered in Paleocene time and were most abundant in the Eocene Epoch, after which they declined to minor importance. It is important to take note of this early evolution of the prosimians, because it means that the evolutionary line of Man and the other anthropoids is as old as that of most of the other mammals, following a parallel course of evolution. However, important evolutionary radiation of the higher primates was long delayed and occurred only after that of the other mammals had been largely completed.

In Oligocene time there evolved from the prosimians three primate groups—the New World monkeys, the Old World monkeys, and primitive ape-like *hominoids.* This evolution is not adequately documented by fossil evidence, but seems to have occurred rather rapidly. The hominoids are considered more closely related to the Old World monkeys than to the New World monkeys, since the former are more advanced in development.

The hominoids can be subdivided into two classes: apes and men. The common ancestor to living apes (except gibbons) and men seems to have been an early hominoid known as *Dryopithecus* (formerly known as *Proconsul*). Fossil remains of Dryopithecus are found in Miocene and Pliocene strata and consist largely of skull fragments and jaws (Figure 30.27). It is not known whether these early apes were tree-dwellers or ground-dwellers. In any case, they gave rise to the chimpanzees, gorillas, and orangutangs, as well as to the oldest-known fossil man, *Ramapithecus.* Distinction between a man and an ape in these fossils of Miocene and Pliocene age is based on dentition. Jaw fragments of *Ramapithecus* collected in India have well-preserved teeth, and these are distinctly man-like in contrast with teeth of apes (Figure 30.28). We shall continue the story of the evolution of Man in our review of the Pleistocene Epoch (Chapter 41).

The primates showed a number of important specializations that led to their rapid evolutionary radiation late in the Cenozoic Era. In adapting to forest-living, the ability to judge distances accurately at close range was a necessity and led to development of binocular vision, in which the eyes came forward on the head to lie in the same plane and hence to secure maximum overlap of vision. The senses of smell and hearing were secondary in importance, so that the olfactory equipment underwent some decline. The need to grasp tree limbs firmly led to an evolution of the hands and feet in which a thumb and first toe became opposed to the remaining four digits. Most important of all was the large increase in brain size and the consequent increase in intelligence and in ability to control the limbs. Good binocular vision enabled the hands and feet to be put to use in manipulating food and various objects, ultimately leading to the use of tools by men.

## Finishing touches to the present continental architecture

By late in the Cenozoic Era, in Miocene and Pliocene times, orogeny, vulcanism, epeirogenic crustal warpings and continental denudation brought the continents into essentially the configurations in which we find them today. The complex arrangement of exposed shields, covered shields, marginal geosynclines, basin-and-range faulted structure, alpine mountain arcs, island arcs, and trenches has been described in earlier chapters. Crustal spreading is believed to be a continuing process, while seismic and volcanic activity leave no doubt that we are still in the midst of major crustal activity.

The most important changes in continental architecture during the middle and late Cenozoic took place along what are now the primary mountain and island arcs. In the western United States Pliocene and Pleistocene time saw the elevation of the Sierra Nevada and various coastal ranges by faulting on a grand scale. The Cascade Range was built of lavas and volcanic cones, and this activity has not yet ceased. Outpourings of basaltic lavas in the Columbia Plateau occurred throughout Miocene and Pilocene time, with some activity lingering through to Holocene time.

Elsewhere in the world, orogeny in middle and late Cenozoic time continued in the Andes, the Alps, and the Himalaya, raising enormous rock masses high in elevation and culminating in folding and overthrusting of strata as young as Pliocene age and even of Pleistocene age.

From the standpoint of Man, the most important epoch of the Cenozoic Era is the Pleistocene. This

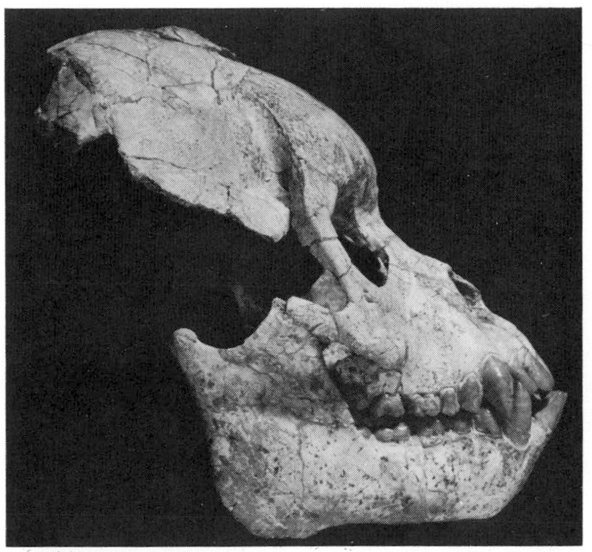

A B

**FIGURE 30.27.** *Dryopithecus,* a fossil ape from South Africa, living during the Miocene and Pliocene epochs. (*A*) Fossil skull found in 1948. (*B*) Restoration of *Dryopithecus* by Wilson. [Both illustrations reproduced by permission of the Trustees of the British Museum (Natural History).]

final two-million-year episode in the earth's history, in which modern Man evolved, saw the finishing touches to details of the landscape we know through the action of glacial ice, streams, waves, and wind. In Part Four we shall examine the activities and resultant landforms of these several forms of erosion, transportation, and deposition acting throughout Pleistocene and Holocene time.

**FIGURE 30.28.** Teeth and jaw fragment of *Ramapithecus,* the oldest fossil man, living in the Miocene and Pliocene epochs. This specimen was found in 1932 in India. (Courtesy of Peabody Museum of Natural History, Yale University.)

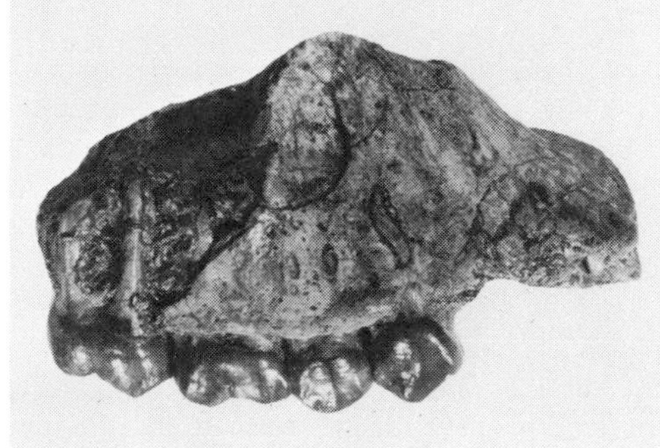

## References for further study


Colbert, E. H. (1955), *Evolution of the Vertebrates,* New York, Wiley, 479 pp.

Savage, J. M. (1963), *Evolution,* New York, Holt, Rinehart and Winston, 160 pp.

Colbert, E. H. (1965), *The Age of Reptiles,* New York, Norton, 228 pp.

Kay, M., and E. H. Colbert (1965), *Stratigraphy and Life History,* New York, Wiley, 736 pp.

Laporte, L. F. (1968), *Ancient Environments,* Englewood Cliffs, N.J., Prentice-Hall, 115 pp., chaps. 3, 6.

McAlester, A. L. (1968), *The History of Life,* Englewood Cliffs, N.J., Prentice-Hall, 151 pp.

Dunbar, C. O., and K. M. Waage (1969), *Historical Geology,* 3rd ed., New York, Wiley, 556 pp.

# 31

# The geology of planetary space

THAT THERE SHOULD be an application of geology, which deals with Earth's[1] minerals and rocks, to the vast regions of "space," a word that implies the complete absence of matter, may seem at first thought to be unreal. Yet there are many forms of matter existing in what was formerly thought to be largely empty space of the solar system. This matter exists in several states—as gas molecules and ionized particles, as liquids, and as solids. The moon, the planets and their satellites, and the asteroids are, of course, the principal bodies of solid matter to which geological investigations can be applied. There are also comets and meteoroid swarms, representing aggregations of matter, most of which is highly diffused and consists of extremely small particles.

One of the most important advances in science in the past decade or two is in the field of lunar and planetary geology. New and highly sophisticated instruments of astronomy, physics, and chemistry are being used in this expanded investigation. Not only are these instruments being operated from Earth's surface, but they are also being carried into the upper atmosphere by rockets and balloons and into space by vehicles that orbit Earth and Moon or pass close to the planets. Landing of men and instruments upon the lunar surface has been achieved, allowing samples of mineral matter to be returned to Earth for study and permitting first-hand examination of lunar materials in place.

We also have stepped up our scientific effort in analyzing and interpreting the solid objects that penetrate Earth's atmosphere and reach its solid surface. At the present time Earth receives a rain of solid objects from space. For the most part these are extremely tiny particles that fail to pass through the atmosphere, but a few objects are many tons in

[1] In this chapter, as in Chapters 4 and 5, Earth, Moon, and Sun are capitalized as proper names, to be consistent with the names of the other planets.

mass and impact the lithosphere. Earth's far-reaching gravitational field draws toward it and entraps small masses that by chance pass nearby. Literally, the planets are sweeping up debris from the solar system. It takes only a moment's reflection to make us aware that the quantity of space debris must have been vastly greater at earlier stages of planetary history, unless space objects are somehow being produced as fast as they are entrapped. Such reasoning leads to the hypothesis that the planets and their satellites grew to their present dimensions by the infall of objects of many sizes.

On Earth the processes of weathering, erosion, and sedimentation quickly erase an impact scar. Few can be found. But on the Moon such features are preserved in abundance and invite study. Paradoxically, we may learn much about the history of Earth from studying its satellite companion. Perhaps we need to rephrase the prophetic line, "Speak to the Earth and it shall teach thee," to read "Reach to the Moon and she shall teach thee." Investigation of the Moon is understandably at the forefront of physical science research today.

## Testimony of the meteorites

We cannot take samples of the matter comprising the Earth's mantle and core, although the project MOHOLE raised hopes of obtaining sample material directly from the upper mantle. However, for what it is worth in allowing controlled inferences, the evidence supplied by meteorites has been exploited with interesting results, both as to the composition of Earth's interior and the age of the members of the solar system.

Unlike the silent atmospheric penetration of the meteor, which leaves only a passing streak of light, the fall of a large meteorite is accompanied by a brilliant flash of light and by sounds resembling thunder or cannon fire. Frictional resistance with the atmosphere causes the outer surface of the object to be intensely heated, vaporized, and in consequence severely eroded. However, this heat does not penetrate to the interior of a meteorite, which reaches the earth with its original composition and structure unchanged. The single mass may explode before the impact, showering fragments over a wide area. The observed arrival of a meteorite and subsequent collection of the fragments is designated as a *fall.* Collection of a meteorite whose fall was not observed is designated as a *find.* Examples of large meteorites are shown in Figure 31.1.

Meteorites have been intensively studied, not only as to chemical composition and structure, but also as to age. They fall into three classes: (1) The *irons* (*siderites*)[2] are composed almost entirely of a nickel-iron alloy in which the nickel content ranges from 4% to 20%. (2) At the other end of the series are the *stones* (*aerolites*),[2] consisting largely of silicate minerals, mostly olivine and pyroxene, and with only 20% or less nickel-iron. Plagioclase feldspar may also be present. (3) An intermediate class of meteorites consists of the *stony irons* (*siderolites*),[2] in which silicate minerals and nickel-iron occur in about equal proportions. The nickel-iron may form a continuous medium in which spherical bodies of silicate minerals are enclosed.

[2] Terms in parentheses are now considered obsolete, but will be encountered in readings on the subject.

A

B

**FIGURE 31.1.** Two varieties of meteorites. (*A*) This stony meteorite, weighing 745 lbs (338 kg), is the largest single stony meteorite of which the fall has been observed. It struck the ground at Paragould, Arkansas, on February 17, 1930, forming a huge fireball visible over thousands of square miles. Height of the meteorite is about 2 ft (0.6 m). (Yerkes Observatory.) (*B*) The Willamette meteorite, an iron meteorite, weighs 15½ tons (14 metric tons) and is over 10 ft (3 m) long. The huge cavities were produced by rapid oxidation of the iron during fall through the atmosphere. (Courtesy of American Museum of Natural History—Hayden Planetarium.)

Structures of the meteorites have aroused much interest in their similarities to and differences from terrestrial rocks. The nickel-iron of an iron meteorite typically shows crystalline structure. When a polished surface is etched, there appear distinctive line-patterns known as *Widmanstätten figures* (Figure 31.2*B*), unknown in terrestrial iron, from which the interpretation can be made that the alloy has cooled very slowly from a high temperature. This evidence suggests that the iron meteorites are disrupted fragments of larger original masses, such as might be found in the cores of planets.

One class of stony meteorites, the *chondrites,* possess an internal structure never observed in rocks of

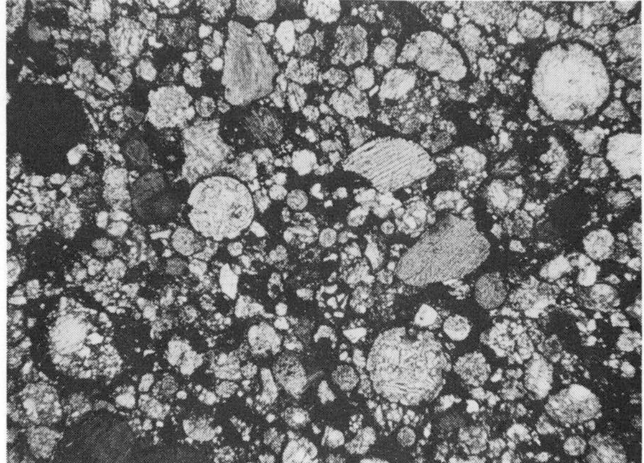

A

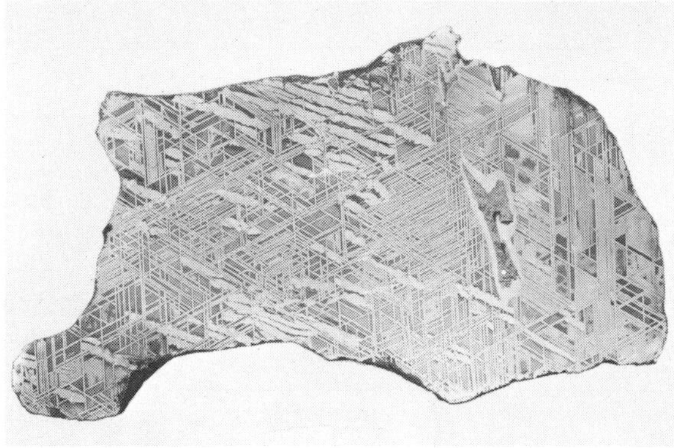

B

**FIGURE 31.2** (*A*) Microscopic photograph of a thin slice of a chondrite meteorite, showing an area about 0.4 in. (1 cm) across. [From John A. Wood (1968), *Meteorites and the Origin of Planets,* New York, McGraw-Hill, p. 18, Figure 2–3. Used with permission of the publisher.] (*B*) Widmanstätten figures etched into an iron meteorite. (Smithsonian Astrophysical Observatory photograph, courtesy of J. A. Wood.)

Earth. Olivine or pyroxene crystals occur in small rounded bodies (*chondrules*) on the order of 0.04 in. (1 mm) in diameter (Figure 31.2*A*). This structure is certainly important in the origin of the stony meteorites, but the significance is not known. However, another group of stony meteorites (*achondrites*) possesses a coarse-grained structure that resembles the structure of Earth's plutonic igneous rocks.

When the meteorites of observed falls are cataloged, their relative abundance turns out to be about as follows: stones, 94%; irons, 4½%; stony irons, 1½%. The stony meteorites are thus preponderant in bulk and most of these are chondrites possessing the unique structure noted above as not found in terrestrial rocks. These facts suggest as a working hypothesis that the chondrites represent distributed fragments of the earliest planetary bodies to be formed in the solar system. The nickel-iron meteorites can be interpreted as cores of these planetary bodies in which the process of differentiation had taken place. Stony meteorites having textures resembling terrestrial igneous rocks point to the possibility that melting and recrystallization had taken place to some degree in these original planetary bodies.

Age determinations of meteorites have been made, using the uranium–lead, potassium–argon, and rubidium–strontium methods described in Chapter 26. There is a high degree of agreement in the results pointing to the time of formation of all types of meteorites at 4.5 billion years before present. It has already been noted that this age is about 1 billion years greater than that of the oldest known crustal rocks on Earth.

We conclude from the study of meteorites that the first large solid objects of the solar system were formed rapidly by aggregation of iron-magnesium silicates and nickel-iron (and of many less abundant elements) and that this event took place about 4½ billion years ago. These first large bodies have been named *planetoids,* which simply means "bodies resembling the planets." Within the larger planetoids some melting and recrystallization evidently took place, accompanied by differentiation of the nickel-iron into core material. Melting by radiogenic heat and differentiation of silicates from nickel-iron calls for a planetoid as large as Earth or Venus. Disruption of such a planetoid into fragments, which became the asteroids and meteoroids, obviously took place at a subsequent time. The effect of exposure to cosmic rays provides evidence of the age of disruptive collisions in which meteorites were reduced to fragments on the order of 3 ft (1 m) diameter. Typically this age is on the order of one-half billion years for irons and 20 million years for stones.

The assumption that the terrestrial planets were created out of the same substance as the disrupted planetoids led to the accepted hypothesis that the Earth's core is composed of nickel-iron and the mantle of iron-magnesium silicates. This conclusion is greatly strengthened by independent evidence of the density and related physical properties of the Earth's interior derived from study of earthquake waves (Chapter 23).

## Impact features on Earth

Have meteorites of great size struck the Earth's surface to produce recognizable impact features? The largest known single meteorite is the Hoba iron, found in Southwest Africa; it weighs about 66 tons (60 metric tons) and measures 9 by 9 by 3 ft (3 x 3 x 1 m). The next five in order of size are irons weighing roughly half as much as the Hoba meteorite. However, no stony meteorites have been found whose weight is over one ton. The largest single stony meteorite observed to fall, pictured in Figure 31.1, weighs one-third of a ton.

Rarely has an observed meteorite fall produced craters of measurable dimension. One of them was the Siberian Sikhote Alin fall of February 12, 1947, witnessed by many persons. The largest iron fragment recovered weighed 2 tons (1800 kg). Funnel-shaped craters as large as 92 ft (28 m) in diameter were produced by the larger iron fragments. Soviet scientists deduced from the observed trajectory of the meteoroid trail that it was a small asteroid traveling at a speed of 25 miles per second (40 km per sec).

We therefore turn to prehistoric impacts of enormous meteorites capable of producing rimmed craters with

**FIGURE 31.3.** Oblique air view of Barringer Crater in northern Arizona. (Yerkes Observatory.)

diameters of 500 to 5000 ft (150 to 1500 m) and larger. Several fine examples of almost perfectly circular large craters with sharply defined rims have been found and examined over the continental surfaces of Earth (see Figure 31.3). In addition, there are many more circular rock structures which prove upon examination to show intense disturbance and alteration of the rock in which they occur. Altogether, perhaps fewer than one dozen large, rimmed craters and about 50 circular structures are known. The widespread availability of air photographs, combined with satellite photography, has brought the discovery of many structures of possible meteoric impact origin. We are, of course, excluding from this discussion all known volcanic craters constructed of lava and volcanic ash, as well as obvious calderas, the large craters produced by explosive demolition of a preexisting volcanic cone (Chapter 21).

At the outset, we must recognize that there exists a wide range of opinion as to the origin of circular structures, and of certain sharp-rimmed deep craters as well. Because we are treating these features under a discussion of meteorite impacts, that origin may seem to be implied to be the favored hypothesis. However, a substantial number of geologists who have given intensive study to circular structures hold that they may have been formed by internal earth processes—for example, by uplift under pressure of rising magma, followed by collapse. Explosion by volcanic gases is also postulated as a cratering mechanism and has had many adherents, who refer to the circular forms as *cryptovolcanic structures.* Those who hold that the circular structures are extraterrestrial in origin, resulting from impact of large objects from space, refer to the same forms as *astroblemes* (freely translated as "starwounds"). While originally possessing sharp-rimmed craters, the astroblemes today represent only the deeply eroded basal parts of the original impact structures.

Perhaps the finest example of a large circular rimmed crater of almost certain meteoritic impact origin is the Barringer Crater (formerly known as Meteor Crater) in Arizona (Figure 31.3). The diameter of this crater is 4000 ft (1200 m) and its depth almost 600 ft (180 m). The rim rises about 150 ft (46 m) above the surrounding plateau surface, which consists of almost horizontal limestone strata. Rock fragments have been found scattered over a radius of 6 mi (10 km) from the crater center, while meteoritic iron fragments numbering in the thousands have been collected from the immediate area. Other evidence of severe shock forces and high temperatures comes from the finding of closely fractured rock, silica glass, and a unique silica mineral known as *coesite.* The latter was produced by severe shock pressures from a pure sandstone formation underlying the limestone of the plateau. Although boreholes and shafts were put down in the bottom of the crater in an attempt to locate a large iron body, none was found. It has been calculated that an impacting meteorite capable of producing such a crater would have disintegrated and partially vaporized during impact, leaving no single large mass intact. Carefully derived estimates of the impacting object specify that it was a 63,000-ton ($56 \times 10^6$ kg) iron meteorite about 100 ft (30 m) in long dimension, and that it was traveling at about 34,000 miles per hour (15 km per sec) when impact occurred.

Figure 31.4 shows inferred steps in the formation of a simple meteorite crater of moderate size, such as the Barringer Crater. Kinetic energy, estimated to be on the order of $10^{21}$ to $10^{28}$ ergs, is almost instantly transferred to the ground by a shock wave, which intensely fractures and disintegrates the rock around the point of impact. As the shock wave is reflected back to the meteorite body, it is fragmented into thousands of pieces and partly vaporized as well. Large amounts of fragmental debris are then thrown out, while the solid bedrock is forced upward and outward to create the crater rim. A great deal of rock material falls back into the crater, filling in the bottom, where melted rock may be concealed.

A number of other craters of generally accepted meteoritic origin deserve mention. Comparatively small but abundantly endowed with nickel-iron fragments are the Odessa craters in Texas, evidently formed by two large impacting fragments. A group of smaller craters in Argentina, the Campo del Cielo swarm, are associated with meteoritic iron fragments and silica glass. Within Australia four outstanding crater localities are known, all with meteoritic iron. One of these, the Wolf

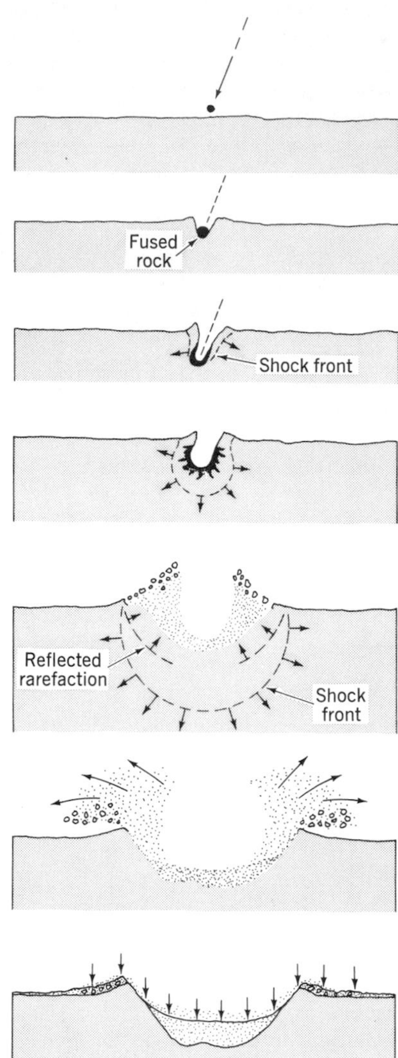


**FIGURE 31.4.** Hypothetical stages in the formation of a meteorite impact crater. [Modified from E. Anders (1965), *Scientific American,* October 1965, p. 34. Data of E. M. Shoemaker and U.S. Geological Survey.]

Creek Crater, is remarkably perfect in form, the rim being 2800 ft (850 m) in diameter (Figure 31.5). In Estonia, the Kaalijarv Crater is accepted as being of meteoritic origin, as is the Aouelloul Crater in Mauritania. Altogether, the list consists of only eight craters (or crater groups) with which meteoritic iron is associated.

Of those well-formed large craters whose origin is disputed, and which have not revealed meteoritic iron, the New Quebec Crater of Canada is perhaps the most outstanding (Figure 31.6). It is exceptionally large: two miles (3.2 km) in diameter, and 1300 ft (400 m) deep. The rim rises 300 to 500 ft (90 to 150 m) above the surrounding land surface. The bedrock, which consists of gneiss and granite of the Canadian Shield, is intensely fractured. Similar in some respects is the Ashanti Crater of Ghana, which contains a lake over 6

**FIGURE 31.5.** Oblique air view of Wolf Creek Crater, Western Australia. The crater is about 0.5 mi (0.8 km) in diameter, and the rim rises about 200 ft (60 m) above the flat sediment-filled floor. (Photograph by courtesy of R. M. L. Elliott, West Australian Petroleum Pty. Limited.)

mi (10 km) in diameter. This crater also lies in ancient shield rocks.

Large circular structures lacking a rim or crater, presumably because of erosional removal, run to much larger diameters than the craters listed above. About

**FIGURE 31.6.** Vertical air view of New Quebec Crater (Chubb Crater), located at about lat. 61° N., long. 73½° W. in northern Quebec. The depression, 2 mi (3.2 km) wide and 1300 ft (400 m) deep, is formed in gneisses of Precambrian age. (Mosaic air photograph by courtesy of K. L. Currie, Geological Survey of Canada, Dept. of Energy, Mines & Resources.)

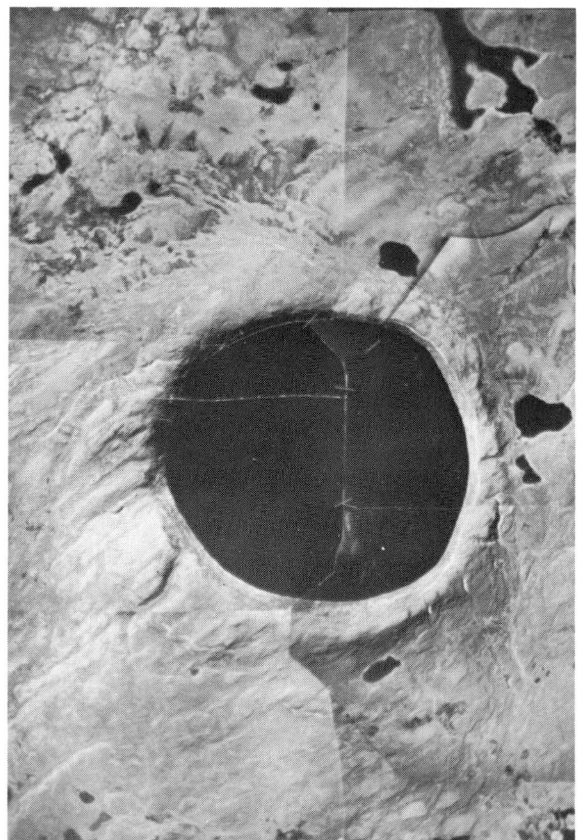

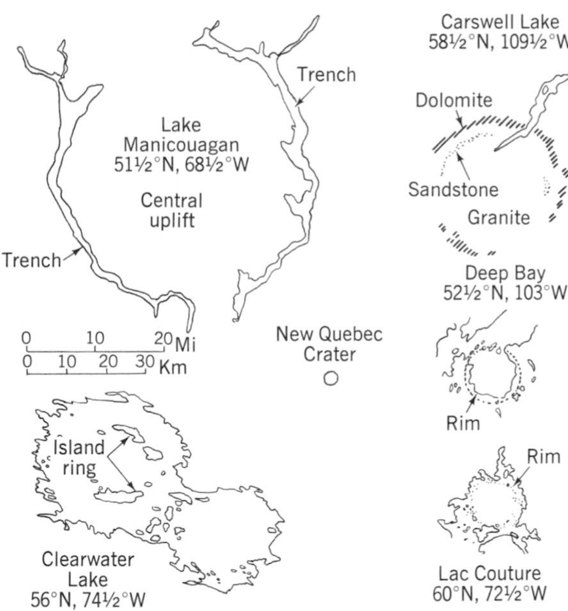


**FIGURE 31.7.** Large circular structures of the Canadian Shield. Solid lines are lake shorelines. New Quebec Crater, shown for scale comparison, is pictured in Figure 31.6. [After M. R. Dence (1965), *Annals New York Acad. Sci.*, vol. 123, p. 943, Figure 2.]

a dozen such structures have been found in the Canadian shield. Typically, they are represented by circular depressions containing lakes (Figure 31.7). If these structures are astroblemes, as some investigators claim, they represent extremely ancient impacts, perhaps dating back as far as 200 to 300 million years, when the Canadian Shield had been reduced to a low continental platform.

From a review of craters and circular structures of our Earth we can draw the conclusion that impacts by large meteorites have been extremely rare events in recent geologic time. Perhaps the number has been on the order of a half dozen occurrences in a million years. Moreover, possible meteor impact features of greater age are widely scattered and the number of impacts appears to have been small over the past half billion years. But these frequencies are what we might expect, on the assumption that meteorites are not being produced in the modern solar system. If they represent space debris that continues to be swept up by planets and satellites, the frequency of impacts should be small in later geologic eras compared with a high frequency in the early stages of planetary formation. We must therefore look to a celestial body on which impact features would have been preserved with little or no erosion for the entire 4½ billion years since Earth and the other planets formed. Two such bodies are available for study. They are our Moon and the planet Mars. Perhaps in the future Mercury will also provide a third body for study.

## Tektites

Among the most puzzling and controversial natural mineral objects found on Earth's surface are small pieces of glass ranging in size from a sand grain to individuals weighing as much as 2 lbs (1 kg). These glass objects are named *tektites.* The collection and scientific study of tektites spans the past 200 years, yet evidence as to their age and mode of origin is largely a product of intensive research through use of modern tools and disciplines of science applied within the past decade or two.

One of the most interesting and unique features of tektites relates to their shapes. Usually smoothly rounded in contour, they take the symmetrical forms of buttons, dumbbells, tear-drops, disks, winged bodies, and rods (Figure 31.8). The glass is colored green, brown, or amber. In the past they have been collected for use as ornaments and were even shaped by Stone-Age Man into weapon points.

Facts concerning the areas of concentration of tektite finds are quite well understood and free of controversy. There appear to be five world localities of occurrence, designated as *strewnfields* (Figure 31.9). Largest of the strewnfields is the Australasia field, which includes southern Australia, the Philippine Islands, Indonesia, and parts of Indochina and China. Recently, extremely minute tektites, known as *microtektites,* have been found in deep-sea sediments from a broad area of the Indian Ocean, as shown in Figure 31.9, and constitute a part of the single Australasia strewnfield. A second strewnfield is that of the Ivory Coast. Microtektites have also been recovered from deep-sea sediments off this coast. A third locality is in Czechoslovakia. Here tektites occur in small areas in Moravia and Bohemia. The name *moldavites* has been locally applied to these tektites. A fourth strewnfield is the southern United States, where tektites have been found at two localities, one in Texas and one in Georgia. A fifth strewnfield is in the Libyan desert.

The age of tektites, representing the time at which they last solidified from a molten state, has been measured through the potassium–argon age determination method. Within each strewnfield the age is the same for all specimens, but ages differ greatly from one strewnfield to another. The results are:

| | |
|---|---|
| Australasia field | 700,000 years |
| Ivory Coast field | 1.1 million years |
| Czechoslovakia field | 15 million years |
| United States field | 34 million years |
| Libya field | 34 million years |

Microtektites of the Indian Ocean are found in sediments deposited near the close of the Matuyama geomagnetic reversal, an event dated at 700,000 years, and hence in agreement with the geochemical date for tektites on land in the Australasian strewnfield.

Facts concerning the chemical composition of tektites must also be taken into account in hypotheses of their origin. All are glasses high in silica, which ranges from 70% $SiO_2$ in the Australasian tektites to as high as 97.6% $SiO_2$ for those of the Libyan strewnfield. Aluminum oxide is the second-ranking constituent, forming about 13% of the Australasian tektite glass. Iron, magnesium, and calcium are important lesser constituents. Tektite glass is unique in having a very high melting point (higher than that of Pyrex glass) and a low coefficient of expansion. Chemically, then, tektite

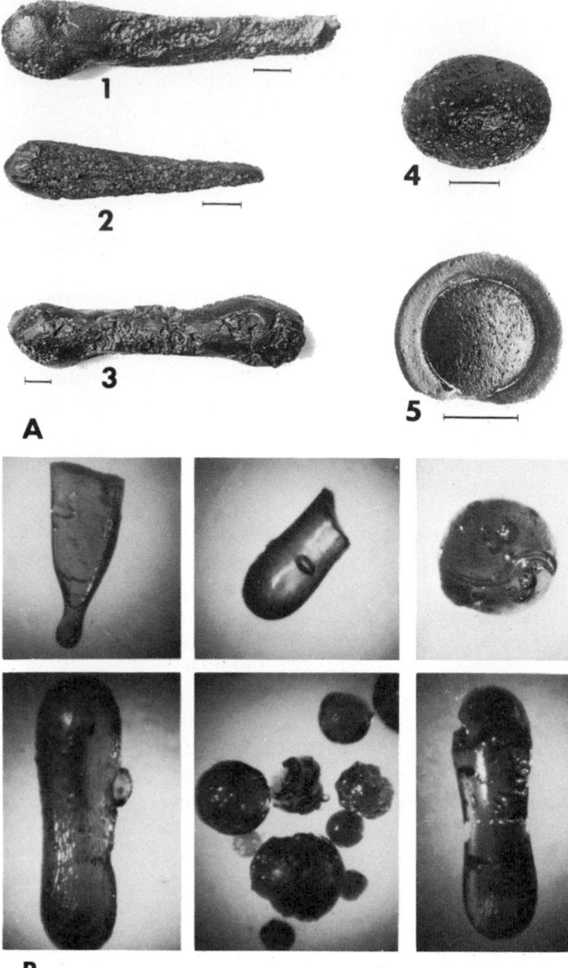

**FIGURE 31.8.** (*A*) Tektites: *1* and *2*, teardrop forms, Lang Bien, South Vietnam; *3*, dumbbell, Tan Hai Island, China; *4*, spherical form, Philippine Islands; *5*, flanged button form, Australia. Length of bar: 1 cm. (Photographs by Virgil E. Barnes, Director of Tektite Research, Bureau of Economic Geology, University of Texas at Austin.) (*B*) Microtektites from deep-sea cores off the Ivory Coast. All are less than 0.05 in. (1.3 mm) in size. (Courtesy of Billy P. Glass, Lamont-Doherty Geological Observatory of Columbia University.)

glass with its high silica content is not the same as any glass that might be produced by melting of a stony meteorite.

The shapes of tektites show clearly that they solidified from droplets free to adjust their outlines to surface tension. Moreover, many show markings, such as grooves, that suggest the effects of attrition by air resistance during their fall. All opinion seems to be in agreement that tektites solidified from liquid drops falling through the atmosphere.

Until about a decade ago, the most commonly held hypotheses of tektite origin invoked an extraterrestrial source. One such hypothesis is that a disrupted planetoid provided tektites as well as the more generally recognized forms of meteorites. Under this hypothesis, tektites are classed as one variety of meteorite, along with stones and irons.

If the tektite material was derived from a disrupted planetoid, the high-silica rock must have been already segregated from more basic rock within the planetoid before its disruption. Layers or pools of glassy silicate have been postulated as forming upon the surface of the planetoid, providing a source of tektite glass.

Another extraterrestrial hypothesis holds that tektite glass is derived from comets. Melted by intense heat from passage near the sun, the silicate remains of the comet were intercepted by the Earth and provided the molten matter for a shower of tektites.

A still different extraterrestrial hypothesis, defended by John A. O'Keefe and others, suggests that huge meteoritic masses, impacting the surface of the Moon, forced lunar surface matter into space orbits, and that some of these chunks of lunar materials reached the Earth. This hypothesis faces the difficulty of explaining how high-silica rocks came to exist on the Moon's surface. Lunar rocks thus far analyzed are mafic in composition, a fact that might appear to rule out a lunar origin for tektites. However, glassy matter in lunar rock samples chemically resembles some tektites, so that a lunar origin of tektites is not ruled out.

The lunar hypothesis has been modified to suggest that large solid masses, thrown from the Moon by an impacting meteorite, came into elliptical orbit as Earth satellites. Finally these objects entered the Earth's atmosphere at low grazing angles. Intensely heated by atmospheric friction, the surfaces of these satellites were fused and gave off droplets which solidified into tektites during downward fall through the atmosphere. This hypothesis explains the broad pattern of tektite distribution over vast strewnfields.

A different group of hypotheses regards tektite glass as being of terrestrial origin, derived from melting of rocks of the earth's surface. Melting occurred through the impact of large meteorites, producing craters from which surface material was thrown upward into the atmosphere in a molten state. The tektites were formed as these melted particles fell back through the atmosphere. One line of evidence has recently been brought forward to support the terrestrial hypothesis. If the tektite glass was derived from surface rocks of the Earth, the age of the mineral matter prior to its melting should agree with the age of rocks in the supposed area of impact of the meteorite.

Based upon the ratio of isotopes of strontium and rubidium, it has been possible to derive the age of the original rock material from which the glass of tektites was formed. When this is done, the age of the Australasian, Czechoslovakian, and United States tektite materials proves to be similar, about 300 to 400 million years. In the case of the Czechoslovakia area, crystalline rocks of the tektite region are also of 300-million-year age and it can be reasoned that these rocks provided the source of those tektites. Upon similar age analysis, tektite material of the Ivory Coast field yields an original age of 2 billion years, which is the same as for shield rocks exposed in an area of Ghana about 200 mi (300 km) east of the tektite field —moreover, a possible meteorite crater, today containing Lake Bosumtwi, can be postulated as the point of impact of the meteorite that produced these tektites.

Diversity of hypotheses of tektite origin is extreme.

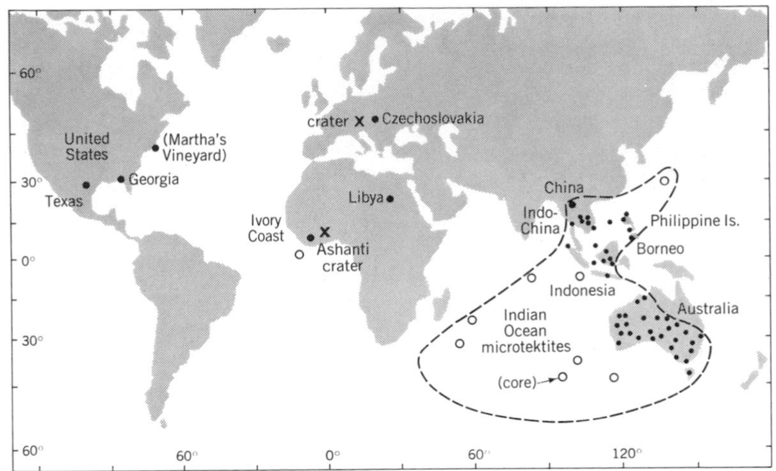


**FIGURE 31.9.** World distribution of tektites. Black dots show generalized positions of tektite localities. Open circles show locations of deep-sea cores in which microtektites have been found. [Data from V. Barnes, (1961), *Scientific American,* November 1961; and W. Gentner *et al.* (1970), *Science,* vol. 168, p. 359, Figure 1.]

The various lines of evidence seem uncompromisingly at odds. Perhaps the only area of complete agreement among carefully-considered hypotheses of tektite origin is that the showers of droplets were generated in some manner by collisions of extraterrestrial masses with Earth and its atmosphere. Further sampling of the Moon's surface may ultimately decide whether the tektite glass could be of lunar material, although evidence found thus far is indecisive on this question. In the meantime, intensive researches by scientists in many disciplines—among them geochemistry, geology, astronomy, planetary science, and lunar science—are sure to bring new evidence to bear upon this most puzzling problem of the small glass objects.

## The lunar environment

If we are to interpret correctly the physical features of the Moon's surface, it will first be necessary to consider the surface environment of that satellite. Environmental factors include the Moon's gravity field, lack of both atmosphere and hydrosphere, intensity of incoming and outgoing radiation, and surface temperatures. All of these factors show striking differences when compared with the environment of Earth.

Gravity[3] on the Moon's surface is about one-sixth as great as on Earth. Therefore, an object that weighs 6 pounds on Earth will weigh only 1 pound on the Moon. This relatively small gravity is of great importance in interpreting the Moon's surface and history. For example, rock of the same strength as rock on Earth could stand without collapse in much higher cliffs and peaks on the Moon than on Earth. Objects thrown upward at an angle from the Moon (as when the Moon is struck by a large meteoroid) will travel much higher and farther than under the same impetus on Earth. Lack of sufficient gravity has cost the Moon the loss of any atmosphere that it may have once possessed, since the escape velocities of the gas molecules will be comparatively low.[4] Lack of a lunar atmosphere is shown by the fact that the rays from a star are instantaneously cut off as the Moon's edge passes over the star. Were a gaseous envelope present on the Moon, those rays would be bent, causing the light to be cut off over a definite span of time and a slight alteration by refraction of the star's apparent position.

Lacking an atmosphere, the Moon's surface intercepts the Sun's radiation on a perpendicular surface with the full value of 2 langleys per minute. The Moon's albedo (percent of reflected energy) is small (only about 7%), thus most incoming solar energy is absorbed by the Moon's surface. The effect is to cause intense surface heating during the long lunar day of about two weeks' duration (Figure 31.10). With the Sun's rays striking at a high angle for several days continuously, surface temperatures at lunar noon reach 214° F (101° C). Correspondingly, conditions on the dark side of the Moon reach opposite extremes of cold during the long lunar night. With no atmosphere to return long-wave radiation, surface temperatures

[3] Gravity is defined as the attraction which Earth or Moon exerts upon a very small mass located at its surface.
[4] Earth's escape velocity is 7 mi (11.2 km) per second, in comparison with only 1½ mi (2½ km) per second for the Moon.

**FIGURE 31.10.** Surface temperatures to be expected on the Moon at various times of the lunar day and night. [After F. L. Whipple (1968), *Earth, Moon, and Planets,* 3rd Ed., Cambridge, Mass., Harvard Univ. Press, p. 135, Figure 99.]

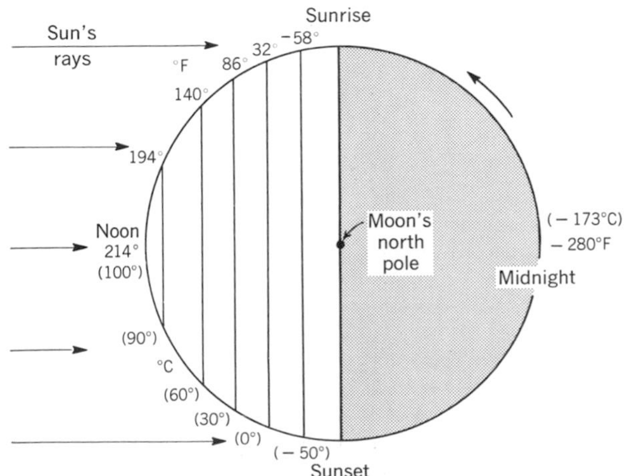

drop to values estimated at below −280° F (−173° C).

Of particular interest is the sudden drop in lunar surface temperature when sunlight is abruptly cut off by a lunar eclipse. In one such instance the surface temperature fell from 160° F (71° C) to −110° F (− 79° C) in only one hour. This drop of 270 F° (150 C°) is vastly greater than any natural temperature drop on the earth's surface in a comparable period of time and may be a significant mechanism in causing the rupture of exposed rocks.

From the scientific standpoint, such huge temperature ranges are of interest because of the possible effect upon minerals exposed at the Moon's surface. The expansion and contraction that crystalline minerals undergo when heated and cooled can bring about the disintegration of solid rock into small particles. These variations can also cause loose particles to creep gradually to lower levels on a sloping ground surface. These effects may be unusually important on the Moon, because without an atmosphere and running water ordinary terrestrial processes of weathering, erosion, and transportation cannot act upon the Moon.

The Moon's surface contains no bodies of standing water, hence there are no features of wave and current erosion. Without streams and water bodies, the Moon has no mechanisms or receiving areas for accumulation of water-laid sedimentary strata.

## The lunar surface

Astronomers and geologists have for decades been documenting the Moon's relief features, a field of study that has been called *selenography*. As the advent of the great telescopes permitted more and more details to be revealed, progress was made in mapping and interpreting details of the lunar surface. Information on magnitude of the relief features came from measurement of the shadows they cast under the Sun's rays at a low angle. But it was not until the successful use of space vehicles equipped with cameras that minute details were revealed and experimental investigations of the surface directly performed.

In 1963 and 1964, three United States *Ranger* space-

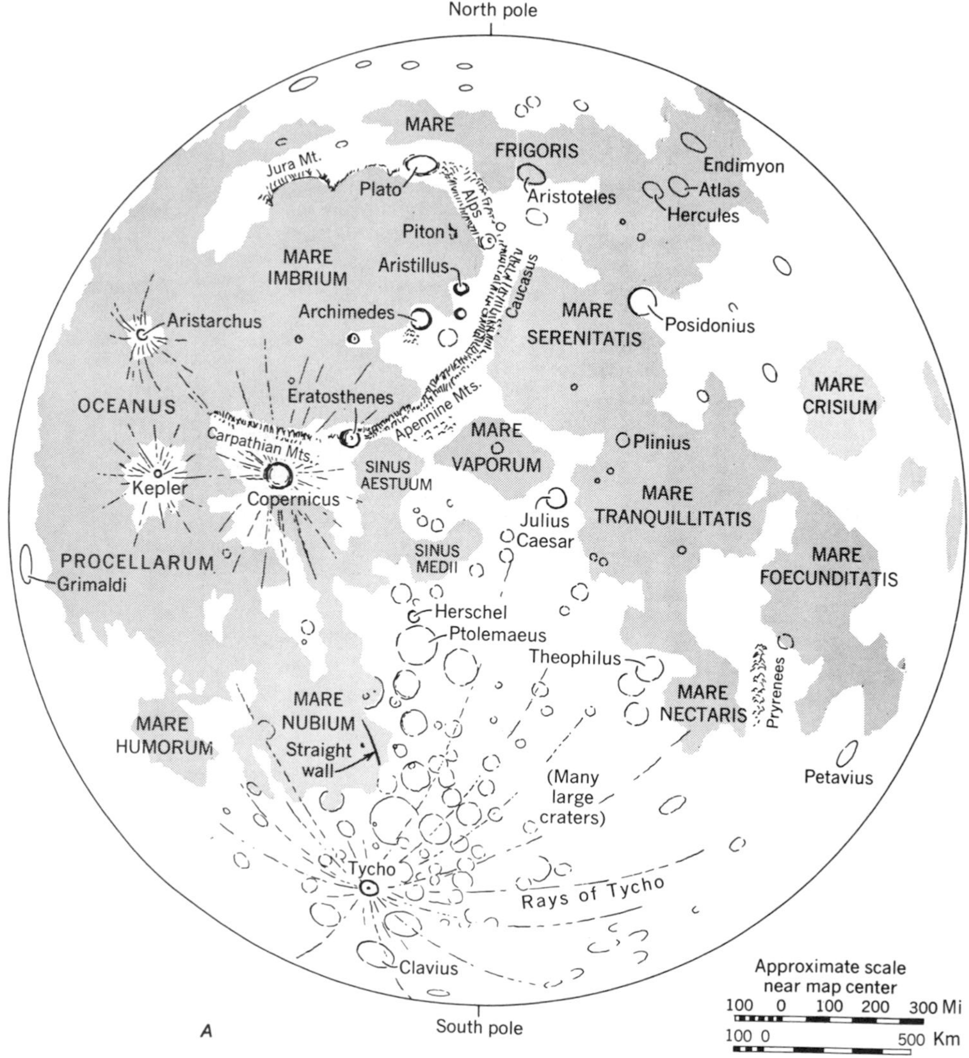


**FIGURE 31.11.** (*A*) Sketch map of the major relief features of the moon. This diagram may be used as an aid in identifying areas and subjects in the lunar photographs of this chapter. The Moon is shown here as it appears to the unaided eye or through binoculars, whereas most astronomical telescopes invert the image. (*B*) The Moon as it would appear if its whole disk could be simultaneously illuminated from a source at the same altitude. (Yerkes Observatory.)

*B*

craft impacted the lunar surface, sending back some 17,000 pictures from a wide range of elevations. Photographs made from distances as close as 1000 ft (300 m) revealed features as small as 18 in. (45 cm) across. There followed landings by *Surveyor* spacecraft, making direct physical and chemical tests of lunar surface materials as well as photographs of the ground immediately surrounding the vehicle. By 1968, five *Lunar Orbiter* vehicles had completed their missions of photographing the lunar surface from heights as low as 35 mi (56 km). A total of almost 2000 vertical photographs, at least 10 times sharper than the best taken by telescopes from Earth, were obtained for the nearside of the Moon, as well as almost complete coverage of the previously unknown farside. Scientific analysis of this plethora of information will require years for full exploitation.

In 1969 and 1970 manned space vehicles of *Apollo 9, 10, 11,* and *12* missions circled the Moon at low levels and descended to the lunar surface, permitting photographic negatives in color to be brought back to Earth. Extremely high resolution photographs were thus obtained (see Figure 31.15).

As anyone can easily see by use of a small telescope or binoculars, the first major subdivision of the Moon's surface is into light-colored areas and dark-colored areas (Figures 31.11 and 31.12). The former constitute the relatively higher surfaces, or highland (upland) areas, and can be collectively termed the *terrae.* This Latin word reflects the earliest interpretations of Galileo, that these areas were dry lands. The dark-colored areas, the low-lying smooth lunar plains, are named the *maria,* plural of the Latin word *mare* for "sea." Galileo applied this term to what he believed to be

**FIGURE 31.12.** The fully illuminated Moon as seen from Apollo 11 spacecraft at a distance of about 11,000 mi (17,-700 km). The photograph is centered on Mare Crisium (see Figure 31.11*A*), while Mare Serenitatis lies at the upper left. Radial rays from several great craters appear as light-colored streaks. (NASA photograph.)

true seas of liquid. Of the nearside of the Moon, about 60% is terrae, about 40% maria.

Lunar highland areas, or terrae, exhibit a wide range of relief features. Most outstanding are the great mountain ranges, of which there are 20 major groups on the nearside. Perhaps the most spectacular of these are the Appenines rimming the Mare Imbrium on the southwest side (Figure 31.13). Several peaks within the Appenines rise to heights of 12,000 to 16,000 ft (4 to 5 km) above the nearby mare surface. The highest and most massive mountains are those of the Leibnitz range, near the lunar south pole, which have peaks rising to heights of 35,000 ft (11 km). Elsewhere, the highland terrain consists of gently rolling surfaces with slopes less than 10° from the horizontal, and of rough areas with slopes exceeding 10°.

Lunar maria of the nearside are divided into ten major named areas, in addition to a single vast area, Oceanus Procellarum (Figure 31.11). Although maria outlines are in places highly irregular, with many bays, it is noteworthy that a circular outline is persistent for several, and particularly striking for Mare Imbrium.

Most spectacular of the Moon's surface features are the *craters.* Even under the low magnification of a small telescope the large craters form an awe-inspiring sight when seen in a partial phase of the Moon. Craters are abundant over both the terrae and maria surfaces. Using telescopes alone, some 30,000 craters have been counted on the nearside with diameters down to 2 miles (3 km). This number has been increased to an estimated 200,000 with space-vehicle photography and includes recognizable craters as small as 2 ft (0.6 m) across. On the lunar nearside there are 150 craters of

**FIGURE 31.13.** Mare Imbrium, with its bordering mountains, the Jura, Alps, Caucasus, Apennines, and Carpathians; and the great craters Plato, Aristillus, Archimedes, and Eratosthenes. Note the spine-like peak, Piton. Identify these features with the aid of Figure 31.11. (The Hale Observatories.)

diameter larger than 50 mi (80 km). Largest of these is *Clavius,* 146 mi (235 km) in diameter and surrounded by a rim rising 20,000 ft (6 km) above its floor. (See south polar area in Figure 31.11.) *Tycho* and *Copernicus* are among the most striking of the large craters (Figure 31.14).

The forms of large craters fall into several types. In some the floor is flat and smooth, and the rim is sharply defined and abrupt. In others, such as Copernicus, the floor is saucer-shaped, while the rim consists of multiple concentric ridges. Particularly interesting are systems of *rays* of lighter-colored surface radiating from certain of the larger craters—for example, Copernicus (Figure 31.14). In several of the large craters there is a sharply defined *central peak,* which must be taken into account in interpreting the origin of craters. That of Eratosthenes shows up particularly well in Figure 31.14.

Small lunar craters, down to the limits of resolution are almost perfectly circular and have a cup-shaped interior and a prominent rim (Figure 31.15). However,

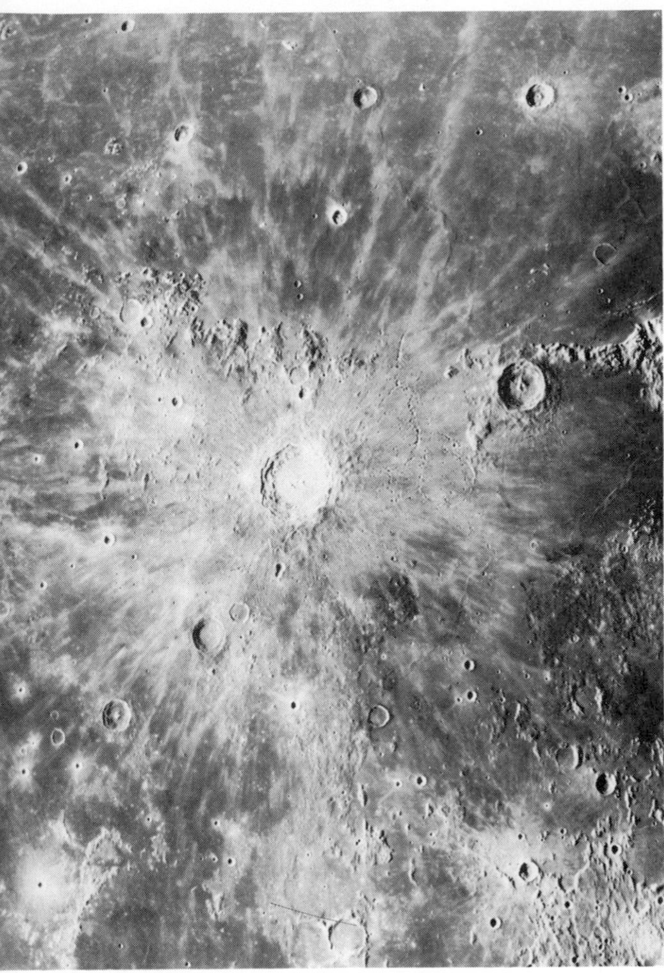

**FIGURE 31.14.** Copernicus, the great lunar crater lying south of Mare Imbrium (see Figure 31.11). Note the rays—radial streaks of lighter-colored material. The conspicuous crater lying east-northeast of Copernicus is Eratosthenes. (The Hale Observatories.)

**FIGURE 31.15.** Censorinus (*arrow*), one of the freshest craters on the Moon's nearside, shows a sharp rim and surrounding zone of light-colored soil surface. Crater rim is about 4 mi (7 km) in diameter. (Apollo 10 photograph by NASA.)

these well-defined forms grade into less distinct craters with low slopes and into shallow depressions. The impact origin for almost all of these smaller craters is generally accepted. A few are fresh in appearance, with a litter of boulders on the rim and within the crater itself. The supposedly newer craters are frequently lighter in color than the surrounding surface. The more subdued craters appear to be older and have lost their sharpness through slow processes of mass wasting (Figure 31.16). These grade into the oldest forms, which have lost their rims and show only a shallow depression. A few small craters are elliptical in outline and may represent the secondary fall of masses dislodged by much larger impacts.

Taking into account lunar craters of all sizes, it has been shown that the number of craters per unit of area is inversely proportional to the square root of the crater diameter. Consequently the number of large craters is few, and that of very small craters is legion.

Yet another class of distinctive lunar surface features are the *rilles*. Some are remarkably straight, taking the form of a narrow trench up to 150 mi (240 km) long. Others are irregular in plan, and a few are sinuous, suggestive of terrestrial meandering rivers (Figure 31.17). Most of the straight rilles are interpreted as fracture features in brittle rock of the lunar crust. Related features are the straight cliffs, or *walls*, which may be fault escarpments. A particularly striking example is the Straight Wall in Mare Nubium (Figure 31.11), which is 800 ft (240 m) high and may represent a fault that broke the mare surface.

Study of Ranger and Lunar Orbiter photographs has revealed many classes of minor details that are as yet little understood. Particularly prevalent in areas of rough terrain are minute systems of parallel ridges and troughs. Many of the steep slopes exhibit step-like terraces near the base.

The farside of the Moon has now been photographed in detail by Lunar Orbiter spacecraft and by astronauts of Apollo spacecraft, the first human beings to see that side of the Moon. The lunar farside is heavily cratered and generally lacking in extensive maria (Figure 31.18).

## Origin of the great craters and maria

Origin of the great craters and the circular-rimmed maria cannot be discussed without placing the subject in the general context of the Moon's total constitution. Two widely divergent hypotheses have found supporters throughout the long history of *lunar geology*, or *selenology*, the science analogous to terrestrial geology. One extreme view holds that the lunar craters and maria are largely of volcanic origin. This hypothesis implies a long history of intrusion and extrusion of molten rock from the Moon's interior. Source of the heat may be

**FIGURE 31.16.** Subdued old craters in the southeastern part of Mare Tranquillitatis contrast with sharply defined craters of much smaller size and younger age. Area shown is about 3 × 4 mi (5 × 6½ km). (Lunar Orbiter III photograph by NASA.)

**FIGURE 31.17.** Hadley's Rille, a sinuous canyon-like feature, crosses a cratered plain and ends in a highland area. North is at the bottom of this Lunar Orbiter V photograph, spanning an area about 30 mi (50 km) wide. Location: 2°27′ E., 24°47′ N. (NASA photograph.)

radiogenic, as in the Earth. Circular depressions of the great craters are explained by the collapse of volcanoes as magma is removed from below. The maria are interpreted as vast lava fields produced by extrusion of basalt magma from deep sources. The volcanic interpretation encounters difficulty on a number of points. True volcanic cones, such as those found in abundance on Earth, are not present, and photographs rarely show features that can be interpreted as lava flows. Moreover, if the Moon's interior is sufficiently heated to produce plutonic rocks, there should also be found orogenic belts of folding and faulting such as characterize the Earth. Except for fracture lines, which are numerous, mountain-making forms of crustal uplift and compression seem to be totally lacking. The high lunar mountain ranges seem, instead, to constitute rims of circular maria or of large craters.

The second major hypothesis of the Moon's geology may be described as the *meteoritic* (or *impact*) *hypothesis,* and includes the assumption that the Moon is a cold body without internal rock melting and volcanic action. One of the strong advocates of the meteoritic theory was the distinguished American geologist Grove Karl Gilbert, who published his explanation in 1893. Among the modern group of scientists who have contributed details to the impact hypothesis is Professor Harold C. Urey. His modified explanation is often referred to as the Urey-Gilbert hypothesis. According to Gilbert, the great craters were produced by large meteorites, in the manner which we have previously discussed in connection with terrestrial meteorite craters. However, the lunar craters are much larger than those on Earth and require explanation of the characteristic central peak. It has been suggested that the central peak lay directly beneath the center of impact-explosion, and that since the shock wave was directed downward, the underlying rock remained intact while that surrounding it was blown outward (Figure 31.19). The rays which emanate from several large craters are explained as debris deposits thrown out over long distances from the explosion centers (Figure 31.14).

Under the Urey-Gilbert hypothesis, the rimmed maria, of which there are at least five on the lunar nearside, are the old impact scars of enormous masses, probably asteroids. The case of Mare Imbrium is particularly striking (Figure 31.13), as Gilbert pointed out. Urey also reconstructed the Imbrium collision, considering it as involving impact of an object about 125 mi (200 km) in diameter approaching from a low angle. The impact raised a great wave of rock that spread outward, coming to rest in a great arc of mountain ridges. Gilbert had proposed that the heat of impact melted a vast quantity of lunar rock that subsequently solidified as the mare surface.

## Mascons and the Moon's figure

Some investigators claim that the hypothesis of a cold lunar interior is supported by an analysis of the Moon's shape, or figure. Recall, as background for the discus-

**FIGURE 31.18.** Photographed by Lunar Orbiter IV spacecraft from a distance of 1850 mi (3000 km), the eastern limb of the Moon cuts the sphere from top to bottom in a vertical line. The heavily cratered lunar farside lies to the left. The lunar equator is represented by a horizontal line crossing the center of the photograph. (NASA photograph.)

sion, that the oblate ellipsoidal figure of the Earth represents a close adjustment of its figure to its rate of rotation (Chapter 2) and, moreover, that most of the Earth's crust shows very low isostatic anomalies (Chapter 25). These facts indicate that the Earth's highly heated interior is capable of deforming at depths below about 25 mi (40 km) to achieve an equilibrium figure with respect to the centrifugal force of rotation, as well as to maintain isostatic equilibrium despite inequalities of mass from place to place within its crust. If the Moon has a cold interior, possessing considerable strength with which to resist unbalanced forces, its figure might show marked departures from an equilibrium figure with respect to its rotation and particularly with respect to the tidal forces that would tend to deform it into a prolate ellipsoid with the long axis lying in the Earth-Moon line.

**FIGURE 31.19.** Cross section of a lunar crater, according to the meteorite-impact hypothesis of origin. The vertical scale is greatly exaggerated. [After R. A. Lyttleton (1956), *The Modern Universe,* New York, Harper & Row, p. 70, Figure 28.]

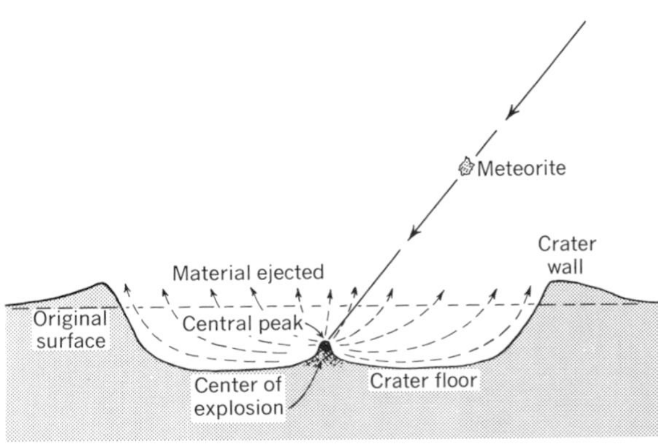


There must exist an elongation of the Moon's figure along the Earth-Moon axis in order to stabilize the synchronization of its rotation and revolution. As measured along this axis, the Moon's radius is estimated to be more than 0.6 mi (1 km) longer than the polar radius. The magnitude of such an equatorial elongation is much larger than can be attributed to flexing of a spherical Moon under existing tidal forces. From tidal forces alone, the radius along the Earth-Moon axis should be only about 210 ft (64 m) longer than the polar radius. Need for postulating the 1-km equatorial bulge arises from the nature of the Moon's motions, particularly the librations mentioned in Chapter 8. Assuming the

Moon to be completely homogeneous in composition throughout, the bulge is required to explain the observed librations. Accepting this assumption and the reality of the postulated bulge, some investigators have felt that the hypothesis of a cold lunar interior is supported.

Recently, new evidence has come to light concerning inequalities of mass distribution within the Moon and bears on the Urey-Gilbert hypothesis of maria origin. If each rimmed mare represents the impact of an enormous mass, such as an asteroid, we might expect a deficiency of mass under the mare, because a body impacting at asteroid velocities of 10 km per sec would cause throwout of much more than its own mass. Evidence seems to be to the contrary. Lunar Orbiter satellites have recorded the Moon's gravity field in great detail. The resulting map shows definite concentrations of mass, known as *mascons,* under the centers of the ringed maria of the lunar nearside (Figure 31.20). These concentrations are particularly strong under Mare Imbrium and Mare Serenitatis. Determination of gravity on the lunar farside is prevented by the fact that no radio-wave reception is possible while the satellite is on the farside of the moon. Existence of mascons located on the lunar nearside and farside, but not on the lunar limbs (sides) would account for the Moon's librations.

In Chapter 9 it was explained that tidal friction has slowed the Moon's rotation to the extent that the sidereal period of rotation is now exactly equal to the lunar sidereal period of revolution, hence that the Moon continually presents the same side to the Earth. The concentration of mascons on the lunar nearside, in greater total mass than elsewhere, might explain the fixation of the Moon with respect to Earth in the position we find it today. As the Moon's rotation with respect to Earth gradually decreased to zero, that part of the Moon bearing the largest mass concentration would, because of its greater gravitational attraction, have come to occupy a position closest to the Earth.

**FIGURE 31.20.** Gravity map of the lunar nearside. Lines show equal variation of gravitational acceleration in milligals. Major mascons coinciding with ringed maria are *I,* Imbrium; *S,* Serenitatis; *C,* Crisium; *N,* Nectaris. [After W. M. Kaula (1969), *Science,* vol. 166, p. 1585, Figure 1.]

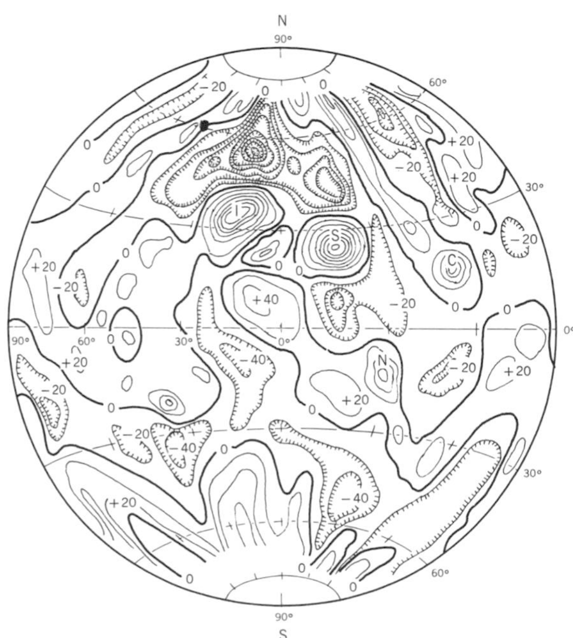


## The Martian surface

Do the surfaces of planets, other than Earth, show the scars of impacts? The outer planets, with their great distances and dense atmospheres, reveal nothing of this nature. Venus, though close to Earth, conceals her surface beneath a very dense atmosphere. Mercury, without an atmosphere, is a likely candidate for showing a heavily scarred surface, but, because of its distance from the Earth and nearness to the Sun, observations have not yet been made.

Mars, another near neighbor, was photographed by U.S. Mariner 4 spacecraft in 1965, and by Mariner 6 and 7 spacecraft in 1969. Series of photographs showed that part of the Martian surface is heavily cratered in the Southern Hemisphere (Figure 31.21). The sizes and numbers of craters per unit of area on Mars are quite similar to corresponding data for the lunar uplands.

It has been noted, however, that the craters of Mars are shallower and have lower rims and flatter floors than lunar craters of the same size. That some forms of erosion or blanketing processes, albeit much less effective than those on Earth, operate on Mars is suggested by the subdued crater forms. The atmosphere of Mars, consisting largely of carbon dioxide, is highly rarified, with a surface pressure of only about 5 mb, compared with 1000 mb for Earth. There is no suggestion of the action of running water on Mars, but rock weathering and wind action could be effective.

**FIGURE 31.21.** Cratered surface of Mars photographed by Mariner 6 spacecraft at a distance of about 2150 mi (3460 km). The area shown spans about 550 × 400 mi (885 × 640 km). The largest crater visible (lower right) is about 160 mi (260 km) in diameter. North is down. Location: long. 15° E., lat. 16° S. (NASA photograph.)

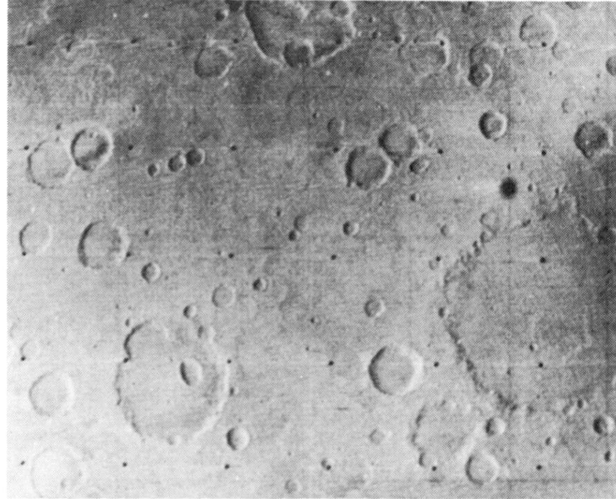

Mariner 6 and 7 photographs revealed two important types of terrain in addition to the cratered surfaces. One of these is described as *chaotic terrain,* in which relief features are irregular, suggesting to interpreters that the Martian surface has in places undergone collapse, as if material had been withdrawn from beneath (Figure 31.22). A third type of surface, described as *featureless terrain,* appears as a smooth, light-colored plain.

The dark-colored, heavily cratered terrain of Mars is interpreted as original, or primeval Martian surface, comparable with the lunar uplands, and presumed to date from the time of formation of the planet some 4.5 billions of years ago. The chaotic terrain seems to have been affected by some unknown crustal processes at a later time in the planet's history. The featureless terrain is also considered younger than the cratered surface. Although processes of erosion and blanketing seem to have been at work on the Martian surface, photo interpreters have as yet not found any tectonic or topographic forms comparable to those known on Earth.

**FIGURE 31.22.** Chaotic terrain of Mars, photographed by Mariner 6 spacecraft. Upper photograph covers an area measuring about 500 mi (800 km) from top to bottom. Lower photograph shows a small part of the upper, greatly enlarged. (NASA photograph.)

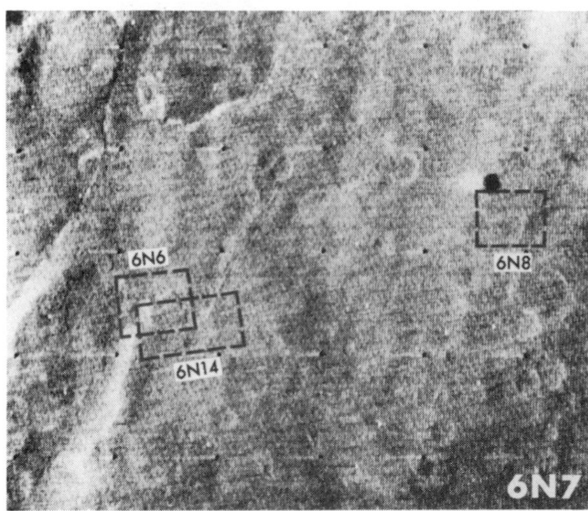


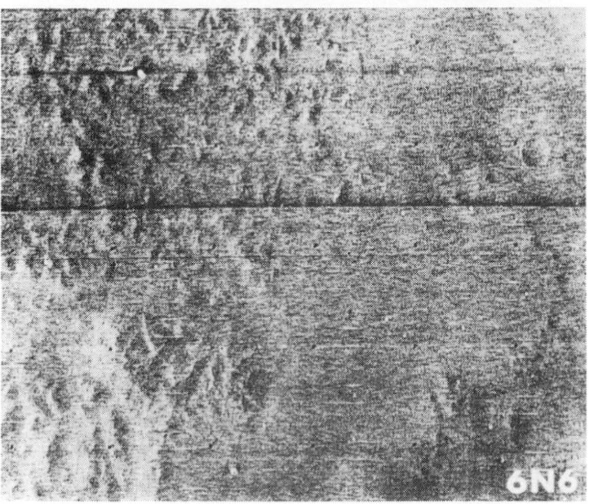


Thus we can tentatively conclude that there can have been little or no tectonic activity on Mars. We see no indications of the processes of orogeny or vulcanism that have characterized Earth's geologic history. Without the internal melting of rock and the resulting rise of magma to the Martian surface, the processes of outgassing[5] would necessarily have been very slow. Perhaps therein lies part of the explanation of the extreme thinness of the Martian atmosphere.

Carrying this discussion further to include Venus, the very high density of that planet's atmosphere suggests that outgassing may have occurred in large quantities and that therefore the crust of Venus has been subjected to intensive tectonic activity, along with much vulcanism and intrusion of magma arising from great depth. If so, the surface of Venus, like that of Earth, may preserve few if any impact features of great age, such as have been found on Mars. We might therefore anticipate the discovery of orogenic mountain ranges and many volcanoes on Venus.

## Lunar surface materials and rocks

The first samples of lunar soil and rock were obtained in July of 1969 by astronauts of the Apollo 11 mission from Mare Tranquillitatus. The surface materials here consist of unsorted fragmental debris ranging from dust to blocks almost 3 ft (1 m) across. On the rim and floor of a nearby crater some 100 ft (30 m) deep were found blocks as large as 16 ft (5 m) across. The layer of loose material, which can be termed *regolith,* has been estimated to have a depth of 10 to 20 ft (3 to 6 m) between craters. The larger rock fragments of which samples were taken are considered to be derived locally from bedrock by the force of impacting meteorites. However, a few small fragments may have come great distances from great craters such as Theophilus and Tycho.

The uppermost few inches of fine-grained surface material at Tranquillity Base has been described as brownish to medium-gray cohesive soil consisting of grains in the size range of silt to fine sand. The material is easily penetrated. Upon compaction it becomes stronger and shows cohesion, as illustrated by the clear footprints of the astronauts (Figure 31.23).

Rock samples collected from Tranquillity Base are all of igneous mineral composition and fall into three classes. First is a fine-grained crystalline igneous rock with vesicular texture. *Vesicular* refers to presence of *vesicles,* small spheroidal cavities assumed to have been formed by gas bubbles, as in scoriaceous lavas. A second rock type is medium-grained crystalline igneous rock, containing larger irregular cavities (*vugs*) (Figure 31.24). A third rock type is breccia, consisting of mixtures of fragments of mineral grains or igneous rocks mostly smaller than 0.2 in. (0.5 cm) in diameter. The finer particles of the breccia consist largely of glass, in either rounded or angular grains.

A particularly interesting feature of the rock samples

[5] Outgassing means the emanation of volatile elements from within the planet, resulting in the formation of an atmosphere. This subject is discussed in detail in Chapter 27.

**FIGURE 31.23.** Astronaut's footprint in the lunar soil. Notice the many miniature craters in the surrounding surface. (Apollo 11 photograph by NASA.)

A

B

**FIGURE 31.24.** Lunar rocks collected by astronauts of the Apollo 11 mission at Tranquillity Base. (*A*) Holocrystalline rock of granular texture, showing glass-lined surface cavities. Specimen is about 8 in. (20 cm) high. (*B*) Close-up photograph of a vuggy, somewhat shattered, coarsely crystalline rock without glassy pits. Area shown is about 0.8 in. (2 cm) across. (NASA photographs.)

is the presence of surface pits lined with glass. These pits average less than 0.04 in. (1 mm) across. The pits, the rounding of gross shape of the fragments, and a lighter-colored surface than the inside rock suggest that some process of erosion has been in operation, possibly of the nature of impacts by small particles.

All of the crystalline rocks are interpreted as volcanic, formed at or close to the lunar surface by solidification of magma. Rocks of the first type described above consist of about one-half pyroxene, about one-quarter calcic plagioclase feldspar, and considerable ilmenite. Also present is some olivine and a number of other minerals in smaller amounts. The second type of crystalline rock proved to be of very similar mineral composition to the first. In short, they are basic (mafic) igneous rocks and may be considered analogous with terrestrial basalts. There are, however, certain important differences between the lunar rocks and the terrestrial basalts. First, the abundance of pyroxene in the lunar rocks is considerably greater relative to plagioclase feldspar. Second, the abundance of ilmenite, an oxide of titanium and iron ($FeTiO_3$), is strikingly high. The lunar rocks are almost totally lacking in water and in the ferric form of iron. This composition suggests that the rock crystallized in an oxygen-poor and water-poor environment. In view of the high titanium and iron content of the lunar rocks, they cannot be matched to any of the common terrestrial basalts and must have had a quite different geochemical evolution.

The lunar regolith and breccias, taken together, are interpreted as produced by intense shock and partial melting, which can be described as a form of *impact metamorphism*. Melting is indicated by the presence of glass. Particularly interesting are the glass spherules (Figure 31.25) which are interpreted as "splash" phenomena—that is to say, minute droplets which cooled quickly into spheroidal shapes. In view of the great abundance of impact craters of all sizes on the lunar surface, the presence of a large amount of regolith and breccia of impact origin is to be expected. Craters as

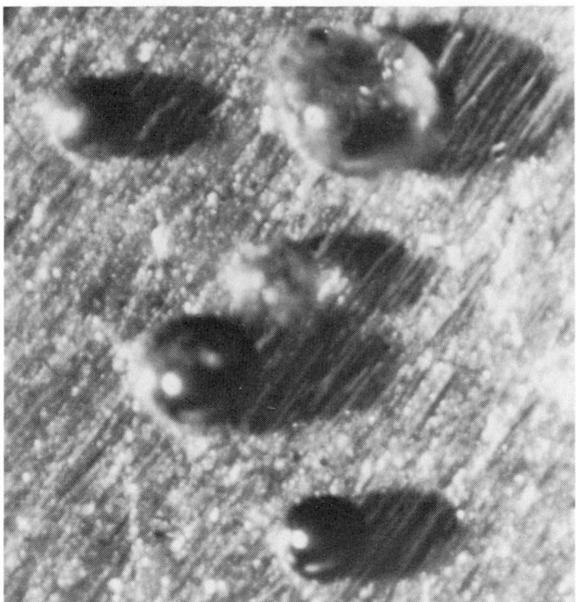

**FIGURE 31.25.** Glass spherules from the lunar regolith. Largest spherule is 0.016 in. (0.4 mm) in diameter. Spherules rest on an aluminum dish with a striated surface. (Apollo 11 photograph by NASA.)

small as 0.8 in. (2 cm) in diameter were observed at Tranquillity Base.

Analyses of lunar material showed extremely minute quantities of organic matter, and these can be accounted for by contamination during the processes of collecting and returning the samples to earth. It is concluded that organic matter is present in lunar rocks in less than one part per million. The presence of life, present or past, seems to have been completely ruled out of the lunar surface environment.

Age determinations yielded figures of −3.3 to −3.7 billion years for basaltic crystalline rocks of the Tranquillity Base. This figure is quite close to the age of the oldest terrestrial rocks. A figure of −4.6 b.y. was obtained for breccia and lunar regolith. A single rock fragment unlike other rocks of Tranquillity Base yielded an age of −4.4 b.y. This fragment may have come from possibly older rock of the lunar highlands. If breccia and lunar regolith are representative of the original lunar crust, the Moon must have originated about the same time as the earth, namely about −4.6 to −4.7 b.y.

One interpretation of an age around −3.6 b.y. for crystalline igneous rocks of the Tranquillity Base is that an important event in lunar history occurred at this time. The event was one of melting and may possibly have been of more than local occurrence. The cause of such a *thermal episode* can be referred to one of two sources —massive bombardment of the lunar surface by meteorites, or internal heating from radiogenic sources.

Late in 1969 the Apollo 12 spacecraft landed at a point in the Ocean of Storms on the western side of the lunar nearside. A radiometric age of −3.4 b.y. has been determined for igneous rock from that locality, an age about the same as for rocks at Tranquillity Base. Breccias were almost totally lacking among the samples returned for study. Moreover, the proportion of titanium proved to be about half that in samples from Tranquillity Base. Large individual crystals, up to 4 in. (10 cm) in length, were found in rocks from the Apollo 12 site, whereas crystals in the Tranquillity Base rocks are all much smaller. Evidently the lunar surface has a geologically varied composition.

One small rock specimen from the Apollo 12 site has yielded an age of −4.6 b.y., equal to that of meteorites and equivalent to the inferred age of accretion of the Moon and planets. The specimen is of unusual chemical composition with respect to both meteorites and terrestrial rocks, in that it contains unusually high concentrations of radioactive thorium, potassium, and uranium.

In 1970 scientists of the Smithsonian Astrophysical Observatory analyzed a small sample of lunar regolith from Tranquillity Base. The material was shaken on a sieve with openings 0.01 in. (0.25 mm) in diameter. The 25% of material retained on the sieve was found to consist of tiny rock and glass fragments, and glass spherules. The rock fragments represent a sample of the lunar bedrock that has been crushed, dispersed, and repeatedly mixed by successive meteorite impacts. The fragments must have traveled varying distances from point of origin, some coming from great distances along crater rays. A surprising discovery was that while most fragments are of basaltic composition, similar to that of the large rock specimens, about 6% proved to be of the composition of anorthosite, a terrestrial rock consisting largely of calcic plagioclase feldspar (see Table 20.4 and Figure 21.7).

On the reasonable assumption that a small percentage of the tiny rock fragments could easily have come from the lunar highlands, lying some 30 mi (50 km) to the south of Tranquillity Base, the Smithsonian scientists have suggested that the highlands are underlain by a crust of anorthosite, derived by differentiation of a magma produced by partial melting of the outer layer of the Moon during a brief episode of intense heating. Chemical analysis of the lunar surface by Surveyor 7 at a location on the lunar highlands supports the hypothesis that highlands bedrock is of anorthosite composition. The specific gravity of anorthosite (about 2.9 g/cc) is substantially less than that of lunar basalt (about 3.3 g/cc). If isostasy prevails over the lunar crust, highlands of anorthosite should stand higher than maria surfaces of basalt. Gravity measurements derived from satellite orbits show no gravity anomaly associated with the lunar highlands, an observation in agreement with the hypothesis of an anorthosite layer resting in isostatic equilibrium with respect to a denser basalt layer. If so, the Moon has a crustal structure analogous in some respects to the Earth's arrangement of a high-standing felsic continental crust and a low-lying basaltic oceanic crust.

## Origin of the Moon

Finally, we turn to consider the origin of the Moon as the smaller member of that "binary planet," the Earth-

Moon pair. We shall accept the hypothesis of a cold Moon whose surface was severely scarred by infall of huge bodies, probably asteroids, during the final stages of its formation. Those events probably took place rapidly. Infall of objects continued through the remainder of geologic time, producing the craters, large and small, and causing local melting upon impact. But what of the formation of the Moon as a spherical body?

Four basic hypotheses, or groups of hypotheses, of the Moon's origin have been given serious consideration by astronomers and geophysicists, although only three of these are now credited with a substantial degree of plausibility. The hypotheses are listed below with names and dates of investigators who proposed each hypothesis or a modification of it:

1. Binary-system hypothesis, Kuiper, 1956.
2. Capture hypothesis. Gerstenkorn, 1955; Alfvén, 1963; Urey, 1963; Singer, 1967.
3. Fission hypothesis. Darwin, 1898; Wise, 1963; Cameron, 1964; O'Keefe, 1969.
4. Coagulation (or many-moon) hypothesis. Ruskol, 1960; McDonald, 1964.

The *binary-system hypothesis* supposes that both Moon and Earth grew as independent bodies by gradual accumulation from diffuse cold gases and dust. It is postulated that the Moon was close to Earth during the growth of both bodies, so that there was a binary planet from the outset. A major weakness of this hypothesis is that the Moon has a low density and lacks an iron core. It is difficult to explain the accretion of large amounts of iron by the Earth, but not by the Moon. Further difficulties exist in explaining how the two bodies were prevented from falling together, or falling apart. For these reasons the binary-system hypothesis is not now given serious consideration.

A *capture hypothesis* was proposed by H. Gerstenkorn in 1955, and further developed by H. Alfvén in 1963. Both of these investigators supposed that the Moon entered Earth's gravity field with a retrograde orbit. The Moon spiralled in toward Earth, underwent a reversal of orbit, and spiralled out in direct motion. Harold C. Urey in 1963 also postulated capture of the Moon, which, as we have seen, was regarded by him as an older body than Earth. S. F. Singer, in 1967, also proposed lunar capture, but with the Moon approaching Earth in a hyperbolic orbit of direct motion. The capture hypotheses can explain the lower density of the Moon by reason of different conditions prevailing during accretion far from Earth, although those special conditions are difficult to justify.

Recall, from Chapter 27, that Professor Preston E. Cloud has introduced the possibility of lunar capture at −3.6 b.y., giving rise to a thermal event in which outgassing was speeded up by tidal flexing due to the Moon's proximity. It is interesting to note that the age of −3.6 b.y. for igneous rocks at Tranquillity Base on the Moon seems to correlate with this event.

The *fission hypothesis,* touched upon in Chapter 9, requires that the Moon represent a mass which broke away from a fast-spinning Earth. Recall that Sir George Darwin described the process of *rotational fission* which he arrived at by looking back toward a point in time at which the Earth's speed of rotation was much faster than now. The centrifugal force of rotation, together with the Sun's tide-raising force, induced a tidal bulge in Earth. The bulge then separated and moved away from Earth, forming the Moon.

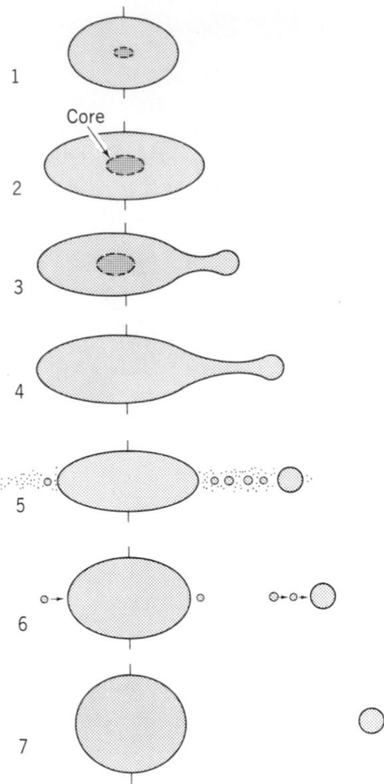


**FIGURE 31.26.** Stages in fission of the Earth-Moon body to produce the Moon. [After D. U. Wise (1963), *Jour. Geophys. Research,* vol. 68, p. 1547, Figure 1.]

The strongest argument urged against Darwin's hypothesis, and one which caused it to be shelved for a long period of time, was that the total energy and angular momentum of Earth at the time of its fission would have had to be greater than the present quantities within the Earth-Moon pair by a large factor. The present energy is only about 6% of that original required value, and the angular momentum only about 27%. Although some energy is dissipated in tidal flexing (refer to Chapter 9), the loss would not be nearly sufficient to account for the difference.

In reviving the fission hypothesis in 1963, Donald U. Wise made the suggestion that the high rate of spinning needed to throw off the Moon developed as the Earth's metallic core was separated from the silicate mantle rock and brought a great mass closer to the Earth's center. When the rate of spin increased to the point that the period of rotation was 2.65 hours, centrifugal force in the equatorial belt would have balanced gravitational attraction, allowing the development of the bulge and its fission. Figure 31.26 shows stages in fission as envisioned by Professor Wise.

A. G. W. Cameron, in 1964, suggested that the fission process, instead of taking place in the plastic manner shown in Figure 31.26, occurred suddenly by the throwing off of small fragments of the Earth near its equator, and that these fragments then accumulated into the Moon.

There has been one strong point of evidence in favor of the fission hypothesis. The Moon's average density is known to be 3.34 g/cc, about the same as Earth's mantle rock averages (3.3 to 3.9 g/cc). The Earth-material which would have broken free would have been composed largely of mantle rock. Thus the low density of the Moon is explained, along with its lack of any substantial quantity of free iron.

Not surprisingly, Darwin and others speculated that the lunar material came from the present area of the Pacific Ocean basin. We do not need to entertain this idea, in view of our knowledge of the processes of crustal separation and continental growth, but it was an intriguing possibility at the time it was put forward.

As stated in earlier paragraphs, rock samples brought to the Earth by Apollo missions 11 and 12 have proved to be mineralogically quite unlike the terrestrial basalts of the oceanic crust. This evidence seems on the face of it highly unfavorable to the fission hypothesis, although the lunar rock samples come from only two localities, both in maria. It should also be remembered that the surface zone of the oceanic crust is comparatively very young, perhaps 130 m.y. or less, whereas the lunar igneous rocks have been dated as −4.6 and −3.6 b.y., which prevents any meaningful comparison.

The *coagulation* (or *many-moon*) *hypothesis* has in common with the binary-system hypothesis the postulate that Moon and Earth grew at the same time in close proximity. However, the many-moon hypothesis proposes that the lunar matter was dispersed into smaller fragments in a ring about the Earth. As proposed by Gordon J. F. MacDonald in 1964, there were originally several small moons of various sizes in orbit around the Earth. The largest moon, with a mass about ¼ to ⅓ that of the present Moon, orbited closest to the Earth. As it spiralled outward, this largest moon collided with and captured the other smaller moons in succession. A great advantage of the many-moon hypothesis is that the dispersal of the present lunar mass into several small masses greatly reduces the tide-raising effect that a single moon close to Earth would exert.

Professor MacDonald was led to the inference that under the many-moon hypothesis the Moon's surface is quite young, in fact not older than −1.5 b.y. As we now know, lunar rocks have ages at least as old as −3.6 b.y., an observation that would appear to render the many-moon hypothesis untenable as outlined. This hypothesis also faces the problem of explaining how the small satellites were originally formed or captured, and why they lacked free iron in the same proportions found in Earth.

## Review of a system

We have examined abundant and varied evidence that the collision of objects traveling at high speed in interplanetary space has been a process of great importance in the early history of the planetary bodies. Such collisions continue today. Seen in the collective view, these collisions constitute a physical system in which the inherited kinetic energy of masses in motion is abruptly transformed by impact into high-energy shock waves which produce severe physical rupture of the receiving body. Ultimately, the converted energy is dissipated in the form of heat and leaves the solar system by long-wave radiation. The total process is therefore one involving the gradual decline in the total energy of the solar system.

The system of collisions apparently plays a major role in the formation of the large bodies of the solar system, since by gravitational attraction of larger bodies for smaller ones the growth of planets by accretion is a reasonable mechanism. There is also reason to suppose that the opposite result—that of fragmentation into small particles—has resulted from a related disruptive process, as in the case of the fragmentation of comets passing close to the Sun.

Dr. Robert Jastrow has aptly noted that "The Moon is a Rosetta Stone of the planets."[6] Because processes of rock disintegration and transport act with extreme slowness on the lunar surface, and because her crust is cold and motionless, our close satellite carries the entire record of 4½ billion years of solar-system history on her intensely illuminated surface. We have only to decipher the sharply-etched lunar markings to read a history that on Earth has been largely erased by the continuum of atmospheric processes and a succession of crustal upheavals, intrusions, and volcanic outbursts.

## References for further study

Nininger, H. H. (1952), *Out of the Sky; An Introduction to Meteoritics,* New York, Dover Publications, 336 pp.

Mason, B. (1962), *Meteorites,* New York, Wiley, 274 pp.

Mason, B. (1966), *Principles of Geochemistry,* New York, Wiley, 329 pp., chap. 2.

Fairbridge, R. W., ed. (1967), *Encyclopedia of Atmospheric Sciences and Astrogeology,* New York, Reinhold, 1200 pp. See: Astroblemes, Astrogeology, Australites, Explosion craters, Mars, Meteorite flux and infall, Meteorites, Moon, Tektites.

Lyttleton, R. A. (1968), *Mysteries of the Solar System,* Oxford, Clarendon Press, 261 pp., Chap. 6.

Whipple, F. L. (1968), *Earth, Moon, and Planets,* Cambridge, Mass., Harvard Univ. Press, 297 pp., chaps. 8, 9.

Wood, J. A. (1968), *Meteorites and the Origin of Planets,* New York, McGraw-Hill, 117 pp.

[6] R. Jastrow (1967), *Red Giants and White Dwarfs,* New York, Harper & Row. See p. 73.

# FOUR

# The continental surfaces

*Waterfalls at Ocho Rios, Jamaica. Fritz Henle from Monkmeyer.*

# 32

# Weathering, soils, and mass wasting

THE STUDY OF the origin and evolution of the relief features of the landscape, or *landforms,* visible upon the earth's surface constitutes a branch of the earth sciences known as *geomorphology,* closely affiliated with physical geology and hydrology. Although historically geomorphology has dealt largely with the surfaces of the continents, it may be extended to include the origin of the relief features of the continental shelves and ocean basins. In the study of landforms it is essential that the various landscape features be sorted out according to groups or classes containing those forms similar both in processes of origin and in configuration. The geomorphologist is therefore strongly interested in the physical, chemical, and organic processes by which the landscape is developed. He finds that he must look to the geologic processes and structures of the earth's crust beneath him, as well as to the climatological influences of the atmosphere above him, in order to understand the configuration of the surface, for this is the surface of discontinuity between lithosphere and atmosphere.

The shaping of the continental landscape could not take place in the way it does without the presence and action of water. Weathering of rock and the erosion, transportation, and deposition of mineral particles by streams, glacial ice, and ocean waves and currents requires water in the liquid or solid state. In earlier chapters we have studied water in atmosphere and oceans, including its changes of state and those phases of the water balance dealing with transport of water vapor across parallels of latitude. Precipitation of water upon the lands furnishes the fluid medium of most geomorphic processes, as well as the potential energy whereby the flow systems of streams and glaciers are powered. It is obvious, then, that *hydrology* must be studied in conjunction with geomorphology. Hydrology, broadly defined, is the science of water, with special reference to its distribution and movement. In this part of the book we shall complete the examination of the hydrologic cycle and the evaluation of the earth's water balance.

## Endogenetic and exogenetic processes

In the broadest sense all landforms fall into two great classes, the products of two great classes of geomorphic processes. The *endogenetic processes,* meaning that they are internally powered, include tectonic activities that dislocate the crust and volcanic processes that construct new landforms by extrusions of magma. New relief features thus created can be designated as *initial landforms* (Figure 32.1). The initial landforms are acted upon by the *exogenetic processes* powered by external sources of energy, largely solar. These processes or agents of landmass denudation yield the *sequential landforms.* The adjective "sequential" here refers to the orderly succession of landforms created by erosion, weathering, and mass wasting.

The sequential landforms can in turn be subdivided into two varieties, *erosional* and *depositional.* Erosional landforms are those resulting from the progressive removal of earth materials, and depositional landforms from the accumulation of the products of erosion. In the example shown in Figure 32.1, erosion by runoff on slopes and in streams has carved a host of erosional landforms, consisting of canyons and the intervening divides and peaks. Deposition of sediment by streams has at the same time been forming a type of depositional landform known as an *alluvial fan.* Each agent of erosion produces a characteristic assemblage of erosional and depositional landforms.

In summarizing this introduction to geomorphology, it might be said that all landscapes of the continents reflect the existing stage in a great conflict between endogenetic processes and exogenetic processes.

**FIGURE 32.1.** Two great classes of landforms: (*A*) Initial; (*B*) Sequential. (© 1960, John Wiley & Sons, New York.)

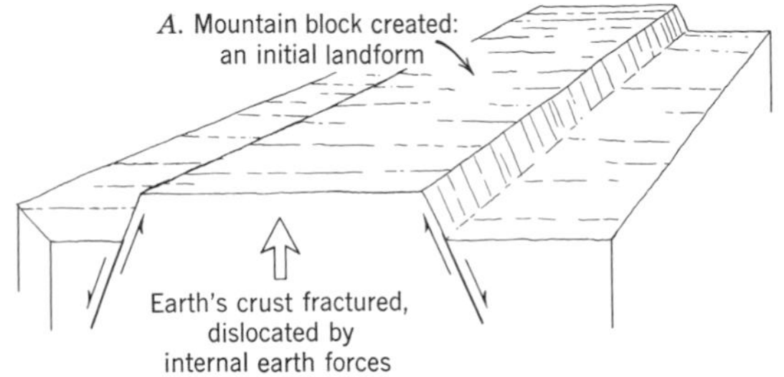


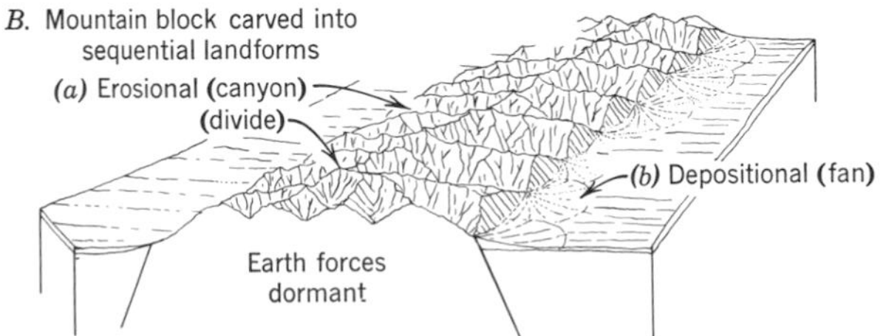


Where endogenetic processes have been recently active, through orogeny and vulcanism, there exist rugged alpine mountain chains and high plateaus. Where exogenetic processes have been given opportunity to operate with little disturbance for vast spans of time, the landmasses have been reduced to low plains. In many periods of the geologic past continental relief was generally low, and the subsidence of continental crust allowed shallow seas to spread far inland. At such times the exogenetic processes dominated. The continents today are, in contrast, generally high in elevation and rugged in relief, suggesting that we live at a time when the endogenetic processes have temporarily gained the upper hand on a world-wide scope.

## Agents of landscape development

Almost all sequential landforms are shaped or greatly modified by the *active agents* of landform development: flowing water (overland flow and channel flow), waves and associated coastal currents, glacial ice, and wind. All these active agents consist of fluids (in the broad sense) and are acting directly or indirectly under the force of gravity or the atmospheric pressure-gradient force. The fluid agents are engaged in *erosion,* which is the flow of water, ice, or air over the solid ground surface to dislodge in one way or another particles of soil, overburden, or bedrock. The particles are then carried as sediment to progressively lower and more distant locations.

The *passive agents* of landform development fall into two major groups. The *weathering processes*—including all forms of mechanical disintegration and chemical decomposition of mineral matter—act continuously on all soil, overburden, and bedrock lying close to the surface where atmospheric influences are felt. The products of weathering tend to remain in place where formed unless they are moved under the force of gravity or by fluid agents. The *mass-wasting processes* include all forms of downslope movement of soil, overburden, or bedrock under the direct influence of gravity, but without the action of a fluid agent, as in the erosion processes. Mass wasting represents the spontaneous yielding of earth materials when gravitational force exceeds the internal strength of the material. Therefore mass wasting involves the sliding, rolling, and flowage of masses of soil, overburden, and bedrock to lower positions, but it is regarded as a passive agent because it provides no means of transport to distant places.

The exogenetic processes—consisting of the combined agents of erosion, weathering, and mass wasting—reduce a landmass to progressively lower levels, a total process termed *denudation.*

## A dynamic approach to geomorphology

The approach to geomorphology must be a dynamic one, stressing the action of forces to dislocate and transport masses. Force acting through distance constitutes work in the mechanical sense. Energy must be transformed when work is done. Therefore each of the agents of landscape development can be regarded as being involved in a system of energy transformation and mass transport.

The endogenetic processes are responsible for raising large masses of rock above sea level. In so doing, they furnish every particle of the elevated mass with a supply of potential energy. Work is required to achieve the mechanical and chemical breakdown of this rock into soil and sediment. As individual sediment particles move from high to low levels, the potential energy of position is transformed into kinetic energy of motion, which in turn is dissipated through friction and is transformed into heat. Such is the nature of the geologic aspect of denudation.

The exogenetic processes operate on solar energy. Some of this energy is utilized directly when solar heating and evaporation occur under direct impact of the sun's rays. But most of the exogenetic processes are powered indirectly through motions of the atmosphere and oceans and attendant processes of condensation. Thus streams and glaciers depend upon precipitation to deposit water at high elevations on land, which gives the water an initial store of potential energy to be expended in flow to lower levels. Wind is a fluid flow induced by pressure gradient forces. Kinetic energy of moving air powers two active agents of erosion and transportation. First is the direct frictional drag of air over the ground surface, called *wind action,* which results in certain forms of erosion and deposition. Second, winds blowing over ocean surfaces generate waves. Energy transferred to waves ultimately is transported to the shores of the continents, where it is absorbed in erosion and transportation of mineral matter.

To sum up, the exogenetic processes fall into three groups; (a) those sustained by direct input of solar radiation, (b) those that are simple gravity-flow systems (mass wasting, streams, and glaciers), and (c) those which derive energy from atmospheric motion (wind action and wave action).

## Nature of weathering

The weathering processes may be thought of as leading to the preparation of parent matter of the true soil and, from the geological standpoint, as the preparation of sediment for transportation (Chapter 22). One aspect of weathering is the breaking up of hard strong bedrock, occurring in large masses, into particles ranging down through the various grades of clastic particles to the minute chemical ions. As breakdown occurs, the total surface area of the particles in a given bulk volume is enormously increased, facilitating complex chemical changes.

Another aspect of weathering is the change in chemical composition of the rock-forming minerals, through reaction with acids and water, to yield new minerals that will remain indefinitely without further change under the conditions of temperature, pressure, and moisture prevailing at the earth's surface. The processes and products of mineral alteration have been discussed in Chapter 22.

A third aspect of weathering is the continual agitation of the soil and weathered overburden as soil-mosture content increases and decreases seasonally (Chapter 33) and as soil temperatures rise and fall daily and seasonally (Chapter 14). Drying and wetting, freezing and thawing, growth and decay of plant roots, and the burrowing and trampling of the soil by animals continually agitate the soil. Such disturbances affect the soil rhythmically long after the mineral matter has been reduced to minute particles and the principal chemical changes have largely occurred.

Looking at these three aspects of weathering, then, we see that certain one-way, or irreversible, changes have superimposed upon them a pattern of rhythmic fluctuations in physical and chemical state, so that weathering is indeed a most complex natural phenomenon.

## Geometry of rock disintegration

Geologists use a set of terms to describe the various ways in which bedrock is reduced to individual masses and particles. These terms do not refer to the forces and weathering processes that cause breakup, but merely to the geometrical variations that may occur.

*Granular distintegration* consists of the grain-by-grain breakdown of rock masses composed of discrete mineral crystals and usually refers to the coarse-grained igneous and metamorphic rocks—such as granite, gabbro, and gneiss—and to the coarse clastic sediments—such as sandstone and conglomerate (Figure 32.2). The individual mineral grains simply separate from one another along their natural contacts to produce a coarse sand or gravel in which each particle has much the same shape and size as in the original rock.

In *exfoliation* solid rock bodies break apart in shells and plates, or scales, conforming roughly with the configuration of the outer surface (Figure 32.2). The planes of fracture are thus roughly parallel with the outer rock surface and are new fractures rather than previously existing natural surfaces of breakage. Exfoliation can occur on a very large scale, with individual plates of rock many feet thick, or on a very small scale, with layers a small fraction of an inch thick. Exfoliation affects many varieties of rocks and can be caused by a variety of processes, both physical and chemical.

As explained in Chapter 20, most bedrock is so fractured by systems of joints that it is rare to find flawless bodies of rock (monoliths) more than a few feet across. Most joints occur in parallel sets, and there are often two or more sets intersecting at large angles. Consequently most bedrock is already broken into blocks from a few inches to a few feet across. When stresses are exerted upon jointed rock, the rock comes apart rather readily along these planes by a type of disintegration called simply *joint-block separation* (Figure 32.2). Of course, a single joint block may undergo subsequent granular disintegration or exfoliation, or both.

Where a very hard rock is subjected to severe stresses, it may rupture into highly irregular angular blocks. In this form of breakup, described as *shattering,* the fractures may cut across mineral grains and other structures in the rock (Figure 32.2). Shattering

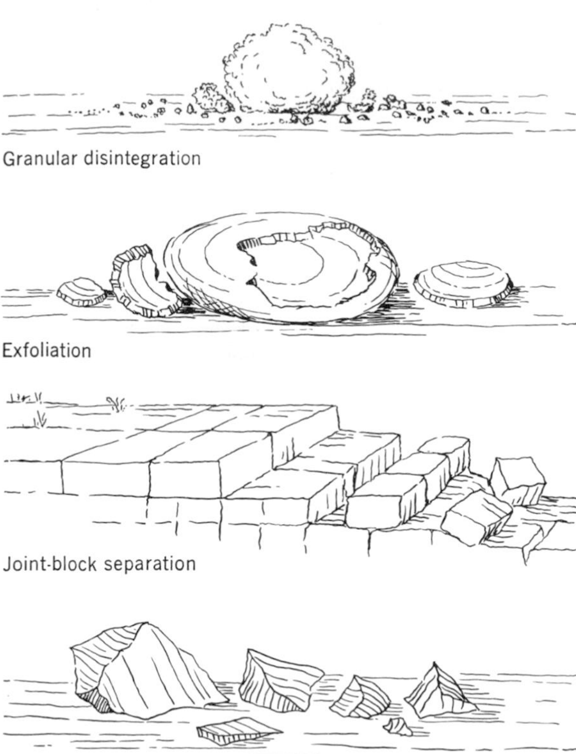


**FIGURE 32.2.** Four geometrical patterns of rock breakup. (© 1960, John Wiley & Sons, New York.)

is well illustrated by the effects of blasting bedrock with explosives or of a hammer blow on a boulder of hard rock such as quartzite or granite.

Other natural structures of rocks influence the geometry of breakup. In sedimentary strata the bedding planes (stratification planes) provide planes of weakness along which the rock can split. Slate tends to split along its cleavage surfaces to produce thin plates, and schist to give slab-like fragments determined by foliation. The chemical action of acids upon a rock surface will commonly produce shallow cup-like hollows or grooves separated by sharp ridges.

## Physical (mechanical) weathering

Treated first are the physical processes in which mechanical stresses act upon rock, causing distintegration. These processes constitute the initial, or primary, breakdown of bedrock into fragments whose surfaces are in turn exposed to chemical weathering.

In climates of the middle and high latitudes and at high altitudes, alternate freezing and melting of water in the soil and rock provides a powerful mechanism of rock breakup. Soil water and water that has penetrated the joint planes, bedding planes, foliation planes, and other openings of the rock are transformed into ice crystals of needle-like form. Growing masses of such crystals exert great pressures upon the confining rock walls, causing joint blocks and bedding layers to be heaved up and pried free of the parent mass. Freezing of water that has soaked into the pore spaces of a rock can produce shattering into angular fragments.

The results of disintegration of bedrock by freezing water, a process commonly referred to simply as *frost action,* are most conspicuous above the timber line in high mountains and at lower levels in arctic latitudes. The ground may be covered with large angular blocks of fresh rock in an accumulation known as a *felsenmeer* (literally, a rock sea), or *boulder field* (Figure 32.3). Frost shattering is particularly active on the steep rock walls rising above alpine glaciers, for here the meltwater produced in the warmth of the summer days percolates into joint cracks to refreeze at night, a process repeated many times in each season.

Formation of ice bands and layers in the soil is a widespread occurrence in winter in the colder climates. Where the soil is rich in fine-grade silt and clay, soil water tends to freeze in the form of horizontal ice layers that consist of narrow ice crystals perpendicular to the surface. Therefore as the ice layer thickens a strong upward pressure is exerted upon the overlying soil layer, thus lifting, or *heaving,* the soil. Because of the irregularity of growth of the ice layers, frost heaving is uneven and produces mounds of soil.

An interesting effect of ice-crystal growth in soils (*ground ice*) is the moving of larger fragments of rock —in the size range of pebbles, cobbles, and boulders —upward toward the surface or laterally to form rows. Where a rock fragment lies close to the surface, soil heat is conducted more rapidly to the surface, causing the growth of ice under the rock. Continued thickening of the ice layer heaves the rock fragment upward, causing it to rise to the surface, or even to be lifted above the surrounding ground surface. In arctic environments, particularly in the tundra climates, the larger fragments tend to be moved sidewise as well as upward by such frost action and to be sorted out into narrow bands, which intersect to form a net-like pattern consisting of *stone polygons* (or *stone rings* or *stone nets*) (Figures 32.4 and 32.5). These forms are

**FIGURE 32.3.** Quartzite blocks above timberline, making up a felsenmeer at about 12,000 ft (3,700 m) elevation on the summit of Medicine Bow Peak, Snowy Range, Wyoming. (Photograph by A. N. Strahler.)

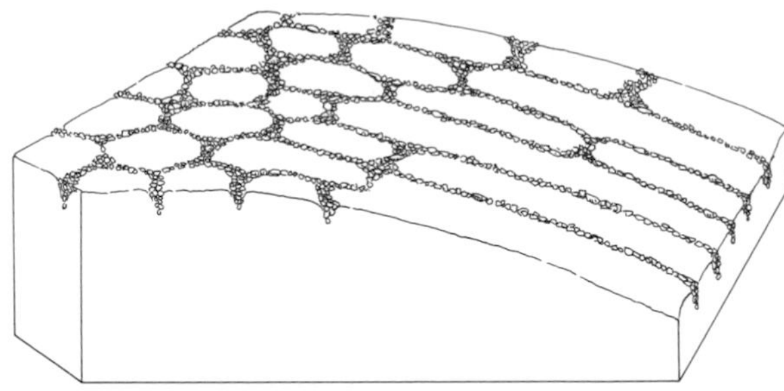

**FIGURE 32.4.** Stone polygons grading into stone stripes on an arctic slope. [After C. F. S. Sharpe (1938), *Landslides and Related Phenomena,* New York, Columbia Univ. Press.]

closely related to the tundra polygons and other forms of patterned ground, all formed by the growth of ice wedges or by shrinkage due to desiccation (Figure 32.6).

In the dry climates—steppes and deserts of the low and middle latitudes—an important agent of rock disintegration is *salt-crystal growth,* a process quite similar physically to ice-crystal growth. Such climates have long drought periods in which evaporation can occur. Water films are drawn surfaceward by capillary-film tension and moisture is steadily evaporated, permitting dissolved salts to be deposited in openings in the rock and soil. Although minute in size and appearing fragile, the growing salt crystals are capable of exerting powerful stresses. Even the hardest rocks (also concrete, mortar, and brick) can be reduced to a sand by continued action of the process. Hence the granular disintegration of rocks in dry climates is often a conspicuous process. Sandstones are particularly affected, for ground water may emerge gradually near the base of a sandstone cliff, supplying water and dissolved salts for continual evaporation (Figure 32.7). As the rock disintegrates and the sand particles are blown away or washed out in rainstorms, the rock wall recedes to produce a *niche,* or in some cases a shallow cave, or even a *rock arch* (Figure 32.8). Such well-protected re-

**FIGURE 32.5.** Stone polygons on Grinnel Peninsula, northwest Devon Island. The rock fragments are of limestone. (Photograph by J. W. Kerr.)

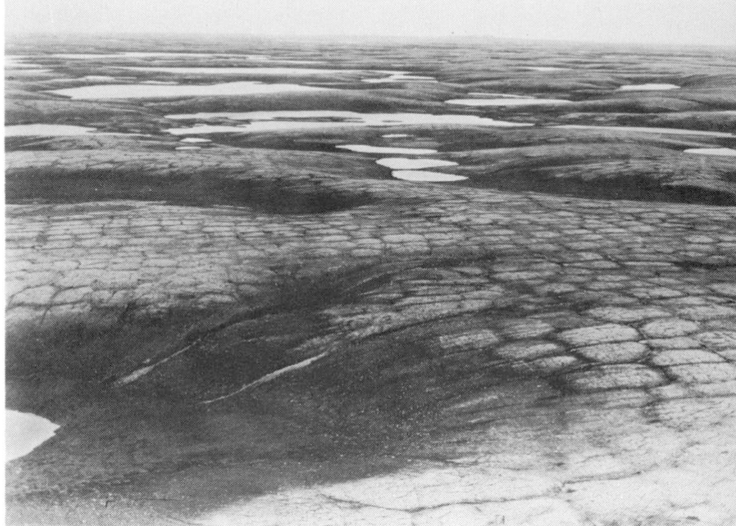

**FIGURE 32.6.** Air view of tundra polygons on Wollaston Peninsula, Victoria Island, lat. 70° N., long. 112° W. (Photograph by A. L. Washburn, Arctic Institute of North America.)

cesses were used by Indians of the southwestern United States as sites for dwellings.

The simple process of wetting and drying of soil and rock can result in forces capable of agitating soil and disintegrating rock. Clay consisting of *colloids* has a strong affinity for water and will swell greatly when permitted to adsorb water. Thus certain of the shales and those siltstones and sandstones containing clay particles tend to disintegrate by moisture adsorption on exposed surfaces. Some shales actually disintegrate spontaneously into a mass of tiny chips, a process known as *slaking.* Clay-rich soils—swelling when wet, contracting when dry—are continually affected by changes in moisture content. In this manner *soil cracks* and *mudcracks* are formed (Figure 32.9).

Rock distintegration is commonly attributed to temperature changes alone. It is well known that most crystalline solids expand when heated and contract when cooled. It is reasoned that because the heating

**FIGURE 32.7.** Sandstone has disintegrated at the base of a high cliff, resulting in a niche and cliff overhang. (© 1960, John Wiley & Sons, New York.)

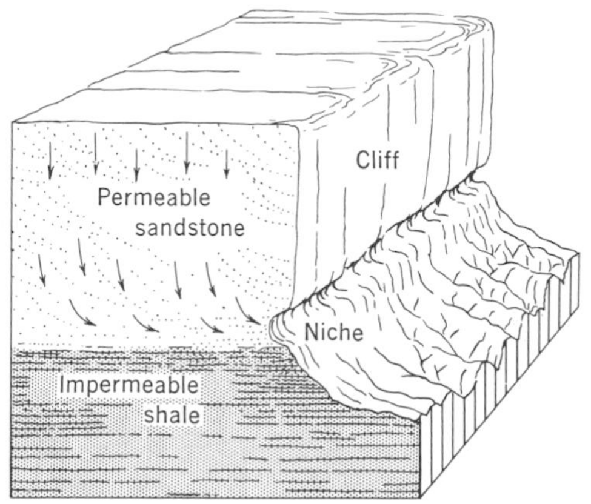

**FIGURE 32.8.** Rock arches resulting from granular disintegration of sandstone. Arches National Monument, Utah. The rock of which the arch is composed is the Entrada sandstone formation. (Photograph by A. N. Strahler.)

of rock will cause expansion of the minerals, the rock may be broken. Sudden and intense heating by forest and brush fires causes severe flaking and scaling of exposed rocks. Also, we know that primitive mining methods included the building of fires upon a quarry floor to cause slabs to break free. But it is uncertain that the daily temperature cycle under solar heating and nightly cooling produces sufficiently great stresses to cause fresh hard rock to break apart. Laboratory tests have shown that rocks can stand the equivalents of centuries of daily heating and cooling without showing signs of disintegration. It is at least reasonable to suppose, however, that expansion and contraction through daily temperature changes may assist in breaking up rocks already affected by other stresses and by chemical decay.

Closely related to physical weathering, and commonly included as one of the processes, is the rupturing of otherwise solid bedrock as a result of the spontaneous volume expansion which the rock undergoes when it is relieved of the confining pressure of overlying and surrounding rock. In quarries of such massive rocks as marble and granite it is a well-known phenomenon that the rock rifts loose in great slabs or sheets, sometimes with explosive violence. When such a slab is cut into a block, the block expands measurably. As a vertical saw cut is made, the cut immediately narrows, and rock expansion continues slowly thereafter for many days.

**FIGURE 32.9.** Mudcracks. Individual blocks are about 1 ft (0.3 m) across. (Photograph by G. K. Gilbert, U.S. Geological Survey.)

This evidence shows that most massive rocks, such as the igneous and metamorphic types, are under a state of slight compression when deeply buried, because of confining pressures of overlying rock or because of orogenic strain that has not been relieved. As the denudation of the landmass proceeds, such rocks are gradually brought nearer the surface. Free of load or of confining rock on the sides, the mass expands. Usually the expansion results in the splitting off of shells of rock up to several feet thick to produce *sheeting structure* (Figure 32.10). Where great bodies of granitic rock are subject to formation of sheeting, dome-like mountain summits, known as *exfoliation domes,* are produced. Fine examples are seen in the Yosemite National Park, where individual rock shells are 20 to 50 ft (6 to 15 m) thick (Figure 32.11). Sheeting in granite of a coast line will result in bedrock slabs dipping seaward everywhere along the shore.

Still another physical-weathering process is that of the action of growing plant roots, exerting pressure upon the confining walls of soil or rock. This process is

**FIGURE 32.10.** Sheeting structure in the Rock of Ages Granite Quarry, Barre, Vermont. The undulating horizontal lines represent natural parting surfaces in the granite. (Photograph by B. Rothstein from Cushing.)

**FIGURE 32.11.** North Dome (*left of center*) and Basket Dome (*right of center*), two great exfoliation domes of Yosemite National Park, California. (Photograph by Douglas Johnson.)

of importance in the breakup of rock already affected by other physical and chemical processes.

## Chemical weathering

Chemical changes in the rock-forming minerals represent responses to the change of environment of the mineral matter from one of great heat and confining pressure deep within the crust to one of low atmospheric temperatures and pressures with the presence of abundant free oxygen and water. Mineral alteration is discussed in Chapter 22. Chemical reactions of original minerals with water (*hydrolysis*), with oxygen (*oxidation*), and with carbonic acid (*carbonation*) are perhaps the dominant groups of chemical changes that the igneous and metamorphic rocks undergo. In contrast, the clastic sedimentary rocks, having been produced under an atmospheric environment, are little subject to further reactions with water, oxygen, or carbonic acid. Another group of chemical reactions are those involving weak acids produced from the decay of vegetative matter.

Chemical decay of joint blocks of igneous rock takes two forms. Granular disintegration, commonly affecting the coarse-grained igneous rocks, tends to produce rounded egg-shaped boulders (Figure 32.12). The products of disintegration, in the form of a coarse sand or gravel of individual mineral crystals, are swept away by overland flow to become the sediment load of streams. The finer-grained igneous rocks are commonly affected by *spheroidal weathering,* a form of exfoliation in which the joint blocks are modified into spherical cores surrounded by shells of decayed rock (Figure 32.13).

**FIGURE 32.12.** Rounded boulders produced by granular disintegration of rectangular joint blocks of granite. (Based on a drawing of W. M. Davis; © 1960, John Wiley & Sons, New York.)

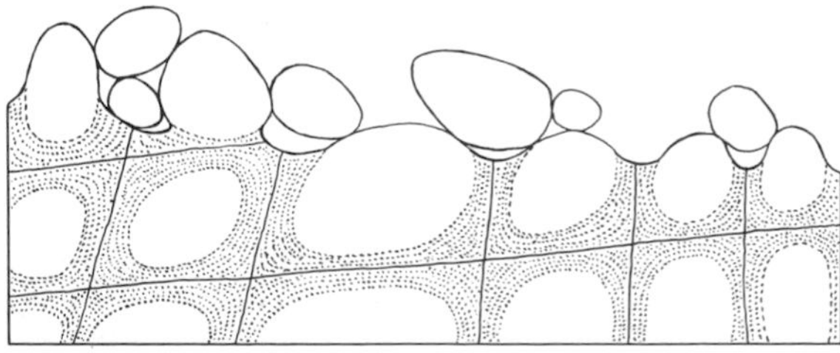

**FIGURE 32.13.** Spheroidal weathering of a boulder of gabbro from the Palisades of the Hudson River, New Jersey. (Photograph by Douglas Johnson.)

In the humid equatorial and tropical climates, chemical decay of igneous and metamorphic rocks extends to depths as great as 300 ft (90 m) and has produced a thick layer of soft clay-rich rock known as *saprolite.* Examples may be found throughout the Piedmont and Appalachian regions of the southeastern United States. Saprolite is easily removed by power shovels with little or no blasting required and contrasts strongly in engineering properties with the dense strong parent rock from which it is formed. Its development of abundant clay minerals with plastic behavior greatly reduces the ability of the saprolite rock to support heavy engineering structures.

Although carbonic acid plays an important role in the decomposition of many mineral and rock varieties, its effects are most striking in the weathering of the carbonate rocks—limestone, dolomite, and marble. Carbonic acid combines readily with calcium carbonate to produce the highly soluble salt calcium bicarbonate, which is carried away in runoff. Limestone surfaces commonly show elaborate pits, grooves, and cup-shaped hollows on exposed surfaces (Figure 32.14). Deep below the surface, ground-water circulation permits carbonic acid to act upon limestone strata to produce cavern systems (Chapter 33).

It is interesting to note that the action of carbonic acid is conspicuous in cold climates, where chemical weathering generally is very slow. Hydrolysis and oxidation are inhibited by the low temperatures in the cold climates, but strongly activated in the warm climates. Hence it is often said that weathering processes at high latitudes and high altitudes are dominantly physical, and those of the warm humid climates are dominantly chemical. In very dry deserts chemical weathering is greatly reduced in intensity, although the effects of hydrolysis and oxidation are clearly seen.

## Weathering and soils

All plant and animal life of the lands is dependent for survival upon the true soil, or *solum,* which comprises a mineral layer at best only a few feet thick over much of the continental surface. Prolonged action of weathering processes combined with organic activity of plants and animals brings the soil layer into physical and chemical equilibrium with the prevailing climatic factors of heat and moisture. Place-to-place variations in character of the soil are apparent through differences both in chemical composition and physical texture of the soil itself and in the characteristic forms of natural vegetation it bears. At the risk of oversimplification, we shall attempt only to differentiate five *soil-forming regimes,* or *pedogenic regimes.* Figure 32.15 is a schematic representation of soil profiles produced in four of the regimes.

**FIGURE 32.14.** Deeply pitted surface of limestone, near Fremantle, Western Australia. (Photograph by Douglas Johnson.)

**Laterization** Consider first the pedogenic regime of *laterization,* which operates in an environment of prevailingly warm temperatures and abundant precipitation occurring year-around or in a long rainy season. This is the environment of equatorial lands and of those parts of tropical lands having a monsoon climate. Intensity of bacterial activity, a major factor in soils of moist climates, is determined largely by temperature.

The relations of bacterial activity to temperature are shown diagrammatically in Figure 32.16. On this graph the vertical scale represents the intensity, or rate, at which vegetative matter is either produced or destroyed, and the horizontal scale gives average annual air temperature. One curve shows the activity of the larger plants, or *macroflora,* which produce vegetative matter by photosynthesis. Two other curves show the activity of bacteria, which consume vegetative matter produced by macroflora—one curve for *aerobic bacteria* (those which require oxygen), the other for *anaerobic bacteria* (those which do not use oxygen). The activity of aerobic bacteria, which live in the well-drained and aerated soils, exceeds that of macrofloral growth at an average temperature of about 77° F (25° C), which is equaled or exceeded year round in the equatorial rainforests. Because the rate of bacterial activity above this temperature exceeds the rate of macrofloral production, the soil is lacking in *humus,* the partially decomposed remains of vascular plants.

The activity of anaerobic bacteria does not exceed macrofloral production until a still higher temperature, well above 95° F (35° C), is reached. Such a high average annual temperature is not found in any climate. Thus in the poorly drained soils of meadows and swamps, where the soil is saturated and oxygen kept out, the humus is not consumed, even in warm climates, and it can accumulate as thick deposits of peat.

In humid low latitudes the percolation of great quantities of rainfall through the soil causes silica ($SiO_2$) to be removed, a process termed *desilication* (Figure 32.15*A*). Soluble salts, including such bases as calcium, sodium, and potassium, are also completely removed. What finally remains in these tropical soils is a group of highly stable oxides and hydroxides of iron, manganese, and aluminum. These form such minerals as *limonite* and *bauxite,* which are not soluble in the soil water of the warm humid climates. The iron and aluminum are supplied by alteration of mineral matter such as that of igneous rocks (Chapter 22). Soils containing these hydroxide minerals in abundance are known generally as *latosols.* Distribution of latosols can be seen on the world map of soils, Appendix 2.

The color of latosols is typically a reddish-brown or chocolate-brown. Horizons are not apparent. Small irregularly shaped nodules of hydroxides are distributed throughout the soil. The soil is favorable for the growth of a native vegetation consisting of *rainforest.*

As explained in Chapter 22, excessive accumulations of hydroxides of iron and aluminum lead to the formation of laterite, which may take the form of rock-like layers beneath the surface. Laterite is of common occurrence in regions of wet-dry tropical climate (monsoon climate).

**Podzolization and gleization** A second pedogenic regime is that of *podzolization,* characteristic of moist climates with long cold winters. Such climates are widespread in latitudes 45° to 65° in North America and Eurasia, and at high altitudes generally throughout the middle latitudes. Referring again to Figure 32.16, we find that at colder mean annual temperatures the production of plant matter by macroflora exceeds the rate of its destruction by aerobic bacteria. So in cold moist climates humus accumulates in substantial quantities. Organic acids produced in the decomposition of plant matter pass downward through the soil (Figure 32.15*B*). Hydrogen ions of the acid solution replace ions of the bases, which are leached from the soil and are exported from the region as runoff in streams. Colloidal mineral and humus particles are also carried down from a thin upper layer of the soil, termed the *zone of eluviation,* resulting in a characteristic ashen-gray horizon, labeled $A_2$ in Figure 32.15*B*. These materials accumulate in the underlying *zone of illuviation,* forming a dense horizon designated as the *B* horizon. Figure 32.17 is a photograph of a typical *podzol* soil exhibiting the distinctive horizons produced under the regime of podzolization.

Podzols are rated low in fertility for agricultural purposes because strong leaching has removed bases

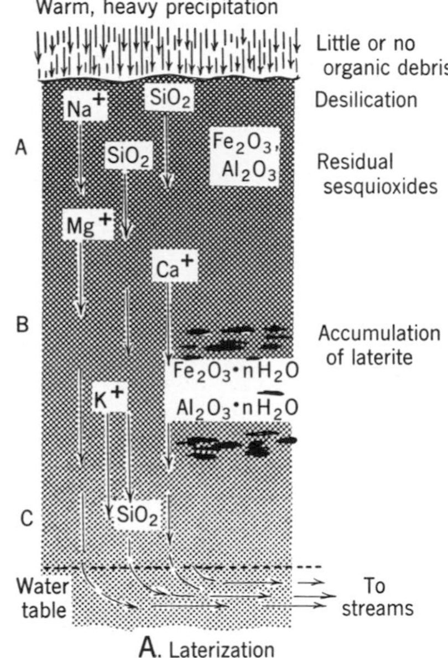


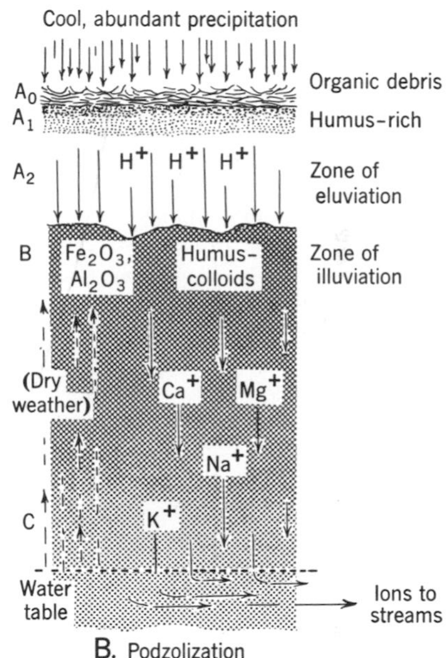


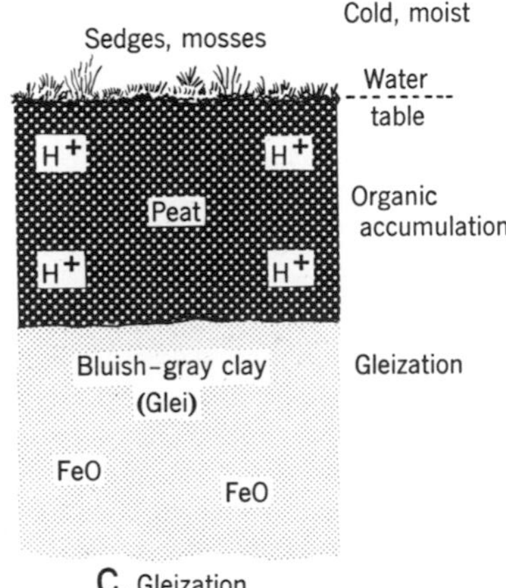


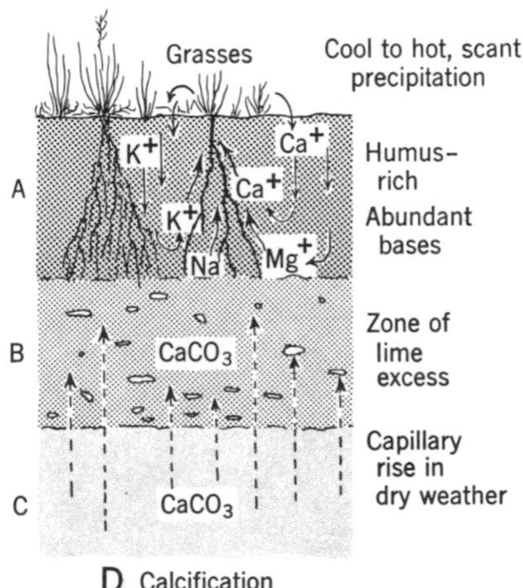


**FIGURE 32.15.** Schematic diagrams of soil development under four pedogenic regimes. (© 1965, John Wiley & Sons, New York.)

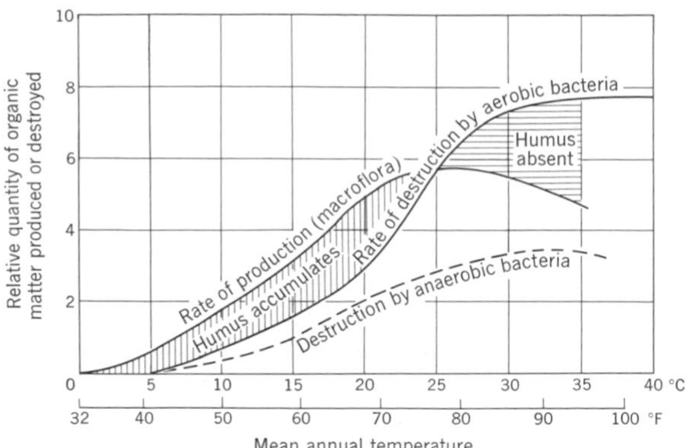


**FIGURE 32.16.** Relative rates of production and destruction of plant matter as dependent upon average annual temperature. [After M. W. Senstius (1958), *Amer. Scientist,* vol. 46.]

needed for many crops and has resulted in an acid soil. Whereas the coniferous trees and certain broad-leafed evergreens thrive on the podzols, the addition of lime and fertilizers is necessary for successful agricultural production.

A third pedogenic regime is *gleization* (*glei* is pronounced "glay"), operating in cool moist climates where water drainage is impeded and conditions of saturation prevail much of the time. Bogs and wet meadowlands in middle and high latitudes are favorable to gleization, and much of the wet arctic tundra is affected by this process. As shown in Figure 32.15*C*, gleization is characterized by a thick upper horizon of organic accumulation, which may be peat. Beneath the peat is typically a dense bluish-gray clay known as the *glei horizon.* Here, because of a deficiency of free oxygen, the iron oxide is in the reduced state, as ferrous oxide (FeO).

**Calcification and duricrust** A fourth regime is *calcification,* characteristic of soils in regions deficient in soil moisture. Such climates include the semi-arid steppes and deserts, found widely distributed from tropical to middle latitudes. Calcification is found where annual evaporation on the average exceeds annual precipitation. The effects of this moisture imbalance are illustrated in Figure 32.15*D*. During dry periods or dry seasons soil water rises toward the surface and is evaporated, leaving behind calcium carbonate (mineral calcite), which forms nodules or lenses in the soil. This zone of carbonate accumulation is designated the *B* horizon. Figure 32.18 shows a profile of one of the major varieties of soils produced under a regime of calcification. Although no deposits of carbonate matter are visible, the *B* horizon has a distinctive prismatic structure.

The most widespread type of natural vegetation in a regime of calcification is grasslands. The grasses are deep-rooted and bring up to the surface the bases they require for growth (Figure 32.15*D*). Thus there is a recycling of the bases, which might otherwise be permanently removed from the soil in periods of excess

**FIGURE 32.17.** Podzol soil profile developed on sandy granitic till in Maine. (Photograph by C. E. Kellogg; courtesy of Soil Conservation Service, U.S. Department of Agriculture.)

rainfall. Partial decay of grass roots adds substantial amounts of humus to the uppermost or *A* horizon, which is typically brown to black. Soils produced in the regime of calcification are extraordinarily rich in nutrients needed for the cultivation of grains. Major wheat producing regions of the world lie under this pedogenic regime.

Calcification may proceed to an advanced state in which accumulation of calcium carbonate assumes the form of a rock-like layer. The material is known variously as *caliche, lime-crust,* or *calcrete.* This hard layer is often difficult to distinguish from a stratum of limestone deposited in an aqueous medium.

We have seen that both laterization and calcification produce rock-like crusts within the soil, but under quite different climatic conditions and with unlike chemical compositions. The term *duricrust* has been applied to

**FIGURE 32.18.** Profile of a brown soil developed on loess in Colorado. The *B* horizon shows prismatic structure. (Photograph by C. C. Nikiforoff; courtesy of Soil Conservation Service, U.S. Department of Agriculture.)

a wide variety of such phenomena. Indurated soil produced under laterization is often called *ferricrete,* recognizing the abundance of ferric iron oxide ($Fe_2O_3$). In addition to crusts of calcrete and ferricrete, there are regions in which crusts are produced by the accumulation of silica—this material can be designated *silcrete.* Duricrusts of both lateritic and siliceous compositions are widespread in tropical regions of Africa, India, and Australia. Strongly resistant to erosion, these duricrusts form a protective capping layer over upland surfaces. Similar processes of accumulation of calcium carbonate, iron oxide, or silica in the outermost zone of exposed bedrock masses produces an extremely hard protective crust. The phenomenon is known to geologists as *case-hardening.*

**Salinization** Fifth among the pedogenic regimes is *salinization,* or accumulation of soluble salts in the soil zone. This process occurs in poorly-drained places in desert climates, where water received as stream flow from surrounding highlands is evaporated on the floors of basins. Common salts found in these soils are sulfates and chlorides of calcium and sodium. Gypsum (hydrous calcium sulfate) is a particularly common mineral in such localities and may form a dense crust. Soils developed under a regime of salinization can support only a sparse vegetation of salt-tolerant plants and may be totally devoid of vegetation.

## Mass wasting

Although the force of gravity acts constantly upon all soil, overburden, and bedrock, the internal strength of these materials is ordinarily sufficient to keep them in place, thus we rarely see soil or rock moving spontaneously except when carried by an active agent of erosion. Wherever the ground has a measurable slope with respect to the horizontal, a proportion of the acceleration of gravity is directed downslope parallel with the surface. Every particle has at least some tendency to roll or slide downhill and will do so whenever the downslope force exceeds the resistive forces of friction and cohesion that tend to bind the particle to the rest of the mass.

The downslope force increases as the sine of the angle of the slope measured from the horizontal. Thus on a slope of 30° the force acting on a unit of mass is just half the total gravitational force, but on a slope of 60° it is about 87%. Hence, as everyone knows, the tendency to slide is greater on steeper slopes, but it is not often appreciated that the tendency increases most rapidly in the lower range of angles, from 0° to 45° or so, and thereafter less rapidly. Above 70° the slope behaves almost as if it were perpendicular. From these facts we might reason that precipitous slopes will be rare in nature simply because they waste away so rapidly that, when formed by any geologic agent, they do not endure for long. On a percentage basis the total area of land slopes steeper than 45° is very small indeed, although it is the few steep mountain slopes that are readily visible from afar and therefore attract our attention. By far the greatest proportion of the earth's land surface is in slope less than 5°, and on such subdued relief the effects of mass wasting are rarely noticed.

The forms of mass wasting range from the great catastrophic slides in alpine mountains, involving millions of cubic yards of rock and capable of wiping out a whole town, down to the small flows of saturated soil seen commonly along the highways in early spring. But extremely slow movement of soil, imperceptible from one year to the next, also acts on almost every hillside.

**Soil creep (surficial creep)** Careful inspection of a hillside may reveal evidence that the soil has been very slowly moving downslope rather steadily over a long period of time, a phenomenon termed *soil creep* or *surficial creep* (Figure 32.19). If an outcrop of a distinctive type of rock is present high up on the slope, one may find that the larger joint blocks have moved away from their original locations and that smaller fragments of the rock are being carried far down the slope in the soil mass. Yet it is unlikely that these particles have at any time slid or rolled rapidly. Where steeply dipping layered rocks such as slates or shales underlie a hillside, the upper edges of the layers are commonly turned downhill as if bent, the result of slow creep distributed on countless joint fractures and bedding or cleavage surfaces in the rock (Figure 32.20). Trees, posts, poles, and monuments may be found tilted downhill, suggesting rotation as the soil has crept

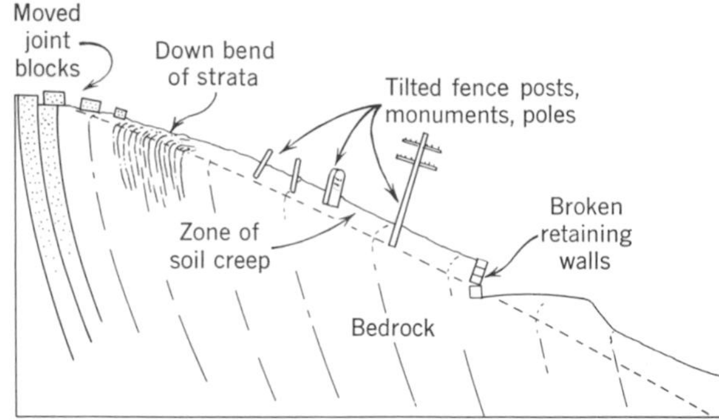


**FIGURE 32.19.** Commonplace evidences of the almost imperceptible downslope creep of soil and weathered rock. (© 1960, John Wiley & Sons, New York.)

downslope, the surface layers moving more rapidly than those at depth. Retaining walls paralleling the slope may be found to be tipped over and broken, suggesting a yielding to the pressure of soil creep.

The mechanism of soil creep is a combination of the various weathering processes that agitate the soil acting in concert with the force of gravity. Whatever mechanism disturbs the soil induces downslope movement of the particles, because gravity exerts an influence on the motions and its influence is in the downslope direction. Consider, as an illustration, that dry sand is poured into a conical pile on a table. Once the motions of the grains have ceased, there is no further change of the slope of the sand because the forces of friction exceed the downslope component of the force of gravity. Now let the table be tapped repeatedly, sending a series of shock waves through the sand. With each tap the sand slope is lowered, and consequently the conical pile lowers and widens. Each mechanical shock momentarily reduces the friction between sand grains, and at that instant the force of gravity moves the grains a very slight distance downslope.

**FIGURE 32.20.** Downbend by creep of the upper edges of near-vertical shale strata, Maryland. (Photograph by G. W. Stose, U.S. Geological Survey.)

In nature, disturbances of soil result from many causes. Growth and melting of ice crystals, drying and wetting accompanied by shrinking and swelling of the soil, and the volume expansion and contraction from temperature changes are important physical causes. The growth of plant roots, pushing aside the soil, with later collapse of root cavities after the roots have decayed, is an important vegetative process. Burrowing by many forms of animal life, with later closing of the cavities, is a biological cause. Trampling of slopes by large animals—such as deer, bison, and cattle—may cause downslope soil creep.

**Earth flowage** In hilly and mountainous regions of humid climate, yielding of soil, overburden, or bedrock rich in clay minerals (e.g., clay soils, clay-rich glacial debris, or shales) takes the form of *earthflows.* These are tongue-like masses that have flowed a limited distance down the hillside, perhaps coming to rest before reaching the base, or in some cases turning and flowing downvalley for a short distance. At its upper end the earthflow leaves a depression bounded on the uphill side by a curved *scarp* (Figure 32.21). At its lower end the earthflow bulges convexly downslope in a *toe.* Where the hillside flattens to a broad valley floor, the toe spreads out into a broad rounded mass resembling a pancake. Where the valley is relatively narrow, the toe forms a dam, sometimes creating a lake (Figure 32.22).

Earthflow is a form of mass wasting in which behavior of the earth material is that of a *plastic solid.* Any mixture of solid particles (sand, silt, or clay, for example) with a liquid such as water or oil forms a variety of plastic solids characterized by a certain degree of strength. Such a mixture will resist flowage up to a given limit, the *yield stress,* but above this yield stress it will flow much as a true liquid. Of course, if the quantity of water is small relative to the amount of solid matter, the material will resist flowage to the point that it will come to rest on a relatively steep slope, as in the earthflow. The presence of clay particles tends to reduce the resistance to flowage by providing a form of lubrication. Moreover, clays tend to absorb and hold water, thus aiding in the accumulation of the necessary water to give a mixture of soft consistency.

The scientific study of the behavior and physical properties of soil, overburden, and weak rocks under unequal stresses is treated in *soil mechanics,* an engineering phase of the earth sciences involving

**FIGURE 32.21.** Earth flows on steep mountain slopes in a humid region. (After a sketch by W. M. Davis; © 1960, John Wiley & Sons, New York.)

**FIGURE 32.22.** This great earthflow occurred in 1925 in the Gros Ventre River valley of Wyoming. A shale mass of 50 million cu yds (38 million cu m) descended 2000 ft (600 m) to form a dam 250 ft (75 m) high, ponding the river to produce a lake 5 mi (8 km) long. (Photograph by A. N. Strahler.)

fundamental principles of physics. Most of the man-made forms of mass movements caused during construction and excavation are similar in principle to the naturally occurring types of mass wasting. Much is to be gained by applying the principles of soil engineering to an explanation of the natural phenomena.

Some earthflows, particularly those large flows affecting weak bedrock, start out with a very slow flowage but increase in rate because the mixing of the water with the mineral particles reduces the internal resistance to flow. In such cases the flow develops more fluid-like behavior and may travel a considerable distance downvalley as a long narrow tongue. Rate of motion is probably on the order of several feet per hour. Shallow earthflows in soil may become stiffer in consistency after a few yards of travel because of drainage of the soil water, hence they may come to rest on the hillside.

*Solifluction,* an arctic variety of earth flowage, is an important process in the development of the landscape in regions of tundra climates. In these regions the permanently frozen subsoil (permafrost) acts as a barrier to downward percolation of water released in the spring by the melting of the snow cover and ice in the surface layer of the soil. Unable to escape by drainage, moisture builds up until the thawed soil is saturated and exceeds its yield stress, resulting in slow flowage of a shallow layer. The result is a succession of *solifluction terraces* and *solifluction lobes* (Figure 32.23). Motion is on the order of a few yards per year, with motion of a few inches per day at the maximum.

**Mudflow** Where the proportion of water to mineral matter is large, there may be produced a rather fluid mixture capable of traveling rapidly in stream-like masses down the channels of streams, a form of mass wasting termed *mudflow.* In nature there are all gradations between earthflow and mudflow, and it is not practical to try to draw a precise line of distinction.

One type of mudflow, common in arid regions, originates in the watersheds of streams high in a mountain range. Here torrential thunderstorm rains may wash vast quantities of loose soil and weathered overburden down steep mountain slopes into the ad-

**FIGURE 32.23.** Solifluction on this Alaskan tundra slope has produced lobelike masses of soil, locally termed "earth runs." (Photograph by P. S. Smith, U.S. Geological Survey.)

**FIGURE 32.24.** Mudflows issuing from the mouths of canyons in a semi-arid region. (© 1960, John Wiley & Sons, New York.)

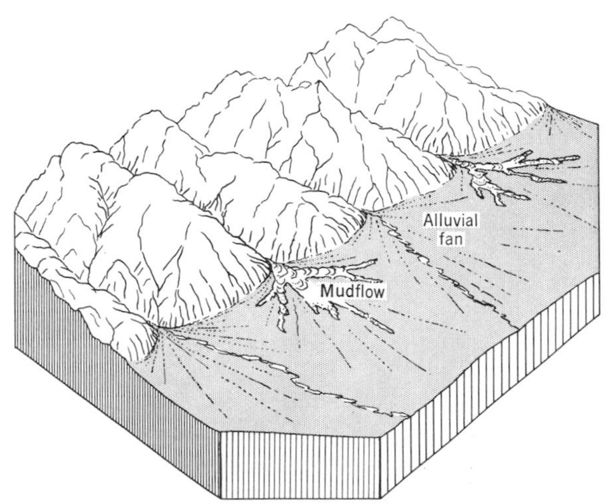

**FIGURE 32.25.** A small mudflow resulting spontaneously from rapid summer melting of soil ice in the arctic tundra. The central stream is about 2 ft (0.6 m) wide. De Salis Bay, Banks Island, lat. 71½° N. (Photograph by A. L. Washburn, Arctic Institute of North America.)

jacent channels. As the heavily laden stream flow progresses down valley, the loss of water by seepage and the increasing proportion of solid matter picked up from channel floors and banks cause the stream to thicken into a mudflow. The mudflow may attain the consistency of ready-mix concrete and will continue downvalley, where it commonly spreads out upon the plain at the foot of the mountain range (Figure 32.24). Eventually thickening of the mud by loss of water causes the yield stress to increase above the gravitational stress, at which point flowage will cease.

Mudflows of the mountainous deserts are a serious threat to life and property because they may emerge from canyons with little warning and spread over populated lands. The *debris flood,* a disastrous flood occurring in such localities as Los Angeles and Salt Lake City, is a form of flowage intermediate between the turbid flood of a mountain stream and a true mudflow.

Mudflows are also produced on the slopes of active volcanoes where torrential rains saturate freshly fallen volcanic ash. Herculaneum, a Roman village at the western base of Mt. Vesuvius, was thus buried in the eruption of A.D. 79. Other types of mudflows, in high alpine mountains and in arctic regions, can result from rapid melting of snow and ground ice (Figure 32.25). In other cases an earthflow originating in highly weathered rock rich in clay minerals may become increasingly fluid as it travels and change to a mudflow.

**FIGURE 32.26.** Slide and slump are two basic forms of landsliding. (© 1960, John Wiley & Sons, New York.)

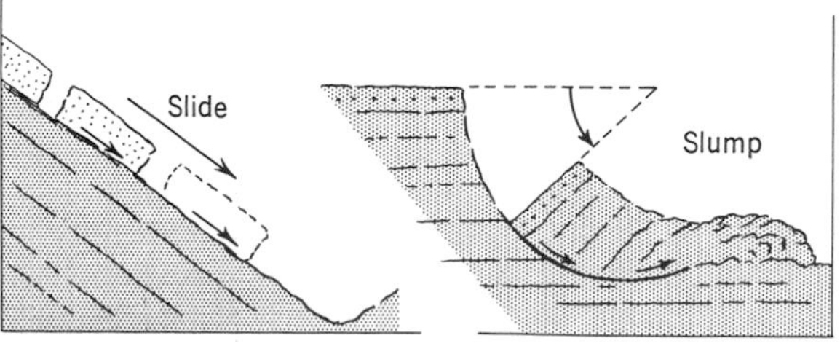


**Landslide** Although the term *landslide* is often used in reference to any form of rapid mass wasting, including earthflow, it is correctly limited to the rapid sliding of large masses of bedrock without plastic flowage in the early stages. Most landslides as they travel undergo a distintegration of the rock mass into a debris of assorted sizes that may travel with a gross flowage motion and produce a tongue-like body of rubble. In the early stages, however, the landslide moves with one of two basic types of motion: *rockslide,* in which a single block slides on its lower surface on a bedding plane, joint plane, or fault plane; and *slump,* in which a block slips on a curved fracture plane rotating backward upon a horizontal axis as it sinks (Figure 32.26).

Rockslides are found in high mountain ranges of the alpine type where steep rock walls have previously been formed by glacial erosion (Chapter 40). Many rockslides have been reported in the Alps, Canadian Rockies, and mountains of Norway (Figure 32.27). One slide may involve many millions of cubic yards of rock and can travel with the speed of a freely falling object. Towns, highways, and railroad lines in the path of the slide are obliterated. Immediate causes of rockslides are not often evident, and the time of their occurrence cannot be predicted. In some cases hydrostatic pressure of water in the rock interstices may have pried the block loose. An earthquake shock may set off a slide, an example being the Madison landslide caused by the Hebgen Lake earthquake of 1959 in Montana.

Slumping of bedrock masses on a vast scale is found along cliffs of sedimentary strata or lavas (Figure 32.28). Blocks as long as a mile or more and with a thickness of a thousand feet are known. Steepening of the cliff by running-water erosion of shale formations in the cliff base precedes the slump. Although hundreds of such large slump blocks are known in the semi-arid regions of the Colorado Plateau and Columbia Plateau, nearly all appear to be at least some thousands of years old and may have occurred under climatic conditions perhaps more moist than exist there today.

The slumping of masses of soil and overburden is commonly seen on a small scale in the banks of streams or along cliffs cut into by wave action. The upper parts of many earthflows show slumping, with the characteristic block-like and stepped appearance.

In both rockslide and slump the earth material behaves essentially as an *elastic solid*—that is, as a brittle substance that yields by elastic bending when unequal stresses are applied. Such yielding in rock would be imperceptible, but when the strength of the rock is exceeded a sudden rupture occurs and the detached mass moves with great rapidity.

**Rockfall and talus** On any near-vertical cliff of rock fragments are continually being pried free by the processes of physical weathering already described. The fall of any such fragment, whether it be merely a sand grain or a huge mass weighing hundreds of tons, is described simply as *rockfall.* Although the fragment may bounce or roll down the cliff face, its descent is approximately at the speed of a freely falling body accelerating under the force of gravity. Most large falling rock masses shatter into many smaller fragments strewing the base of the slope (Figure 32.29).

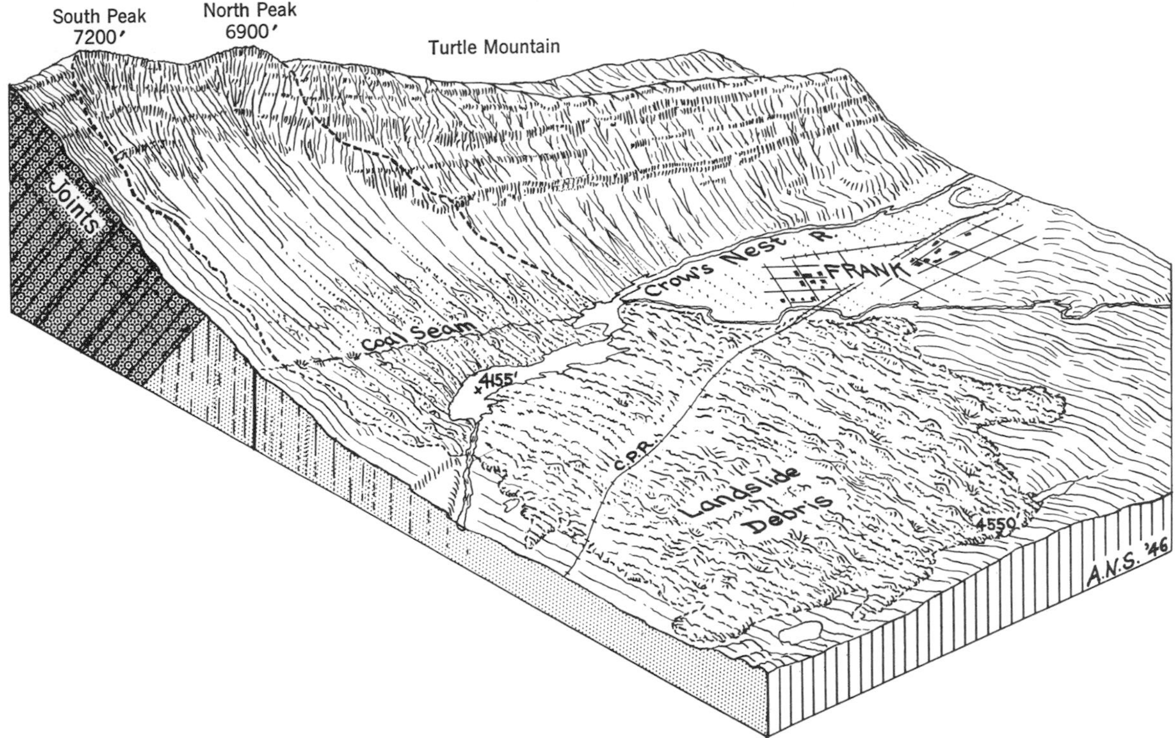


**FIGURE 32.27.** Block diagram of the Turtle Mountain landslide which occurred near Frank, Alberta, in 1903. A great limestone mass, some 40 million cu yds (32 million cu m), slid from the mountainside between South and North Peaks, descended 3000 ft (900 m) to the valley floor, then spread widely as a sheet of bouldery debris. Seventy lives were lost in the town of Frank. (Based on data of the Canadian Geological Survey, Department of Mines. © 1960, John Wiley & Sons, New York.)

Rockfall continued from a cliff face over many decades and centuries eventually builds a *talus slope* of loose rock fragments (*talus*) at the cliff base (Figure 32.29). Normally the cliff has recesses and ravines tending to funnel the fragments into a chute-like exit, causing the pile of fragments to take the shape of a *talus cone* (Figure 32.30). Material constituting talus is also referred to as *slide rock.* The surface slope is remarkably constant at an angle of close to 35° with the horizontal.

**FIGURE 32.28.** A slump block descending from a cliff of horizontal strata rotates backwards on an axis parallel with the cliff. (© 1960, John Wiley & Sons, New York.)

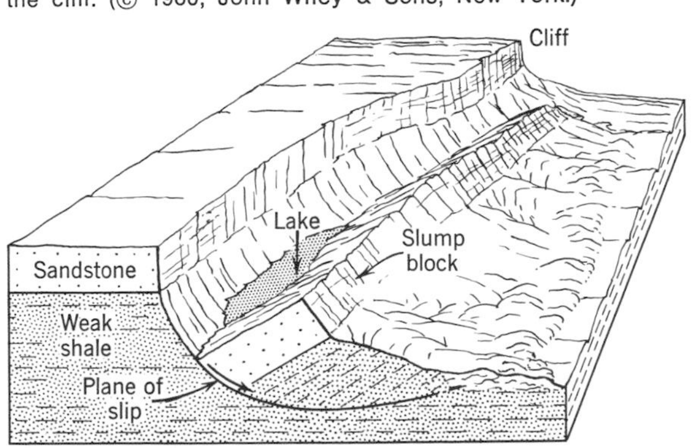


The maximum angle of slope that can be held by a pile of loose coarse grains—whether of slide rock, sand, or gravel—is termed the *angle of repose.* Although this angle increases slightly as the size of fragments decreases, it is rarely less than 34° or higher than 37° in natural slopes composed of mixtures of sizes. Increased angularity of the particles and greater roughness of their surface texture yield the somewhat steeper repose angles.

**FIGURE 32.29.** Talus cones of quartzite fragments, Snowy Range, Wyoming. (Photograph by A. N. Strahler.)

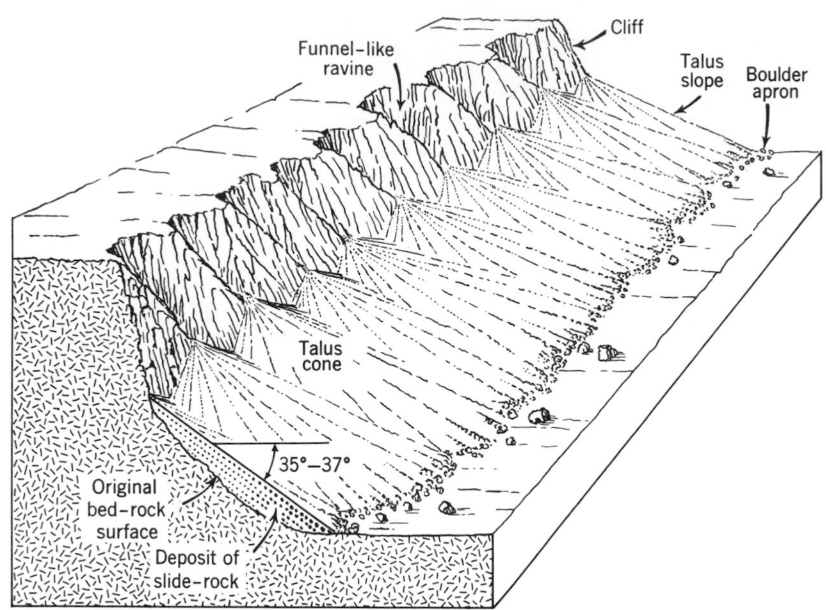


**FIGURE 32.30.** Talus cones. (© 1965, John Wiley & Sons, New York.)

In simple talus cones, particles tend to be finer near the apex, coarser near the base, because the greater momentum and radius of the larger particles permits them to travel farther. Very large fragments may roll well beyond the base of the talus cone.

This chapter has dealt with the passive agents of denudation—weathering and mass wasting. Weathering prepares the bedrock for erosion and transportation by active agents, of which flowing water is the most important. We shall therefore turn in the next two chapters to the movement of water below and above the ground surface.

## References for further study

Sharpe, C. F. S. (1938), *Landslides and Related Phenomena,* New York, Columbia Univ. Press, 137 pp.

Lobeck, A. K. (1939), *Geomorphology,* New York, McGraw-Hill, 731 pp., chaps. 1, 3.

Fairbridge, R. W., ed. (1968), *The Encyclopedia of Geomorphology,* New York, Reinhold, 1295 pp.

Strahler, A. N. (1969), *Physical Geography,* 3rd ed., New York, Wiley, 733 pp., chaps. 18, 19.

Thornbury, W. D. (1969), *Principles of Geomorphology,* 2nd ed., New York, Wiley, 594 pp., chaps. 3, 4.

# 33

# Water in the subsurface zone

THAT PART OF HYDROLOGY concerned with the earth's water budget includes the gains and losses of water among atmosphere, oceans, and lands and the total rates of transformation from vapor state to liquid or solid state and retransformation to vapor state. Such interchanges of water form part of the hydrologic cycle, in which moisture is traced through a number of possible circuits. In a more restricted sense, hydrology is concerned largely with the water that falls on the lands and with its movements over the ground surface, through soil and rock, and in streams, marshes, and lakes.

The practical hydrologist classifies water that flows on the land surface or lies ponded in lakes and marshes as *surface water* and water that lies beneath the land surface—enclosed in pores of the soil, overburden, or bedrock—as *subsurface water.* Subsurface water is in turn subdivided into *soil water,* which is moisture found in the soil or residual overburden within a few feet of the surface, and *ground water,* found in bedrock or in thick masses of overburden many feet below the surface.

Soil water has been intensively studied by the soil scientist and agricultural engineer because of its essential role in the growth of plants. Ground water is usually investigated by the geologist and civil engineer because the storage and movement of ground water is strongly influenced by the types of rocks and structures present and the flow of the water responds to laws of fluids treated in the science of hydraulics.

In this chapter some elementary principles of both soil water and ground water are introduced to give a unified picture of the movements of water from the time that it falls as precipitation, through its progress under the surface, to the time that it reemerges into streams and bodies of standing water. In Chaper 34 the surface flow of water is considered under the general heading of *runoff.* If we add what has been already said of the oceanic circulation (Chapter 16), the movement of air masses (Chapter 19), and the distribution of precipitation on a global scale (Chapter 18), as well as what is included in Chapter 40 concerning the nourishment and wastage of glaciers, we shall have secured a picture of the scope of general hydrology as a basic earth science.

## The hydrologic cycle and world water balance

The continuous interchanges of geographical position and physical state of water constitute the *hydrologic cycle,* shown schematically in Figure 33.1. Could we trace a given molecule of water, it might be found to follow one of a number of circuits including the vapor, liquid, and solid states. As the principal reservoir of the earth's water, the oceans form a convenient point at which to start the analysis of the hydrologic cycle. An estimated 80,000 cubic miles of water evaporates annually from the ocean surface, and about 15,000 cubic miles evaporates from the lands, including lakes and marshes (Figure 33.2). Thus a total of 95,000 cubic miles of water evaporates, and an equal amount must be returned to the earth's surface annually by precipitation. Of this, about 24,000 cubic miles falls as rain or snow upon the land surfaces. These figures show that the quantity precipitated upon the lands is some 60% greater than the amount of water that is returned to the atmosphere by evaporation from the land. We are led to conclude that the remaining precipitation on land, 9000 cubic miles, or about 40%, is returned annually to the oceans by liquid or glacial flow over and beneath the ground. The most obvious part of this return flow is, of course, by streams emptying into the oceans, but some water seeps into the ground and, as ground water, passes beneath the lands into the coastal ocean waters.

**FIGURE 33.1.** The hydrologic cycle. (© 1960, John Wiley & Sons, New York.)

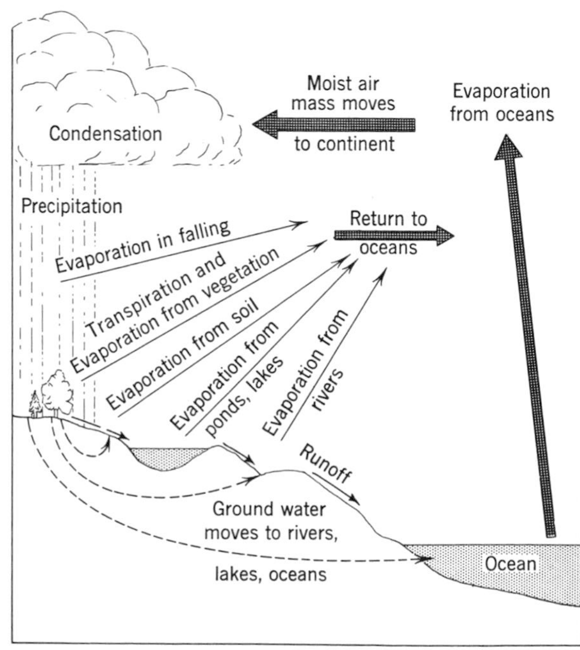


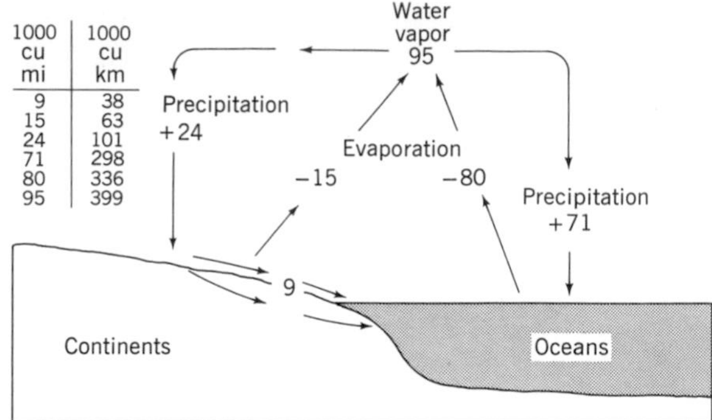


**FIGURE 33.2.** Schematic diagram of the world's water balance.

The figures given in Figure 33.2 represent a rough numerical estimate of the components of the earth's *water balance.* Recall that in Chapter 18 the water balance of the atmosphere was developed in terms of a simple equation including the terms *P,* for precipitation, *E,* for evaporation, and *G,* for the net gain or loss of water held in the system. Using these same terms, the water balance of either the world continents taken together or the world ocean can be stated as follows:

$$P = E + G + R$$

where *P, E,* and *G* are defined as above, and *R* is runoff (positive when out of continents, negative when into oceans). Since the annual change in stored water must be very small on large areas of the globe taken together, the term *G* can be neglected, simplifying the equation to:

$$P = E + R$$

For the continents: $24 = 15 + 9$ (units of 1000 cu mi)
For the oceans: $71 = 80 - 9$

Taking the entire globe as a unit, the runoff terms sum to zero, leaving only:

$$P = E$$

Substituting the numerical data: $24 + 71 = 15 + 80$

Water in storage is distributed very unevenly among its three states in various places over the globe (Table 33.1). Over 97% is in the world ocean, and most of the remainder is locked up in icecaps and glaciers. Subsurface water constitutes a very much greater volume than surface water on the lands, roughly by a factor of 30 times. Notice how trivial is the volume of water held in the entire atmosphere, yet the hydrologic cycle depends upon atmospheric transport of water in order to function.

We have seen in earlier chapters how the water vapor from maritime air masses moves landward, where rapid condensation produces precipitation. By direct evaporation some of the falling rain and snow may return immediately to the vapor state (Figure 33.1), and some

**TABLE 33.1. ESTIMATED DISTRIBUTION OF THE WORLD'S WATER***

| Location | Surface Area sq mi | Surface Area sq km | Water Volume cu mi | Water Volume cu km | Percent of Total |
|---|---|---|---|---|---|
| Surface water | | | | | |
| Fresh-water lakes | 330,000 | 860,000 | 30,000 | 125,000 | 0.009 |
| Saline lakes and inland seas | 270,000 | 700,000 | 25,000 | 104,000 | 0.008 |
| Average in stream channels | ... | ... | 300 | 1,250 | 0.0001 |
| Subsurface water | 50,000,000 | 130,000,000 | | | |
| Soil moisture and intermediate-zone (vadose) water | | | 16,000 | 67,000 | 0.005 |
| Ground water within 0.5 mi (0.8 km) depth | | | 1,000,000 | 4,170,000 | 0.31 |
| Ground water, deep-lying | | | 1,000,000 | 4,170,000 | 0.31 |
| Total liquid water in land areas | | | 2,070,000 | 8,637,000 | 0.635 |
| Icecaps and glaciers | 6,900,000 | 18,000,000 | 7,000,000 | 29,200,000 | 2.15 |
| Atmosphere | 197,000,000 | 510,000,000 | 3,100 | 13,000 | 0.001 |
| World ocean | 139,500,000 | 360,000,000 | 317,000,000 | 1,322,000,000 | 97.2 |
| Totals (rounded) | | | 326,000,000 | 1,360,000,000 | 100 |

* Data from Dr. Raymond L. Nace, U.S. Geological Survey, 1964.

of that which lands on foliage and on the ground may also evaporate directly. The excess precipitation may run off into streams or may sink into the soil and bedrock. Soil moisture lying close to the ground surface may be taken up into the foliage of plants, to be released into the atmosphere as vapor. Some soil moisture is evaporated directly from the ground surface in periods of dry weather. That which has sunk to greater depths becomes a part of the ground-water body and moves slowly through the rock, eventually to emerge in streams, marshes, lakes, or the sea.

With this general sketch of the various possible paths of travel of water in the hydrologic cycle, we turn to the details of water behavior on or within the soil.

## Infiltration and runoff

In the natural undisturbed state most soil surfaces can absorb the water from light to moderate rains and transmit it downward by a process termed *infiltration.* Natural passageways are available between individual soil grains and between the larger aggregates of soil where previous drying has caused cracks to form, where borings by worms and other animals have been made, where decay of plant roots has left openings, and where the alternate growth and melting of ice crystals has disrupted the soil. Such openings tend to be kept clear by the protective mat of decaying leaves and plant stems, and the mat also acts to break the force of falling raindrops. When rain falls too rapidly to escape downward through the soil passages, the excess quantity escapes as runoff—a surface layer of water following the slope of the ground—in a process known as *overland flow.*

We have noted that the intensity of rainfall is measured in depth of water accumulated per unit of time (Chapter 18). Imagine that the rain is caught in a straight-sided, flat-bottomed container and that none is lost by splashing out or by evaporation. The depth in inches of accumulation per hour represents rainfall intensity (Figure 33.3). If the container is imagined to have a porous bottom, like a sieve, the water will leak through, lowering the level at a certain rate, representing the rate of infiltration into the soil, the *infiltration capacity.* Now, if the rainfall rate exceeds the infiltration rate, the container will fill until it can hold no more. When both the storage capacity and the ability of the soil to transmit water to greater depth are exceeded, the excess escapes as overland flow. Thus we can also measure runoff by overland flow in units of inches or centimeters per hour.[1]

The ability of soils to absorb rainfall, or the infiltration capacity, is ordinarily rather great at the very outset of a rain that follows a period of dryness. This is because the soil is in a contracted state and has many large openings. As wetting proceeds, however, the soil takes up water and swells, closing the larger openings. Moreover, the sponge-like capacity of the soil pores to hold water is quickly met, after which the infiltration capacity is sharply reduced. Thus if we should make a graph of the rate at which the infiltration

[1] Strictly speaking, runoff rate, or intensity, is defined as volume of water (cubic inches) derived from an area of ground surface (square inches) per hour, but this reduces to depth (inches) per hour.

**FIGURE 33.3.** Rainfall, infiltration, runoff, and overland flow.

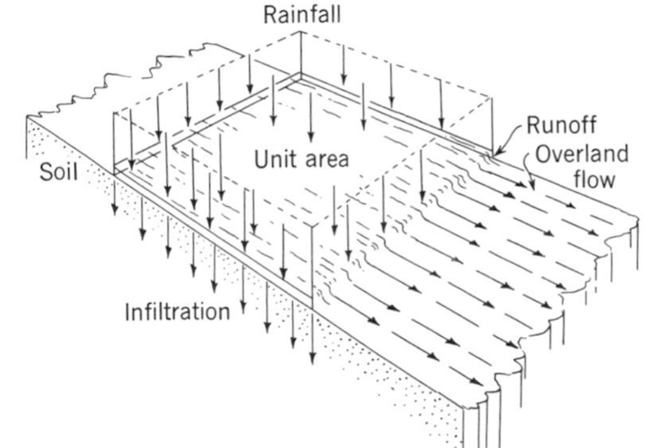

capacity changes with time, we would see that the initial value is high—perhaps 2 to 3 in. (5 to 8 cm) per hour—but falls rapidly within the first hour and thereafter levels off and becomes relatively constant at a much lower rate (Figure 33.4).

Where a sandy or gravelly soil is present, there is little or no swelling of the soil when it is wet, and because the soil pores are relatively large and freely interconnected, the infiltration capacity remains high even after prolonged rain. In contrast, in clay-rich soils the infiltration capacity quickly falls to a very low value, as shown in Figure 33.4*A*. In areas subject to grazing by livestock, trampling of the soil surface causes the soil pores and larger openings to be sealed, thereby reducing infiltration (Figure 33.4*B*). Thus overgrazed land tends to have greater runoff and to be subject to excessive soil erosion. Land bearing an undisturbed forest cover maintains a higher infiltration rate than deforested land, because the canopy of foliage and the litter of fallen vegetation protect the soil from rain beat, keeping the soil passages from being sealed (Figure 33.4*C*).

**FIGURE 33.4.** Rate of infiltration of rainfall varies with soil texture and land usage. (© 1960, John Wiley & Sons, New York. Data by Sherman and Musgrave; Foster.)

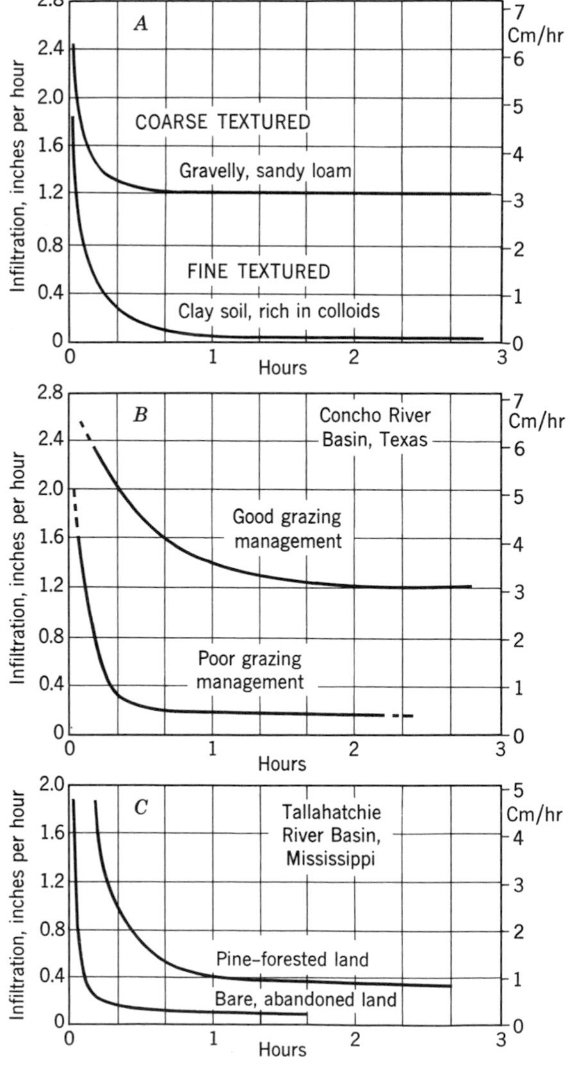


As Man has cleared the world's forests for agriculture and used the natural grasslands for grazing of herds of cattle and sheep, he has caused radical decreases in the infiltration capacity of the soil. These changes in turn have tended to increase the rate of runoff that is produced from a given intensity of rain. Widespread soil erosion has resulted, often with severe gullying and a depletion of the soil- and ground-water reserves (Chapter 34).

## Zones of soil water

Water is held in the soil, overburden, and bedrock in different ways, depending upon the degree to which it occupies all the available interconnected pore spaces. Let us suppose that after a period of heavy rains, during which time much water has percolated downward through the soil, a rainless period ensues. There will come a point when gravity is no longer capable of moving the remaining water downward to lower levels because the water is in the form of thin films clinging to the soil grains with a force stronger than the force of gravity.

Let us examine the several states of soil water, starting with the lowermost level. Below the *water table,* all pore space is water-filled and constitutes the zone of saturation, or *ground-water zone* (Figure 33.5). Water in this zone is able to move very slowly downward and toward streams or lakes under the influence of gravity, hence the water table slowly sinks during periods between rains. The movement of ground water and the form of the water table are discussed in later paragraphs of this chapter.

Above the water table, soil water takes the form of *capillary water,* that is, water drawn upward against the force of gravity by a force known as *capillary ten-*

**FIGURE 33.5.** Zones of subsurface moisture.

Ground surface

| | | |
|---|---|---|
| Discrete film zone | Water in discrete films. Air-filled voids continuous. | Zone of condensation and evaporation |
| — — — — — | — — — — — | CAPILLARY FRINGE — — — |
| Continuous film zone | Capillary films continuous and connected. Air voids also interconnected. | Zone of capillary movement |
| Capillary moisture zone | Capillary water fills all voids, except for trapped air-bubbles. | |
| | | GROUND WATER TABLE — |
| Ground water zone | All voids filled. Water moves under gravity. | Zone of gravity flow |

*sion.* We can think of a porous soil as consisting of countless tiny tubes, frequently uniting and dividing, but nevertheless behaving much as a bundle of tiny glass tubes held vertically with the lower ends immersed in a jar of water. Water would rise in these capillary tubes to a limiting height of several inches to several feet above the water level in the jar, depending on the diameter of the tubes. The smaller the diameter, the higher the capillary rise. The water surface at the upper end of the tube has a *capillary film,* or *skin,* of surface water molecules that cling to one another. This film tends to creep upward along the sides of the tube, drawing the water column upward. Similarly, in soils a zone of capillary water lies above the water table. In gravels and coarse sands the rise is only a fraction of an inch, but in fine silts it may be several feet. This is because the smaller the soil particles, the smaller the diameters of openings between the grains.

The zone lying above the water table is thus occupied by capillary water almost completely filling the pores of the soil, and it is termed the *capillary-moisture zone* (Figure 33.5). This moisture is available to plants. During dry periods evaporation into soil air may remove water from the upper fringes of the capillary zone, but more will be drawn upward to take its place.

Still higher is a zone in which moisture is in the form of connected films of capillary moisture which do not fill all the pore space. Here soil air can move freely through connected openings between soil grains and water films. This zone is known as the *continuous-film zone.* The water here is that which is left behind after the drainage of soil in periods between heavy rains.

In the uppermost moisture zone, tiny fragments of capillary-moisture films cling to the soil grains at the points where grains touch. This zone is called the *discrete-film zone,* the word "discrete" here meaning "separated from one another." The tiny films tend to bind together the soil particles of silt size and thus give cohesion to the soil. In dry weather the films shrink through evaporation, causing the soil to become harder and stronger, because their binding force becomes greater as the individual films become smaller.

Where colloidal clays are present in the uppermost zone of the soil, moisture is also held in the soil in the form of water molecules attracted by unlike electrical charges to the surfaces of the colloidal particles. Such moisture is sometimes referred to as *hygroscopic moisture.* Neither this type of moisture nor the discrete capillary films adhering to larger grains can be completely lost from the soil by evaporation during dry periods. It would be necessary to bake the soil in an oven at high temperature to obtain complete drying. Generally speaking, coarse-grained sandy soils can hold little moisture in extreme drought, whereas the silt and clay soils may retain a considerable amount.

During long-continued heavy rains or when a snow cover is melting, infiltration continues under the force of gravity, carrying the water down to successively greater depths. Soil pores soon become filled with water, with only a small amount of free air remaining entrapped in bubbles. The soil may, for a time, become almost completely saturated with water. Downward percolation continues beyond the soil-water belt into the *intermediate belt,* a zone too deep to be reached by plant roots. Water may ultimately reach the groundwater zone below (Figure 33.6).

After the rain has ceased, water continues to drain downward under the influence of gravity, but some remains held in the soil, clinging to the soil grains in thin capillary films. Capillary water in the discrete film zone of the soil remains held in place until gradually dissipated by evaporation or drawn into root systems.

After a soil has been saturated by prolonged rains and then drains until no more water moves downward under the force of gravity, the soil is said to be holding its *field capacity* of water. Most excess water drains out in a day's time, and usually not more than two or three days are required for gravity drainage to cease. Soil-moisture content can be stated in terms of the equivalent depth in inches of water in a given thickness of soil. At field capacity, soil-moisture content ranges from 1 to 4 inches per foot of soil, depending upon soil texture (Figure 33.7). Sandy soils have a low field capacity, which is rapidly reached because of the ease with which the water penetrates the large openings. Clay soils have a high field capacity, but require much

**FIGURE 33.6.** Phases of the hydrologic cycle in the zones of soil water and ground water. (© 1960, John Wiley & Sons, New York.)

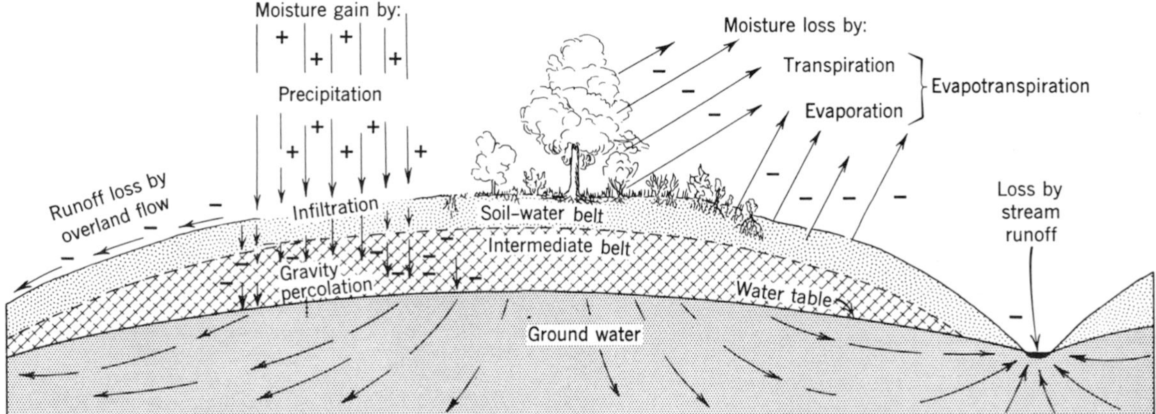

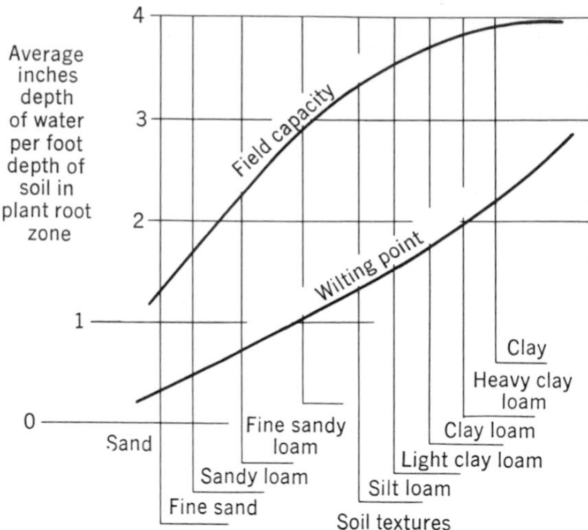


**FIGURE 33.7.** Texture of a soil determines its field capacity for moisture and the wilting point. [© 1960, John Wiley & Sons, New York; Data by Smith and Ruhe (1955), *Water; Yearbook of Agriculture, 1955,* Washington, D.C., U.S. Gov't. Printing Office.]

longer periods to attain it because of the slow rate of water penetration.

A comparable but lower value of soil moisture is the *wilting point,* below which foliage wilts because of the inability of the plants to extract the remaining moisture (Figure 33.7).

## Evaporation and transpiration

During dry warm periods between rains the soil gradually gives up its moisture by means of two mechanisms. First, moisture evaporates directly from the soil, the drying progressing slowly downward. The water vapor gradually diffuses outward into the free atmosphere or is forced out of the soil by alternations of atmospheric pressure. In humid continental climates drying during a single summer season will not affect more than the uppermost foot of soil, but in the tropical deserts, arid for many years at a time, drying by evaporation will be effective to depths of many feet.

Second, soil water drawn into the roots of plants is carried to the foliage and there exuded to the atmosphere through leaf pores in a process known as *transpiration.* Loss of soil water by transpiration can extend to the depth of root penetration, often many feet down, and defines the *soil-water belt,* a layer in which moisture is available to plants. During a single growing season a field of corn may transpire an amount of soil water equal to a water depth of almost 1 ft (30 cm), while a grove of trees may in the same time transpire a quantity equal to a depth of over 2 ft (60 cm). A soil surface clothed with vegetation is far more rapidly depleted of its moisture than a bare surface.

For convenience in stating total soil-moisture loss in studies of hydrology and climatology, the combined effects of direct evaporation and plant transpiration are referred to as *evapotranspiration.*

## The annual cycle of soil moisture

The characteristic annual cycle of changes in soil-moisture content deserves study because it leads to a better understanding of principles of ground-water movement, surface runoff, and various aspects of the sculpturing of the land by running water.

As an illustration, changes in soil moisture were followed throughout the year 1944 in a test plot at an agricultural experiment station at Coshocton, Ohio (Figure 33.8). The example is generally representative of what might be expected throughout the humid middle-latitude climates of North America and Europe.

In late winter and early spring, melting of snow and soil ice releases much water, which infiltrates the surface, raising the moisture content to exceed the field capacity and causing the soil for a time to be completely saturated. Surplus water runs off to produce spring floods, whereas some percolates down through the intermediate belt to reach the ground-water zone. The soil is in a soft state, easily yielding to a weak mud when churned up by wheels or hoofs.

As April passes into May, air temperatures increase and new foliage appears. The resulting great increase in evapotranspiration causes a rapid decline in soil moisture throughout May and June to amounts far below the field capacity. Although an occasional rainstorm may temporarily cause a small increase in soil moisture, the summer months constitute a period of severe moisture deficit, for the losses by evapotranspiration normally continue to be heavy through midsummer.

As autumn sets in, with lowering of air temperatures and the dropping of foliage, evapotranspiration is reduced, while rainfall replenishes soil moisture. Thus we see a sharp rise in the curve in late November and throughout December. Depending upon rainfall in the particular year, field capacity may be regained before soil moisture is frozen.

## The soil-water balance

The annual cycle of soil-water changes can be presented in quantitative terms through the equation of soil-water balance calculated for each month of the year, using values of a particular year or the averages of many years. Using terms equivalent to those stated earlier in this chapter for the world water balance the equation is as follows:

$$P = E + G + R$$

where $P$ is precipitation,

$E$ is actual evapotranspiration,

$G$ is change in soil-water storage in the zone available to plants,

$R$ is water surplus, which eventually becomes runoff.

The terms of the equation are illustrated in Figure 33.9 as applied to a soil column of unit cross section ex-

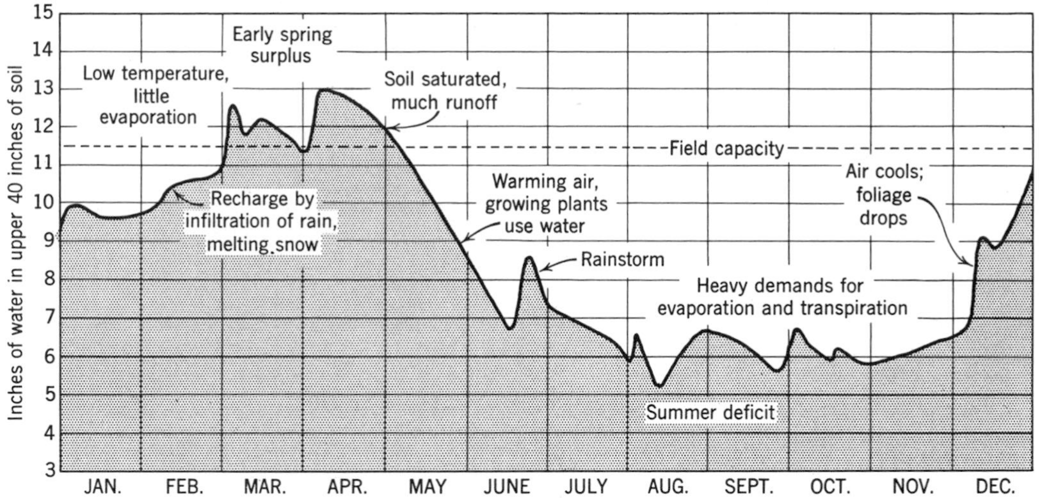


**FIGURE 33.8.** Annual cycle of soil moisture. (© 1960, John Wiley & Sons, New York. Based on data of Thornthwaite and Mather.)

tending from the ground surface (including plant surfaces) to the lower limit of root penetration. All terms are in units of depth (inches or millimeters).

The annual cycle of water balance components is best understood by use of actual examples, shown in graphic form in Figure 33.10 and in tabular form in Table 33.2. Consider first the example of Seabrook, New Jersey, which lies in a humid continental climate with a warm summer and a moderately cold winter. Precipitation is substantial in all months, but shows a marked maximum in summer and a minimum in late fall. Evapotranspiration is close to zero in the winter months because the soil moisture is frozen most of the time and plant transpiration is practically nil. Evapotranspiration begins a sharp rise in spring, peaking in July, then falling again to low values. Consequently there is a period of four successive months in summer when evapotranspiration exceeds precipitation, depleting the soil moisture—this is the period of soil-moisture *utilization.* Altogether, 100 mm of water was drawn from the soil to meet the water balance. In October precipitation again exceeded evapotranspiration, and soil-moisture *recharge* began. In early December the 100 mm of water drawn from storage had been replaced. From that point on, through the winter and early spring, a *water surplus* prevailed, totalling 378 mm for the year. This surplus leaves the soil column as runoff, both as overland flow and as ground-water flow, although the runoff is considerably delayed.

Because the changes in stored water, $G$, sum out to zero for the entire year, the water balance equation for the year can be simplified to read

$$P = E + G$$

The monthly and annual values in Table 33.2 should be carefully checked against the step-graph of Figure 33.10.

The second example, Berkeley, California, represents a Mediterranean-type climate with a long dry summer and a mild but wet winter. The total annual precipitation

**TABLE 33.2. ANNUAL CYCLE OF WATER-BALANCE COMPONENTS FOR LOCATIONS IN HUMID CONTINENTAL AND MEDITERRANEAN CLIMATES***

| | | Jan. | Feb. | Mar. | Apr. | May | Jun. | Jul. | Aug. | Sept. | Oct. | Nov. | Dec. | Year Total |
|---|---|---|---|---|---|---|---|---|---|---|---|---|---|---|
| *Seabrook, N.J.* | | | | | | | | | | | | | | |
| Precipitation | $P$ | 87 | 93 | 102 | 88 | 92 | 91 | 112 | 113 | 82 | 85 | 70 | 93 | 1108 |
| Evaporation | $E$ | 1 | 2 | 16 | 46 | 92 | 129 | 147 | 130 | 92 | 53 | 19 | 3 | 730 |
| $(P-E)$ | | +86 | +91 | +86 | +42 | 0 | −38 | −35 | −17 | −10 | +32 | +51 | +90 | +378 |
| Storage Change | $G$ | 0 | 0 | 0 | 0 | 0 | −38 | −35 | −17 | −10 | +32 | +51 | +17 | 0 |
| Surplus | $R$ | 86 | 91 | 86 | 42 | 0 | 0 | 0 | 0 | 0 | 0 | 0 | 73 | 378 |
| *Berkeley, Calif.* | | | | | | | | | | | | | | |
| Precipitation | $P$ | 130 | 112 | 94 | 37 | 24 | 5 | 1 | 1 | 13 | 31 | 62 | 106 | 616 |
| Evaporation | $E$ | 26 | 32 | 45 | 56 | 65 | 61 | 48 | 34 | 32 | 39 | 43 | 28 | 509 |
| $(P-E)$ | | +104 | +80 | +49 | −19 | −41 | −56 | −47 | −33 | −19 | −8 | +19 | +78 | +107 |
| Storage Change | $G$ | +104 | +22 | 0 | −19 | −41 | −56 | −47 | −33 | −19 | −8 | +19 | +78 | 0 |
| Surplus | $R$ | 0 | 58 | 49 | 0 | 0 | 0 | 0 | 0 | 0 | 0 | 0 | 0 | 107 |

* Data from C. W. Thornthwaite and J. R. Mather (1955), *The Water Balance,* Centerton, N.J., Drexel Institute of Technology, Laboratory of Climatology, 86 pp., Table 2.1.

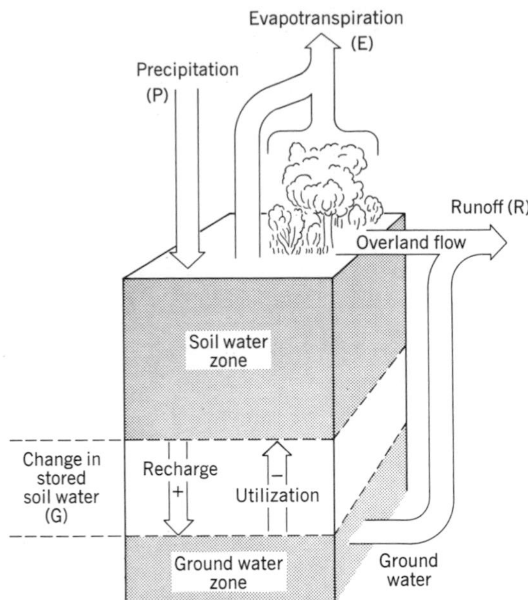


**FIGURE 33.9.** Soil-water balance for a soil column of unit cross section.

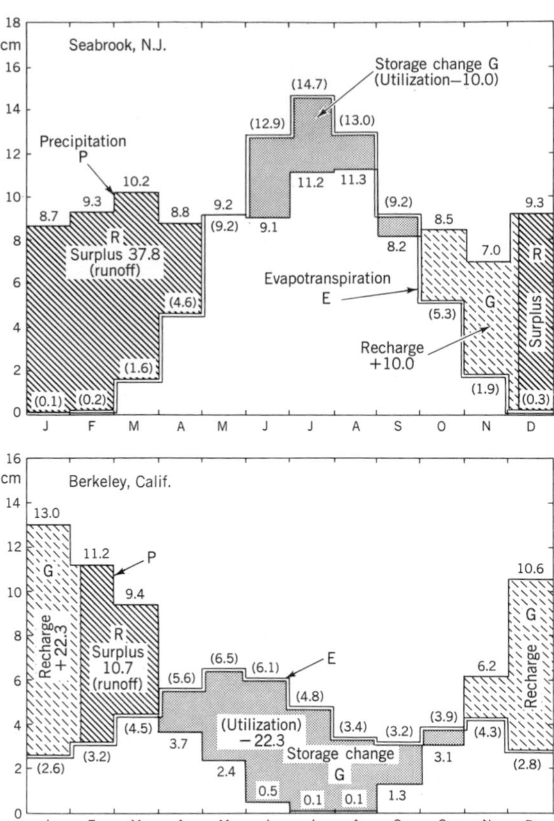


**FIGURE 33.10.** Water balance for Berkeley, California, and Seabrook, New Jersey. [Data from C. W. Thornthwaite and F. R. Mather (1955), *The Water Balance,* Centerton, N.J., Drexel Inst. of Tech., p. 26, Table 2.1.]

is about half that at Seabrook. Note first how the precipitation declines from high values in the winter to near-zero values in mid-summer. The curve of evapotranspiration is rather moderate in range. During the winter plant growth continues in this climate, which means that there is no period of strongly suppressed evapotranspiration. Beginning in April, evapotranspiration exceeds precipitation and soil moisture utilization becomes heavy. If it were not for the fact that natural vegetation of this region is adapted to reducing its transpiration rate to low values, plants could not long survive without irrigation. Because of this adaptation, evapotranspiration falls off in summer and soil moisture utilization diminishes toward the end of the long drought. Recharge, which begins in November, is not completed until February. The total surplus is therefore small—only about one-third as large as for Seabrook.

Analysis of the annual cycle of soil-water balance has many uses; it enables water resources to be calculated for any region. Estimates of irrigation needs and of the quantities of surplus water that can be drawn upon for irrigation and hydroelectric power can be derived from such data.

## Global water balance by latitude zones

For the earth as a whole the water balance equation can be applied to entire 10-degree latitude zones encircling the globe. The result is a meridional profile which averages out the differences between continents and ocean basins (Figure 33.11). Runoff, as defined in this latitudinal treatment, includes all net flow of water into or out of the latitude belt, and includes ocean current transport as well as stream flow. Notice the large water surplus in the equatorial belt, the two zones of moisture deficit over the subtropical high pressure belts, and the two middle-latitude zones of surplus. Poleward of 70° both precipitation and evaporation are very small, showing a net surplus. This graph should be studied in conjunction with Figures 16.17, 16.18, and 18.29. Note particularly how the meridional transport of water vapor (Figure 18.29) completes the atmospheric portion of the hydrologic cycle. The contribution of the oceanic circulation to the global water balance is not shown by these diagrams, since it is concealed within the runoff term, *R.* We do know that the Atlantic and Indian Oceans import water from the Arctic and Pacific Oceans and that the quantities involved in this transfer are comparable to the quantities of runoff from the lands to the oceans.

## Ground water

By percolation under the force of gravity, water that has infiltrated the soil and cannot be held there makes its way down to the *ground-water zone,* defined as the zone in which subsurface water occupies all the interconnected openings in the rock and moves under the force of gravity. Ground water is said to occupy the

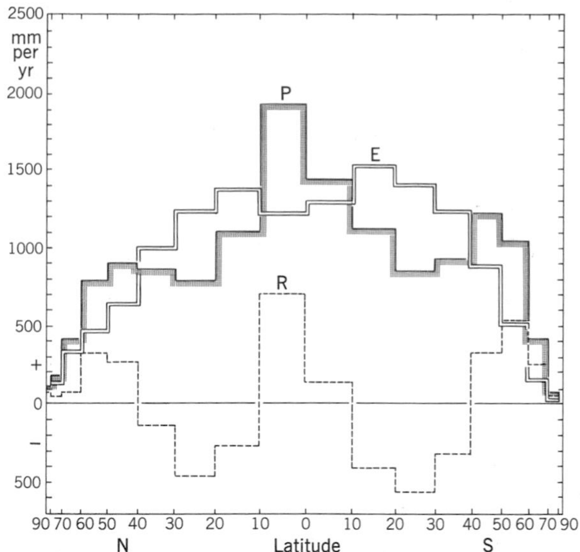


**FIGURE 33.11.** Water balance for ten-degree zones of latitude. [Data from W. D. Sellers (1965), *Physical Climatology,* Chicago, Univ. of Chicago Press, p. 5, Table 1.]

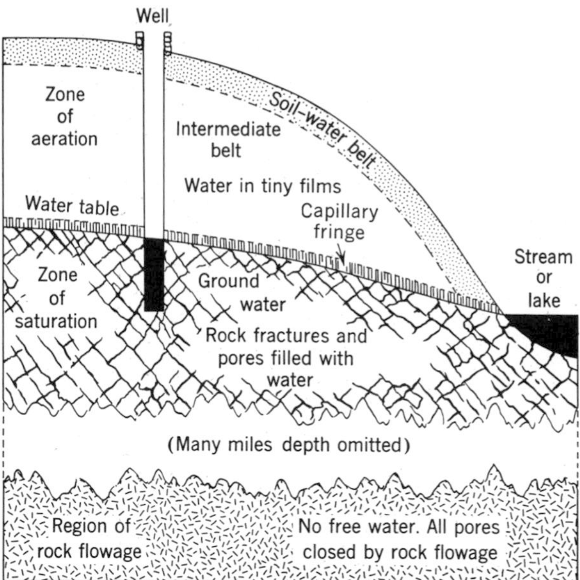


**FIGURE 33.12.** Schematic cross section through the various moisture zones and belts of soil and bedrock. (© 1960, John Wiley & Sons, New York. Based on data of Ackerman, Colman, and Ogrosky.)

*zone of saturation* and is distinguished from the *zone of aeration* which lies above it and is not completely saturated (Figure 33.12).

Moisture of the zone of aeration includes that of both soil-water belt and intermediate belt. Where the ground-water zone lies close to the surface, the zone of aeration may be only a few inches thick, or it may be entirely missing where the water table is exposed in a marsh or lake. In hilly and mountainous areas the zone of aeration may be as much as several hundred feet thick.

The upper surface of the ground-water zone is termed the *water table* (Figure 33.12). Its position may be approximately determined by noting the level at which water stands in wells that penetrate the ground-water zone. Capillary tension draws water upward into the pore spaces of the overlying intermediate belt, completely filling the available space to a height ranging from 1 in. (2.5 cm) or less in sands and gravels to as much as 2 ft (60 cm) or more in silts. This added layer of saturation, held by capillary tension, is termed the *capillary fringe*. Strictly speaking, the water table lies at the upper limit of the capillary fringe, but in practice the *piezometric surface,* or level of standing water in the large opening of a well, is defined as the ground-water table.

Where there are many wells closely spaced over an area, the configuration of the water table can be shown by connecting the levels of standing water in the wells (Figure 33.13). The water table will be found to be highest in elevation under the interstream divides and lowest along the lines of valleys, where it may intersect the surface in the channels of streams or at the shores of lakes and marshes.

**Ground-water motion** Water in an open body, such as a lake, assumes a horizontal surface because there is little resistance to flowage. In the ground-water zone, however, gravity movement is through the very tiny spaces between mineral grains and the thin cracks of joints in bedrock, which greatly resist flowage. Consequently percolating water reaching the water table under the divides cannot escape readily and tends to accumulate, raising the water table and causing it to maintain a sloping surface in rough conformity with the ground surface (Figure 33.13). Difference in level between the water table under a divide and at the low point of a valley constitutes a *hydraulic head* and causes the water to flow very slowly within the ground-water body, following curved paths much like those

**FIGURE 33.13.** Relation of the water table to the ground surface. (© 1960, John Wiley & Sons, New York.)

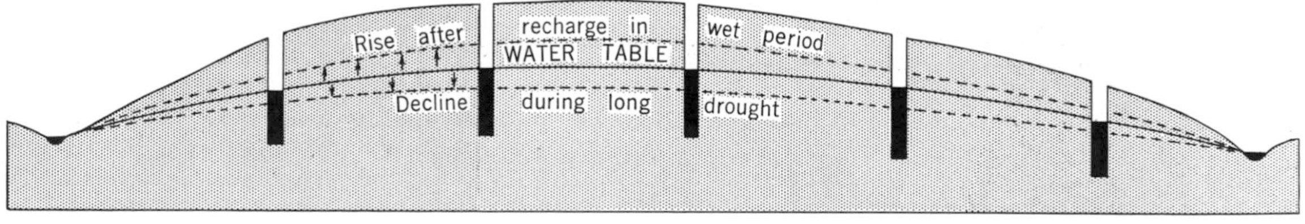

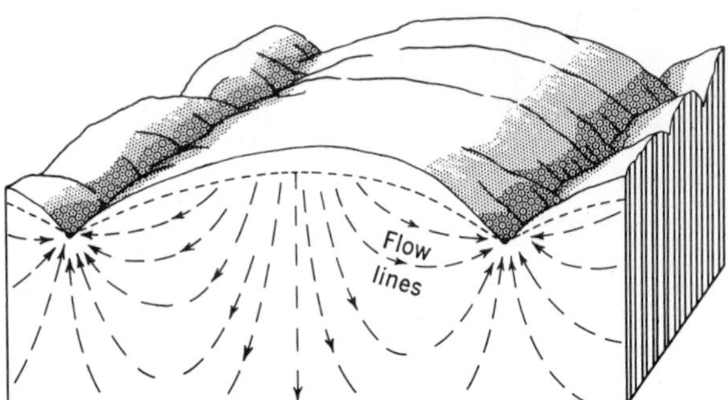


**FIGURE 33.14.** Ground water follows strongly curved paths of travel where the subsurface material is uniform throughout. (© 1960, John Wiley & Sons, New York. Based on data of M. K. Hubbert.)

shown in Figure 33.14. A particular molecule of water, if it could be traced, might follow a curving path that carries it deep into the bedrock and returns it by upward flow to the line of a stream channel, where the water escapes into the stream as surface runoff. Flow velocity is highest near the line of escape, as suggested by the close crowding of arrows in Figure 33.14.

Strange as these curved flow paths may seem, they conform to laws of physics of fluids. The cementation of rocks and slow movement of mineral matter from one region to another within the bedrock may be attributed to the slow circulation of ground water. Were it not for this flow mechanism, the ground-water body would be completely stagnant and certain important geological processes could not take place.

**Ground-water recharge** With a generally constant climatic environment the water table will become approximately fixed in position, and the rate of addition to the ground-water body, or rate of *recharge,* will on the average balance the rate at which water is returned to surface flow by seepage in streams, lakes, and marshes. But should there occur a period of unusually dry years, the water table will slowly fall; if there is a period of unusually wet years, it will gradually rise (Figure 33.13).

Seasonal fluctuations in the level of the water table are to be expected in climates having alternately dry and wet seasons (Mediterranean climates and wet-dry tropical climates) or alternately warm and cold seasons (humid continental climates and humid subtropical climates). A seasonal decline in the water table results from the cutting off of recharge during a dry season or when soil moisture is solidly frozen. A seasonal rise results from the percolation of excess infiltration through the zone of aeration.

The rhythm of water-table fluctuation is illustrated in Figure 33.15. Note that the water table fell steadily throughout the summer months (equivalent of period of moisture deficit in Figure 33.8), for during this time the precipitation was absorbed and held in the soil-water belt to be returned to the atmosphere by evapotranspiration. Only in late winter or early spring did the water table begin to rise, for at this time there was a water surplus percolating through the intermediate water belt to recharge the water table. Note that the severe drought of August through November 1930, when less than 1 in. (2.5 cm) of rain fell per month, caused a further decline in the water table and delayed recharge until the following spring.

## Effluent and influent streams

The conditions of water-table configuration and recharge described above apply primarily to regions of humid climate. In arid regions, where streams supplied by runoff from mountain watersheds flow across adjoining plains underlain by coarse alluvium composed of sand and gravel, the water table under the valley alluvium is recharged by downward seepage from the

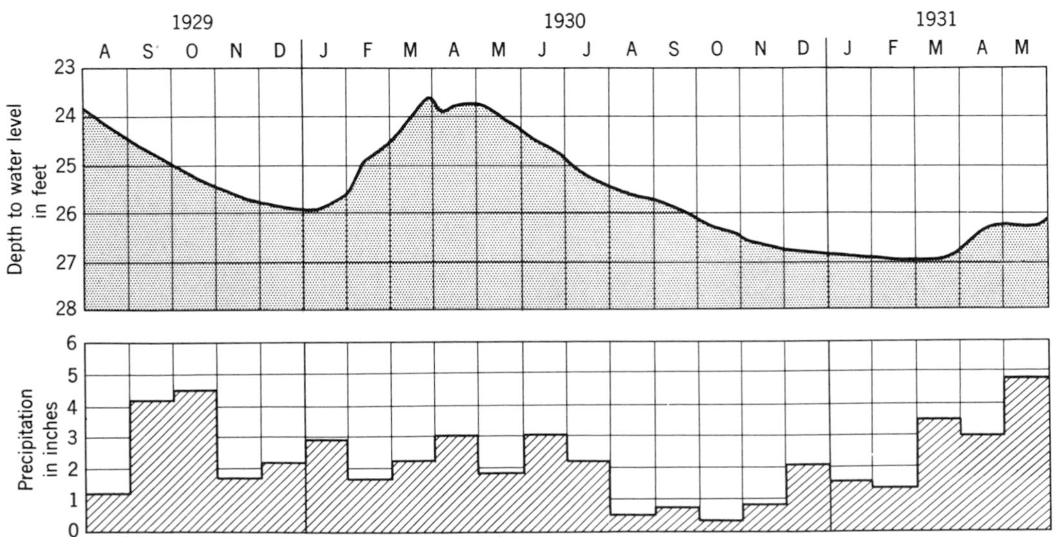


**FIGURE 33.15.** Seasonal fluctuations in the height of water in an observation well in Washington, D.C., (© 1960, John Wiley & Sons, New York. Based on data of O. E. Meinzer.)

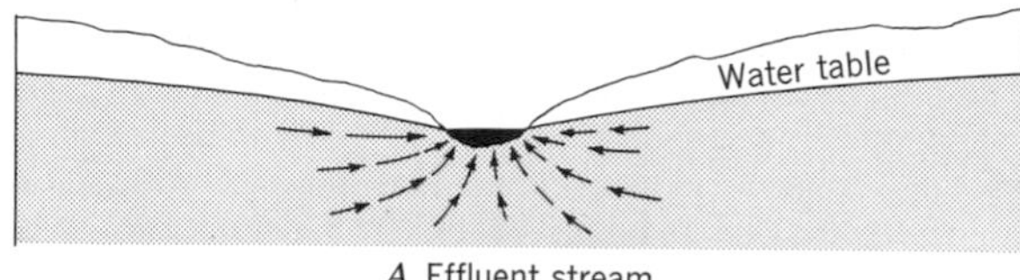


*A* Effluent stream

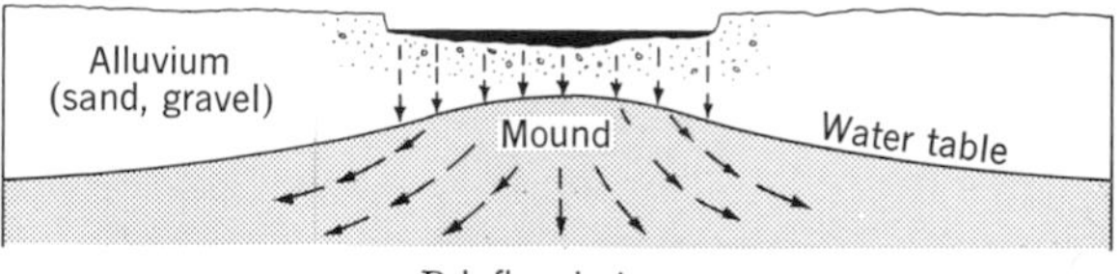


*B* Influent stream

**FIGURE 33.16.** Effluent and influent streams.

stream channel, which is the reverse of the flow conditions in a humid region (Figure 33.16).

A stream that provides water by seepage to the water table below is termed an *influent stream* and produces a water-table *mound* beneath its channel (Figure 33.16*B*). A stream that receives water by seepage from the water table is, in contrast, termed an *effluent stream* (Figure 33.16*A*).

Desert streams thus tend to disappear as they flow across a dry alluvial plain. By seepage the ground water normally reappears through the surface of the plain at lower elevations, often in a central basin or depression, where it evaporates and the dissolved salts remain behind.

## Porosity and permeability

Ground water may saturate any type of geologic material, whether it be the bedrock or the residual and transported overburden. The bedrock may be of any variety of igneous, sedimentary, or metamorphic rock, and the overburden may be of any of several types ranging from dense clays to coarse gravels. Consequently the flow of ground water and the quantity which can be held is subject to many variations. It is with such variations that the ground-water geologist, or *hydrogeologist,* is concerned. He must apply the laws of physics of fluids to varied and complex geologic conditions.

The total volume of pore space within a given volume of rock is termed the *porosity* and gives an indication of the ability of a rock to hold a fluid in storage. Variations that may be expected in the porosity of various types of rocks are obvious from considerations of their origins and compositions. Clastic sedimentary rocks, such as sandstone and conglomerate, can have high porosity because of the relatively large openings possible between the well-sorted rounded grains of quartz of which most sandstones are composed (Figure 33.17*A*). It also follows that transported overburden of stream-laid gravels and sands or beach deposits composed largely of hard, well-rounded, coarse mineral grains will have a high porosity. Where sands are mixed with silts, the porosity is reduced because the fine particles are fitted into the openings between the large grains (Figure 33.17*B*).

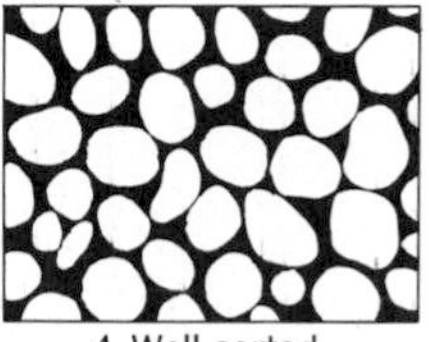

*A* Well sorted

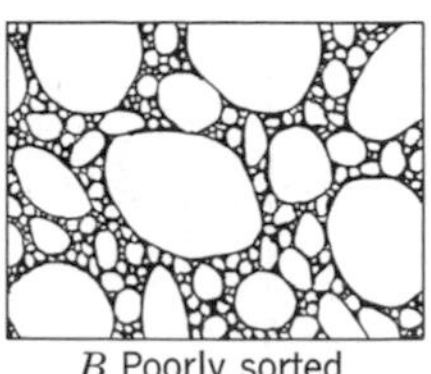

*B* Poorly sorted

**FIGURE 33.17.** Pore space is relatively greater in well-sorted sediment than in poorly sorted sediment.

Soft clays and muds also have a high original porosity, but when compacted into shale they have extremely low porosity. Some rock masses have large openings. Limestone, for example, may have cavernous openings resulting from solution. Scoriaceous lavas have numerous bubble-like cavities formed by expanding gases.

Certain of the very dense rocks, such as igneous and metamorphic varieties, have negligible pore space in the fresh unweathered state because the mineral crystals are tightly intergrown. Most bodies of such rock are, however, broken by numerous joint fractures and faults, so that the rock mass as a whole has interconnected openings and will permit water to be held as well as moved through the mass (Figure 33.12).

Even though a rock may have a high porosity, water cannot move freely through the rock mass unless the openings are interconnected and of sufficient diameter to permit flow. Therefore the property of *permeability,* or relative ease with which water will move through the rock under unequal pressure, is of primary importance in determining the rate of ground-water movement and the amount of water that can be withdrawn by pumping from wells. Permeability of unconsolidated sands and gravels is extremely high, while that of dense clays and shales is extremely low, to the extent that such materials can be described as *impermeable* for all practical purposes. Permeability of sandstone formations is commonly high, but may be greatly reduced if the pores are closed by cementation of mineral matter. Igneous and metamorphic rocks, where broken by numerous joint fractures and faults, may have high permeability. Similarly, the scoriaceous zones and interbedded volcanic-ash layers within a series of basaltic lava flows give the mass as a whole a very high permeability in a direction parallel with the beds, whereas the dense basalt of individual lava layers may be almost impermeable.

The downward extent of ground water is a matter of much interest to the geologist. Experience shows that very little ground water can be obtained from extremely deep wells, that is, water wells over 2 mi (3 km) deep. At much greater depths, high confining pressures tend to close the pores in the rock so as to limit the space available for holding water. At depths below 10 mi (16 km) the region of rock flowage is gradually entered. Here the yielding of rock under great confining pressure closes all original openings, and no water can enter or remain in the rock. Notice in Table 33.1 that ground water is divided into two categories—that within 0.5 mi (0.8 km) of the surface and available for use, and that at greater depth, not available in useful quantities. The

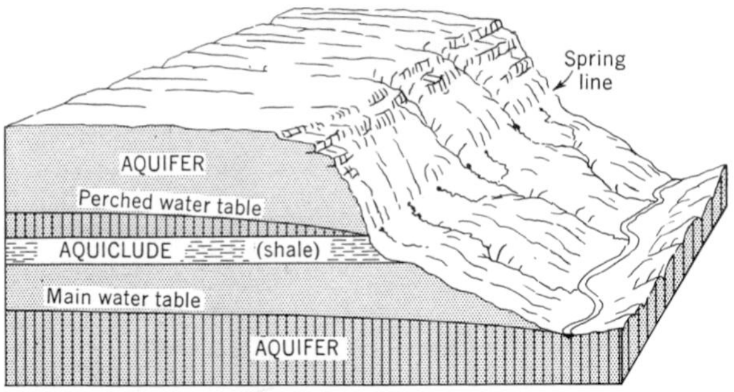

**FIGURE 33.18.** A perched water table and spring line. (© 1960, John Wiley & Sons, New York.)

total quantity of ground water is estimated to be about equally divided between these two zones.

## Aquifers and aquicludes

Layered rocks may offer strongly contrasting zones of permeability lying one above the other, particularly where sedimentary strata of varying types are interlayered. The geology of an area thus exerts a strong control on the movement of ground water. Figure 33.18 shows thick layers of sandstone with a shale bed between.

A sandstone layer, being high in porosity and permeability, can hold and transmit large quantities of water, hence it is designated as an *aquifer.* A shale layer, impermeable in nature, prevents flow of ground water through itself and deflects flow above it, hence it is designated an *aquiclude.*

The shale layer in Figure 33.18 is blocking the downward percolation of water to the main water table below, causing a *perched water table* to be formed in the overlying aquifer. Water from this table emerges in the valley side along a horizontal line in the form of slow seepages and trickles, termed *springs* or *seeps* (Figure 33.18). The main water table, intersecting the stream channel, is recharged at more distant points where the overlying aquiclude is absent or broken.

Springs are usually insignificant features, going unnoticed because of a concealing cover of vegetation, and commonly ceasing to flow in the summer season. Some, however, yield substantial flows of water. A most impressive example is the Thousand Springs of the Snake River Canyon in Idaho, where highly permeable layers of scoriaceous basalt are exposed (Figure 33.19).

## Artesian flow

A particularly interesting type of flow is found in the *artesian* spring or well, where water is forced upward under natural pressure to rise above the surface of the ground. Geologic conditions necessary to artesian flow are illustrated in Figure 33.20. An aquifer, consisting of an inclined sandstone layer, receives water along its exposed outcrop at a relatively high position. The water moves through the aquifer and is confined between aquicludes of shale. Thus water beneath the valley floor is under hydrostatic pressure from the weight of overlying water in the aquifer. If a well is now drilled into the aquifer under the valley floor, the water will be forced to the surface by the hydrostatic pressure and may emerge as a copious flow continuously maintained by the pressure difference, or head, between the well and the intake area. Natural artesian springs can occur where faulting has produced a natural passageway for water through the aquiclude.

Where the sedimentary strata have a very gentle dip, artesian wells may be located at great distances from the intake region. In many regions artesian wells are a major source of water supply. Of particular importance are those in arid plains adjacent to mountain ranges on which the intake areas are provided with abundant recharge by orographic precipitation.

## Pump wells (gravity wells)

Most water wells are simply tubes or shafts drilled or dug to a depth below the water table and are supplied by gravity flow from the surrounding ground-water zone. If left undisturbed, the water level comes to rest at the level of the water table. Water must be drawn or

**FIGURE 33.19.** Thousand Springs, Idaho. Located on the north side of the Snake River Canyon, nearly opposite the mouth of the Salmon River, these great springs extend for 0.5 mi (0.8 km) along the edge of a layer of scoriaceous basalt. The discharge is nearly constant at 500 cu ft (14 cu m) per second. (Photograph by I. C. Russell, U.S. Geological Survey.)

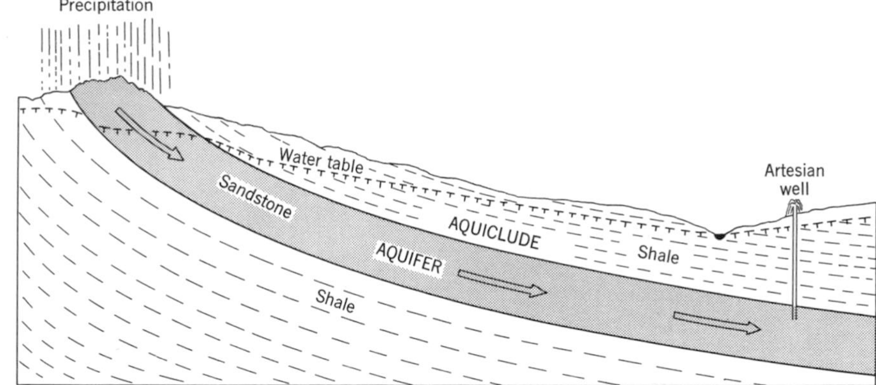


**FIGURE 33.20.** Schematic structure section showing conditions favorable to the occurrence of artesian flow.

pumped to the surface. For effective and prolonged use a well must be protected from collapse by means of a solid casing, which may be a masonry wall (in the case of a dug well) or a steel pipe (in the case of a drilled well). Perforations through the lower part of the casing permit water to enter.

Dug wells, excavated by hand labor, are usually less than 50 ft (15 m) deep and are effective where the water table lies close to the surface in a thick layer of overburden, such as alluvium. A dug well for domestic use may yield as little as a few gallons per day or as much as 500 gallons (2000 liters) per minute in a highly permeable deposit. Drilled wells, which may have diameters up to 18 in. (45 cm), can be driven to depths of over 1000 ft (300 m) and, with powerful pumps, will furnish as much as many millions of gallons per day if located in highly permeable material.

Pumping of water from a well commonly exceeds the rate at which water can enter the well, so that the water level drops progressively lower (Figure 33.21), depressing the water table into a conical form, or *cone of depression,* surrounding the well. The *drawdown* is the difference in height between water table and water level in the well. Formation of the cone of depression actually increases the rate at which water flows into the well, thereby increasing the yield of the well, but this effect is limited. Beyond a critical limit of drawdown the yield no longer increases.

**FIGURE 33.21.** Rapid pumping of a well causes drawdown and a cone of depression. (© 1960, John Wiley & Sons, New York.)

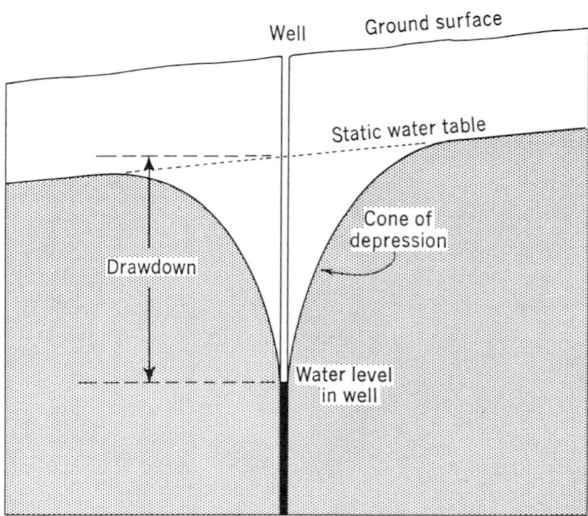


The cone of depression may extend several miles from a large well, and the combined effect of closely spaced wells is to depress the water table generally. Heavy pumping may thus exceed the rate of natural recharge, and the water table will continue to fall, eventually leading to a serious decline in water yield. In arid regions, particularly, the ground water stored in alluvial deposits can be withdrawn much faster than it is restored by influent seepage from surface streams. In humid regions careful regulation of pumping and the artificial recharge of the ground-water table by waste water pumped down into recharge wells can bring about a balance in the rates of withdrawal and recharge.

## Relations of salt and fresh ground water

Of considerable scientific interest is the relation of fresh ground water to salt ground water in coastal areas and beneath islands. Figure 33.22 is a highly diagrammatic cross section of the ground-water relations under an island or in a long narrow peninsula. Fresh water, being less dense than salt, forms a ground-water body resembling a huge lens, with convex surfaces above and below. The fresh-water body actually floats upon the salt, much as the hull of a ship displaces water and floats at rest. Normally the densities of fresh water to salt water are in the ratio of 40:41. Thus the elevation of the upper surface of the water table above sea level is one-fortieth as great as the depth of the base of the fresh-water body below sea level. For example, if the bottom of the fresh-water lens lies 400 feet below sea level, the ground-water table will rise 10 feet above sea level.

As the shoreline is approached, the contact between fresh and salt water rises in elevation and emerges on the sea floor along a line close to the land. As the arrows in Figure 33.22 indicate, the fresh ground water follows deeply curving paths, and these paths turn upward and seaward to emerge under the ocean close to the coast. The salt ground water remains essentially stagnant beneath the fresh. Some mixing, or diffusion,

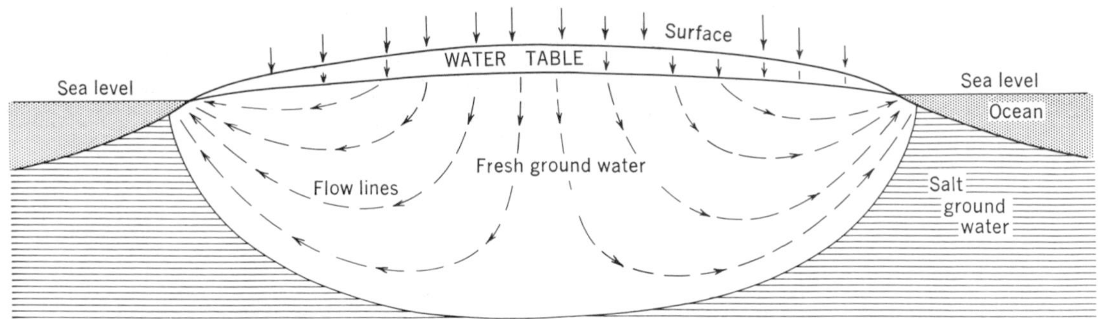


**FIGURE 33.22.** Relation of fresh to salt ground water under an island or peninsula. (© 1960, John Wiley & Sons, New York. Based on data of G. Parker.)

of the salt and fresh water will occur through the effects of tidal changes in ocean level.

One problem of practical interest is that the rapid pumping of water from wells located close to a coastline will draw the salt-water–fresh-water contact landward until the salt water begins to be drawn into the well, contaminating the fresh-water supply. If pumping is stopped for a long period, the salt water will again be pushed seaward, a process that can be hastened by pumping fresh water down into the contaminated wells or into new wells in the vicinity so as to create a barrier of fresh water.

## Limestone caverns

Carbonate strata, or limestones, composed largely of carbonates of calcium and magnesium, are highly susceptible to the action of carbonic acid found in rainwater, soil water, and ground water. Effects of this acid action, which can be called *carbonation,* are obvious in the etched surfaces of exposed limestone masses (Figure 32.14), but they are particularly important in the development of caverns in bedrock of the ground-water zone.

When carbon dioxide gas is dissolved in water, *carbonic acid* is produced:

$$\underset{\text{Water}}{2H_2O} + \underset{\text{Carbon dioxide}}{2CO_2} \rightleftharpoons \underset{\text{Carbonic acid}}{2H_2CO_3}$$

In the chemical reaction between carbonic acid and mineral calcite the acid is written as consisting of two hydrogen ions and two bicarbonate ions. The hydrogen ion acts upon the carbonate ion in the calcite to yield carbon dioxide and water. The calcium ion joins the two bicarbonate ions to become *calcium bicarbonate,* which is a highly soluble salt:

$$\underset{\text{Calcite}}{CaCO_3} + \underbrace{\underset{\text{Hydrogen ion}}{2H^+} + \underset{\text{Bicarbonate ion}}{2(HCO_3)^-}}_{\text{Carbonic acid}}$$

$$\rightleftharpoons \underbrace{\underset{\text{Calcium ion}}{Ca^{2+}} + \underset{\text{Bicarbonate ion}}{2(HCO_3)^-}}_{\text{Calcium bicarbonate}} + \underset{\text{Water}}{H_2O} + \underset{\text{Carbon dioxide}}{CO_2}$$

Although the normal solution of atmospheric carbon dioxide in rainwater constitutes a weak acid, the carbon dioxide produced in the humus layer of soil by plant decay gives to soil water a much higher concentration of carbonic acid. It is believed that much of the solution of limestone in humid regions can be attributed to acid produced in the soil layer and in the layer of raw humus that overlies it.

In humid climates lowering of the land surface by carbonation is a comparatively rapid process in areas underlain by limestone or marble, as compared with the rates at which sandstones, quartzites, other metamorphic rocks and igneous rocks are reduced in the same regions. As a result, carbonate rocks typically form valleys and lowlands in humid climates. In one study of a small valley in Pennsylvania, with a drainage area of about 100 sq mi (260 sq km), chemical analysis of stream water leaving the valley showed that about 260 tons (234 metric tons) of rock are carried away annually in solution. At that rate the limestone surface would be lowered at the rate of about 1 ft (30 cm) per 1000 years.

Limestone caverns consist of interconnected passageways and rooms forming highly complex systems. Patterns of joints in the limestone exert a strong control over the network of passages (Figure 33.23). Variations in composition among individual limestone beds will also help to control spacing of passages.

**FIGURE 33.23.** Map of a portion of Anvil Cave, Alabama. (Courtesy of W. W. Varnedoe and the Huntsville Grotto of the National Speleological Society.)

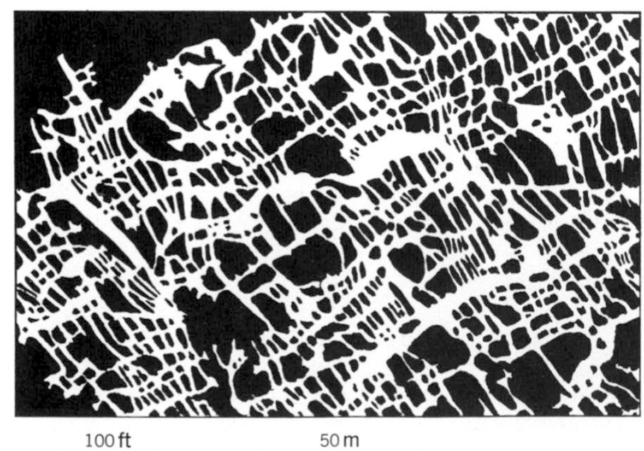

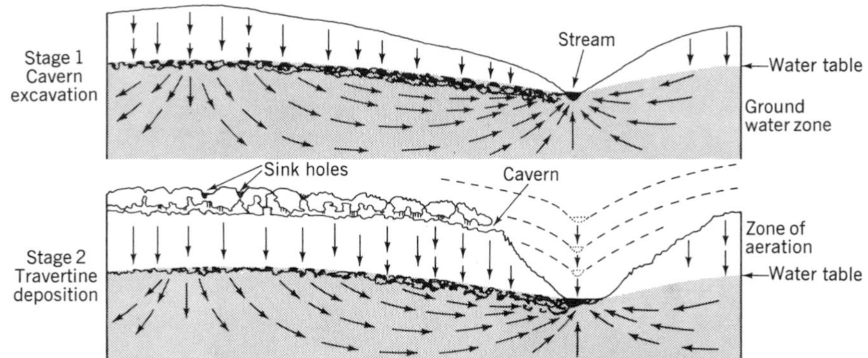


**FIGURE 33.24.** Stages in cavern development.

It is now generally agreed that many, if not all, cavern systems are excavated in the ground-water zone. As suggested in Figure 33.24, water percolating downward in the zone of aeration reaches the water table, below which it moves as ground water with extreme slowness along curved paths indicated by the arrows. Carbonic acid reaction with limestones is believed to be concentrated in the uppermost part of the ground-water zone. Here passageways are enlarged and the calcium bicarbonate is carried into streams and out of the region.

In a second stage, shown in Figure 33.23, the stream has deepened its valley and the water table has been lowered accordingly. New caverns are being formed at the lower level, while those previously formed are now in the zone of aeration. Percolating water is now exposed to the air on ceilings and walls of the caverns.

The carbonic acid reaction is reversible, so that under favorable conditions that permit some of the dissolved carbon dioxide in the solution to escape into the air as a gas, calcite is precipitated as a mineral deposit:

$$\underset{\text{Carbonic acid}}{H_2CO_3} + \underset{\text{Calcium bicarbonate in solution}}{Ca^{2+} + 2(HCO_3)^-}$$

$$\rightarrow \underset{\text{Carbon dioxide gas}}{2CO_2} + \underset{\text{Water}}{2H_2O} + \underset{\text{Calcite precipitate}}{CaCO_3}$$

Precipitation of calcium carbonate on the inner surfaces of caverns occurs as *travertine,* a banded form of calcite. Encrustations forming where water drips from cave ceilings constitute *dripstone,* while encrustations made in moving water of pools and streams on cave floors form *flowstone.* Dripstone and flowstone accumulate as elaborate encrustations, known popularly as "formations," that give many caves their great beauty.

Certain scenic features of caverns are illustrated in Figure 33.25. From ceiling points where the slow drip of water takes place, spike-like forms known as *stalactites* are built downward. From points on the cavern floor upon which there falls a steady drip of water, post-like columns termed *stalagmites* are built upward. Stalactites and stalagmites may join into *columns,* and the columns forming under a single joint crack may fuse into solid *walls.* Growth below a joint crack may produce a *drip curtain.* Blocks of limestone fallen from the ceiling pond the runoff along the cavern floor, making pools in which *travertine terraces* are formed.

After cavern development has been in progress for a long period of time the land surface above is deeply pocked with depressions, which are parts of the old cavern system lying close to the surface. These depressions are termed *sinks,* or *sinkholes* (Figure 33.26). They may be partly filled with clay soil and can hold ponds or marshes, or may be cultivated if the soil is well drained. Some sinks are gaping holes or fissures leading down to open caverns beneath.

## Karst landscapes

To the landscape of a region of carbonate rocks bearing a well-developed subterranean drainage system and largely devoid of surface streams the name *karst* is given, after a type region in the Dalmatian coastal belt of Yugoslavia. A number of distinctive landforms of the karst regions, as well as a cycle of regional development, is shown in Figure 33.27.

Rock fins separated by deep grooves and developed by weathering of exposed limestone are referred to as *lapiés* (Block *A*). As caverns are deepened and enlarged, large funnel-shaped sinkholes, called *dolines,* are developed (Block *B*). Collapse of caverns and coalescence of dolines forms still larger flat-floored depressions known as *poljes* (*C*). Ultimately all the limestone layer may be removed, except for a few isolated remnants known as *hums* (Block *D*).

Regions of karst topography, each somewhat different from the other but all representing an advanced state of solution activity in limestone, are found in the Mammoth Cave region of Kentucky, in southern Indiana, the Causses region of France, the Yucatan Peninsula, and in parts of Cuba and Puerto Rico.

## Hot springs, geysers, and fumaroles

At a number of widely separated localities, ground water emerges in *hot springs* at temperatures not far below the boiling point of water, which is 212° F (100° C) at sea-level pressure. In certain of these localities, periodic jet-like emissions of steam and hot water occur from small vents and are known as *geysers.* The heated water emitted by hot springs and geysers is

FIGURE 33.25. Stalactites and stalagmites. Indian Echo Cave, near Hummelstown, Pennsylvania. (Photograph by D. L. Babenroth.)

largely ground water that has been heated by contact with rock, itself heated by rising hot gases released from magmas at depth.

Vents which emit volcanic gases are known as *fumaroles*. Gas temperatures at fumaroles are often far above the boiling point of water and have been measured as high as 650° F (320° C). In Chapter 27 the role of hot springs, fumaroles, and geysers as sources of atmospheric volatiles was examined. Table 27.5 gives analysis of gases from these sources —recall that over 99% of the gas is water. Probably only 1% or less of the water in hot springs and geysers is juvenile water of magmatic origin.

The superheated steam of fumaroles provides valuable sources of natural heat with which to operate power plants. Most of this steam and its associated gases are believed to be volcanic in origin, in contrast with hot springs, which consist largely of recirculated ground water.

Because the heated ground water is highly active chemically, it dissolves unusually large amounts of mineral matter, most of which is silica or calcium carbonate, depending upon the composition of the bedrock through which the solutions move. Upon reaching the surface the hot water is rapidly cooled and must precipitate much of the dissolved mineral matter. En-

FIGURE 33.26. A sinkhole about 60 ft (18 m) deep on the Kaibab Plateau, Arizona, elevation 8500 ft (2500 m). Horizontal limestone strata outcrop on the far wall of the depression. (Photograph by A. N. Strahler.)

FIGURE 33.27. Evolution of a karst landscape. (Drawn by E. Raisz. © 1960, John Wiley & Sons, New York.)

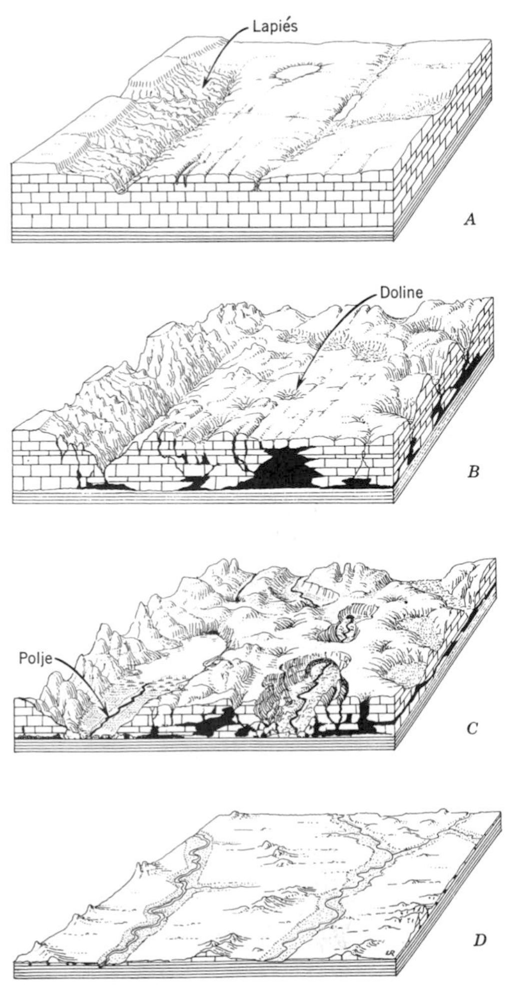

**FIGURE 33.28.** This early photograph of Mammoth Hot Springs, Yellowstone Park, Wyoming, was taken by the pioneer photographer, W. H. Jackson, in 1870. (U.S. Geological Survey photograph.)

crustations are thus built up close to the springs and gradually spread laterally in flat-topped terraces which may be stepped, one above the other (Figure 33.28). Terraces formed of silica, known as *siliceous sinter* (or *geyserite*), are typical of hot springs in which water rises through igneous rocks. Where limestone bedrock furnishes calcium carbonate, the deposits are of travertine, as in the case of Mammoth Hot Springs, pictured in Figure 33.28. Certain algae thrive in the pools of hot water and these may also precipitate calcium carbonate. Cones of siliceous sinter are built around the orifices of geysers.

Geyser action consists of the occasional or periodic emission of a column of steam and water droplets under high pressure from a small vent (Figure 33.29). This action can be explained by the *Bunsen theory,* which makes use of the principle that the boiling point of water is raised with increasing hydrostatic pressure at increasing depth. For example, at a depth of 150 m (500 ft) the boiling point is about 200° C (390° F). The geyser is thought to consist of a long narrow tube with tortuous shape and numerous constrictions (Figure 33.30). It fills with ground water entering from passageways in the surrounding rock. Gradually the water temperature rises by conduction of heat from the enclosing rock until the boiling point is approached throughout a large part of its length. Boiling point is first reached near the base of the tube, converting water to steam, which lifts the entire water column. Displaced water pours out of the geyser vent and the hydrostatic pressure, and along with it the boiling point, are lowered simultaneously at all points in the column (Figure 33.30*B*). With sufficient lift, the entire column passes the boiling point and conversion to steam takes place

**FIGURE 33.29.** Waikite Geyser, Rotorua, North Island, New Zealand. (Photograph by New Zealand Tourist Bureau.)

**FIGURE 33.30.** Schematic diagram of the Bunsen geyser theory.

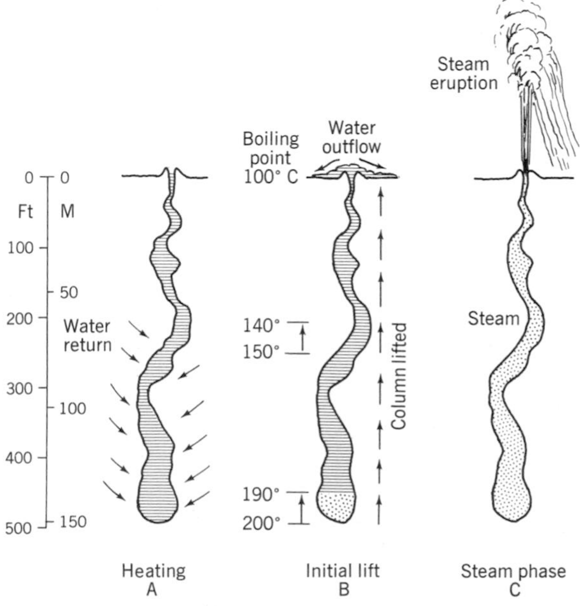

suddenly throughout the entire tube. Under tremendous pressure the entire column of water and steam is ejected within a few minutes, after which eruption ceases.

In 1969 a successful man-made geyser was put into operation in a geothermal locality in Oregon. It was made by boring a hole 6 in. (15 cm) in diameter to a depth of 115 ft (35 m). The geyser erupts once in every 8 to 10 hours.

Old Faithful, in Yellowstone National Park, is perhaps the best known geyser of all. It erupts for about 4 minutes at intervals averaging close to one hour. With each eruption about 10,000 gallons (40 kiloliters) of water are discharged in a column that may rise to a height of 150 ft (45 m). Almost all of the world's geysers are located in three places: Yellowstone Park in Wyoming, Iceland, and New Zealand.

In addition to the hot springs associated with magmatic activity, there are countless springs of warm water known simply as *warm springs* or *thermal springs.* For example, Warm Springs in Georgia emit water at a temperature of 88° F (31° C). This water is ground water that has followed a permeable rock layer downward to a depth of almost 4000 ft (1200 m), where it is heated according to the normal geothermal gradient. A favorable geologic structure enables the water to return to the surface as a warm spring.

## Subsurface water in review

In this chapter we have traced water in the liquid state through a highly complex set of paths in the soil, overburden, and bedrock. Obviously, water confined in minute interconnected pore spaces behaves in a very different manner from free water in streams, lakes, and ponds. Upward movements of water in capillary films and in the rising paths of ground-water motion seem strange to surface-dwellers accustomed to seeing water run only downhill.

The subjects covered in this chapter are remarkably diverse in character, ranging from the environmental aspects of soil water to the geologic processes of ground water. Yet all are parts or byproducts of one link in the hydrologic cycle. The grand concept of a global water balance ties all of the diverse fragments into a unified pattern, which is that of an open system of mass transport powered by solar energy and governed by the earth's gravity field. In the next chapter we will examine a closely related part of the mass transport system, that of surface flow of water in another link of the hydrologic cycle.

## References for further study

Meinzer, O. E. (1923), *The Occurrence of Ground Water in the United States with a Discussion of Principles,* U.S. Geological Survey, Prof. Paper 489, 321 pp.

Lobeck, A. K. (1939), *Geomorphology,* New York, McGraw-Hill, 731 pp., chap. 4.

Thomas, H. E. (1951), *The Conservation of Ground Water,* New York, McGraw-Hill, 321 pp.

U.S. Dept. of Agriculture (1955), *Water; Yearbook of Agriculture, 1955,* Washington, D.C., U.S. Govt. Printing Office, 751 pp.

Todd, D. K. (1959), *Ground Water Hydrology,* New York, Wiley, 336 pp.

Sellers, W. D. (1965), *Physical Climatology,* Chicago, Univ. of Chicago Press, 272 pp., chap. 7.

Thornbury, W. D. (1969), *Principles of Geomorphology,* 2nd ed., New York, Wiley, 594 pp., chaps. 13, 22.

# 34

# Runoff of surface waters

CHAPTERS 18 AND 33 traced the movement of water from the vapor state in the atmosphere, through precipitation and infiltration, to ground water, covering atmospheric and subsurface parts of the hydrologic cycle. In this chapter we consider the forms of surface-water flow, both over the slopes of the land and in stream channels, collectively designated as *runoff.* It has already been explained that runoff may be derived both from direct surface accumulation of precipitation that does not infiltrate and from ground water outflowing along lines where the water table intersects the surface in streams, lakes and marshes.

Runoff, in its attempts to progress efficiently to lower levels and eventually to reach the sea, organizes itself into *drainage systems,* each consisting of a more or less leaf-shaped or pear-shaped area of the land bounded by a drainage divide, defining a *drainage basin,* and possessing a narrow mouth through which water and mineral matter are discharged by a single channel. Within the drainage basin is a system of branching stream channels toward which the ground surfaces slope. Given ample time, freedom from disturbing outside forces, and the absence of strong inequalities of rock resistance, the drainage system and its associated land slopes become so adjusted as to dispose efficiently of the runoff and mineral waste, with the ultimate goal of reducing the land to a surface of faint relief close to sea level. We may think of the drainage basin as a converging mechanism designed to integrate and funnel the widely spread forms of runoff into progressively narrower and more intense lines of flow.

Two fields of the earth sciences are joined in the study of drainage systems: hydrology and geology. Where interest lies particularly in the water itself, with emphasis upon the quantity of water moved in a given time and the relation between precipitation and runoff, studies fall within the scope of hydrology and are treated as a branch of civil engineering. Where interest is centered on the processes of erosion and transportation going on within the drainage system and upon the geometrical forms of the channels and land slopes, studies are carried out by geologists.

The efforts of both hydrologists and geologists are joined in the Water Resources Division of the U.S. Geological Survey, the agency given responsibility for assessing the surface- and ground-water resources of the United States. Other agencies also have an interest in study of runoff. The Forest Service is concerned with runoff and other hydrologic problems of the national forests, whereas the Soil Conservation Service views runoff problems as related to soil erosion and agricultural land use. Where engineering works are constructed and maintained for irrigation, for navigability of rivers, and for flood controls, runoff is a concern of the U.S. Bureau of Reclamation (Department of Interior) and the U.S. Army Corps of Engineers.

## Overland flow

The term *overland flow* is given to the movement of runoff downslope on the ground in a more or less broadly distributed sheet or film, or in very shallow interconnected rills. In contrast, *channel flow* (*stream flow*) occurs in a long, narrow, trough-like depression bounded by banks or valley walls that slope toward the channel.

Overland flow taking the form of a thin continuous film over relatively smooth soil or rock surfaces is designated as *sheet flow*. Where the surface is pitted or has obstructing masses in the form of soil mounds, boulders, or fallen vegetation, runoff takes the form of small rivulets overflowing from one hollow to the next. On a grass-covered surface the countless stems cause the flow to be subdivided into a pattern of many intertwining flow lines. Such flow may not be noticed, even in a heavy rain yielding much runoff. Similarly, in a heavy forest the accumulation of fallen vegetation may completely mask from view a substantial rate of overland flow.

Consider the stages in production of overland flow on a vegetated land slope. Assume that rain sets in after a summer period of many days of drought. Should there be a canopy of foliage, much of the rain that first falls will cling in droplets to the surfaces of the leaves and stems, a process termed *interception* (Figure 34.1). Should the rain cease, the intercepted moisture would be returned to the atmosphere by evaporation without even reaching the ground. Rain reaching the ground at first infiltrates at a rapid rate, so that a short rain, though heavy, may produce no runoff.

As explained in Chapter 33, the infiltration rate rapidly diminishes with time, thus there comes a point at which a moderate to heavy rain will begin to produce an excess of water available to form overland

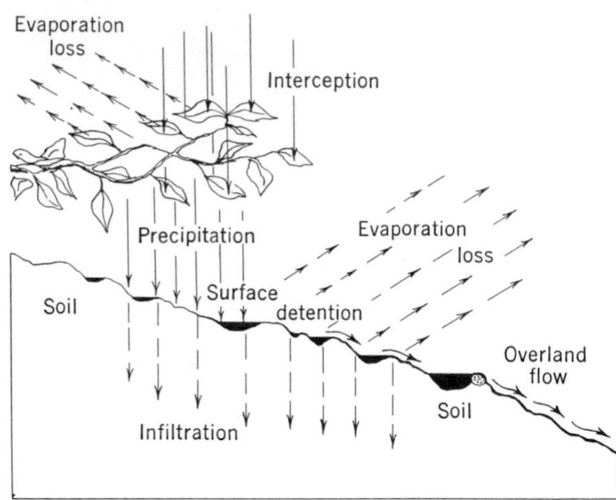


**FIGURE 34.1.** Evaporation, interception, and surface detention detract from precipitation before it can enter the ground or produce overland flow. (© 1960, John Wiley & Sons, New York.)

flow. First, however, the excess precipitation will accumulate in tiny pools in natural hollows in the soil or behind small dams of pebbles or fallen leaves and twigs. The holding of water in such natural cavities is termed *surface detention* (Figure 34.1). Should the rain cease within a short time, the water thus detained may be lost by evaporation and give no overland flow. Assuming, however, that the rain is intense and long continued, there comes a point when the excess water begins to flow down the slopes as overland flow.

How much overland flow reaches the base of a long narrow strip of sloping ground? First, the rate of runoff from any square foot of the surface will depend upon the degree to which the rate of rainfall exceeds the rate of infiltration. For example, if rain is falling at the rate of 0.3 in. per hour and the soil surface has a constant infiltration rate of 0.2 in. per hour, the runoff will have a rate of 0.1 in. per hour.

A second consideration will be the length of the slope over which the runoff passes. Each square foot of the ground must receive and pass on all the runoff yielded from the entire strip of ground lying upslope from it. Consequently the runoff rate increases in direct proportion to length of slope. One might suppose from these considerations that the layer of overland flow becomes deeper as the length of slope increases, but actually depth may increase very little downslope because the velocity of flow increases downslope. Runoff reaching the base of the slope may flow directly into a stream channel (Figure 34.2) or may disappear under a layer of coarse sand or gravel, should such a deposit lie at the base of the slope.

## Stream channels

A *stream channel* is simply a long, narrow, sloping trough shaped by the concentrated flow of water in a manner most effective for moving the mixture of water and sediment supplied by runoff and by ground-water

FIGURE 34.2. This heavy overland flow from a corn field occurred on an eight percent slope following a torrential summer thunderstorm rain. Channel flow is seen in the ditch in the foreground. (Photograph by Soil Conservation Service, U.S. Department of Agriculture.)

seepage from the enclosing drainage basin. Channels range in size from insignificant brooks one can step across in a single stride, to the trenches of great rivers hundreds of feet wide. Taking the mile-wide Mississippi River as an extreme example, we see that natural stream channels can range from 1 ft (0.3 m) or less to 5000 ft (1500 m) or more in width, a 5000-fold ratio in size.

Channels do not necessarily need to contain flowing water to be so defined. Many channels of desert streams are dry most of the time, yet they bear the unmistakable markings of rapidly flowing water and are occupied by raging torrents on the rare occasions of flood. In the air photograph of Death Valley (Figure 26.9) hundreds of dry channels, termed *washes,* can be seen, along with several larger dry river channels. Even in a humid region the smallest channels normally become dry in the summer season, when the water table falls so low that no ground water can seep into the stream.

To describe a stream channel and the flow of water in it, hydraulic engineers use a set of terms and definitions that constitute, collectively, the *hydraulic geometry* (Figure 34.3). Stream *depth, d,* is measured at any desired point. *Width, w,* is the distance across the stream from bank to bank. Cross-sectional area, *A,* is given for a vertical cross section at right angles to direction of flow. The length of the line of contact of water with channel, measured along the cross section, is termed the *wetted perimeter, P.* Units of feet or meters are used.

Division of the cross-sectional area, *A,* by wetted perimeter, *P,* gives the *hydraulic radius, R.* For a broad shallow stream the hydraulic radius will be very nearly the same as the average depth. To express deepness and shallowness of a stream channel, the *form ratio*—or ratio of average depth, *d,* to width, *w*—is a useful quantity, because a ratio does not express actual size. For example, a form ratio of 1:160 means that the stream is 160 times as wide as it is deep, on the average.

Of great importance in describing a stream channel is the *gradient,* or *slope, S.* The slope of a large river can be given as the angle of the water surface with respect to the horizontal. Because this angle is usually very small, the slope is more commonly given as the vertical drop in feet per mile of horizontal distance, or as the *percent of grade,* the ratio of vertical drop to horizontal distance in the same units. Thus a gradient of 0.05, or 5 percent, means a vertical drop of 5 feet for each 100 feet of horizontal distance. In giving the gradient of a small shallow stream or of a dry channel, the gradient of the channel floor is determined, often from topographic contours on maps, and it would differ little from the water-surface gradient if averaged over an appreciable distance.

## Stream flow

Every particle of water in a stream is drawn vertically downward under the force of gravity, so that the water

FIGURE 34.3. Geometric elements of a stream channel and distribution of speeds of flow. (© 1960, John Wiley & Sons, New York.)

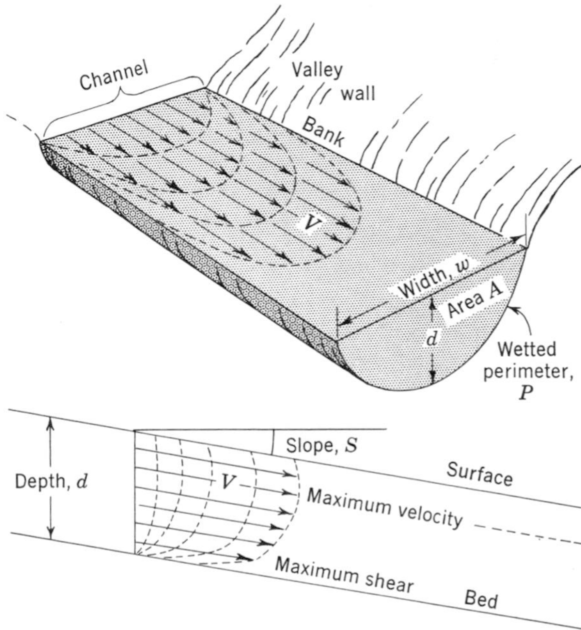

exerts a pressure upon the channel walls proportional to the water depth. A part of the force of gravity acts in the downstream direction, parallel with the stream bed, tending to cause flow of one water layer over the next lower layer in a type of motion known as *shear.* The fluid may be thought of as having almost infinitely thin layers of water molecules, each layer slipping over the layer below, much as playing cards slip over one another when the deck of cards is pushed along a table top. The layer immediately in contact with the solid bed does not slip, but each higher layer slips over the one below, so that the forward motion, or *velocity, V,* increases from the bed upward into the stream.

Dotted lines in Figure 34.3 show the successive positions that would be occupied by water particles starting out together on a vertical line. We see that velocity increases very rapidly from the bed upward, then increases less rapidly, so that the maximum velocity is found at a point about a third of the distance from the surface (Figure 34.3). Similarly, on the stream surface velocity increases from zero at the banks to a maximum near the center line. The rate of shear, which is the same as the rate of change in velocity, is greatest near the bed and banks of the stream.

The foregoing statements imply that each particle of water moves downstream in a direct simple path. Such would be the case in true *laminar flow,* or *streamline flow,* which occurs in fluids when their motion is very slow. In most forms of runoff, including most overland flow and nearly all stream-channel flow, the water particles describe highly irregular paths of travel, resembling a tortuous corkscrew motion including sideways and vertical movements. Such motion, described as *turbulent flow,* consists of innumerable eddies of various sizes and intensities continually forming and dissolving. The velocity, *V,* referred to above, and the simple paths of flow shown by the arrows in Figure 34.3 are merely the average velocities and average paths of the particles at given levels in the stream.

Turbulent flow in fluids is of great importance in the processes of erosion by running water, waves and tidal currents, and wind, because the transportation of fine particles held in *suspension* in the fluid depends upon the upward currents in turbulence to support the particles. Without turbulence particles could only be rolled or dragged upon the bed or lifted a short distance above it.

Because of the differences in average flow velocity from point to point in a stream, a single statement of velocity is needed to apply to the stream as a whole. This is the *mean velocity* and is approximately equivalent to six-tenths of the maximum velocity, but this ratio depends upon relative stream depth.

The quantity of water that flows through a stream channel in a given period of time, the *discharge,* is a most important characteristic of the flow from the standpoint of describing the magnitude of the stream. Discharge, *Q,* is defined as the volume of water passing through a cross section in a short unit of time. Commonly the units are in terms of cubic feet per second, abbreviated as *cfs,* or simply stated as *second-feet*

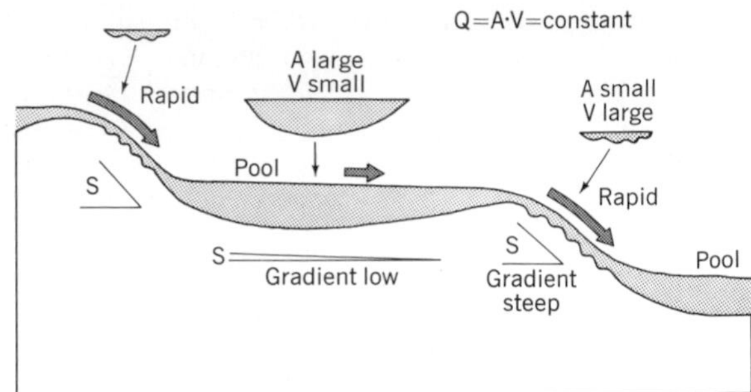


**FIGURE 34.4.** Relations among cross-sectional area (*A*), mean velocity (*V*), and gradient (*S*) in a stream of uniform discharge.

(in metric units—cubic meters per second, *cms*). Discharge is computed by multiplying the mean velocity, *V,* times the cross-sectional area, *A,* in the formula $Q = AV$.

If a long stream channel is to conduct a given discharge through its entire course, the discharge must be constant at all cross sections, otherwise water would accumulate by ponding. Hence the product of cross-sectional area and mean velocity must be constant in all cross sections along the stream. If the stream becomes narrower, with reduced cross section, it must have a proportional increase of velocity. If the velocity should increase because of a steepened gradient, the cross-sectional area of the stream will become smaller. The same river that flows slowly in a broad channel on a low gradient will flow swiftly in a narrow stream when it enters a gorge of steep gradient. The equation $Q = AV$ is known as the *equation of continuity* of flow, because a stream that is neither gaining nor losing water at any point on its course must keep the discharge constant by appropriate combinations of cross-sectional area and velocity (Figure 34.4).

## Stream energy and velocity

The flowing of a stream requires that energy be changed continuously from one form to another. Shear within the water is resisted by a property of stickiness in the fluid, known as *viscosity.* Energy must be consumed in overcoming this resistance to flow. At first stream energy exists in the *potential* form, by reason of the stream's height or altitude at the upper end of the course. As the water drops in level downstream, the potential energy is transformed into kinetic energy, the energy of motion.

If the stream offered no resistance to flow, the water would accelerate continuously, just as an object accelerates when falling in a vacuum. But the increasing rate of flow in the stream is met by increasing internal resistance from the viscosity of the water, hence the velocity quickly reaches a constant value. In overcoming resistance kinetic energy is transformed into heat energy at a constant rate. Actually, the stream should become warmer by its own flow, but the rise in temperature is not measurable.

We have seen that stream velocity increases when the slope, or gradient, increases, for then the downslope force component of gravity is greater. A stream will also become swifter if its channel shape is altered to offer less resistance to flow along its wetted perimeter. If the stream becomes broader and shallower, its perimeter becomes longer, compared with the area of cross section, thus offering more resistance to flow and causing a decrease in velocity. A channel is most efficient when it has the least perimeter for the given cross-sectional area—that is, when it has the maximum hydraulic radius (because $R = A/P$). A semicircular channel is the most efficient form, but is rarely approached in nature. Other considerations, such as the necessity of transporting sediment and the weakness or strength of the materials composing the channel walls, enter into the form of a natural stream channel.

Still another primary factor controlling velocity is the roughness of the stream bed. Flow over a bed consisting of cobbles or boulders or having wavelike ripples of sand will be less efficient than flow over a very smooth bed, such as one of fine clay or of highly polished rock.

In summary, a stream whose discharge is kept constant throughout its length will have its mean velocity determined by the stream gradient and by the cross-sectional area, form, and roughness of its channel (Figure 34.4).

Where a stream has an increase in discharge because of the onset of a flood, the water deepens and the velocity is increased. An increase in cross-sectional area also takes place with increasing discharge, but the depth usually increases in greater ratio than does the width. Changes of this sort are explained in Chapter 35.

## Relation of velocity to depth and slope

Hydraulic engineers have tried for almost two centuries to establish a useful mathematical relationship among observed values of stream velocity and both depth and gradient (slope). First to make this attempt was a French engineer, whose formula of 1775 is known as the *Chezy equation:*

$$V = C\sqrt{R \cdot S}$$

where $V$ is mean stream velocity,
$R$ is hydraulic radius,
and $S$ is slope, as percent grade.

The term $C$ is a numerical constant. We can rewrite the Chezy equation as follows:

$$V = C \cdot \sqrt{R} \cdot \sqrt{S}$$
$$\text{or } V = C \cdot R^{1/2} \cdot S^{1/2}$$

In words, this equation states that the mean velocity varies as the square-root of hydraulic radius and as the square-root of slope. Hydraulic radius is essentially equivalent to the average stream depth. An increase of velocity with increase in depth is to be expected (when slope is held constant) because the frictional resistance with the bed has less influence for deeper water than for shallower. The increase of velocity with steeper slope (holding depth constant) is intuitively obvious, since the component of gravitational force acting parallel with the stream bed is greater when slope is steeper.

That velocity increases about as square-root of slope can be easily demonstrated with a small laboratory flume of rectangular cross section. By means of blocks the flume can be raised successively through slopes of 1, 2, 3, and 4 percent. By controlling the flow of water, depth can be kept constant at all values of slope, although the discharge must also be increased to maintain constant depth. Surface velocity is measured by timing the travel of floating particles, and this is converted to mean velocity by multiplying by 0.7. Mean velocity can also be derived by measuring the discharge of the flume and dividing by cross-sectional area. Table 34.1 summarizes the data of a typical experiment. The plotted points in Figure 34.5 show reasonably close approximation to a straight line, as required by the Chezy equation.

**FIGURE 34.5.** Plot of mean velocity against square-root of slope. (Data from Table 34.1.)

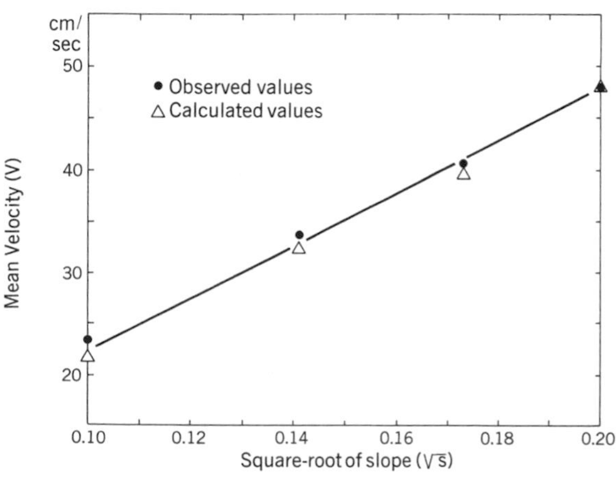


**TABLE 34.1. EXPERIMENTAL FLUME DATA ON RELATION OF VELOCITY TO SLOPE***

| Slope | Square Root of Slope | Observed Mean Velocity, cm/sec | Calculated Mean Velocity ($V = Q/A$), cm/sec |
|---|---|---|---|
| 0.01 | 0.100 | 23.2 | 21.7 |
| 0.02 | 0.141 | 33.8 | 32.2 |
| 0.03 | 0.173 | 40.5 | 39.6 |
| 0.04 | 0.200 | 48.0 | 48.0 |

* Data obtained by A. N. Strahler.

The Chezy equation has been revised a number of times on the basis of additional measurements. In wide use today is the *Manning equation:*

$$V = \frac{1}{n} R^{2/3} \cdot S^{1/2}$$

While the square-root relationship remains unchanged for slope, the exponent for hydraulic radius has been raised to the two-thirds power. The constant, *n,* is a numerical estimate of the roughness of the stream bed, and measures the total effect of various forms of irregularities in the configuration of the bed and alignment of the channel. When c.g.s. units are used, the value of *n* runs from 0.015 to 0.060 in natural streams.

## Stream gauging

The responsibility of measuring, or *gauging,* the principal streams of the United States is in the hands of the U.S. Geological Survey, through its Water Resources Division. Cooperating with state and municipal agencies, the Geological Survey maintains over 6000 gauging stations on the nation's principal streams and their tributaries. Discharge figures, published in a series of water-supply papers, provide essential information for the planning of flood-control devices and the construction of dams for water power and irrigation.

The simplest measurement to be taken is that of the height of stream surface, termed the *stage.* This may be done by attaching a scaled rod, or *staff gauge,* to a bridge pier or abutment, where it can be read directly as required. When a continuous record of stage is needed, a *stilling tower* is constructed beside the stream (Figure 34.6). This structure is merely a masonry or concrete *stilling well* connected by a pipe to the stream channel so that the water level in the well matches that of the stream surface (Figure 34.7). A float, connected by a wire to a recording mechanism, rises and falls with the water level and produces a continuous record of stage.

Determination of stream discharge requires that the cross-sectional area and mean velocity be measured directly. For this purpose a *current meter* is lowered into the water at regular intervals of horizontal distance and depth so as to give the average velocity at each of many points, forming a regular grid pattern over the entire cross section (Figure 34.7). The current meter consists of a set of revolving cups whose rate of turning is proportional to the stream velocity (Figure 34.8). The turning of the cups causes an electric circuit to be broken repeatedly, sending a series of clicks to headphones worn by the observer. A count of the clicks in a given span of time will establish the velocity.

The Price current meter, shown in Figure 34.8, is capable of measuring velocities in the range from 0.2 to 20 ft (0.06 to 6 m) per second. Measurements can be made from a bridge or, where no bridge is available, from a cable car running on a cable suspended across the river (Figure 34.7). Depth measurements are made along with the current measurement, making it possible to determine a profile of the stream bed and the stream's cross-sectional area. Mean velocity can be computed by averaging the individual readings of the entire cross section. Discharge then follows from the formula $Q = AV$.

**FIGURE 34.6.** Recording gauges are housed in this concrete stilling tower. The channel cross section is artificially controlled at this point. Fish Creek, near Duarte, California. (Photograph by U.S. Geological Survey.)

Obviously stream gauging requires considerable time and effort, and it would not be practical to carry on a continuous series of current-meter readings. Fortunately, a simple method of estimating discharge by means of stage reading alone is available in the *rating curve,* or *stage-discharge curve* (Figure 34.9). To prepare such a curve, discharge is measured by current meter for several discharges covering a wide range of values. These data are plotted on a graph of stage (gauge height) versus discharge, and a smooth curve is drawn to connect and extend the points. Once drawn, the curve serves to give a quick estimate of discharge for any measured stage. For example, in Figure 34.9 a stage height of 20 feet gives an estimated discharge of about 16,500 cfs. Rating curves must be recomputed and corrected at intervals of time because the channel form may change somewhat through flood erosion. The curves are most effective when used in a

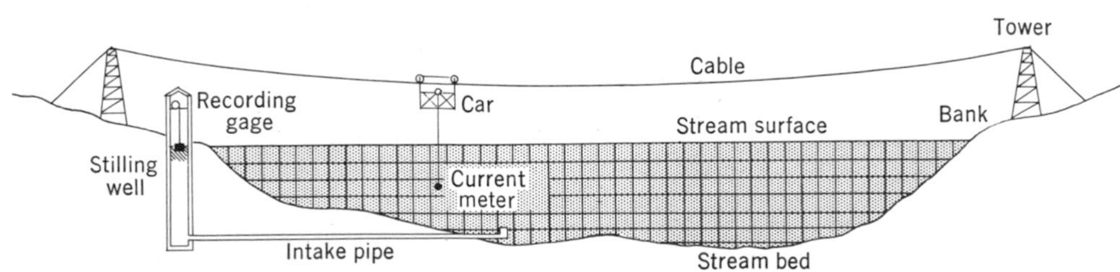


**FIGURE 34.7.** Schematic diagram of a stream gauging installation. (© 1960, John Wiley & Sons, New York.)

**FIGURE 34.8.** Stream-gauging apparatus for use on a large river. A convenient bridge permits the current meter (*right*) to be lowered by a power winch at any desired point. (Photograph by U.S. Geological Survey.)

highly stable reach of a river, as where bridges and other engineering works give the channel a fixed form.

## Drainage networks

In analyzing a drainage network, the stream channels are traced out in full upon a map or air photo to include all clearly defined flow lines, even those which carry water only in times when overland flow occurs.

**FIGURE 34.9.** By means of this rating curve the discharge of Levisa Fork, Kentucky, could be estimated from stream stage. The curve shown here was used in the period October, 1945, to January, 1946. [© 1960, John Wiley & Sons, New York. Data from W. G. Hoyt and W. B. Langbein (1955), *Floods,* Princeton, N.J., Princeton Univ. Press, p. 69, Figure 23.]

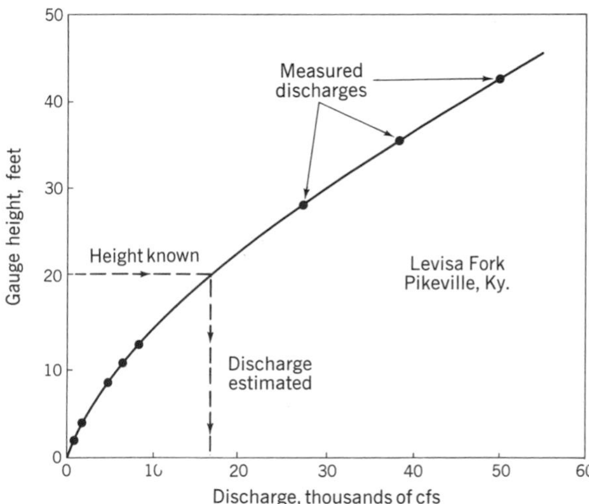


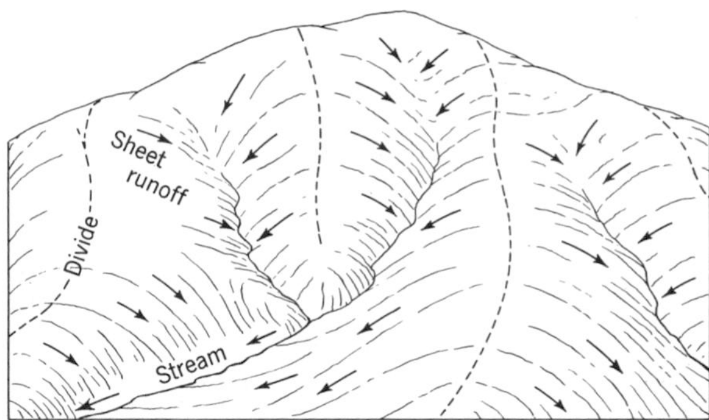


**FIGURE 34.10.** Finger-tip stream channels are fed by overland flow from small watersheds. (© 1960, John Wiley & Sons, New York.)

Surface slopes converge toward the head of each of the smallest, or finger-tip, channels where runoff collects in sufficient quantity to scour a permanent channel and to maintain it against the filling action of soil creep, slope wash, and vegetative growth (Figure 34.10). During the long period of time within which the landscape evolves by fluvial-denudation processes, the runoff of all available ground becomes apportioned to the individual channels in such a manner that each channel obtains just the amount of runoff needed to sustain it. Furthermore, the gradients of both valley walls and channels become adjusted between themselves to permit a generally uniform disposal of rock waste.

As channels join each other, at angles that are usually acute, the discharge of water and sediment load is funneled into exit channels of progressively larger dimensions. Although the flow paths are not the shortest possible, they are the most economical under the requirement that each unit of channel length be provided with a proportionate surface area of runoff.

## Playfair's law

The first meaningful generalization about the relation of stream systems to their valleys was made in 1802 by an English geologist, John Playfair, who stated:

> Every river appears to consist of a main trunk, fed from a variety of branches, each running in a valley proportioned to its size, and all of them together forming a system of valleys connecting with one another, and having such a nice adjustment of their declivities that none of them join the principal valley either on too high or too low a level; a circumstance which would be infinitely improbable if each of these valleys were not the work of the stream which flows in it.

The above pronouncement, now known as Playfair's law, suggests that the channel dimensions, discharges, and gradients of streams bear some definite mathematical relation to the areas of the contributing watersheds. Playfair was primarily concerned with providing a convincing argument that streams are the agents that have carved the valleys they occupy—a principle then in dispute—but his law has since been developed into a rigorous quantitative set of geometrical relations describing stream systems that have been under the processes of fluvial denudation for a long period of time and that have underlying bedrock that is generally uniform in its resistance to weathering and stream erosion.

## Stream orders and stream numbers

If we are given a map of a complete stream-channel network of a drainage basin, as shown in Figure 34.11, it is possible to subdivide the net into individual *channel segments,* defined by stream junctions, and to designate by integer numbers the segments in terms of orders of magnitude within a hierarchy. Every finger-tip channel, from its point of origin to its first point of junction, is designated as a channel segment of the *first order.* The junction of any two first-order channels produces a segment of the *second order,* the junction of any two second-order segments produces a segment of the *third order,* and so forth. The junction of a single first-order segment with a second-order or higher-order channel does not, however, produce any change in the order of the segment it joins.

When this ordering system is applied throughout the entire drainage network, it will be found that a single trunk-stream segment bears the highest order designation. Where a large stream network is taken into consideration, the order of any segment will, on the average, reflect the magnitude of the channel in terms of its channel dimensions, discharge, and contributing watershed area. A relatively large sample must be taken to reveal consistent relations, because individual segments may be much longer or shorter than the average and there will be many chance distortions in the pattern of the network.

**FIGURE 34.11.** System of assigning orders to the stream segments within a drainage basin. (© 1960, John Wiley & Sons, New York.)

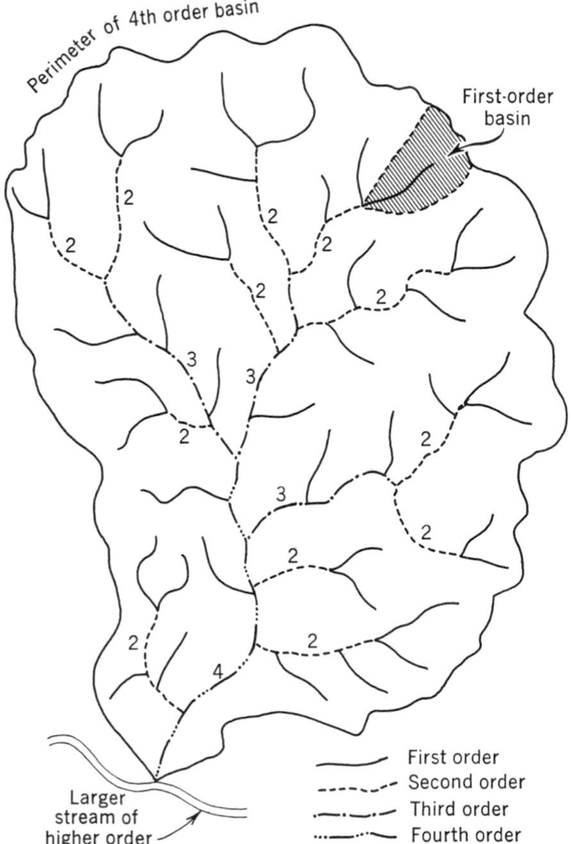


The first step in stream-network analysis is to count the numbers of stream segments of each order. The example in Table 34.2 is taken from a carefully surveyed detailed map of a small drainage network typical of the Big Badlands of South Dakota.

**TABLE 34.2. STREAM ORDERS AND NUMBERS, BIG BADLANDS, SOUTH DAKOTA***

| Stream Order | Number of Stream Segments | Bifurcation Ratio |
|---|---|---|
| 1 | 139 | |
| | | 3.02 |
| 2 | 46 | |
| | | 4.18 |
| 3 | 11 | |
| | | 3.66 |
| 4 | 3 | |
| | | 3.00 |
| 5 | 1 | |

* Data from K. G. Smith (1958), *Geol. Soc. of Amer. Bulletin,* vol. 69, pp. 975–1008. (See Figure 14.)

The ratio of the number of stream segments of a given order to the number of segments of the next higher order is termed the *bifurcation ratio.* In the example cited above, this ratio ranges from as low as 3 to over 4 between the various orders. These observed differences can be attributed to chance variations that may affect any stream network.

The accumulated data of many stream networks involving thousands of stream segments have revealed the principle that in an area of uniform climate, uniform rock type, and uniform history of geologic development the bifurcation ratio tends to be constant from one order to the next, hence that a single ratio characterizes the entire network. Commonly the bifurcation ratio falls between 3 and 5. Rarely is the theoretical minimum possible value of 2 approached.

There follows from observation a *law of stream numbers:* The numbers of stream segments of successively lower orders in a given basin tend to form a geometric progression, commencing with a single trunk segment of the highest order and increasing according to a constant bifurcation ratio. For example, given a bifurcation ratio of exactly 3 and a trunk-stream segment of the sixth order, the numbers of segments within the system will be 1, 3, 9, 27, 81, and 243.

Any geometric progression, such as the number series 1, 3, 9, 27, 81, 243, represents a constant ratio of increase. Therefore, if we should plot the numbers of stream segments on a constant-ratio (logarithmic)

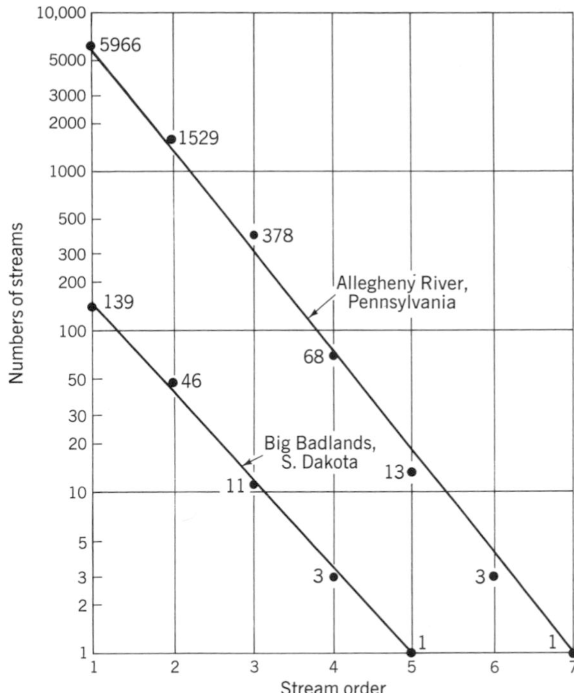


**FIGURE 34.12.** Plot of numbers of stream segments against stream order for two stream systems of vastly different size. The plotted information is also given in Tables 34.2 and 34.3. [Data of Marie E. Morisawa (1962), and Kenneth G. Smith (1958).]

scale against stream orders on a uniform (arithmetic) scale, the points should fall close to a straight line. Figure 34.12 shows the data of Table 34.2 plotted on such a graph, known as a *semi-logarithmic plot.* The five points do not conform exactly with the fitted straight line, but departures from this line are small.

Table 34.3 gives network data for a portion of a large drainage basin, that of the Allegheny River in the Appalachian Plateau region of Pennsylvania. Numbers of stream segments for this basin are also plotted against order in Figure 34.12.

## Stream lengths, basin areas, and channel slopes

Inspection of the segments of various orders in Figure 34.11 shows that on the average the second-order segments are longer than those of first order, that third-order segments are longer than second-order segments, etc. To study this matter further, examine the data of Table 34.3 for the Allegheny River drainage basin.

Although the master stream of this basin is given as of the seventh order, its length and area are stated with reference to a stream gauge and do not reveal the full segment dimensions. Therefore only the first six orders should be considered in analyzing the data.

The mean length of segments of each order is converted into *cumulative mean length,* by adding the mean length of each order to the sum of those of lower orders. When this is done, the cumulative mean length of segments of any one order is approximately three times the average cumulative length of segments of the next lower order, this relation being expressed by the *length ratio.*

Extensive observations of drainage networks show that the cumulative length ratio tends to remain constant within a given drainage system. It is therefore possible to state a *law of stream lengths:* the cumulative mean lengths of stream segments of successively higher orders tend to form a geometric progression beginning with the cumulative mean length of the first-order segments and increasing according to the length ratio.

Figure 34.13 shows the cumulative length data of Table 34.3 in a semi-logarithmic plot against stream order. Except for the first order segments, all points lie very close to the fitted straight line. Also shown on this same graph is a plot of cumulative length data for

**TABLE 34.3. ALLEGHENY RIVER DRAINAGE BASIN CHARACTERISTICS***

| Stream Order | Number of Segments | Bifurcation Ratio | Mean Length of Segments, miles | Cumulative Mean Length, miles | Length Ratio | Average Watershed Area, square miles |
|---|---|---|---|---|---|---|
| 1 | 5966 | | 0.09 | 0.09 | | 0.05 |
| | | 3.9 | | | 3.3 | |
| 2 | 1529 | | 0.3 | 0.4 | | 0.15 |
| | | 4.0 | | | 2.7 | |
| 3 | 378 | | 0.8 | 1.2 | | 0.86 |
| | | 5.7 | | | 3.1 | |
| 4 | 68 | | 2.5 | 3.9 | | 6.1 |
| | | 5.3 | | | 2.8 | |
| 5 | 13 | | 7 | 11 | | 34 |
| | | 4.3 | | | 2.9 | |
| 6 | 3 | | 20 | 31 | | 242 |
| | | 3.0 | | | | |
| 7 | 1 | | 8+ (not complete) | | | 550 (not complete) |

* Data from Marie E. Morisawa (1962), *Geol. Soc. of Am. Bulletin 73,* see p. 1037.

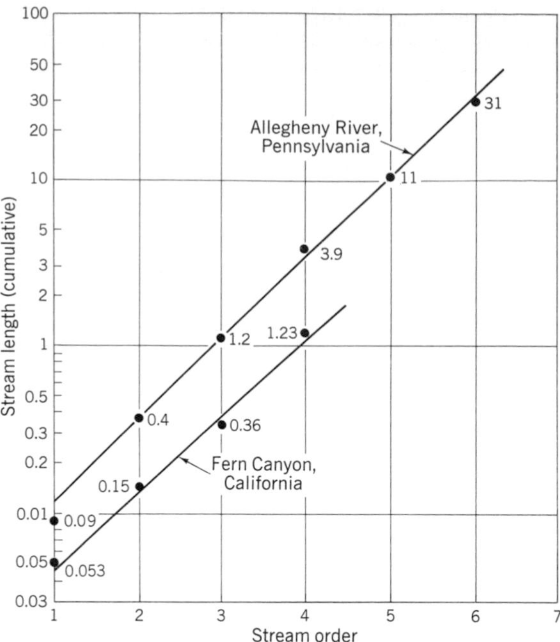


**FIGURE 34.13.** Plot of cumulative mean stream length against stream order. [Data of Marie E. Morisawa (1962), and James C. Maxwell (1960).]

Fern Canyon, a small watershed in the San Gabriel Mountains of California.

Each first-order stream segment of a drainage network receives runoff as overland flow from contributing slopes of a *first-order basin,* examples of which are shown in Figure 34.14. A second-order basin includes two or more first-order basins, in addition to which there are *interbasin areas* from which overland flow passes directly into the second-order channel segment. Thus the basin area of a segment of any higher order includes all areas of basins of lower orders in the system, plus all interbasin areas.

**FIGURE 34.14.** Nested arrangement of basins of first and second orders with interbasin areas.

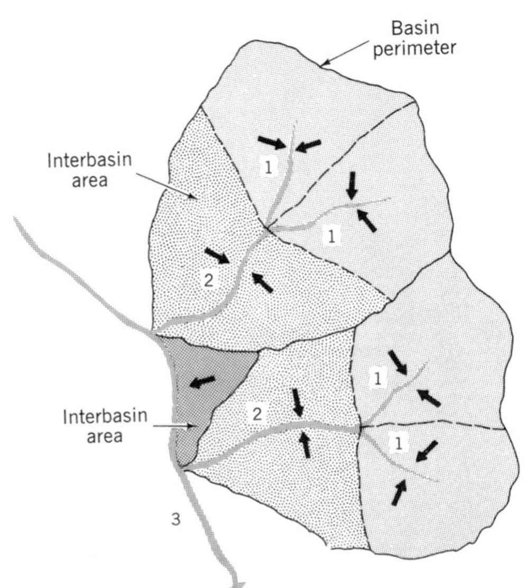


Studies of many drainage basins have shown that basin area tends to increase with order in a manner similar to that shown by increase of cumulative stream length with order. This relationship is stated in a third law of drainage basin geometry: The mean basin areas of successive stream orders tend to form a geometric series beginning with mean area of the first-order basins and increasing according to a constant *area ratio.* Figure 34.15 is a semilogarithmic plot of basin area against order for the Allegheny River data of Table 34.3, and for Fern Canyon, California.

An almost universal characteristic of drainage basins that have had ample time to adjust their geometry to prevailing conditions of hydrology and geology is that the slope, or gradient, of the first-order streams is, on the average, steeper than the average slope of the second-order streams, and that the average gradient diminishes with each integer increase in order. Reasons for this downstream decrease in channel slope are explained in Chapter 35.

The nature of downstream decrease in channel slopes can be seen in an example, for which data are given in Table 34.4. For each stream order in the drainage basin of Home Creek, Ohio, the mean channel slope is given as a ratio of vertical drop to horizontal distance. The *slope ratio,* or ratio of mean slope of one order

**FIGURE 34.15.** Plot of mean basin area against stream order. [Data of Marie E. Morisawa (1962), and James C. Maxwell (1960).]

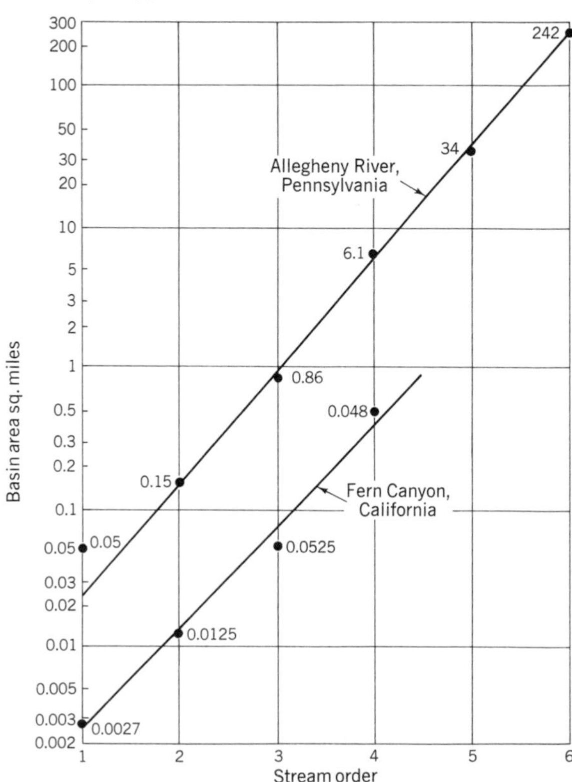

**TABLE 34.4. CHANNEL SLOPES OF THE HOME CREEK, OHIO, DRAINAGE BASIN***

| Order | Mean Channel Slope | Slope Ratio |
|---|---|---|
| 1 | 0.181 | |
| | | 0.48 |
| 2 | 0.087 | |
| | | 0.32 |
| 3 | 0.028 | |
| | | 0.32 |
| 4 | 0.009 | |
| | | 0.56 |
| 5 | 0.005 | |

* Data from Marie E. Morisawa, 1959.

to that of the next higher order, is given in a third column. In this example the ratios range from about one-half to one-third, with an average of about 0.4.

On the basis of extensive data on channel slopes, a law of stream slopes has been formulated: The mean slopes of stream segments of successively higher orders in a given basin tend to form an inverse geometric series, decreasing according to a constant slope ratio.

Figure 34.16 is a semilogarithmic plot of mean channel slope against stream order for the data of Home Creek. The data conform rather well to the requirements of the law of stream slopes, but with deviations that are to be expected in a natural system.

The laws of stream numbers, lengths, basin areas, and channel slopes were derived by a distinguished hydrologist, Robert E. Horton, on the basis of actual stream network data and are empirical in nature. Each law can be given formal statement as a mathematical equation. Together these laws can be regarded as a modern quantitative expression of Playfair's law to the effect that streams run in valleys proportioned to their sizes and that they have a good adjustment of their declivities (slopes).

**FIGURE 34.16.** Plot of mean channel slope against stream order. [Data of Marie E. Morisawa (1959).]

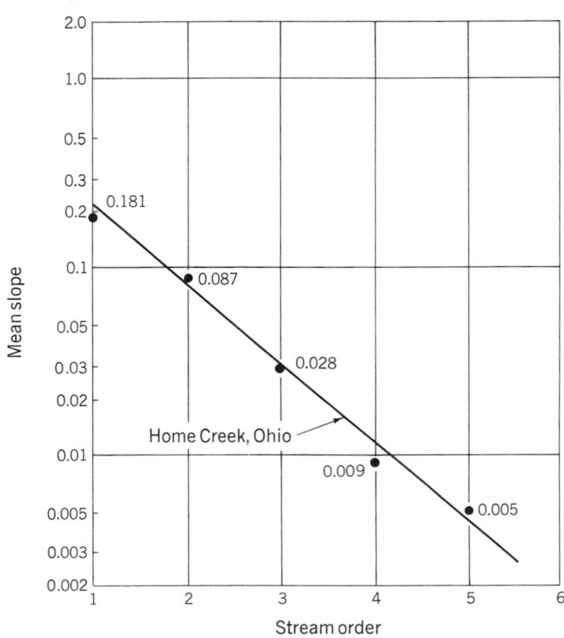


## Stream discharge and basin area

It is to be expected that the stream discharge will tend to increase with increasing basin area, since the discharge is derived from overland flow and ground-water seepage from precipitation falling upon that watershed. When the mean annual discharge, as calculated from stream gauge records, is plotted against the total area of watershed lying above that gauge, a simple relationship of discharge to basin area is revealed (Figure 34.17). Although the data are plotted on a double-logarithmic graph, the straight line of best fit is so inclined that the discharge increases in direct proportion to the increase in drainage area. Once the existing relationship has been established for a given watershed, it is possible to make good estimates of the mean annual discharge at any given point on a trunk stream by merely measuring the watershed area lying above that point.

## Drainage density

Badlands—those areas of intricately eroded landforms found in barren regions where weak clays and shales are exposed in a dry climate—often show miniature mountain ranges and valleys strikingly resembling in form the great mountain ranges of the earth. Within badlands a drainage basin of, say, the fifth order of magnitude may be only a few yards in length, whereas in a mountain region, such as the Appalachians, a fifth-order basin may be several miles in length. Maps

**FIGURE 34.17.** Plot of mean annual stream discharge against drainage basin area. [Data of John T. Hack (1957), *U.S. Geol. Surv. Professional Paper 294-B,* p. 54, Figure 15.]

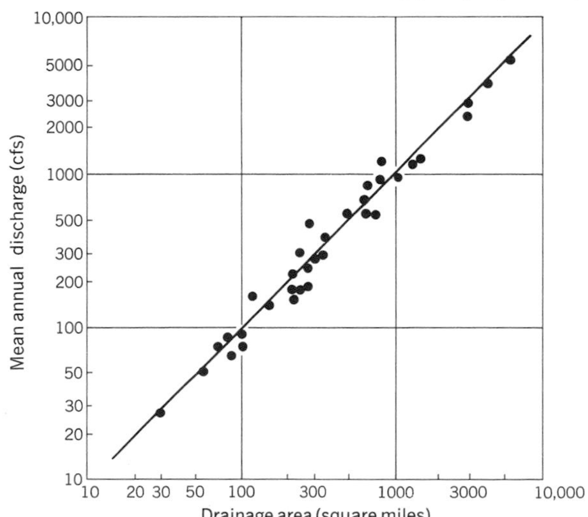

of the drainage networks of both basins, if reduced to equal dimensions, might prove quite indistinguishable in regard to the stream pattern and its component parts.

Clearly, drainage networks can take a wide range in fineness or coarseness of pattern, just as a woven fabric can range from an extremely fine silk cloth to coarse burlap. In drainage systems the scale of fineness or coarseness of the pattern is described by a measure termed the *drainage density,* computed by measuring the total length of all channels in the basin and dividing by the area of the basin:

$$\text{Drainage density} = \frac{\text{total length of stream channels, mi}}{\text{basin area, sq mi}}$$

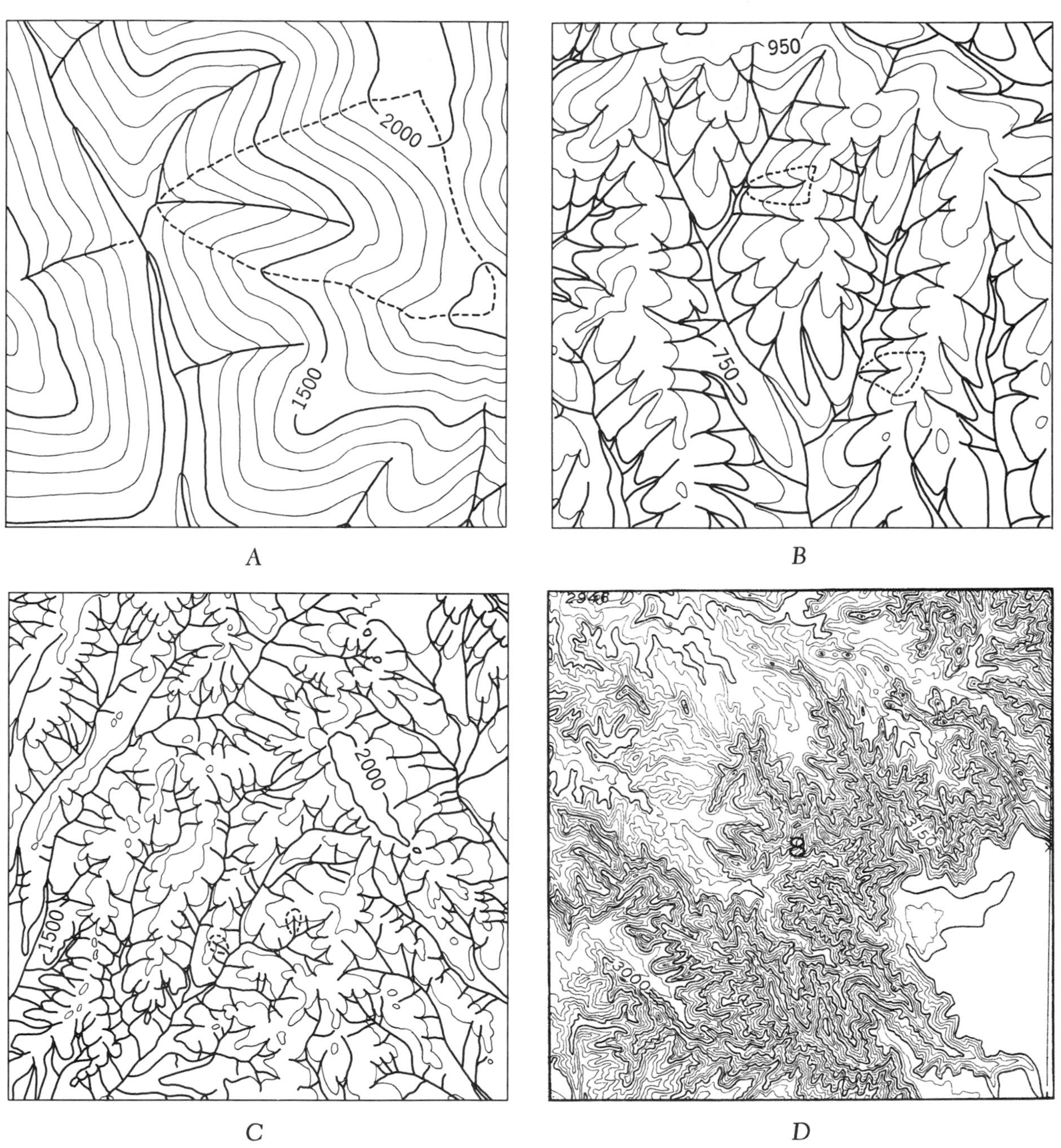


**FIGURE 34.18.** Each of the above maps covers 1 sq mi, but the total length of stream channels found in each area is greatly different from one map to the next. (© 1960, John Wiley & Sons, New York. Based on maps of the U.S. Geological Survey.) (*A*) Low drainage density (coarse texture) in Driftwood, Pennsylvania, quadrangle. (*B*) Medium drainage density (medium texture) in Nashville, Indiana, quadrangle. (*C*) High drainage density (fine texture) in Little Tujunga, California, quadrangle. (*D*) Badlands, where drainage density is extremely high (ultrafine texture) in Cuny Table West, South Dakota, quadrangle.

**FIGURE 34.19.** Ultrafine texture of badlands is illustrated by this vertical air photograph of 1 sq mi (2.6 sq km) of the Big Badlands of South Dakota. Compare with Figure 34.18*D*, a similar example from the same region. North is toward the bottom. (U.S. Department of Agriculture.)

If, for example, a drainage density of 15 is obtained, we can say that there are 15 miles of channel length for every square mile of surface.[1]

Examples of various drainage densities are shown in Figure 34.18. Each map covers 1 sq mi (2.6 sq km). Map *A* illustrates very low drainage density, averaging from 3 to 4 miles of channel per square mile. Note that a single first-order drainage basin is over one-third of a mile across. Low drainage density, which we may also describe as *coarse texture,* is typical of regions of extremely resistant rock, particularly basins eroded in massive sandstone strata. Map *B* illustrates medium drainage density in the range 12 to 16. Such areas are widespread in humid climates of the central and eastern United States over a wide variety of rock types. Map *C* illustrates high drainage density, ranging from 30 to 40. Such *fine texture* is typical of regions of relatively weak rocks in a semiarid climate where vegetative cover is sparse. Map *D* illustrates *ultrafine texture* of drainage network with drainage density running from 200 to 400. This is an area of badlands, essentially the same as that illustrated in the air photograph of Figure 34.19.

Several factors control drainage density. Physical properties of the bedrock or overburden into which the valleys are carved is a primary control. If the region is one of very hard massive rock, such as granite or thick sandstone strata, drainage density tends to be low because a large surface area of runoff is required to produce the channel discharge needed to erode and maintain a channel in such rock. If the underlying material is highly permeable, low drainage density will be favored because much of the precipitation is infiltrated and a large surface area is required to furnish the runoff needed for maintenance of a channel. If the underlying material is impermeable, as in a dense clay or shale, much of the precipitation runs off as overland flow and is therefore more effective in sustaining channels. Thus clay, which combines weakness with low permeability, yields the highest drainage densities.

[1] Metric units may also be used. To convert to kilometers per square kilometers, multiply drainage density values by 0.62.

Still another factor is the presence of a vegetative cover. Where plant growth is dense, the surface is made more resistant to erosion, hence the drainage density tends to be lower than in a corresponding area barren of vegetation. We might also reason that in a region where rainfall is more intense, yielding more storm runoff, drainage density will tend to be higher than it would be in a region where rainfall intensity is lower.

## Relation of stream flow to rainfall

One important aim of the science of hydrology is to relate the changes in discharge of streams to the characteristics of rainfall and to variations in runoff attributed to overland flow and to influent seepage from the ground-water body. When rainfall records are compared with runoff records by means of graphs, certain basic principles emerge.

As a simple case, consider the runoff from a very small drainage basin, about one acre (0.4 hectare) in area, as a result of a heavy rainstorm lasting about an hour. The information is treated by means of a *hydrograph* (water graph) on which time is scaled in minutes on the horizontal axis and the amounts of rainfall and runoff on the vertical axis (Figure 34.20). Rainfall

**FIGURE 34.20.** Receipt and outflow of water are accounted for on this hydrograph of a 1-acre (0.4-hectare) drainage basin near Hays, Kansas, during a brief afternoon rainstorm in summer. [© 1969, John Wiley & Sons, New York. Data from E. E. Foster (1949), *Rainfall and Runoff,* New York, Macmillan, p. 306, Figure 114.]

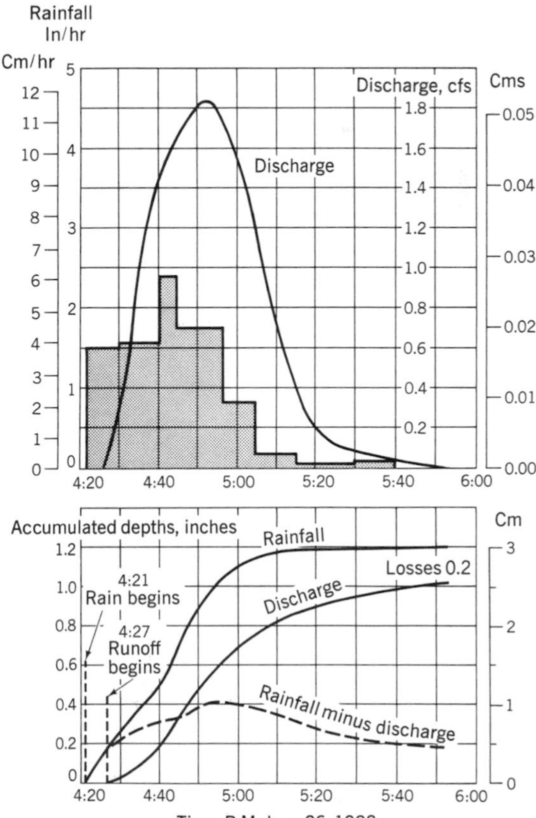

is measured with a rain gauge (Chapter 18) at intervals of 5 or 10 minutes. This information is plotted as a step graph in the upper part of Figure 34.20. The rain began at 4:21 P.M. and continued at an intense rate for 40 minutes, after which it quickly subsided and stopped completely by 5:40.

Discharge from the outlet of the drainage basin, shown by a smooth curve in Figure 34.20, began at 4:27, rose rapidly to a peak rate of over 1.8 cfs (0.05 cms), then fell rapidly and stopped completely at about 5:50. These graphs show us that there is a distinct *time lag* (in this case 6 minutes) between time of onset of rain and time of the first runoff at the basin exit. The lag is attributed to surface detention on the ground slopes and to absorption by the soil of the first rain because of a high initial infiltration capacity.

In the lower half of Figure 34.20 the same data are plotted in a somewhat different way, the rainfall and runoff being accumulated from beginning to end so that the total yield is shown for any given instant. Rainfall and discharge are both scaled in units of inches of depth[2] and can be compared directly. Rainfall exceeded discharge throughout the entire period. When both rainfall and runoff had ceased, the total rainfall was 0.2 in. (0.5 cm) greater than the runoff. What happened to this 0.2 in. of rainfall? It was lost or detained by a combination of evaporation and infiltration, and hence never reached the mouth of the basin.

Consider next a much larger drainage basin, that of Sugar Creek, Ohio, with 310 sq mi (805 sq km) of watershed area. The outline of the basin is shown by a dashed line in Figure 34.21, which is a map of the Muskingum River watershed with isohyets drawn for a rainstorm of August 6 and 7, 1935. Rainfall on the Sugar Creek watershed ranged from 5 to 9 in. (13 to 23 km), but the average accumulated depth for the watershed was 6.3 in. (16 cm). In Figure 34.22 is a hydrograph based on the records of a stream gauge at Strasburg, Ohio. Here discharge is plotted in depth equivalent in inches per hour, the same units used for rainfall, so that the rainfall and runoff can be compared directly. Notice that Sugar Creek was carrying a

[2] Discharge, $Q$, in cfs, is divided by the basin area, in square feet, to give feet of depth per second. This figure is converted to inches and totalled for any desired interval of time.

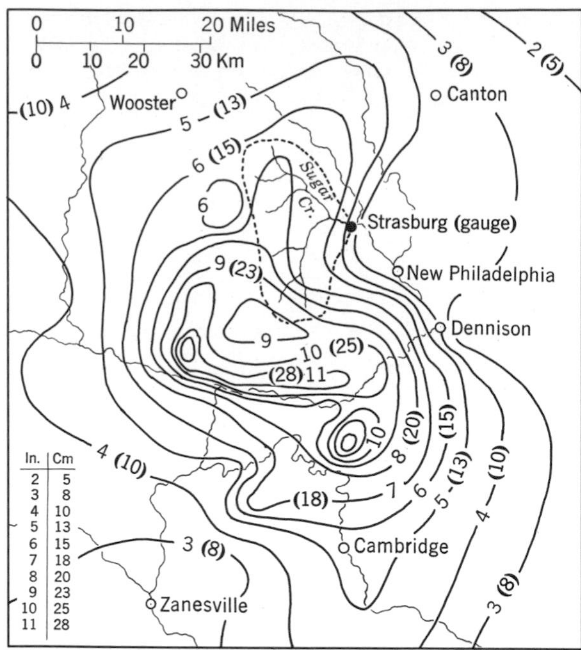


**FIGURE 34.21.** Isohyets in inches of a one-day summer rainstorm in northern Ohio, August 6–7, 1935. Centimeters in parentheses. [© 1965, John Wiley & Sons, New York. Based on a map by W. G. Hoyt and W. R. Langbein (1955), *Floods,* Princeton, N.J., Princeton Univ. Press, p. 44, Figure 12.]

small discharge before the rainstorm. That flow may be attributed to the seepage of ground water into the channel, providing *base flow.* Runoff at the gauge did not begin to increase sharply until the rain was almost over, a lag of many hours. The peak discharge was reached about 18 hours after the rain began, then decreased gradually. Lag in this case is due in part to the initial infiltration rate, but more particularly to *channel storage,* which is the ability of many branching stream channels to hold water in the manner of a temporary reservoir and hence to store water as runoff increases.

**FIGURE 34.22.** Hydrograph of the Sugar Creek watershed, showing the relation of flood crest to period of rainfall. [© 1965, John Wiley & Sons, New York. Data from W. G. Hoyt and W. R. Langbein (1955).]

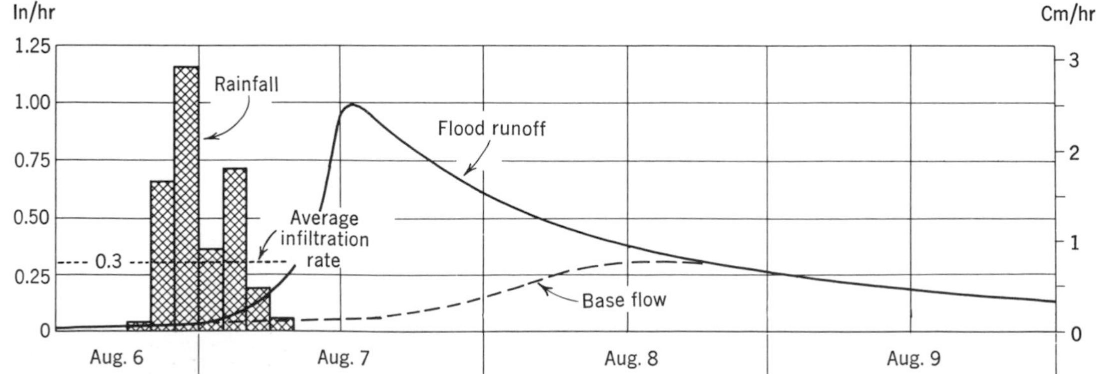

During the prolonged rainstorm over the Sugar Creek watershed, water infiltrating the ground percolated down to the water table, recharging the ground water body and causing an increase in the contribution to streams by base flow. The dashed line in Figure 34.22 shows the slow rise of base flow during August 7 and 8, with the cessation of surface runoff, until it provided almost the entire flow of the stream.

A computation of the total storm runoff showed that only about 3 in. (8 cm) of water was discharged by the stream through the Strasburg gauge, whereas an average of 6.3 in. (16 cm) had fallen. The missing 3.3 in. (8 cm) was lost by evaporation or infiltrated the surface to be held as moisture in the soil-water and intermediate belts, or was added to the ground water.

In summary, the larger the watershed, the longer the lag between rainfall period and peak discharge, and the slower the rate of decline of discharge after the peak has passed. In other words, with increasing basin size the discharge is both delayed in time of peak and drawn out in duration.

## Base flow and surface water flow

In regions where the water table is normally high and is intersected by the channels of larger streams—that is, in those climates having an excess of precipitation over evapotranspiration—hydrographs plotted over a period of many months show water contributions from both base flow and surface-water flow (overland flow). An illustration is provided by the Chattahoochee River, a stream of considerable magnitude, draining an area of 3350 sq mi (8700 sq km) in the southern Appalachian Mountains (Figure 34.23).

During October, 1931, when the summer moisture deficit prevailed, discharge was small—about 1000 cfs (30 cms)—and was due entirely to base flow. But a succession of winter rainstorms caused sharp discharge peaks of 15,000–20,000 cfs (400–600 cms), between which peaks the flow subsided to a moderate level. As the enlarged hydrographs of January 1932 show, each discharge peak was produced by direct surface flow accompanying the storm runoff. The discharge did not quite subside to equal the base flow of 4000 cfs (110 cms) before the next storm came along and raised the discharge. The winter season of moisture surplus thus shows its effects strongly in a seasonal rise of base flow.

To point up some of the effects of climate and geology on stream discharge, three hydrographs are shown in Figure 34.24 for a one-year period. All three streams have small watersheds, 150 sq mi (390 sq km) or less. Ecofina Creek, gauged at Bennett, Florida, is remarkable in having a relatively high and constant value of base flow with only small peaks. This results from the presence of a cavernous limestone underlying the watershed. Rainfall infiltrates readily, with very little surface runoff, and moves readily through solution passages to emerge as springs and thus to provide base flow for the stream. The second example, Potato Creek at Thomaston, Georgia, shows a low base flow combined with sharp peaks produced by rainstorms in winter, but also with rainstorm peaks in the summer months. This hydrograph is typical of small mountainous watersheds in a humid subtropical climate. The hydrograph of Antelope Creek at Red Bluff, California, seems to resemble that of Potato Creek, but there is a distinct difference in that the months of July through October have only base flow, reflecting the long and severe summer drought of the Mediterranean-type climate.

Study of the hydrograph of a large stream, the Missouri River gauged at Omaha, Nebraska, shows still other climatic influences (Figure 34.25). The Missouri, a major tributary of the Mississippi, drains some 323,000 sq mi (840,000 sq km), including a large semiarid plains region and headwaters in the Rocky Mountains. Judging from the records of two years, 1941 and 1942, we see that the flood peaks occur in the months of March through June and are derived from snowmelt, beginning on the High Plains in early spring and continuing into the higher mountain watersheds in early summer. The relatively low flow of the winter months can be explained by the frozen condition of soil moisture gen-

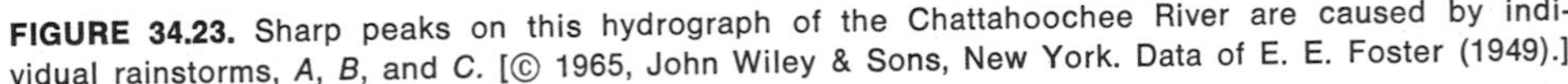

**FIGURE 34.23.** Sharp peaks on this hydrograph of the Chattahoochee River are caused by individual rainstorms, *A*, *B*, and *C*. [© 1965, John Wiley & Sons, New York. Data of E. E. Foster (1949).]

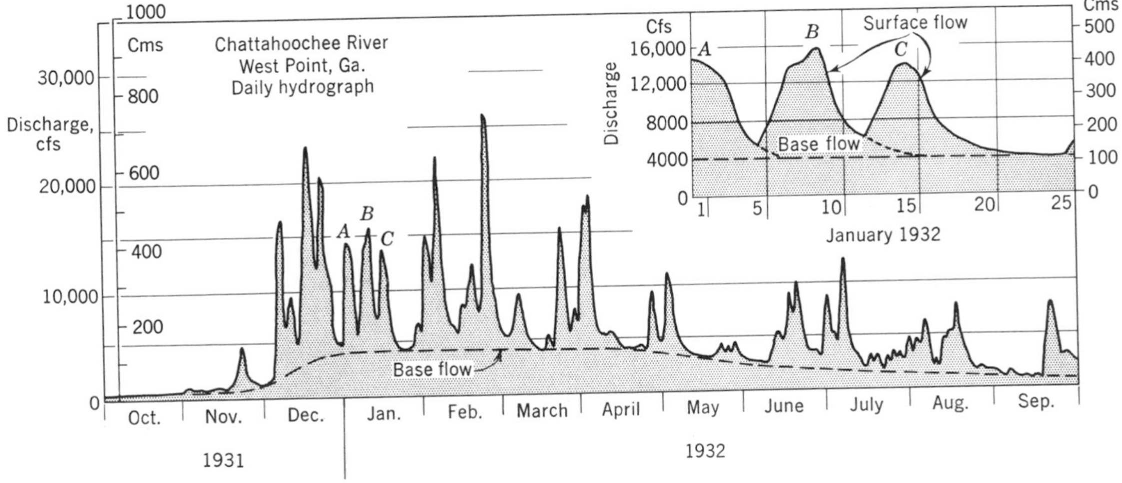

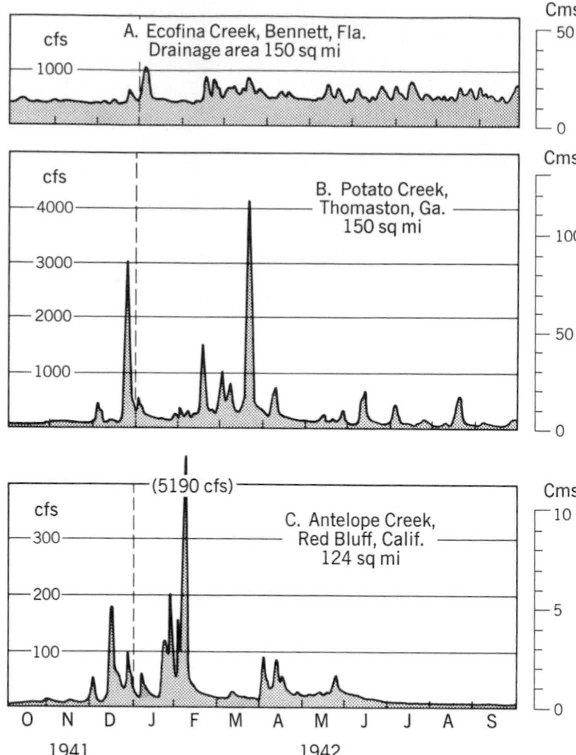


**FIGURE 34.24.** Differences in climate, relief, and rock type of their watersheds cause basic differences in these three hydrographs. [© 1965, John Wiley & Sons, New York. After E. E. Foster (1949).]

erally and the relatively small precipitation during those months. Base flow, which is down to a low value of about 10,000 cfs (280 cms) in winter, rises to more than 20,000 cfs (560 cms) in summer, when groundwater recharge has occurred.

## Floods

Despite the fact that everyone is familiar with river floods through photographs seen in newspapers and on television, it is not easy to give a simple and widely acceptable definition of what constitutes a flood. Most streams have a rather clearly defined channel whose walls are scoured sufficiently by high discharges that little or no vegetation can flourish there, whereas the adjoining ground normally supports a vegetative cover of forest, grasses, or crops. A stream whose discharge just fills the clearly defined channel is said to be in the *bankfull stage.* Closely coinciding with the bankfull stage is a stream height designated by hydrologists of the U.S. Weather Bureau as *flood stage,* the critical upper limit above which overbank flooding sets in, inundating the adjoining flat ground, known as the *floodplain,* and thereby constituting a *flood.* A floodplain may be present on one or both sides of the channel and is inundated by flood water about once per year, on the average, in those climates where a season of water surplus is characteristic (Figure 34.26). Where a river occupies a narrow rock gorge, there may be no convenient reference level, such as a floodplain, by which to judge the occurrence of a flood.

At long intervals—such as every 20, 50, or 100 years, on the average—there occur discharges of far greater magnitude than those expected annually. Such rare floods inundate ground surfaces lying well above the floodplain and may cover broad, flat, step-like expanses of ground known as *terraces* (Chapter 35).

**The flood wave** The rise and fall of stream stage during passage of a flood is termed the *flood wave.* The highest point, or *crest,* travels downstream to reach progressively lower elevations along the system. Principles governing the form and height of the flood wave are the same as those governing the lesser peak discharges already discussed. An example is taken from the Savannah River and its tributaries in South Carolina and Georgia (Figure 34.27). Near Clayton, Georgia, the Chattooga River, draining only 203 sq mi (526 sq km), experienced its peak discharge of about 7000 cfs (200 cms) only about one day after the occurrence of the storm, then quickly subsided.

The flood wave continued downstream for 65 mi (105 km) to Calhoun Falls, South Carolina, where the flood crested late on the second day with a peak discharge of 46,000 cfs (1400 cms) derived from a watershed of almost 2900 sq mi (7500 sq km). At Clyo, Georgia, 95 mi (153 km) farther downstream, where the watershed area is almost 10,000 sq mi (26,000 sq km), the flood crest of 64,000 cfs (2000 cms) arrived on the fifth day. As plotted on the upper hydrograph of Figure 34.27, it is clear that the lag in arrival of flood crest increased downstream and that peak discharge also increased. The duration of the flood also increased downstream.

To compare the characteristics of the three gauging stations independent of the magnitude of the flood, the lower part of Figure 34.27 shows the discharge per square mile of watershed plotted against time in days. The area under each line on the graph is the same,

**FIGURE 34.25.** Discharge of the Missouri River at Omaha, Nebraska, shows a strong seasonal cycle. [© 1965, John Wiley & Sons, New York. After E. E. Foster (1949).]

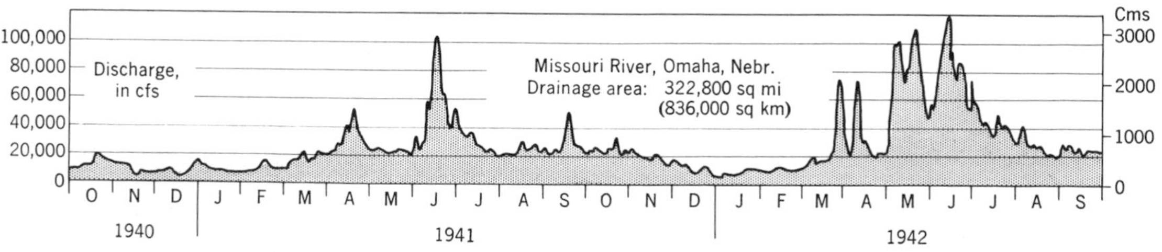

**FIGURE 34.26.** The floodplain of the Washita River, near Davis, Oklahoma, was almost completely inundated in this flood of 1950. A meander bend of the river channel is marked by a double line of trees. The channel carries most of the discharge because of its much greater water depth and velocity of flow, whereas water spread over the floodplain is moving very slowly. (Photograph by Soil Conservation Service, U.S. Department of Agriculture.)

only the curve form differs. Here we see clearly the sharp peaking and rapid dropoff of discharge in the small watershed, contrasting to the broadly attenuated flood wave farther downstream.

**Prediction of floods** At strategic points along major river systems of the United States are located 85 offices of ESSA-U.S. Weather Bureau from which the River and Flood Forecasting Service operates. River-stage and flood forecasts are issued by each office to the communities of the associated district. Flood warnings are widely publicized and close cooperation is maintained with the municipal authorities, the American Red Cross, the U.S. Army Corps of Engineers, and the U.S. Coast Guard. Thus evacuation of persons from threatened areas and the protection of property can be handled with maximum efficiency.

The study of long periods of record of river stages enables the U.S. Weather Bureau to estimate the probability of a given stage being reached in any month of the year. Four examples of expectancy graphs have been selected for illustration (Figure 34.28). The Mississippi River at Vicksburg, Mississippi, illustrates the greatest of North American rivers in a characteristic annual cycle of flood stages occurring in late winter and spring and of relatively small maximum stages in late summer and fall.

The Colorado River at Austin, Texas, illustrates a river situated in a semi-arid plains region. Floods in the summer months result from torrential rains derived from moist tropical air masses invading from the Gulf of Mexico. Some of this rainfall is from tropical storms (hurricanes) which occur in late summer and early fall. Note that the lowest observed maximum discharges are about the same for each month, for at such levels of discharge the river comes close to running dry.

The third illustration, that of the Sacramento River at Red Bluff, California, shows a strong annual cycle, with winter floods and only very low maximum discharges in the dry summer. Compare this graph with Figure 33.10, and note how closely the precipitation graph of the Mediterranean climate of Berkeley, California, coincides with the cycle of maximum flows of record.

Finally, the Connecticut River at Hartford, Connecti-

**FIGURE 34.27.** A flood wave traveling downstream is shown in these hydrographs of the Savannah River system in South Carolina and Georgia. [© 1965, John Wiley & Sons, New York. After W. G. Hoyt and W. B. Langbein (1955), *Floods,* Princeton, N.J., Princeton Univ. Press, p. 39, Figure 8.]

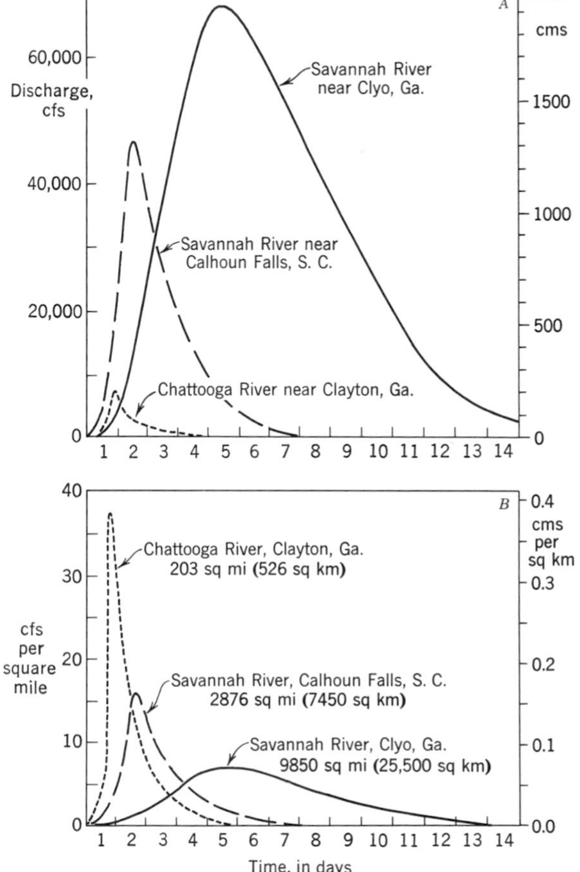

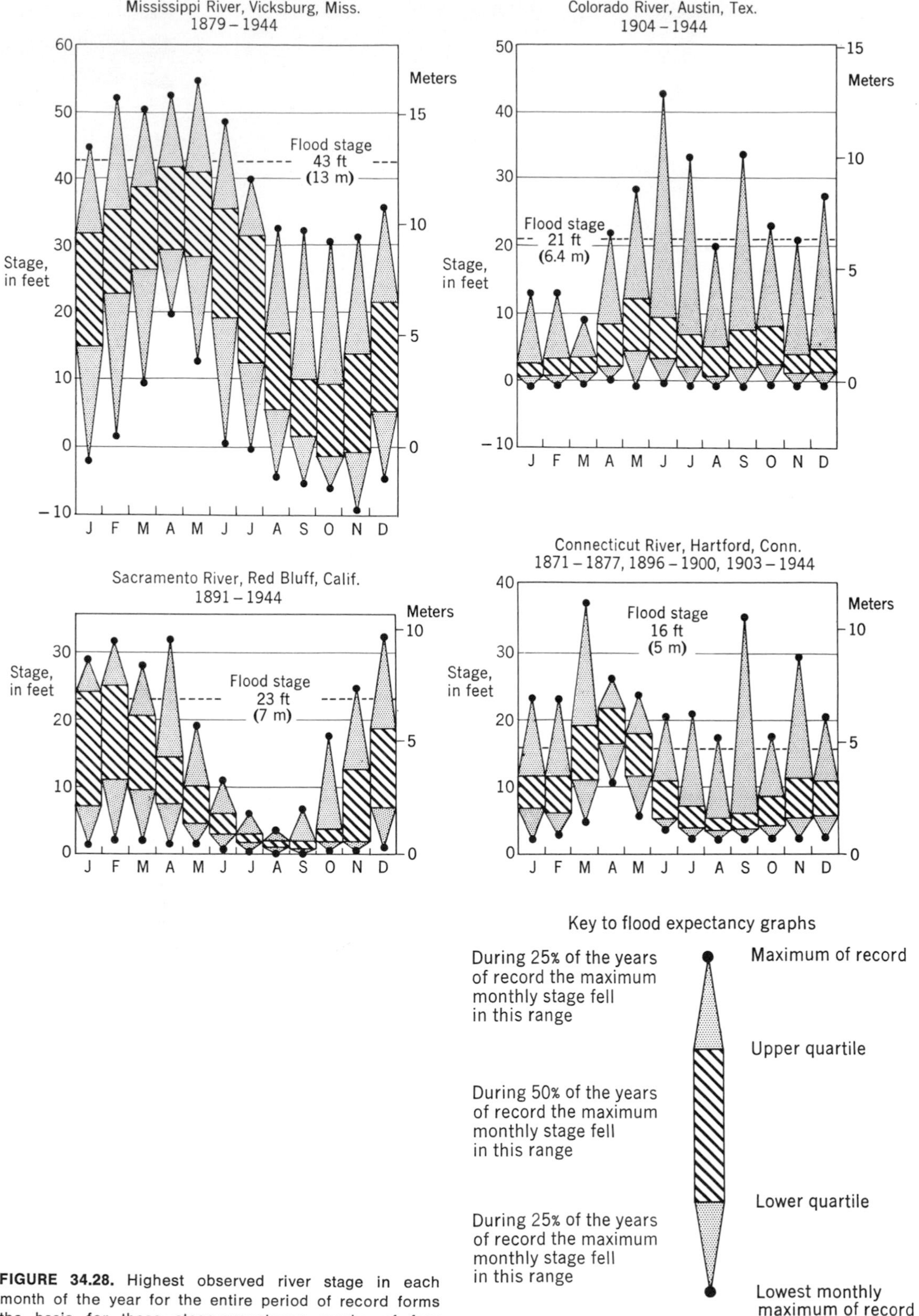


**FIGURE 34.28.** Highest observed river stage in each month of the year for the entire period of record forms the basis for these stage-expectancy graphs of four representative American rivers. [© 1965, John Wiley & Sons, New York. Data of ESSA Weather Bureau.]

**FIGURE 34.29.** During the flood of March, 1903, this artificial levee along the Mississippi River at Greenville, Mississippi, proved barely high enough to contain the river. A break in the levee (distant point, marked X) is permitting river water to pour out and spread over the floodplain at the left. (Photograph by Mississippi River Commission.)

cut, shows an annual cycle of maximum flows not unlike the Mississippi, but much more subdued in amplitude. Maximum stage is greatest in the spring, when the rapid melting of snow and thawing of soil water furnishes much runoff. There is a general decline in summer, but because of occasional hurricane rainfalls September and November have exceptionally high observed discharges. The maximum of record for September occurred in 1938, when a hurricane added torrential rains to a watershed already nearly saturated by heavy rains occurring a few days previously.

**Flood control** In general, reduction of flood-peak discharges can be brought about by two forms of control. First, storm runoff on slopes of the smaller tributary basins can be detained and delayed, thus passing the flow to downstream parts of the system more gradually. Second, the lower reaches of larger streams can be improved in efficiency or can be provided with protective structures to confine peak discharges to the natural channel.

Under the first program, watershed slopes can be treated by reforestation and by crop planting in contour belts and terraces so as to increase the infiltration capacity of the surface and thereby reduce the rate of runoff. To these measures may be added the construction of many small dams, usually of compacted earth, to store floodwaters temporarily and distribute the downstream discharge over a long period of time. Watershed treatment also has the beneficial effects of reducing soil erosion, hence of reducing the undesirable effects of sedimentation upon the stream channels and of increasing recharge to the ground-water zone.

Control of inundation on floodplains may be based on one of two principles. First, a system of *levees,* or *dikes,* can be built adjacent to the channel to contain overbank flow in stages at which the water would otherwise overspread the floodplain (Figure 34.29). Most levees are broad earth embankments, although flood walls of reinforced concrete can be used where a city lies close to the river channel. If overtopped by an unusual flood discharge, the levee may be broken at a low point to produce a great breach, known as a *crevasse,* through which the floodwater will quickly flow to inundate the floodplain (Figure 34.30).

The lower Mississippi River, under the supervision of the Mississippi River Commission from 1897 to 1934, was controlled by a vast levee system designed to protect the floodplain from inundation. The system has been continuously improved and now includes over 2500 mi (4000 km) of levees, in places up to 30 ft (10 m) high.

A second principle of river control is that of channel modifications designed to shorten the length of the stream and hence to steepen the gradient. The resulting increase in velocity of flow reduces the area of cross section, hence lowering the height of water at flood crest. Shortening is accomplished by the artificial cutoff of meander bends (Chapter 35).

## A gravity flow system in review

Runoff of water over the land surfaces and its streams constitutes a fairly simple gravity-flow system powered by solar energy. The water mass, arriving as precipitation, has the potential energy of its elevation above sea level. As this water flows to lower levels potential energy is transformed into kinetic energy, which in turn is dissipated through frictional resistance and escapes from the system, eventually to be lost by long-wave radiation to outer space. Runoff thus participates in both

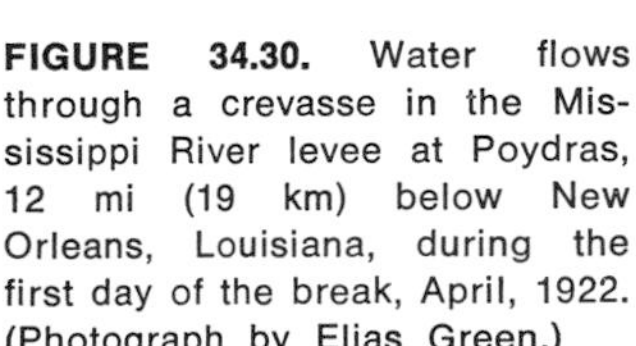

**FIGURE 34.30.** Water flows through a crevasse in the Mississippi River levee at Poydras, 12 mi (19 km) below New Orleans, Louisiana, during the first day of the break, April, 1922. (Photograph by Elias Green.)

the water balance and the radiation balance of planet Earth.

Ground-water flow represents a sluggish branch of the gravity flow system, but is important in sustaining stream flow over long periods when overland flow is not occurring.

We have seen that the gravity flow of water organizes itself into channel networks together with contributing areas of runoff, all adjusted to the optimum balance between the need to possess contributing surfaces, yet at the same time to move the water out of the region as efficiently as possible. But streams also must entrain and transport detrital mineral matter, thus the forms of stream channels and drainage basins must also be shaped to serve a geological function. In the next chapter we shall look into the geological work of overland flow and streams as exogenetic processes whereby the landscape is carved and the denudation of continents is carried out.

## References for further study

Foster, E. E. (1948), *Rainfall and Runoff,* New York, Macmillan, 487 pp.

Linsley, R. K., M. A. Kohler, and J. L. H. Paulhus (1949), *Applied Hydrology,* New York, McGraw-Hill, 698 pp.

Colman, E. A. (1953), *Vegetation and Watershed Management,* New York, Ronald Press, 412 pp.

Hoyt, W. G., and W. B. Langbein (1955), *Floods,* Princeton, N. J., Princeton Univ. Press, 469 pp.

U.S. Dept. of Agriculture (1955), *Water, Yearbook of Agriculture, 1955,* Washington, D.C., U.S. Govt. Printing Office, 751 pp.

Wisler, C. O., and E. F. Brater (1959), *Hydrology,* 2nd ed., New York, Wiley, 408 pp.

Strahler, A. N. (1969), *Physical Geography,* 3rd ed., New York, Wiley, 732 pp., chap. 28, appendix IV.

# 35

# Geologic work of running water

TO THE GEOLOGIST streams are much more than simply mechanisms for the discharge of runoff from the lands; they are major agents of land sculpture, creating a vast array of erosional and depositional landforms, besides transporting sediment and depositing it in basins and shallow seas where it will be transformed into sedimentary rock. In combination with weathering, mass wasting, and overland flow—a total process we may call *fluvial denudation*—streams are responsible for creating most of the landscapes seen on the surfaces of the continents. True, glacial ice is a dominant agent in high mountains, wind creates conspicuous forms in a few desert and coastal localities, and wave action shapes the shorelines. But from the standpoint of total surface area affected, fluvial denudation is the predominant agent of landscape evolution.

## Erosion by overland flow

The flow of a sheet or film of water over the soil surface exerts a *shearing stress,* or *drag,* upon the mineral grains. If this stress is sufficient to overcome the cohesive forces binding a grain to the parent mass, the grain is *entrained* into the flowing layer and is rolled, dragged, or carried downslope. The progressive removal of grains in this manner is described as *soil erosion.*

Greatly aiding the process of erosion on barren soil surfaces is *splash erosion,* the dislodgment and movement of soil particles under the impact of falling raindrops (Figure 35.1). Contained in the geyser-like spray of droplets are particles of clay and silt, which may be lifted to heights of 2 ft (0.6 m). Within a single violent rainstorm drop impacts can

**FIGURE 35.1.** The fall of a large raindrop upon a wet soil surface produces a miniature crater and throws grains of silt and clay high into the air. (Official U.S. Navy photograph.)

cause the disturbance of as much as 100 tons of soil per acre (225 metric tons per hectare). On a sloping surface particles thus agitated creep gradually downhill. Splash erosion is an important process on rounded divides and hill summits where overland flow is not normally effective. Moreover, openings of the soil surface tend to become clogged by splash action, causing a reduction of infiltration capacity and a consequent increase in rate of runoff.

Of considerable interest to geologists and soil scientists are the factors that govern the intensity of soil erosion by overland flow. We have already seen that the smaller the infiltration capacity of the soil and the longer the ground slope, the greater the flow over a given patch of ground, hence the more rapid the soil erosion. Another factor is the resistance of the surface to the entrainment of particles. A good vegetative cover, particularly a grass sod, breaks the force of falling raindrops and absorbs the energy of the overland flow, thus tending to reduce the rate of soil erosion. Hence even under heavy and prolonged rains a thickly vegetated slope may yield very small quantities of mineral solids, whereas the barren slopes of a desert landscape or the unprotected surface of a cultivated field will produce large quantities of sediment with each rainstorm.

Finally, the factor of *slope,* or inclination of the ground surface from the horizontal, is important in soil erosion. It is easy to see that as the ground slope steepens, the force of gravity acting parallel with the surface in increased, and that hence the velocity of the flow is increased and the eroding stress becomes greater. In general, then, the rate of erosion increases with the steepness of the slope. On the other hand, the steeper the slope, the less rainfall intercepted by

**FIGURE 35.2.** Shoestring rills on a barren 55% slope, Ventura County, California. At the left, weeds are taking hold to form a protective cover. (Photograph by Soil Conservation Service, U.S. Department of Agriculture.)

**FIGURE 35.3.** A great gully system in Stewart County, Georgia, in 1936. Such severe gullying has now been largely controlled. (Photograph by Soil Conservation Service, U.S. Department of Agriculture.)

**FIGURE 35.4.** Potholes carved in lava near Crater Lake, Oregon. (Photograph by A. K. Lobeck.)

a unit of ground surface, until on a vertical surface no vertically falling rain can be caught at all. Combining the two effects, we find that the most intense soil erosion may be expected on slopes having an inclination of about 40° from the horizontal. Rate of erosion increases most rapidly in the range from horizontal up to 30° or so.

## Normal and accelerated erosion

To the geologist, whose viewpoint spans vast periods of time and whose interest is in processes acting on a continental scale, erosion of the soil is a process of nature whereby the many landscape features of the earth's surface are slowly carved. Soil erosion is, to him, a normal geologic process associated with the hydrologic cycle. In humid climates, where vegetation is dense, soil erosion is normally very slow, and the characteristic soil profiles are maintained as erosion proceeds. In arid climates, especially where rock is of a weak and highly impermeable nature (as in the Badlands of South Dakota), normal erosion is rapid and furnishes vast quantities of sediment to streams. We conclude, therefore, that there is a *geologic norm* of soil erosion appropriate to the particular conditions of climate and bedrock prevailing in an area.

Where man has cut the forests and converted the land to agricultural uses, or where a forest or prairie fire has destroyed the vegetation, there may be a sudden large increase in the erosion rate, producing a state known as *accelerated erosion.* Soil horizons are removed at a much faster rate than they can be formed, resulting in a rapid decline in fertility of the soil. Streams become burdened with quantities of sediment far in excess of the normal amounts to which their courses have been adjusted.

Applying our knowledge of the factors affecting the rate of soil erosion, we see that accelerated erosion comes about because the resistance of the surface and the rate of infiltration have been sharply reduced by destruction of the vegetative cover. Not only is a greater proportion of overland flow then produced from a given rain, but also the ease with which the mineral grains are entrained is also increased.

## Forms of accelerated erosion

Clearing of forest and cultivation of the ground create the opportunity for splash erosion to seal the soil openings and hasten sheet flow. Soil is removed by sheet flow in relatively thin uniform layers by a process termed *sheet erosion,* which may escape notice. Gradually, however, the fertile upper horizons of the soil are lost, and eventually only the infertile subsoil or bedrock remains.

Soil removed in sheet erosion is carried to the base of the slope. Here it may accumulate in thin layers to form a deposit known as *colluvium,* or *slope wash.* Some particles will, of course, be carried into stream channels, to be deposited as *alluvium* on the valley floor. The term *sedimentation,* which in general geo-

**FIGURE 35.5.** Hydraulic action by a stream in flood removed glacial sands and gravels from an area 1 mi (1.6 km) wide and 3 mi (5 km) long, destroying eight large farms and leaving the trench shown here. Cavendish, Vermont, November, 1927. (Wide World Photos.)

logic usage simply means the accumulation of any sediment, is applied in agricultural engineering studies to the accumulation of both colluvial and alluvial deposits derived from accelerated soil erosion. Sedimentation can bury fertile agricultural land under a coarse permeable layer unfit for cultivation.

On steep slopes laid bare of vegetation, intense runoff forms long narrow channels termed *shoestring rills* (Figure 35.2). Although resembling stream channels, such rills merely score the surface and do not have adjoining ground surfaces sloping toward them. Moreover shoestring rills are often seasonal features, obliterated by freeze and thaw in winter or by plowing of the land.

Shoestring rills can coalesce and deepen to form *gullies* of awesome proportions (Figure 35.3). Gully development is particularly striking in regions underlaid by a thick layer of weathered overburden (saprolite), in regions with a weak wind-transported silt (loess), or in regions with a soft shale bedrock.

Allowed to continue unchecked, severe gullying will produce a landscape resembling the badlands (Figure 34.19). Applying the basic principles of slope erosion already referred to, engineers of the Soil Conservation Service have effectively halted accelerated soil erosion by construction of terraces (to reduce slope steepness and length), by cultivation in contour belts (to reduce length of slope exposed by tillage), by planting trees and vines (to reduce surface erodibility and increase infiltration), and by building check dams in gully floors (to induce gully sedimentation and filling). Much badly abused land has been removed permanently from cultivation and restored to forest cover. Since major soil-conservation efforts began in the 1930s vast strides have been made in soil-erosion and sediment control throughout the United States, but much remains to be done to reduce undesirable effects to the practical minimum.

## Work of streams

Streams perform three closely interrelated forms of geologic work: erosion, transportation, and deposition.

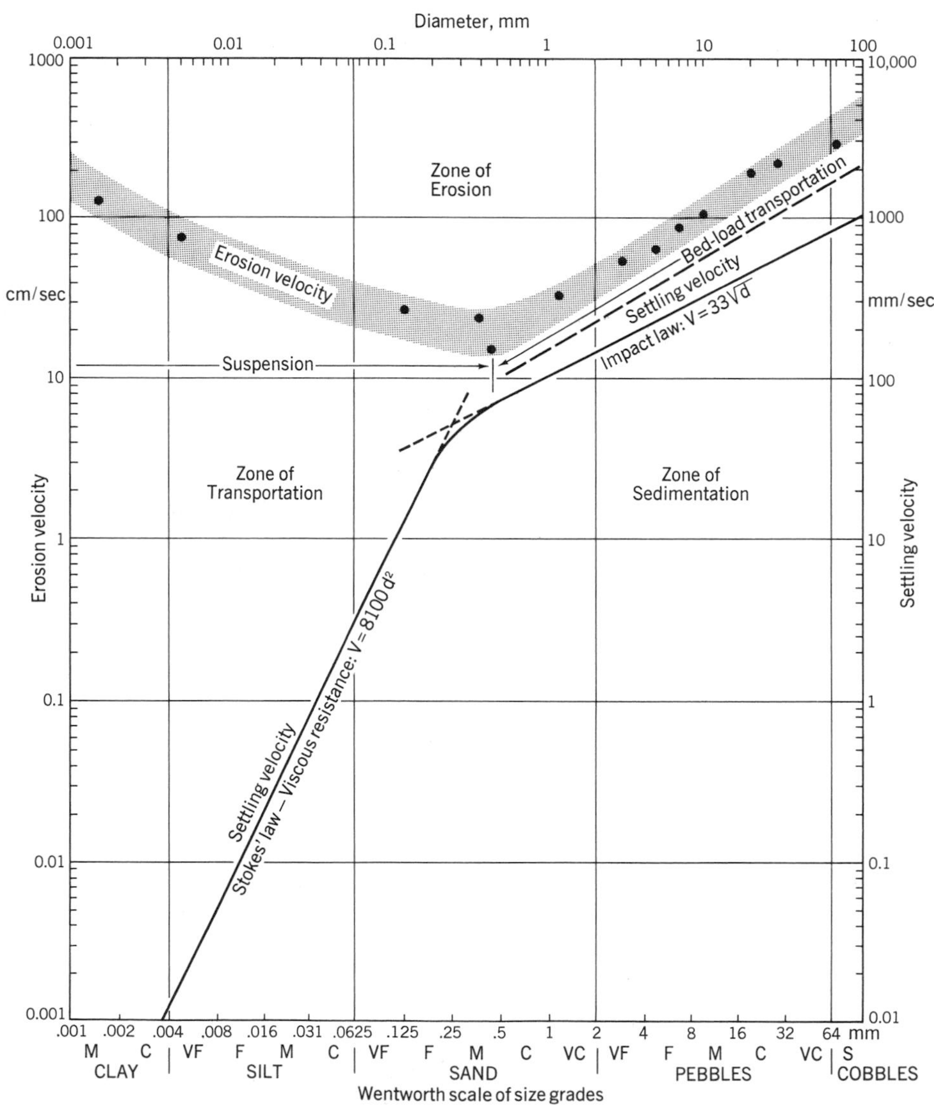


**FIGURE 35.6.** Logarithmic graph of the relations among erosion velocity, settling velocity, and grain diameter, defining zones of erosion, transportation, and sedimentation. [Based on data of F. Hjulström (1935), *Bull. Geol. Instit. of Upsala,* vol. 25, p. 295, Table 7, and p. 298, Figure 18; and W. W. Rubey (1933), *Amer. Jour. Sci.,* vol. 24, p. 334, Figure 1.]

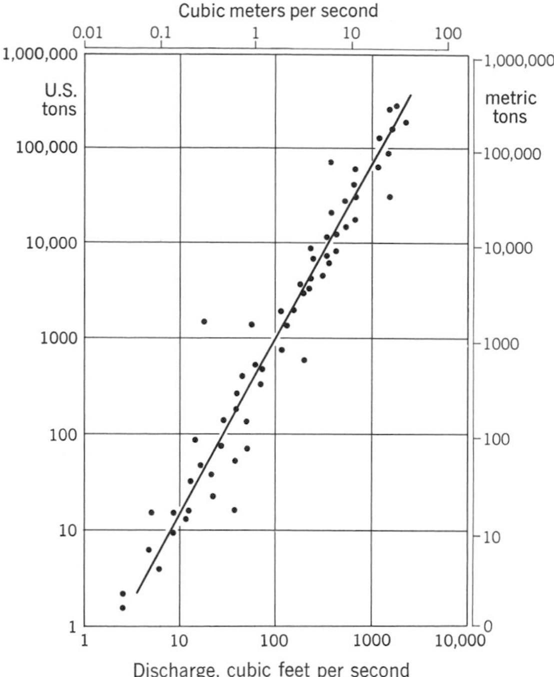


**FIGURE 35.7.** Graph of the relation of suspended load to discharge for the Powder River at Arvada, Wyoming. The dots suggest individual observations. The sloping line shows the average trend of all observations. [Modified from L. B. Leopold and T. Maddock (1953), *U.S. Geol. Surv. Professional Paper 252,* p. 20, Figure 13.]

*Stream erosion* is defined as the progressive removal of mineral matter from the surfaces of a stream channel, whether the exposed material consists of bedrock, residual or transported overburden, or soil. *Stream transportation* is the movement of eroded particles in chemical solution, in turbulent suspension, or by rolling and dragging along the bed. *Stream deposition* consists of the accumulation of any transported particles on the stream bed, on the adjoining floodplain, or on the floor of a body of standing water into which the stream empties. These phases of geologic work cannot be separated one from the other, because where erosion occurs there must be at least some transportation, and eventually the transported particles must come to rest.

The nature of stream erosion depends upon the materials of which the channel is composed and the means of erosion available to the stream. One simple form of erosion is by *hydraulic action,* the effect of pressure and shearing force of flowing water exerted upon grains projecting from the bed and banks. Weakly consolidated bedrock and various forms of uncemented transported and residual overburden are readily worn away by hydraulic action alone, but the process has little effect on strongly bonded bedrock.

Mechanical wear, termed *abrasion* (or *corrasion*), occurs through the impact of rock particles carried in the current striking against the exposed bedrock of the channel surfaces. Small particles are further reduced by crushing and grinding when caught between larger cobbles and boulders. Chemical reactions between ions, carried in solution in stream water, and the exposed mineral surfaces result in a form of erosion designated *corrosion,* which is essentially the same as chemical rock weathering described in Chapter 32.

Abrasion of hard-rock channels yields a variety of minor erosional forms such as chutes, plunge pools, and a type of cylindrical pit known as a *pothole* (Figure 35.4). The pothole is deepened by a spherical or discus-shaped stone, the *grinder,* rotated by the force of helical water currents in the cylinder.

Hydraulic action is the dominant process of stream erosion in weak alluvial deposits of floodplains. In flood stage the swift highly turbulent flow on the outside of stream bends undermines the channel wall, causing masses of sand, gravel, silt, or clay to slump and slide into the channel, an activity described as *bank caving.* Huge volumes of sediment are thus incorporated into the stream flow in times of high stage, and the channel may shift laterally by many yards in a single flood (Figure 35.5).

Three forms of stream transportation of mineral mat-

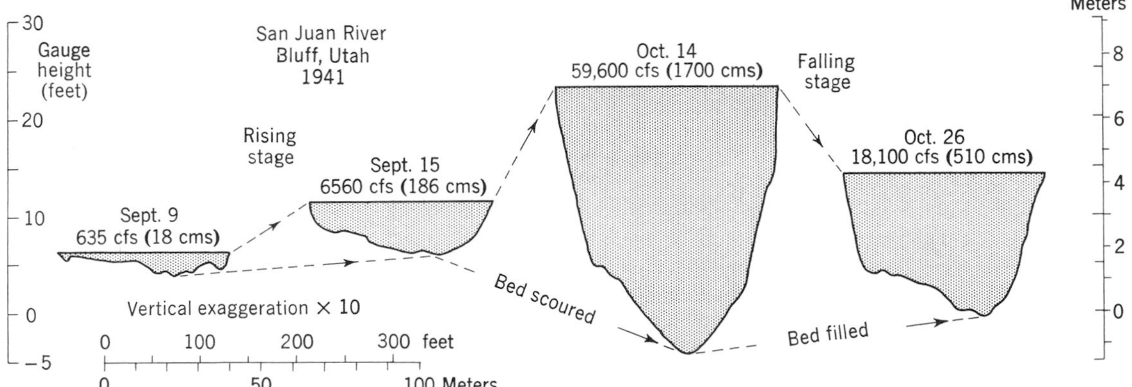


**FIGURE 35.8.** These cross sections of the San Juan River show great changes as the river first rises in flood stage, then falls. [© 1960, John Wiley & Sons, New York. Based on data of L. B. Leopold and T. Maddock (1953), *U.S. Geol. Surv. Professional Paper 252,* p. 32, Figure 22.]

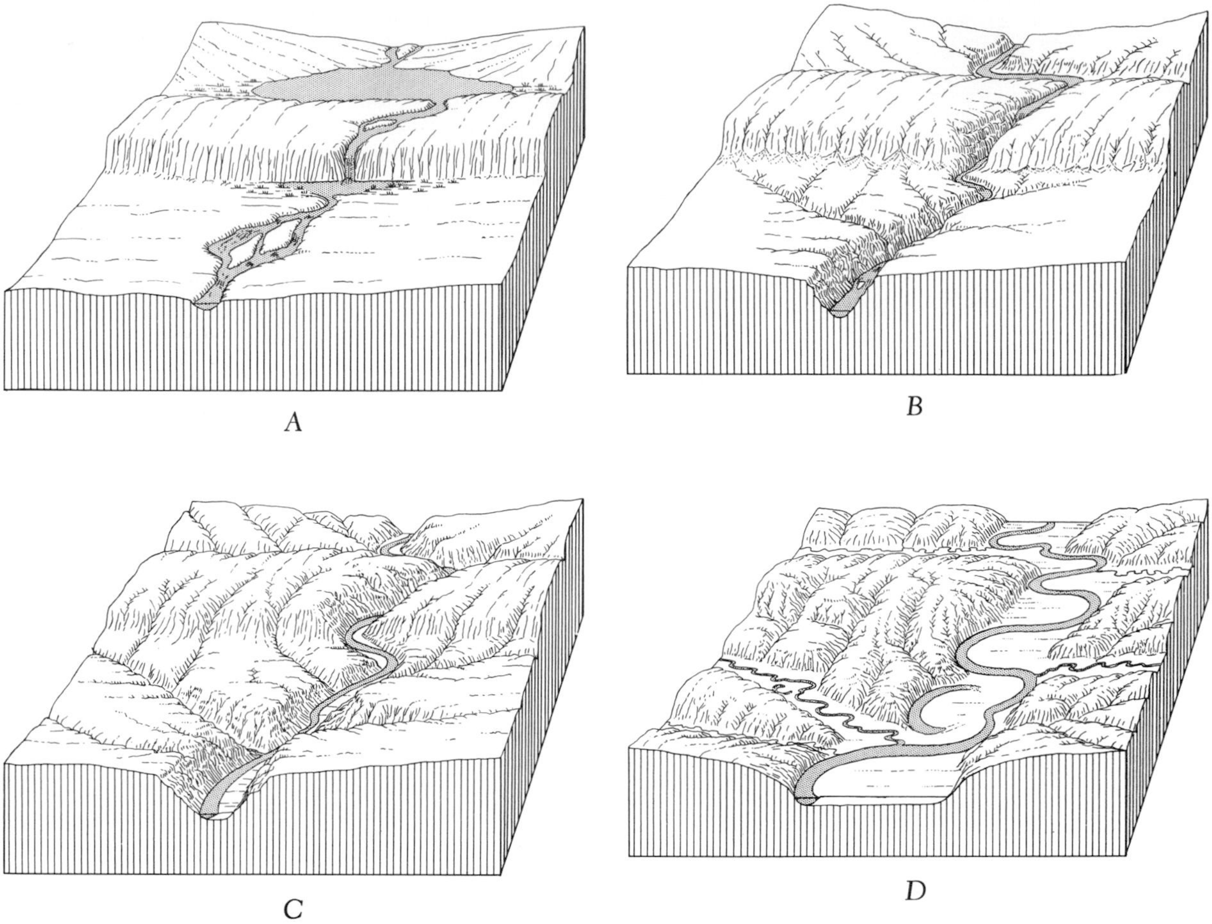

A

B

C

D

**FIGURE 35.9.** Evolution of a stream and its valley. (*A*) Initially the stream has lakes, falls, and rapids. (*B*) Erosion of a rock gorge occurs rapidly, draining the lakes and reducing the falls. (*C*) The stream becomes fully graded, permitting a narrow floodplain to be formed. (*D*) Enlargement of the floodplain allows meanders to shift more freely between valley walls. (© 1960, John Wiley & Sons, New York. Based on drawings by Erwin Raisz.)

ter can be distinguished. First, corrosion yields chemical ions that may travel downstream indefinitely. Such matter, referred to by hydraulic engineers as constituting the *dissolved solids,* does not appreciably affect the mechanical behavior of the stream.

Second, particles of clay, silt, and sometimes fine sand are carried in *suspension,* a form of transport in which the upward currents in eddies of turbulent flow are capable of holding the particles indefinitely in the body of the stream. Material carried in suspension is

**FIGURE 35.10.** The narrow winding rock gorge of the Little Colorado River in nothern Arizona. (Photograph by Barnum Brown, American Museum of Natural History.)

referred to as the *suspended load* and constitutes a large share of the total load of most streams. The more intense the turbulence of the stream, the greater the total quantity and the larger the particles that can be held in suspension. Clay particles, once lifted into suspension, are so readily carried that they travel long distances. Silts settle rapidly when turbulence subsides. Coarse sands are rarely transported in suspension except in the highly turbulent flow of floods. As a result, suspension provides a means of separating solid particles of various size grades and carrying each size fraction to a different location, a process known as *sorting.* (Other sorting mechanisms exist.)

Third of the modes of transportation is that of rolling or sliding of grains along the stream bed, a motion that can be conveniently included in the term *traction.* Particles thus in motion are referred to collectively as the *bed load* of the stream. Traction results both from the direct pressure of the water flow against the upstream face of a grain and from the dragging action of the water as it flows over the grain surface. In bed-load movement, individual particles roll, slid, or take low leaps downstream, then come to rest among other grains. The shear of water close to the stream bed also subjects particles to a lifting force, not unlike that which gives an airfoil its lift. Small grains responding to the lifting force may be carried upward into the turbulent zone of the stream, where they are carried away in suspension.

**Erosion velocities and settling velocities** The key to understanding how sediments are sorted according to size grades during transport by water currents can be found by analyzing in quantitative terms the relative ease with which particles are set in motion as compared with the ease with which they are held in suspension. Consider, first, the requirements of current velocity for the entrainment of particles on the bed of a stream. Many observations have been made, both in natural streams and in laboratory flumes, of the minimum velocity required to set in motion particles of a given grade size. One of the pioneer investigators of this problem was G. K. Gilbert, who in the early 1900s experimented with traction of coarse detrital materials in flumes, seeking an answer to the problem of choking of stream beds with debris as a result of uncontrolled hydraulic mining of gold-bearing gravels in the Sierra Nevada of California.

When stream velocity steadily increases there comes a critical point, designated the *erosion velocity,* at which particles of a given size begin to roll or slide on the stream bed or are lifted up into suspension. You might think that erosion velocity must increase as the size of particles is increased, since the larger the grains, the greater the stress required to set them in motion. Examine the figures in Table 35.1. Contrary to what one might expect, the erosion velocity of colloidal clay is quite high—about the same as for coarse pebbles—while the lowest erosion velocity is for medium sand.

Evidently two factors control erosion velocity. (1) *Cohesion,* which is greatest in fine clays and diminishes to nothing in sand, tends to increase resistance to erosion. (2) *Particle size* directly affects erosion velocity beginning with sand grades. So we see that the most easily entrained bed material is sand, for it is unimpeded by cohesion and is least impeded by particle size resistance.

The data of Table 35.1 are plotted in Figure 35.6. A

**TABLE 35.1. EROSION VELOCITIES FOR VARIOUS SIZE GRADES***

| Wentworth Grade | Mean Diameter, mm | Mean Velocity, cm/sec |
|---|---|---|
| Fine clay (colloidal) | 0.0015 | 130 |
| Very fine silt (noncolloidal) | 0.005 | 76 |
| Fine sand | 0.13 | 27 |
| Medium sand | 0.38 | 24 |
| Medium sand | 0.45 | 15 |
| Very coarse sand | 1.2 | 34 |
| Very fine pebbles | 3 | 54 |
| Fine pebbles | 5 | 64 |
| Fine pebbles | 7 | 85 |
| Medium pebbles | 10 | 104 |
| Coarse pebbles | 20 | 190 |
| Coarse pebbles | 30 | 220 |
| Very coarse pebbles | 70 | 270 |

* Data from G. K. Gilbert and F. Hjulström.

FIGURE 35.11. The valley walls of a graded stream gradually recline in angle through action of weathering, mass wasting, and slope erosion by overland flow. (© 1960, John Wiley & Sons, New York. After a drawing by W. M. Davis.)

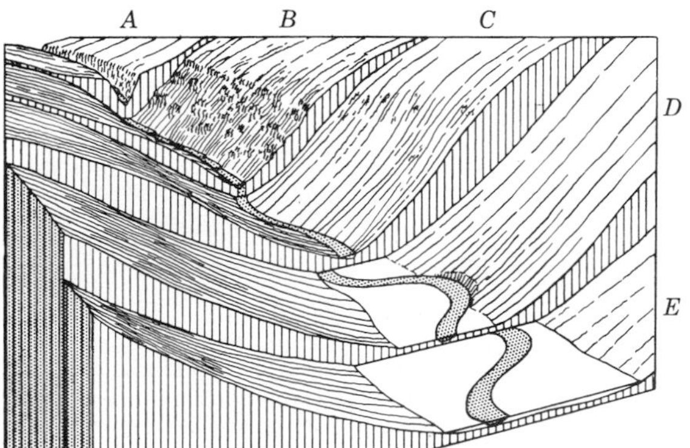


FIGURE 35.12. A graded stream, cutting laterally on the outside of a bend, produces a floodplain along the inside of the bend. (© 1960, John Wiley & Sons, New York.)

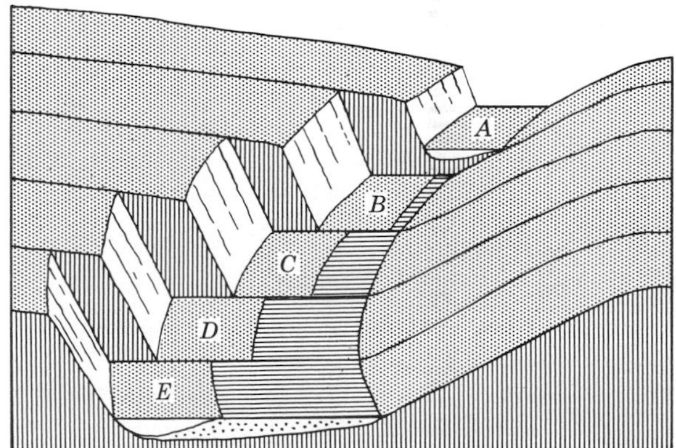

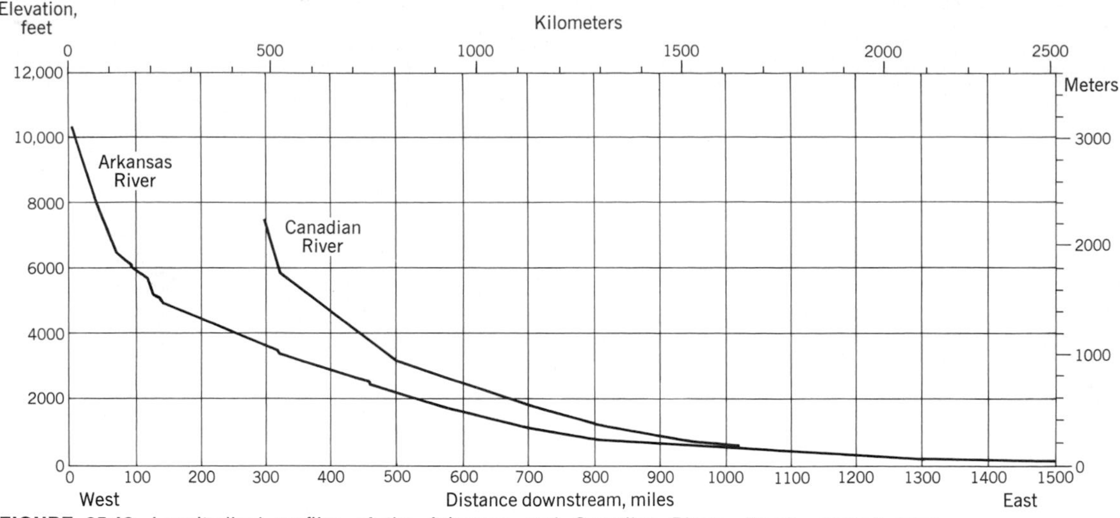


**FIGURE 35.13.** Longitudinal profiles of the Arkansas and Canadian Rivers. Poorly graded upper portions reflect effects of glaciation and rock inequalities. (© 1969, John Wiley & Sons, New York. Data of Gannett, U.S. Geological Survey.)

shaded band has been drawn to show approximately the way in which the curve runs. The area of the graph above the shaded band has been labeled "zone of erosion" and represents the velocities at which specific particle grades will be eroded from the stream bed. Below the shaded band is a zone on the graph labeled "zone of transportation." Here we encounter the principle that particles, once lifted into suspension or set to rolling on the stream bed, will continue in motion at lower velocities than were required to entrain them.

This principle requires some knowledge of *settling velocity,* which is the terminal velocity with which a particle falls through still water. Obviously, the smaller the particle, the slower will be its rate of settling. A line on the graph of Figure 35.6 shows how settling velocity is related to particle size.

For coarse grades (medium sand and larger) settling velocity varies as the square root of particle diameter. This relationship is known as the *impact law* and is represented by the following simplified equation:

$$V = 33\sqrt{d}$$

where V is settling velocity in cm per sec, and *d* is diameter in cm of a spherical grain of quartz. The numerical constant, 33, is approximately right for water at a temperature of about 16° C (61° F).

For particles smaller than fine sand, settling velocity is determined by viscous resistance of the fluid, to which *Stokes' law* applies. Simplified for spherical quartz grains at 16° C, this law is represented by the following equation, using units of centimeters and seconds:

$$V = 8100\, d^2$$

Both impact law and Stokes' law plot as straight lines on the logarithmic-scaled graph of Figure 35.6. They are connected by a curving line in the region where their effects overlap.

Particles of clay and silt, once entrained, rise quickly into the body of the stream and are carried in suspension. As Figure 35.6 shows, the settling velocities of the finest particles are extremely low and are easily exceeded by the upward components of motion in the turbulent eddies of the stream. Consequently the fine clays continue in transportation almost indefinitely, while the coarser silts settle out only when stream velocity has dropped to low values. In this way clay is carried to the sea, where it contacts salt water and undergoes clotting into larger particles, a process known as *flocculation.* Silts settle out in sluggish waters of inundated floodplains and over deltas in standing water.

Particles of medium to coarse sand and larger particles travel as bed load in a stream. These particles cease to move at velocities only slightly less than the erosion velocities required to entrain them. Conse-

**FIGURE 35.14.** Features of an alluvial river and its floodplain. *A*, alluvium; *B*, bluffs; *F*, floodplain; *L*, levee; *O*, oxbow lake; *Y*, yazoo stream. (© 1960, John Wiley & Sons, New York. Based on a drawing by Erwin Raisz.)

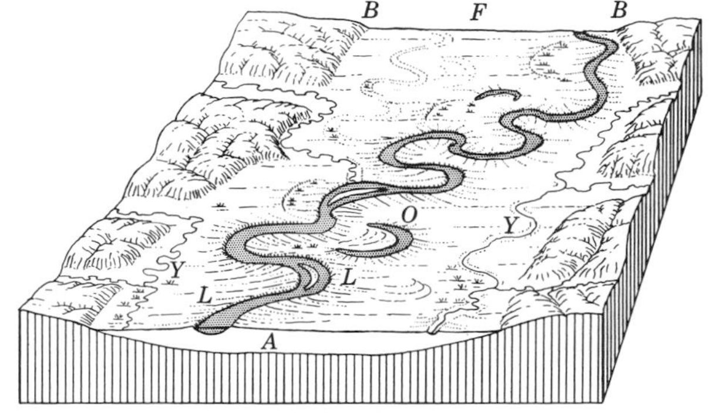

**FIGURE 35.15.** Air view of meanders, oxbow lakes and marshes, and bar-and-swale topography. Mudjalik River, northern Saskatchewan. (Royal Canadian Air Force official photograph, No. A1814-27.)

quently, as shown on the graph of Figure 35.6, the region of bed load transportation is a narrow zone. The principle that emerges is as follows: When a mixture of clay, silt, and coarse particles (sand grains and larger) has once been set in motion by increasing velocity of a stream, the reverse process of deposition during falling velocity quickly affects the coarse grades, which cease to move; the silts and clays, however, continue to be transported in suspension and do not settle out until velocity has dropped to comparatively low levels. Therein lies the answer to the sorting of sediment by streams.

**Load of streams** The solid load of a stream can be stated in units of weight of sediment moved past a fixed cross section in a unit of time, for example, *tons per day.* At certain of the stream-gauging stations operated by the U.S. Geological Survey measurements are regularly made of the quantities of load being moved in both suspension and traction. Measurement of the suspended load is the less difficult procedure of the two, and much is known about the characteristics of various rivers in regard to the changes of suspended load with discharge and the total load moved in suspension each year.

It is well-known that the suspended load increases very rapidly as the discharge increases. Figure 35.7 is a graph relating suspended load to discharge in the Powder River, Wyoming. Likewise, bed load increases greatly with increasing discharge. From Figure 35.7 it can be seen that a ten-fold increase in discharge brings about almost a 100-fold increase in suspended load. Obviously the great bulk of sediment is moved at relatively high stream stages, whereas relatively little is moved at low stages, when the water of the stream becomes quite clear.

Table 35.2 gives examples of the concentration of suspended sediment in four large rivers. Rivers differ greatly in their typical suspended loads, depending upon the environment of the watershed. The Missouri River, for example, derives much suspended load from badlands and other barren surfaces of the semi-arid Great Plains region, whereas the eastern tributaries to the Mississippi—such as the Ohio and Tennessee, with forested watersheds in a humid climate—contribute a much smaller proportion of suspended load. The Hwang Ho (Yellow River) of China drains an arid region of silts (loess) and can receive vast quantities of suspended matters to give an extraordinarily high concentration.

The ratio of suspended load to bed load in a stream will range from predominantly suspended load in streams of humid climates (the Mississippi carries about 90 percent of its total load in suspension) to perhaps

**FIGURE 35.16.** Development of simple alluvial meanders from an initially straight reach of a stream. [After G. H. Matthes (1941), *Transactions Amer. Geophys. Union,* vol. 22.]

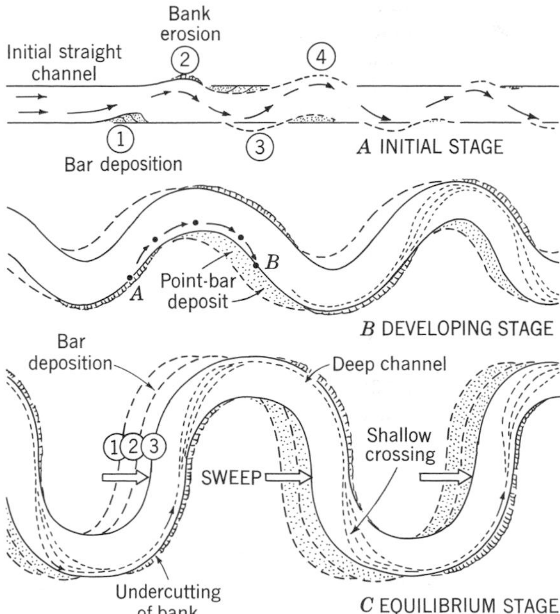

an equal amount of both forms of transport in streams of semi-arid and arid regions. The latter streams tend to have broad shallow channels of relatively steep gradients well adapted to moving coarse materials in traction, whereas the streams of humid climates tend to be relatively narrow and deep, with lesser gradients,

**TABLE 35.2. SUSPENDED SEDIMENT IN SOME LARGE RIVERS***

| | Suspended Sediment, parts per million | Fraction by Weight |
|---|---|---|
| Mississippi River | | |
| Yearly average | 550–600 | 1/800–1/1660 |
| Flood stage (up to 2,000,000 cfs) | 2,600 | 1/400 |
| Low stage (70,000 cfs) | 50 (water blue, clear) | 1/20,000 |
| Missouri River | | |
| Flood stage | 20,000 | 1/50 |
| Colorado River (before Hoover Dam) | | |
| Flood stage (50,000–70,000 cfs) | 40,000 | 1/25 |
| Hwang Ho (Yellow River), China Flood stage | Weight of solids may be greater than weight of water | |

* Data from G. H. Matthes (1951), *Scientific American,* vol. 184, no. 4, pp. 19–23.

a combination better suited to carrying more fine material in suspension.

## Channel changes in flood

Persons watching a river rise to bankfull stage as a flood wave passes see only the increase in height of the stream surface, for the water is turbid and hides what goes on beneath. By means of stream gauging at various stages of discharge, the hydraulic engineer is made aware of important changes in the bed of the stream.

Figure 35.8 shows a typical set of changes in channel cross section during rise and fall of stage over a period of a few weeks. As discharge increases, cross-sectional area increases. At first, as the stream surface rises, the bed remains at about the same level or may actually be raised by deposition, because the initial rise in discharge is accompanied by a sharp increase in bed load. Then, as discharge continues to increase, the increasing velocity of the stream greatly increases its transporting power and the bed is strongly scoured, deepening the channel by several feet. Later, as discharge falls, bed materials cease to be moved and are deposited in layers on the stream bed, restoring the channel approximately to its previous depth.

Because a stream is subjected almost constantly to either an increasing or a decreasing discharge, one can infer that the channel is almost continuously being either scoured or filled. Alluvial deposits are thus being continuously *reworked* by a stream, often through a depth of many feet.

The maximum load that a stream can transport as bed load under given conditions is known as its *tractive capacity.* It is known that the tractive capacity increases by about the third to fourth power of the average stream velocity. Hence, if velocity is doubled, the capacity can be increased by 8 to 16 times. But the velocity of a stream is, as we have seen in Chapter 34, determined by the magnitude of discharge, the stream gradient or slope, and the efficiency of the channel, both in regard to depth/width ratio and bed roughness. Tractive capacity is especially strongly affected by downstream slope of the bed, because not only does a steeper slope result in higher velocity of the water, but also particles may be dragged or rolled more easily on a steeper slope.

The hydraulic engineer and geologist also use the term *tractive competence,* which is the ability of a stream to move bed materials in terms of the largest particles that can be rolled or dragged. Obviously, when a stream increases in velocity it can move larger particles, because more pressure and dragging force can be exerted upon them. From laboratory experiments it has been observed that the weight of the largest particle that a stream can move on its bed varies about as the sixth power of the mean velocity. As in the case of capacity, competence is strongly affected by the gradient of the stream. Huge boulders can be rolled down the channel of a mountain stream of very steep gradient, whereas the same boulders would be immovable in the bed of a large river of low gradient.[1]

## Stages of stream gradation

The nature of stream action and the attendant landforms can be studied by the device of setting up a hypothetical life history of a stream and considering the stages of development (Figure 35.9). The stream history is imagined to begin on a newly formed landmass not previously subject to the processes of fluvial erosion.

[1] This principle is illustrated in Grand Canyon, where boulders brought down in floods from steep side canyons form great accumulations, making rapids in the channel of the Colorado River.

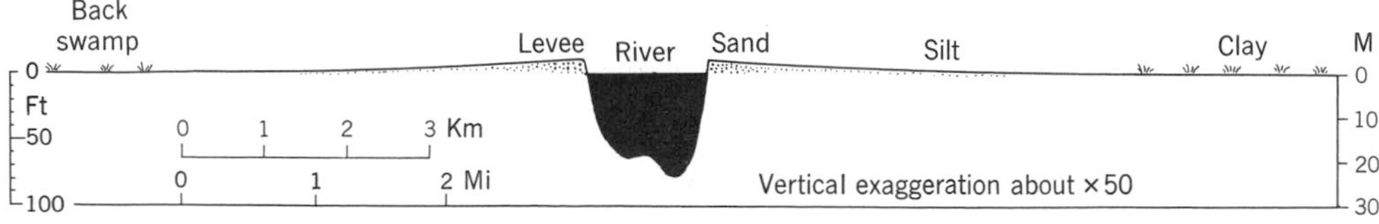


**FIGURE 35.17.** A transverse profile, greatly exaggerated, showing relation of natural levee to river channel.

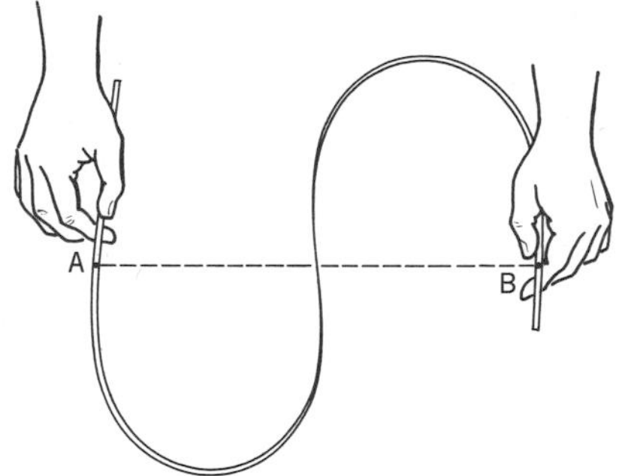


**FIGURE 35.18.** A thin strip of spring steel, held in an S-shaped bend, closely resembles the curve form of a freely meandering stream. The distance *A–B* is the meander wave length. [Sketched from a photograph by L. B. Leopold and W. B. Langbein (1966), *Scientific American,* June 1966, p. 67.]

For example, a continental shelf rapidly upraised from beneath the sea and faulted into blocks would present a landscape of closed depressions and alternating steep and gentle slopes, as suggested in Block *A* of Figure 35.9. Surface runoff immediately organizes itself into a crude and inefficient drainage system consisting of a series of lakes and marshes connected by narrow streams passing over the steep fault scarps in a succession of falls and rapids.

Intense channel abrasion at those points where the stream passes over steep falls quickly forms narrow gorges. As the rock barriers are reduced, lakes and marshes are lowered and finally drained, as Block *B* shows. Although now possessed of a continuous narrow channel, the stream has many rapids along its course. The transporting capacity of the stream exceeds the sediment load available, and thus the stream channel consists largely of exposed bedrock. Abrasion continues rapidly and the channel is lowered, causing the steep-walled rock gorge to be deepened. The result may be a canyon of spectacular proportions (Figure 35.10). Weathering, sheet erosion, and mass wasting act upon the rock walls to widen the canyon (Figure 35.11). Rock fragments that roll, slide, or are washed down to the stream are swept away as suspended and bed load.

Note that in Block *B* of Figure 35.9 many new stream branches are shown as being formed and extended away from the main stream. As these branches cut their valleys new sources of sediment are created and the total load of the main stream steadily increases. At the same time the gradient of the main stream is becoming less steep, hence the stream's capacity to transport load is becoming less. Obviously it is only a matter of time before the increasing supply of coarse sediment being fed into the stream matches the stream's capacity for bed load transportation.

This point in the life history of the stream is a most important one, for when the stream is receiving and transporting sediment to the limit of its capacity the period of rapid channel downcutting comes to an end and the channel is said to be *graded.* Rapids will have been removed by abrasion and the channel will have formed a smoothly decreasing slope throughout its length. A layer of bed materials (sand, gravel, and cobbles) will normally cover the channel floor and will be continually reworked as the stream stage rises and falls.

**FIGURE 35.19.** Logarithmic plot of meander wave length against mean annual discharge for 31 rivers. [U.S. Geological Survey data from C. W. Carlston (1965), *Amer. Jour. Science,* vol. 263, p. 868, Table 1.]

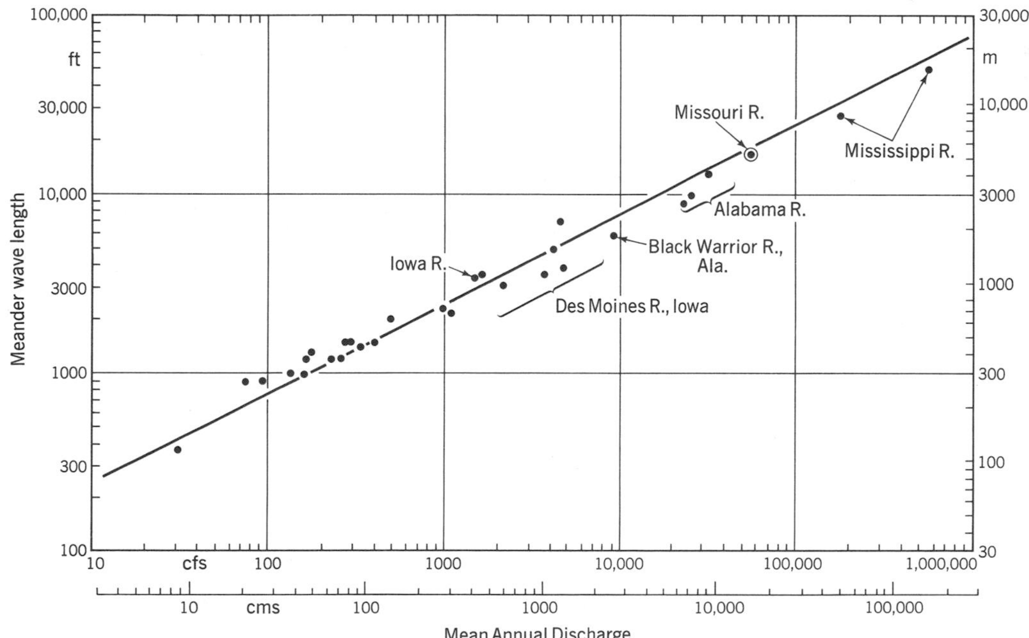

Once graded, the main stream begins to produce a new landform—the floodplain—by cutting horizontally on the outsides of the stream bends (Figure 35.12). This activity, termed *lateral planation,* resembles the action of a saw turned on its side and takes place principally in times of bankfull and flood discharges, when the stream has great energy and scours both the banks and the bed. On the insides of the bends bed load is deposited in the form of sand and gravel bars, creating a widening belt of nearly flat ground. When extreme floods occur this low ground is inundated and is the site of deposition of silt that is settled out from the turbulent water. The silt layers thus accumulate to produce a flat fertile floodplain.

In Block *C* of Figure 35.9 the main stream is shown to be graded and to be producing the first narrow areas of floodplain. As the floodplain is widened by further lateral planation the valley walls are less frequently undermined and therefore decline in steepness by the action of weathering and mass wasting (Figure 35.11).

In Block *D* of Figure 35.9 the floodplain has widened to the degree that a wave-like succession of channel bends, termed *meanders,* is able to form. Widening of the valley occurs only where the outside of a meander bend impinges upon the valley wall.

## The equilibrium profile; baselevel

The downstream changes in slope (gradient) of a river may be studied by means of the *longitudinal profile,* a graph in which stream elevation is plotted on the vertical axis (ordinate) and the horizontal distance on the horizontal axis (abscissa), as shown in Figure 35.13. The vertical scale is greatly exaggerated in the plotting of a stream profile. Characteristically the longitudinal profile of a graded stream, known as the *equilibrium profile,* is upwardly concave and shows a decreasing gradient from head to mouth.

The stream mouth enters a body of standing water at a very low but distinct surface slope. The level of the body of standing water effectively limits the downcutting of the stream and therefore constitutes the *baselevel* of the stream. Sea level, projected inland beneath the stream system, forms the baselevel for fluvial denudation of the lands.

Why is the longitudinal profile of a graded stream upwardly concave? In other words, why does the slope of a graded stream become progressively less downstream? Consider first that in most stream systems, particularly those of humid lands, stream discharge increases progressively downstream because tributaries enter the main channel, bringing the runoff of an increasingly large watershed area into the main channel. There is also a downstream increase in the load of the main stream because each tributary contributes a share.

One of the fundamental laws of streams, the *law of declivities,* was set forth in 1877 by the distinguished American geologist G. K. Gilbert to explain the downstream decrease in stream slope. Gilbert reasoned that as a stream grows larger (that is, as the magnitude of discharge increases downstream) the stream becomes more efficient mechanically, losing a smaller proportion of its energy in friction with the channel walls. Because

**FIGURE 35.20.** Idealized map and profiles of a meander bend of the lower Mississippi River. Arrows show position of fastest current.

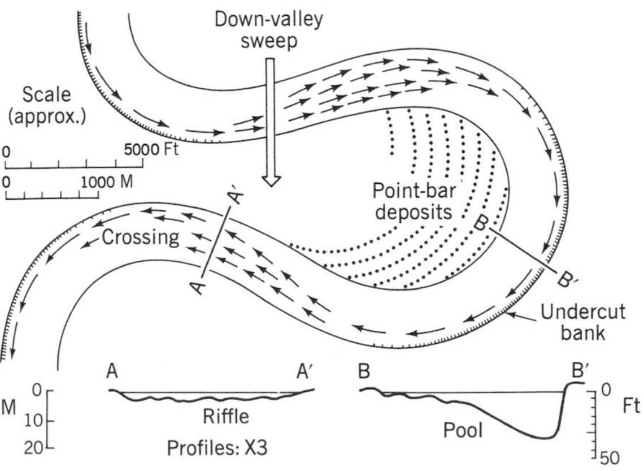


**FIGURE 35.21.** Growth of a meander bend and its cutoff are seen in maps of four Mississippi River surveys, superimposed. (© 1965, John Wiley & Sons, New York. Data of U.S. Army Corps of Engineers.)

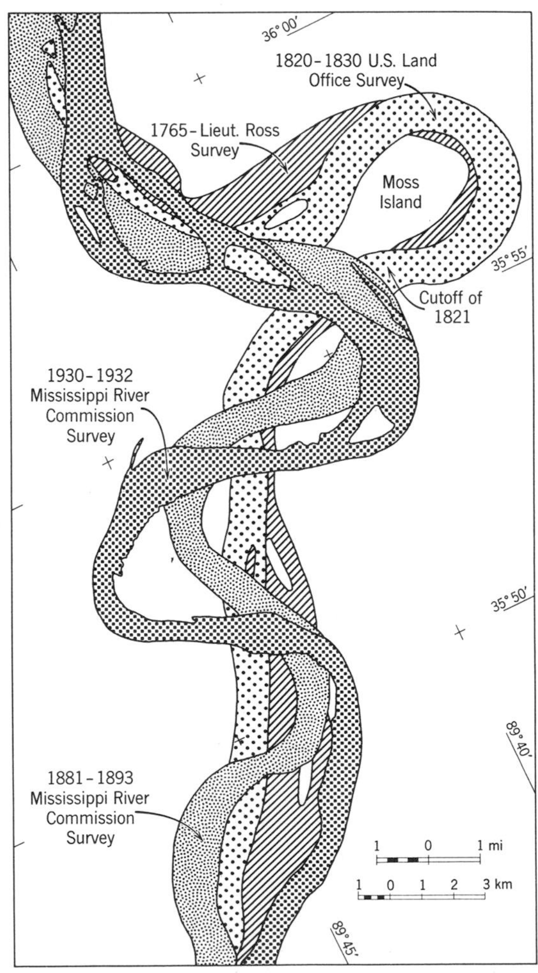

FIGURE 35.22. Oblique air photograph, looking north, of the Mississippi River, showing three artificial meander cutoffs made by the Corps of Engineers to reduce river length. Taken in 1937, this photograph shows sediment plugs blocking the ends of Bachelor Bend, which formerly flowed past the city of Greenville, Mississippi. (Photograph by War Department, Corps of Engineers.)

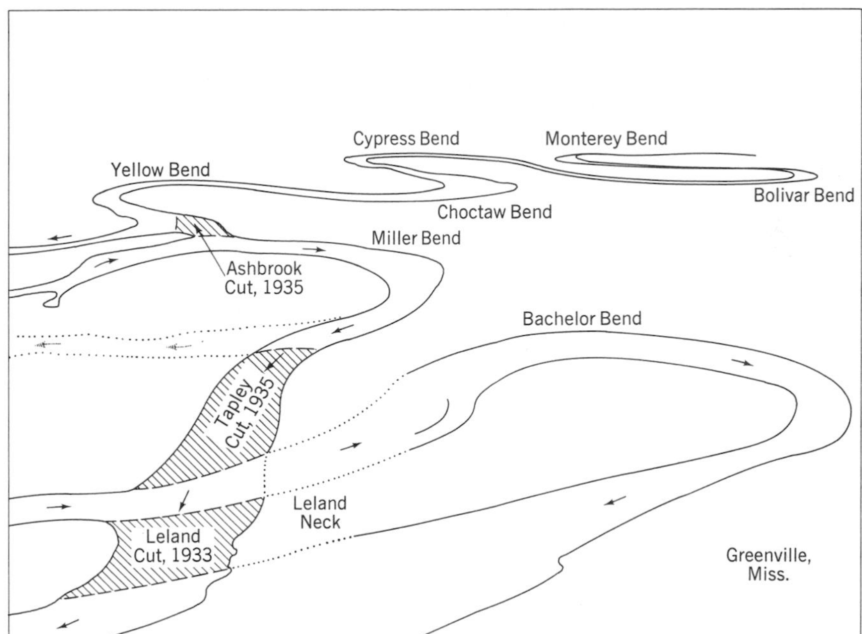


proportionately less energy is lost in friction, the larger stream can maintain sufficient velocity to carry its load on a lesser slope.

It is important to keep in mind that the graded stream is the product of a long period of adjustment through progressive downcutting (or upbuilding, in some cases). During this long period the stream has so adjusted its gradient that throughout its entire length the gradient is of just the right amount to permit the load to be carried through the system.

In explaining profile concavity, we must also take into account that in most river systems the particles making up the stream bed become finer, on the average, from the head to the mouth. This postulate has led geologists to conclude that a steeper slope is required near the headwaters to transport the coarser particles and that the slope diminishes progressively downstream in close relation to the decrease in particle size.

Many people think of a stream system as consisting of swiftly flowing mountain torrents near the headwaters, leading downstream to great main rivers of stately or majestic aspect, implying that the larger rivers have relatively slower rates of flow. Actually most rivers show a gradual but small downstream increase in the average velocity of flow. Decrease in slope would tend to cause slower flow, but the increasing depth of the river downstream acts more effectively to cause a velocity increase, hence the net effect is one of increasing velocity.

## Alluvial rivers

Many of the world's graded rivers occupy broad floodplain belts over which the depth of alluvium equals or exceeds the depth to which scour takes place in time of flood. Designated *alluvial rivers* by hydraulic engineers, these streams flow on very low gradients and have extremely sinuous bends known as *alluvial meanders* (Figures 35.14 and 35.15).

Alluvial rivers may develop in the later stages of the life history of a stream, outlined above, by continued lateral planation. It is also possible for an alluvial river to form upon delta deposits which the stream itself has built into a shallow bay or estuary. Still another region of origin of alluvial rivers is upon the smooth gently sloping surface of a lake floor or shallow sea that has been exposed by withdrawal of the water.

Meanders originate from the enlargement of bends in the path of flow of the stream. For example, the growth of a sand bar along the side of a straight channel will deflect the lines of flow toward the opposite bank, where undercutting takes place and a bend begins to form (Figure 35.16*A*). Material from the undercut bank is carried a short distance downchannel, forming another bar, which in turn deflects the flow to the opposite side to develop a second bend. Once a bend is produced, centrifugal force continues to thrust the flow toward the outside of the bend, resulting in continued undermining and the enlargement of the bend until a meander loop is formed.

On the inside of the bend a series of arcuate sand and gravel bars accumulates to produce a *point-bar deposit* (Figure 35.16*B*). Ideally we might expect a uniform series of meander bends to reach an optimum size suited to the magnitude of the stream and thereafter to cease growth. A downvalley shift, or *sweep,* of the entire system of bends would continue because of the inclination of the alluvial valley in the direction of the stream's mouth (Figure 35.16*C*). But because of inequalities of erodibility in the materials constituting the floodplain deposits, a meander may become constricted, creating a narrow *meander neck,* and the neck may be cut through by bank caving or by overflow in time of flood, permitting the stream to bypass the bend and thereby to produce a *cutoff.* The cut-off meander bend is quickly sealed off from the main stream by silt deposits and becomes an *oxbow lake.* Gradual filling of the lake results in an oxbow swamp or marsh (Figure 35.15).

In the discussion of floods (Chapter 34) it was noted that many alluvial rivers of humid climates have a yearly flood of such proportions that the water can no longer be contained within the channel and spreads out upon the floodplain. Such overbank flooding permits fine-grained sediment (silts and clays) to be deposited from suspension in the relatively slowly moving water covering the floodplain. The sediment is laid down in layers, which may be called *overbank deposits.*

Adjacent to the main channel, in which flow is relatively swift because of greater depth, the coarsest sediment—sand and coarse silt—is deposited in two bordering belts. After many floods there are thus built up lateral zones of somewhat higher ground, termed *natural levees* (Figure 35.14). The highest points on the levees lie close to the river bank. There is a gentle slope away from the river down to the low-lying marshy areas of floodplain some distance from the river. Figure 35.17 is a greatly exaggerated cross section of the Mississippi River showing its flanking levees. Levee height is generally 12 to 15 ft (3.5 to 4.5 m) above the surrounding floodplain, and slopes are on the order of 3 to 4 ft per mi (0.5 to 0.7 m/km) away from the river. In times of overbank flood the channel of an alluvial river is often clearly delineated by a double line of trees growing on the levees and projecting above the flood waters (Figure 34.26).

**FIGURE 35.23.** A braided stream fed by glacier meltwater. Peters Creek, Chugach Mountains, Alaska. (Photograph by Steve McCutcheon, Alaska Pictorial Service.)

The presence of a natural-levee system along an alluvial river has a curious effect upon the junction of tributaries. Streams entering upon the floodplain cannot flow directly into the master stream because the levee acts as a barrier. Instead the tributary turns downvalley and parallels the main stream, often for many miles, before a junction is made (Figure 35.14). Such a stream of deferred junction on a floodplain is termed a *yazoo stream,* after the Yazoo River (Tallahatchie River) of Mississippi.

**Meander form and development** The form and size range of alluvial meanders make interesting subjects for mathematical analysis. Scientists of the U.S. Geological Survey have found that the form of meander curves is mathematically similar to curves formed by elastic

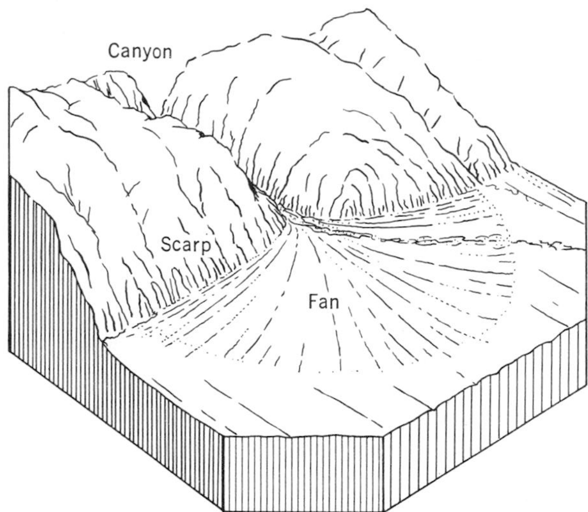


**FIGURE 35.24.** An alluvial fan. (© 1960, John Wiley & Sons, New York.)

**FIGURE 35.25.** An alluvial fan at the margin of Death Valley, California. Shoreline of pluvial Lake Manly follows the outer fan margin. (Photograph by M. A. Melton.)

bending in a thin strip of spring steel (Figure 35.18). In the case of the spring this shape represents the curve of least work, and in the case of the meander bend it tends to minimize the change in direction of the channel at all points on the curve.[2]

Meander curves show a high degree of geometrical similarity over the entire range of sizes. That is to say, the meanders of a small meadow brook would closely resemble the meanders of a great alluvial river, such as the Mississippi, when the channels of both are drawn to such scales that the average *meander wave length* is the same in both examples. By meander wave length is meant the horizontal distance between corresponding points on the transverse reaches of alternate bends (Figure 35.18).

The wave lengths of meanders are obviously closely related to the size of the stream, which can be measured in several ways—for example, in terms of channel width, area of channel cross section, or magnitude of discharge. Perhaps the best measure of size of a stream is its mean annual discharge. Other useful measures of discharge are those made when the channel is at or close to the bankfull stage.

Figure 35.19 is a graph in which meander wave length has been plotted against mean annual discharge on logarithmic scales. The plotted points represent measurements at 31 places taken on streams having as small a drainage area as 46 sq mi (100 sq km) to the Mississippi River with a drainage area of over one million sq mi (2.6 million sq km). Superimposed upon these points is a straight line so drawn that the meander wave length varies as the square root of the mean annual discharge. Although the line of best fit to the plotted points is slightly different, the square root relationship is a good generalization. It would also be found that the average meander width, measured between lines tangent to the outsides of the bends, increases as the square root of mean annual discharge. Consequently it may be stated as a sound generalization that meander width tends to increase in direct ratio with meander wave length, which accounts for the maintenance of a uniform shape.

[2] This curve is known as a *sine-generated curve* and minimizes the sums of the squares of changes in direction, as compared with other possible curves.

**Channel forms of the Mississippi River** The channel of an alluvial river shows striking variations in form and depth, depending upon its position with respect to the meander bends. Figure 35.20 shows that on the outsides of the meanders the channel is deepened into a *pool* which lies close to the outside or *undercut* bank. Swiftest current threads are found over the deepest zone and thus run close to the undercut bank. In the transverse reaches, where curvature reverses direction, the channel becomes shallow and irregular because of the formation of bars in the stream bed. This zone constitutes the *riffle.* Because at this location the lines of swiftest current change sides, the riffle is known in navigational terms as the *crossing.* Riffles and pools are typical of the beds of straight reaches of streams as well as of meanders.

In the Mississippi River, pools are scoured to depths of 60 to 80 ft (18 to 24 m) below the level of mean low water, whereas maximum depths in the zone of the riffle, or crossing, are only 15 to 20 ft (5 to 6 m) below that same reference level. Thus, surprisingly enough, for about 470 mi (760 km) upstream from its mouth the Mississippi River has parts of its bed below sea level.

The Mississippi River between 1765 and 1932 experienced 19 natural cutoffs in the distance from Cairo, Illinois, to Baton Rouge, Louisiana (Figure 35.21). These cutoffs shortened the river by about 250 mi (400 km), whereas lengthenings of channel in the same period totalled about 500 mi (800 km). The total length remained essentially constant. Channel shortenings not accounted for by cutoffs occurred in part by crosscutting of open bends (*chute* diversions) and in part by

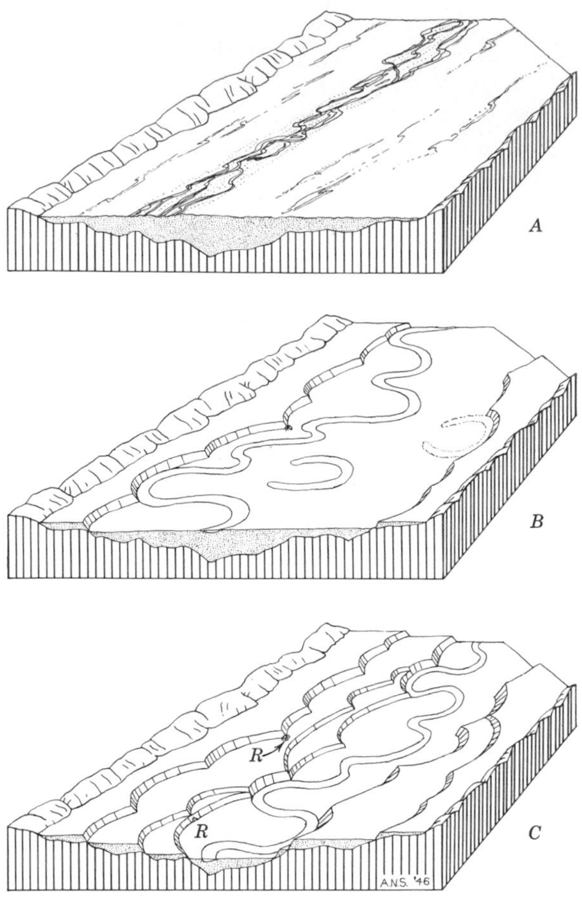


**FIGURE 35.26.** Formation of alluvial terraces. The letter *R* in Block *C* refers to a point where a terrace is defended by a rock outcrop. (© 1960, John Wiley & Sons, New York.)

straightening of open bends. After 1932 the river channel was radically altered by artificial cutoffs to achieve flood control (see Chapter 34). Figure 35.22 shows three such engineering changes shortly after they were made.

After a cutoff has occurred the ends of the abandoned loop are quickly sealed by sediment, creating an oxbow lake, which gradually fills with very fine sediment, largely fine clay, deposited in floods. These dense tough deposits of the Mississippi alluvial plain are termed *clay plugs* and may be from 100 to 150 ft (30 to 45 m) thick. In contrast, the point-bar deposits are comprised of about half sand and half silt. As new meander bends grow their shapes are influenced by the encounter with resistant clay plugs, whereas the point-bar deposits are easily eroded. Thus the variations in composition of the alluvial layer contribute to distortions of shape of growing meanders and tend to induce cutoffs to occur.

## Aggrading streams; alluvial fans

When rock waste, particularly the coarse material carried as bed load, is supplied to a stream by its tributaries and by runoff from adjacent slopes in greater quantity than the stream is capable of transporting, the excess load is spread along the channel floor, raising the level of the entire channel. Such upbuilding is termed *aggradation,* in contrast to *degradation,* which is the process of downcutting carried on by a stream capable of transporting more load than it is supplied with.

A stream channel in which aggradation is in progress is typically broad and shallow. Aggradation takes the form of deposition of long narrow bars of sand and gravel, which tend to divide the flow into two or more lines (Figure 35.23). The flow thus subdivides and rejoins in a manner suggesting complexly braided cords, giving rise to the descriptive term *braided stream,* in contrast to the typical single-channel form of streams whose sinuous meander loops have already been described. As channel aggradation proceeds, the stream is shifted laterally to flow in lower adjacent ground and will thus move widely from side to side wherever there are no confining valley walls.

Perhaps the most common cause of aggradation in stream channels is the combination of arid climate

**FIGURE 35.27.** Terraces cut by the Shoshone River, west of Cody, Wyoming, rise like broad flights of steps. (Photograph by Frank J. Wright.)

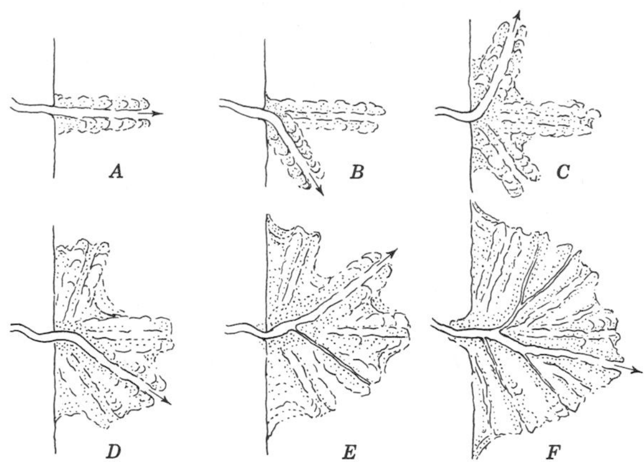


FIGURE 35.28. Stages in the development of a simple delta built into a lake in which wave action is slight. (© 1960, John Wiley & Sons, New York. Based on data of G. K. Gilbert.)

FIGURE 35.29. Oblique air view of the Kander River delta, Lake Thun, Switzerland. Note the jet of sediment-laden water being projected into the lake. (Swissair photograph.)

and mountainous relief, as in the southwestern United States. Barren steep mountain slopes shed large quantities of coarse debris when eroded by runoff of torrential rains. Floods in the mountain valleys are thus characterized by a large proportion of coarse bed load carried downvalley on steep gradients. Where a canyon emerges upon a piedmont valley floor of gentle slope, aggradation occurs because the stream is not able to transport its load on a sharply reduced gradient. Moreover, stream discharge may diminish rapidly in the lowland region because of influent seepage and evaporation. Free to shift from side to side as aggradation occurs, the stream spreads its excess load in the form of an *alluvial fan* (Figure 35.24).

The alluvial fan takes the form of a sector of an upwardly concave low cone steepening in gradient toward an apex situated at the canyon mouth. At its outer edge the fan slope grades imperceptibly into the flatter plain. As one might suspect, the diameter of particles constituting the fan is greatest near the apex, where much bouldery material may be found, and grades to progressively finer particles toward the periphery. Large fans of mountainous deserts may be several miles in radius from apex to outer edge (Figure 35.25), but much smaller fans are common. One can often observe miniature alluvial fans only a few feet in radius forming at the mouths of small gullies where soil erosion is in progress. In the larger desert fans mudflow layers are common (see Figure 32.24).

From the standpoint of ground water, alluvial fans are of extremely great importance in arid climates because they act as ground-water reservoirs. Water enters near the fan apex by influent seepage and moves downward and outward along the layers of sorted gravels and sands, filling the interstices. Wells driven into the alluvium of the lower slopes of the fan will often prove to have artesian flow, because sloping impermeable mudflow layers interbedded with the permeable gravels form aquicludes which confine the water under pressure. Great as the water resources of

FIGURE 35.30. Internal structure of a simple delta built into a lake. (© 1960, John Wiley & Sons, New York.)

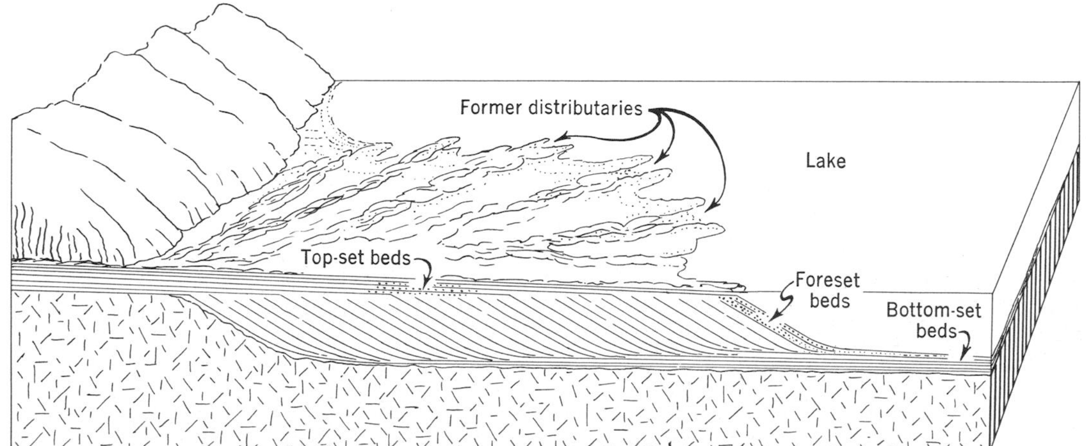

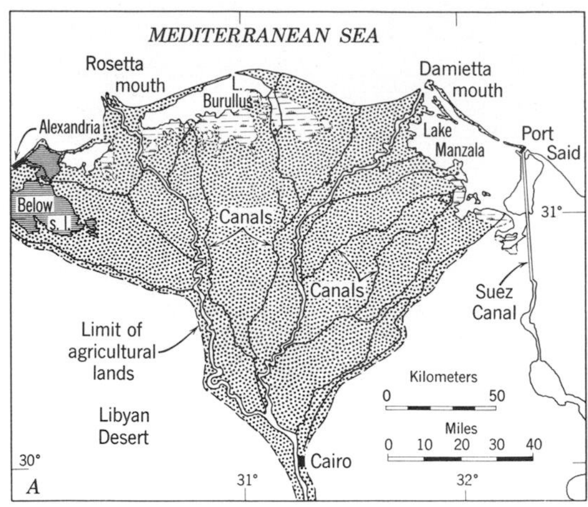


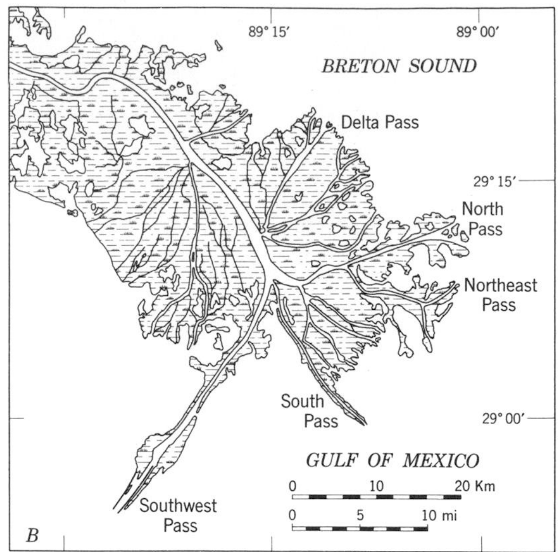


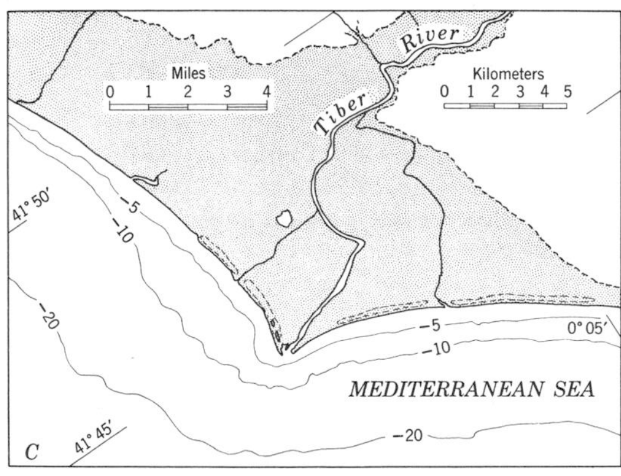


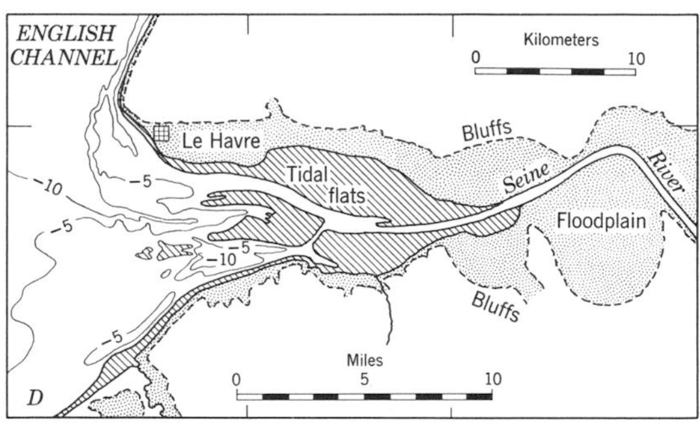


**FIGURE 35.31.** Delta outlines. (*A*) Arcuate shoreline form of the Nile delta. The basic outline is triangular. (*B*) The Mississippi delta is of the branching, bird-foot type. (*C*) A simple cuspate form is shown by the Tiber delta. Wave action rapidly redistributes the sediment. (*D*) Estuarine delta of the Seine River. (© 1965, John Wiley & Sons, New York.)

alluvial fans are, the long-term supply is effectively limited by the slow rate of recharge—often extremely slow—thus extensive pumping for irrigation can exhaust the water supply in a comparatively short time.

## Alluvial terraces

The term *terrace,* in its broadest sense as a landform, is simply any relatively long narrow element of gently sloping ground surface bounded along one edge by a more steeply descending slope and along the other by a more steeply rising slope. There are many varieties and origins of terraces. One particularly interesting variety related to stream action is the *alluvial terrace,* so named because the terrace is shaped by stream erosion in a valley deposit of alluvium.

Essential steps in the evolution of alluvial terraces are illustrated in Figure 35.26. First (Block *A*), a valley is filled with alluvium by an aggrading stream until the valley floor is broad and flat. Aggradation might result from a change to a more arid climate or from the greatly increased load derived from a melting glacier in the upstream region.

In Block *B* we see that the stream has changed its role from one of aggradation to one of degradation and has begun to cut down into the alluvial deposit, at the same time shifting laterally and planing its floodplain in the easily eroded material. There now appears a single terrace, whose surface is the remnant edge of the original floodplain and whose boundary on the valleyward margin is formed by steeply descending scarps carved by meander growth.

Cause of degradation might be found in a change to a more humid climate, for the growth of a denser vegetative cover would tend to hold back the coarser debris from the streams and thus reduce the stream loads in both quantity and size of particles. A similar effect would follow the disappearance of glaciers, if such had been the cause of the initial aggradation.

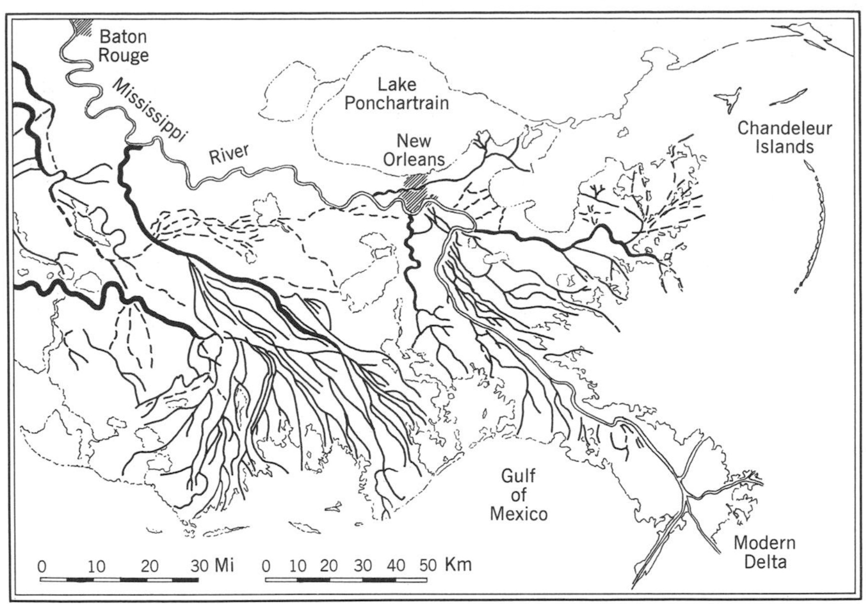


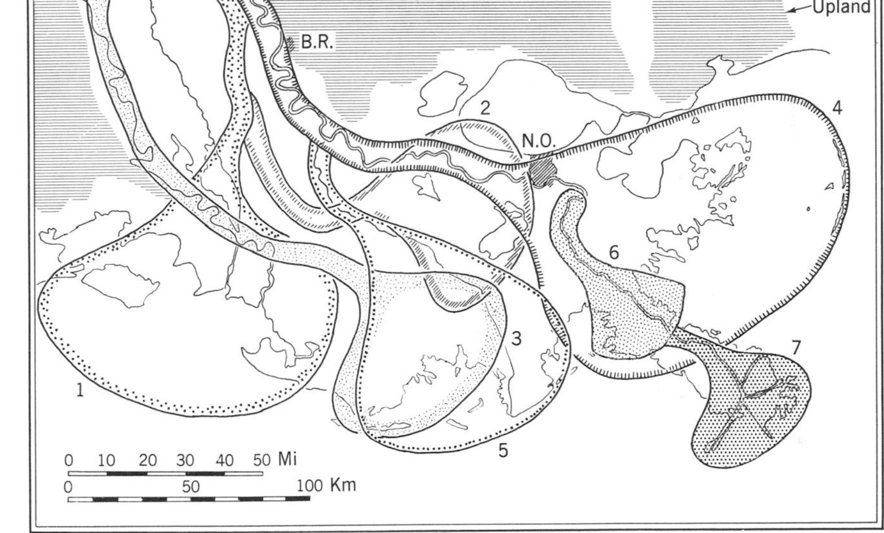


**FIGURE 35.32.** Deltaic plain of the Mississippi River. *Upper map:* Abandoned river courses and distributaries are shown by bold lines. *Lower map:* Seven deltas, numbered in order from oldest to youngest. The lower map covers a larger area than the upper map. [Redrawn and simplified from maps by C. R. Kolb and J. R. Van Lopik (1966), in *Deltas in Their Geologic Framework,* M. L. Shirley, Ed., Houston, Texas, Houston Geol. Soc., p. 22, Figure 2, and p. 31. Figure 8.]

In Block *C* of Figure 35.26 degradation has proceeded further, and a series of alluvial terraces, resembling a flight of broad stairs on the valley wall, has been carved (Figure 35.27). Once formed, a terrace may be protected from later undermining by the presence of an outcrop of resistant rock at the base of the terrace (letter *R* in Block *C*). Such terraces are described as being *rock defended.*

## Deltas

A stream reaching a body of standing water, whether a lake or the ocean, builds a deposit, the *delta,* composed of the stream's load. The growth of a simple delta can be followed in stages, shown in Figure 35.28. For simplicity we imagine that the water body is not appreciably affected by waves and tides. The stream enters the standing water body as a jet whose velocity is rapidly checked (Figure 35.29). Sediment is deposited in lateral embankments in zones of less turbulence on either side of the jet, thus extending the stream channel into the open water. The stream repeatedly breaks through the embankments to occupy different radii and in time produces a deposit of semicircular form, closely analogous to the alluvial fan (which is in a sense a terrestrial delta).

In cross section the simple delta consists largely of steeply sloping layers of sands, termed *foreset beds* (Figure 35.30), which grade outward into thin layers of silt and clay, the *bottomset beds.* As the delta grows, the stream will aggrade slightly and spread new layers of alluvium, the *topset beds.* An important factor in causing the finer suspended particles to settle close to the stream mouth is the presence in sea water of dissolved salts, which act to cause the particles to clot together, or *flocculate,* into aggregates of such size that they readily sink to the bottom.

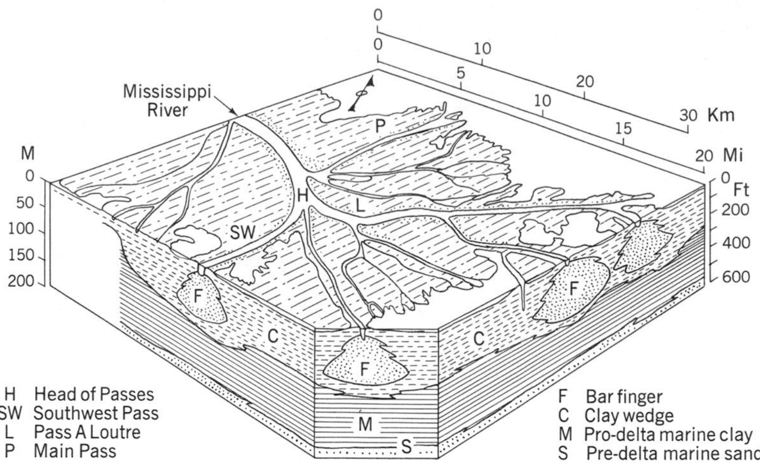


**FIGURE 35.33.** Block diagram showing structure and sedimentary units within the modern bird-foot delta of the Mississippi River. [Simplified from a diagram by H. N. Fisk, E. McFarlan, Jr., C. R. Kolb, and L. J. Wilbert, Jr. (1954), *Jour. of Sedimentary Petrology,* vol. 24, p. 77, Figure 1.]

Form and structure of large marine deltas are strongly influenced by the initial configuration of the shoreline, waves and tides, changes of sea level, and subsidence of the delta. Figure 35.31 illustrates a variety of outlines shown by deltas. The Nile delta takes the triangular shape of the capital Greek letter *delta,* from which the landform was originally named. From an apex at Cairo, *distributary channels* branch in a radial arrangement. Sediment reaching the Mediterranean Sea from the principal distributary mouths is swept along the coast by wave-induced currents to form curved bars enclosing shallow lagoons. The delta shoreline is thus *arcuate* in plan, bowed convexly outward.

The Mississippi River delta, Figure 35.31*B,* is described as a *bird-foot delta* because of the long extensions of its branching distributaries into open water. The Tiber River delta (Figure 35.31*C*) represents a *cuspate* (tooth-shaped) form in which a single dominant mouth builds the delta forward into deeper water while wave action sweeps the sediment away from the mouth to form two curving beaches, concave toward the sea. Still another variety, the *estuarine* delta, fills a long narrow estuary that resulted from drowning of the lower part of the valley (Figure 35.31*D*).

**The Mississippi River delta** The delta of the Mississippi River has been intensively studied by geologists, whose findings illustrate principles of sedimentary facies (Chapter 28). Numerous borings have revealed the composition and structure of both the modern delta and of several older deltas which together comprise an enormous *deltaic plain.* Figure 35.32 consists of two maps of the Mississippi delta region. Map *A* shows the patterns of abandoned channels and distributaries as well as the present channel. Map *B* shows by shaded

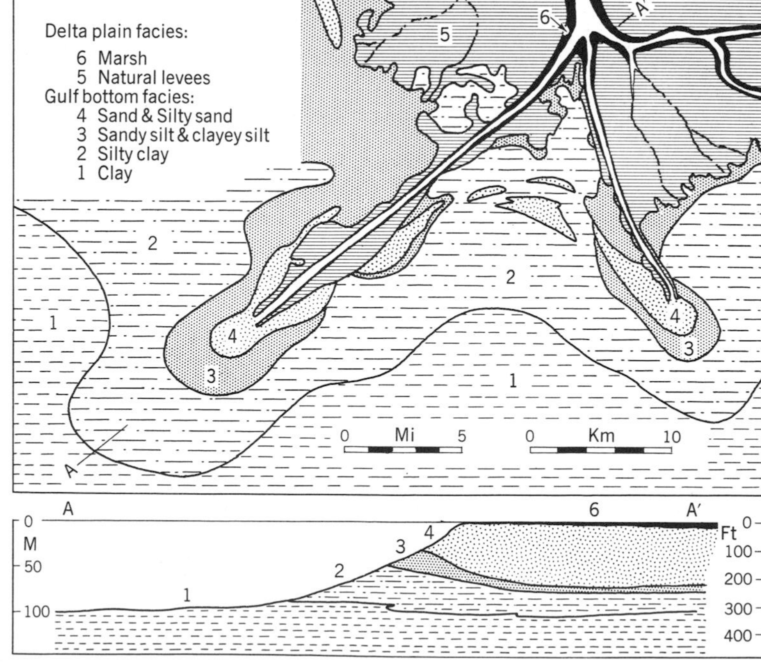


**FIGURE 35.34.** Facies map and structure section of the modern delta of the Mississippi River. [Simplified from H. N. Fisk, E. McFarlan, Jr., C. R. Kolb, and L. J. Wilbert, Jr. (1954), *Jour. of Sedimentary Petrology,* vol. 24, p. 87, Figure 8, and p. 92, Figure 12.]

bands the outlines of six older delta lobes and the modern lobe, which constitutes a *subdelta* of the entire complex. Starting over 5000 years ago, each of the older deltas in succession built a fan-shaped deposit, not greatly unlike the Nile delta, in the form of radiating distributary channels. Diversions of the main river channel upstream from the delta shifted the zone of accumulation alternately eastward and westward, as the numbered sequence on the map shows. Recent subsidence has resulted in partial inundation of the older delta plains.

The modern Mississippi River bird-foot delta differs from the earlier deltas in having broadly-branched distributaries. Moreover, the modern delta is being constructed in deeper water—over 300 ft (90 m)—than its predecessors. Figure 35.33 shows the structure of the modern delta by means of a block diagram. Advancing distributary mouths have built deep but narrow *bar fingers* of sand upon earlier deposits of marine clays and upon a thin layer of prodelta clays and silts that were laid down seaward of the advancing sands. As the bar fingers grew clays and silts were deposited between the fingers.

Facies of sediment of the modern bird-foot delta platform are shown in Figure 35.34. Notice the succession of deposits encountered at increasing depth outward from the ends of the distributaries (passes). These are foreset beds and grade outward and downward from sand, through silt mixtures, to clay (bottomset beds) spread over the ocean floor at a depth of about 300 ft (90 m). The topset strata, which form the present delta plain lying close to sea level, are natural levees bordering the distributary channels and deposits of organic-rich clay and silt in salt marshes between the distributaries.

Not all sediment is deposited by stream discharge through the principal passes. Here and there the levee is broken by a crevasse through which flood waters discharge sediment to be spread in fan-like accumulations upon tidal deposits. The crevasse is eventually abandoned and its deposits subside, to be covered again by tidal waters.

Altogether, the modern bird-foot delta contains about 27 cu mi (113 cu km) of sediment, deposited in about 450 years. The yearly increment is about 0.06 cu mi (0.25 cu km), or about 500 million tons (455 million metric tons). This total stream load, suspended load and bed load combined, consists of about 25% sand, 30% silt, and 45% clay.

**The Catskill Delta of Devonian age** Large accumulations of deltic sediments are found in the stratigraphic record. Examples were cited in Chapter 28 from the Permian and Triassic strata of the Grand Canyon region. A classic example, illustrating deltaic facies and their interpretation, is that of Devonian strata of the Catskill region of New York state. Figure 35.35 shows both an east-west cross section through the Devonian strata as they are today, and a restored cross section of the geosyncline as it appeared after Devonian sedimentation had been completed.

Rapidly rising highlands to the east provided streams with abundant sediment, which was spread as a delta or series of deltas across what is now the Catskill

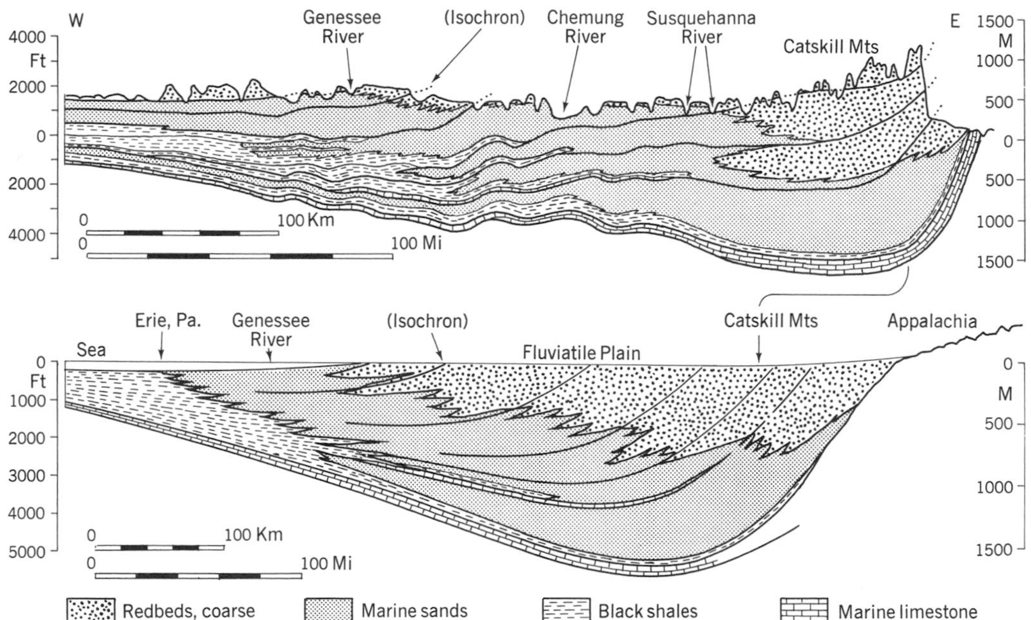


**FIGURE 35.35.** The Catskill Delta of the Devonian Period. *Above:* East-west profile and stratigraphic cross section of the Devonian strata, showing conditions today. Strata exhibit minor folding. *Below:* Restored stratigraphic section at the close of Devonian sedimentation. [Upper section after G. M. Friedman and K. G. Johnson (1966), in *Deltas in Their Geologic Framework,* M. L. Shirley, Ed., Houston, Texas, Houston Geol. Soc., p. 174, Figure 2, modified from J. G. Broughton. Lower section after M. Kay and E. H. Colbert (1965), *Stratigraphy and Life History,* New York, Wiley, p. 218, Figure 11-9.]

Mountains region. These sediments were red beds of coarse sandy texture. Westward the delta sediments graded into finer sands and then into marine black shales. As the restored section shows, the deltaic facies spread progressively farther westward, overlapping the marine facies. Behind the spreading delta lay an expanding fluviatile plain. Lines of equal time (isochrones) show how this overlap occurred.

## References for further study

Powell, J. W. (1875), *Exploration of the Colorado River of the West and Its Tributaries,* Washington, D.C., U.S. Govt. Printing Office, 291 pp.

Lobeck, A. K. (1939), *Geomorphology,* New York, McGraw-Hill, 731 pp., chaps. 5, 6, 7.

Leopold, L. B., M. G. Wolman, and J. P. Miller (1964), *Fluvial Processes in Geomorphology,* San Francisco, Freeman, 552 pp.

Shirley, M. L., Ed. (1966), *Deltas in Their Geologic Framework,* Houston, Texas, Houston Geol. Soc., 251 pp.

Morisawa, M. (1968), *Streams; Their Dynamics and Morphology,* New York, McGraw-Hill, 175 pp.

Thornbury, W. D. (1969), *Principles of Geomorphology,* 2nd ed., New York, Wiley, 594 pp., chaps. 5, 6, 7.

# 36

# Systems of fluvial denudation

IN THE PRECEDING four chapters emphasis was upon the contemporary aspect of processes of denudation and activities within the hydrologic cycle. In this chapter we shall look further into the long-term geological aspect of denudation in order to place the exogenetic processes in the perspective of geologic history.

## Concept of the denudation system

That part of the continental crust lying above sea level, which is the baselevel for reduction by streams, constitutes the *available landmass* subject to denudation and to ultimate removal. However, to this landmass as it exists at any one moment must be added the crustal mass that will rise under isostasy to replace in part any rock mass that is removed in the denudation process. Estimates vary as to what factor to allow for isostatic replacement, but ratios on the order of 3:4 to 4:5 are considered realistic. Using the second of these ratios, the removal of 5000 ft of rock would be accompanied by uplift of 4000 ft and would result in a net lowering of the land surface of only 1000 ft. Thus the available landmass includes the crustal mass furnished by isostatic replacement.

The available landmass provides potential energy of position for a denudation system that is activated by exogenetic agents powered by solar energy. Two forms of work must be done within this system. First, energy must be expended to reduce the strong dense bedrock to a clastic state or weaken it greatly so that it can be moved to lower levels by mass wasting or by processes of overland flow. Weathering encompasses these preliminary physical and chemical changes essential to denudation. Energy for weathering processes comes from external sources—from sensible atmospheric heat and heat stored in water in its liquid and vapor states, and to some degree directly from incident solar radiation. The second form of work is that of abrasion and transportation by overland flow. This fluid flow, as we have seen, is a system of mass transport and energy transformation powered by gravity in which potential energy of position of water and rock particles is transformed into kinetic energy of flow and ultimately dissipated as heat from resistance. Water is brought to high elevations on land by atmospheric processes, which are exogenetic and powered by solar energy. Rock is brought to high elevations by endogenetic forces which are powered by internal sources of energy probably dependent upon radiogenic heat (Chapter 23).

In summary, the available landmass upon which denudation acts is provided by endogenetic systems of mass transfer, but the reduction of the landmass is achieved by exogenetic systems expending solar energy. The two systems come into accidental linkages at various times and places over the earth. An alpine mountain system is raised by orogenic and volcanic processes at a time and place that depends upon large-scale crustal tectonic processes totally unrelated to world patterns of incoming solar radiation, atmospheric circulation, precipitation, and evaporation (as witness the eruptions of volcanoes in almost any latitude on the globe). The global tectonic patterns of moving crustal plates, spreading mid-oceanic rift zones, and island arcs in compression, along with their seismic and volcanic activity, are completely unrelated in any systematic way to the basic planetary systems of atmospheric circulation. So it is in an almost accidental manner that the great mountain chains transgress the flow paths of the easterlies and westerlies, disrupting what would otherwise be a rather simple system of global climates. The climatic differences, in turn, influence denudation processes and rates from place to place over the globe. Geologic and climatic controls together act in many combinations to regulate the denudation process.

## Rates of orogenic uplift

Let us take up first the case of an active orogenic belt along the continental margin. Disregarding the horizontal movements involved in folding and overthrust faulting, consider for the moment only the lifting of the crustal mass. Rates of uplift during orogeny can be estimated from the ages of late Cenozoic strata found today at high positions in the mountain zone, but these estimates deal with long time spans within which uplift rates may have been unevenly distributed.

Some rough values of maximum rates of uplift by orogenic processes can be obtained from the data of geodetic surveys. Precise leveling, discussed in Chapter 11, has been repeated in a number of instances along survey traverse lines crossing active mountain blocks. For example, leveling surveys in 1906 and 1944 across the San Bernardino fault block near Cajon Pass in California showed a rise in elevation of about 8 in. (20 cm), which is at the rate of about 17 ft (5 m) per 1000 years. A number of other similar measurements in California showed rates of uplift ranging from 15 to 40 ft (4 to 12 m) per 1000 years, with an average of about 25 ft (7.5 m) per 1000 years. Comparable rates have been measured in orogenic belts in such widely separated places as the Persian Gulf area and in Japan. Epeirogenic uplift of certain parts of the stable continental crust is estimated to be on the order of 3 ft (1 m) per 1000 years.[1]

Using the rate of uplift of 25 ft per 1000 years, a mountain summit might rise from sea level to an elevation of 20,000 ft (6 km) in 800,000 years, assuming none of its mass to be removed by denudation processes. This extrapolation suggests that a full-sized mountain range might be created in a time span less than one-half the duration of the Pleistocene Epoch. Considering the durations of even the individual epochs of the Cenozoic Era, orogenic uplift appears to be an extremely rapid process in comparison with the uninterrupted spans of time in which denudation operates. Even the towering Himalaya range might well have been raised through a large part of its height in 2 million years, although the total uplift probably took much longer because of slower rates operating during much of the orogeny.

## Observed denudation rates

Geologists and hydrologists have made a number of attempts to estimate the rates of continental denudation by using long-term measurements of suspended and dissolved solids in major streams. There are also some estimates of solids yielded by small watersheds, based upon the accumulation of sediment in man-made reservoirs.

Table 36.1 summarizes recently compiled data on mean annual stream loads, both solid and dissolved, and the derived denudation rates. Figure 36.1 is an

[1] Data on uplift rates from J. Gilluly (1949), *Geol. Soc. Amer. Bull.*, vol. 60, pp. 561–590; and S. A. Schumm (1963), U.S. Geol. Survey, Professional Paper 454-H, 13 pp.

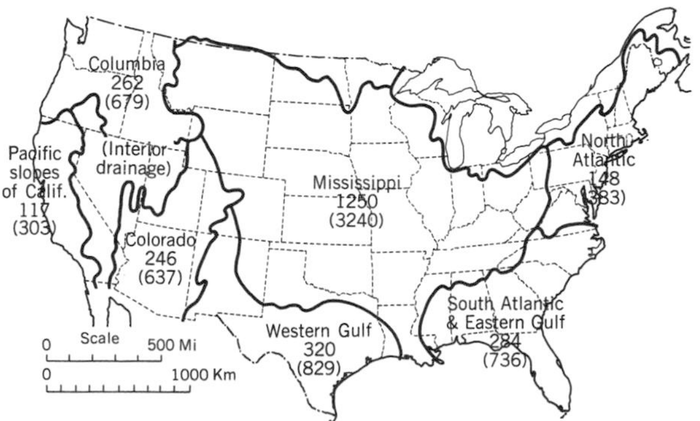


**FIGURE 36.1.** Index map showing drainage areas listed in Table 36.1. Figures give areas in thousands of sq mi, with units of thousands of sq km in parentheses. [After S. Judson and D. F. Ritter (1964), *Jour. Geophys. Research,* vol. 69, p. 3396, Figure 1.]

**TABLE 36.1. DENUDATION RATES FOR MAJOR REGIONS OF THE UNITED STATES***

| Drainage Region | Load, tons/sq mi/yr | | | Denudation, per 1000 yrs | | Denudation, per million yrs | |
|---|---|---|---|---|---|---|---|
| | dissolved | solid | total | ft | cm | ft | m |
| Colorado River | 65 | 1190 | 1255 | 0.54 | 16.5 | 540 | 165 |
| Pacific slopes, California | 103 | 597 | 700 | 0.30 | 9.1 | 300 | 91 |
| Western Gulf | 118 | 288 | 406 | 0.18 | 5.3 | 180 | 53 |
| Mississippi | 110 | 268 | 378 | 0.17 | 5.1 | 170 | 51 |
| S. Atlantic and eastern Gulf | 175 | 139 | 314 | 0.13 | 4.1 | 130 | 41 |
| N. Atlantic | 163 | 198 | 361 | 0.16 | 4.8 | 160 | 48 |
| Columbia | 163 | 125 | 288 | 0.13 | 3.8 | 130 | 38 |
| Average | 121 | 340 | 461 | 0.20 | 6.1 | 200 | 61 |

* Data for solid loads by S. Judson and D. F. Ritter (1964), *Jour. Geophys. Res.*, vol. 69, p. 3399, Table 3; for dissolved loads, by D. A. Livingstone (1963), U.S. Geol. Survey, Prof. Paper 440-G, Chapter G.

outline map showing the drainage regions and their areas. Notice the high rate for the Colorado River region. This area includes semi-arid plateaus, basin-and-range desert, and part of the Rocky Mountains. Here sparseness of vegetation and an abundance of weak sedimentary rocks and alluvium facilitate erosion. High rates for the Pacific slopes reflect rugged terrain and high elevations of recently uplifted mountain blocks. Rates for much of the central and eastern United States are comparatively low because of moderate to low relief and widespread cover of forest or grasslands. (Data of the Columbia region are based upon too short a term of record to warrant evaluation.)

The relationship between dissolved load and solid load is an interesting one. Figure 36.2 is a graph in which solid load is plotted against dissolved load. The dashed line shows a distinct trend—that areas yielding the largest total load tend to have the highest ratios of solid load to dissolved load. In a dominantly arid climate, such as that of the Colorado River region, little water is available in the soil- and ground-water zone for reaction of carbonic and other acids with rock, hence dissolved load is small in quantity and in ratio to solid load. In humid climates, such as the eastern United States, there is a water surplus and abundant soil and ground water, while at the same time vegetation holds back solids from entrainment in overland flow. Here dissolved load is important both in total quantity and in ratio to solid load.

**FIGURE 36.2.** Logarithmic plot of solid load against dissolved load for drainage areas shown in Figure 36.1, using data of Table 36.1. [Data of S. Judson and D. Ritter (1964), *Jour. Geophys. Res.*, vol. 69, p. 3399, Table 3.]

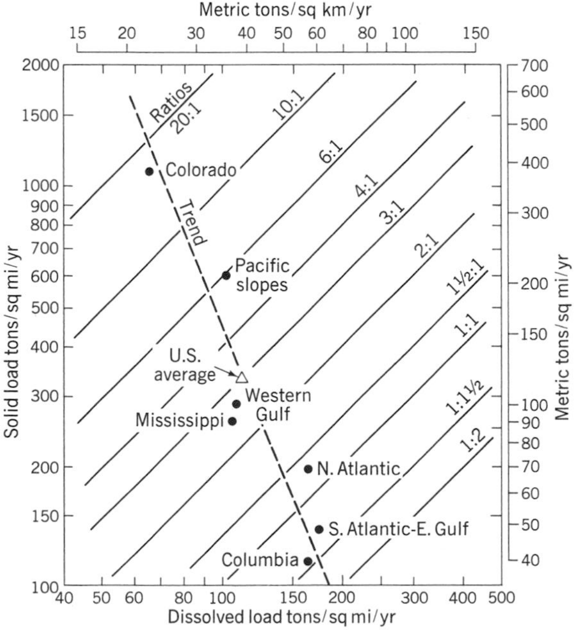


Extending his estimates of present denudation rates to other parts of the world, Professor Sheldon Judson has analyzed data of the Amazon River and Congo River basins (Table 36.2). Land erosion rates are known to have been greatly increased by Man's activity in deforestation and cultivation. Therefore the observed data of solid load have been reduced considerably, to represent an estimated geologic norm. Notice in Table 36.2 that the solid load of the combined United States regions has been reduced to about one-quarter of the value given in Table 36.1, with the result that the estimated denudation rate is about halved.

One might reason that rivers of the wet equatorial regions would carry the highest quantities of dissolved solids. However, Table 36.2 shows that both the Amazon and Congo basins yield much smaller amounts of dissolved solids per unit of area than do the humid eastern areas of the United States (Table 36.1). The explanations may lie in part in the effects of prolonged chemical alteration and leaching of equatorial soils and saprolite, which have been carried to the point that comparatively little further chemical activity can now take place.

## Maximum denudation rates

Denudation rates are strongly influenced by elevation of the surface of a landmass above baselevel. The higher a mountain block rises, the steeper will be the gradients, on the average, of streams carving into that mass. Because stream abrasion and transportation ability (both capacity and competence) increase strongly as gradients become steeper, the rate of denudation will be highest for the most highly elevated crustal mass and will diminish as elevations become lower. Also to be taken into account is the heightened intensity of

**TABLE 36.2. ESTIMATED DENUDATION RATES FOR THREE WORLD REGIONS***

| Region | Load, tons/sq mi/yr dissolved | solid | total | Denudation rate ft/1000 yr | cm/1000 yr |
|---|---|---|---|---|---|
| Amazon River basin | 95 | 225 | 320 | 0.15 | 4.7 |
| Congo River basin | 103 | 35 | 138 | 0.07 | 2.0 |
| United States | 111 | 95† | 206 | 0.10 | 3.0 |
| Weighted means | 103 | 138 | 241 | 0.12 | 3.6 |

* Data from S. Judson (1968), "Erosion of the Land," *Amer. Scientist*, vol. 56, no. 4, pp. 356–374, Table 2. Includes data of R. J. Gibbs (1967), "Geochemistry of the Amazon River System," *Geol. Soc. Amer. Bull.*, vol. 78, pp. 1203–1232.
† Solid load reduced to adjust for estimated increased erosion because of Man's activity.

rate of rock break-up with increasing altitude because of frost action.

Based upon measured volumes of sediment brought by streams from small watersheds in mountainous areas, denudation rates of 3 to 5 ft (1 to 1.5 m) per 1000 years are about the maximum that can be expected as average values for high mountain masses.[2] These rates are very much greater than for large continental areas of moderate to low elevation. As Table 36.1 shows, average denudation rates for the eastern and central regions of the United States run from 0.13 to 0.17 ft (4 to 5 cm) per 1000 years, although much higher values are found locally in small areas of highly erodible soil and rock.

We can conclude that rates of uplift of a landmass during orogeny are faster, by a factor of perhaps 5 to 10 times, than the maximum rates of denudation of the uplifted masses. This disparity easily accounts for the presence of great alpine ranges such as the Himalaya, Alps, and Andes.

[2] Based on data of S. A. Schumm (1963), U.S. Geol. Survey, Professional Paper 454-H, pp. H3–H4.

**FIGURE 36.3.** Schematic diagram of denudation of a landmass following orogenic uplift.

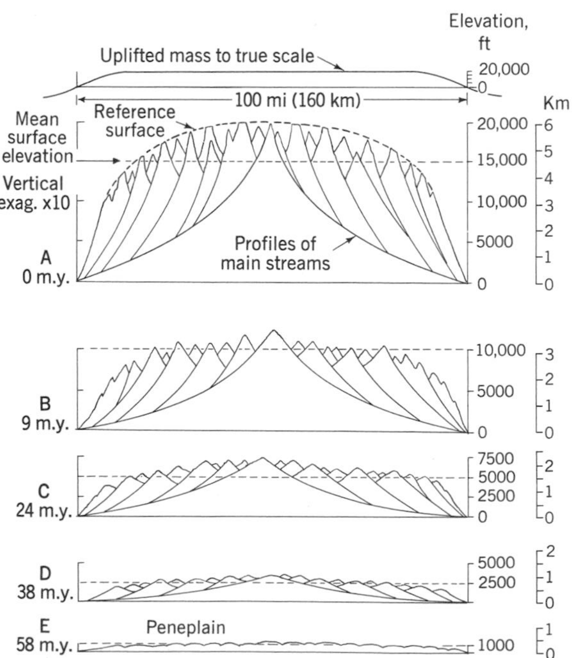


## A model denudation system

Using certain reasonable assumptions, we can devise a model of the denudation process and from it perhaps obtain some idea of the order of magnitude of time spans involved in reduction of a mountain mass to a peneplain.

First, it is assumed that during orogeny a substantial crustal mass is arched up (or lifted as a block along boundary faults) (Figure 36.3). Arbitrarily we assign a width of 100 mi (160 km) to the uplifted mass, for this is about the order of magnitude of width of a number of present-day ranges, including the Alps, Carpathians, Pyrenees, Caucasus, Alaska Range, Sierra Nevada, Cascades, Rockies, and Appalachians. Length of the uplift is not important in this analysis—a segment some tens of miles long will do. The uplifted mass is bordered by low areas, at or below sea level, which can serve as receptors of detritus. An initial surface of reference, close to sea level, is raised to a summit elevation of, say, 20,000 ft (6 km). In Figure 36.3 a dashed line shows how this reference surface has been deformed by the orogenic uplift. In Figure 36.4, a graph on which elevation is plotted against time, orogeny is shown by the steeply rising dashed line. Orogeny is given a span of 5 million years (m.y.), but most of the rise in elevation occurs within 2 m.y. Uplift tapers off in rate and becomes zero at zero reference time.

Denudation has been in progress during the uplift, increasing in intensity as elevation increases. The elevated mass has been carved into a maze of steep-walled gorges organized into a fluvial system of steep-gradient streams. The profile of the rugged mountain mass and the main stream system are suggested in greatly exaggerated scale in Stage *A* of Figure 36.3. Let it be assumed that at time-zero the average elevation of the eroded surface lies at 15,000 ft (4.6 km). Thus some 5000 ft (1.5 km) of rock has been removed during orogenic uplift.

Starting at time-zero, a denudation rate of 3.5 ft (1.05 m) per 1000 yr is assumed for the entire surface. However, with decreasing elevation the rate of denudation itself diminishes in such a constant ratio that one-half of the available landmass is removed in each 15 m.y. period. We may call this time unit the *half-life* of the available mass. An additional assumption is that isostatic restoration occurs constantly in the ratio of four-to-five. The initial rate of net lowering of the surface will be only one-fifth of the denudation rate, or 0.7 ft (21 cm) per 1000 yr. In million-year units, this net lowering rate is 700 ft (213 m) per m.y. at time-zero

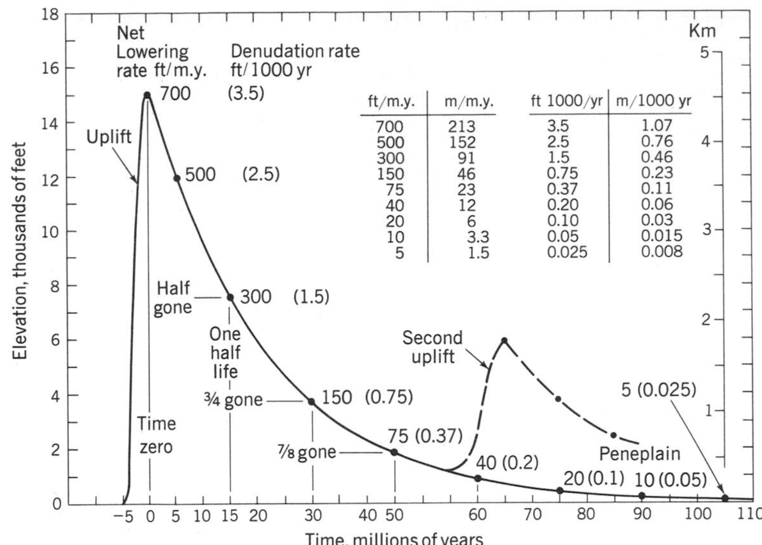


| ft/m.y. | m/m.y. | ft 1000/yr | m/1000 yr |
|---|---|---|---|
| 700 | 213 | 3.5 | 1.07 |
| 500 | 152 | 2.5 | 0.76 |
| 300 | 91 | 1.5 | 0.46 |
| 150 | 46 | 0.75 | 0.23 |
| 75 | 23 | 0.37 | 0.11 |
| 40 | 12 | 0.20 | 0.06 |
| 20 | 6 | 0.10 | 0.03 |
| 10 | 3.3 | 0.05 | 0.015 |
| 5 | 1.5 | 0.025 | 0.008 |

**FIGURE 36.4.** Arithmetically scaled graph of elevation change with time during landmass denudation, assuming a half-life of 15 million years and an initial net lowering rate of 700 ft (213 m) per million years.

(Figure 36.4). As shown by labels on the descending curve of Figure 36.4, when the elevation is reduced to 7500 ft (2.3 km) at the end of 15 m.y., the net rate of lowering will have fallen to about 300 ft (91 m) per m.y.

What we are describing here is a negative-exponential decay process not unlike the mass rate of decay of radioactive isotopes (Chapter 23). The curve of elevation flattens with the passage of time. Rates of denudation comparable with those observed today in the central and eastern United States are attained when the average elevation is about 1000 ft (0.3 km), after a lapse of some 60 m.y. Thereafter further decline in elevation is extremely gradual.

Figure 36.5 shows the exponential decay of elevation with time on a semi-logarithmic graph. Here the curve of Figure 36.4 appears as a straight line. Any one

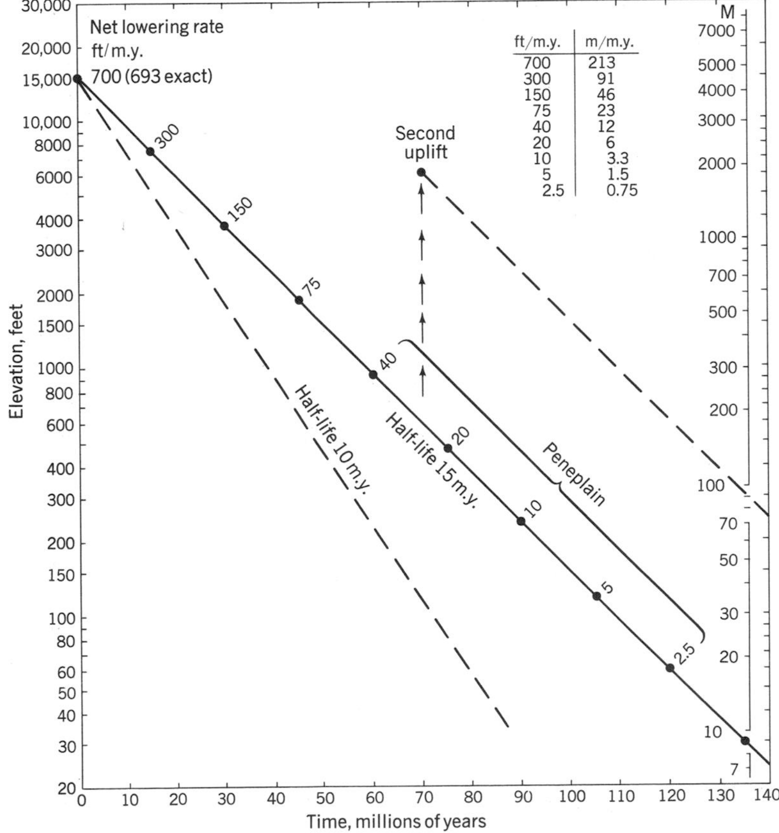


| ft/m.y. | m/m.y. |
|---|---|
| 700 | 213 |
| 300 | 91 |
| 150 | 46 |
| 75 | 23 |
| 40 | 12 |
| 20 | 6 |
| 10 | 3.3 |
| 5 | 1.5 |
| 2.5 | 0.75 |

**FIGURE 36.5.** Semi-logarithmic graph of landmass denudation, using the same parameters as in Figure 36.4.

**FIGURE 36.6.** The San Gabriel Mountains, near Montrose and Altadena, California. (Photograph by A. N. Strahler.)

of a large number of arbitrary initial values of elevation and net lowering rates might be substituted for the values shown. In all cases the progress of denudation would be represented on the graph by a straight line sloping downward to the right. More rapid change rates will be shown by steeper lines, meaning that low elevations will be achieved in shorter elapsed times. For example, as shown on Figure 36.5, if an initial net lowering rate of about 1050 ft (320 m) per m.y. is assumed, the half-life will be 10 m.y. The particular values selected for illustration seem to be commensurate with what is known about denudation rates.

Figure 36.3 shows a succession of imagined profiles of the landmass as it is lowered. The gradients of the streams are shown as declining with time, while the valley-side slopes become less steep. The over-all ruggedness of the landscape therefore decreases with time and gradually assumes a more subdued aspect (Figures 36.6 and 36.7). When the average elevation is reduced to 1000 ft (0.3 km) and less, the land surface may be considered to represent a peneplain. The word "peneplain" was coined by a geomorphologist, Professor W. M. Davis, from two words: "penultimate" and "plain." It is evident from the nature of the exponential-decay curve that zero elevation can never be reached. Instead, elevation approaches zero as time approaches infinity. Thus our model of denudation has no ultimate stage. In this context, the word "peneplain" is appropriate. Attainment of a peneplain in an uninterrupted denudation span of 40 to 70 m.y. is not an unreasonable guess, considering that most of the geologic periods are about of that order of duration. Continuous sedimentation throughout a single geologic period can thus be roughly equated to the contemporaneous denudation of an adjacent mountain mass produced by orogeny at the start of the period.

The denudation process can be interrupted at any point by renewal of orogenic uplift. A new curve of denudation then follows the cessation of uplift (Figures 36.4 and 36.5). Interruption can occur early in the denudation process, when elevations are high and relief is strong, or it may occur in the peneplain stage, when relief is low and even a minor crustal uplift can have radical effects. In later paragraphs the manifestations of such interruptions upon the landscape forms will be examined.

## Slopes and denudation

We found in Chapter 34 that stream systems tend to follow certain geometrical laws relating stream orders to stream lengths, basin areas, and channel slopes. Because stream channels transport loads of detritus supplied from the adjacent land slopes that form the valley walls, channel slopes must maintain an adjustment to the quantity and caliber (fragment size) of those loads. A load consisting of coarse fragments requires a steep channel gradient for transport, since the particles travel as bed load and considerable force of current is required to move them. On the other hand, a load of fine particles (silt and clay) travels largely in suspension and can be moved on a low stream gradient, provided only that the water is sufficiently turbulent to keep the particles in suspension.

In a recently uplifted mountain mass stream gradients will initially be steep because the average drop in elevation from the summit region to the surrounding lowlands occurs in a relatively short distance. Therefore deep canyons will be quickly carved into the uplifted block. The steep walls of these canyons will contribute large quantities of coarse rock fragments that will roll or slide into the canyon bottoms or will be swept down by storm runoff (Figure 36.8). This is why talus slopes are common features of the lower walls of many canyons. Steep channel gradients are required to move this coarse debris downvalley. Thus both the stream channel and its contributing valley-wall slopes evolve synchronously and maintain a reasonable degree of adjustment, one to the other, so far as their gradients are concerned. Rapid vertical and lateral cutting by the stream tends to cause steepening of the valley walls, and this action in turn maintains the rate of supply of detritus to the channel. The mutual adjustment is such that in a graded stream the ability of the stream to transport load is matched to the quantity of load supplied.

In the model of landmass denudation illustrated in Figure 36.3 both channel slopes and valley-wall slopes are shown to be steepest in the early stage of denudation, when average elevations are highest. Erosion rates are most rapid at this time and consequently within the total system the most rapid rates of energy transformation are found at this time. However, as the net lowering of land surfaces continues the potential energy of the system is steadily reduced, with the result that erosion rates diminish. A reduction in rate of down-cutting of stream channels (because average elevation drop in the given horizontal distance is reduced) reduces also the rate at which valley walls are subjected to undermining. Under the attack of weathering, mass wasting, and overland flow the valley walls can now be reduced to lower angles of inclination. Reduction in angle tends also to reduce the rates of

**FIGURE 36.7.** The Blue Ridge Upland in North Carolina. (Photograph by Frank J. Wright.)

slope wasting and hence to reduce the rate of production of debris, as well as to reduce the average size of the particles. In response, stream channels become graded to lower slopes.

Evidence of slope measurements made at a wide variety of geological regions, ranging in relief from high rugged mountains to low plains, supports the principle of synchronous reduction of slopes of stream channels and their contributing valley-side slopes as average elevation of the landmass diminishes. Figure 36.9 is a graph with double logarithmic scales on which the mean angle of valley-side slope is plotted against the mean channel slope. Each point represents a particular region in which sample measurements were taken. Although the points lie in a scattered band, it is evident that they tend to fall upon a sloping line in such a way that high angles of valley-side slopes are associated with steep channel gradients, while low valley-side slope angles are associated with gentle stream channel gradients. The ratio between the two slope values is not constant, but ranges from about 5:3 in the high-value range of the graph (upper right) to about 4:1 in the low-value range (lower left). This change in ratios suggests that valley-side slopes do not decline as rapidly in angle as do the associated channel slopes.

**FIGURE 36.8.** Steep-walled valley with straight slopes, Cabrini Canyon, Verdugo Hills, Los Angeles County. (Photograph by A. N. Strahler.)

The trend-zone shown in Figure 36.9 can serve as a model of geometrical change throughout the denudation of a landmass. Starting at time-zero, following the completion of orogeny, the stage of denudation would be represented by a point at the upper-right end of the trend-line. With the passage of time the representative point would be shifted down the trend-zone. In the peneplain stage the point would be found near the lower end of the zone. The denudation process spans millions of years, whereas the geologist has only a few decades in which to observe change. He therefore forms an array of many examples caught in various stages of development and from these reconstructs a model of the total pattern of change through time.

## Evolution of hill slopes

Accompanying the reduction of surface slopes throughout denudation is a gradual modification of the profiles of the valley walls and intervening divides and summits. These surfaces may be referred to as *hill slopes.* Figure 36.10 shows successions of such slope profiles, illustrating two models of slope evolution.

In early stages slopes tend to descend to stream channels with essentially straight profiles and narrow or sharp-crested divides. Slope profiles of this type are illustrated in Figure 36.8. In the model for a humid climate, as relief decreases the valley sides decline in angle of slope, and simultaneously the divides become more broadly rounded because of the increasing influence of soil creep and rain beat (raindrop impact). (Rounded divides and summits are illustrated by badlands of the Chinle formation, Figure 36.11, although the climate is semiarid.)

In later stages, particularly in humid climates having dense vegetation and thick residual soils, the hill-slope

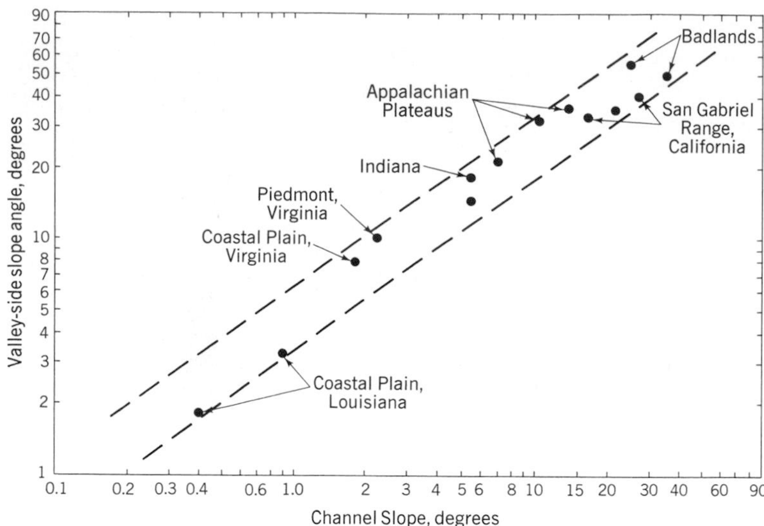


**FIGURE 36.9.** Logarithmic plot of mean valley-side slopes against mean channel slopes for sample regions differing greatly in relief and climate. [Data compiled by A. N. Strahler (1950), and E. Surovell (1968).]

profile develops a characteristic flattening near the base, giving the entire profile a sigmoid (S-shaped) curve. The basal flattening of profile may be produced by an accumulation of colluvium (slope wash) brought down by overland flow from the higher slopes. The colluvial slope merges with the floodplain.

Hill-slope profiles evolve in a somewhat different manner in arid climates than in humid. Following the early period of rapid denudation, the gradation of the major streams is typically followed by a retreat of the valley walls in a succession of parallel planes, as suggested in the right-hand side of Figure 36.10. At the foot of the retreating slope is a widening surface of comparatively low gradient, the *pediment,* across which flowing water transports the detritus from the base of the steep slope to the main channel. Divides are lowered because of the intersection of retreating steep slopes, narrowing the residual mass between them. Ultimately retreat of the steep slopes eliminates the higher mass entirely and pediments merge into a surface of low relief designated a *pediplain.* This model of hill-slope development, which is well demonstrated on a small scale in badlands (Figure 36.11), is characterized as a phenomenon of *parallel retreat* of slopes, as distinguished from *reclining retreat* seen in the model typical of humid climates.

As we shall find in Chapter 37, inequalities of rock resistance have strong control over the evolution of hill-slope forms. The idealized models presented here assume that the rock mass is homogeneous throughout, as is often the case in areas of plutonic igneous bodies and in thick sequences of shales.

**FIGURE 36.10.** Schematic diagram of hill-slope evolution with decreasing relief in humid and arid climates.

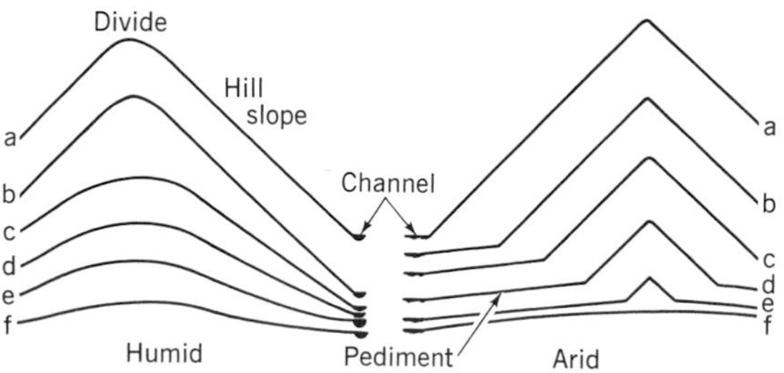


## Peneplains of the geologic past

Few good examples of peneplains in the formative process can be cited in the world today. Two reasons may contribute this deficiency of examples. First, the continents today stand relatively high, for the most part, because of the recency of world-wide orogenic and volcanic activity in the Cenozoic Era. Second, it is difficult to ascertain whether a broad plain lying close to sea level has been produced by erosion or by deposition. The Amazon-Orinoco lowland of northern South America may well represent a peneplain of the present day, if it should prove on further investigation to be largely a region of older bed rock reduced by erosion to its present level.

That peneplains have been produced in the geologic past is well documented by the study of unconformities exposed over long distances in the walls of canyons and cliffs. This topic has been explained in Chapter 28, using Grand Canyon as a classic region for the display of a major unconformity. (The outline of geologic history of the Precambrian rocks of Grand Canyon as given in Chapter 28 should be reviewed at this point.) Referring to Figure 36.12 we see that the tilted Algonkian strata rest unconformably upon Archean granites and schists, the surface of separation being an ancient peneplain of fluvial denudation. Beveling both Algonkian and Archean rocks is a second younger peneplain bearing monadnocks of resistant quartzite and forming the uneven surface upon which the Cambrian strata were deposited.

The significance of these unconformities in terms of vast cycles of fluvial denudation was first recognized by Major John Wesley Powell, leader of a pioneer voyage down in the Colorado River in 1869. Let us read his own words in which he attempted to interpret what he saw.

Referring to the Paleozoic strata, lying across the beveled edges of the tilted Algonkian strata, Powell wrote:[3]

The beds, themselves, are records of the invasion of the sea; the line of separation, the record of a long time when the region was dry land. The events in the history of this intervening time, the period of dry land, one might suppose were all lost.

Referring next to the unconformity between the Algonkian strata and the more ancient Archean schists upon which they lie, he stated:

Here, then we have evidences of another and more ancient period of erosion, or dry land. Three times has this great region been left high and dry by the ever shifting sea . . . and three times have the clouds gathered over the rocks, and carved out valleys with their storms. . . . The plateaus and mountains of the first and second periods have been destroyed or buried; their eventful history is lost; the rivers that ran into the sea are dead.

Reviewing the history of this threefold assemblage of rock units, Powell summarized:

We have looked back unnumbered centuries into the past, and seen the time when the schists in the depths of the Grand Canyon were first formed as sedimentary beds beneath the sea; we have seen this long period followed by another of dry land—so long that even hundreds, or perhaps thousands, of feet of beds were washed away by the rains; and, in turn, followed by another period of ocean triumph, so long, that at least ten thousand feet of sandstones were accumulated as sediments, when the sea yielded dominion to the powers of the air, and the region was again dry land. But aerial forces carried away the ten thousand feet of rocks, by a process slow yet unrelenting, until the sea again rolled over the land, and more than ten thousand feet of rocky beds were built over the bottom of the sea; and then again the restless sea retired. . . . Thus ever the land and sea are changing; old lands are buried, and new lands are born, and with advancing periods new complexities of rock are found; new complexities of life evolved.

Of course, where sedimentary strata of marine deposition now overlie an extensive erosion surface carved on older rocks we must take into account that

[3] J. W. Powell (1875), *Exploration of the Colorado River of the West and Its Tributaries,* Washington, D.C., U.S. Govt. Printing Office, 291 pp.

**FIGURE 36.11.** Badlands of the Chinle formation, Painted Desert, Arizona. (Photograph by A.T.&S.F. Railway.)

the action of waves and currents may have had an important effect in modifying the peneplain as it was gradually submerged and overlapped by the sea. It seems entirely reasonable that a slow submergence would permit wave action to erode an appreciable thickness of bedrock from the peneplain, thus producing a *marine peneplain,* somewhat different in its surface features from the peneplain of fluvial denudation. One might deduce that the marine peneplain would more closely resemble a geometrically plane surface. The role of wave action in continental denudation and the evidence of marine erosion as seen in unconformities are discussed in Chapter 38.

Because the earth's crust is affected spasmodically by epeirogenic warpings, a peneplain is eventually elevated or depressed, bringing to an end the epoch of continuous fluvial denudation (Figure 36.13). If uplift occurs, a new landmass is brought above base-level and denudation is revived with an intensity appropriate to the height of elevation. This event is described as *rejuvenation.* Now, however, the drainage systems are already well established, hence general valley entrenchment quickly ensues. The peneplain surface is gradually destroyed, but it may persist in the form of flat-topped divides forming a generally

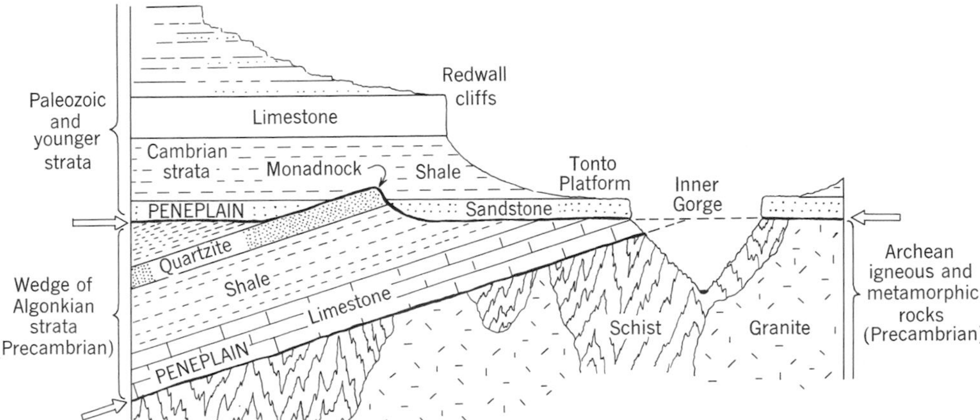


**FIGURE 36.12.** Schematic cross section through the inner reaches of the Grand Canyon of the Colorado River, Arizona, showing ancient peneplains.

A

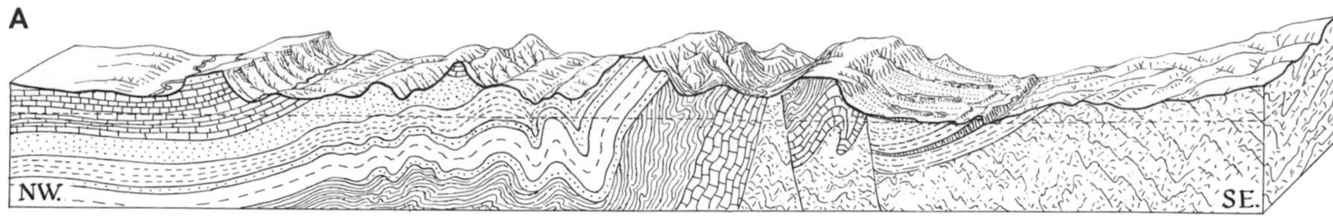


B

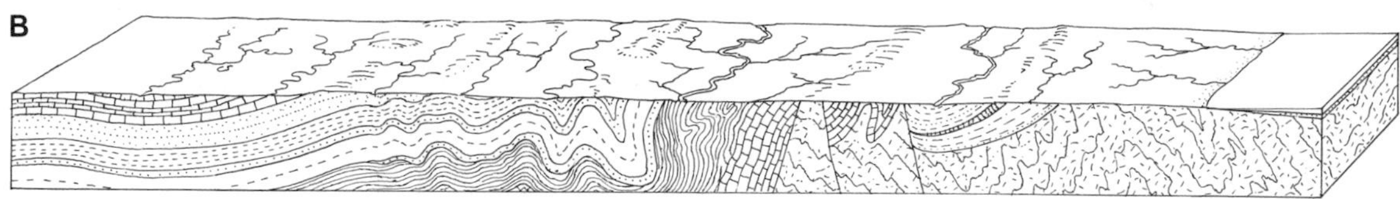

C

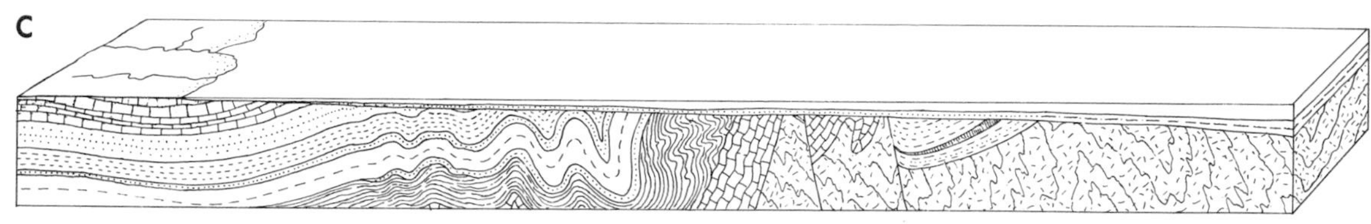

D

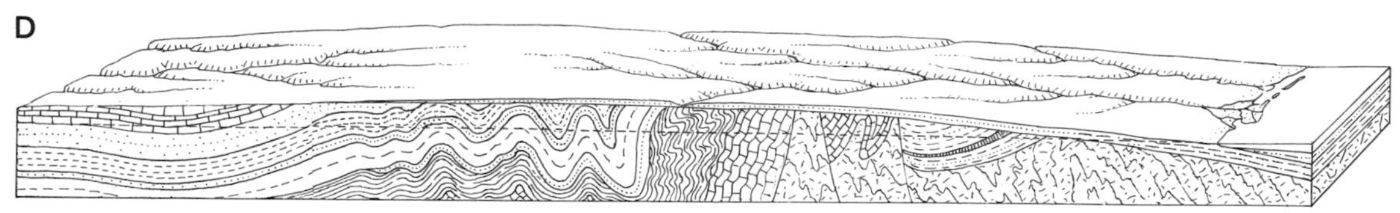

**FIGURE 36.13.** Development of peneplains of the eastern United States in the Mesozoic and Cenozoic Eras. (Drawn by Erwin Raisz; reproduced by permission of Columbia Univ. Press.) (*A*) Mountainous relief of the late Triassic and early Jurassic periods follows block faulting. (*B*) Jura-Cretaceous peneplain bevels fold and fault structures. (Fall Zone peneplain.) (*C*) Continental subsidence brings Cretaceous seas over the peneplain. Strata are deposited. (*D*) The continent is uparched. Consequent streams flow seaward on the cover of Cretaceous strata. (*E*) By Miocene time another peneplain has been formed. (Schooley peneplain.) (*F*) Again the continent is broadly upwarped and streams are rejuvenated. (*G*) By late Pliocene time a younger and lower peneplain has developed on the zones of weakest rock. (Harrisburg peneplain.) Resistant rocks form bold monadnock ridges. (*H*) A slight uplift, followed by minor entrenchment of streams, completes the topography as seen today.

accordant upland level, as shown in Block *G* of Figure 36.13. Figure 36.14 illustrates the contrast between the gently undulating peneplain surface and the steep-sided trenches carved into it by streams experiencing an intensification of erosional activity. Ultimately all vestiges of the peneplain surface will be destroyed, but its effects persist in a uniformity of summit levels throughout the area.

Uplifted and dissected peneplains are widespread over the continents today. One good example is the *Piedmont peneplain,* forming a zone 100 mi (160 km) wide and 750 mi (1200 km) long through Maryland, Virginia, the Carolinas, and Georgia. Carved on a belt of igneous and metamorphic rocks of varied types, this peneplain was completed in the late Cenozoic Era and subsequently uplifted a few hundreds of feet. It is now dissected to a rolling landscape of low hills over which summit levels are remarkably accordant. Stone Mountain, a monolithic stock of granite, rises sharply above the surrounding peneplain (Figure 36.15). A prominent hill or mountain of this type, owing its existence to superior resistance to erosion, is known as a *monadnock.*

Older than the Piedmont peneplain, and therefore found only at the summit level of the higher ridges of parts of the Appalachian Mountains and New England, is the *Schooley peneplain* (Figure 36.13*E*). Although widespread over the eastern United States in the mid-Cenozoic Era, only vestiges of this peneplain remain in the uniform summit levels of ridges upheld by the

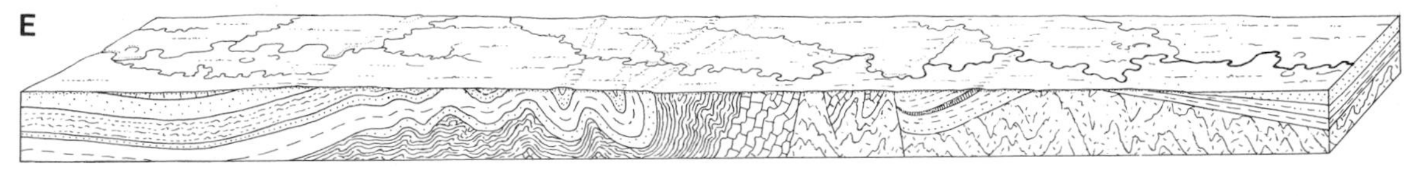


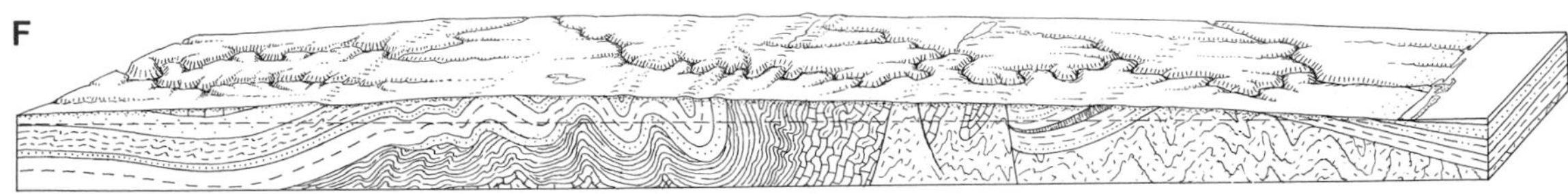


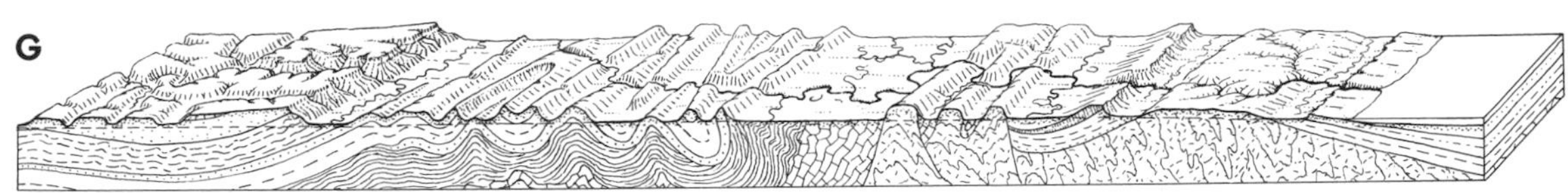


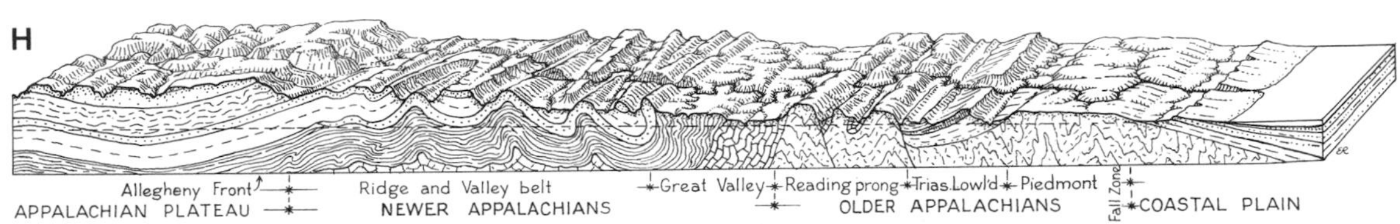


most resistant quartzites and gneisses of the Appalachians.

## Stream rejuvenation; entrenched meanders

In the normal evolution of a stream, as explained in Chapter 35, the condition of grade with respect to the baselevel is quickly achieved. At this point the erosional activity of the stream changes from one of dominant downcutting to one of lateral cutting, producing the floodplain. At any time in the course of this developmental history the baselevel of the stream may fall appreciably relative to the mouth of the stream. Such a change may come about because of a lowering of sea level or because the continental crust locally rises. The establishment of a relatively lower new baselevel has a profound effect upon the graded stream, because the extended portion of the stream to its new mouth is usually on a much steeper gradient than the stream had previously established near its mouth (Figure 36.16).

As suggested by successive profiles *A* through *F* in Figure 36.16, the steepened portion of the stream is a zone of intense erosion because stream velocity is greatly increased and the stream capacity exceeds the load. Here channel degradation occurs and there may be formed a series of rapids as the erosion acts on bedrock masses of varied resistance. The reach of the stream experiencing degradation spreads rapidly upstream and a narrow steep-walled gorge or canyon is produced, contrasting sharply with the broad-floored valley previously present.

The renewal of downcutting by a stream as a result of crustal rise or a drop of sea level is the precursor to rejuvenation of the entire landscape, because its effects travel upstream into all branches of the system and ultimately bring on an intensification of the total denudation process. A common effect of rejuvenation is the production of a *rock terrace,* representing the broad valley floor of the previous graded state into which the rejuvenated stream has carved a narrow inner gorge (Figure 36.17).

In an extreme case of rejuvenation the floodplain meanders of an alluvial river may become deeply *incised,* or carved, into the underlying bedrock (Figure 36.18), producing *entrenched meanders* that form a winding river gorge. An example is the gorge of the Moselle River in western Germany (Figure 36.19), interpreted as the result of rejuvenation of a meandering river.

## Rejuvenation and isostasy

The simple model of denudation proposed in an earlier part of this chapter included the assumption that

**FIGURE 36.14.** The St. John peneplain, southeast of Barranquitas, Puerto Rico, is represented by a rolling upland surface at an elevation of about 2000 ft (600 m). The peneplain, of Miocene age, is now deeply trenched by the Rio Usabón flowing in the steep-walled Canyon de San Cristobal. (Photograph by R. P. Briggs, U.S. Geological Survey.)

isostatic compensation is continuously in progress and keeps pace with mass removal. It seems unlikely that such an assumption is valid. Instead, because the lithosphere has a certain amount of strength, it is more likely that isostatic compensation during denudation takes place in short episodes separated by long periods

**FIGURE 36.15.** Stone Mountain, near Atlanta, Georgia, is a body of massive light-gray granite almost free of joint fractures. Because of its superior resistance to forces of weathering and erosion, the granite stands some 650 ft (200 m) higher than the surrounding Piedmont plateau. (U.S. Air Force photograph.)

when the crust does not rise. In other words, until a certain minimum mass of rock has been removed the isostatic imbalance is not enough to deform the lithosphere. After a critical point, further removal triggers a rather rapid uplift to bring about a new isostatic equilibrium.

In view of the likelihood of spasmodic isostatic uplifts, the simple model curve of denudation must be broken into a series of small steps, as shown in Figure 36.20. In this case it has been assumed that isostatic compensation occurs quickly after 1000 ft (300 m) of rock has been removed. However, the uplift is only 80% of that amount, or 800 ft (244 m). Each such uplift starts a new phase of denudation, but because the crust remains fixed during this denudation the net lowering rate is the same as the denudation rate for the given altitude. As a result the early part of the denudation phase is one of rapid mass removal, but this rate falls off in a negative-exponential curve. The model can be constructed for other assumed requirements for triggering isostatic uplift. Also, it would be more realistic to allow a definite time span for isostatic uplift, which would soften the teeth of the curve.

Examination of the new model of denudation shown in Figure 36.20 leads to some interesting deductions. While landmass elevations are high, above about 4000 ft (1200 km), episodes of isostatic uplift and subsequent denudation occur in quick succession—e.g., at about 1-m.y. intervals. Because the changes in level constitute a small relative fraction of the total elevation, there would probably be no appreciable effects upon profiles of the streams and their valley-side slopes. However, when the elevation of the landmass is in the peneplain region—in the 1000-ft (300-m) range (about at the 60-m.y. mark on the graph)—the

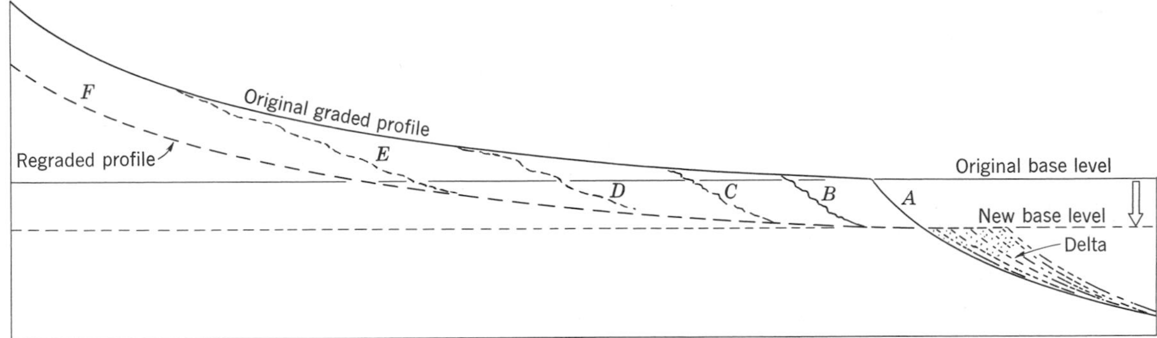


**FIGURE 36.16.** A drop of baselevel initiates regrading of the stream profile. Changes progress headward from *A* through *F*, until grade is reestablished.

isostatic uplift not only approximately doubles the thickness of the available landmass but also brings on a very sharp increase in denudation rate. The result is a profound rejuvenation of the landscape. The peneplain is then sharply incised by the principal streams and the new set of steep slopes contrasts sharply with the subdued slopes of the remaining parts of the peneplain. As redesigned, the denudation model accounts for episodic uplift of otherwise tectonically stable crustal regions, such as the Appalachians.

Other causes of epeirogenic uplift are not excluded by the model of episodic isostatic uplift. For reasons that are obscure, epeirogenic movements, both up and down, can be expected as a result of large-scale motions of the lithospheric plate in the processes of continental drift.

It is interesting to find that negative isostatic anomalies on the order of 20 to 40 milligals exist over wide areas of the Appalachians, exposed shield, covered shield, and Rocky Mountains. There are also many small areas of positive anomalies in these regions, but the tendency toward negative values is quite marked. Dr. George P. Woollard, a leading authority on gravity measurements and their interpretation, states that "changes in crustal thickness due to surface erosion [are] going on at a faster rate than can be compensated through crustal buoyancy."[4] He goes on to say that all mountain ranges show a history of basal planation followed by rejuvenation. In old mountain ranges, such as the Appalachians, this sequence has been repeated several times. In the Rockies rejuvenation has occurred at least once since the range was reduced to low relief following its uplift in the Laramian orogeny of Cretaceous time. Dr. Woollard expects that the isostatic anomalies will be about zero when a mountain range is originally formed, but that negative anomalies will develop after reduction to a low surface of erosion. Positive anomalies might be expected following rejuvenation if the momentum of crustal uplift carried the base of the crust to a level above that required for perfect equilibrium.

Here we have an example of the interrelationship between geomorphology and geophysics. It serves as a reminder that no field of specialization in the earth sciences can be investigated effectively without calling upon other branches of specialization for information essential to the explanation of a given phenomenon.

[4] Quoted and paraphrased with the author's permission from G. P. Woollard (1966), *The Earth Beneath the Continents*, Geophysical Monograph 10, Washington, D.C., Am. Geophys. Union, p. 584.

## Denudation in an arid climate

Desert regions differ strikingly in appearance from humid regions because of differences in landforms and vegetation. Despite the fact that many of the most arid deserts experience heavy rains only at intervals of several years, the evidences of the action of running water are clearly seen in the presence of numerous dry channels. On the rare occasions when heavy downpours produce much runoff, the eroding and transporting power of overland flow and channel flow is fully equal to that in any humid region. The absence of a vegetative cover is an important factor, for without the protective effect of vegetation there is nothing to stop overland flow from sweeping great quantities of coarse particles of weathered rock down the slopes

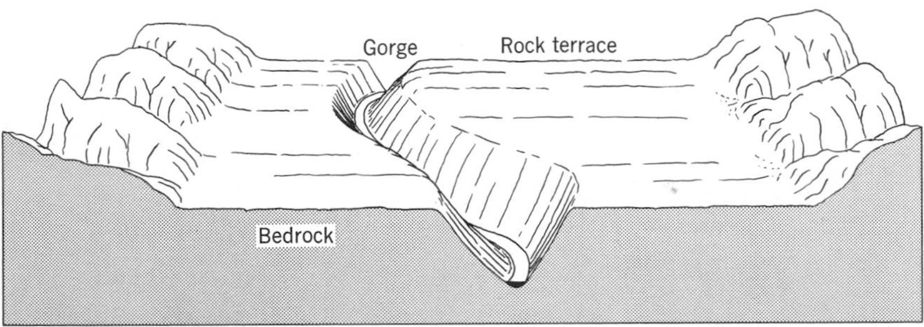


**FIGURE 36.17.** A rock terrace, formerly a floodplain belt, borders a steep-walled inner gorge resulting from stream rejuvenation.

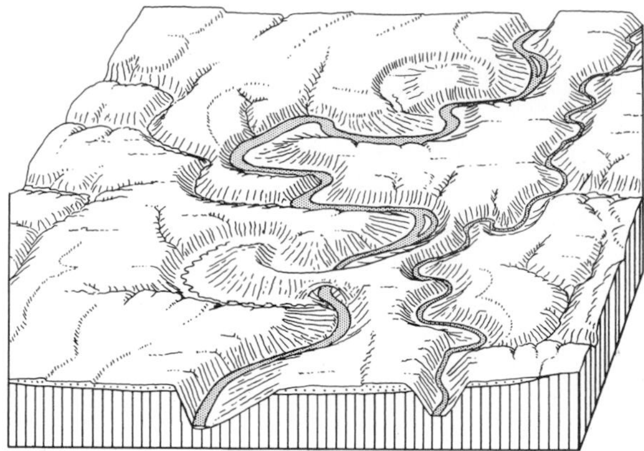

**FIGURE 36.18.** Entrenched meanders with cutoffs and a natural bridge. (© 1960, John Wiley & Sons, New York. After a drawing by Erwin Raisz.)

and into adjacent channels. Charged with a heavy load of debris, the raging torrent sweeps down steep canyon grades and spreads out upon the adjacent valley floor.

Much desert rainfall, especially that of mountainous deserts, is from local convectional storms (thunderstorms). These tend to cover only small areas, hence runoff may be limited to a single small watershed. Unlike the regional floods of river systems in humid lands, described in Chapter 34, desert floods affect only short reaches of stream systems and the water is rapidly lost by evaporation and influent seepage. Thus the debris load is carried only short distances—usually from a mountain range to the adjacent valley floor, where it accumulates in alluvial fans.

An idealized model of fluvial denudation in a mountainous desert region is illustrated by block diagrams of Figure 36.21. Orogeny has elevated a large fault block (right) and an anticlinal arch (left). Between them is a down-faulted depression. Summit elevations may range from 5000 to 10,000 ft (1.5 to 3 km) and valley floors from a few hundred feet down to elevations below sea level, as at *D* in Block *A*. For purposes of illustration little denudation is shown to have occurred during orogeny. Nevertheless, processes of fluvial denudation are at work from the very beginning,

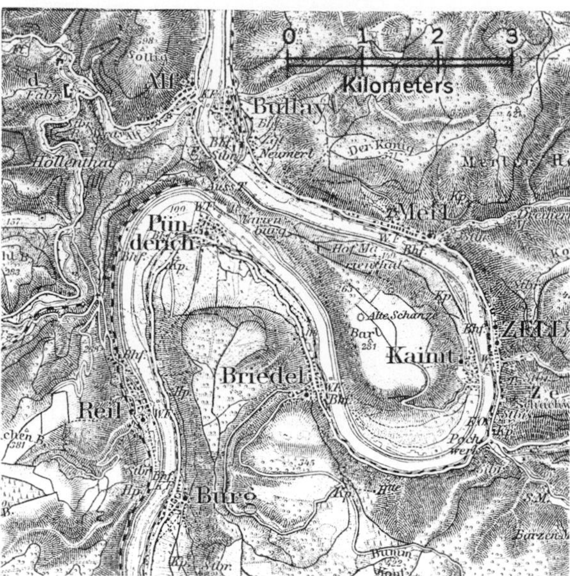


**FIGURE 36.19.** Entrenched meandering gorge of the Moselle River, Eifel district of western Germany. (Portion of Sheet 504, Cochem, Germany, 1:100,000, 1890.)

dissecting the rising masses and filling the depressions with alluvium even as they are being formed.

The fault depression shown in Block *A* receives sediment from adjacent mountain slopes, but it does not fill with water to form a lake because evaporation greatly exceeds precipitation in the arid climate. Block *B* shows the effects of prolonged denudation and sedimentation. The mountain blocks have been carved into an intricate system of valleys and ridges. The intermontane basins are now filled with hundreds of feet of alluvium, which is spreading over upon the ragged mountain borders. Far out upon the alluvial valley are flat *playa* surfaces, underlain by fine silts and clays, at times inundated by shallow ephemeral lakes, the evaporation of which causes dissolved salts to accumulate upon the playa surface.

As denudation proceeds, the mountain ranges are reduced both in elevation and in extent, shrinking along the margins at the expense of the rising and expanding

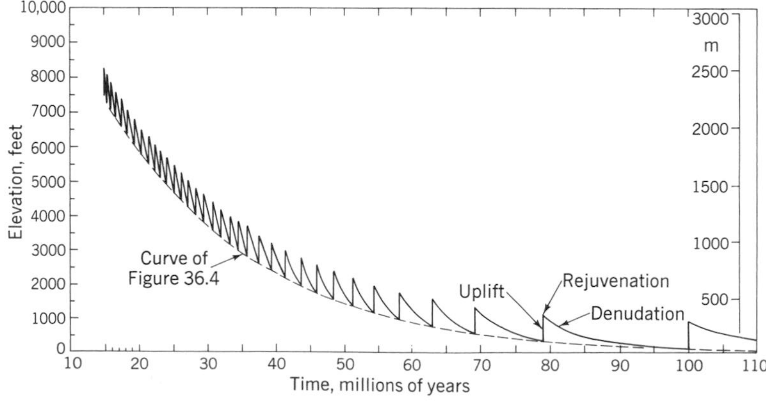


**FIGURE 36.20.** Plot of elevation against time for modified model of landmass denudation assuming a succession of abrupt isostatic uplifts. Compare with Figure 36.4.

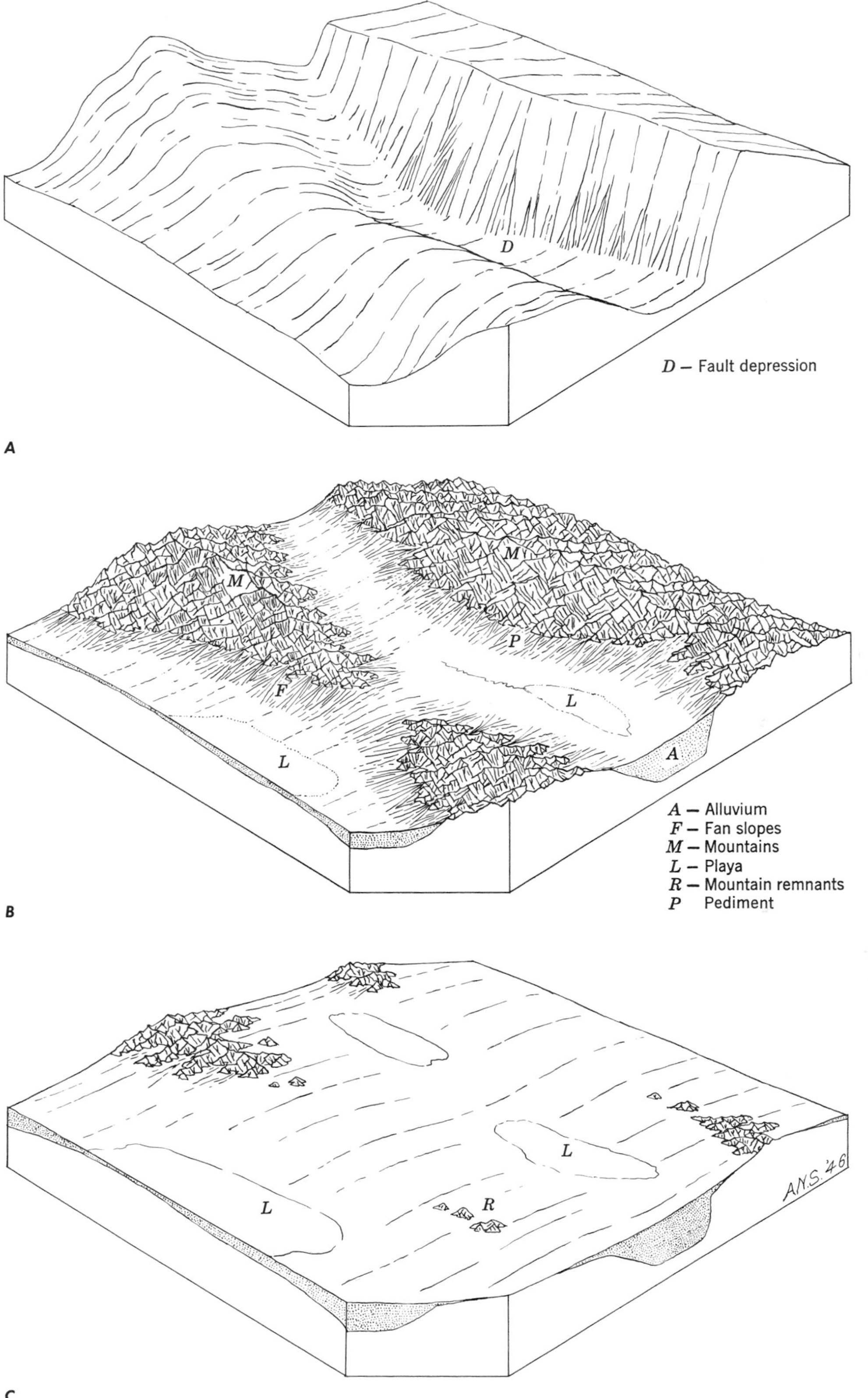


**FIGURE 36.21.** Fluvial denudation in a mountainous desert region. (*A*) Maximum tectonic relief. (*B*) Mountain blocks deeply dissected and intermontaine basins partly filled. (*C*) Small residual mountain masses, vast alluvial surfaces, and playa floors. (© 1960, John Wiley & Sons, New York.)

**FIGURE 36.22.** A rock pediment, now bared by erosional removal of the thin alluvial cover. Western side of Dragoon Mountains, near Benson, Arizona. (Photograph by Douglas Johnson.)

surface of alluvial deposition. Figure 26.9 shows a desert landscape similar to that depicted in Block *B* of Figure 36.21.

In an advanced stage of denudation, shown in Block *C*, mountain areas shrink to small remnants with many isolated fragments known as *inselbergs* (island mountains) detached from the main mass by the surrounding sloping sea of alluvium.

As the mountain base is worn back, there may be produced a sloping platform of bedrock thinly covered by layers of alluvium of growing fans. This rock surface is a pediment (Figure 36.22). Zones of rock pediment are shown fringing the mountain bases in Block *B* of Figure 36.21 at points indicated by the letter *P*. Pediments become broader until the intervening mountain mass is entirely consumed, leaving a thinly veneered pediment surface in its place, as suggested in Block *C*.

Completion of denudation results in a pediplain formed in part of the eroded bases of the mountain blocks and in part of thick alluvial deposits. Such a pediplain may be formed without reference to the sea as a controlling baselevel because the drainage has been in the form of local interior systems. The pediplain may thus be formed hundreds of feet above sea level.

The cycle of fluvial denudation in a desert climate is well illustrated in the Great Basin physiographic province of southern Oregon, Nevada, western Utah, and southeastern California, and in the Mojave and Sonoran Deserts extending farther south and east. Recently uplifted fault blocks are characteristic of northern Nevada and southern Oregon. Advanced denudation is illustrated in central and southern Nevada and in the Death Valley region (Figure 26.9). Pediplain development can be found in southwestern Arizona.

## The role of denudation throughout geologic time

The principal geologic role of the continental denudation process has been that of producing sediment, part of which becomes consolidated sedimentary rock of the continents and part of which enters the deep ocean basins. Professor Sheldon Judson has estimated the components of a mass-transfer system from continents to oceans (Table 36.3). Stream transport has been adjusted to a value estimated to have been in effect before man's intervention in normal erosion processes. Although these figures are subject to some uncertainty in view of the lack of sufficient basic information, they show clearly that streams contribute almost all of the total mineral matter entering the oceans. Furthermore, since most of the sediment accumulates in water depths less than 10,000 ft (3 km), much of it remains near the continental margins.

**TABLE 36.3. ESTIMATED MASS TRANSPORT OF MINERAL MATTER FROM CONTINENTS TO OCEAN BASINS***

| | Million metric tons per year |
|---|---|
| Mass derived from continents: | |
| by stream transport | 9.3 |
| by wind transport | 0.06 to 0.36 |
| by glacier transport | 0.1 |
| Mass from extraterrestrial sources | 0.00035 to 0.14 |
| Total entering ocean basins | 9.6 approx. |
| Mass of sediment deposited in oceans: | |
| in water depths less than 10,000 ft | 5 to 10 |
| in water depths over 10,000 ft | 1.2 |
| Total accumulation in ocean basins | 6.2 to 11.2 |

* Data from S. Judson (1968), *American Scientist,* vol. 56, no. 4, p. 371.

Let us now consider the production and accumulation of sediment in terms of geologic time, using the annual rate of 10 million ($10^{10}$) metric tons as a round figure taken from Table 36.3. It has been estimated that the total existing world mass of sediments, including the sedimentary rocks, is $1.7 \times 10^{18}$ metric tons, which is about 200 million times the annual increment. Consequently all of the known sediment of the earth could have been furnished by continental denudation in about 200 m.y., or since late Triassic time. However, sedimentary rocks (now metamorphosed) have been dated as 3 b.y. old, or even older, thus it is certain that many times over the mass of sedimentary material has been produced than now exists. What became of this enormous mass of sediment? The answer lies in the rock-transformation cycle, explained in Chapter 20. While some sedimentary strata became metamorphic rocks without undergoing melting, it seems inescapable that most of the sediment eventually was melted to produce magmas deep within orogenic belts. These magmas intruded higher parts of the crust to become batholiths of plutonic igneous rock, largely of granitic composition. Vast areas of such granitic igneous rock must have been exposed over the continental shields for vast spans of geologic time. Therefore the same mineral matter must have been recycled repeatedly, passing through the sequence of denudation, sedimentation, metamorphism and remelting, intrusion, crustal uplift, and again release by denudation to begin the next cycle.

Having placed the role of denudation in its geologic perspective, we turn in the next chapter to the control exerted upon landforms by the existing inequalities of rock resistance developed by crustal evolution in the past. Such is the inheritance of geologic history visited upon the environment of today.

## References for further study

Schumm, S. A. (1963), *The Disparity Between Present Rates of Denudation and Orogeny,* U. S. Geol. Survey, Professional Paper 454-H, Washington, D.C., U.S. Govt. Printing Office, 13 pp.

Leopold, L. B., M. G. Wolman, and J. P. Miller (1964), *Fluvial Processes in Geomorphology,* San Francisco, Freeman, 522 pp., chaps. 3, 8, 12.

Fairbridge, R. W., ed. (1968), *The Encyclopedia of Geomorphology,* New York, Reinhold, 1295 pp. See Arid cycle, Continental erosion, Denudation, Humid cycle, Slope analysis, Slopes.

Judson, S. (1968), "Erosion of the Land, or What's Happening to Our Continents?," *Amer. Scientist,* vol. 56, no. 4, pp. 356–374.

Thornbury, W. D. (1969), *Principles of Geomorphology,* 2nd ed., New York, Wiley, 594 pp., chaps. 5, 6, 8, 11.

# 37

# Landform and rock structure

FOR SIMPLICITY, the processes of weathering, mass wasting, and erosion by running water have thus far been treated as if they operate upon geologic materials of generally uniform composition and structure. Thus the model of landmass denudation has been based upon the assumption of a homogeneous rock body lying beneath the surface. One can find regions of the continents underlain by a single rock type, such as a large granite batholith, to serve as ideal locations to illustrate the ideal denudation system. But by far the largest proportion of the continental crust has inequalities in both resistance and structural arrangement of bedrock masses which appreciably modify landform development.

Rock masses that resist decay and disintegration by weathering or that by reason of their strong internal cohesion resist the erosion of running water are more slowly reduced by the process of fluvial denudation than adjacent rock masses more susceptible to weathering and erosion. Over a long period of time, differences develop in topographic relief corresponding with the differences in resistance presented by the bedrock elements. Characteristic patterns of ridges, valleys, and escarpments thus emerge, and drainage patterns are deformed to fit along zones of least rock resistance.

## Erosion forms of horizontal layers

Vast areas of the continental shields bear covers of marine sedimentary strata laid down upon a basement of ancient igneous and metamorphic rocks that had been reduced to

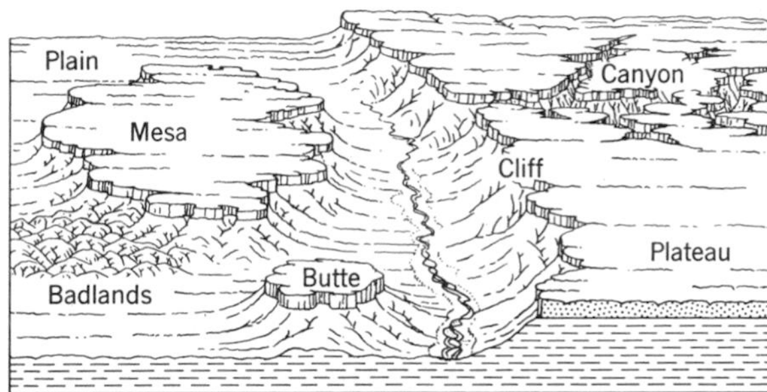


**FIGURE 37.1.** Landforms of horizontal strata evolving in an arid climate. (© 1960, John Wiley & Sons, New York.)

peneplains and submerged to become the floors of shallow inland and marginal seas. Although the aggregate thickness of these strata is in places several thousand feet, a figure that seems large to a human being, the deposits are actually relatively thin in comparison with the strata accumulated in subsiding geosynclinal troughs.

Over large parts of the continental shields strata of Paleozoic, Mesozoic, and Cenozoic ages have been raised in broad crustal upwarpings, or epeirogenic uplifts, involving little or no tilting, folding, or faulting. A particular sandstone layer, for example, may have been raised to elevations of several hundred to a few thousand feet above sea level with so little disturbance that it is inclined only a fraction of a degree from the horizontal. Such a departure from horizontality is scarcely detectable within a distance of several miles, and for all practical purposes we regard the layer as horizontal.

In the United States much of the region lying between the Rockies and the Appalachians is underlain by nearly horizontal strata. Another large region is that of the Colorado Plateau of Arizona, Utah, New Mexico, and Colorado. It is from these areas that we draw type examples of the landforms developed in horizontal strata.

The plateau basalts, described in Chapter 25, also constitute large expanses of near-horizontal layered rocks. Examples are the Columbia Plateau region of Washington, Oregon, and Idaho and the Deccan Plateau of western India.

**FIGURE 37.2.** Map of a portion of the Grand Canyon, showing characteristic benching of horizontal strata. The area shown, about 6 mi (10 km) across, occupies the northwest quarter of the Bright Angel Quadrangle. The isolated butte to right of center is Shiva Temple. Granite Gorge of the Colorado River crosses the bottom of the map. [From C. E. Dutton (1882), *Tertiary History of the Grand Canyon District,* U.S. Geol. Survey, Monograph 2, Washington, D.C., U.S. Govt. Printing Office, Plate 42, ff. p. 258.]

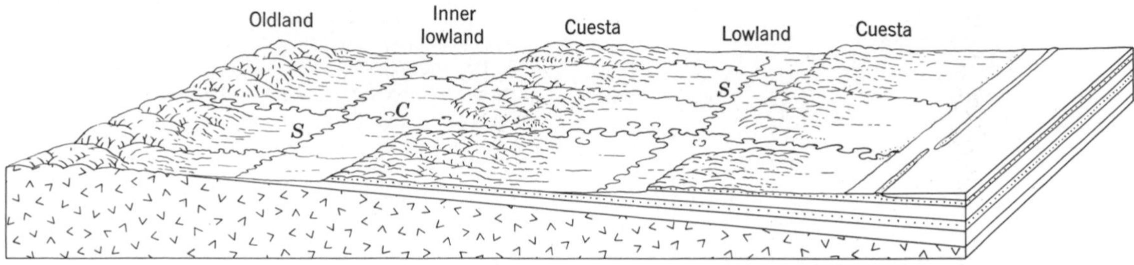


**FIGURE 37.3.** Landforms of a broad coastal plain. (© 1960, John Wiley & Sons, New York. Based on drawings by A. K. Lobeck.)

Details of landscape development in horizontal strata are illustrated in Figure 37.1. A cap rock of resistant sandstone maintains a nearly flat *plateau* surface, its edges standing as nearly vertical *cliffs* kept in sharp definition by constant undermining of weak shale beds beneath. Continued erosion causes a portion of the plateau to become detached. The resulting flat-topped mountain, bounded on all sides by steep cliffs, is termed a *mesa*. As a mesa shrinks by wastage of its surrounding cliffs it assumes the form of a small flat-topped hill, a *butte*.

Where several weak and resistant strata are found in alternation, the wasting back of a canyon wall produces a composite slope consisting of a succession of cliffs and intervening gentle slopes (Figure 37.2). A widening bench may be formed on the upper surface of a particularly thick massive layer. In time this bench may be expanded to a width of many miles by removal of the overlying strata. The resulting plateau-like surface is termed a *stratum plain* or *stripped structural surface*.

Drainage patterns developed upon horizontally layered rocks are of the *dendritic* form, described and illustrated in Chapter 34. Such a pattern develops in the absence of any systematic orientation of controlling structures within the rock. Although the alternating weak and resistant layers of a sedimentary sequence constitute a system of inequalities of resistance in the vertical direction through the mass, any given layer is uniform in the horizontal direction, hence it does not introduce any appreciable large-scale control over the direction taken by the growing finger-tip streams in the early stages of dissection.

Areas of horizontally layered rocks in a humid climate may not exhibit prominent cliffs, plateaus, or esplanades, particularly if strong inequalities in rock resistance are lacking and the masking cover of vegetation, soil, and residual overburden is thick.

**FIGURE 37.4.** Cuestas and lowlands of Mississippi and Alabama. (© 1965, John Wiley & Sons, New York. Based on a diagram by A. K. Lobeck.)

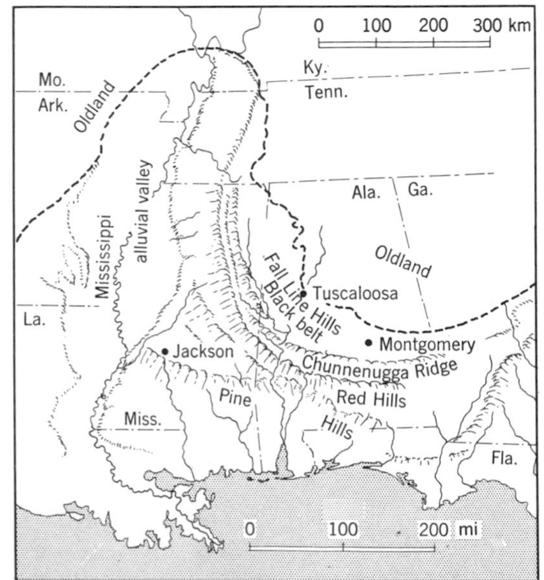


## Gently inclined strata—coastal plains

Most marine sedimentary strata deposited upon a sloping continental shelf during the Mesozoic and Cenozoic Eras and since uplifted by epeirogenic crustal movements possess a persistent seaward dip of perhaps 1° or 2° at most. This attitude results in part from the original slope of the deposit and in part from a crustal warping accompanying emergence. Such strata constitute a *coastal plain* (Figure 37.3). Because the deposition of the strata took place to the accompaniment of a series of marine invasions and retreats, individual stratigraphic units tend to thin to a feather-like edge toward the land and to thicken seaward.

When brought above sea level for the last time, the coastal plain presents a very smooth sloping plain across which flow streams bringing runoff from the region of older land, or simply, the *oldland*. Any stream that comes into existence upon a newly formed land surface by following the direction of the initial sope is termed a *consequent stream*. Streams crossing the new coastal plain are described as *extended consequent streams* because they were extended in length as emergence of the plain progressed.

After the processes of fluvial denudation have begun to act upon the poorly consolidated clays and sands of the coastal plain there emerge belts of low hills, representing exposed sand layers. Although the sand is not indurated, it resists erosion because of its high capacity for infiltration, for even heavy rains produce little overland flow on sand. Separating the hill belts are broad low valleys where the surface is underlain by layers of soft clays. The hill belts are *cuestas* and the valleys are *lowlands* (Figure 37.3).

As the lowlands have been excavated a new set of

**FIGURE 37.5.** A cuesta of the Paris basin, France. The view is toward the south. (Photograph by Douglas Johnson.)

streams, following the lowlands and joining the consequent streams at right angles, has appeared. These are *subsequent streams* formed by extending themselves headward along a belt or zone of weaker rock.

Some coastal plains, composed of poorly consolidated sands and clays, give only poorly defined cuestas appearing as belts of hills with indistinct ragged borders. An illustration is the coastal plain of Alabama and Mississippi (Figure 37.4). Other coastal plains—usually those of somewhat older geologic age, including Mesozoic strata (Jurassic and Cretaceous ages)—have highly indurated layers of sandstone, limestone, or chalk (a form of limestone) that strongly resist erosion and stand out in sharp contrast to the lowland belts of clay and shale. A good illustration is the *Paris basin* of northern France (Figure 37.5), where cuestas possess an abrupt steep face, termed the *inface,* opposite to the direction of dip, and a gentle descent on the *backslope* in the direction of dip. Another good example is the coastal plain of southeastern England (Figure 37.6), in which two cuestas are strongly defined—an inner one of Jurassic limestone and an outer one of Cretaceous chalk.

The gently dipping strata of coastal plains form ideal structures for the accumulation of artesian groundwater supplies. Sandy strata outcropping in cuestas serve as intake areas for precipitation. Many miles downdip artesian flow is obtained from the aquifer, there buried deeply beneath impermeable shales and clays.

Not all gently dipping layered rocks are in coastal plains. Any shield area within the continent may be warped into broad arches and saddles to produce zones of low dip, on the order of 1° to 3°. The result may be a series of cuestas and lowlands. A good example of a cuesta of Paleozoic strata is the Niagara cuesta, of massive Silurian limestone, that runs across western New York State, through southern Ontario, then between Lake Huron and Georgian Bay, and finally curves south to form the Door Peninsula in Wisconsin.

Niagara Falls, formed at the point where the north-flowing Niagara River crosses the Niagara cuesta, illustrates a basic principle of the control of rock structure upon the gradient of a large stream (Figure 37.7). The resistant Lockport limestone sustains the channel of the river upstream from the falls, but weak shales beneath the limestone are continually undermined, perpetuating the abrupt drop of the river profile (Figure 37.8). The falls have retreated about 6.5 mi (10.4 km) from the line of the Niagara escarpment, where the falls originated some 20,000 to 35,000 years ago.

**FIGURE 37.6.** Topographic diagram of southern England and Wales, showing cuestas and lowlands. *J*: Jurassic. *K*: Cretaceous. *O*: Oxford. *C*: Cambridge. *E*: Educational Lowland. (After a drawing by W. M. Davis.)

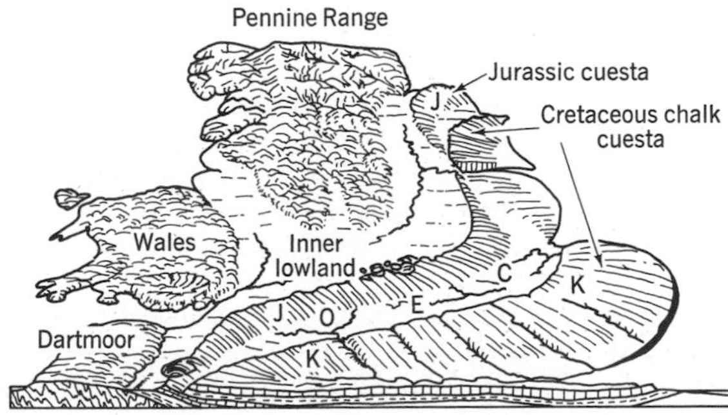


## Domes in layered rocks

An interesting tectonic structure of shield areas bearing a sedimentary cover is sharp upward doming. Typically

**FIGURE 37.7.** Bird's eye view of the Niagara Escarpment and Niagara River, looking southwest from a point over Lake Ontario. (Redrawn from a sketch by G. K. Gilbert, 1896.)

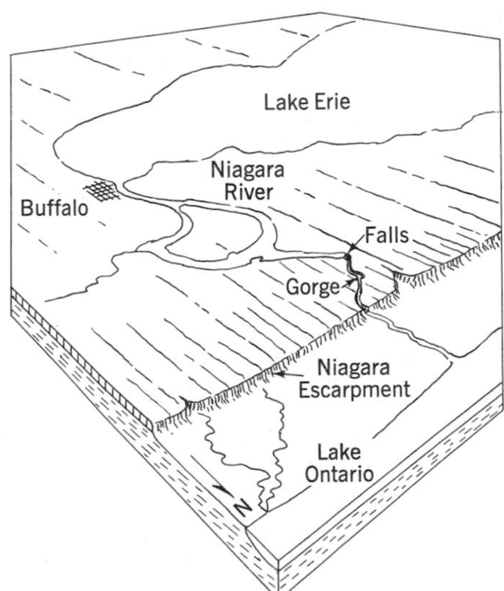

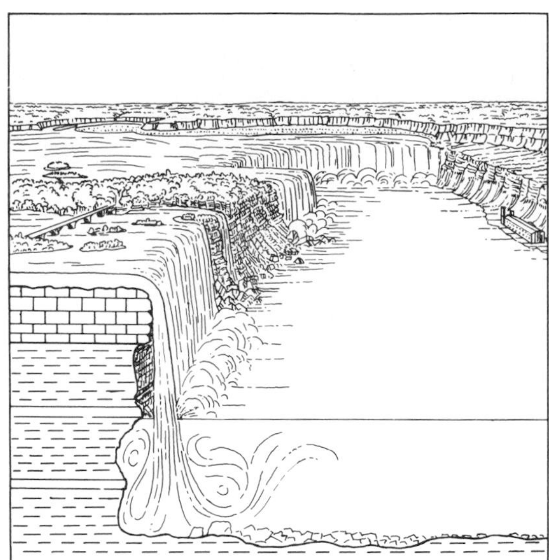

**FIGURE 37.8.** Cross section and sketch of Niagara Falls, showing cap rock of Lockport dolomite and underlying weak shales. (© 1960, John Wiley & Sons, New York. Drawn by Erwin Raisz and based on an illustration by G. K. Gilbert, 1896.)

these *domes* are nearly circular (Figure 37.9). The sedimentary strata are sharply flexed upward around the base and the central part is elevated to heights of several hundreds or even a few thousands of feet. On the dome flanks the strata dip at angles from 20° or 30° to 60°, or even more. Sedimentary domes may be from 5 to 100 mi (8 to 160 km) across the base (Figure 37.10).

As denudation progresses, strata are removed from the center of the dome and are eroded outward to become sharp-crested ridges termed *hogbacks* (Figure 37.11). A hogback is distinguished from a cuesta in having steep slopes on both flanks, but a hogback may gradually merge into a cuesta where the dip of the strata becomes gradually less, as shown in Figure 37.12.

**FIGURE 37.9.** The Richat structure, Mauretania, Africa, photographed from Gemini 4 spacecraft. Erosion of a nearly circular sedimentary dome has revealed a concentric system of ridges and valleys. (NASA photograph.)

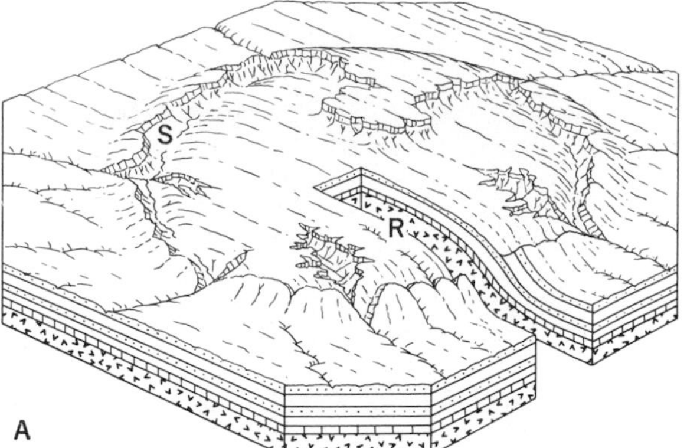


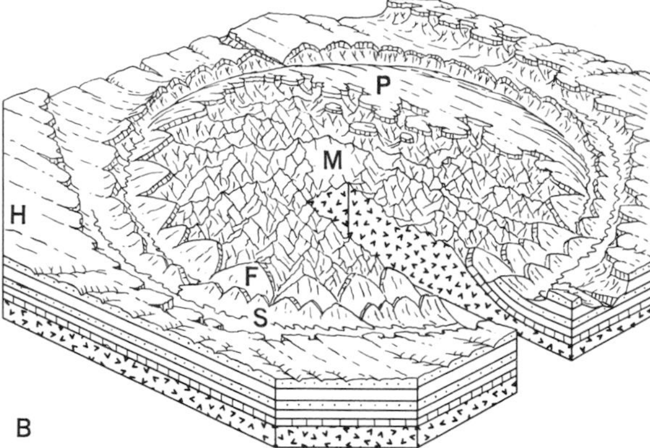


**FIGURE 37.10.** Landforms of a mountainous dome: (*A*) Early stage in removal of sedimentary cover; (*B*) Fully dissected dome with exposed core. *S*: subsequent stream. *R*: stripped sandstone formation. *P*: stripped limestone formation. *H*: horizontal strata. *F*: flatiron. *M*: crystalline rocks. (© 1960, John Wiley & Sons, New York.)

When a mountainous dome is deeply dissected, the central region may have been completely stripped of sedimentary strata, leaving exposed a mass of older igneous or metamorphic rock constituting the *core* of the dome (Figure 37.10). A sandstone layer resting directly upon the older rock now develops a series of triangular-shaped plates termed *flatirons.* Beyond these are hogback ridges separated by narrow circular valleys occupied by subsequent streams.

The drainage pattern of a mountainous dome consists of *radial* elements and *annular* elements—the latter are subsequent streams. The total effect is that of a trellis pattern bent into a circular form (Figure 37.13).

The origin of domes is not always readily apparent. Some small domes are caused by the intrusion of igneous rock in the form of a laccolith (Chapter 21) and are therefore described as *laccolithic domes* (Figure 37.14). Others of large size and with a generally flattened summit, such as the Black Hills uplift, are caused by deep-seated forces associated with mountain uplift.

**FIGURE 37.11.** Hogbacks of dipping sedimentary strata, Virgin Anticline, southern Utah. Virgin River cuts across strata in a watergap (*foreground*). (Photograph by Frank Jensen.)

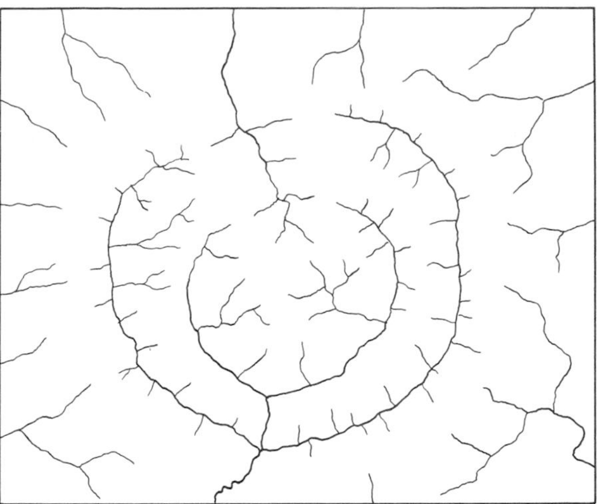

**FIGURE 37.13.** Radial and annular drainage on a dissected dome. (© 1960, John Wiley & Sons, New York.)

## Erosion of folded strata

Erosional landforms developed on a series of simple open folds are illustrated in Figure 37.15. As shown in Block *A,* a particularly massive resistant formation of sandstone has been almost stripped clean of overlying weak formations of shale. Bold *anticlinal mountains* are formed by the anticlinal arches, and deep *synclinal valleys* coincide with the synclinal troughs. Major streams that originally crossed the anticlines may maintain their transverse courses by cutting deep steep-walled *water gaps* across the anticlinal mountains.

Next the crests of the anticlines become breached by narrow valleys that grow along the mountain crests. These *anticlinal valleys* are occupied by subsequent streams and continue to lengthen and deepen until the anticline is completely open out along its length. On the flanks of the anticline the sandstone formation now presents its upturned edges to form *homoclinal mountains,* which are essentially the same features as the hogback ridges previously described as located on the flanks of a dome.

In the more deeply eroded folds shown in Block *B,* the sandstone formation, referred to above, is entirely eroded from above the anticlines, but persists along the synclinal axes, where it forms long, narrow, flat-topped *synclinal mountains,* much like long mesas but with shallow summit valleys extending along the center line of the mountain. A *trellis drainage pattern* is associated with dissected folds (Figure 37.16).

The folds illustrated in Figure 37.15 are idealized by showing the crests of the anticlines and troughs of the synclines as maintaining horizontality. The condition pictured is rarely found extending for any appreciable distance along the folds. Most fold crests, when followed for long distances, alternately plunge downward and then rise again in a series of undulations, as if the folds were themselves warped by a series of transverse waves of greater length.

Where plunging folds are eroded, the homoclinal mountains form *zigzag ridges* (Figure 37.17). Where the ridge crosses a plunging anticline a steep-walled *cove* is formed. Where a syncline is crossed a long spade-like mountain with steep walls around the end and sides is

**FIGURE 37.12.** Gradation of hogbacks into cuestas as dip decreases. *H*: hogback. *S*: subsequent valley. *Cu*: cuesta. *M*: mesa. *E*: esplanade. *Cl*: cliff. *P*: plateau. (© 1960, John Wiley & Sons, New York. Based on a drawing of W. M. Davis.)

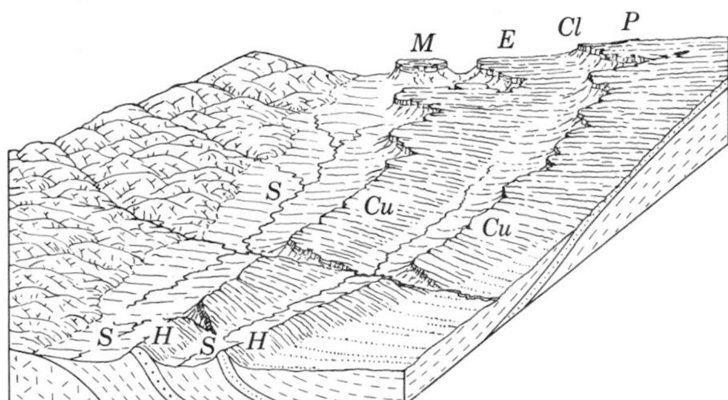


**FIGURE 37.14.** Structure section through Navajo Mountain, Utah, a laccolithic dome. (© 1965, John Wiley & Sons, New York. Based on data of H. E. Gregory.)

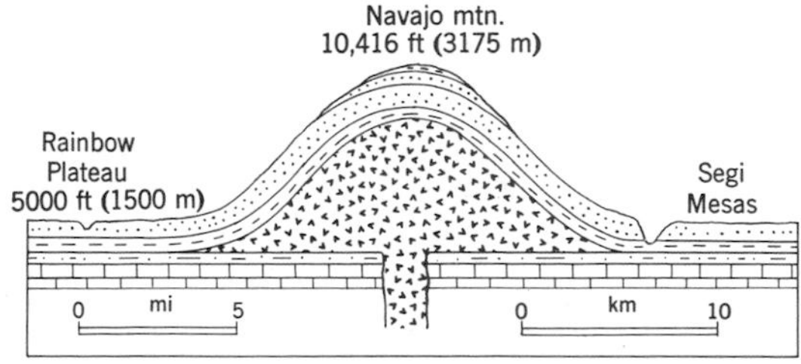

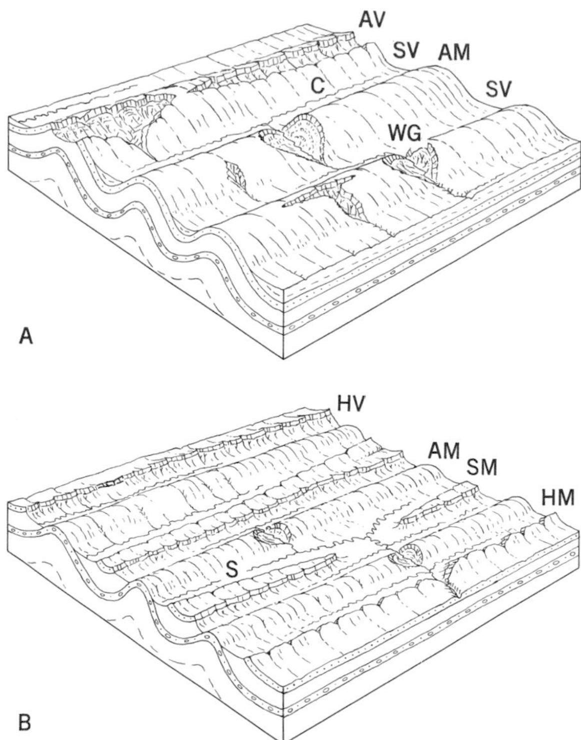


**FIGURE 37.15.** Landforms on open, parallel folds. (*A*) Strong relief, corresponding to a single resistant sandstone formation. *AV*: anticlinal valley. *SV*: synclinal valley. *AM*: anticlinal mountain. *WG*: watergap. (*B*) Relief increasing in complexity on two resistant formations. *HV*: homoclinal valley. *SM*: synclinal mountain. *HM*: homoclinal mountain. *S*: subsequent stream. (© 1960, John Wiley & Sons, New York.)

formed. Good examples of zigzag ridges are found in the Appalachians of central Pennsylvania and throughout the extensions of this fold belt southwestward into Maryland, West Virginia, Virginia, Tennessee, and Alabama (Figure 37.18). Of particular interest in folded strata of Pennsylvanian age are the layers of anthracite coal that now remain only in the synclinal troughs (Figure 37.19).

The structures and landforms of layered rocks should be thought of as forming a gradational series of forms,

**FIGURE 37.16.** Trellis drainage pattern. (© 1965, John Wiley & Sons, New York.)

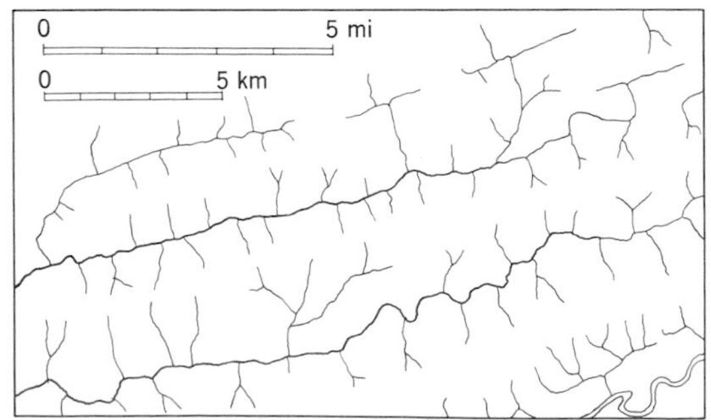


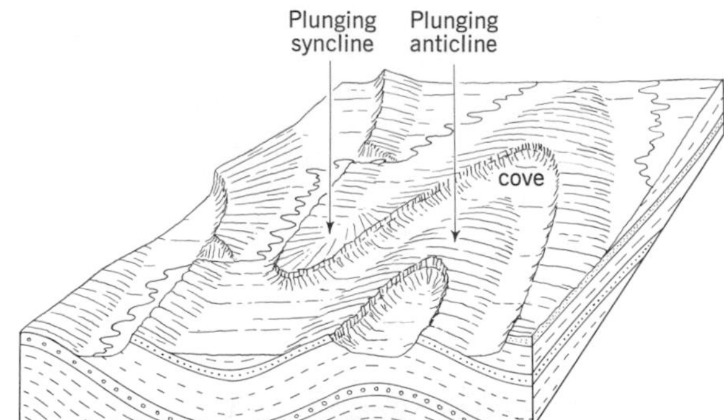


**FIGURE 37.17.** Zigzag ridges developed on plunging folds. (© 1960, John Wiley & Sons, New York. Based on a drawing by Erwin Raisz.)

rather than as falling into distinct categories. Thus horizontal strata traced from one region to another may grade imperceptibly into gently dipping strata and take the form of broad low domes or folds. We shall then find that the mesas and plateaus give way to cuestas, which in turn give way to narrow hogbacks, as suggested in Figure 37.12. Some domes of sedimentary strata are nearly circular in outline, whereas others are strongly elliptical and can be equally well described as doubly plunging anticlines (see Figure 26.12).

## Erosional forms of metamorphic rocks

Much of the area of the continental shields is underlain by metamorphic rocks—gneisses, schists, slates, quartz-

**FIGURE 37.18.** Zigzag ridge in plunging folds, south of Hollidaysburg, Pennsylvania. Nearer bend is a plunging syncline. The more distant bend (at right) is a plunging anticline enclosing a cove. Resistant stratum is the Tuscarora formation, a quartzite of Silurian age. (Photograph by John S. Shelton.)

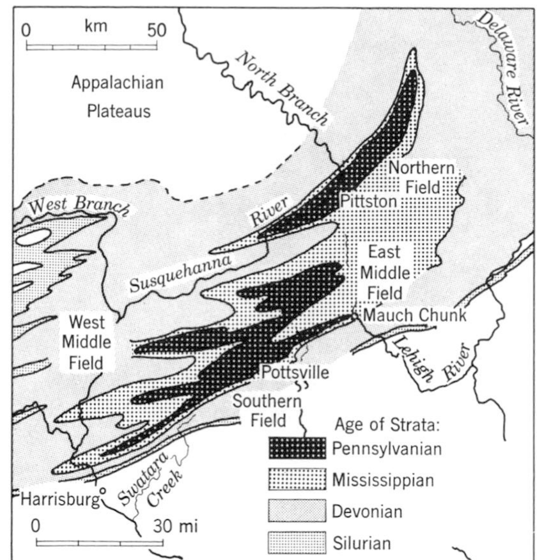


**FIGURE 37.19.** Geologic map of anthracite coal basins of eastern Pennsylvania. Dark areas are synclinal troughs. (© 1965, John Wiley & Sons, New York.)

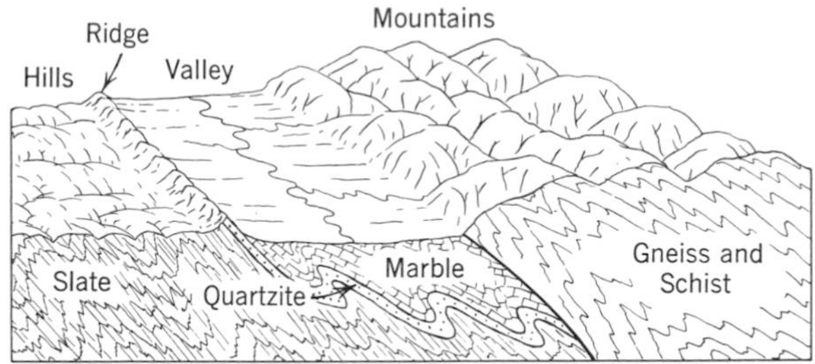


**FIGURE 37.20.** Relation of metamorphic rock belts to topography. (© 1960, John Wiley & Sons, New York.)

ites, and marbles—representing the greatly altered and deformed sedimentary strata of ancient geosynclines compressed and intruded in the root zones of orogenic belts of the Precambrian and Paleozoic Eras.

A common attribute of metamorphic rocks is that they tend to lie in roughly parallel belts and zones—e.g., belts of gneiss or schist paralleling belts of slates, marbles, and quartzites (Figure 37.20). The result of such an arrangement is that the regional topography is one of valleys, hill belts, and mountain ridges arranged in parallel zones. Thrust faults commonly separate rocks of one belt from those of another and may bring together rocks of contrasting resistance to erosion, producing sharply defined escarpments.

In general, where denudation progresses in a humid climate we shall find that quartzite strongly resists weathering and erosion to form bold ridges much like the homoclinal ridges of a belt of open folds, but much less regular in plan and in profile. In contrast, marbles are susceptible to solution removal and form the lowest valleys. Slate is of intermediate resistance and produces belts of hills. Gneisses are often highly resistant to denudation and produce mountainous belts. Schist varies greatly in its resistance, depending upon its structure and composition.

Topography of metamorphic rocks is illustrated in its many forms throughout New England and the older Appalachians, including the Blue Ridge Mountains and the Piedmont Plateau. In the Green Mountains of Vermont are found valleys developed on marbles infolded and infaulted between ridges of schist and gneiss. The Hudson and New Jersey Highlands (Figure 26.25) represent a broad mountainous band of resistant gneisses, with some bodies of intruded granite. In the region of Harpers Ferry, West Virginia, great ridges of quartzite rise above lowlands of schist.

**FIGURE 37.21.** Erosional development of a tilted fault-block mountain. (© 1960, John Wiley & Sons, New York. Based on a drawing of W. M. Davis.)

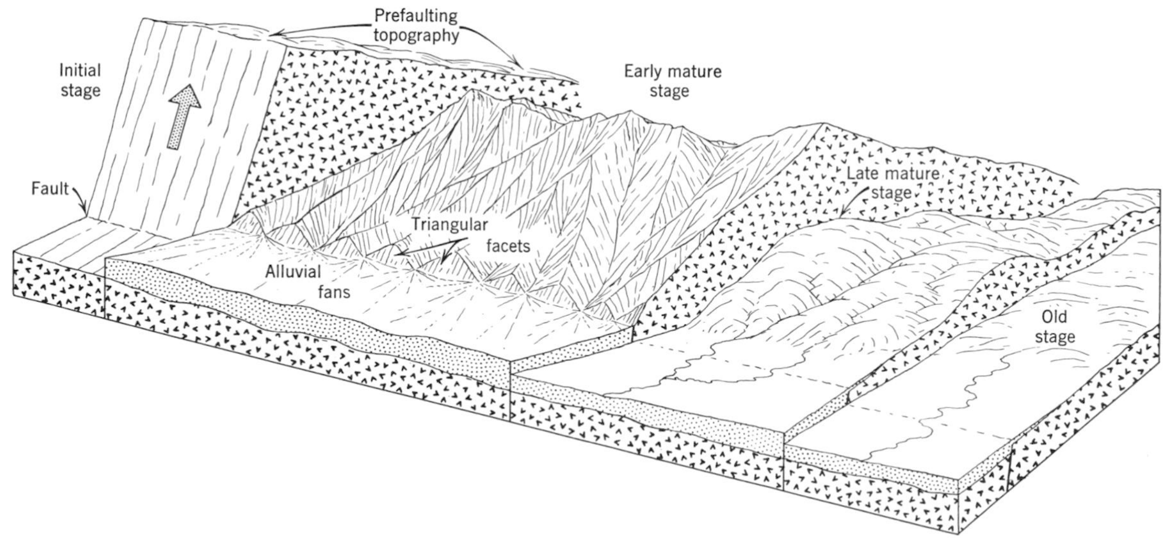

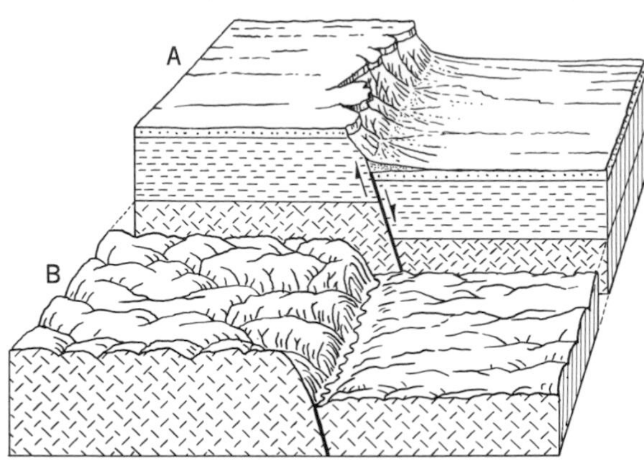


FIGURE 37.22. (*A*) Fault scarp resulting from recent faulting. (*B*) Fault-line scarp resulting from erosion along an inactive fault.

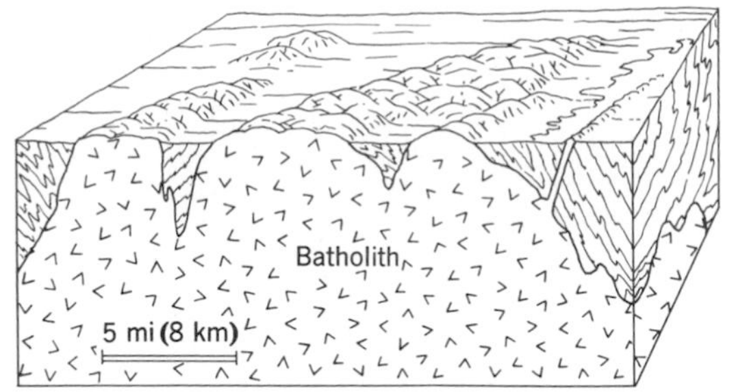


FIGURE 37.24. A batholith exposed by erosion. (© 1965, John Wiley & Sons, New York. Based on a drawing by C. R. Longwell, A. Knopf, and R. F. Flint.)

## Fault-block mountains

Long-continued vertical movement along great normal faults brings into existence fault-block mountains and associated downfaulted valleys. A single block may be tilted during faulting to produce a highly asymmetrical mountain mass, or it may be elevated more or less uniformly as a great horst (Figure 26.8).

A tilted-block mountain produced by faulting undergoes a series of denudational changes shown in Figure 37.21. Canyons are rapidly carved into the fault scarp, dissecting the block and pushing the drainage divide back toward the center line. Small remnants of the fault plane may remain at the mountain base as *triangular facets* truncating the ends of the spurs between canyons. In an arid climate alluvial-fan deposits are built rapidly at the mountain base, covering the fault line. Eventually the block is reduced to a range of hills, then finally to a peneplain or a pediplain. In these later stages the fault line, if not renewed by recent faulting, is deeply buried under alluvium.

Fault-block mountains are abundant in the Basin and Range physiographic province of southern Oregon, Nevada, western Utah, southeastern California, western and southern Arizona, and parts of New Mexico. Blocks showing little dissection can be seen in southern Oregon, where faulting has raised great masses of basaltic

FIGURE 37.23. A fault-line scarp in ancient rocks of the Canadian Shield. The body of water resting against the scarp is MacDonald Lake, located near Great Slave Lake, Northwest Territories. (Royal Canadian Air Force photograph No. A5120-105R.)

FIGURE 37.25. The Idaho batholith of Cretaceous age, exposed in the Sawtooth Mountains of south central Idaho. View is northward. (From *GEOLOGY ILLUSTRATED* by John S. Shelton. W. H. Freeman and Company. Copyright © 1966.)

**FIGURE 37.26.** Dendritic drainage pattern on igneous rock of the Idaho batholith. (© 1965, John Wiley & Sons, New York.)

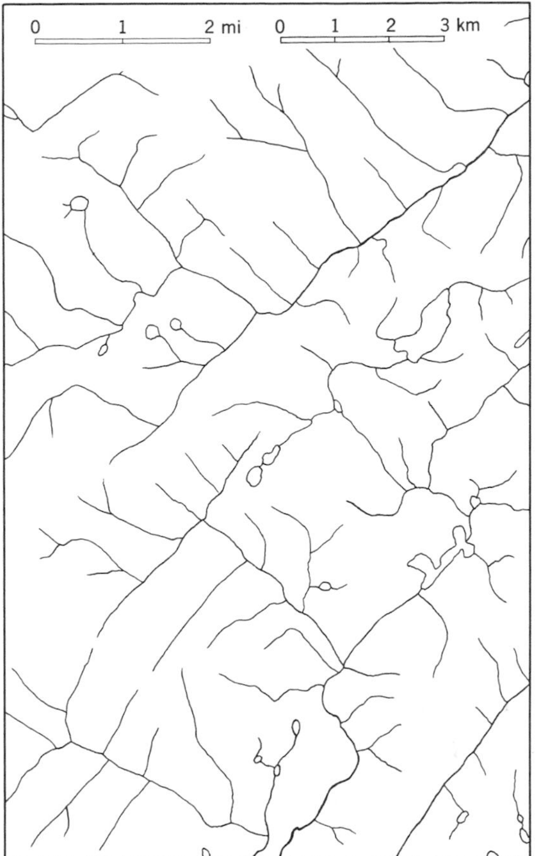


**FIGURE 37.27.** A rectangular drainage pattern consisting of subsequent streams located on fault zones. Adirondack Mountains, New York. (© 1965, John Wiley & Sons, New York.)

lavas into tilted blocks. Farther south, in Nevada, Utah, and California, are numerous deeply dissected blocks (see Figure 37.32).

## Fault-line scarps

Many of the straight steep scarps located along the line of a fault are not produced directly by fault movements of recent geologic date. They are, instead, *fault-line scarps* produced by erosional removal of weaker rock from one side of an older fault plane produced at a date far back in geologic time (Figure 37.22). Stage *A* represents a recently formed fault scarp in weak sedimentary strata. After extensive erosion, shale stripped away from the resistant basement rock, causing the appearance of a fault-line scarp (Stage *B*). This landform takes the general position of the original fault scarp but is formed of rock that was deeply buried at the time of the fault movement.

Fault-line scarps are common features of the ancient crystalline rocks of the continental shields (Figure 37.23). Fault structures can persist despite deep erosion because the fault plane extends far down into the crust.

## Landforms on plutonic igneous rocks

Exposure of a batholith by erosional removal of the covering rock takes place at a rather advanced time in the denudation of orogenic belts, since these enormous bodies of granitic rock are emplaced deep in the root zone of the mountain mass (Figure 37.24). Examples of batholiths are given in Chapter 21. The extent of Cretaceous batholiths in western North America is shown in Figure 30.21.

Some batholiths, or portions of batholiths, are of uniform composition and structure throughout and are largely lacking in conspicuous faults, thus the entire mass may be described as a homogeneous rock body (Figure 37.25). In such cases streams flowing on the rock of the batholiths form a highly uniform dendritic drainage pattern not readily distinguishable from the pattern found in horizontally layered rocks (Figure 37.26). Other batholiths are broken by prominent faults along which subsequent streams develop, producing the rectangular drainage pattern illustrated in Figure 37.27.

## Erosional development of stratovolcanoes

The succession of landforms resulting from the erosion of an extinct stratovolcano and a caldera is illustrated in a series of block diagrams in Figure 37.28. Block *A*

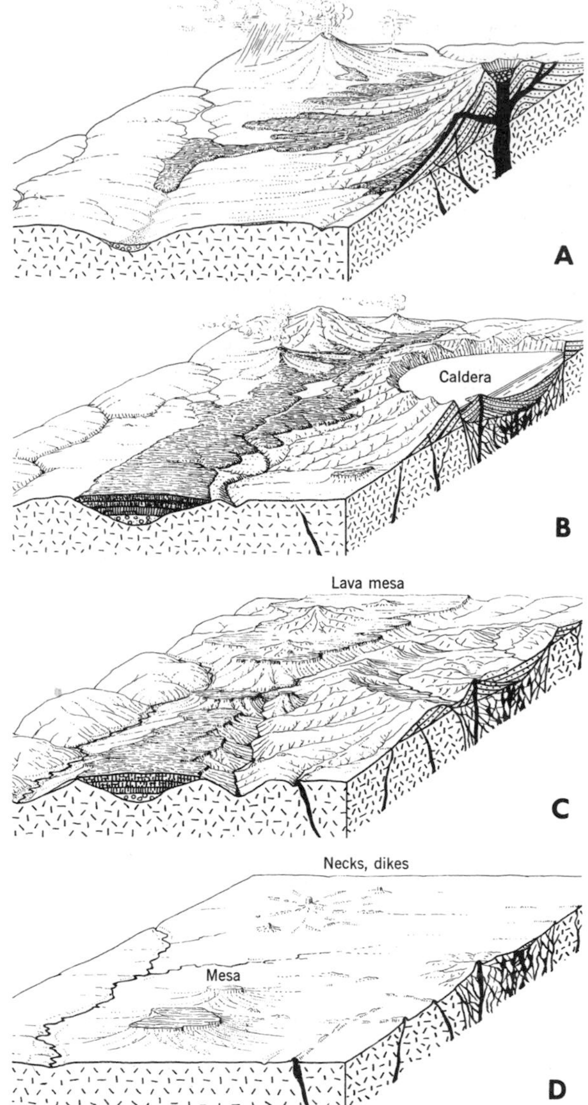


FIGURE 37.28. Stages of erosional development of volcanoes. (© 1960, John Wiley & Sons, New York.)

shows newly formed stratovolcanoes and associated lava flows. Although running water attacks a volcanic cone as it is being built, the continual addition of lava and ash to the slopes of the cone maintains its form until volcanic activity ceases. Block *B* shows one of the cones to have been destroyed by explosion, leaving a caldera. More lava flows have been extruded, filling a stream valley.

In a later stage of dissection (Block *C*), the cones and caldera have been cut up into systems of radial valleys and ridges. The crater rim is eventually breached by streams, so as to conduct the runoff out of the central depression by surface flow and to drain any lake that may have existed in the crater.

Long after the volcanic cone has been entirely removed by denudation, there remain projecting above

FIGURE 37.29. Agathla Peak, a volcanic neck in northern Arizona. Behind the peak are seen horizontal sedimentary strata which formerly enclosed the volcanic rock. (Photograph by Barnum Brown, American Museum of Natural History.)

the land surface erosion remnants of the magma that solidified within the central *volcanic neck* (Figure 37.29) and in near-vertical radial *volcanic dikes,* as suggested by Block *D* of Figure 37.26. Where the neck and dikes are surrounded by weak shale they rise as a conspicuous steep-sided peak with walls radiating like spokes from the hub of a wagon wheel.

Probably the best-known locality for illustration of radial patterns of volcanic dikes is the Spanish Peaks area in southern Colorado. Here the dikes form narrow walls of rock traceable for miles across country (Figure 37.30). At some points two dikes cross each other, producing an oblique intersection of the rock walls.

FIGURE 37.30. A vertical dike of volcanic rock exposed by erosion to produce a wall-like landform. West Spanish Peak (*background*) is an intrusive igneous body surrounded by metamorphosed sedimentary strata. Locality is south central Colorado. (Photograph by G. W. Stose, U.S. Geological Survey.)

**FIGURE 37.31.** Major geomorphic subdivisions of North America. [After A. K. Lobeck (1948), *Physiographic Diagram of North America,* New York, Hammond Incorporated.]

## Geomorphic Provinces of the United States and Canada

The geomorphologist recognizes distinctive regions of landform assemblages sharing many characteristics in common within each region but distinctively different from those of adjacent regions. Such regions are known as *geomorphic provinces.* The primary basis for defining a geomorphic province is the geologic structure and age of the bedrock, since, as we have seen in the present chapter, landform and structure are closely related. A secondary basis for distinguishing between geomorphic provinces and between subprovinces is that of geologic process. Basically there are two processes of importance in this connection: fluvial denudation and continental glaciation. A tertiary basis of subdivision, usually applied to subdivisions within the provinces, is that of relief, including the extent to which fluvial dissection has developed.

According to a classification system applied by Professor Armin K. Lobeck, North America north of about the 20th parallel of latitude consists of 28 geomorphic provinces grouped into five major divisions (Figure 37.31). Table 37.1 lists the five major divisions and the 28 geomorphic provinces, together with dominant rock type and structure and relief characteristics. Figure 37.32 is an outline map of the 48 United States and southern Canada showing boundaries of those geomorphic provinces falling within the limits of the map area. Figure 37.33 is a *physiographic diagram* employing a conventionalized pictorial representation of the relief of the provinces. It should be kept in mind that the table and maps involve considerable generalization and cannot take account of many secondary structures and rock types occurring within each province.

## References for further study


Dutton, C. E. (1882), *Tertiary History of the Grand Canyon District,* U.S. Geol. Survey, Monograph 2, Washington, D.C., U.S. Govt. Printing Office, 264 pp. (out of print.)

Lobeck, A. K. (1939), *Geomorphology,* New York, McGraw-Hill, 731 pp., chaps. 4, 13–19.

Thornbury, W. D. (1965), *Regional Geomorphology of the United States,* New York, Wiley, 609 pp.

Shelton, J. S. (1966), *Geology Illustrated,* San Francisco, Freeman, 434 pp.

Hunt, C. B. (1967), *Physiography of the United States,* San Francisco, Freeman, 480 pp.

Thornbury, W. D. (1969), *Principles of Geomorphology,* New York, Wiley, 594 pp., chaps. 9, 10, 19.

**TABLE 37.1. GEOMORPHIC DIVISIONS OF NORTH AMERICA***

| Major Division | | Geomorphic Province | Predominant Rock Ages |
|---|---|---|---|
| I. CANADIAN SHIELD | | 1. Laurentian Upland | Precambrian |
| | | (2. Arctic archipelago)† (3. Greenland) | |
| II. ATLANTIC PLAIN | | 4. Atlantic and Gulf coastal plain | Cretaceous, Cenozoic |
| | | 5. Continental shelf | Cenozoic |
| III. APPALACHIAN HIGHLANDS | | 6. New England-Maritime | Precambrian, Paleozoic |
| | | 7. Older Appalachians | |
| | | 8. Triassic lowlands | Triassic |
| | | 9. Newer (Folded) Appalachians | Paleozoic |
| | | 10. Appalachian Plateau | Paleozoic |
| IV. INTERIOR PLAINS | | 11. Interior low plateaus | Paleozoic |
| | | 12. Central lowland | Paleozoic, Cretaceous, Pleistocene |
| | | 13. Ozark Plateau | Paleozoic, minor Precambrian |
| | | 14. Ouachita Mountains | Paleozoic |
| | | 15. Great Plains | Cretaceous, Cenozoic |
| V. NORTH AMERICAN CORDILLERA | A. Rocky Mountain system | 16. Southern Rocky Mountains | Precambrian–Cenozoic |
| | | 17. Middle Rocky Mountains | |
| | | 18. Northern Rockies | Precambrian–Cenozoic |
| | B. Intermontane plateau system | (19. Arctic Rockies) | |
| | | (20. Central Alaska uplands & plains) | |
| | | (21. Interior plateaus of Canada) | |
| | | 22. Columbia Plateau | Cenozoic |
| | | 23. Colorado Plateau | Paleozoic–Cenozoic, minor Precambrian |
| | | 24. Basin and Range | Precambrian–Cenozoic |
| | | 25. Mexican highlands | |
| | C. Pacific mountain system | 26. Sierra–Cascade–Coast mountains | Mesozoic–Cenozoic |
| | | 27. Pacific troughs | Cenozoic |
| | | 28. Pacific Coast ranges | Precambrian–Cenozoic |

* After A. K. Lobeck (1948), *Physiographic Diagram of North America*, New York, Hammond Incorporated.
† Provinces in parentheses are not shown in Figures 37.32 and 37.33.

| Predominant Rock Type and Structure | Characteristic Relief | Typical Upland and Summit Elevations feet | meters |
|---|---|---|---|
| Metamorphosed sediments, volcanics, and intrusives. Local thin sedimentary cover | Low hills to low mountains; many lakes | 1000–2500 | 300–760 |
| | | | |
| Unsolidated sedimentary strata, low seaward dip | Undulating plains, floodplains, hill belts (cuestas) | 0–800 | 0–240 |
| Unconsolidated sediments | Gently undulating ocean floor | to −600 | to −180 |
| Folded overthrust sediments, metamorphics, igneous instrusives | Rolling hills to subdued mountains | 1000–5000 | 300–1500 |
| | Rolling hills (Piedmont)<br>Subdued mountains (Blue Ridge) | 300–1500<br>3000–6000 | 90–460<br>900–1800 |
| Redbeds and basaltic lavas in isolated basins | Undulating lowlands, narrow ridges | 500–800 | 150–240 |
| Open folds, overturned folds, thrust sheets | Parallel and zigzag ridges and valleys | 2000–3000 | 600–900 |
| Horizontal to gently dipping strata | Rugged hills and low mountains | 1200–4000 | 360–1200 |
| Horizontal to gently dipping strata; broad domes and basins | Undulating plains to rugged hills; escarpments | 500–1000 | 150–300 |
| Horizontal strata. Pleistocene cover in parts | Plains, low hills; moraine belts | 600–1200 | 180–360 |
| Horizontal strata | Rugged hills, low mountains | 1200–2500 | 360–760 |
| Folded and overthrust strata | Parallel and zigzag ridges and valleys | 500–2500 | 150–760 |
| Horizontal strata; isolated domes | Plains, low hills and escarpments, badlands; isolated mountains | 2000–5000 | 600–1500 |
| Anticlinal uplifts and domes; basin sediments; volcanics | High, rugged mountains; intermontane plains | 10,000–14,000 | 3000–4300 |
| Sedimentary strata; batholiths; faulted mountain blocks | High, rugged mountains; narrow intermontane basins | 9000–12,000 | 2700–3600 |
| | | | |
| Basaltic lavas; fault blocks | Rolling plateaus; isolated mountains | 2000–5000 | 600–1500 |
| Horizontal strata broken by faults and monoclines; minor volcanics | High plateaus, steep escarpments, deep canyons | 6000–11,000 | 1800–3300 |
| Fault blocks of complex structure; alluvium-filled basins | High rugged mountains; broad intermontane plains | 4000–12,000 | 1200–3600 |
| Metasediments, batholiths, volcanics, upfaulted blocks (Sierra Nevada) | High rugged mountains; deep narrow valleys | 8000–14,000 | 2400–4300 |
| Thick sediments in subsiding basins | Extensive plains; low hills | 200–500 | 60–150 |
| Upfaulted blocks of complex structure | Rugged mountains; narrow intermontane lowlands | 8000–10,000 | 2400–3000 |

**FIGURE 37.32.** Geomorphic provinces of the 48 contiguous United States, southern Canada, and northern Mexico. [After A. K. Lobeck (1948), *Physiographic Diagram of North America,* New York, Hammond Incorporated.]

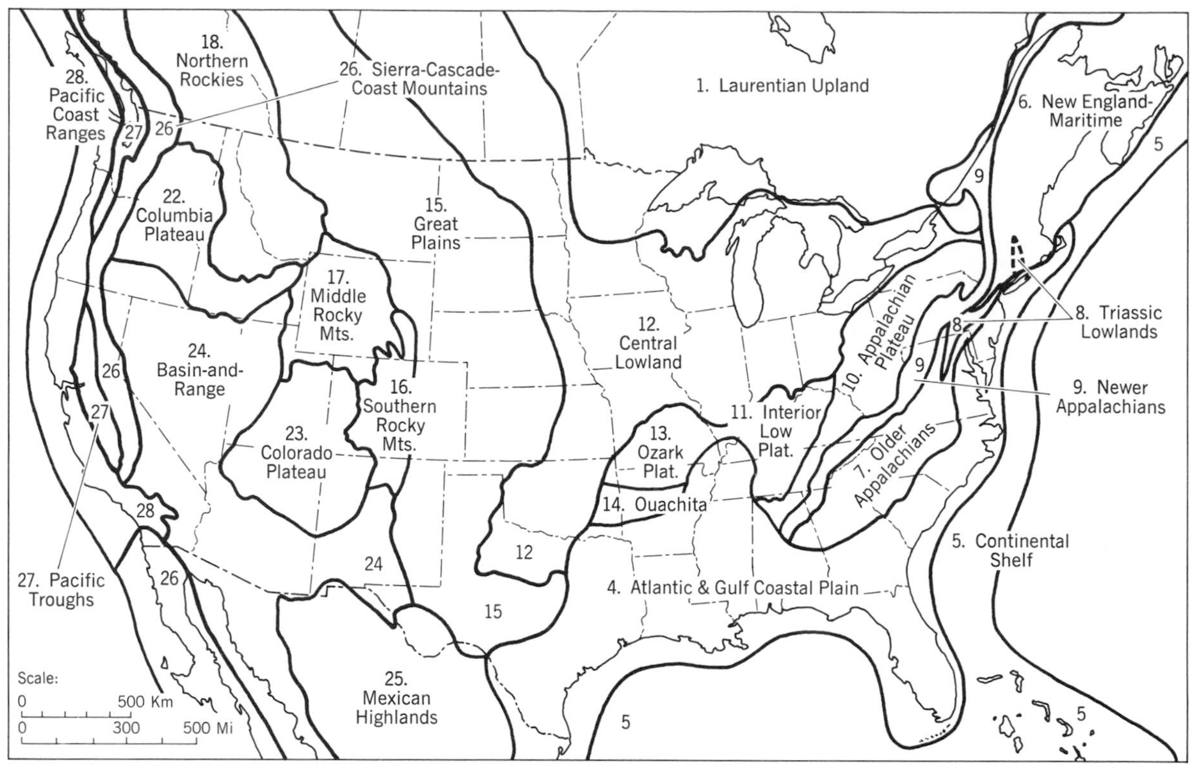


**FIGURE 37.33.** Physiographic diagram of the 48 contiguous United States, southern Canada, and northern Mexico. [A. K. Lobeck (1948), *Physiographic Diagram of North America,* New York, Hammond Incorporated. Reproduced by permission of Hammond Incorporated.]

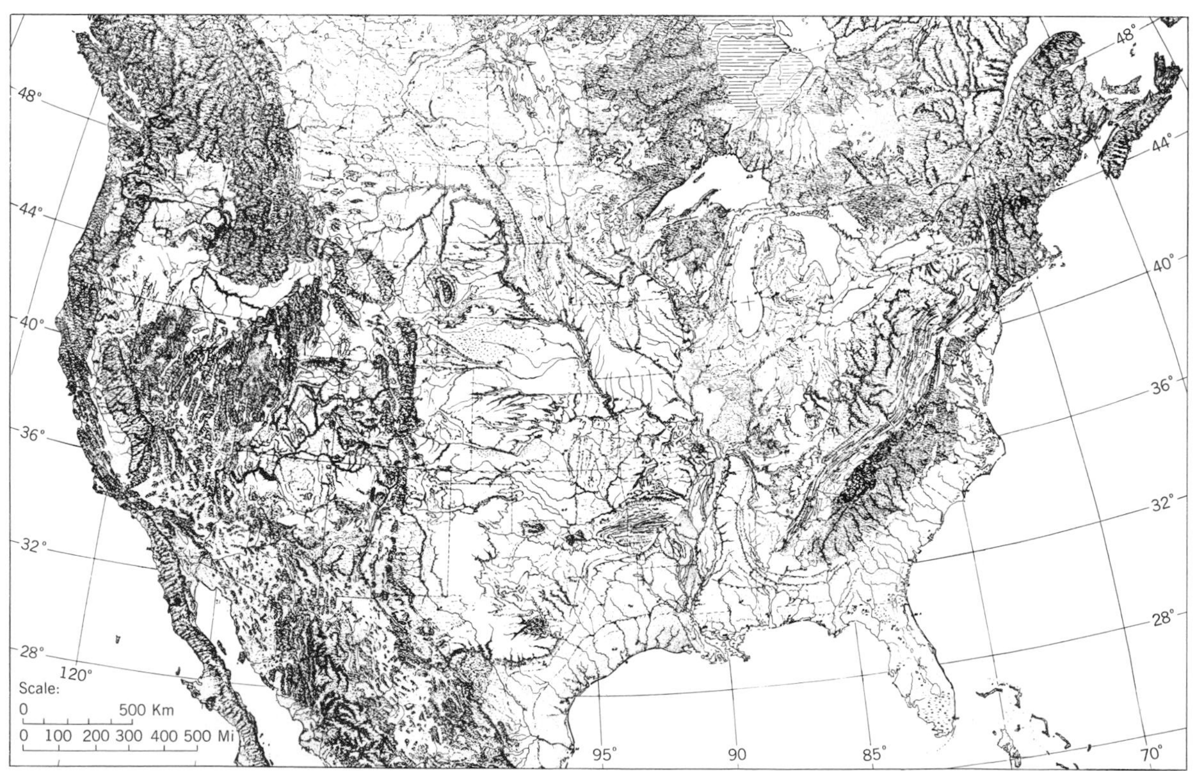

# 38

# Shoreline processes and forms

THE SHORES OF ALL CONTINENTS and islands and of all inland lakes are shaped by the unceasing work of waves. Energy derived from winds is carried forward by deep-water waves, and as they reach the shallow waters of a coast line their energy of orbital motion is transformed into currents and surges possessing great ability to erode rock and to transport sediment

Chapter 17 dealt with the formation of waves by wind, their refraction in shallow water, and their final transformation into breakers. Longshore and rip currents were described as agents capable, respectively, of transporting sediment parallel with and away from the breaker zone.

In this chapter we turn our attention first to the zone of breakers and surf, a zone of land alternately covered by water and exposed to the air. We shall consider the characteristic landforms developed by waves and currents acting upon various types of materials.

## The surf zone

After a breaker has formed and collapsed the wave is transformed into a landward moving sheet of highly turbulent water, the *swash* (or *uprush*) (Figure 17.17). Most shores have a rather gently sloping surface of sand or rock up which the swash of large waves can surge to reach a point several feet higher than the still water level. Opposed by a component of the force of gravity acting in the downslope (seaward) direction and acted upon by frictional resistance with the surface over which it passes, the swash is rapidly slowed

**FIGURE 38.1.** Abrasion platform at low tide. A pocket beach is at lower left. Pacific coast, south of Cape Flattery, Washington. (Photographer not known.)

and finally stopped. The water then begins to pour seaward down the slope in a reverse flow termed the *backwash* (or *backrush*). Return flow is generally less turbulent and shallower than the swash.

Swash and backwash together constitute an alternating water current exerting a frictional drag against the surface over which it moves and capable of moving rock particles of a wide range of sizes, from fine sand to cobblestones and boulders, depending upon size of the breaking waves and steepness of slope of the beach.

Just as a stream adjusts its slope and shapes its channel to suit the conditions of discharge and sediment load imposed upon it, so the swash and backwash shape the land into a sloping surface appropriately adjusted to the wave form and energy and to the type of sediment available.

## Wave erosion; marine cliffs

Where waves break upon a coast of hard bedrock and there is little sediment available, a gently sloping rock surface is gradually carved to accommodate the swash and backwash. This surface, the *abrasion platform,* may be completely covered at high tide, but it is exposed in a broad zone, often many yards wide, at low tide (Figure 38.1). Fragments the size of pebbles and cobbles, serving as tools for abrasion, litter the surface of the wave-abraded platform, whereas sand and finer particles are held in turbulent suspension and moved seaward into deeper water. In many respects the rock abrasion platform shaped by surf action is analogous to the rock channel of a stream of steep gradient whose transporting capacity is great and exceeds the supply of available detritus.

**FIGURE 38.2.** Wave-carved notch (*left*) at the base of a marine cliff. The rock bench in the center is an abrasion platform developed by high-tide surf, west of Auckland, New Zealand. (Photograph by Douglas Johnson.)

Just as the ungraded stream occupies a steep-walled rock gorge, so the shoreline being carved into bedrock possesses a steep *marine cliff* rising abruptly from the inner edge of the abrasion platform. The swash of storm waves thrusts rock fragments with great violence against the cliff base, eroding the cliff base and developing a *wave-cut notch* (Figure 38.2). Such undermining leads to falling and slumping of masses of bedrock from the cliff face, furnishing blocks for fragmentation into sediment of many sizes. The waves are thus engaged in a process of lateral planation much like that carried on by a stream in a flood stage as it undercuts the canyon wall on the outside of a bend.

The development of an abrasion platform and marine cliff are shown in Figure 38.3. Initially (Block *A*) the sea has come to rest against a steeply sloping landmass of resistant bedrock, into which it has carved, first, a small notch, the *nip.* Gradually the abrasion platform is developed and widened (Block *B*) as the detritus is swept seaward to accumulate in deeper water. Inequalities in resistance of the bedrock cause narrow zones to be more rapidly excavated, leading to the formation of *crevices* and *sea caves.* Remnants of bedrock projecting seaward may be cut through to produce *arches,* and these may collapse, leaving columnar rock *stacks* (Figure 38.4).

Block *C* illustrates a more advanced stage, in which the broad expanse of shallow water over the abrasion platform absorbs much of the energy of the breaking waves, leaving little energy to be expended in attack upon the cliff base. In this stage a beach is normally present.

From the engineering standpoint the ability of waves to erode a shoreline is a matter of considerable interest

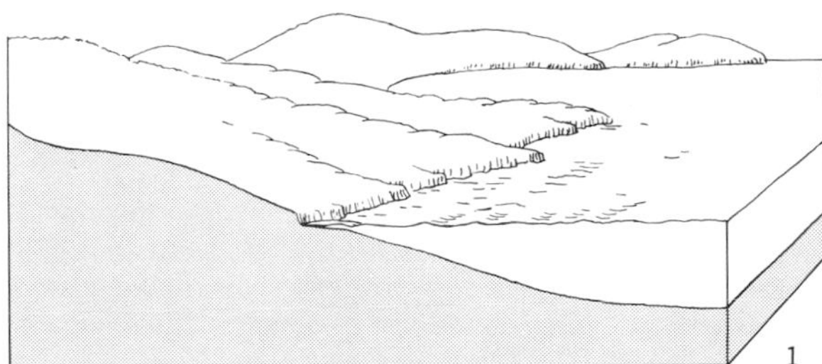

**FIGURE 38.3.** Stages in the evolution of a marine cliff. (After a drawing by Erwin Raisz.) (*A*) A small cliff, or nip, is first cut. (*B*) As wave erosion continues the cliff grows higher and many details appear. *A*: arch; *B*: beach; *C*: cave; *N*: notch; *P*: abrasion platform; *R*: crevice. (*C*) Equilibrium profile established.

and importance. A rapid cutting back, or *retrogradation,* will destroy valuable shore properties (Figure 38.5). An example of rapid cutting back of a cliff in weak glacial deposits is the outer shore of Cape Cod. The Highland Light has had to be moved three times since it was first installed. Retrogradation along the eastern shore of Cape Cod has proceeded at a rate of between 2 and 3 ft (0.6 to 0.9 m) per year for at least a century.

Breaking storm waves damage such protective engineering structures as sea walls, jetties, and dikes (Figure 38.6). Kinetic energy of waves in deep water increases as the square of the wave height, hence we should expect a great increase in erosive power of breaking waves as breaker height increases. Consequently by far the most significant wave erosion occurs in times of storms, particularly those coinciding with high-tide levels. Storm waves 18 ft (5.5 m) high can exert breaking pressures of over 2000 lb per sq ft (10,000 kg per sq m) upon exposed rock surfaces and can shift blocks of stone or concrete weighting from 2 to 10 tons. Much higher pressures have been measured, momentarily up to 14,000 lb per sq ft (70,000 kg per sq m) upon sea walls exposed to breaking storm waves.

**FIGURE 38.4.** The chalk cliffs of the Normandy coast, France, with an arch and a stack. (Photographer not known.)

## Beaches

A *beach* may be defined as a relatively thick accumulation of sand, gravel, or cobbles in the zone of breakers and surf. A beach is therefore a depositional landform

**FIGURE 38.5.** Storm waves have rapidly undermined this marine cliff, composed of weak glacial sands and gravels. Suffolk, England. (H.M. Geological Survey.)

**FIGURE 38.6.** Storm waves breaking against a sea wall at Hastings, England. (Photographer not known.)

in contrast to the abrasion platform and marine cliff, which are erosional landforms. In certain respects beaches are analogous to the alluvial deposits of a floodplain, particularly to the point-bar deposits of meandering rivers or to alluvial fans. In all these cases moving water shapes excess quantities of detritus into sorted and layered deposits. For both river and beach deposits the accumulation is closely associated with a condition of grade, or equilibrium, in that the deposition represents an attempt by the fluid agent to restore and maintain an equilibrium profile despite a continuous series of disturbances tending to upset the equilibrium.

Beaches are formed of sediment produced by wave

**FIGURE 38.7.** This beach ridge of pebbles and cobbles has been built by the swash of breaking storm waves, thrusting the rock fragments landward. Jessops Neck, Long Island. (Photograph by A. C. Veatch, U.S. Geological Survey.)

erosion or brought to the shore at various points by streams draining the land. Clay and silt, readily held in suspension, are unable to remain in the zone of breakers and surf, hence they diffuse seaward to settle upon the continental shelf in deeper water.

The first beach to form on a coast line having resistant bedrock and characterized by abrasion platforms and cliffs is the *shingle beach,* or *cobble beach,* composed of well-rounded fragments the size of pebbles, cobbles, or, rarely, small boulders (see Table 22.3). Shingle beaches are narrow and have a very steep seaward slope (Figure 38.7). Commonly the landward side of the shingle ridge is also very steep. As swash rides up a shingle beach the water rapidly percolates into the coarse shingle, to the extent that all the water may be absorbed and no backwash can result. Particles are thrust up the beach and accumulate in a steep slope, the steepness of which is limited by the ability of the rounded particles to maintain stability against the pull of gravity. Shingle beaches commonly form first in the most sheltered locations—in re-entrants and bayheads between rocky promontories—and are called *pocket beaches* (Figure 38.1). They are commonly crescentic in plan and are concave toward the sea.

Where large quantities of sediment are available—as where large rivers are building their deltas or where the coast line is composed of sandy sedimentary strata or of glacial outwash sands—beaches are broad and continuous along the coast. Figure 38.8 shows in profile the characteristic form elements of such sand beaches. The *foreshore* is that sloping zone over which the swash and backwash act. It is bounded on the landward side by the limit reached by swash at high tide and on the seaward side by the breaker zone. Commonly a sand or gravel *bar* is present beneath the point where the breakers form (Figure 38.9). Although usually covered by water, the bar crest is exposed at low water of spring tides. Between the bar and the foreshore slope is a *trough,* representing the zone of extreme turbulence at the point where the breakers collapse. Where turbulence is great, even the largest particles are momentarily lifted into suspension. Therefore sediment tends to drift away from this zone to positions of less turbulence, either landward or seaward, and a trough results. Seaward of the bar lies the *offshore,* a sloping sand surface extending out into deeper water and covered at all times by water. No clearly defined outer limit can be set for the offshore. Two, three, or more bars separated by troughs exist in the offshore zone of some coasts.

The bar and trough arrangement is, for some beaches at least, a characteristic feature of the winter season, when waves are large and steep, but it is replaced in summer by an abrupt downward inflection of the profile known as a *step* (Figure 38.9). The step is composed of gravel and marks the point of breaker formation of the relatively small waves and swells prevailing in summer. In general, small waves of low steepness tend to cause a movement of sand inshore from deeper water, causing a summer accumulation, or *progradation,* of the beach, whereas the large steep waves of winter storms tend to cause a sand movement in the seaward direction, de-

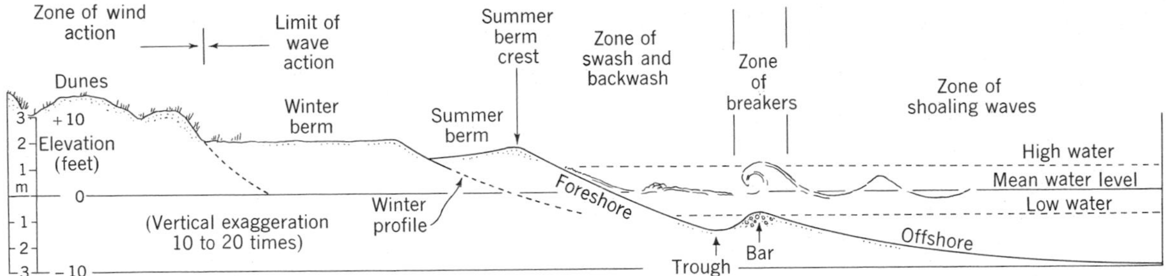


**FIGURE 38.8.** Characteristic elements and zones of the profile of a sand beach.

pleting the beach and increasing the water depth, as suggested in Figure 38.9.

Progradation by summer waves builds a new sand deposit, the *summer berm,* taking the form of a bench several yards wide (Figure 38.8). The *berm crest,* or line of contact between berm and foreshore, is commonly slightly higher than the inner part of the berm, and swash of spring tides may spill over the berm. Landward of the summer berm there is typically present a somewhat higher bench, the *winter berm,* built by the swash of large waves. In rare storms of great violence the entire winter berm may be cut away and the waves may reach the belt of sand dunes lying landward of the beach. After such extreme retrogradation the winter berm will be built back. Actually three or more berms may be found on a broad sand beach, each associated with a different set of wave conditions.

## Littoral drift

In the foregoing discussion we have assumed that the wave crests are parallel with the water line and that each wave breaks at the same instant along its entire length. If such were the case, sediment moved by swash and backwash would travel landward and seaward in paths exactly normal to the beach—i.e., along the line of the profiles shown in Figure 38.8 and 38.9. Actually, on most beaches waves approach the shore with some degree of obliquity at almost all times, as suggested in Figure 17.20. Despite the effect of wave refraction tending to bend the wave front so that the waves will approach the shore in a parallel manner, waves reach the breaking point with an oblique trend, causing the swash to be directed obliquely up the foreshore, as shown in Figure 38.10. As a result, particles carried in the swash ride obliquely on the beach face, but tend to be brought back in the normal downslope direction by the backwash. With each cycle of such movement the particles are moved along the beach by an increment of distance that may amount to several feet. Multiplied by countless repetitions, this lateral movement, termed *beach drift,* accounts for transport of vast quantities of sediment and is of primary importance in development of various kinds of beach deposits along a coast.

In the offshore zone the oblique approach of waves also results in lateral movement of sediment. As noted in Chapter 17, wave orbits in shallow water are transformed into simple back-and-forth water movements at the bottom. Sand thus dragged back and forth forms into very small ridges and troughs known as *oscillation ripples*. Now, if the wave approach is oblique to the contour of the slope, the sand not only will move back and forth normal to the slope, but will also creep parallel with the shoreline in a type of movement similar to the beach drifting but very much slower.

Still another mechanism causes lateral sediment movement in the offshore zone, the *longshore current.* As explained in Chapter 17, surface water of the waves

**FIGURE 38.9.** Characteristic beach profiles of winter and summer in middle latitudes.

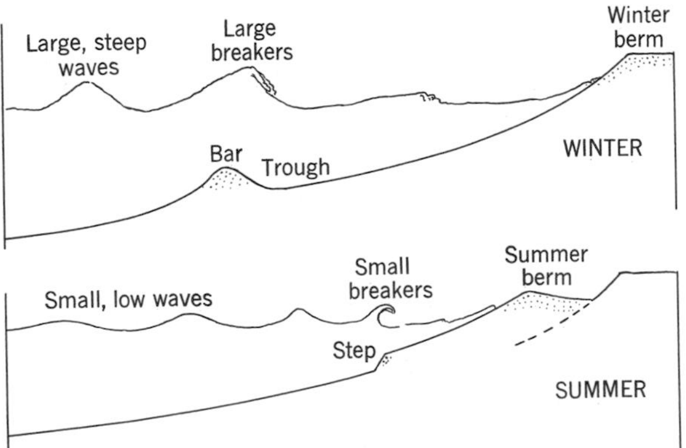


**FIGURE 38.10.** Beach drift of sand, caused by oblique approach of swash. (© 1960, John Wiley & Sons, New York.)

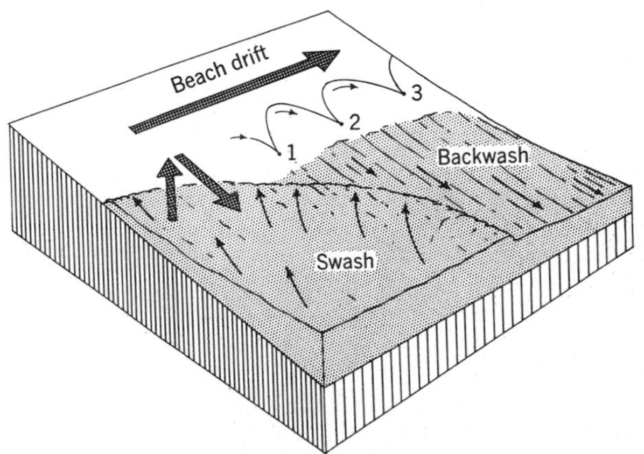

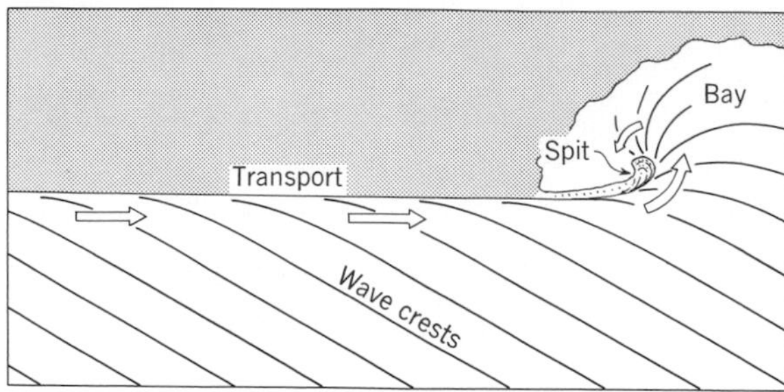


FIGURE 38.11. Littoral drift along a straight section of coast line, ending in a bay.

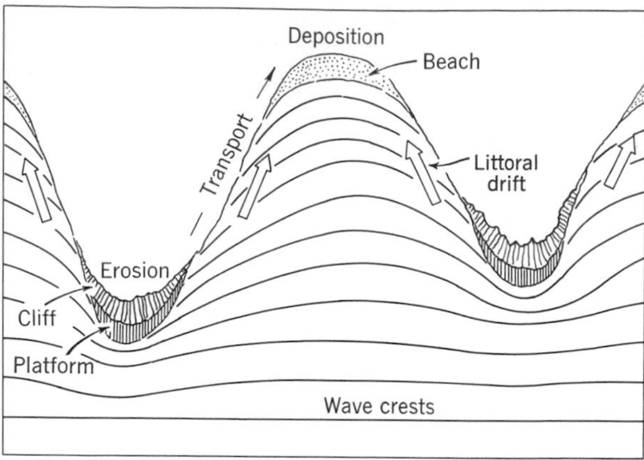


FIGURE 38.12. Littoral drift along bay sides on an irregular coast line. (Compare with Figure 17.15.)

is moved in the direction of wave travel by mass transport, which is particularly developed with steep waves. Also, water may be dragged landward by onshore winds. Water thus moving landward tends to raise the water level, and the excess must escape in some manner. Under favorable conditions of waves and winds the water escapes by flow parallel with the shore as a longshore current with sufficient velocity to move sediment. Longshore currents are most strongly felt in the breaker zone. Sediment movement by this process is termed *longshore drift.*

Both beach drift and longshore drift operate at the same time and in the same direction. Their combined effect in moving sediment may be called *littoral drift.*

Littoral drift may operate on both straight and embayed coast lines, as illustrated in Figures 38.11 and 38.12. Along a straight coast drift will carry sediment continuously along the beach, often for many tens of miles, much as bed load is carried by a river. However, if the coast line undergoes an abrupt change in direction, as where a bay is encountered, sediment is carried out into open water to form a *sandspit,* a finger-like extension of the beach. Refraction of waves around the end of the spit causes the end to curve landward in a characteristic spiral of lessening radius and the spit is described as *recurved* (Figure 38.13). In pursuing our analogy of surf zone to stream, the spit may be thought of as analogous to a stream's delta, for it is a growing deposit of sediment built into open water.

The case of an embayed coast is shown in Figure 38.12. As explained in Chapter 17, wave refraction causes a height increase in waves and breakers against the promontories, resulting in erosion of an abrasion platform and a marine cliff (Figure 17.15). Detritus thus produced moves by littoral drift along the sides of the bays, where wave approach is oblique. Sediment movement is directed along both sides of the bay toward the bayhead and accumulates there, producing the crescentic pocket beach previously referred to in the discussion of shingle beaches.

We can readily deduce the trend in evolution of an embayed coast line by imagining that the promontories are progressively eroded back while the bayheads are are being filled by a widening beach. In due time the result will be a straight shoreline formed of sections of wave-cut cliff alternating with sections of broad beach. Thus a fundamental law of shoreline evolution is that any shoreline of irregular plan tends to be reduced in time to a simple straight (or broadly curving) shoreline along which the drift of sediment is continuously in one direction for any given direction of wave approach. Removal of irregularities in shoreline plan by wave processes is analogous in some ways to the removal of falls and rapids by a stream to reach the condition of grade.

## The shore profile of equilibrium

As in the case of the graded stream, the continued action of waves produces an equilibrium profile where

FIGURE 38.13. A small recurved sand spit. Grand Traverse Bay, Lake Michigan. (Photograph by I. C. Russell, U.S. Geological Survey.)

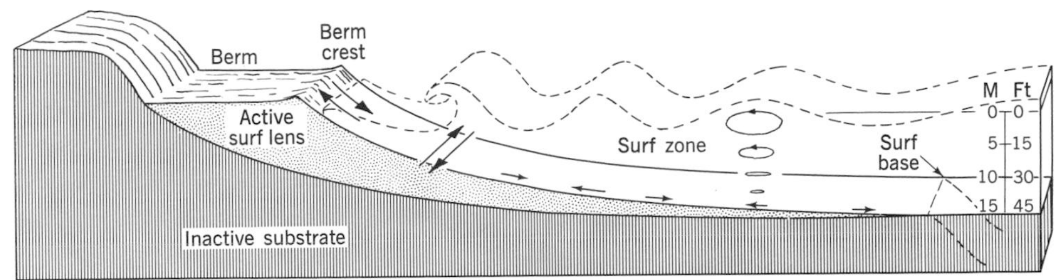


**FIGURE 38.14.** Idealized diagram of the equilibrium shore profile. (Wave size exaggerated.)

there is abundant coarse detrital material—sand and gravel—with which to shape the profile and modify it rapidly in response to changing wave conditions. These continual modifications are analogous to the continual scour and fill of a stream channel in response to changes in discharge and load (see Figure 35.8).

Figure 38.14 shows an idealized shore profile of equilibrium of unit width developed on a lens of sand, designated the *surf lens*.[1] This active lens, which can be reworked by wave action, extends seaward to the *surf base* at a depth of about 40 to 50 ft (12 to 15 m), depending upon average energy of incoming waves. The profile is so adjusted that landward push of sand by forward drag of wave orbits and swash just balances the seaward movement of sand by backwash and reverse drag of wave orbits. It must also be remembered that littoral drift of sand will be occurring in a direction parallel wih the shoreline, but transverse to the profile. When equilibrium prevails, the mass flow of sand through the profile by littoral drift is so adjusted that sand neither accumulates nor is removed.

When waves of a given height and steepness have been in action for a sufficiently long time, the profile transforms and dissipates wave energy without retrogradation, progradation, or change in slope angle of the profile. The waves in combination with the profile constitute an *open system* in which there is an input of kinetic energy from the waves, an energy transformation into surges of water, and a dissipation of energy through the resistance of fluid flow and the motion of bed materials back and forth. The open system also includes inflow and outflow of matter by littoral drift entering and leaving through the side boundaries of the system. In a condition of *steady state* the rates of inflow and outflow of energy and matter are unchanging with time and the profile assumes an unchanging geometry. When there is any change in rates of flow of energy or of matter the steady state is upset. The geometry of the system then undergoes appropriate changes and a new steady state is quickly achieved.

Seasonal adjustments of the equilibrium profile, as well as adjustments accompanying alternate periods of storm waves and weak waves with low swells, are normal in the regime of any shoreline. These fluctuations cause no net long-term change in the equilibrium profile.

One set of changes in the equilibrium profile can be brought about by changes in rates of littoral drift of sand through the system. If more sand arrives than leaves, there is an accumulation upon the surf lens. The profile is then built out in the seaward direction. The resulting progradation leaves a series of *beach ridges,* representing older berms (Figure 38.15*A*).

Progradation is sometimes concentrated in one locality along a coast because littoral drift converges upon that locality from both directions. A *cuspate foreland* is then constructed and builds seaward as a prominent cape. One striking example is the Dungeness Foreland of southeastern England (Figure 38.16). Another example is Cape Kennedy (formerly Cape Canaveral) in

[1] This model of an equilibrium profile is based upon R. S. Dietz (1963), *Geol. Soc. Amer. Bull.*, vol. 74, pp. 971–989.

**FIGURE 38.15.** (*A*) Progradation, producing successive beach ridges. (*B*) Retrogradation, resulting in cutting back of berm and removal of beach.

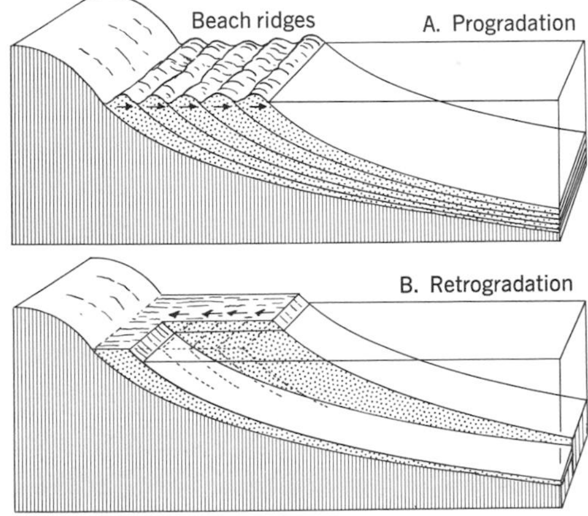


**FIGURE 38.16.** Curving beach ridges from Dungeness Foreland, on the Dover Straits of England. [From D. W. Johnson (1919), *Shore Processes and Shoreline Development,* New York, Wiley, p. 423, Figure 130.]

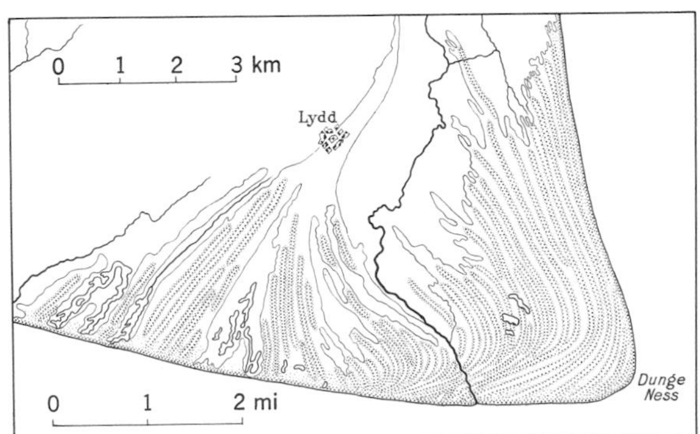

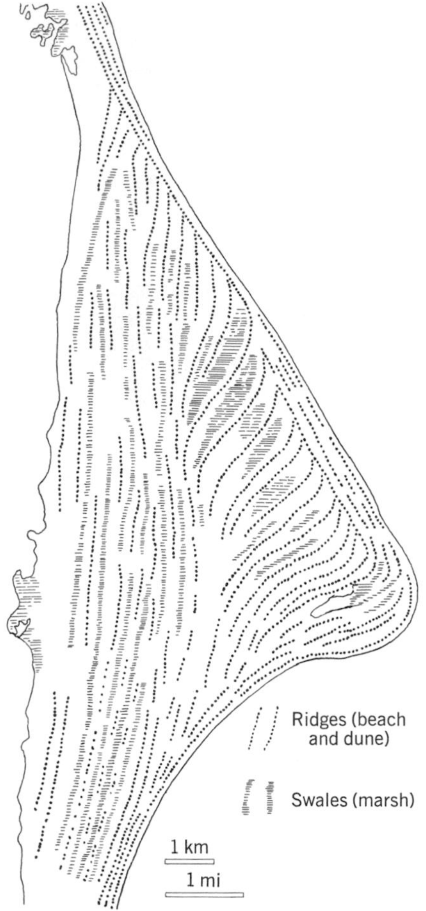


FIGURE 38.17. Map of Cape Canaveral (renamed Cape Kennedy), Florida, as it appeared about 1910, prior to Man-induced modification. Ridges close to the Atlantic shore (*right*) are beach ridges, whereas those farther inland are dune ridges built upon older beach ridges. [Redrawn from D. W. Johnson (1919), *Shore Processes and Shoreline Development,* New York, Wiley, p. 420, Figure 129.]

Florida, conveniently formed and situated to serve as a launching base for spacecraft (Figure 38.17).

Where more sand leaves than enters the surf zone by littoral drift the profile will be moved landward, a process of retrogradation. This change may result in complete removal of the surf lens and wave attack will begin again upon the underlying coastal materials (Figure 38.15*B*).

A second set of changes in the equilibrium profile is related to relative changes of sea level with respect to the land. Rise or fall of the sea level is referred to as *eustatic* change, which may result from changes of ocean volume due to the growth or melting of ice sheets, or from other causes. Relative rise of sea level, whether by eustatic rise or negative epeirogenic movement of the continental crust, results in *submergence,* and relative fall of sea level in *emergence*. These latter terms are useful where the nature of the sea level change cannot be determined.

As shown in Figure 38.18*A,* a submergence is met by

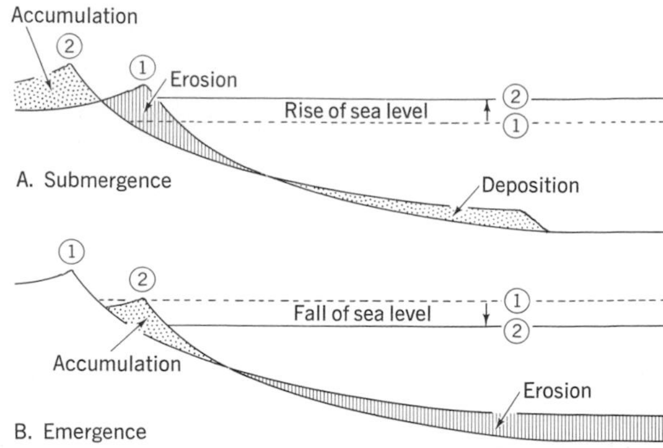


FIGURE 38.18. Schematic diagrams showing, *A,* effects of submergence and, *B,* effects of emergence upon the equilibrium profile.

a landward shift of the equilibrium profile, during which erosion occurs in the inner beach zone while deposition occurs in the outer surf zone. Current action may also deposit a layer of sediment in deeper water of the shelf zone. Some sand will also be moved landward to construct a new higher berm. Emergence, shown in Figure 38.18*B,* will be met by a seaward shift in the equilibrium profile, requiring deposition in the upper beach zone and erosion in the outer surf zone. Erosion by currents may also be required in deeper water. Both submergence and emergence can be slow and uniform in rate, or the changes may be sudden (as in the case of crustal change associated with faulting). During slow changes the equilibrium profile can be continuously maintained, whereas if rapid changes occur equilibrium is destroyed and must be reestablished on a new profile.

More-or-less continuous emergence produces a coastline consisting of numerous parallel sand ridges, representing the abandoned berms. Between these *beach ridges* are *swales,* which may be occupied by marshes. The eastern coast of Florida in the vicinity of St. Augustine offers a good example of the effects of gradual emergence.

## Elevated shorelines

When the development of a shoreline is interrupted by a sudden rise of the coast or a rapid lowering of water level, an *elevated shoreline* is formed. This landform is not a true shoreline because it is no longer shaped by waves and currents. Instead the processes of weathering, mass wasting, and running water will begin to destroy the shoreline form and eventually obliterate it entirely.

Elevated shore lines are common along the continental and insular coasts of the Pacific Ocean, because here rapid uplift of a crustal block along an active fault is an event of frequent occurrence. Typically a wave-cut cliff and marine bench are thus brought to positions well above the limits of wave attack. Repeated uplifts result in a series of elevated shorelines in a step-like arrangement. Fine examples are seen on the western slope of San Clemente Island, off the California

**FIGURE 38.19.** Air view of a series of marine terraces representing elevated shorelines. Western side of San Clemente Island, California. (Photograph by courtesy of Robert S. Dietz.)

coast (Figure 38.19). Geologists refer to such elevated benches as *marine terraces.*

In the discussion of changes of land and sea levels during the Pleistocene and Holocene epochs (Chapter 41) a number of examples of elevated shorelines are shown. These include phenomena of isostatic crustal rise following disappearance of the ice sheets and related crustal tilting. Also considered in Chapter 41 are

**FIGURE 38.20.** Evolution of an embayed coast. *BHB*: bayhead beach. *BHD*: bayhead delta. *BMB*: bay-mouth bar. *BSB*: bayside beach. *CB*: cuspate bar. *CD*: cuspate delta. *CH*: cliffed headland. *CS*: cuspate bar. *CT*: complex tombolo. *DT*: double tombolo. *HB*: headland beach. *I*: inlet. *L*: lagoon. *LB*: looped bar. *RS*: recurved spit. *S*: spit. *T*: tombolo. (© 1960, John Wiley & Sons, New York.)

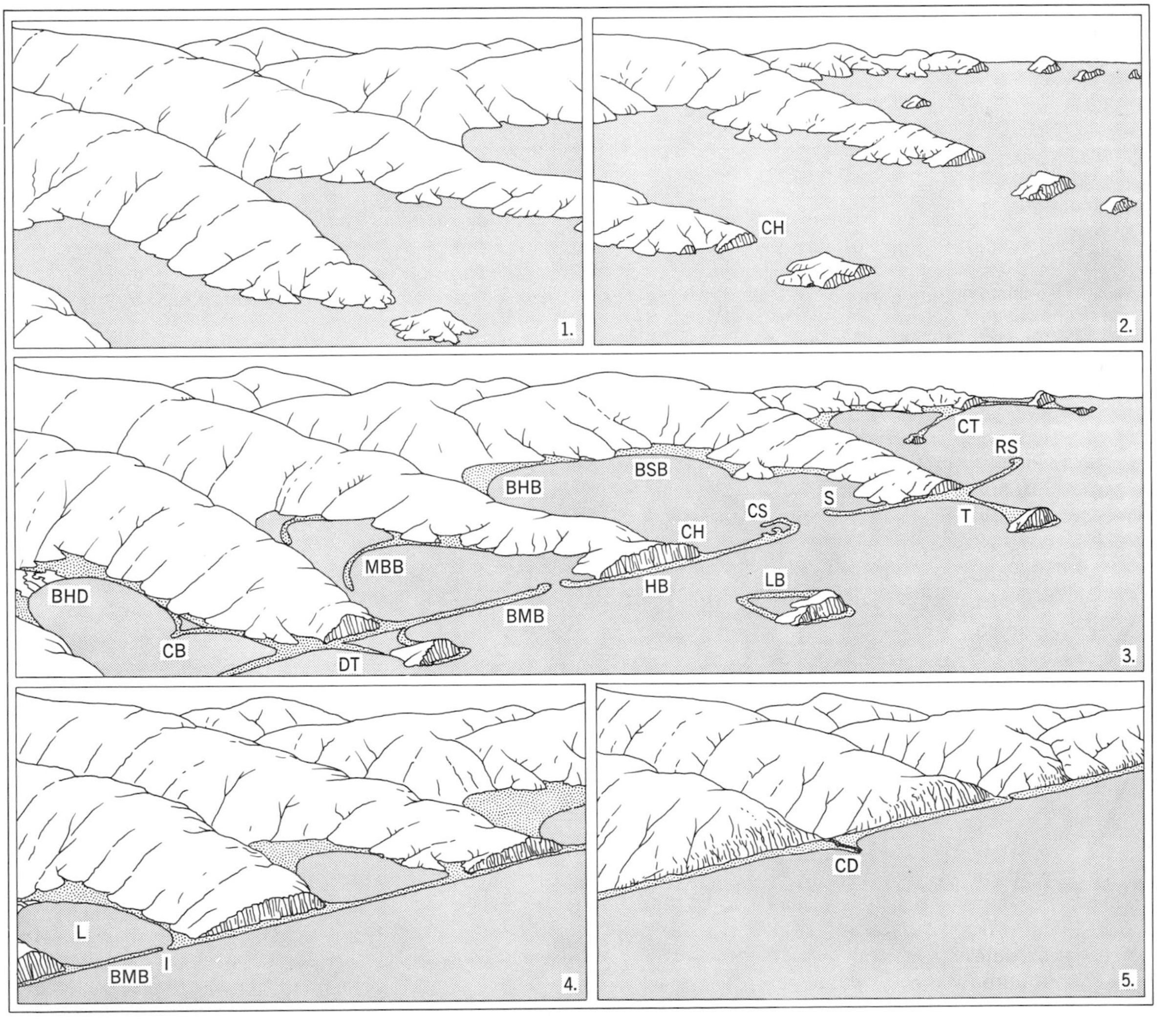

the elevated shorelines of inland lakes, resulting from the shrinkage of those lakes because of climatic change.

## Evolution of an embayed coast

Further details of evolution of an embayed coast are found by examining the sequential development of such a shoreline, beginning with a new shoreline that has come into existence through a partial drowning of the coast. The first frame of Figure 38.20 represents a landscape previously carved into stream valleys and divides by the processes of fluvial denudation. It is supposed that the coastal region subsided or that the sea level rose, or both, bringing the water line to a position against the hill slopes. Obviously the valleys now are occupied by bays, while the divides and hilltops form peninsulas and islands projecting into the sea.

The early phase of development (Frame 2) is almost wholly one of erosion, resulting in *cliffed headlands.* As erosion progresses smaller outlying islands are beveled, marine cliffs increase in height, and abrasion platforms are broadened. Presently the supply of sediment becomes sufficient to permit accumulations in the form of *headland beaches* at the bases of marine cliffs, spits of recurved and complex form, and *bayside* and *bayhead beaches* (Frame 3). Islands may become tied to the mainland by sand bars of a variety termed *tombolos* (Figure 38.21).

In a still more advanced stage of development all outlying islands have been removed by wave erosion (Frame 4). Bays are sealed across by *bay-mouth bars,* enclosing *lagoons* of open water in the bays. Bay-mouth bars may possess a narrow *tidal inlet* through which water alternately moves seaward and landward in response to falling and rising tide. Lagoons are progressively filled by silt and clay brought from streams emptying into the lagoons. Particularly important is the fact that the shoreline is now straightened to a simple line consisting of cliff segments alternating with bar segments. Retrogradation continues, however, and in the most advanced stage (Frame 5) the shoreline has been cut back to the innermost limit of the original bayheads. Now all the shoreline is one zone of erosion in bedrock. Sediment brought from the land is projected directly into the open ocean from *cuspate deltas.* This sediment is carried by littoral drift along the continuous beach in a direction dictated by prevailing direction of approach of waves and swells.

**FIGURE 38.21.** Two tombolos connecting an island with the mainland. (© 1960, John Wiley & Sons, New York. Based on a drawing by W. M. Davis.)

The development of shore forms outlined above would be modified somewhat if initial topography were different. For example, if relief of the submerged landscape were low, the marine cliffs would be small. If the landscape were one carved by glaciers into glacial

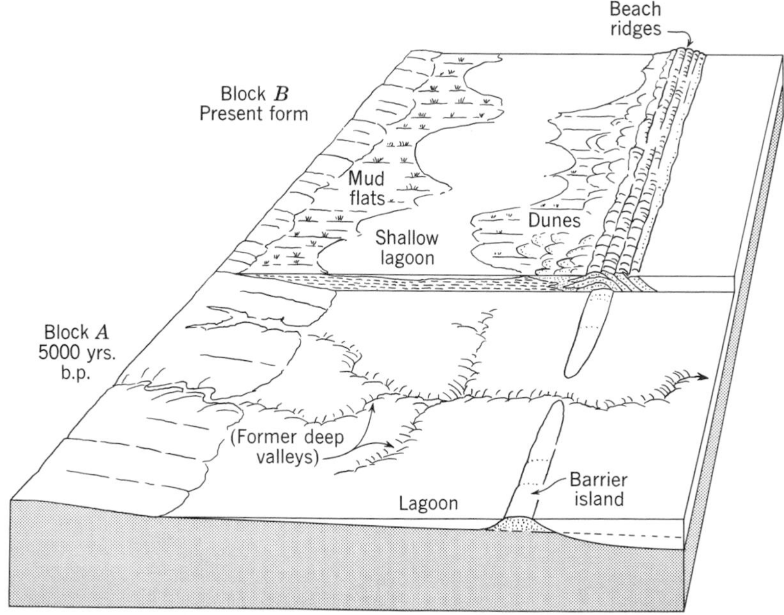


**FIGURE 38.22.** Development of a barrier island along the Gulf Coast of Texas. [Suggested by data of H. N. Fisk (1959), *Proc. 2nd. Coastal Geography Conf.,* Washington, D.C., Nat. Acad. of Sci.]

troughs the initial configuration of the coast line would be different. Nevertheless, the general process of headland wave attack, sealing off of bays by bars, and ultimate straightening of the shoreline would follow in the sequence described.

## Evolution of a gently sloping coast

In extreme contrast to embayed coasts of strong relief, with their highly irregular initial plan, are those coasts along which the water line has come to rest against a gently sloping plain of very low relief. Such a condition might result from the epeirogenic uplift of a continental coastal plain, causing the inner edge of the continental shelf to emerge. Because the shelf is normally a site of accumulation of sedimentary strata, we should expect a very smooth surface to appear and the resulting water line to be simple in plan. Another circumstance for production of an initial shoreline of very gentle seaward slope is that of the rapid postglacial rise of sea level, permitting the water to encroach upon a glacial outwash plain or perhaps upon a broad deltaic or alluvial plain.

Figure 38.22 shows the development of a part of the Gulf Coast of Texas, along which an epeirogenic upwarping brought marine strata of late Cenozoic age above sea level. As we know—from the fact that wells are drilled for petroleum many miles out to sea along the Gulf coast—the submarine topography is in general one of very gradual deepening with distance from shore. In Block *A* of Figure 38.22, representing conditions about 5000 years ago, sea level had made a rapid rise following the melting of the ice sheets and then rested against a gentle slope. Breaking storm waves quickly threw up a sand bar immediately seaward of the breaker line. Scour took place over a broad zone seaward of the bar because the water depth there was initially less than that demanded for an equilibrium profile. The new bar was rapidly built above sea level by swash, creating a narrow *barrier bar,* or *barrier island,* which cut off from the open sea a narrow zone of shallow water, the *lagoon,* lying between the barrier and the mainland.

Sea level continued to rise and the barrier island continued to be built upward by the addition of sediment brought by littoral drift from mouths of larger streams. Simultaneously the lagoon floor received sediment derived from many smaller streams that drained into it, hence it remained shallow despite the rising sea level. The barrier island became wider as new storm berms were added, and these have given a corrugated form to the island. Sand dunes were formed by strong onshore winds. The sand was blown into the lagoon beyond, where it now forms a deposit overlapping silts and clays previously laid down. As found today (Block *B*), large areas of the lagoon are filled to elevations of 1 to 3 ft (0.3 to 0.9 m) above sea level by sands, silts, and clays, forming *mud flats.*

A somewhat similar arrangement of barrier island and lagoon is found along the south shore of Long Island, New York, but it has resulted from quite different geological events (Figure 38.23). Here during the Wisconsinan glaciation the ice sheet advanced to a position along the north shore of the island. Melt-water streams built a vast outwash plain sloping gently southward to

**FIGURE 38.23.** Coastal features and moraines of western Long Island, New York. (Based on maps of the U.S. Geological Survey.)

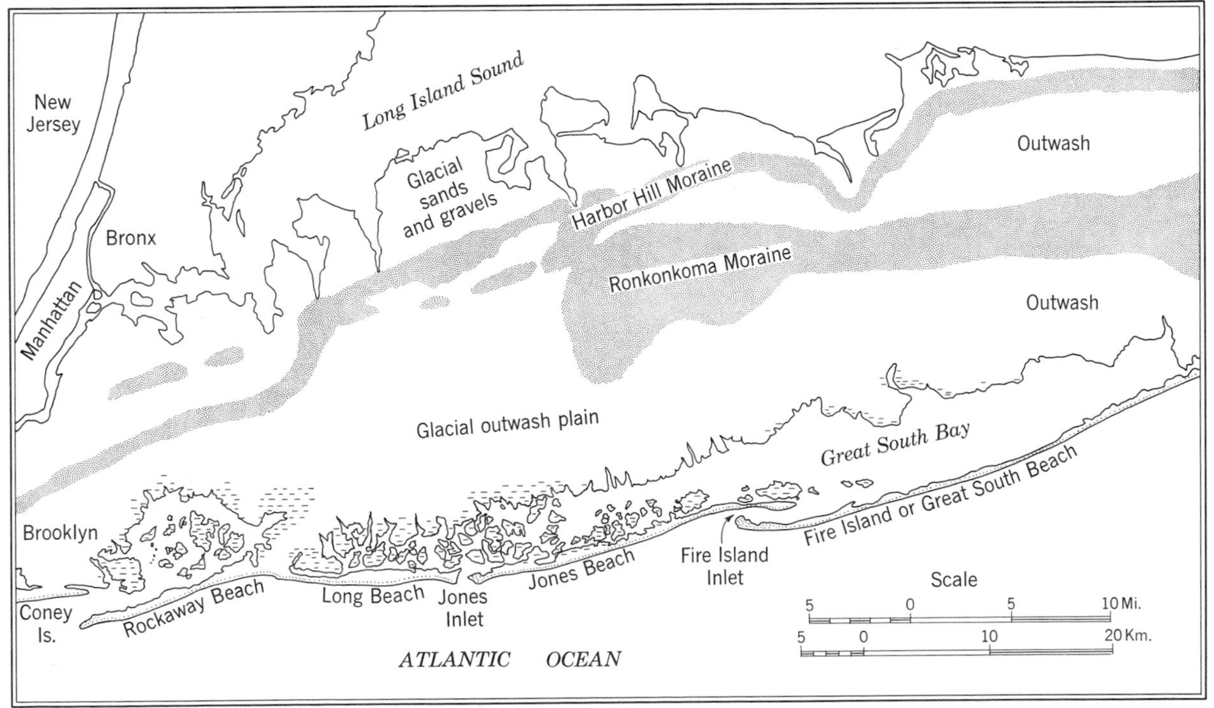

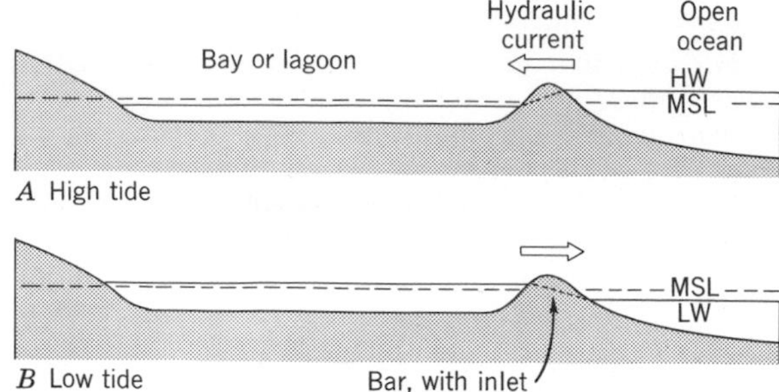


**FIGURE 38.24.** Hydraulic currents set up by rise and fall of the tide.

the shoreline, which was then some miles farther south than now because of lowered sea level. Rapid post-glacial rise in sea level inundated the outer slope of the outwash. Simultaneously the original beach was built upward as a barrier island, keeping pace with rising sea level, and thus enclosing a lagoon of increasing width.

## Tidal inlets and deltas

Where the range of tide is appreciable and the lagoons and bays are large, barrier islands and baymouth bars maintain narrow openings, termed *tidal inlets,* through which water flows alternately landward with rising tide and seaward with falling tide (Figure 38.24). (The nature of these flood and ebb currents is explained in Chapter 9). Because of the narrowness of the inlet, water level of the open ocean rises more rapidly than the level in the lagoon, with the result that a hydraulic gradient is created, much like a rapid in a river. A powerful current streams landward through the inlet, scouring the opening and carrying sediment into the lagoon, where a *tidal delta* is formed (Figure 38.25). Sediment comprising this delta is derived largely of sand carried to the inlet by littoral drift along the seaward side of the bar. When the tide level of the open ocean falls, a reverse hydraulic gradient is set up and a strong tidal current flows seaward through the inlet and tends to form a second delta, but rapid littoral drift generated by large waves of the open sea minimizes the formation of this deposit.

Tidal inlets are modified in response to the prevailing movement of sediment by littoral drift along a coast. As a rule, the bar on the updrift side of the inlet is prograded (built out) and that on the downdrift side is retrograded (cut back) so that an offset form develops, as shown in Figure 38.26. Finally, the ends of the baymouth bar (or barrier island) show a considerable overlap and the tidal inlet is greatly lengthened. The bar end that is being lengthened takes the form of a recurved spit and may show many curving beach ridges as evidence of its stages of growth.

Tidal inlets may be created by a severe storm in which onshore winds coinciding with high water of spring tides cause storm swash to break over a low point in the barrier island. If conditions are favorable, powerful currents responding to a hydraulic gradient will scour a large gap within a few hours. East Moriches Inlet, shown in Figure 38.25, illustrates such a storm break. An inlet thus formed may be subsequently closed by shore drift of sediment into the opening, or it may remain as a permanent feature maintained by tidal-current scour. Large-scale current ripples attest to the speed and erosional capability of tidal currents (Figure 38.27).

## Tidal flats and salt marshes

Bays and lagoons of any origin shut off from the open ocean are gradually filled by layers of clay and silt brought into the quiet water by streams draining the land. The sediment is distributed over the bay by ebb

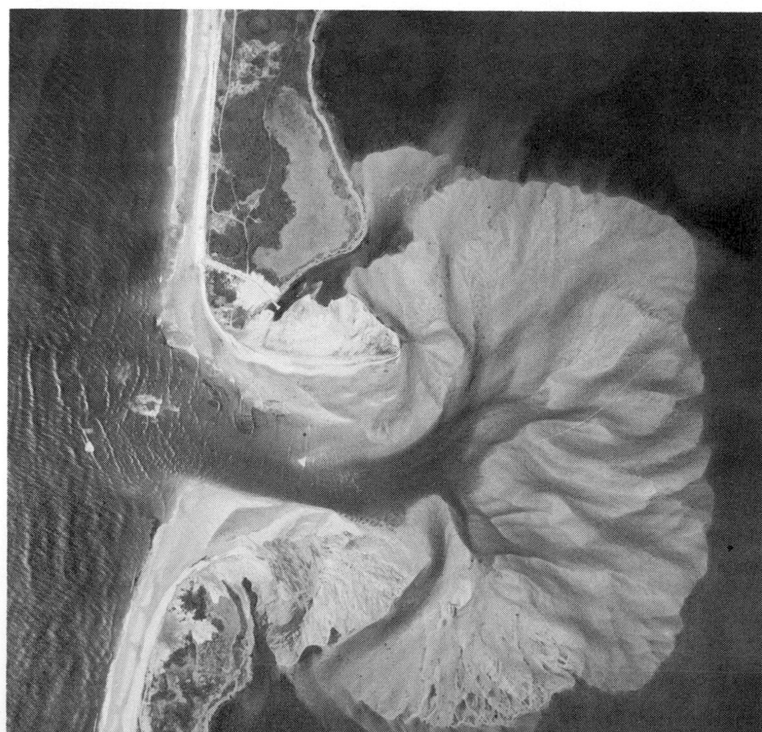

**FIGURE 38.25.** A great storm of March, 1931, cut this breach through Fire Island, allowing tidal currents to carry sediment from the open Atlantic Ocean (*left*) into the lagoon (*right*) and construct a tidal delta. The entire area shown is about 1 mi (1.6 km) across. East Moriches Inlet, Long Island, New York. (U.S. Air Force photograph.)

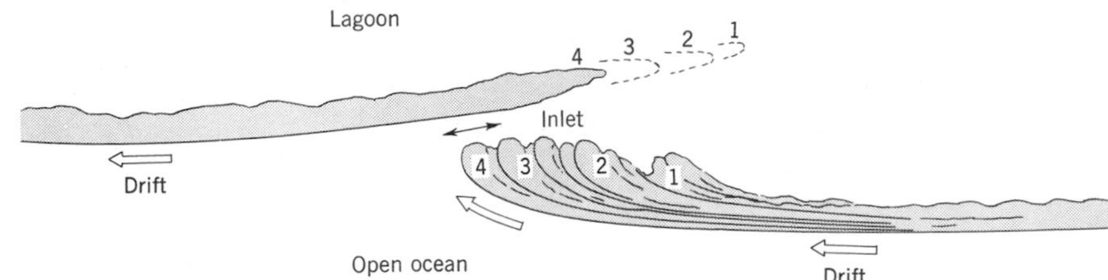


FIGURE 38.26. Migration of an inlet in a barrier island.

and flood tidal currents. Clays of the type illustrated in Figure 22.3 upon reaching the saline water of the bay or lagoon flocculate and settle to the bottom, where they adhere and form sediment layers. Figure 38.28 shows the chain-like structure produced by flocculation. Sediment of this type has a very large proportion of water-filled voids and is capable of a high degree of compaction if drained of water.

Organic matter, both that carried in suspension in streams and that produced by growth of plants and animals on the bottom, may constitute a substantial proportion of the sediment. Gradually the sediment is built upward until the upper surface is approximately at the level of low tide. The result is a mud flat, or *tidal flat,* exposed at low water of spring tides but covered at high water (Figure 38.29).

Ebb and flood currents maintain a branching system of *tidal streams* scoured by flow in alternating directions (Figure 38.30). A completed tidal-channel network consists of trunk streams joined by tributaries of smaller dimensions and discharges, just as for ordinary fluvial systems on the land. There are, however, many interconnections among the lower-order channels. Highly sinuous meanders are characteristic of tidal streams.

Upon the tidal mud flats a salt-tolerant vegetation takes hold, eventually forming a resistant mat of plant roots. More sediment is trapped by plant stems, and the level of the deposit is built up to the mean level of high tide. The resulting surface is described as a *tidal marsh,* or *salt marsh* (Figure 38.30). Tidal flats and tidal marshes encroach in succession upon the open water until the entire bay or lagoon is filled, except for the system of tidal channels. Where sea-level rise has been gradual, salt-marsh vegetation has maintained its growth at tide level by building newer layers upon old. In this manner layers of *peat* are produced.[2]

FIGURE 38.27. Large sand ripples produced by ebb tide currents. Avon Estuary, Nova Scotia. Current direction is indicated by the arrow. (Photograph by Canada Department of Mines and Technical Survey, Ottawa.)

## Common types of shorelines

It has long been a goal of geomorphologists to set up a logical classification scheme in which every segment of the world's shorelines can find its place. Despite the widespread use of several different classifications, none has been fully accepted because none has proved completely adequate. In this chapter it will suffice to call attention to some of the common varieties of shorelines.

In foregoing paragraphs one major variety of shoreline was treated in detail: the embayed coast produced by partial submergence of a fluvially eroded landmass (Frame 1*A* of Figure 38.31). The term *ria shoreline* has been applied to this variety. A good example is found along the Brittany coast of France, in the vicinity of Brest, and another along the coast northeast of Auckland, New Zealand.

Erosion by ice sheets may have so modified the fluvially eroded topography that submergence has produced an embayed coast in which the valleys show some degree of straightening and deepening by ice, hilltops are blunted by ice erosion, and deposits of till block smaller valleys. Such a shoreline is well illustrated by the coast of Maine between Portland and Eastport.

Coastal regions of fluvially eroded topography having very low relief produce still another minor variety of embayed coast when partially submerged (Frame 1*B*). Estuaries extend far inland and show a tree-like branch-

[2] Not to be confused with peat formed in fresh-water bogs. (See Chapter 22.)

FIGURE 38.28. Honeycomb structure of particles in flocculated sediment of brackish water of tidal lagoons.

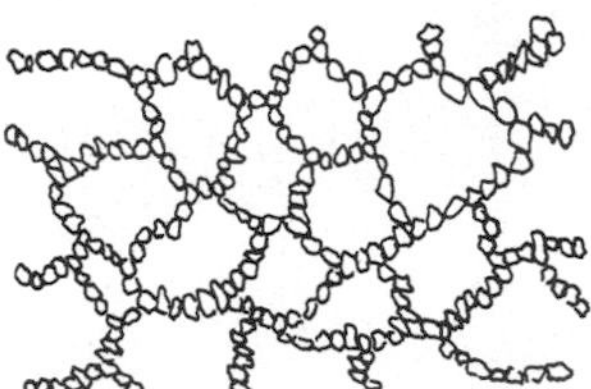

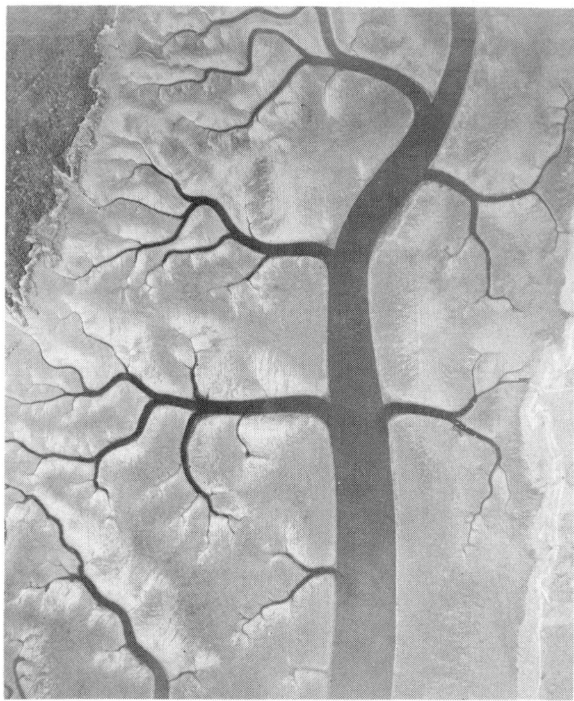

**FIGURE 38.29.** Tidal mudflats and tidal channels at low water near Yarmouth, Nova Scotia. This vertical air photograph covers an area about 1 mi (1.6 km) wide. (Royal Canadian Air Force official photograph No. KA51-15.)

ing pattern, as would be expected from inundation of a stream pattern. Fine examples of highly embayed coasts of very low relief are found in the great estuaries of the Atlantic coastal plain, particularly Chesapeake Bay and its branches in Virginia and Maryland.

**FIGURE 38.30.** Tidal creek with sinuous meanders in coastal salt marsh, Rock Creek, Orleans, Massachusetts. (Photograph by Harold L. R. Cooper, Cape Cod Photos, Orleans, Mass.)

Most spectacular of the embayed shorelines are the *fiord coasts,* formed of partially submerged glacial troughs (Frame 1*C*). A characteristic feature of the fiord coast is the straightness, great steepness, and great height of the walls of the embayments, as well as their great depth (see Figure 40.16).

Where Pleistocene ice sheets spread to the continental margins, conditions were favorable for the accumulation of great masses of glacial drift and their subsequent partial submergence. (Landforms of glacial deposition are described in Chapter 40.) Thus the water line may have come to rest against swarms of drumlins (Frame 1*D*) or against masses of deeply pitted outwash formed between stagnant blocks of ice. The resulting embayed shoreline is highly irregular in plan, but the weakness of the glacial drift permits rapid modification where the coast is exposed to waves of the open ocean. Fine examples of partially submerged drumlins are found in the Boston Bay area of Massachusetts. The north shore of Long Island, New York, illustrates an embayed shoreline formed of glacial outwash (Figure 38.23). Here the bays occupy cavities left by the melting of stagnant ice bodies, and the peninsulas represent glaciofluvial deposits built between those ice bodies.

Partial submergence of the terrestrial landforms described above may result from epeirogenic downwarping of the continental margins or from crustal depression under the load of ice sheets. The post-glacial rise of sea level adds to the degree of submergence. Locally, the downfaulting of a block of the earth's crust may cause partial submergence of fluvially eroded topography. Examples might be sought along the earth's great island and mountain arcs of present-day orogenic activity.

A second major shoreline variety, also treated in foregoing paragraphs, is that produced by relative changes of land and sea level to bring the water line against a very gentle sloping plain of low relief (Frame 2*A*). Development of the barrier island and lagoon is characteristic of this type of shoreline.

Frame 2*B* illustrates a variety of shoreline produced by the rapid emergence of a steeply sloping coast. The initial shoreline thus produced will be relatively simple in plan and will receive the full force of wave attack. A marine cliff and abrasion platform will quickly develop. Such shorelines of emergence may be found along the Pacific Coast of the United States—for example, in the Ventura region of California. Rapid emergence may be expected to accompany faulting in an orogenically active belt such as that surrounding the Pacific Ocean basin.

Another major group of shorelines includes those produced by the rapid accretion of new land by accumulations of detrital or organic sediment. *Alluvial-fan shorelines* and *delta shorelines,* pictured in Frames 3*A* and 3*B*, represent sites of rapid accumulation of fluviatile sediment. No changes of sea level relative to the land are required in the formation of these shorelines, although such changes may modify the development. Another type of accretion is represented by *coral-reef shorelines* (Frame 3*D* of Figure 38.31). These features are described in detail in Chapter 25.

The growth of volcanoes and the extrusion of lava flows in coastal locations may cause new masses of

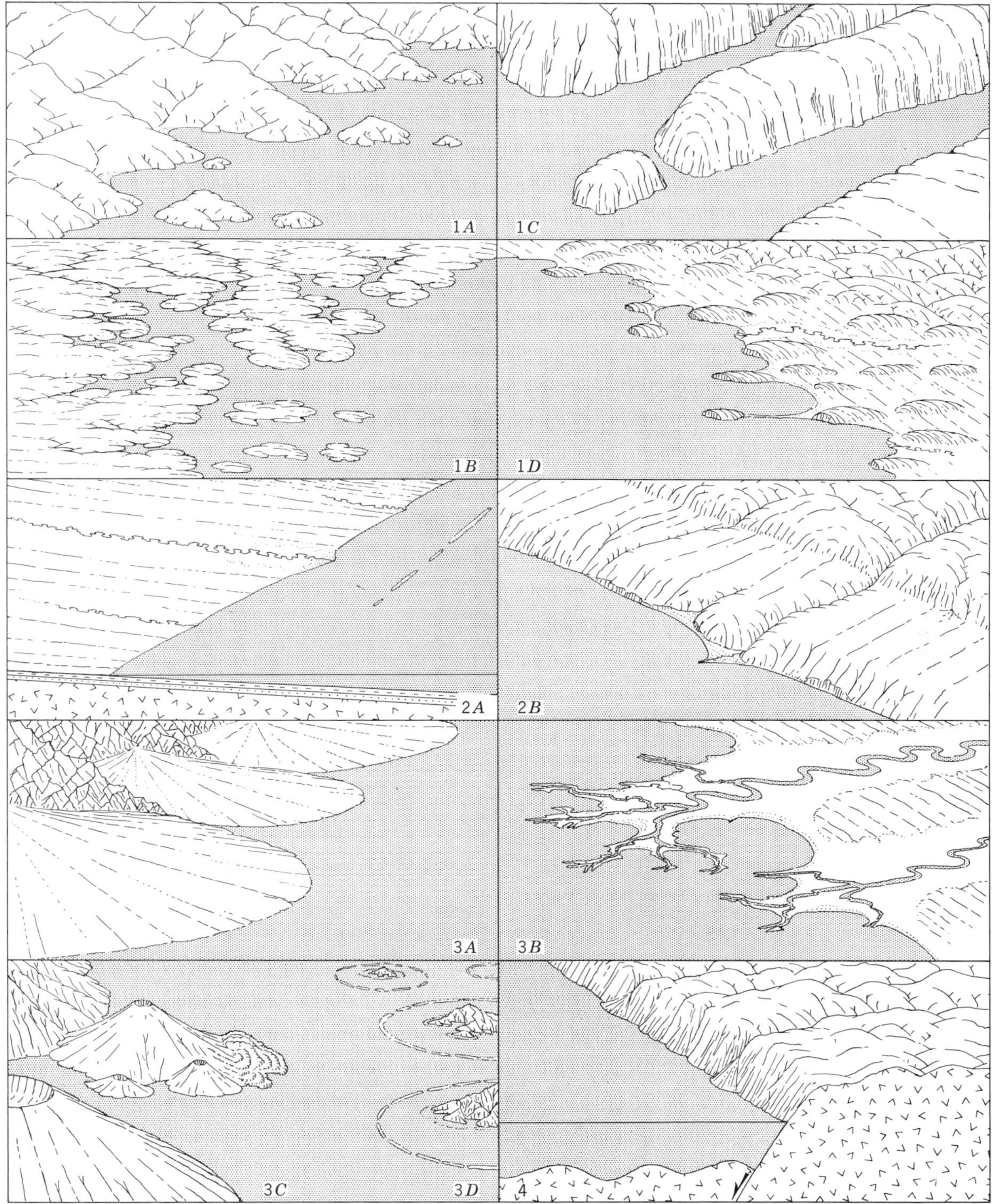


**FIGURE 38.31.** Varieties of shorelines. (*1A*) Ria shoreline. (*1B*) Shoreline of submergence with low relief. (*1C*) Fiord shoreline. (*1D*) Drumlin shoreline. (*2A*) Coastal-plain shoreline. (*2B*) Shoreline of emergence, steeply sloping. (*3A*) Alluvial-fan shoreline. (*3B*) Delta shoreline. (*3C*) Volcanic shoreline. (*3D*) Coral-reef shoreline. (*4*) Fault-scarp shoreline. (© 1960, John Wiley & Sons, New York.)

rock to be built and thus to create a unique variety, the *volcanic shoreline* (Frame 3C). Many fine illustrations are seen in the volcanic island chains of the circum-Pacific orogenic belt. An ideal small-scale example is found in the Wizard Island volcanic cone and its associated lava flow built into Crater Lake, Oregon (Figure 21.23).

Finally, we note a rarely found type, the *fault-scarp* shoreline, formed where normal faulting has recently occurred in a coastal region, dropping a crustal block down so that it is completely submerged. The sea is thus permitted to rest directly against the fault scarp (Frame 4).

## Wave base and marine planation

To what water depths are waves effective as geologic agents? The answer is not a simple one, since it depends upon what effect is specified in the question. The lower limit of wave action effect in agitating bottom material is designated the *wave base.*

Abrasion of hard rock by particles moved back and forth under the influence of shoaling and breaking waves is probably limited to a shallow nearshore zone, perhaps no deeper than 30 ft (10 m). However, the movement of detrital sediment from shallower water to deeper water under the orbital motions of storm waves can extend into much deeper water. Some authorities are of the opinion that the effectiveness of wave action in shaping the shore profile is limited to the upper 65 ft (20 m) of water depth, which has been designated the surf base. Particles of clay and silt grades are thought to be agitated and brought into suspension by orbital drag of storm waves at bottom depths as great as 650 ft (200 m), which is approximately the limit of depth of the continental shelves. Hence in the past this depth has been used to define wave base. There is much doubt today as to the effectiveness of such wave agitation in moving substantial quantities of sediment in depths below 300 ft (100 m), and it seems more likely that bottom currents are principal means of sediment transport over much of the shelf zone.

It is conceivable that, given sufficient time and stability of the crust, wave action in the surf zone might ultimately plane off an entire continent, reducing it to a shallow submarine platform. This process can be called *marine plantation.* The supply of wave energy is practically limitless, since it depends upon wind stress, rather than upon the gravity-flow mechanism required by streams. Moreover, the deep ocean basins provide a sink for almost limitless quantities of detrital material derived from continental denudation.

The prospect of marine planation as a real event in the geologic past becomes somewhat more likely when we consider that fluvial denudation would be active under the same set of stable conditions. Reduction of the landmass to a peneplain would minimize the volume of rock that wave action would need to remove. Even so, the process of marine planation would be extremely slow, since the equilibrium profile of the shore is adjusted to dissipate most of the wave energy in frictional resistance.

There is, however, one set of conditions under which marine planation may have been effective. When a continent that has been reduced to a peneplain undergoes a slow crustal sinking (a negative epeirogenic movement), the action of waves in removing a substantial layer of soil, overburden, and bedrock is greatly facilitated. Deepening of the water by progressive submergence allows more wave energy to act in the surf zone, while at the same time making available space in which the sediments can be deposited. This principle has been discussed in earlier paragraphs.

Marine planation is therefore an event to be anticipated during the slow submergence of a landmass, and we should look for evidences of such action in the unconformities of the geologic record. Two great unconformities of the inner Grand Canyon have been described in some detail in Chapters 28 and 36. (Refer to Figures 28.1, 28.8, and 36.12.) The older of the two unconformities, that which bevels the Archean rocks, is remarkably even. This surface appears to be a true peneplain of fluvial denudation, for it still retains a zone of weathered rock and overburden. Wave action of the advancing seas of Algonkian time was not sufficiently effective to remove but a small part of this weathered material. Evidently, submergence was rapid in this case.

The second unconformity lies beneath the Cambrian Tapeats sandstone and cuts across both Archean and Algonkian rocks. This erosion surface shows many monadnocks of resistant quartzite and was evidently quite hilly when submergence began. Marine action was only moderately effective in modifying this erosion surface. In places all weathered rock was removed, for the rock beneath the unconformity is locally quite fresh. Monadnocks of quartzite show definite indications of wave cutting, for they have steep slopes and basal accumulations of coarse debris, now conglomerate and breccia (Figure 38.32). Possibly wave action cut off large parts of the tops of the monadnocks as submergence progressed.

The evidence from Grand Canyon does not give support to the concept of marine planation as an important process in removing substantial thicknesses of the continental crust. Nevertheless, the possibility that marine planation has been important at other times in the geologic past should not be dismissed.

**FIGURE 38.32.** Diagram of unconformity between Tapeats formation of Cambrian age and Algonkian strata of Precambrian age, Grand Canyon, Arizona. Monadnock of Algonkian strata (*center*) resisted wave attack, by waves of rising sea, approaching from the right. The section is about 600 ft (180 m) long. [After R. P. Sharp (1940), *Geol. Soc. Amer. Bull.*, Vol. 51, p. 1263, Figure 8.]

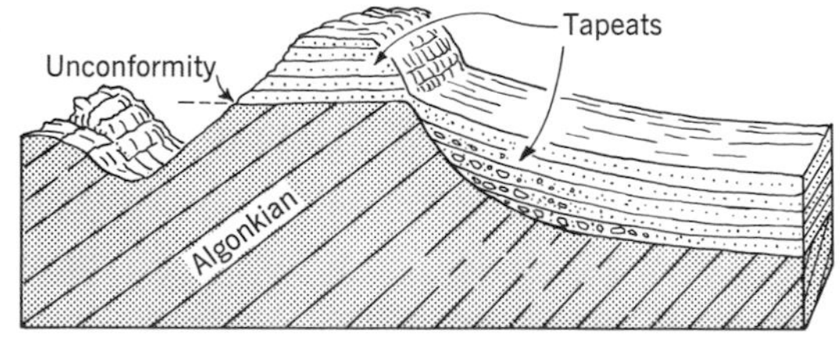

## A system in review

This chapter has dealt with a geologic agent powered by atmospheric circulation, which in turn derives its energy from solar radiation. Unequal heating and cooling of the atmosphere leads to density differences within the atmosphere from one part of the globe to another, resulting in pressure gradients and the ensuing response in the planetary winds. These winds transfer their kinetic energy to ocean waves, which bring an almost continual energy flux to the shores of the continents. Here the energy of water motion is dissipated in motions of water and sediment, and a geologic function is thus performed. But the winds also exert drag forces and lift forces upon the surfaces of the continents. Here the moving air, which is a fluid in its behavior, is able to move particles of mineral matter over the ground surface or lift them high into the air in suspension. It is therefore appropriate that in the next chapter the geologic work of wind should be considered.

## References for further study


Guilcher, A. (1958), *Coastal and Submarine Morphology,* New York, Wiley, 274 pp.

King, C. A. M. (1959), *Beaches and Coasts,* London, Edward Arnold, 403 pp.

Shepard, F. P. (1963), *Submarine Geology,* 2nd ed., New York, Harper & Row, 557 pp., chaps. 6, 7.

Bascomb, W. (1964), *Waves and Beaches,* New York, Doubleday, 260 pp.

Strahler, A. N. (1966), *A Geologist's View of Cape Cod,* Garden City, N.Y., Doubleday—Nat. Hist. Press, 115 pp.

Bird, E. C. F. (1968), *Coasts,* Cambridge, Mass., M.I.T. Press, 237 pp.

Fairbridge, R. W., ed. (1968), *The Encyclopedia of Geomorphology,* New York, Reinhold, 1295 pp. See Bars, Beach, Coastal classification, Coastal geomorphology, Coast lines, Platforms—wave-cut, Terraces—marine, Tidal delta, Tidal inlet.

39

# Wind as a geologic agent

WIND IS A THIRD AGENT of active erosion and deposition capable of producing distinctive landforms. In all probability, an analysis of the world's landscapes would show that landforms produced by wind action are of relatively minor importance compared with those produced by running water, glacial ice, and waves. Nevertheless, in certain favored localities, particularly in the world's deserts and steppes, wind produces depositional features that locally dominate the landscape. Along many of the world's coasts, including those in humid climates, belts of sand dunes are conspicuous landscape elements. From the geologic past enormous accumulations of dune sands have been preserved in the stratigraphic record, as witness the Permian and Jurassic rocks of the walls of Grand Canyon and Zion Canyon (Chapter 28).

Layers of wind-transported silt are widespread over parts of the middle-latitude continents and comprise the parent matter of fertile soils of greatest importance to Man.

## Wind erosion

The flow of air over a solid or liquid surface exerts a dragging force, or *shearing stress,* against that surface. As explained in Chapter 17, air flow over a water surface generates waves, which receive their kinetic energy from the wind. By contrast, air moving over a solid mineral surface, such as bedrock or hardened clay, is quite ineffectual in causing any appreciable change, so greatly does the cohesive strength of the material exceed the stresses exerted by the wind. Only where mineral grains of relatively small size are lying loose upon an exposed surface can wind exploit its full powers of erosion and transportation.

**FIGURE 39.1.** Deflation has lowered the surface in the foreground, as indicated by the remnant knobs of layered sand and silt. Drifts can be seen in the distance. Holt County, Nebraska, 1936. (Photograph by Soil Conservation Service, U.S. Department of Agriculture.)

One form of wind erosion is *deflation,* the lifting and entrainment of loose particles of clay and silt sizes, collectively referred to as *dust,*[1] by turbulent eddies in the wind structure. The process is much like that of suspension of fine sediment in stream flow. Grains are carried up by vertical currents exceeding the setting velocities of the grains in still air. The dust is diffused upward into the atmosphere to heights ranging from a few feet to several miles, depending upon intensity of wind turbulence, duration of the wind, and fineness of the particles.

Deflation occurs where clays and silts in a thoroughly dried state are exposed on barren land surfaces. Such conditions exist in steppes and deserts generally, and locally in desiccated floodplains, tidal flats, and lake beds. Even upon actively forming glacial outwash plains, deflation is active in times of cold, dry weather.

Deflation may result in excavation of shallow depressions, termed *deflation hollows,* or simply *blowouts* (Figure 39.1). Hollows develop where the natural vegetative cover of shrubs or grasses is broken down, exposing the bare soil or overburden to wind. Once formed, deflation hollows hold water after heavy rains and thereby attract grazing animals whose trampling further loosens and disrupts the soil, preparing it for deflation when the soil is again desiccated. Storm runoff attacks the sloping margins of the depressions, washing sediment into the bottom, from where it is later removed by deflation. Thus deflation hollows tend to deepen and enlarge, sometimes growing to widths of 1 mi (1.6 km) or more and to depths of 10 to 50 ft (3 to 15 m).

Deflation may also assist in the excavation of steep-sided pits or bowls in bare rock surfaces. Grains loosened by weathering processes are removed from the hollow by turbulent gusts.

More commonly, deflation produces no distinctive landform but merely removes a layer of uniform thickness from the surface of a plain. Left behind, however, are grains of gravel and pebbles too large to be moved (Figure 39.2). These remnants accumulate into a sheet that ultimately covers the finer-grained material beneath and protects it from further deflation. Such a

[1] Dust carried in suspension by wind is finer than 0.01 mm (10 microns) in diameter—i.e., a silt of medium grade. Dust includes clay particles, 0.004 mm (4 microns) in diameter and finer. (See Table 22.3.)

**FIGURE 39.2.** Pebble-covered surface developed by deflation of a broad gravel-bar deposit of the Colorado River, near Yuma, Arizona. (Photograph by F. J. Wright.)

**FIGURE 39.3.** A ventifact resting in place on a wind-swept gravel surface. A 6-in. (15-cm) ruler indicates size. Wright Valley, McMurdo Sound, Antarctica. (Photograph by R. L. Nichols.)

residual sheet is termed a *desert pavement,* or, in the North African deserts, a *reg.* Desert pavements develop rapidly upon alluvial-fan and terrace surfaces. Exposed surfaces of the pebbles may become coated with a nearly black iridescent substance called *desert varnish.* In some localities the evaporation of capillary water brought surfaceward through the soil leaves behind a deposit of calcium carbonate (caliche) or gypsum that acts as a cement, hardening the pavement into a conglomerate-like slab.

A second form of wind erosion is *sand-blast action,* in which hard mineral grains (usually of quartz) of sand sizes are driven against exposed rock surfaces projecting above a plain. As explained in later paragraphs, sand grains travel close to the ground, hence their erosive action is limited to surfaces lying within a few feet of the flat ground over which the sand is being driven. Sand-blast action probably does not erode resistant bedrock to depths of more than a few inches and is responsible only for minor features such as notches and hollows at the base of a cliff or a boulder.

Most of the spectacular *pedestal rocks,* consisting of large boulder-like masses resting upon thin stalks, are not caused by sand-blast action, as popularly supposed, but are the result of granular disintegration of the basal rock by physical- and chemical-weathering processes.

Sand-blast erosion creates curiously shaped pebbles known as *ventifacts.* When developed to perfection, these objects take the form of elongate, doubly pointed *dreikanter* (from the German words for "three" and "edges"), having three curved faces intersecting in three sharp edges (Figure 39.3). Dreikanter originate from stream-rounded pebbles of hard fine-grained rock such as quartzite, chert, or obsidian. Sand-blast action erodes the windward face of a partially buried pebble. The pebble then turns to rest upon the flattened face, permitting a second face to be cut, and finally a third. Dreikanter and other distinctively pitted, faceted, and polished stones give evidence of aridity of climate when found buried in a sedimentary deposit. For example, the boulders of a residual glacial till (Chapter 40) often show surfaces of wind abrasion, suggesting at least seasonal aridity and strong winds at the time the till was exposed during ice-front retreat.

**FIGURE 39.4.** This rapidly moving cloud is the leading edge of a dust storm. The dust is suspended within turbulent air of a cold front. Coconino Plateau, Arizona. (Photograph by D. L. Babenroth.)

## Dust storms

Winds of high intensity and turbulence, blowing over plains and plateaus at times when the soil is dry, lift great quantities of dust into suspension in the atmosphere, giving rise to a *dust storm* (Figure 39.4). The smaller particles may quickly diffuse to heights of thousands of feet and will travel for hundreds of miles before settling to earth in less turbulent air.

In the United States the passage of a rapidly moving cold front, bringing a turbulent mass of colder air southward over the Great Plains region, is a common cause of a severe dust storm. As the front approaches, a dark dust cloud, representing the leading edge of the front, moves over the plain. When the cloud strikes it may bring semidarkness and reduce visibility to only a few yards. The fine dust, penetrating into all open spaces, makes breathing difficult.

During the cycle of dry years prevailing in the 1930s in the Great Plains region known as the *Dust Bowl,* frequent dust storms occurred because of the combina-

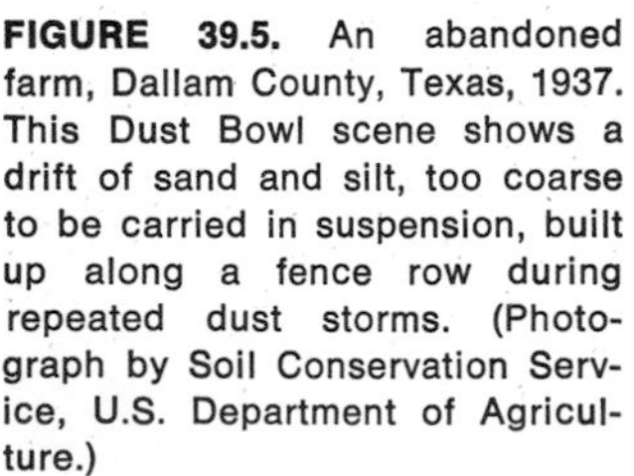

**FIGURE 39.5.** An abandoned farm, Dallam County, Texas, 1937. This Dust Bowl scene shows a drift of sand and silt, too coarse to be carried in suspension, built up along a fence row during repeated dust storms. (Photograph by Soil Conservation Service, U.S. Department of Agriculture.)

tion of drought and vast expanses of cultivated land bared of protective vegetation (Figure 39.5). In the intermontane basins of continental interiors, dust storms are frequent over surfaces underlain by fine silts and clays.

The quantity of dust suspended in a great dust storm has been estimated at values up to 4000 tons per cubic mile of air (875 metric tons per cu km). Thus a storm 300 to 400 mi (500 to 650 km) across might be transporting at one time more than 100 million tons (90 million metric tons) of dust, or enough to produce a mound 100 ft (30 m) high and 2 mi (3 km) across. Repeated many times each year and prolonged over many centuries, dust storms have geologic importance as a method of sediment transport, but their relative importance is difficult to evaluate. Probably the present rates of removal and accumulation by dust storms are a very small fraction of the rates attributable to overland flow and stream flow in the same area.

The importance of air-borne dusts in contributing to pelagic detrital sediment of the deep ocean floors has been discussed in Chapter 24.

## Loess

That thick deposits of wind-transported dust can accumulate under favorable conditions is amply demonstrated by the widespread occurrence in the middle latitudes of surficial layers of *loess,* a porous, friable, yellowish sediment of finely divided mineral fragments mostly in the size range of silt, 0.06 to 0.004 mm (62 to 4 microns) in diameter. Five to thirty percent of the loess may be of clay sizes. In some loess there is 5% to 10% of sand, but these larger grains were transported close to the ground.

Loess, where forming a layer over the upland and divide areas of plains and low plateaus, usually shows no layered structure or stratification, but on the other hand it commonly has a natural vertical parting, or *cleavage,* along which masses readily break away from an undercut bank or cliff. Lack of stratification is attributed to the uniformity of accumulation, probably upon grass-covered surfaces, and to some degree of surficial disturbance by plant and animal action after deposition. The vertical cleavage is perhaps a system of shrinkage cracks resulting from compaction after deposition.

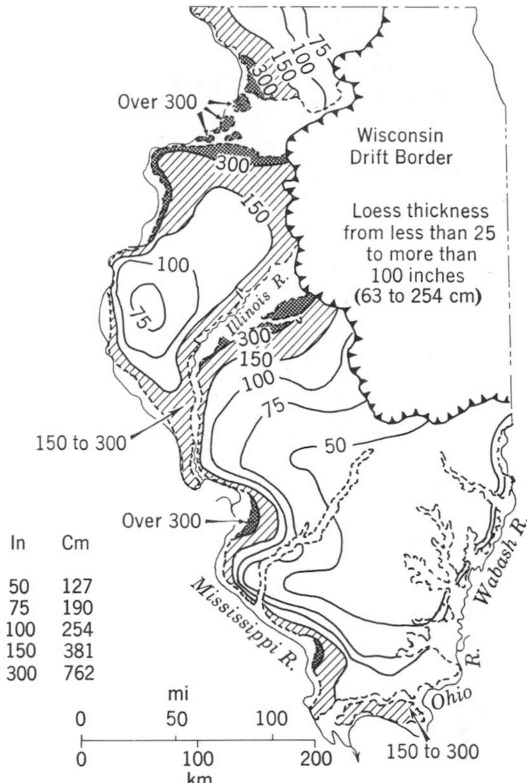


**FIGURE 39.7.** Loess thickness (inches) in Illinois. (© 1965, John Wiley & Sons, New York. Based on a map by R. F. Flint.)

**FIGURE 39.6.** Areas of the central United States covered by important loess deposits (*cross-ruled*) and the Sand Hills, a region of formerly active dunes (*stippled*). (© 1965, John Wiley & Sons, New York. Based on a map by Apfel.)

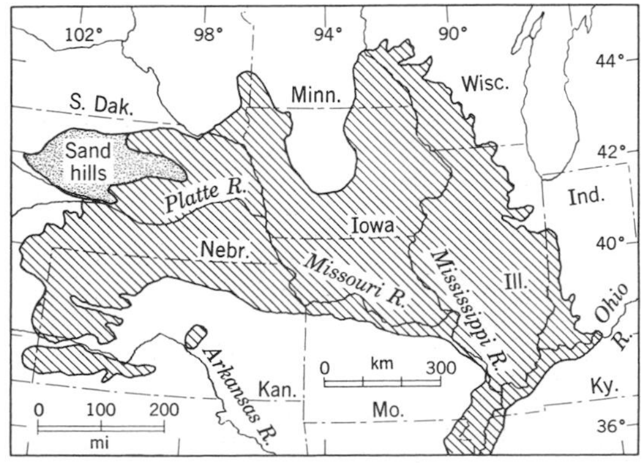


**FIGURE 39.8.** This nearly vertical road cut in thick loess, south of Vicksburg, Mississippi, illustrates the remarkable stability of the undisturbed material. (Photograph by Orlo Childs.)

**FIGURE 39.9.** Oblique air view of deeply eroded loess, Shansi Province, China (lat. 38° N., long. 112° E.). Steep valley sides are artificially terraced to permit cultivation. Flat interstream uplands represent the original depositional surface of the loess, which reaches a thickness of over 100 ft (30 m). (U.S. Geological Survey photograph.)

The mineral composition of loess varies from region to region but is commonly a mixture of mechanically pulverized fragments, dominantly of quartz, but with some feldspar, mica, hornblende, and pyroxene. Characteristically carbonate mineral matter is present in loess, and an unweathered sample will effervesce (froth) when dilute hydrochloric acid is applied to it. Furthermore, small nodules and tubes of calcite (calcium carbonate) are found distributed through the loess. Fossil snail shells occur in large numbers in some thick loess layers.

The grain size and mineral composition of loess of the middle latitudes in the United States and Europe are best explained by the *eolian hypothesis,* that loess is wind-blown dust of Pleistocene age carried from alluvial valleys and outwash plains lying south of the limits of the ice sheets and from glacial deposits uncovered by glacial retreat. Comparisons of loess of Pleistocene age in the central United States with dust from a dust storm in the 1930s showed no important difference in the typical sizes or size range of the particles.

On the other hand, loess deposited on uplands and divides is subject to erosion by overland flow and may be washed down into adjacent valleys, where it is redeposited as an alluvial accumulation. Such *reworked loess* may be stratified and more densely compacted than upland loess of eolian origin.

Strong support for the eolian theory of origin for much of the American loess is found in the patterns of distribution and thickness (Figure 39.6). Most is found in a blanket over the North Central States, with an important extension southward along the east side of the Mississippi alluvial valley and with patches over the High Plains of Oklahoma and Texas. Most of this area lies within and immediately adjacent to the glaciated region.

A study of loess thicknesses shows a characteristic pattern in which the greatest thicknesses, up to 60 to 120 ft (18 to 36 m), are in bluffs immediately adjacent to the eastern edges of river flood-plains. Thicknesses diminish very rapidly eastward from the bluffs, as shown by the lines of equal loess thickness in Figure 39.7. Along the bluffs of the Mississippi River alluvial plain in Mississippi, loess is commonly over 50 ft (15 m) thick (Figure 39.8), but thins rapidly eastward. Close association of these wedge-like loess layers with alluvial floodplains clearly points to the explanation that prevailing westerly winds lifted the silt from the floodplains and deposited it to the lee. Further proof of this explanation is found in the gradation of average grain size from coarsest near the river bluffs to finest at the most distant parts of the loess sheet.

Loess deposits of Europe bear much the same relation to the glaciated region as do those in the United States. Loess forms a nearly continuous sheet in European Russia, where the plains topography was most favorable and the region occupied a leeward position with respect to the ice sheets of northern Europe. The Russian loess is from 30 to 45 ft (9 to 14 m) thick over vast areas. Loess related to ice sheets is also found in Siberia.

**FIGURE 39.10.** Sand movement by saltation and surface creep. (© 1965, John Wiley & Sons, New York. After R. A. Bagnold.)

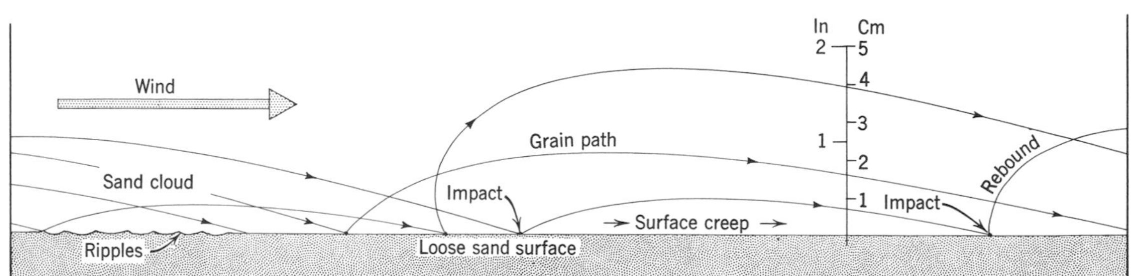

**FIGURE 39.11.** Sand ripples on dune surfaces, Quatif, Saudia Arabia. (Photograph by courtesy of Arabian American Oil Company.)

In northern China loess reaches thicknesses commonly over 100 ft (30 m), and in some places as much as 300 ft (90 m) (Figure 39.9). Just how much of this loess is directly of eolian origin, and how much reworked by streams, is not agreed upon. The dust storms that brought this loess originated from nonglacial regions in the arid interior region of Asia, or more locally from alluvial plains. Loess deposits are also found in Argentina and New Zealand, where they are closely related to glacial deposits.

**FIGURE 39.12.** Relation of rate of sand movement to wind velocity. [After R. A. Bagnold (1941), *The Physics of Blown Sand and Desert Dunes,* London, Methuen, p. 70, Figure 22.]

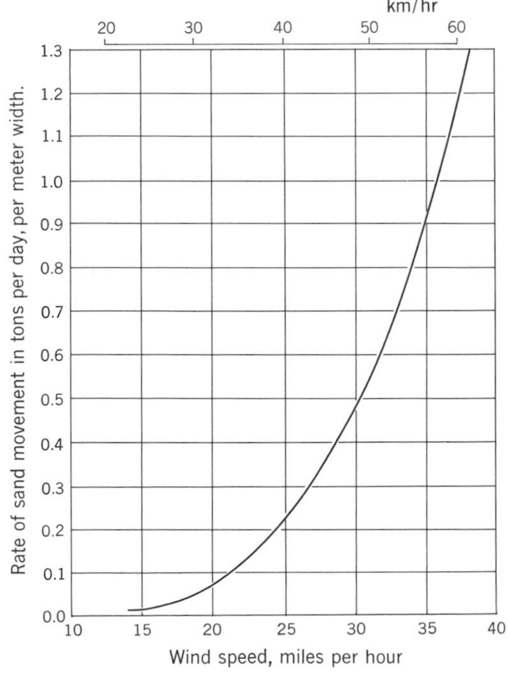


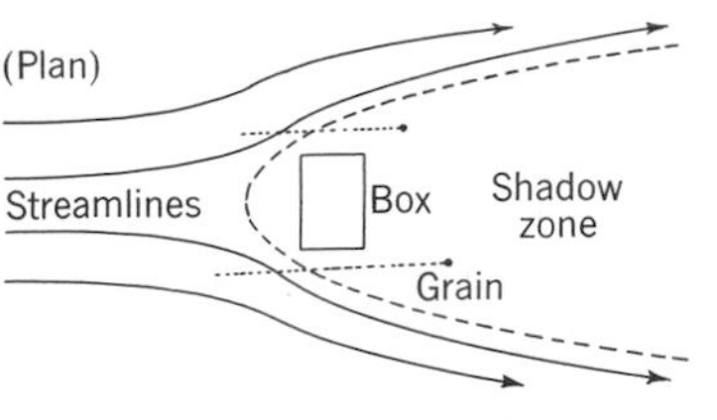


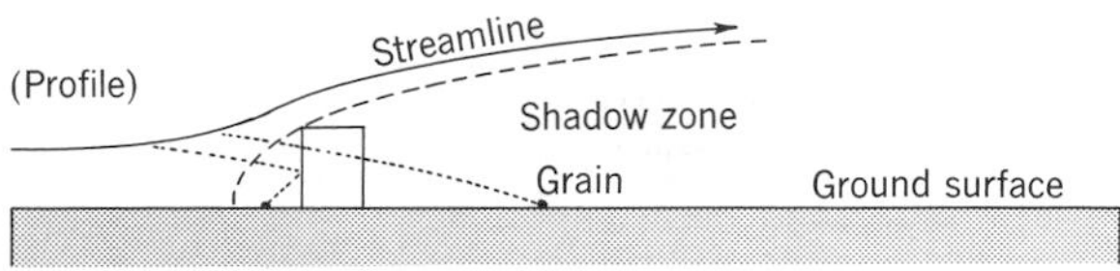


Plan of drift development:

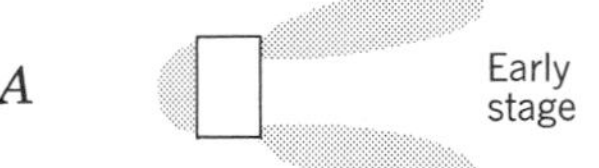


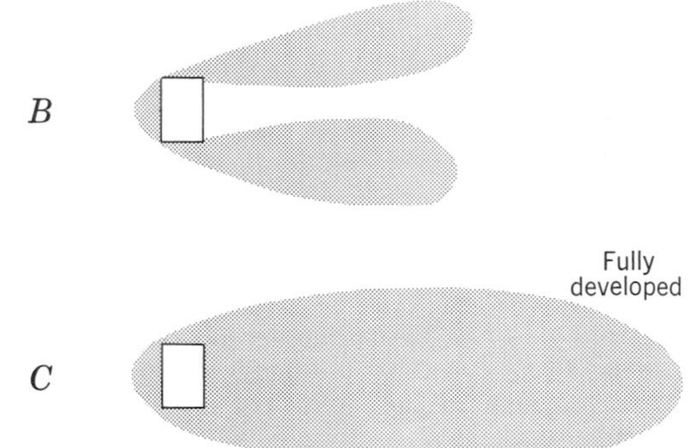


**FIGURE 39.13.** Stages in the formation of a small sand drift accumulating about a box placed on a desert plain across which sand is traveling in saltation. [After R. A. Bagnold (1941), *The Physics of Blown Sand and Desert Dunes,* London, Methuen, p. 190, Figure 63.]

## Transport of sand by wind

Removal of dust in suspension by wind from a mixture of grades, such as an alluvial deposit or beach, leaves the sand and gravel sizes behind. The sand grains travel downwind, staying close to the surface, in a manner described below, and are gradually separated from the gravel particles, which are too heavy to be moved very far by wind. Thus there comes into existence a distinctive body of sediment which we may designate as *eolian sand,* or *dune sand,* most of whose grains are from 0.004 to 0.04 in. (0.1 to 1 mm) in diameter. Wind is thus a most effective sediment-sorting agent.

**FIGURE 39.14.** Long tapering drifts of sand extending to the lee of a row of hills. Note the barchan dunes at the lower left. This vertical air photograph shows an area about 0.4 mi (0.6 km) wide. Desert coast of Peru, latitude about 8½° S. (Courtesy of Ministerio de Fomento, Government of Peru.)

Most dune sands are of the mineral quartz, whose hardness and resistance to chemical decay make it the most durable of the abundant rock-forming minerals. Rarely, dunes are formed of shell fragments, particles of volcanic ash, or grains of gypsum or of heavy minerals such as magnetite. Such unusual compositions are explained by a local abundance of the particular material. Typically, quartz grains of dune sand are beautifully rounded into spherical and egg-shaped grains possessing a frosted surface texture (see Figure 22.9). Although transport by wind is not able to break down the grains into smaller sizes, countless impacts among grains increase their sphericity and cause their surfaces to be covered by microscopic impact fractures. Thus in dune sands we are dealing with particles behaving essentially as highly elastic spheres.

When strong winds blow over a surface of dune sand the grains are carried along in low clouds gliding like a carpet, a phenomenon known as a *sand storm.* Most of the sand is moving in a layer only a few inches off the ground at most, but scattered grains rise as high as several feet. Although the naked eye cannot follow the movement of single grains, the particle paths have been photographed under controlled conditions in laboratory wind tunnels. It is apparent that the grains are engaged in long leaps downwind (Figure 39.10). After impact with grains on the surface, a single grain may rebound high into the air or merely glance off at a low angle. The process of leaping by rebound is termed *saltation.* The rising and falling motions of a particle follow the same laws of motion that they would follow if the grain were shot upward into still air to an equal height. Superimposed upon the rising and falling motion is an increasing forward speed parallel with the ground as the particle is accelerated by force of the wind. The angle of impact of grain path with sand surface is commonly from 10° to 16° with respect to the horizontal. The wind thus imparts kinetic energy to the grain, which, upon impact with the sand surface, dislodges other grains and may project them into the air.

In addition to sand movement by saltation there is set up by grain impacts a slow forward *surface creep* of the sand. The energy of a striking grain is such that it can move a surface grain as large as six times its own diameter or 200 times its own weight. Surface creep causes slow downwind movement of grains too large to engage in saltation, but the smaller grains are traveling much faster in saltation. Thus the smaller grains tend to become separated from the coarse. Separation results in development of sheets of coarse sand or fine gravel from which the fine sand has been largely removed.

We are all familiar with the rippled appearance of dune surfaces. These small ridges and troughs running transversely to the direction of the wind result from uneven movement of grains by surface creep (Figure 39.11).

Where grains of dune sand are traveling in saltation over a sand surface composed of grains of approximately the same diameter, saltation paths are close to the ground, mostly within 6 in. (15 cm), because rebounds are low from impacts among the small easily moved particles. In contrast, grains of dune sand moving across a surface covered by gravel or pebble grains will rebound to heights up to 6 ft (2 m) and hence will attain much greater downward speeds. Therefore for a given wind strength the total rate of movement of sand in saltation is much greater over gravel and pebble surfaces than over dune-sand surfaces. This principle is of fundamental importance in the explanation of sand dunes and will be referred to again.

The rate of movement of sand by wind for any given type of surface and particle size grade depends upon wind speed. Figure 39.12 is a graph showing the relation of rate of sand movement (tons per day per meter

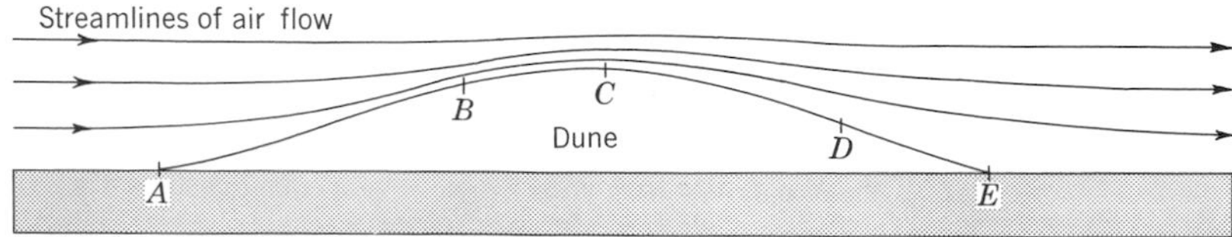


**FIGURE 39.15.** Longitudinal section of a low dune. [After R. A. Bagnold (1941), *The Physics of Blown Sand and Desert Dunes,* London, Methuen, p. 198, Figure 68.]

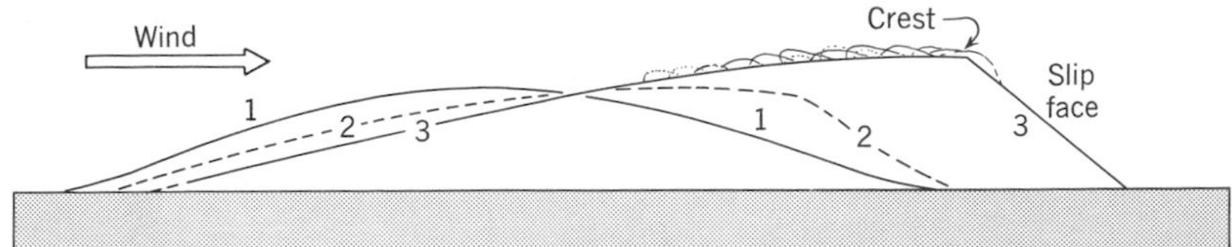


**FIGURE 39.16.** Growth of a dune and development of the slip face. [After R. A. Bagnold (1941), *The Physics of Blown Sand and Desert Dunes,* London, Methuen, p. 202, Figure 71.]

width of cross section) to wind speed, where speed is measured at a height of 1 m (3.3 ft) above the surface. We can see from the upward curve of this graph that rate of movement increases disproportionately with increase in wind speed. Actually, the rate of movement varies about as the cube of wind speed. Thus a wind blowing at 35 mi (55 km) per hour can move in one day the same quantity of sand that a wind of half that speed can move in three weeks.

## Sand drifts and sand dunes

Where saltation and surface creep have had freedom to act upon large supplies of loose sand, there result distinctive depositional landforms that may grow into dominant features of the landscape. Two forms of free sand can be recognized. A *sand drift* is an accumulation of sand formed in the lee of some fixed obstruction, such as a rock or bush. Drifts do not move, but remain attached to the obstacle. A *sand dune* is an individual mound or hill of loose sand rising to a single summit and independent of any fixed surface feature. Dunes are capable of movement downwind while maintaining a characteristic shape, although movement is not a requirement of the form. Dunes are sometimes completely isolated from one another upon a flat surface of coarser grains or bedrock, or they may be joined into a continuous sand layer completely concealing whatever material lies beneath.

Modified dune forms develop in regions sufficiently humid to bear a thin cover of grasses or shrubs. The term *phytogenic dune* is applied to any dune type in which the growth of vegetation plays an important part in determining the dune form.

In addition to drifts and dunes, certain other forms of sand accumulation may occur. Already referred to are the plain-like *sand sheets* of coarse sand or fine gravel formed of grains too large to be transported by saltation. These surfaces are closely related in origin to desert pavement, in that both are covered with large grains from which fine grains have been removed.

**FIGURE 39.17.** Barchan dunes. (© 1960, John Wiley & Sons, New York.)

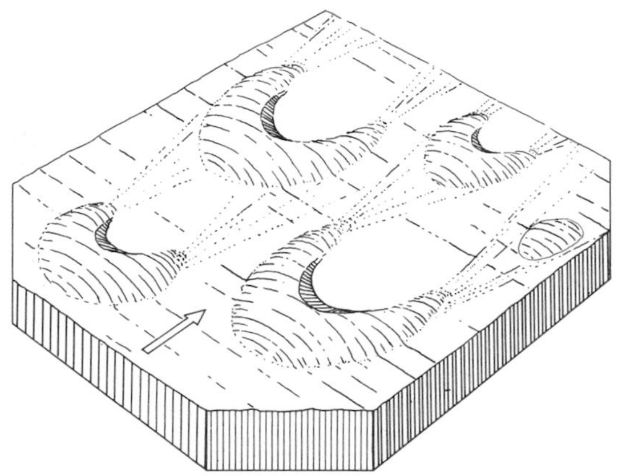

Drifts form because an obstacle gives rise to a *wind shadow* in which air movement is not sufficient to move sand in saltation (Figure 39.13). Grains moving in saltation fall into the shadow zone and are trapped. The growing drift gradually fills the shadow zone and develops the form of a smoothly rounded mound with elliptical outline elongated in the direction of the wind.

Where winds are funneled through a narrow gap in a ridge running transversely to the prevailing wind, a drift forms on the lee side of the gap, gradually growing downwind to become a long, tapered, sharp-crested ridge (Figure 39.14). Such *longitudinal drifts,* which may extend over a quarter of a mile in length, are conspicuous and permanent topographic features of certain desert and steppe lands where ridges or scarps interrupt flat plains or plateaus.

**Dune formation** Suppose that on a flat arid plain a small sand drift has formed over an obstacle. Sand is moving rapidly in saltation across the flat ground, which is pebble strewn and causes high rebounds of the elastic grains. As the grains fall upon the drift of fine sand their rebounds are damped and their rate of movement sharply reduced. The grains are thus delayed as they pass over the drift, much as automobiles are delayed and tend to congregate at the toll booths of a high-speed highway. The drift thus grows in area and height, becoming an increasingly more efficient trap for more sand. Soon the heap has grown far larger than the original drift and is no longer dependent upon the original obstacle. It can then begin a slow downwind migration. At this point a solitary dune has been formed and moves off, leaving a drift about the obstacle to develop another dune.

In Figure 39.15 is shown a growing dune in cross section. Imagine that the wind is initially weak and increases in strength. Streamlines of air flow will be compressed over the dune surface between points *B* and *C,* causing saltation to begin in that zone. The leaping grains are carried forward to the region between *C* and *D,* where they will come to rest. As the wind increases in strength saltation extends upwind to *A* and downwind to *D,* and the entire surface from *A* to *D* is being denuded of surface grains by saltation. Deposition continues in the zone from *D* to *E,* so that as the windward slope of the dune becomes flatter the lee side becomes steeper (Figure 39.16). The entire dune is shifted downwind at the same time.

Ultimately there forms on the lee side a steep *slip*

**FIGURE 39.18.** Barchan dunes formed on a terrace bordering the Columbia River, near Briggs, Oregon. (Photograph by G. K. Gilbert, U.S. Geological Survey.)

*face* having an angle of slope of about 35°. This surface represents the angle of repose of the grains that leap over the dune crest and land within the wind shadow. The slip face is gradually steepened by the rain of sand grains landing upon its upper portion. When the slope angle is thus built up to a point of instability, a layer of sand slides down to the slope base, lowering the slope angle slightly to achieve a stable slope. The slip face thus advances by a succession of slides.

Dunes continue to grow as sand is brought in saltation from upwind sources. As a dune becomes higher, the streamlines of air flow over the dune summit are increasingly compressed, with the result that saltation is intensified. Finally there comes a point when the rate of sand movement over the dune summit balances the rate of receipt of sand by the dune, at which time further dune upbuilding ceases and the dune has reached its maximum dimensions for the given conditions of prevailing winds and sand supply.

**FIGURE 39.19.** A great sea of transverse dunes, bordered by a field of barchan dunes (*lower right*). Imperial County between Calexio, California, and Yuma, Arizona. (Copyrighted Spence Air Photos.)

**Dune types** Dunes take many forms. It would not be easy to compile a complete list of all the varieties that have been described the world over. Nevertheless, a survey of published photographs and descriptions will show that a number of basic types recur with much the same form over a wide range of world regions. Too little is known about the mechanics of dune formation to attempt to classify and explain dunes in terms of their formative processes. We shall instead merely describe a few common types and note the general conditions of formation with which they seem to be associated.

Simplest of the dunes is the *barchan,* or *crescentic dune,* an isolated pile of sand resting upon a flat surface (Figure 39.17). Barchans are among the commonest of dune types and can be found in deserts the world over. Perhaps the best description of the plan view of a barchan is as an ellipse from the end of which a semicircular area has been cut out. The ends of the curved ridge thus remaining are smoothly rounded and descend to the base without any break. The wall of the semicircular cavity consists of a curving slip face. The windward dune slope, which rises smoothly to a broad dome, is abruptly cut off by the slip face to produce a sharp crest (Figure 39.18). Barchans grow to heights of 30 to 100 ft (9 to 30 m) and widths up to 1200 ft (360 m) at the base. Movement of the dune downwind may total several inches per day. Records of individual dunes have yielded rates of moment of 30 to 50 ft (9 to 15 m) per year. Barchans usually are found in groups, or swarms (Figure 39.19), and may form long lines, or chains, across a plain.

In desert localities where a great supply of sand is present, dune sand covers the entire surface and is formed into wave-like ridges separated by troughs and hollows, much as if sea waves in time of storm were frozen into place (Figure 39.19). Such sand waves are described as *transverse dunes,* and the entire assemblage as a *sand sea.* Sand seas of the North African desert are termed *ergs.* Slip faces of a sand sea resemble those of barchans and face downwind. Close relation in origin between transverse dunes and barchans is evident from the fact that toward the edge of a sand sea, where the sand layer thins out, individual transverse ridges become separated by bare ground, then become segmented into individual barchans, as seen in Figure 39.19.

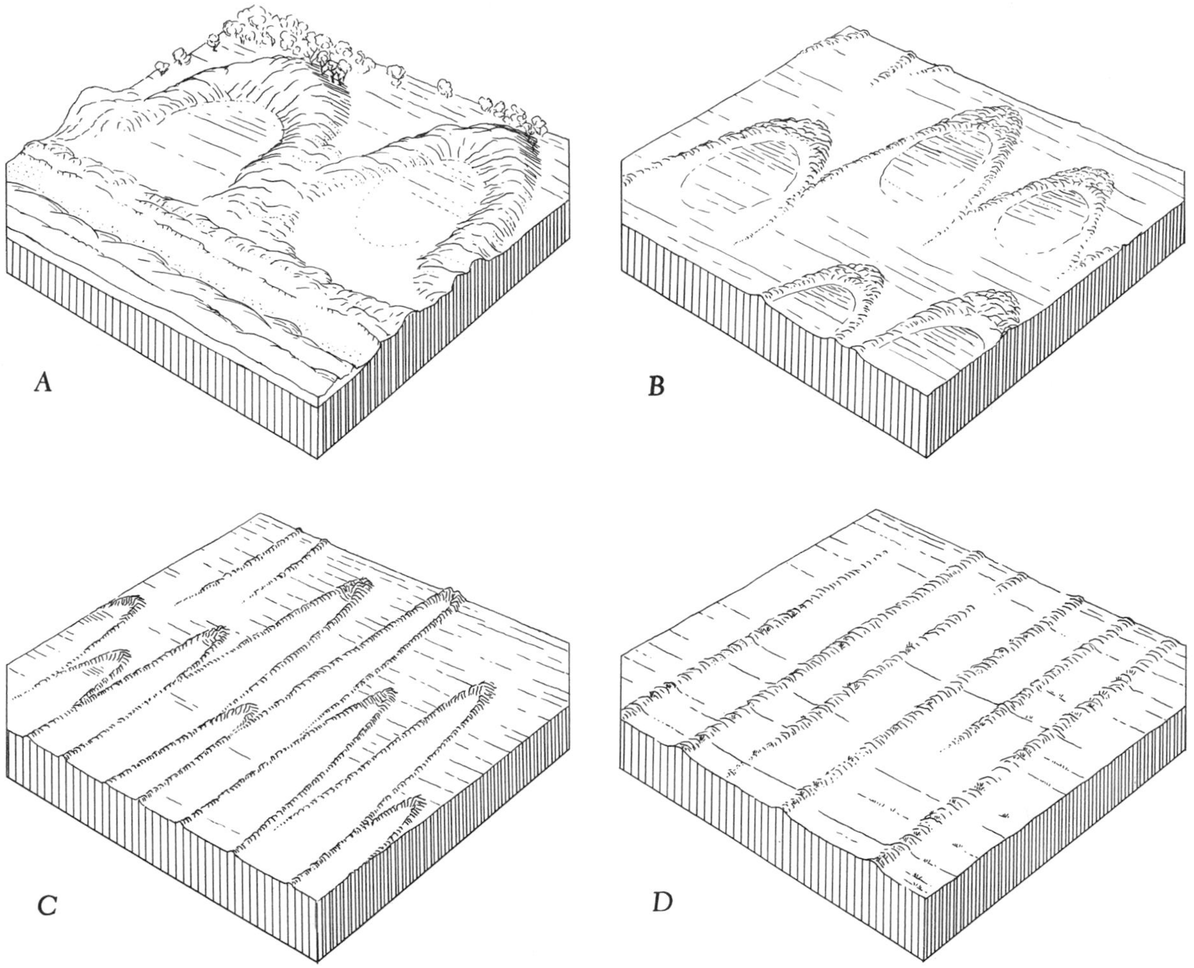

A

B

C

D

**FIGURE 39.20.** Dune varieties. Wind direction is from lower left in every case. (*A*) Coastal blowout dunes. (*B*) Parabolic dunes of a semi-arid steppe region. (*C*) Hairpin dunes, a variety of parabolic dune. (*D*) Longitudinal dunes. (© 1960, John Wiley & Sons, New York.)

Belts of transverse dunes commonly form inland from beaches at localities where sand supply is large but vegetation is absent. An example is seen in the left-hand side of Figure 39.22.

**FIGURE 39.21.** Landward slope of a coastal dune. The slip face is shown advancing over a forest. Cape Henry, Virginia. (Photograph by Douglas Johnson.)

We turn next to a distinctive family of phytogenic dunes characterized by their *parabolic* outlines (Figure 39.20). These dunes are convexly bowed in the downwind direction (opposite to the curvature of the barchan). One variety of parabolic dune forms along coasts, landward of beaches, where strong onshore winds are supplied with abundant sand (Block *A* of Figure 39.20). The sparse vegetative cover of protective grasses and shrubs is locally broken, permitting a deflation hollow to form. Sand is carried from the hollow to the leeward side, building a curved embankment, or rim, which rises in height as the blowout is enlarged. When well-developed, the coastal blowout dune may rise to heights of 100 ft (30 m) and will on the landward side have a slip face that can override an inland forest, killing the trees (Figure 39.21).

Low parabolic dunes are commonly formed in great numbers on semiarid plains and plateaus where the soil or overburden is sandy (Block *B* of Figure 39.20). The dune ridge, which is only a few feet high, is covered by grasses and shrubs serving to trap sand (or coarse silt) derived by deflation from a shallow depres-

**FIGURE 39.22.** Coastal dunes at Pismo Beach, San Luis Obispo Bay, California. Transverse dunes (*light areas*) are advancing upon older stabilized hairpin dunes of parabolic form (*arrows*). (Spence Air Photos.)

sion. In some instances, parabolic blowout dunes have migrated downwind, becoming greatly elongated and assuming a *hairpin* form, as shown in Block *C* of Figure 39.20. A few such hairpin dunes, now fixed by vegetative cover, are seen in Figure 39.22.

On some desert plains dunes take the form of long narrow sand ridges oriented parallel with the prevailing wind direction. They constitute *longitudinal dunes* (Block *D* of Figure 39.20). In coastal localities longitudinal dunes may be merely long narrow bands of loose sand moving by saltation under the force of very strong onshore winds. In some inland tropical regions longitudinal dunes are many feet high and tens of miles long. Variations in form include scalloped sides and various irregularities in plan of the crest.

**FIGURE 39.23.** Star dunes of the Libyan Desert, seen from an altitude of 6 mi (10 km). Dune peaks rise to heights of 300 to 600 ft (90 to 180 m) or more above the intervening level ground. (Photograph by courtesy of Aero Service Corporation, Litton Industries.)

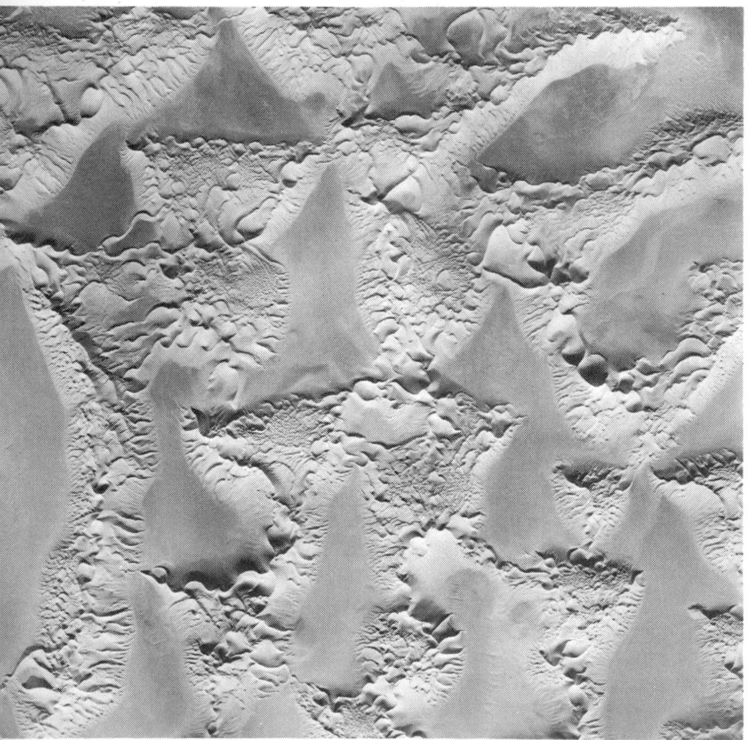

One remarkable dune, a veritable colossus among dune forms, is the *seif dune* of the deserts of Libya and southern Iran. The seif dune may be described as a broad, high, tapering sand ridge longitudinally disposed with respect to the persistent wind. The dune crest, seen in profile, consists of a succession of peaks and saddles. One side of the ridge bears a succession of curved slip faces produced by strong but infrequent winds blowing obliquely across the long axis of the dune. Seif dunes have heights commonly up to 300 ft (90 m) and may range in length from 0.25 to 60 mi (0.4 to 95 km).

A noteworthy dune form of the Sahara and Arabian deserts in the *star dune* (also referred to as a *pyramidal* or *heaped dune*), which takes the form of an isolated hill of sand. In plan the dune base resembles a several-pointed star (Figure 39.23). Sharp-crested ridges converge from the basal points to a central peak in some cases as high as 300 ft (90 m) above the surrounding plain. Star dunes apparently may remain fixed in one position for centuries and have come to serve as desert landmarks, each bearing a local Arabic name.

It should be borne in mind that many dune assemblages are complex in form and are not readily identifiable as belonging to any one of the varieties described above. In some areas several generations of dunes can be recognized and correlated with climatic changes in which dunes are alternately fixed by growth of vegetation and reactivated by breakdown of plant cover in a succeeding dry cycle.

The dune ridge almost universally present on the landward side of sand beaches illustrates the irregular mound-and-hollow form of dunes modified by vegetative cover. These *foredunes,* built of sand driven inland from the berm of the beach, normally rise well above the highest level of attack of swash of storm waves. Thus the dune ridge protects from storm-wave inundation those low-lying areas of tidal marsh that commonly lie on the landward side of a barrier island or barrier beach.

## Wind as a geologic agent—an evaluation

Although the intensive work of wind is limited to those specific places where unattached mineral particles are available in quantity, the wind's activities of erosion and transportation, where they do take place, are significant both in terms of the terrestrial environments of today and in the stratigraphic records of the geologic past. Actively moving dunes constitute almost sterile surfaces in terms of occupation by plants and animals, whereas the belt of fixed coastal dunes serves not only as a protection against wave attack, but also as a unique environment of plants. Dust storms that threaten the comfort and safety of man and animals are at the same time the agencies of deposition of loess, one of the finest of parent bodies for development of fertile soils.

During the Pleistocene Epoch, at times when ice sheets were widespread and large expanses of unprotected detrital materials were exposed to the air, the geologic role of wind was much more important than we find it today. The great fossil dune beds of Permian and Jurassic age in the Colorado Plateau attest to a scale of wind transport and deposition of sand that dwarfs anything found on earth today. Perhaps our judgment of the importance of wind as a geologic agent needs to be tempered by the evidence of the past.

## References for further study

Lobeck, A. K. (1939), *Geomorphology,* New York, McGraw-Hill, 731 pp., chap. 11.

Bagnold, R. A. (1941), *The Physics of Blown Sand and Desert Dunes,* London, Methuen, 265 pp.

Cooper, W. S. (1958), *Coastal Sand Dunes of Oregon and Washington,* Geol. Soc. Amer., Memoir 72, 169 pp.

Shelton, J. S. (1966), *Geology Illustrated,* San Francisco, Freeman, 434 pp., chap. 17.

Thornbury, W. D. (1969), *Principles of Geomorphology,* 2nd ed., New York, Wiley, 594 pp., chap. 12.

# 40

# Glacial processes and forms

BECAUSE MOST OF US have seen ice only in small fragments or thin layers, we think of it as a brittle crystalline solid that fractures easily on impact. When an ice layer has accumulated to a depth of 300 ft (100 m) or more and rests on a sloping surface, the deeper part of the ice behaves as if it were a highly viscous liquid, yielding by slow flowage and carrying downslope the rigid upper crust. Thus there is produced a *glacier,* which we may define broadly as any large natural accumulation of land ice affected by present or past motion.

## Formation of glacial ice

For glaciers to form requires that the quantity of incoming snowfall shall, on the average, year in and year out exceed the average quantity lost yearly by melting and evaporation. We may conveniently combine ice losses by melting and evaporation under the single term *ablation.*

Freshly fallen snow has a very low density—as much as 90 percent of its volume may consist of air-filled voids—but changes quickly set in. The elaborate hexagonal snow crystals change into more-rounded smaller particles. The mass becomes greatly compacted into *old granular snow,* in which the air voids constitute less than 50 percent of the volume. Under the load of newer snow layers and with the aid of some melting and refreezing, the old snow compacts further, reaching the stage where it may be given the name *firn* (also *névé*). Density of firn is greater than about 0.4 g/cc, or four-tenths that of water. As the

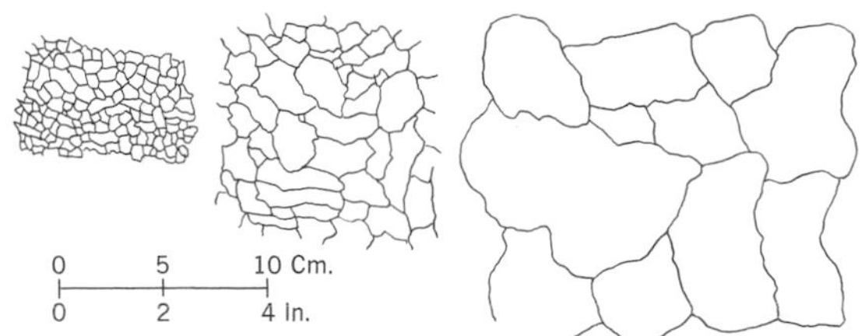


**FIGURE 40.1.** Outlines of individual crystals of glacial ice in a wide range of sizes.

firn is buried still more deeply under new layers of firn and snow it compacts further, to become glacial ice. Although most of the air has by this time been expelled, some is enclosed in bubble holes and the ice density may not be greater than about five-sixths that of water.

Geologists have studied glacial ice as if it were a rock. The ice is sawed into thin layers and placed under a polarizing microscope to reveal its crystalline structure. Glacial ice closely resembles a coarse-grained igneous rock, such as granite, as far as its crystal form is concerned. Individual ice crystals range in diameter from .04 in. (1 mm) near the head of a glacier to 0.8 in. (2 cm) or more in the much older ice near the lower end of a glacier. A simpler method of examining the crystals is to make a pencil rubbing on paper laid over an ice surface that has been slightly etched by melting, for the pencil rubbing will reveal the crystal contacts (Figure 40.1).

Conditions favorable to the accumulation of snow in sufficient depth to form glaciers are commonly met in high mountains and plateaus, both because yearly average temperatures are low and because mountains usually receive heavy orographic precipitation. Thus glaciers exist in equatorial latitudes, although generally well above 15,000 ft (4,500 m) elevation. In cold climates of arctic regions glaciers form at low elevations and commonly extend down to the level of the sea. Windward coasts are highly favorable to the accumulation of glacial ice because of the influx of moisture-laden maritime air masses. Particularly favored are the west coasts of continents in the middle to high latitudes (Chapter 18). In contrast, mountains lying far in the continental interior are poorly situated to receive the heavy snowfall needed to form glaciers.

## Classes of glaciers

Glaciers formed in high steep-walled mountain ranges are typically shaped into long narrow ice streams oc-

**FIGURE 40.2.** Oblique air view of glaciers of the Swiss Alps. *Left,* Glacier d'Argentière with a great ice fall in the lower portion. *Right,* Mer de Glace, famed as the subject of early glaciological observations. (Swissair Photo.)

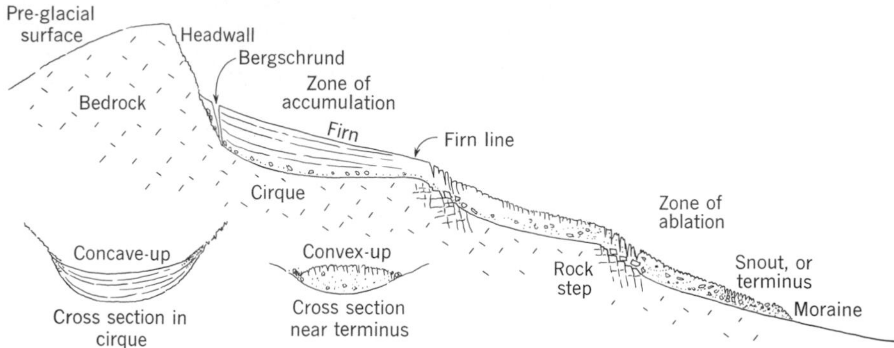


**FIGURE 40.3.** Idealized longitudinal and transverse sections of a simple alpine glacier.

cupying previously carved stream valleys. Such glaciers, which have many of the basic elements of the fluvial drainage system (such as tributary channels leading downgrade to a trunk stream), are classified as *valley glaciers,* or *alpine glaciers* (Figure 40.2). In the high interior area of a large landmass in the high latitudes glacial ice accumulates in vast plate-like bodies termed *icecaps.* Small icecaps a few miles across or a few tens of miles across and roughly elliptical or circular in outline are found today on summit areas of arctic islands such as Iceland, Baffin Island, and Ellesmere Island. Vastly greater ice masses of continental proportions, such as those of Greenland and Antarctica, are termed *continental glaciers,* or simply *ice sheets.*[1] A great ice sheet may reach a thickness of several thousand feet and may cover an area of several million square miles.

[1] In this chapter *icecap* is used for glacial ice bodies largely limited to a mountain mass or high plateau, and *ice sheet* for a larger ice body that spreads far beyond the limits of highlands, covering plains that would not otherwise sustain glaciers.

## Alpine glaciers

The form of a simple alpine glacier is illustrated in Figure 40.3 by longitudinal and transverse cross sections. Snow accumulates at the upper end of the glacier in a bowl-shaped depression, the *cirque,* over a broad expanse of smooth glacier surface, the *firn field.* By slow flowage at depth the glacial ice moves toward the exit of the cirque and may pass over a steepened gradient in the rock floor of the valley, resulting in an *ice fall,* where the rigid surface ice is deeply broken by gaping fractures, termed *crevasses* (Figure 40.2, left). Where the gradient lessens, the crevasses tend to close up, but the surface may be extremely rough because of ablation of surface ice.

From the standpoint of relative gain and loss of mass the glacier may be divided into two parts. The upper part (at higher altitudes), lying in the *zone of accumulation,* receives more snow than it loses by ablation, hence it has a smooth firn surface. The lower part, lying

**FIGURE 40.4.** Shrunken remnant of the Black Glacier, almost buried in its own morainal debris. Bishop Range, Selkirk Mountains, British Columbia. Talus cones have been built from the valley walls. (Photograph by H. Palmer, Geological Survey of Canada.)

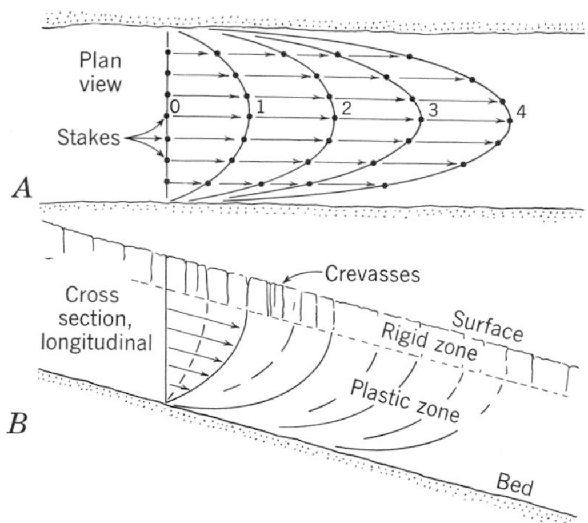


**FIGURE 40.5.** Relative speeds of flowage within a glacier.

**FIGURE 40.7.** Large, unusually deep glacial grooves in massive limestone. Kelley's Island, near the south shore of Lake Erie. (State of Ohio, Department of Industrial and Economic Development.)

in the *zone of ablation,* loses more of its surface to melting and evaporation than it gains yearly by snowfall, hence it is characteristically rough and pitted. Separating the two zones is the *firn line,* where ablation equals accumulation. This line is readily identified as the lower edge of the smooth white-surfaced area of the glacier. Typically the cross profile of the glacier is concave upward in the zone of accumulation and convex upward in the zone of ablation (Figure 40.3).

**FIGURE 40.6.** These sets of chatter marks indicate that ice movement was away from the observer. At the lower left margin of the view is a crescentic gouge. Elmer Creek, west of Richardson Peak, Sierra Nevada Range, California. (Photograph by D. L. Babenroth.)

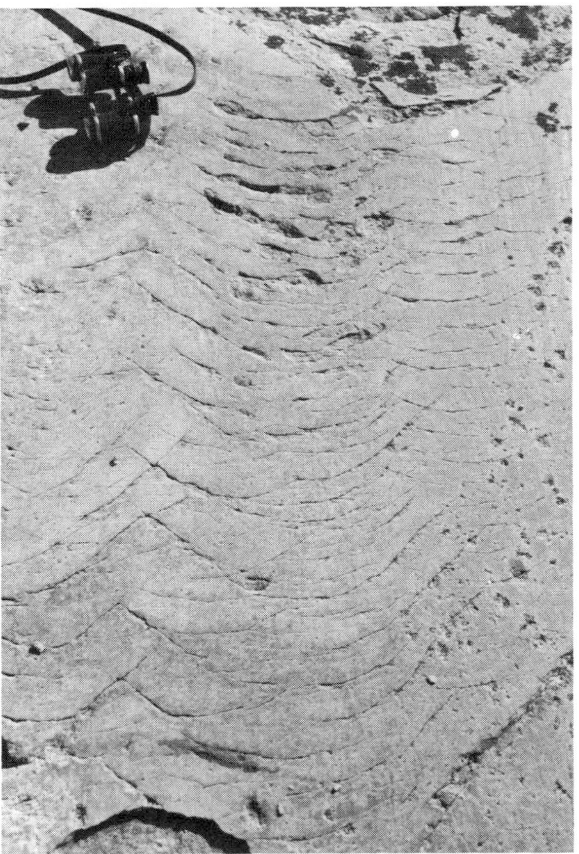

As the glacier extends farther and lower downvalley it encounters progressively warmer climatic zones and suffers progressively greater losses from ablation. At the glacier *terminus* the rigid ice is thrust forward over its own deposits of debris. We may think of a valley glacier as a moving stream, nourished at the upper part, but disappearing by surface loss in the lower part, with balanced rates of gain and loss such that the glacier surface remains approximately constant in form and position, despite the fact that ice is moving from one end to the other. Such constancy of form, while motion continues, is described as *dynamic equilibrium.* As long as glacier equilibrium is maintained, the terminus (end) of the glacier holds to a fixed position and the glacier surface neither rises nor falls in level.

Alpine glaciers illustrate well the concept of an open system and its steady state. Matter enters the system through the upper boundary as snow and leaves the system in the liquid or vapor state. Potential energy of position of the entering matter is converted into kinetic energy of flow under gravity and is transformed into heat through frictional resistance within the ice and along the contact with the rock boundaries. Steady state of the system is equivalent to dynamic equilibrium —it is a state in which the rate of change of velocity is reduced to zero in all points within the flow system.

Glacier equilibrium is easily upset, giving rise to conspicuous changes of form. Suppose, for example, that the rate of nourishment by net gain in snowfall is sharply increased. The ice of the upper end of the glacier thickens and consequently flows more rapidly downgrade. This action moves the glacier terminus farther downvalley in what is described as a *glacier advance.* But the advance brings the glacier terminus to lower levels, where temperatures are higher and ablation more rapid. Soon the rate of ablation balances the rate of ice advance, and the terminus again becomes stabilized.

**FIGURE 40.8.** Sketch of a glacially rounded and plucked rock knob.

Suppose, instead, that the rate of glacier nourishment decreases, as it might if summers become warmer or snowfall is less. The thinning glacier will flow less rapidly and will not be brought to the terminus as rapidly. Now the rate of ablation will be excessive, and the glacier terminus and surface will melt away rapidly, causing the terminus to be displaced upvalley, a phenomenon termed *glacier recession* (Figure 40.4). But as the glacier recedes upvalley less and less of its surface lies in warmer climatic zones, hence ablation is reduced. Again a stage of equilibrium will be established, with the terminus stabilized at a higher level.

From the foregoing analysis we see that glaciers are extremely sensitive indicators of climatic changes. Intensive scientific study is being devoted to documenting the changes in glacier form and attempting to interpret climatic changes that have been responsible. The science of *glaciology,* a branch of the earth sciences devoted to the physics of glacier activity, is thus closely tied in with the earth sciences of climatology and hydrology.

## Rates of glacier flow

The rate of glacier flow has long been a subject of interest to glaciologists. Pioneer scientists in this field—Louis Agassiz, the Swiss-born naturalist, and J. D. Forbes, an English physicist—made observations on glaciers of the Swiss Alps from 1840 to 1842. By planting transverse rows of stakes across the glacier surface and observing the movements of the stakes, both men came independently to the conclusion that surface motion is most rapid near the center, decreasing toward the sides (Figure 40.5). If the line of stakes were to be mapped at equal intervals of time, it would be found to be bent convexly downvalley into a series of parabolic curves, as suggested in Figure 40.5.

Slow surface motion of this type normally goes on at the rate of a few inches to 3 ft (1 m) per day in a valley glacier. Agassiz found that his fastest moving stakes had traveled over 250 ft (75 m) downstream in 1 year. A large boulder resting on the ice moved almost 500 ft (150 m) in 2 years. It should be remembered, of course, that the upper zone of the glacier is composed of brittle ice in the rigid zone. The relative movements of surface points, although resembling flowage of a fluid on a large scale, actually occur by slippage between small blocks formed by the fracturing of the brittle ice. Crevasses are thus produced.

Below the rigid zone the ice within the glacier moves less rapidly with increasing depth, as indicated in Figure 40.5. Thus a straight tube driven vertically through the glacier will gradually be bent into a parabolic curve. Such flowage is described as *laminar.* The *rate of shear,* which is the rate at which any given ice layer moves with respect to the immediately underlying layer, increases with depth and is greatest closest to the bottom.

Close observations on the motions of valley glaciers have revealed that at times and for very short periods the entire glacier is thrust forward as a block and apparently is engaging in a slipping movement at its bed, a phenomenon termed *basal slip,* or *block movement.* Such sudden movement apparently is caused by the application of severe stresses from upstream sections of the ice.

## Glacier erosion and transportation

Just as in the case of streams of water, glaciers represent to the geologist much more than mere systems of water disposal in the hydrologic cycle. Glaciers perform erosion, transportation, and deposition of mineral matter, creating thereby a variety of erosional and depositional features of geologic interest.

Rock fragments are incorporated into glacial ice from the subglacial rock floor and walls. Close to the headwall of the cirque meltwater pouring down from snowbanks above the glacier enters the joint fractures in the headwall rock, where it freezes into seams of ice. Joint blocks are thus pried loose, in the freeze-thaw process described in Chapter 32, to become incorporated into the upper end of the glacier. Beneath the

**FIGURE 40.9.** Lateral and end moraines forming continuous loops and marking the sides and end of a former valley glacier in two positions. (© 1960, John Wiley & Sons, New York. After a sketch by W. M. Davis.)

glacier, ice may flow plastically around joint blocks, then drag them loose when a sudden blockslip movement occurs, an activity termed *glacial plucking.* Blocks of rock being carried within the glacial ice are scraped and dragged along the rock floor, gouging and grooving the bedrock and chipping out fragments of rock, a process of abrasion termed simply *grinding.*

The valley floor formerly beneath a glacier shows a number of interesting erosional features resulting from grinding and plucking. Rock surfaces are generally of hard fresh rock from which weathered rock has been removed. Numerous fine scratches, termed *glacial striations,* mar a surface that may otherwise be highly polished by the action of finely pulverized rock within the moving ice. Such striations mark the lines where sharp corners of large fragments have scraped the surface. Where pressure was strongly applied, the impinging boulders created curved fractures in the bedrock. One fracture type, the *chatter mark,* is bent concavely toward the downstream direction of ice flow (Figure 40.6), and another, the *crescentic gouge,* is reversed in curvature.

In particularly susceptible types of bedrock, such as some limestones, glacial abrasion produces long deep *glacial grooves* paralleling the direction of ice flow and scored by numerous parallel striations (Figure 40.7).

One of the common small landforms produced beneath a glacier is the *glaciated rock knob,* which is simply a hill of bedrock strongly shaped by abrasion and plucking (Figure 40.8). The side of the knob facing upstream with respect to ice flow (*stoss side*) is smoothly rounded by ice abrasion, and the downstream or *lee side* is strongly plucked.[2]

Still another source of glacier load is the rolling and sliding of rock fragments down the steep sides of the cirque and the valley walls adjacent to the ice stream. Such slide rock, taking the form of talus cones and sheets (Chapter 32), brings rock fragments to the glacier margin, where they are dragged along by the moving ice. These marginal embankments of debris are termed *lateral moraines* and can be seen in Figure 40.2. After the glacier has disappeared, these embankments form ridges parallel with the valley walls (Figure 40.9). Where two ice streams join, the debris of the inner lateral moraines is dragged out into the middle of the combined ice streams to form a long narrow line of debris termed a *medial moraine.* Several of these features are visible in Figure 40.10, appearing as parallel lines dividing the glacier into narrow bands. Debris supplied from marginal slopes remains largely on the glacier surface.

In the zone of ablation wasting of the glacier surface, combined with downvalley flowage, brings lower layers of ice progressively nearer to the surface. Here any

[2] The term *roches moutonnées* has long been applied to such a landscape of glaciated rock knobs.

**FIGURE 40.10.** A large branching glacier flowing westward along the northern edge of the Juneau Ice Field, Alaska. Medial moraines show as dark lines and bands. (U.S. Army Air Forces trimetrogon photograph.)

**FIGURE 40.11.** Meltwater issues from a tunnel in stagnant, debris-laden ice at the terminus of the Franz Josef Glacier, South Island, New Zealand. (Official New Zealand Government Photograph.)

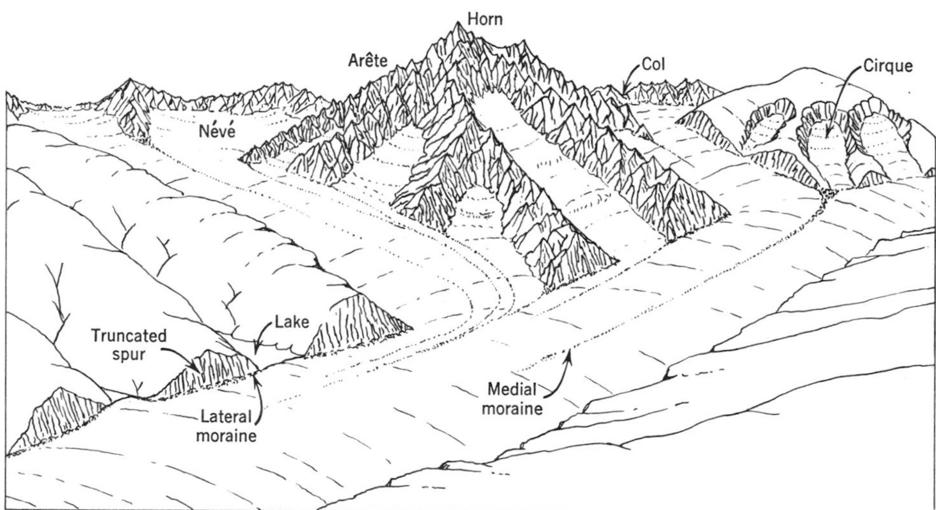


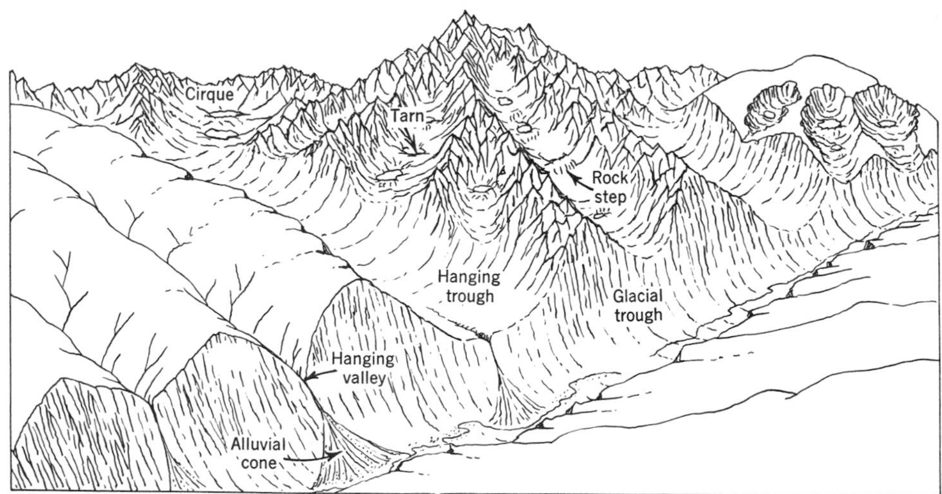


**FIGURE 40.12.** Landscape evolution under alpine glaciation. (*A*) Preglacial topography formed by fluvial denudation. (*B*) Stage of maximum alpine glaciation. (*C*) Post-glacial landscape, following disappearance of all glacial ice. (© 1960, John Wiley & Sons, New York. Based on drawings of A. K. Lobeck and W. M. Davis.)

**FIGURE 40.13.** Steeply rising cirque headwalls culminate in narrow arêtes and sharply pointed peaks in the Sentinel Range, Antarctica. The central peak is Mount Tyree, altitude 16,300 ft (4965 m). (U.S. Geological Survey photograph.)

rock fragments that were incorporated into the ice by plucking and grinding now emerge at the surface, giving the ice a dirt-covered appearance (Figure 40.11).

**FIGURE 40.14.** Lake Ellen Wilson, a rock-basin glacial lake in Glacier National Park, Montana. (Photograph by Douglas Johnson.)

Near the terminus the proportion of solid load to ice increases greatly, until at the very end there is more solid debris than ice (Figure 40.4). This residual mass of rock debris constitutes the *end moraine,* or *terminal moraine,* of the glacier and may take the form of a bouldery embankment curved convexly downvalley (Figure 40.9). The end moraine commonly extends up-

**FIGURE 40.15.** Glacial-trough development. (*A*) Trough filled with ice at stage of maximum glaciation. (*B*) Trough free of ice; U-shaped cross profile. (*C*) Trough floor partly filled with alluvial deposits. (*D*) Trough partly submerged; a fiord. (© 1960, John Wiley & Sons, New York. Based on drawings by Erwin Raisz.)

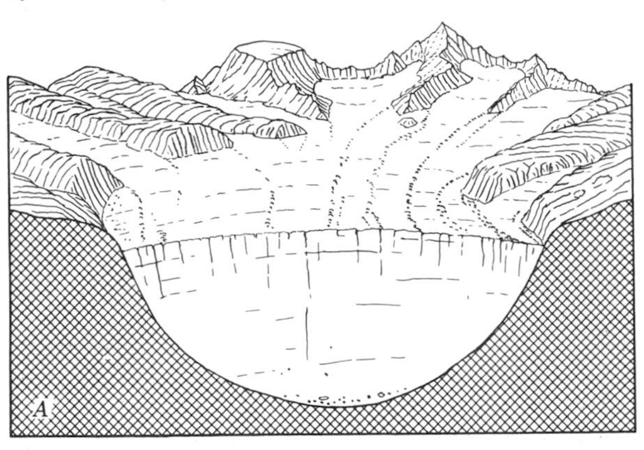


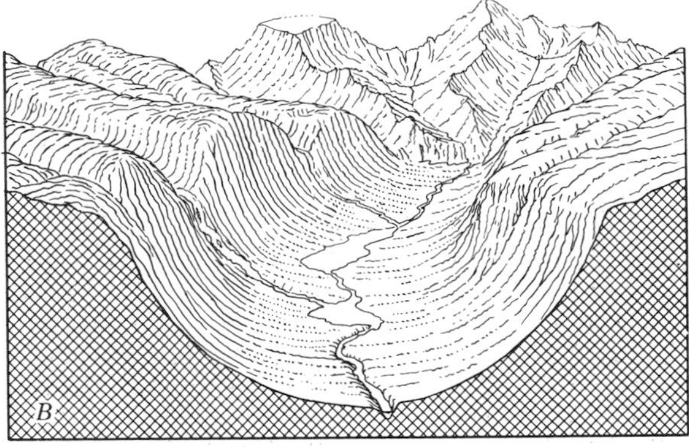


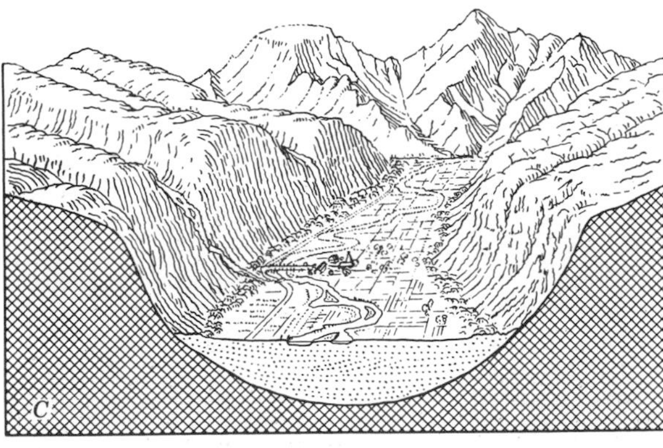

FIGURE 40.16. The Naerö Fiord, Norway. (© Underwood & Underwood.)

valley on either side as a lateral moraine. Because glacial recession leaves the end and lateral moraines largely intact, they serve to document the earlier glacial history of the area and will show the maximum limits of ice advance.

In observing the huge boulders composing glacial moraines, we may fail to realize that much rock is also ground by the glacier into extremely fine particles—of fine silt and clay size—constituting glacial *rock flour.* This material in suspension gives to meltwater streams issuing from a glacier a characteristic milky appearance (Figure 40.11). Settling out in lakes beyond the glacier limit, the rock flour forms layers of silt and clay. Should we examine such sediments under a microscope, we would find that the particles are freshly broken, angular, mineral grains of numerous types rather than being composed of the clay minerals (illite, montmorillonite, or kaolinite) which characterize the clay sediments derived by chemical decay of rock.

## Landforms carved by alpine glaciation

The many spectacular landforms shaped by alpine-glacier erosion can be explained through the use of a series of block diagrams (Figure 40.12). Block *A* shows a mountain region shaped by processes of fluvial denudation in a period of milder climate preceding glaciation. Thick accumulations of soil and weathered overburden mantle the mountain slopes, and divides are broad and somewhat subdued in appearance.

Block *B* shows the same mountain mass occupied by valley glaciers that have been in action for many thousands of years. The higher central summit area has been carved into steep-walled cirques, whose walls meet in sharp-crested divides, termed *arêtes,* that culminate in tooth-like peaks, called *horns* (Figure 40.13). Where two cirques are arranged back to back on opposite sides of a divide, the intervening rock wall may be cut through to form a deep pass, or *col.* Notice that the somewhat lower mountain summit at the far right of Block *B* is only partly consumed by cirque development and that the preglacial mountain surface remains intact over the summit.

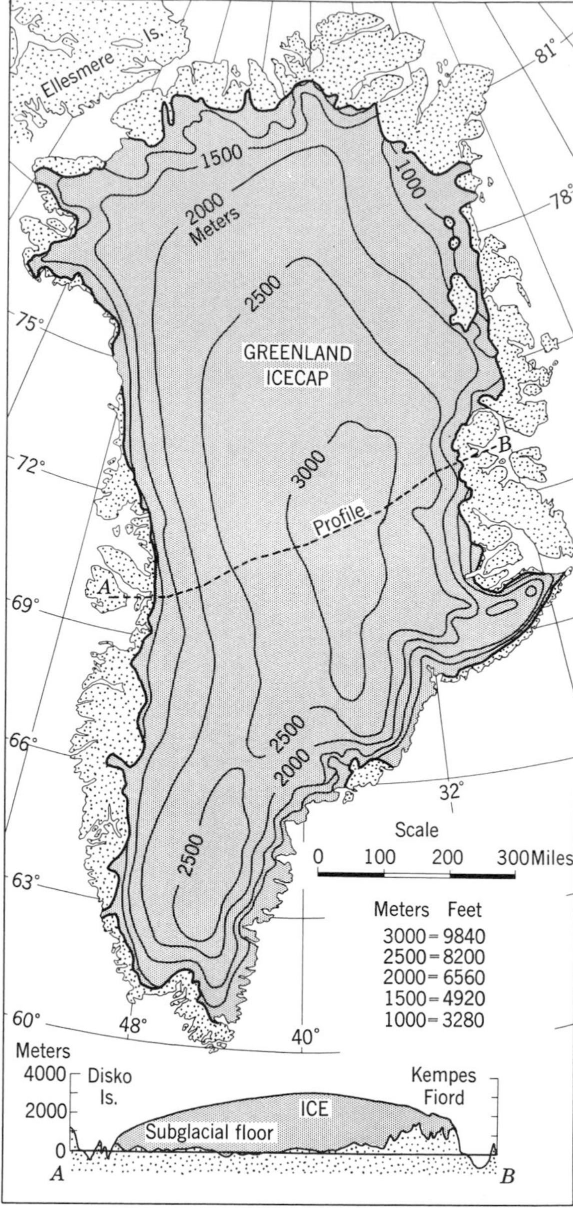


FIGURE 40.17. Greenland and its ice sheet. (© 1960, John Wiley & Sons, New York. Based on a map by R. F. Flint.)

Tributaries enter the main glacier with smoothly accordant ice-surface junctions. Abrasion of the valley walls has planed away projecting spurs of the preglacial stream valleys, producing *truncated spurs.* Where the main glacier blocks a stream valley at relatively low elevations, discharge is ponded in temporary *marginal lakes,* or *ice-dammed lakes.*

Block *C* of Figure 40.12 shows this same region after the glaciers have entirely disappeared because of a general climatic warming. It is in this condition that many of the high mountain ranges of the middle latitudes are seen today. The trunk glacier had eroded a deep U-shaped *glacial trough.* Its smaller tributaries

**FIGURE 40.18.** Ice cliff 50 to 150 ft (15 to 45 m) high at the margin of the Greenland Ice Sheet, Nunatarssuaq, Greenland. The cliff moves forward at about 0.5 in. (1.3 cm) per day. (Photograph by L. H. Nobles.)

also carved troughs, but because these ice streams were of smaller cross section their floors were not so deeply cut, hence they now enter at levels high above the main trough floor. Such tributary forms are termed *hanging troughs.* In the upper reaches of the troughs are many irregularities of gradient, giving a succession of *rock steps* and *rock basins,* which hold lakes. Depressions in the floors of cirques may also hold lakes, called *tarns* (Figure 40.14).

Grandest of all glacially carved landforms are the glacial troughs, which may be thousands of feet deep and tens of miles long (Figure 40.15). After glaciation some troughs have U-shaped cross profiles, with little or no modification by filling (Block *B*), while others have a flat floor because alluvium brought downvalley from receding glaciers by meltwater streams has filled the trough floor to produce a *valley-train deposit* (Block *C*), and still others, cut below sea level in a coastal mountain range, are now invaded by the sea to become *fiords* (Block *D*).

Fiords are characterized by the steepness of their walls and the depth of their floors, often containing water depths of several hundred feet (Figure 40.16). Fiords are widely found along mountainous coasts of arctic and subarctic latitudes. Marine west-coast climates combined with strong relief favored the development of fiord coasts in Alaska and British Columbia, southern Chile, Scotland, and Norway.

## Greenland and Antarctic ice sheets

From the study of small stream-like valley glaciers we turn our attention to the two enormous ice masses of subcontinental size that exist today. Greenland and Antarctica bear these great ice sheets.

The Greenland Ice Sheet occupies some 670,000 sq mi (1,740,000 sq km)—which is 80% of the entire area of the island of Greenland—covering all but narrow land fringes (Figure 40.17). Altogether the ice sheet comprises some 672,000 cu mi (2,800,000 cu km) of ice. In a general way the ice forms a single broadly arched, doubly convex ice lens, smoothly surfaced on the upper side and considerably rougher and less strongly curved on the underside. The mountainous terrain of the coast passes inland beneath the ice with steadily descending summit elevations, giving a central lowland area close to sea level in elevation. The ice margin is in places gently sloping, but elsewhere it forms a steep ramp or a sheer cliff (Figure 40.18). The ice surface is characterized by wind-eroded and drifted features called *sastrugi* (Figure 40.19).

The ice thickness measures close to 10,000 ft (3 km) at its greatest. It is not surprising that the center of Greenland is actually depressed under such a load, in conformity with the principle of isostasy, for 10,000 ft (3 km) of glacial ice is roughly equivalent to a rock layer at least 3000 ft (0.9 km) thick.

The central area of the Greenland Ice Sheet is in the glacial zone of accumulation, hence it is a vast firn field of compacting snow in process of transformation into glacial ice. The firn line lies some 30 to 100 mi

**FIGURE 40.19.** Sastrugi on Greenland Ice Sheet, 5 mi (8 km) from the ice margin, lat. 76° N. (Photograph by L. H. Nobles.)

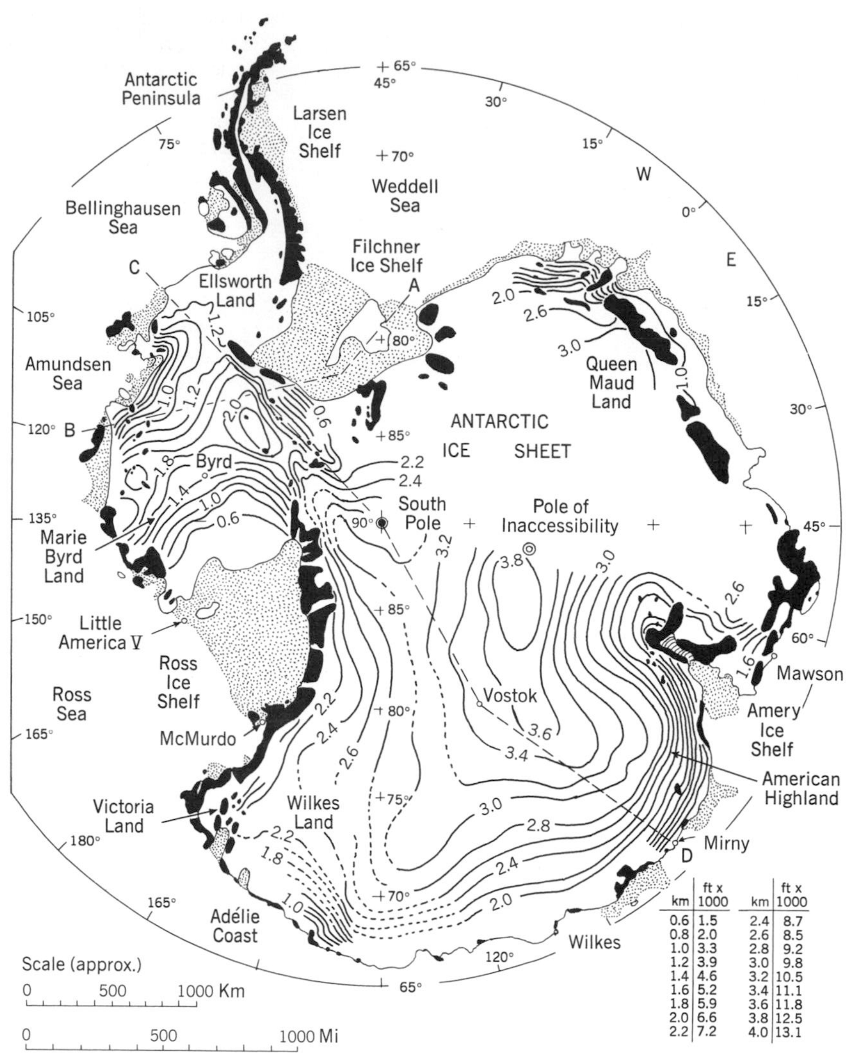


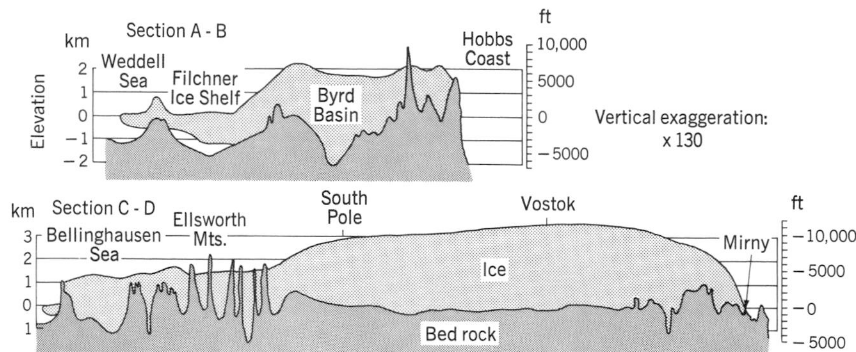


**FIGURE 40.20.** Map of Antarctica showing ice surface elevations by contours with interval of 0.2 km (660 ft). Areas of exposed bedrock shown in black; ice shelves by stipple pattern. [Map redrawn and simplified from C. R. Bentley (1962), *Geophysical Monograph No. 7,* Washington, D.C., Amer. Geophys. Union, p. 14, Figure 2. Cross sections after Amer. Geog. Soc. (1964), *Antarctic Map Folio Series,* Folio 2, Plate 2.]

(50 to 160 km) inland of the ice margin, thus the ablation area constitutes only 15% to 20% of the entire ice sheet.

Because the ice surface slopes seaward, the ice creeps slowly downward and outward toward the margins, where it discharges by glacial tongues—called *outlet glaciers*—closely resembling valley glaciers in form, but fed from a vast ice sheet rather than from a cirque. Some of the outlet glaciers have unusually fast rates of flow, on the order of 100 ft (30 m) per day. Outlet glaciers, reaching the sea in fiords, are the source of North Atlantic icebergs (Chapter 17).

Near the ice borders, where coastal terrain is most mountainous, occasional peaks of bedrock project from beneath the ice sheet. Such rock islands in a sea of ice are termed *nunataks,* from the Eskimo word for these features.

The Greenland Ice Sheet is nourished by snowfall occurring in cyclonic storms traveling generally from west to east across the landmass (Chapter 19). For some time in the recent past the Greenland Ice Sheet was losing mass steadily, but very slowly, as judged from the observed recession of its outlet glaciers and a lowering of ice level along its fringes. However, the ice sheet as a whole is judged to be close to equilibrium at the present time.

Like Greenland, the Antarctic continent is almost entirely buried beneath glacial ice. This is an ice area of just over 5 million sq mi (13 million sq km), or about 1½ times the total area of the contiguous 48 United States (Figure 40.20). Ice volume is about 6 million cu mi (25 million cu km), which is over 90% of the total volume of the earth's glacial ice. (In comparison, the Greenland Ice Sheet has about 8%.)

Intensive study and mapping of the Antarctic Ice Sheet, begun as an IGY study in 1957 and continued since then, has only recently yielded sufficient information for the drawing of a generalized map. Traverses of thousands of miles across the ice sheet have been made to study the area glaciologically. Included are determinations of ice surface elevation, ice thickness (by seismic, gravity, and magnetic observations), annual snow accumulation, and firn properties.

The Antarctic Ice Sheet reaches its highest elevations, almost 13,000 ft (4 km), in a broadly rounded summit located about lat. 82° S., long. 75° E. (Figure 40.20). Surface slope is gradual to within 200 mi (320 km) of the edge of the continent, where a marked steepening occurs, as the crowding of contour lines on the map indicates. Ice thickness is shown on a second map of Antarctica (Figure 40.21). The greatest thicknesses are over 10,000 ft (3000 m). Although in general the ice is thickest where surface elevation is highest (compare the maps), there are important exceptions to this statement. A great subglacial channel, or valley, named the Byrd Basin, has been discovered in the area of Marie Byrd Land. Here an ice thickness of nearly 13,000 ft (4000 m) has been measured, and the rock floor lies some 6500 ft (2000 m) below sea level. (See cross-sections accompanying Figure 40.20.)

The subglacial topography of Antarctica, where known from profiles of traverses along which the ice has been probed by geophysical methods, is in large part mountainous. Mountain peaks and ranges rise above the ice in several belts, mostly close to and parallel with the continental margins. Here the ice

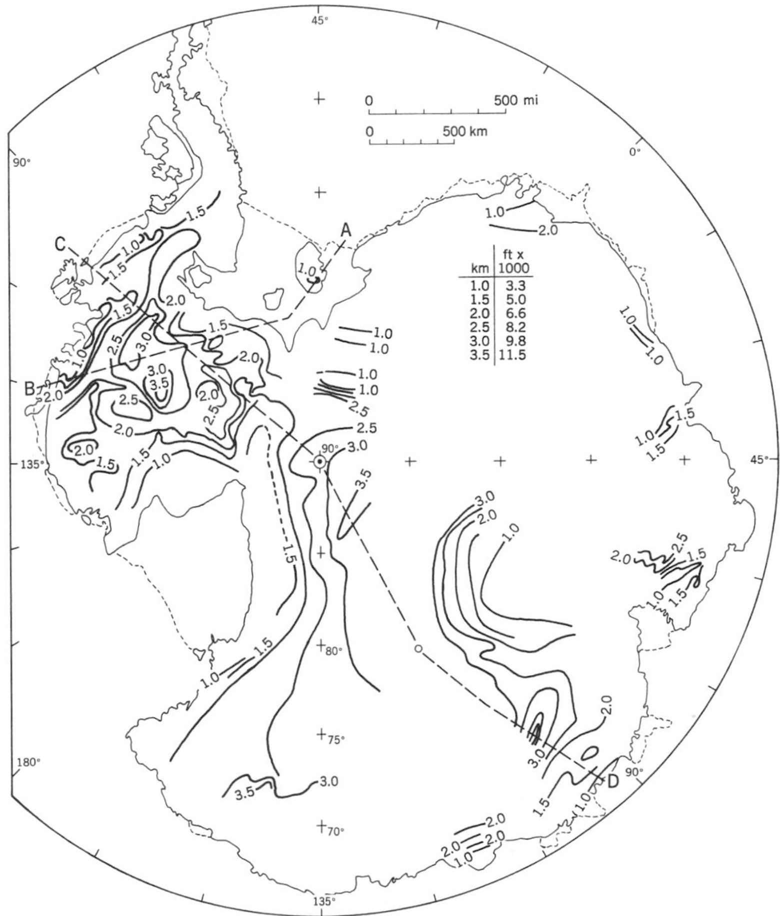


**FIGURE 40.21.** Map of Antarctica showing ice thickness. Isopachs in km; interval is 0.5 km (1640 ft). Dashed shorelines are on ice shelves. [Data from Amer. Geog. Soc. (1964), *Antarctic Map Folio Series,* Folio 2, Plate 3.]

**FIGURE 40.22.** Oblique air view of the head of Shackleton Glacier, Queen Maud Mountains, Antarctica (lat. 85° S., long. 177° W.). The polar ice plateau is seen in the distance. (U.S. Geological Survey photograph.)

moves in outlet glaciers from the interior polar plateau to reach the coast (Figure 40.22). This terrain distribution suggests that the central region has subsided greatly under ice load, as the interior of Greenland seems to have done.

A characteristic feature of the Antarctic coast is the presence of numerous *ice shelves,* which are great plates of floating ice attached to the land (Figure 40.20). Largest is the Ross Ice Shelf, about 200,000 sq mi (520,000 sq km) in area with its surface at an average elevation of about 225 ft (68 m) (Figure 40.23).

**FIGURE 40.23.** The Ross Ice Shelf, Antarctica. The steep ice cliff, from 50 to 150 ft (15 to 46 m) high, presents a formidable barrier. (Official U.S. Coast Guard Photograph.)

Almost as large is the Filchner Ice Shelf bordering the Weddell Sea. Smaller ice shelves occupy most of the bays of the Antarctic coast and in places form a continuous but narrow ice fringe. In general, the ice shelves represent those parts of the ice sheet that have been pushed seaward into water of sufficient depth that the ice is floated off the bottom. The ice shelves are largely maintained by snow accumulation on their surfaces. As explained in Chapter 17, these ice shelves are the source of tabular icebergs of the Antarctic Ocean.

## Water balance of a glacier

Glacial ice masses provide enormous reservoirs for the storage of the world's water, although the total ice volume is only about 2 percent of the world water total (97 percent is in the World Ocean—see Table 33.1). Because its system boundaries are clearly defined, a single glacier or icecap provides a convenient unit for the calculation of a water balance. The water balance equation is a simple one, making use of the same terms as used in Chapter 33 in the water balance of the continents (Table 33.2):

$$G = P - (E + R)$$

where $P$ is accumulation through precipitation, $(E + R)$ is loss through ablation and calving ($E$ represents evaporation; $R$ is melt-water runoff and can include calving),

and $G$ is change in water storage.

Of these terms, accumulation can be measured by means of reference stakes driven into the glacier surface. Losses by ablation and calving will be difficult to measure, but may be arrived at by directly measuring the lowering of the glacier surface during the summer season and the ice volume lost annually at the glacier terminus. Long-term changes in storage may be estimated by surveys of the change in position of the glacier terminus and elevation of its surface. For a glacier in dynamic equilibrium the net annual change in storage will be zero.

## Water balance of Antarctica

Because it involves the world's greatest single accumulation of ice, the water balance of Antarctica is of great scientific interest.[3] As a whole, the Antarctic ice mass shows a net accumulation estimated to average a depth equal to 6 in. (15 cm) of water equivalent per year. Table 40.1 gives estimates of the water balance of Antarctica. Most of the water loss is through melting and calving of outlet glaciers and ice shelves, which constitute a large proportion of the line of contact between ocean and ice. Much smaller losses occur from melting and calving of those parts of the coast line where the ice sheet directly contacts the water. Loss by ablation from the surface of the ice sheet itself is very small. Loss also occurs by bottom melting on the under surfaces of the ice shelves. The sum of all

[3] Data on water budget of Antarctica from F. Loewe. (See reference in Table 40.1.)

**TABLE 40.1. WATER BALANCE OF ANTARCTICA***

| | Billions of metric tons (gt) per year | Length of Productive Coastline, km |
|---|---|---|
| Accumulation (*P*) | +1900 | |
| Ablation Losses (*E* + *R*) | | |
| From ice sheet surface | −10 | |
| From ice sheet contact with ocean | −50 | 10,500 |
| From outlet glacier margins | −520 | 3,000 |
| From shelf ice margins | −880 | 10,500 |
| Bottom melting beneath shelves | −200 | |
| Total ablation | −1660 | |
| Net Accumulation (*G*) | + 240 | |

* Data of F. Loewe (1967), "The Water Budget in Antarctica", *Proc. Symp. on Pacific–Antarctic Sciences,* Tokyo, Japan, JARE Sci. Reports, Special Issue No. 1, pp. 101–110.

estimated losses is 1660 gt (gigatons, or billions of metric tons) per year, as compared with an estimated accumulation through snowfall of 1900 gt per year, for a net gain of 240 gt.

The estimate of a net accumulation over Antarctica is of particular interest in connection with the very slow but definite rise of mean sea level detected by precise leveling surveys (Chapter 11). This rise is estimated at about 1 mm (0.04 in.) per year. Obviously, if the ice volume of Antarctica is increasing, the present rise in sea level cannot be attributed to an increase in oceanic water volume derived from melting ice of Antarctica. The Greenland ice mass is judged to be close to exact balance at the present time and cannot be called upon as a source of increasing oceanic water volume. Therefore, if melting glacial ice is to account for the rise of sea level, it must be provided by the remaining relatively insignificant masses of glaciers and small icecaps, which would have to be losing mass at such a rate that they will all disappear in 500 years. It should be kept in mind, however, that other mechanisms exist for a slow rise in sea level, among them tectonic uplift of a part of the sea floor or a general rise in water temperature.

Water balance of a glacier depends, of course, upon a rate of flow adequate to transport ice from areas of accumulation surplus to marginal zones of net loss by ablation. The Antarctic ice sheet moves outward near its margin at a rate estimated to fall between 80 and 165 ft (25 and 50 m) per year. Rate of movement of outlet glaciers is much faster, estimated at 1300 ft (400 m) per year on the average. A maximum speed of record is 4600 ft (1400 m) per year on the Denman Glacier. For the ice shelves rate of outward movement is even more rapid, on the order of 3300 to 3950 ft (1000 to 1200 m) per year for the Ross and Filchner shelves. Rates of ice movement, combined with estimates of cross-sectional area, provide the basis for estimating the annual losses of water mass at the ice-cap margins. It is estimated that only about 1/10,000 of the total ice mass of Antarctica is involved annually in the exchanges of the water balance. Consequently ice following the longest possible paths of flow may remain in the ice sheet for as long as 100,000 years.

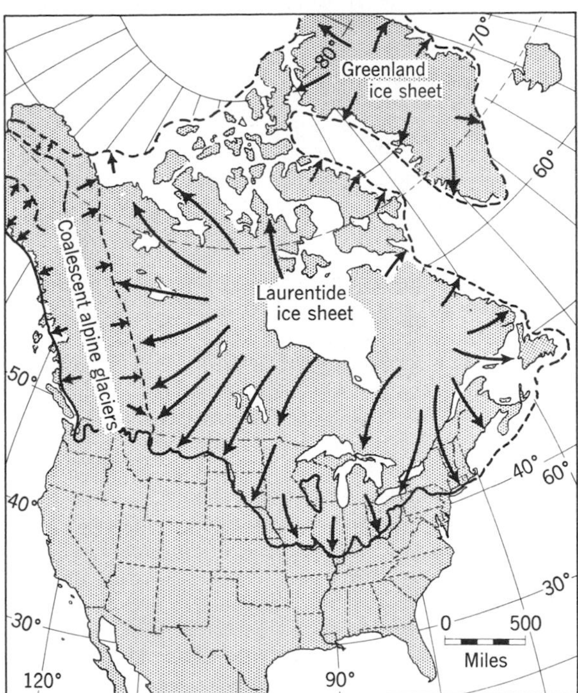


**FIGURE 40.24.** Maximum extent of Pleistocene ice sheets of North America. (© 1960, John Wiley & Sons, New York. Based on data of R. F. Flint.)

**FIGURE 40.25.** Limit of glacial ice of Europe in the last glaciation (solid line), and maximum extent in the entire Pleistocene Epoch (dashed line). (© 1960, John Wiley & Sons, New York. Based on data of R. F. Flint.)

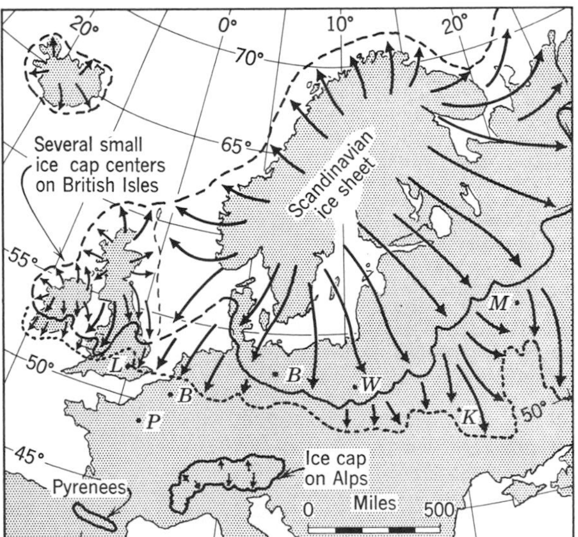

## Pleistocene ice sheets

In the last hundred years, field observations in many parts of the world have provided abundant evidence to show beyond doubt that large parts of North America, Eurasia, and South America were covered by great ice sheets in the Pleistocene Epoch, a unit of geologic time spanning approximately the last 2 to 2.5 million years. Only within the last 10,000 to 15,000 years did these ice sheets disappear from over much of the now heavily populated lands of North America and Europe. Consequently the landforms resulting from glacial erosion and deposition are in many places extremely fresh in appearance and the former ice limits and configurations can be mapped in great detail.

The maximum extent of ice sheets of the Pleistocene Epoch in North America and Europe is shown in Figures 40.24 and 40.25. In North America all of Canada and the mountainous areas of Alaska were covered. Over the Cordilleran Ranges alpine glaciers coalesced into a single icecap which spread westward to the Pacific shores and eastward down to the foothills of the mountains. Much larger was the great *Laurentide ice sheet,* which was centered over Hudson Bay and spread radially. The Laurentide ice sheet inundated the Great Lakes area and spread south into the United States as far as about the line of the Missouri and Ohio Rivers.

In Europe (Figure 40.25) the *Scandinavian ice sheet,* centered over the Baltic Sea, covered all of the Scandinavian peninsula and reached southward and eastward into the Low Countries, Germany, Poland, and Russia. This ice mass also spread westward across the North Sea, where it joined with an ice sheet that covered much of the British Isles. The Alps and Pyrenees ranges bore small icecaps formed by the coalescence of many individual valley glaciers. As would be expected, glacial activity in all the world's high mountain ranges was greatly intensified, with valley glaciers increasing in size and extending into lower altitudes than they do today.

In Siberia icecaps formed upon the uplands east of the Ural Mountains (Figure 40.26). Mountain ranges of northeastern Siberia supported icecaps formed by the coalescence of complex systems of smaller icecaps and valley glaciers. Smaller icecaps also existed over a number of the higher mountain and plateau areas of central and eastern Asia.

In South America the only large ice sheet of the Southern Hemisphere (exclusive of Antarctica) was formed over the Andean Range of Chile and Argentina, largely southward of lat. 40°, by coalescence of valley glaciers and icecaps. At its maximum extent the ice sheet reached to the Pacific Ocean on the west and spread eastward upon the pampas (piedmont plains) of Patagonia for a distance of 100 mi (160 km) or so beyond the base of the Andes.

**FIGURE 40.26.** Glaciated regions in Siberia. Shaded areas show maximum extent of ice in the latest advance, equivalent to the Wisconsinan glaciation. Dashed line indicates maximum limit of known glaciation at any time in the Pleistocene Epoch. [Based on a map compiled by W. R. Farrand (1961), courtesy of the Lamont-Doherty Geological Observatory of Columbia University.]

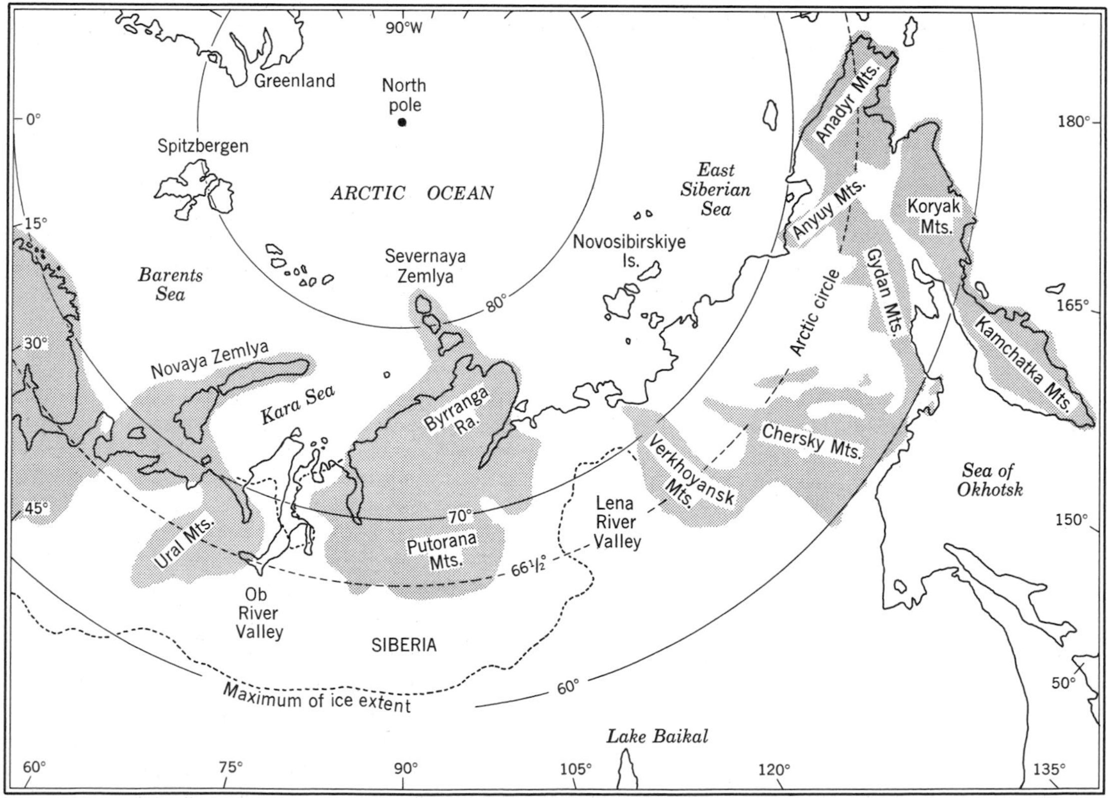

South Island of New Zealand, analogous to the southern Andes in its topography and situation, had an extensive icecap covering a belt 400 mi (640 km) long and 50 mi (80 km) wide. Tasmania also supported an icecap.

The four cycles of ice advance and disappearance within the Pleistocene Epoch are given in Chapter 41. Almost all existing landforms produced directly by Pleistocene glacial action belong to the youngest glacial inundation, the *Wisconsinan Glaciation.*

## Glacial drift

For many decades geologists have applied the term *glacial drift* to all varieties of rock debris deposited in close association with Pleistocene ice sheets. Drift consists of two major classes of materials: (1) *Stratified drift* is made up of sorted and layered clay, silt, sand, or gravel deposited as bed load or deltaic sediment from streams of meltwater, or settled from suspension into bodies of quiet water adjoining the ice. (2) *Till* is an unsorted mixture of rock and mineral fragments of a wide range of sizes—from clay to large boulders—that has been deposited directly from glacial ice. One form, *basal till,* consists of material dragged along beneath the moving ice and plastered upon the bedrock or upon other glacial deposits. Another form, *ablation till,* or *residual till,* consisting of debris held within the ice, is dropped in place as the ice wastes away (Figure 40.27). Moraines usually consist largely of glacial till and were formed under the ice, whereas stratified drift accumulated in favorable locations adjacent to the ice margin, such as valley floors or lake basins.

**FIGURE 40.27.** Basal till and residual till. [From A GEOLOGIST'S VIEW OF CAPE COD by Arthur N. Strahler. Copyright © 1966 by Arthur N. Strahler. Reproduced by permission of Doubleday & Company, Inc.]

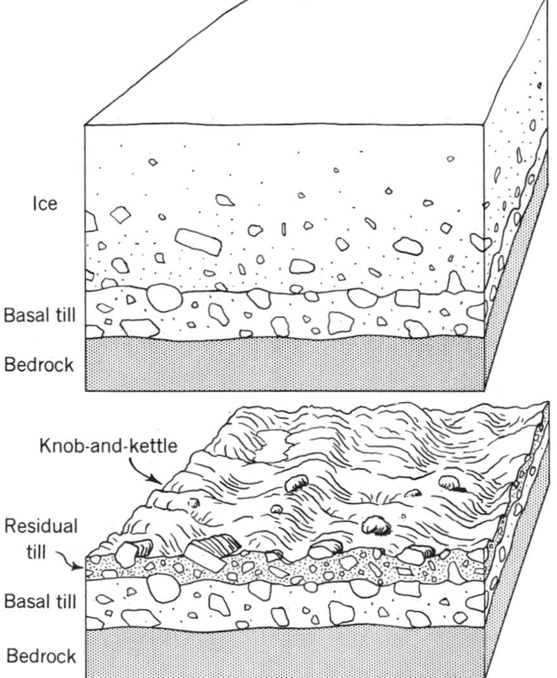


Unusually large rock fragments of boulder size within glacial till are termed *glacial erratics.* Although most erratics are derived from a bedrock source not far away, some have been transported many tens of miles. Where erratics consist of a distinctive rock variety obviously brought from a small area of rock outcrop, lines drawn from these erratics to the parent outcrop form a narrowly radiating pattern indicating approximate direction of ice motion. Such assemblages of erratics constitute *boulder trains.*

Within the area of the United States once covered by Pleistocene ice sheets glacial drift has a thickness averaging from 20 ft (6 m) over mountainous terrain of the northeast to perhaps 50 ft (15 m) or more over the plains of the North Central States. Drift is generally 50 to 200 ft (15 to 60 m) thick in Iowa and over 100 ft (30 m), on the average, in Illinois. As one would expect, the greatest thicknesses occur in preglacial valleys and lowlands and the least over plateaus and hill summits. Consequently the gross effect of continental glaciation has been to reduce the local relief and subdue the slopes.

## Depositional landforms of continental glaciation

The advance and wastage of a great ice sheet leaves a host of distinctive minor landforms. They can best be understood and described with the aid of block diagrams, one showing the ice sheet in place and the other showing the landscape after the ice has disappeared (Figure 40.28). In Block *A* the ice has reached a stable line of advance and is beginning to waste away in place. Previous forward movement of the ice created a terminal moraine at the ice margin. Farther back beneath the ice is a till layer of variable thickness, the *ground moraine.*

From the ice, now become almost stagnant, meltwater issues in numerous streams, some discharging from tubes within and beneath the ice, others flowing down the ice surface itself. Sand and gravel, carried as bed load in the meltwater streams, is spread in sheets in a zone in front of the ice, forming alluvial fans that coalesce into a continuous alluvial sheet, the *outwash plain.* A series of ice blocks, left behind during a previous episode of advance and rapid wastage, are surrounded and perhaps buried in the outwash layers.

At the rear right-hand side of Block *A* the ice sheet has dammed the runoff system to produce a temporary *marginal lake,* into which deltas are being built and on the floor of which fine silt and clay is accumulating.

Disappearance of the ice sheet reveals many more landforms shaped beneath the ice (Block *B*). The terminal moraine now appears as a belt of hilly ground with many deep closed depressions, a type of terrain referred to as *knob and kettle* (Figure 40.29). Sloping away from the terminal moraine is the smooth surface of the outwash plain, pitted here and there by steep-sided depressions, called *kettles,* where ice blocks were buried and in which there may remain lakes (Figure 40.30).

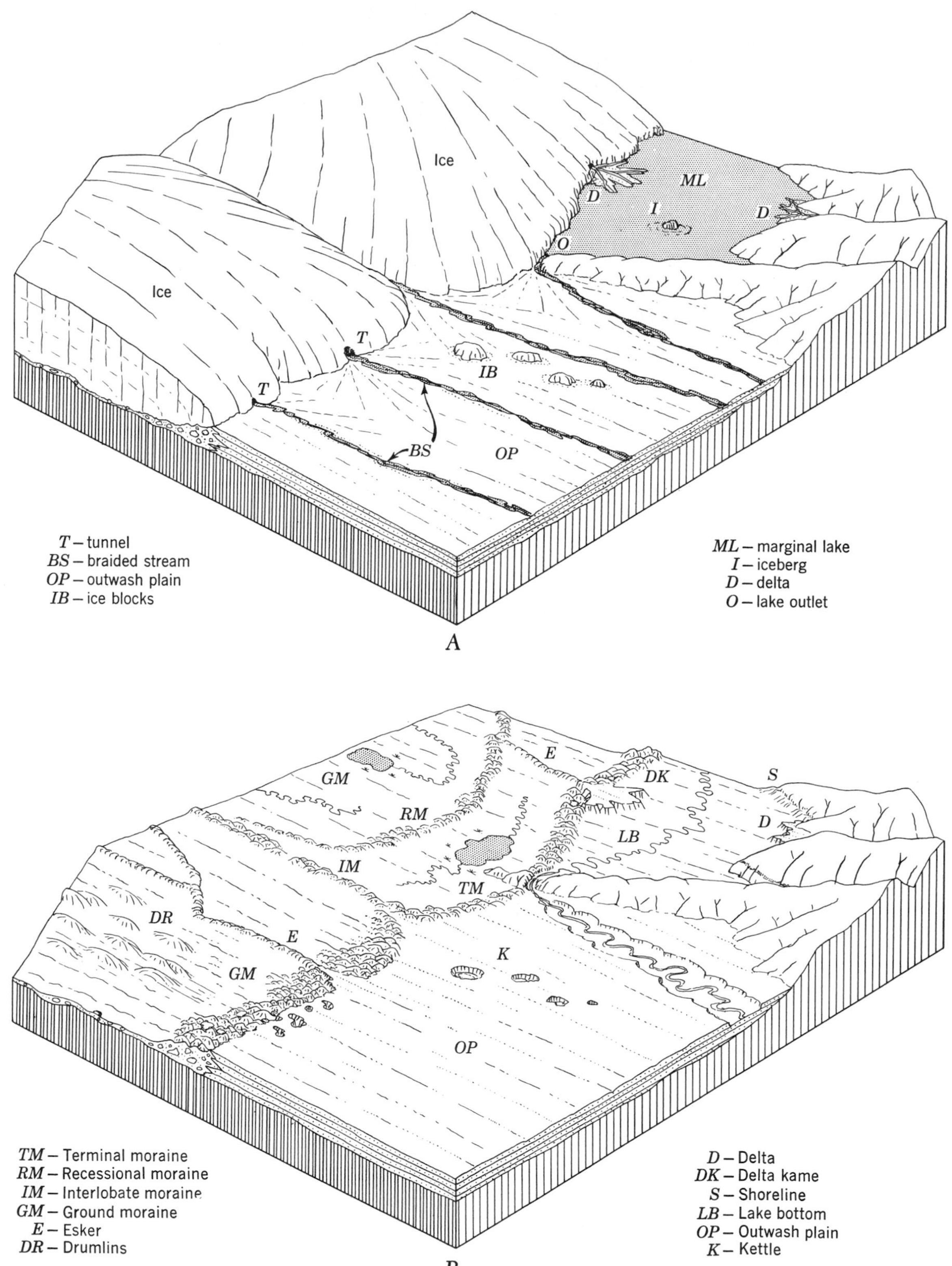


**FIGURE 40.28.** Landforms produced near the margin of an ice sheet. (*A*) Ice margin in almost stagnant condition. (*B*) Ice entirely gone, revealing subglacial forms. (© 1960, John Wiley & Sons, New York.)

**FIGURE 40.29.** Vertical air photograph of a broad moraine belt in southern Saskatchewan, Canada. Numerous kettles pock the surface. The area shown is about 1.5 mi (2.4 km) wide. (Royal Canadian Air Force official photograph, No. A6729-23.)

Behind the moraine is an expanse of poorly drained surface underlain by ground moraine and having many marshes. Rising from this low ground are groups of smoothly rounded hills, called *drumlins,* oval in outline and composed usually of basal till so shaped by the ice flow that the long axes of the hills are roughly parallel to one another and at right angles to the trend of the terminal moraine (Figure 40.31). Drumlins usually occur in groups and are commonly from 0.5 to 1 mi (0.8 to 1.6 km) long and rise to heights of perhaps 75 to 150 ft (22 to 45 m), although wide variation in dimensions and shapes can be seen in any field of drumlins.

Disappearance of the ice may also uncover long narrow ridges of coarse sands and gravels, extending in a sinuous course for miles, roughly parallel with the direction of ice movement (Figure 40.32). These features are *eskers,* the bed-load deposits of subglacial meltwater streams that emerged from tunnels at the ice margin. Some eskers are traceable for tens of miles with few interruptions and may receive tributary eskers, much as streams do.

Most large lobes of an ice sheet, during the period of ice recession, underwent temporary halts and perhaps minor readvances, resulting in the formation of additional moraines, termed *recessional moraines,* each one marking the deposition of till during a temporary halt. Consequently a map of recessional moraines shows concentric patterns of deposits (Figure 40.33). Between adjacent ice lobes are *interlobate moraines* trending roughly parallel with the axes of the lobes.

## Deposits built into standing water

A number of distinctive landforms are found in and around the basins of temporary marginal lakes permit-

**FIGURE 40.30.** A deep kettle pond on Cape Cod. (Photograph by A. N. Strahler.)

**FIGURE 40.31.** Drumlins of glacial till seen in a vertical air photograph. The area shown is about 2 mi (3.2 km) wide. Ice moved from upper right to lower left. The drumlins are 50 to 75 ft (80 to 120 m) high. Locality is near Carp Lake, northern British Columbia. (U.S. Army Air Forces trimetrogon photograph.)

ted subsequently to drain by disappearance of the ice (Figure 40.29). Meltwater streams emerging from the ice built deltas in the marginal lakes. After both ice and lake disappeared, such deltas were left standing as *delta kames,* flat-topped, steep-sided hills of well-sorted sand and gravel (Figure 40.34). They contain the steeply sloping foreset beds typical of small simple deltas (Figure 35.30).

Upon the floors of the marginal lakes were deposited layers of fine silt and clay exhibiting alternate light and dark bands known as *varves.* An individual varve consists of a light band of silt below grading upward into a dark band of fine clay (Figure 40.35). Each varve may represent the deposits of one year, the lighter layer consisting of silt (rock flour) settled out of suspension in the warm season and the thinner darker layer of clay, being the finest material, settled out during the winter when the lake was frozen over and the water quiet.

Where terrain has considerable relief, as in New England or in New York State, long narrow bodies of stagnant ice remained in the larger valleys long after the ice had disappeared from surrounding summit areas. Here were many sites for long narrow marginal lakes to form between the ice and the valley wall, as illustrated in Figure 40.36. Such lakes were the sites of building of many delta kames. Where an aggrading stream ran between the ice and the valley wall, a *kame terrace* was formed, resembling in some respects the alluvial terrace (Chapter 35), but commonly pitted with kettles and possessing an irregular scarp against which the ice had once rested.

In general, delta kames and varved sediments are referred to as *glaciolacustrine* deposits. Kame terraces and other stream-laid sand and gravel deposits, such as outwash plains and the valley trains of alpine-glacial troughs, are *glaciofluvial* deposits. All are forms of stratified drift.

**FIGURE 40.32.** This esker, near Boyd Lake in Canada, crosses irregular hills of glacially eroded bedrock and rock basin lakes. (Photograph by Canadian Department of Mines, Geological Survey.)

FIGURE 40.33. Moraines of the north central United States. (© 1965, John Wiley & Sons, New York. Based on *Glacial Map of North America,* by R. F. Flint and others.)

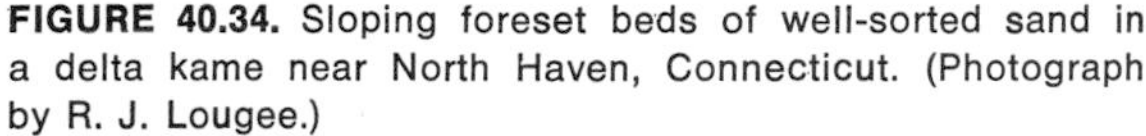

FIGURE 40.34. Sloping foreset beds of well-sorted sand in a delta kame near North Haven, Connecticut. (Photograph by R. J. Lougee.)

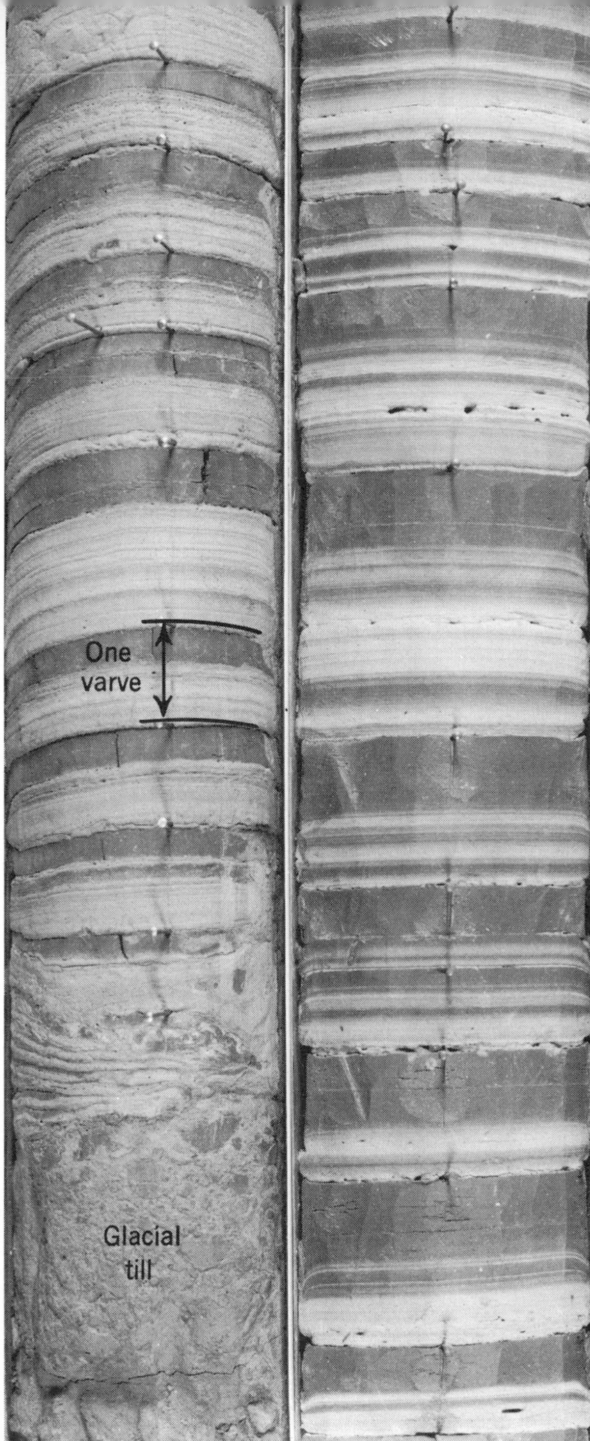


FIGURE 40.35. Varved clays from lake deposits near new York City. Pins mark the divisions between each pair of varves. The sample columns are about 10 in. (25 cm) high. (Photograph by C. A. Reeds, courtesy of the American Museum of Natural History.)

## Erosional landforms of continental glaciation

Because glacial-deposition landforms are the most conspicuous features of glaciated areas such as the north central and northeastern United States, in which occurred the marginal zones of the Pleistocene ice sheets, we may tend to give less thought to the erosional forms made by the ice sheets. In the more central locations of the ice sheets there is less drift and, instead, much heavily abraded exposed bedrock. Such surfaces are typical of the Canadian Shield and the Baltic Shield,

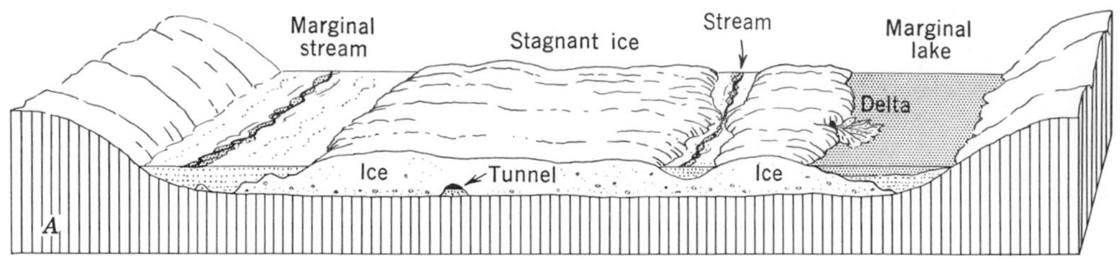


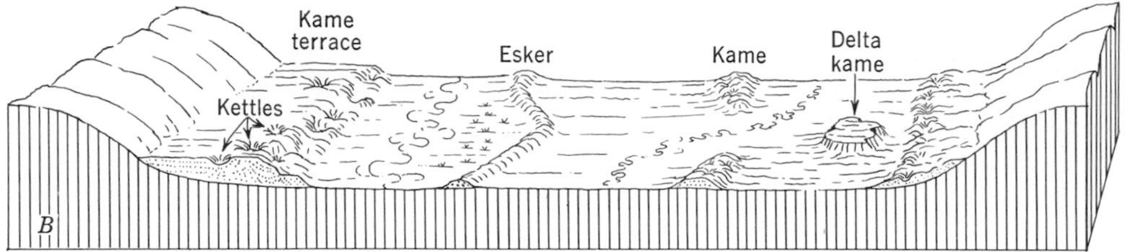


**FIGURE 40.36.** Glacial deposits associated with a mass of stagnant ice In the axis of a broad valley. (© 1960, John Wiley & Sons, New York. After R. F. Flint.)

where countless glacially eroded and drift-blocked lake basins dominate the landscape (Figure 40.32). Glaciated rock knobs and striated and grooved rock surfaces are common.

A few forms of glacial erosion are of major proportions. The Finger Lakes of western New York State are U-shaped troughs, not unlike alpine-glacial troughs, produced by ice erosion where a system of north-south trending stream valleys are inundated by the ice sheet and along which ice flow was intensified. In what is now the Great Lakes region, broad valleys underlain by weak shales were scoured by ice sheets and furnished much of the debris for formation of marginal drift.

## Glacier systems in review

The structure, movements, and effects of glaciers, including icecaps and continental ice sheets, have much in common with systems of overland flow of water, although only the outward forms of valley glaciers closely resemble those of a stream system. All are gravity-flow systems powered by solar energy through the atmospheric lifting of water to a superior elevation, which provides the initial supply of potential energy.

Like streams, glaciers are integral parts of the total hydrologic cycle and take part in maintaining the earth's water balance. Also like streams, glaciers perform the geologic work of continental denudation by eroding and transporting sediment, which is deposited at lower levels.

Unlike fluvial denudation, which has acted over most of the continental surfaces throughout all of recorded geologic time, glacial denudation has been active only in brief and sporadic periods in the past. Because glacial action has been of major importance in the last one to two million years of time and continues to be prominent today, we should not be misled into holding a distorted view of the glacial role in geologic history—it is a very minor role when viewed in the perspective of geologic time.

As we inquire in the final chapter of this book into the many and varied events of the Pleistocene and Holocene epochs, it will become more evident that the terrestrial environment in which Man evolved and lives today is exceptional in many ways to the prevailing tenor of most of recorded geologic time.

## References for further study


Lobeck, A. K. (1939), *Geomorphology,* New York, McGraw-Hill, 731 pp., chaps. 8, 9.

Flint, R. F. (1957), *Glacial and Pleistocene Geology,* New York, Wiley, 553 pp.

Dyson, J. L. (1962), *The World of Ice,* New York, Knopf, 292 pp.

American Geographical Society (1964 and later), *Antarctic Map Folio Series,* New York, Amer. Geog. Soc.

Strahler, A. N. (1966), *A Geologist's View of Cape Cod,* Garden City, N.Y., Doubleday—Nat. Hist. Press, 115 pp.

Thornbury, W. D. (1969), *Principles of Geomorphology,* 2nd ed., New York, Wiley, 594 pp., chaps. 14, 15, 16.

# 41

# The Pleistocene Epoch and Man

AS THE CONCLUDING CHAPTER of this review of the earth sciences we turn to consider the events and problems of the most recent units of geologic time—the Pleistocene and Holocene epochs. Compressed into a time span of only two million years, an almost trivial instant in planet Earth's long history, is a highly complex sequence of environmental changes affecting the atmosphere, the oceans, and the surfaces of the continents. It is perhaps due to the swiftness and intensity of environmental changes within the Pleistocene that the rapid evolution of Man occurred as it did, to the accompaniment of forced geographical displacements and redistributions of faunas and floras.

The Pleistocene inherited from the Pliocene a set of conditions likely to place severe environmental stresses upon plants and animals: The continents stood high, tectonism and vulcanism were active in narrow belts over the globe, and climatic contrasts were intensified from equator to poles. Yet the most potent environmental force, continental glaciation, withheld its action until the Pleistocene. The spread and recession of the great ice sheets dominate the history of the Pleistocene and provide the events upon which the epoch is subdivided into time units.

Referring back to the discussion of nomenclature of the Cenozoic Era in Chapter 30, recall that the conventional, or classical, usage subdivides the era into Tertiary and Quaternary periods, whereas newer usage drops the necessity of naming either period and recognizes only seven epochs, of which the last three are the Pliocene, Pleistocene, and Holocene (see Table 30.1). Use of the term *Quaternary Period* persists today as a convenient handle to designate the combined Pleistocene and Holocene (Recent). Although we shall not refer to the Quaternary Period in this chapter, it is well to keep the term in mind, because it is widely used throughout current publications and emphasizes the unity of the Pleistocene with the Holocene. The world organization of scientists devoted to the investigation of the Pleistocene and Holocene epochs goes by the name of the *International Association for Quaternary Research,* abbreviated to *INQUA.*

## Glaciation and interglaciation

Study of glacial deposits and landforms shows us that the glacial history of the Pleistocene Epoch consisted not of a single cycle of growth and disappearance of ice sheets, but rather of at least four such cycles, each referred to as a *glaciation.* The oldest deposits, those of the first known glaciation, show most strongly the effects of time through the degree of chemical and physical weathering of the component mineral and rock fragments. The degree to which the silicate minerals in tills have been altered to clay minerals and the degree to which calcium carbonate has been leached from masses of glaciofluvial sands and gravels provide evidence that deposits are of different ages.

As with strata of other kinds of sedimentary rock, glacial deposits of each glaciation are commonly found superimposed in order of age. Moreover, the discovery of an ancient soil layer, or *paleosol,* between two layers of glacial material not only serves to separate them into two glaciations but also provides proof of the long time that elapsed between those glaciations. Yet another type of evidence consists of the degree to which landforms of glacial deposition are modified by mass wasting and fluvial erosion. In general, glacial landforms become more subdued with passage of time as their scarps lose sharpness, their depressions are filled, and gullies and new valleys score their poorly consolidated clays and sands.

Another form of evidence of multiple glaciations comes from sediment deposits—usually types formed in bogs, lakes, or estuaries—in which are contained remains of plants and animals known to thrive only in relatively mild climates. Where such deposits separate layers of morainal material they provide evidence of a period of warm climate, or *interglacation,* which separated glaciations.

## Radiocarbon age determination

Assignment of ages in years-before-present to deposits and events of the Holocene Epoch and the last cycle of glaciation and interglaciation of the Pleistocene Epoch has been made possible by the *carbon-14,* or *radiocarbon,* method of age determination. In the earth's upper atmosphere, at levels above 10 mi (16 km), atoms of ordinary nitrogen (nitrogen-14) are subject to bombardment by neutrons created by highly energetic cosmic particles (cosmic rays) penetrating the atmosphere from outer space (see Chapter 6 and Figure 6.21). Upon being struck, an atom of nitrogen-14 absorbs the impacting neutron and emits a proton. The nitrogen atom is thus transformed into an isotope of carbon, *carbon-14,* which quickly combines with oxygen to form carbon dioxide.

Carbon-14 is radioactive and decays back to nitrogen-14. The half-life of carbon-14 is 5730 ± 40 years. (Refer to Chapter 23 for explanation of radioactive decay and half-life, and to Chapter 26 for methods of radiometric age determination.)

The rate of production of carbon-14 in the upper atmosphere is assumed to be constant. Therefore atmospheric carbon dioxide that is taken up by plants and animals will contain a fixed proportion of carbon-14 relative to the total amount of ordinary carbon (carbon-12). From an initial point in time marked by the death of the organism, the proportion of carbon-14 in the organic structure declines steadily, following the exponential curve of decline. By precision measurements of the extremely small amounts of carbon-14 in a sample of organic matter, the age in years of that matter can be estimated to within a fairly small percentage of error. While the very short half-life of carbon-14 makes it an excellent tool for age determinations in the last few tens of thousands of years, the uncertainty of measurement increases at such a rate that the present limit of usefulness is about −40,000 years.

The radiocarbon method of age determination was developed in about 1950 by Willard F. Libby of the Institute for Nuclear Studies of the University of Chicago. Age determinations were made of such materials as charcoal, shells, wood, and peat derived from archaeological sites and glacial deposits. Materials whose age was documented from other historical records served as a check upon the accuracy of the method. By 1952 Libby's laboratory had made age determinations of a large number of carefully selected samples. Other laboratories were soon set up and the radiocarbon method has since been established as one of the most important research tools in geological and archaeological research.

A highly significant event was the dating of wood from trees overwhelmed by the last known ice advance at Two Creeks, Wisconsin (see Figure 41.4). This date, 11,850 ± 100 years before present, proved to be about half the age previously estimated.

In recent years discrepancies have been found in radiocarbon dates as checked against dates determined by such independent means as tree-ring counts and recorded human history. There are reasons to suspect that the rate of production of carbon-14 has not, in fact, been constant in the past. There is no reason to doubt the constancy of interception of cosmic particles by the earth. However, the effectiveness of these particles in penetrating the outer atmosphere, and hence in producing carbon-14, is influenced by the strength of the earth's external magnetic field (Chapter 7). Greater strength of the magnetic field tends to reduce cosmic particle penetration, while a weaker field permits particles to penetrate more readily. The exclusion of cosmic particles during periods of magnetic "bays" in magnetic storms is well documented (Figure 7.31). We have seen that disturbances of the external magnetic field are caused by solar flares, and that the frequency of these flares varies in the same 11-year cycle as does the frequency of sunspots. It is likely, therefore, that the rate of production of carbon-14 follows this and perhaps other cycles of solar activity. In view of observed discrepancies in radiocarbon dates, it is recommended that a given age determination be considered to have a probable absolute error of at least 5%.

## Glacial chronology of North America and Europe

For several decades four glaciations have been recognized in North America, while a similar and possibly equivalent four-glaciation history has been established for Europe on the basis of studies in the Alps. Recently, evidence has been found of two earlier glaciations in the Alps. Evidence of six cold climate episodes is found in northwestern Europe and in Great Britain. Thus the total number of glaciations of the Pleistocene Epoch remains to be established and may even exceed six. Names of the four established glaciations of North America and presumed European equivalents (in parentheses) are given in Table 41.1. Maps of North America, Europe, and Eurasia show maximum extent of Pleistocene ice sheets (Figures 40.24, 40.25, and 40.26).

Maximum southern extent of ice in each glaciation in the north central United States is shown in Figure 41.1. The ice limit of each glaciation is usually marked by a terminal moraine. The ice front advanced in great lobes, whose limits varied both with location and stage. For example, the Kansan ice limit extended beyond those of other ice sheets in northeastern Kansas and northern Missouri, but it was generally surpassed by the younger ice sheets east of the Mississippi River.

Note in Figure 41.1 that an area in southwestern Wisconsin is shown to have escaped inundation by Pleistocene ice sheets. Known as the *Driftless Area,* it was apparently bypassed by glacial lobes moving on either side. Highlands situated south of lake Superior deflected the ice flow to either side of the Driftless Area.

**TABLE 41.1. NORTH AMERICAN AND EUROPEAN GLACIATIONS**

| Glaciations North America | (Alps) | Interglaciations |
|---|---|---|
| Wisconsinan | (Würm) | |
| | | Sangamonian |
| Illinoian | (Riss) | |
| | | Yarmouthian |
| Kansan | (Mindel) | |
| | | Aftonian |
| Nebraskan | (Günz) | |
| ? | | |
| ? | | |
| ? | | |

In the eastern United States the ice limit of only the Wisconsinan Glaciation is sharply defined. A moraine marks the ice margin in northern Pennsylvania and New Jersey, crosses Staten Island and passes over to Long Island at the Narrows of New York Harbor. The moraine belt then follows the north side of Long Island and divides into two lines that continue east and north, constituting the bulk of the islands of Nantucket and Martha's Vineyard and much of Cape Cod (Figure 41.2).

## Stratigraphic sequence within the Wisconsinan Glaciation

Geologists make a distinction between *geologic-climatic* units (glaciations and interglaciations) and *time-stratigraphic* units of the Pleistocene Epoch, on the one hand,

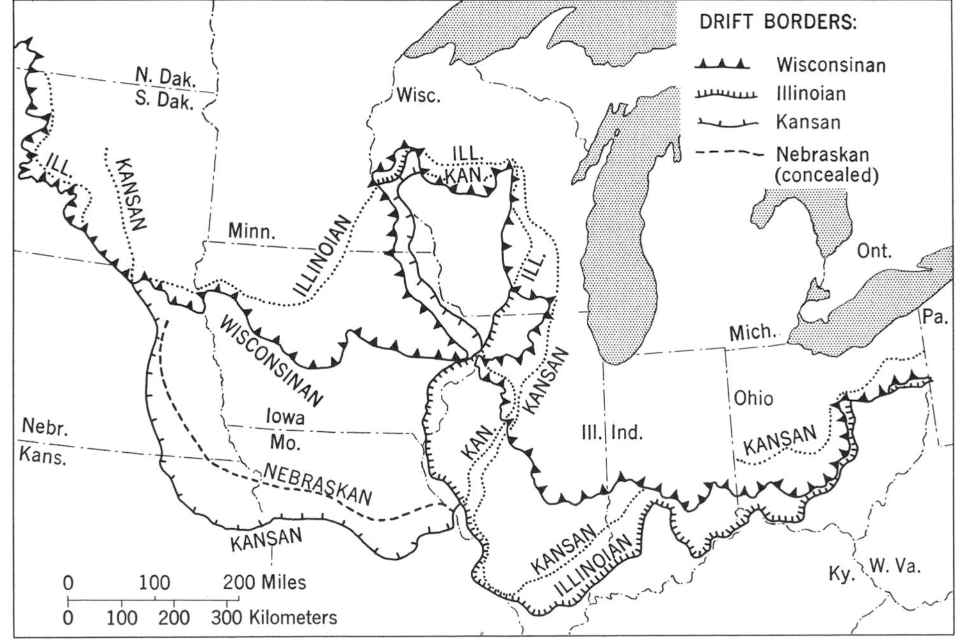


**FIGURE 41.1.** Ice limits in the north central United States for the four glaciations. (© 1965, John Wiley & Sons, New York. Data of R. F. Flint.)

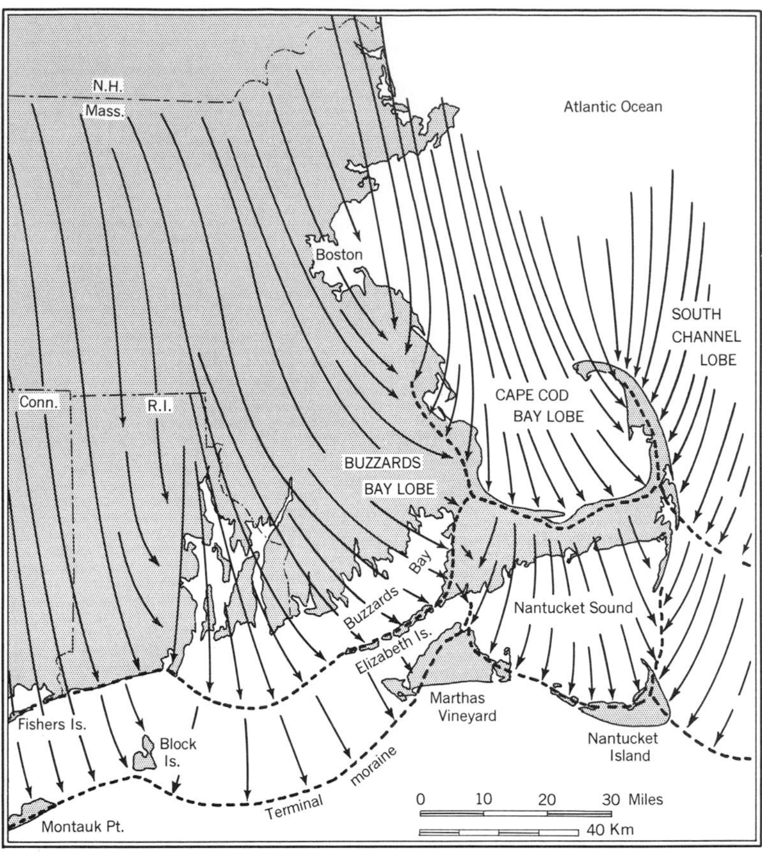


**FIGURE 41.2.** Glacial lobes and moraines of southeastern New England. Arrows show inferred direction of ice movement. [From A GEOLOGIST'S VIEW OF CAPE COD by Arthur N. Strahler. Copyright © 1966 by Arthur N. Strahler. Reproduced by permission of Doubleday & Company, Inc.]

and the sedimentary deposits associated with those events, on the other. All sediments produced during the Wisconsinan Glaciation are said to comprise the *Wisconsinan Stage.* The term "stage" is regarded as a time-stratigraphic unit, since it is defined according to the sedimentary record deposited within specified time limits. Within the Wisconsinan Stage are *substages* consisting of stratigraphic units produced during a number of episodes of glacial advance and recession within any given region. These substages receive names of largely local significance. Within the duration of a given substage the ice front may have advanced one or more times, leaving a till deposit and a terminal moraine. Between ice advances soils were developing on exposed tills, low areas were receiving deposits of glaciolacustrine silts, and bogs were accumulating peat. Forests may have grown on the exposed surfaces, to be overridden by ice of the next advance. In the bordering region south of the glacial limit layers of loess were deposited on uplands, while alluvium was spread over the valley floors.

In the states of Wisconsin and Illinois five substages are recognized within the Wisconsinan Stage. We have selected this region to illustrate the identification of substages because it is centrally located in the continent and is unusually rich in details of Pleistocene stratigraphy. Figure 41.3 is a diagram showing these substages. The vertical axis of the diagram is scaled in time, and the horizontal axis in latitude, north being toward the right. Advance and recession of the ice front is represented by tongues of till deposition entering from the north, reaching a southern limit, then receding north beyond the limits of the diagram. The position and nature of the deposits between tills and in advance of the ice is suggested by various patterns.

Substages in Illinois and Wisconsin are named, from oldest to youngest, *Altonian, Farmdalian, Woodfordian, Twocreekan,* and *Valderan.* Notice the adjectival form of the place names, a requirement of the Code of Stratigraphic Nomenclature for designation of time-stratigraphic units. In conformity with this usage, these substages comprise the *Wisconsinan Stage.* The Altonian Substage is shown to begin at about −75,000 years. However, no radiocarbon dates are available to determine the onset of the Altonian Substage. Silt, peat, tills, and loess of Altonian age rest directly upon soil of the Sangamonian Stage. Four and possibly five ice advances occurred in the Altonian Substage. The Farmdalian Substage is a comparatively short interval of major glacial withdrawal, falling between −28,000 and −23,000 years, during which silt and peat were deposited. There followed the Woodfordian Substage, in which a major ice advance occurred, reaching to the maximum limit of any advance within the Wisconsinan Stage. Ice recession, punctuated by many minor readvances, took place in an interval of about 8000 years, leaving more than 30 recessional moraines in Illinois. A short episode of glacier recession, the Twocreekan

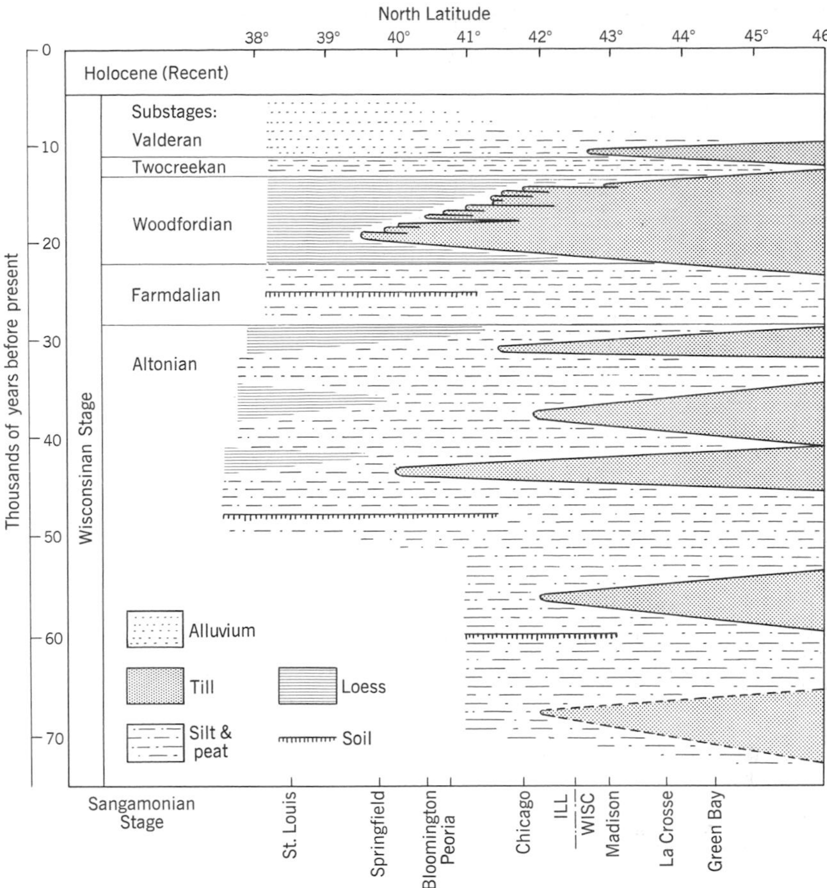


**FIGURE 41.3.** Time–latitude diagram showing sequence of Wisconsinan deposits in Wisconsin and Illinois. Diagram is largely schematic and cannot be interpreted in terms of thicknesses of deposits. [After J. C. Frye, H. B. Willman, and R. F. Black (1965), in *The Quaternary of the United States,* H. E. Wright, Jr., and D. G. Frey, Eds., Princeton, N.J., Princeton Univ. Press, p. 51, Figure 5.]

Substage, saw the deposition of more peat and silt and the growth of forests of spruce, birch, and jackpine (Figure 41.4). Evidences of Man and remains of various mammals are found in this time interval. In the Valderan Substage ice advanced for the last time, overriding the forests and soils of the previous substage. Final ice recession is judged to have occurred at about −10,000 years, which is generally taken as the point in time ending the Pleistocene Epoch and beginning the Holocene Epoch. However, some specialists in the glacial and related deposits of this area extend the Valderan Substage to −5000 years to include alluvial deposits formed following ice recession.

The above chronology of substages of the Wisconsinan Stage is cited as an example of the actual complexity of the record. If one were to look at similar sequences for other parts of North America he would find a somewhat different set of substages and names for each locality. We should expect to find a reasonable agreement on the existence of substages such as the Farmdalian and Twocreekan on the grounds that a major recession of the continental ice sheet must have affected all areas of equivalent latitude at about the same time. We should also expect the major ice advances to be reflected in all records, although ice lobes may have advanced at different rates and to different limits from one region to another.

## History of the Great Lakes

In North America a major phenomenon of late Pleistocene time was the formation of the Great Lakes, five great interconnected inland bodies of fresh water (Figure 41.5). In terms of surface area, the five lakes rank as follows:

| | sq mi | sq km |
|---|---|---|
| Superior (2) | 31,800 | 82,400 |
| Huron (5) | 23,000 | 59,600 |
| Michigan (6) | 22,400 | 58,000 |
| Erie (12) | 9,900 | 26,000 |
| Ontario (14) | 7,500 | 19,400 |

Numbers in parentheses give ranking among all world lakes in surface area. Lake Superior is second only to the Caspian Sea, which is over five times larger. Elevations and depths of the Great Lakes are shown by a profile in Figure 41.6. Superior has the greatest depth, 1330 ft (370 m); Michigan, Huron, and Ontario are of moderate depths, 800 to 900 ft (240 to 275 m); while by comparison Erie is very shallow, 200 ft (60 m).

In preglacial time, the area of the present Great Lakes was occupied by broad stream-eroded lowlands. Except for the basin of Lake Superior, which is entirely within the Canadian Shield, these lowlands were eroded

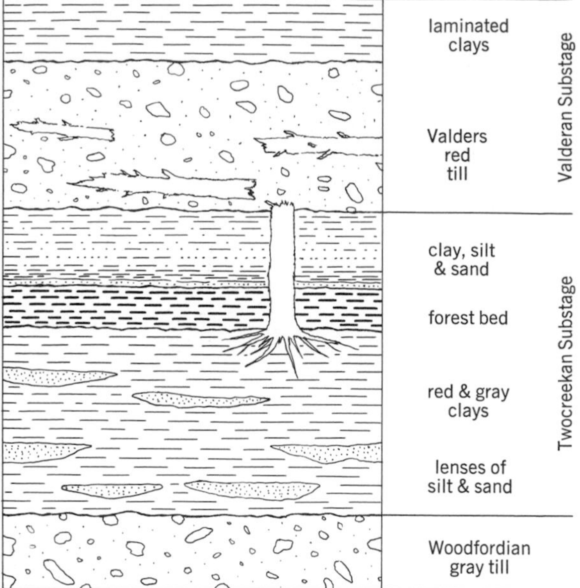


**FIGURE 41.4.** The Two Creeks forest bed, exposed near Manitowoc, Wisconsin, was developed in a substage of mild climate, but was subsequently overridden by ice advance in the Valderan Substage. [After J. L. Hough (1958), *Geology of the Great Lakes,* Urbana, Univ. of Illinois Press, p. 102, Figure 31.]

in weak formations of Paleozoic strata separated by cuestas of more resistant formations. The preglacial lowlands were strongly scoured and considerably deepened by erosive action of successive Pleistocene ice sheets. Debris from the basins provided much of the drift now found in moraine and outwash-plain belts situated south of the Great Lakes.

The Great Lakes came into existence during recessional substages of the Wisconsinan Stage as ice evacuated basins between the ice front and higher ground elevations to the south. Evidence of the existence of these early lakes is found in elevated shorelines, or *strandlines,* marked by beach ridges.

A complicating factor in the history of the Great Lakes has been a downwarping of the earth's crust under the load of glacial ice and a subsequent upwarping following removal of ice load. These effects have been discussed in Chapter 25 in connection with the subject of isostasy and are illustrated by the uplift of the Baltic region in post-glacial time (Figure 25.17). Figure 41.7 is a schematic diagram to illustrate the principle as it applies to the Great Lakes region. In *Phase 1* the crust is shown to be warped down beneath the ice sheet while a proglacial lake lies to the south of the ice front. Wave action in this lake will produce a horizontal strandline. In *Phase 2* the ice front has receded some distance and the crust has risen, warping the first strandline so that it increases in elevation toward the north. In this phase a new horizontal strandline is formed at lake level. In *Phase 3* further ice recession has permitted additional crustal rise, upwarping the strandlines of both the first and second phases.

Figure 41.8 shows elevations of several warped strandlines of northeastern North America. These include marine shorelines as well as lakes. Notice that for Lake Ontario the present elevation of a single strandline is 400 ft (120 m) higher at the northeastern end than at the southwestern end. Degree of warping is less over the western Great Lakes. A dashed line shows the southern limit of warping, or *hinge-line,* which is approximately equivalent to the limit of Wisconsinan ice advance in the New England region.

In the Great Lakes region, several hinge-lines are recognized, as shown in Figure 41.8. These lines refer to lake levels in order of age from south to north. The oldest cuts across Lake Erie, while the youngest cuts across northern Lake Michigan.

Developmental history of the Great Lakes during recessional phases of the ice sheet is extremely complex. We make no attempt here to give a full sequence

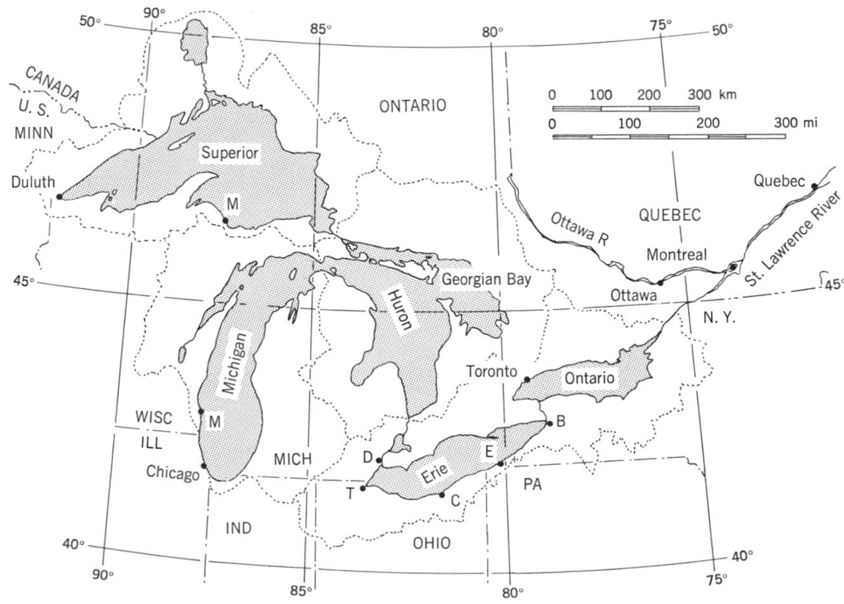


**FIGURE 41.5.** General map of the Great Lakes region. Drainage areas outlined in dotted line. (Based on U.S. Lake Survey charts.)

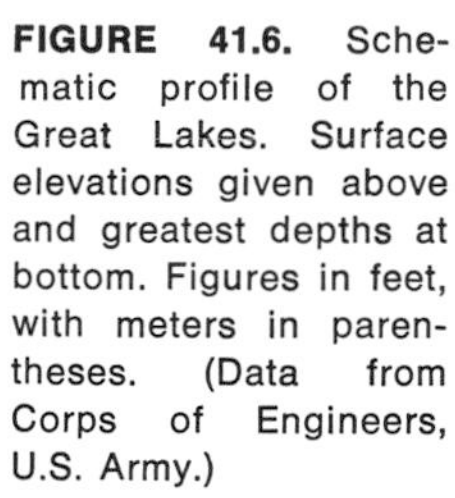

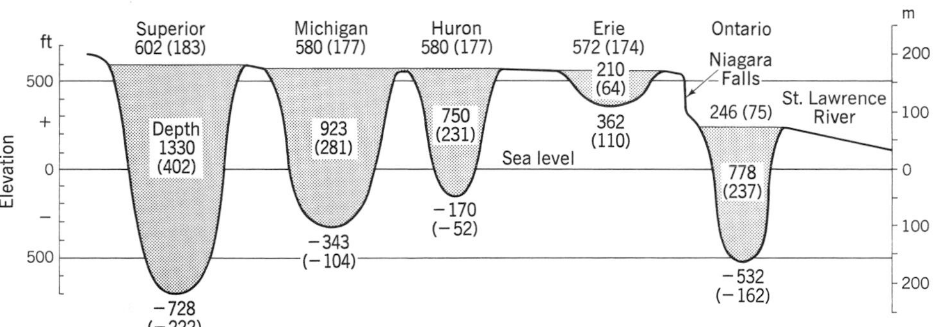


**FIGURE 41.6.** Schematic profile of the Great Lakes. Surface elevations given above and greatest depths at bottom. Figures in feet, with meters in parentheses. (Data from Corps of Engineers, U.S. Army.)

of events, but merely to pick out certain representative and interesting points in time to illustrate the nature of the process. A series of maps in Figure 41.9 shows conditions at these selected points in time.

*Map A* shows conditions between −14,000 and −15,000 years in recessional phases of the Woodfordian Substage. Ice lobes in the basins of Lake Michigan and Lake Erie had receded sufficiently far to form two proglacial lakes, named *Chicago* and *Maumee* respectively. The former drained south by means of the Desplaines River, and the latter drained into the Wabash River. Continued recession (*Map B*) enlarged these lakes, lowering the level of Lake Maumee and allowing it to drain west along the ice front into Lake Chicago. There followed an extensive ice recession interval not shown (Lake Arkona), followed by a readvance (Port Huron). At about −13,000 years the Erie basin was occupied by *Lake Whittlesey* (lower than its predecessor, Lake Maumee), which drained into *Lake Saginaw,* situated in what is now Saginaw Bay of Lake Huron (*Map C*). Lake Saginaw in turn drained into Lake Chicago. There followed a major ice recession, the Twocreekan interval, in which much of the area of the present lake basins was occupied by water and probably drained eastward into the St. Lawrence or Lake Champlain estuaries.

Again the ice advanced. This was the Valderan advance of about −12,000 years, but it did not reach as far as previous advances. Conditions shown in Map C were essentially resumed at the time of maximum Valders advance. Final recession of the ice front now was underway. *Map D* shows conditions later in Valderan time. Ice had receded from the western end of the Lake Superior basin, allowing the formation of *Lake*

**FIGURE 41.7.** Schematic profiles showing crustal warping and strandline deformation accompanying ice retreat. [After R. F. Flint (1957), *Glacial and Pleistocene Geology,* New York, John Wiley & Sons, p. 252, Figure 14.7.]

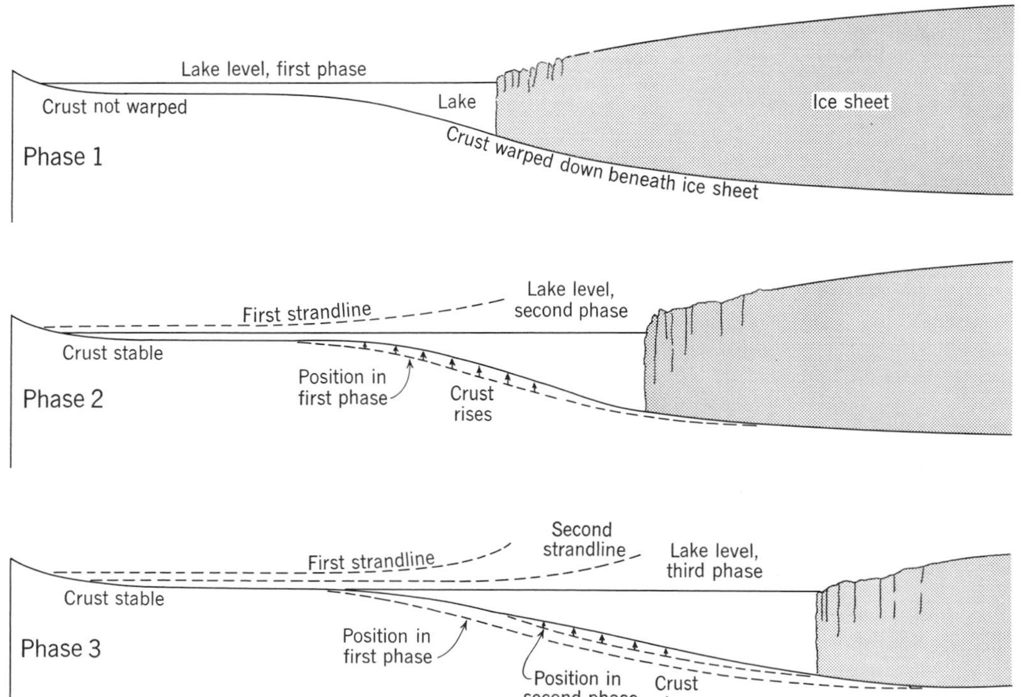

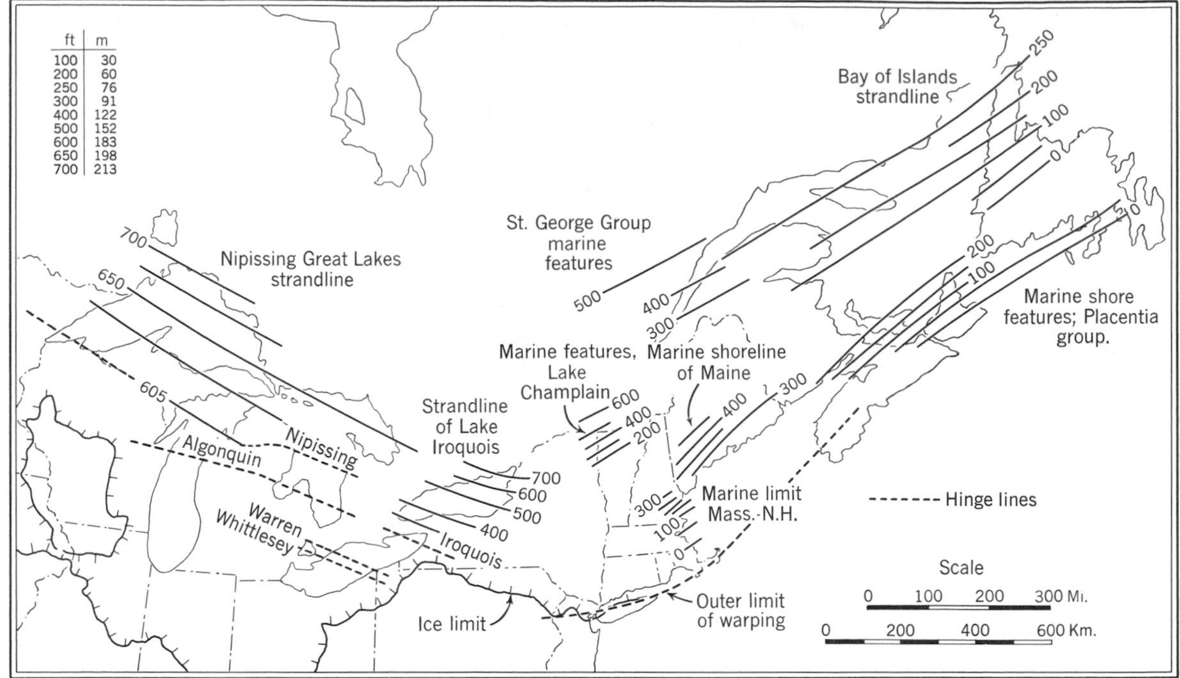


**FIGURE 41.8.** Altitudes of strandlines in eastern North America. Contours (isobases) are in units of feet above sea level. [Modified and simplified from a map by R. F. Flint (1957), *Glacial and Pleistocene Geology,* New York, John Wiley & Sons, p. 251, Figure 14.6. Hinge lines from J. L. Hough (1958), *Geology of the Great Lakes,* Urbana, Univ. of Illinois Press, p. 136, Figure 34.]

*Duluth,* which drained south by way of the St. Croix River. Lakes of the Michigan, Huron, Erie, and Ontario basins were now connected and drainage was eastward through the Mohawk Valley. Note that Huron drained directly into Ontario by means of a channel along the ice front. At about −9000 years, or somewhat earlier, ice recession had opened a northern outlet channel from Georgian Bay of Lake Huron, allowing eastward drainage by way of Lake Nipissing and the Ottawa River into the St. Lawrence estuary (*Map E*).

The opening of this channel initiated an extremely low stage of lake levels, but this was reversed as crustal rebound raised the northern outlet. At about −4000 years, as shown in *Map F,* lake levels had risen again, fusing the three upper lakes into one body (Lake Nipissing), which discharged simultaneously through three outlets—one into Lake Erie, a second by reoccupation of the Chicago outlet, and a third by way of the Ottawa River. Subsequently, because of increased crustal uplift in the north, the northern outlet by way of the Ottawa River was abandoned. Lake levels fell and the Chicago outlet was also abandoned.

## Pluvial lakes of the Pleistocene

One of the nonglacial phenomena correlated with glacial and interglacial stages of the Pleistocene Epoch is the rise and fall of water levels in inland lakes of arid and semiarid regions. Such lakes occupied intermontane basins of the western United States, and, with one exception, had no outlets to the sea. They have been named *pluvial lakes,* the adjective *pluvial* suggesting the increase in depth and extent of the lakes as a result of increased precipitation and reduced evaporation. Figure 41.10 is a map of pluvial lakes of the western United States showing their shorelines when at the maximum stages. Today these basins contain greatly shrunken lakes or are completely dry playas (see Chapter 36). Altogether, about 120 pluvial lakes were in existence in optimum periods of the Illinoian and Wisconsinan glaciations. Many of these overflowed into neighboring lakes of lower elevation.

Largest of the western pluvial lakes was *Lake Bonneville,* of which the present-day shrunken remnant is Great Salt Lake (Figure 41.11). At its maximum extent Lake Bonneville was almost as large in area, 20,000 sq mi (52,000 sq km), as present Lake Michigan and attained a maximum depth of 1000 ft (330 m). At least eight different interpretations of the history of Lake Bonneville have been made since about 1890, when the geologist Grove K. Gilbert published a comprehensive survey of the area. While many of the facts and interpretations which Gilbert put forth are valid today, the additions of evidence have led to increasingly complex histories. A modern interpretation of Bonneville history is shown in Figure 41.12 by means of a time-scaled diagram in which lake surface elevation and average elevation of termini of adjacent valley glaciers are plotted together. It is immediately evident that each rise of lake level is synchronous with an advance of valley glaciers in the nearby Wasatch Mountains. This

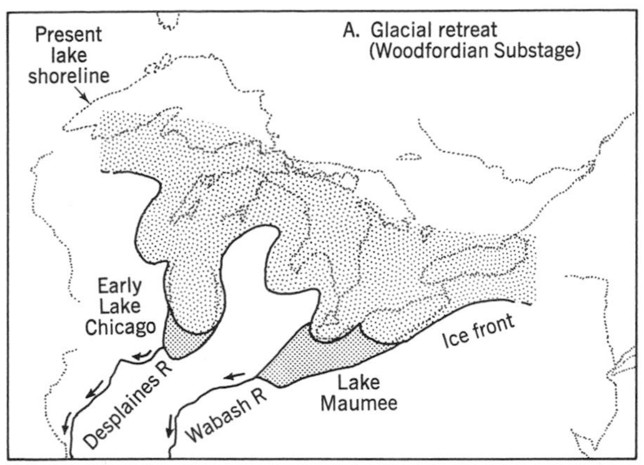


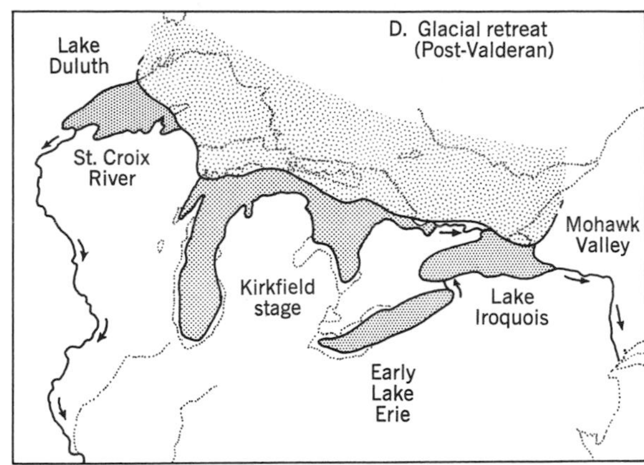


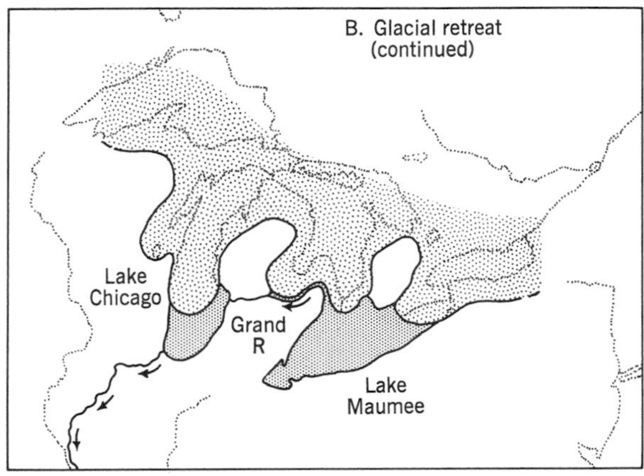


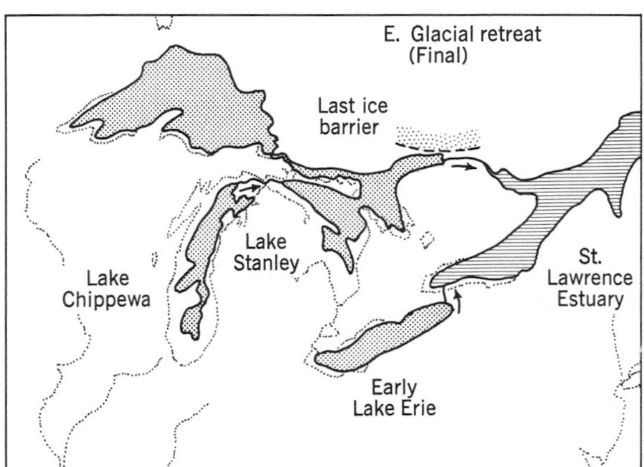


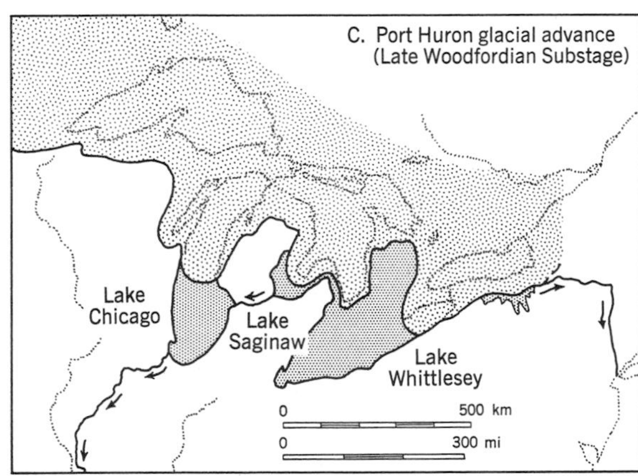


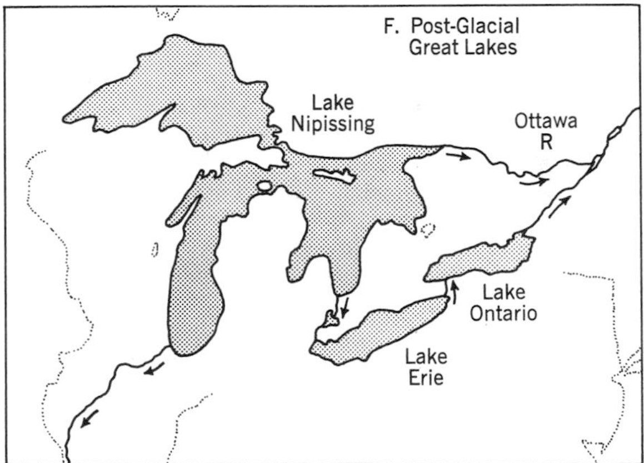


**FIGURE 41.9.** Selected stages in the development of the Great Lakes. (After J. L. Hough, 1958, *Geology of the Great Lakes,* Urbana, Univ. of Illinois Press, pp. 284–296, Figures 54, 56, 60, 69, 73, and 74.)

relationship between glacial maxima and lake level maxima was well established by the early investigators of the pluvial lakes region.

The two oldest pluvial episodes of the Lake Bonneville basin are correlated with the Kansan and Illinoian glaciations, but little is known of their maximum levels. During the Wisconsinan Stage there occurred a major pluvial event, the *Alpine Lake substage,* consisting of perhaps five maxima of lake levels interrupted by low levels. Three of these maxima are shown to coincide with valley-glacier maxima. The Alpine Lake sub-stage seems to correlate in time with ice advances of the Altonian Substage in the central United States (see Figure 41.3). At the maximum height of these cycles of rise,

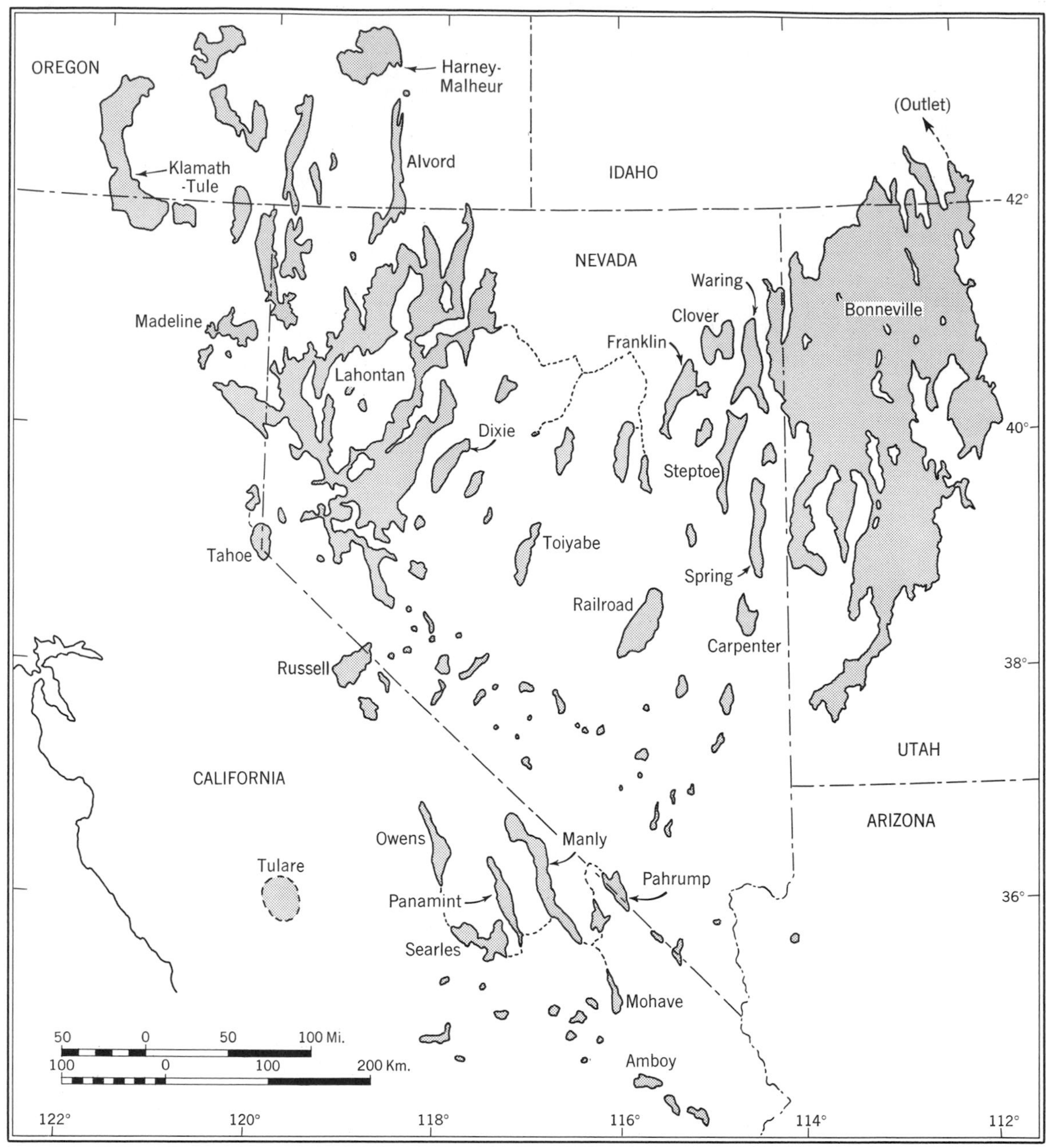


**FIGURE 41.10.** Pluvial lakes of the western United States. Dotted lines are overflow channels. [Based on a map by R. F. Flint (1957), *Glacial and Pleistocene Geology,* New York, John Wiley & Sons, p. 227, Figure 13.2.]

Lake Bonneville overflowed at its north end into a tributary of the Snake River. At this time the highest of the shorelines was cut by wave action. It is now found at an elevation of about 5300 ft (1615 m), or about 1000 ft (330 m) above the present elevation of the lake bed.

The Alpine Lake substage was followed by a dry substage in which the lake diminished to very low levels. An episode of soil formation (Promontory Soil) is associated with this substage, which occurred about between −25,000 and −30,000 years and appears to correlate with the Farmdalian Substage of glacial recession in the central United States.

Again the lake level rose and overflowed through the northern outlet. Two episodes of maximum lake level are recognized within this second pluvial substage, which coincides with glacial advances of the Pinedale glaciation in the Wasatch Mountains (Figure 41.12) and appears to correlate with the Woodfordian Substage in the age range −22,000 to −12,000 years. After the last of the high shorelines had been formed, the lake outlet at the point of overflow was rapidly deepened by erosion in weak alluvial materials and soon reached a bedrock threshold. Wave action at the stabilized lower level cut a prominent shoreline into the mountain slopes

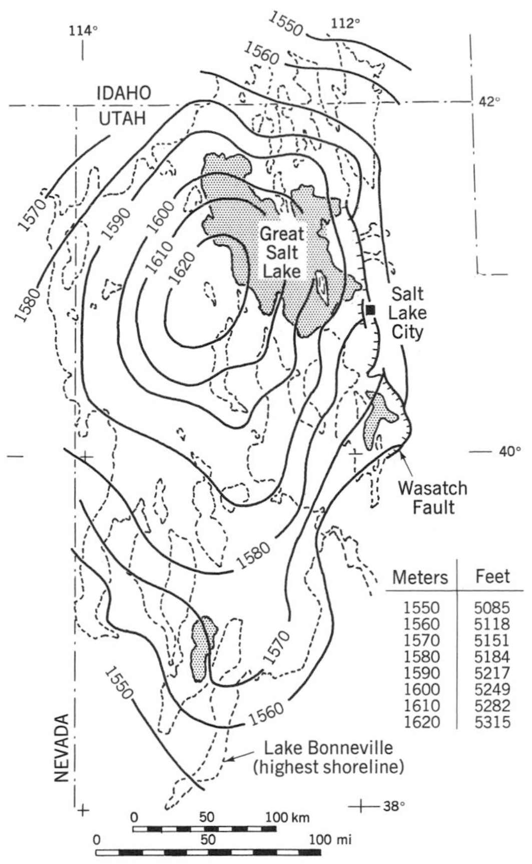


**FIGURE 41.11.** Deformation of the highest shoreline (dashed line) of Lake Bonneville, Utah, shown by elevation contours in meters. [After P. B. King (1965), in *The Quaternary of the United States,* H. E. Wright, Jr. and D. G. Frey, Eds., Princeton, N.J., Princeton Univ. Press, p. 850, Figure 14. Data of M. D. Crittenden, Jr., U.S. Geological Survey.)

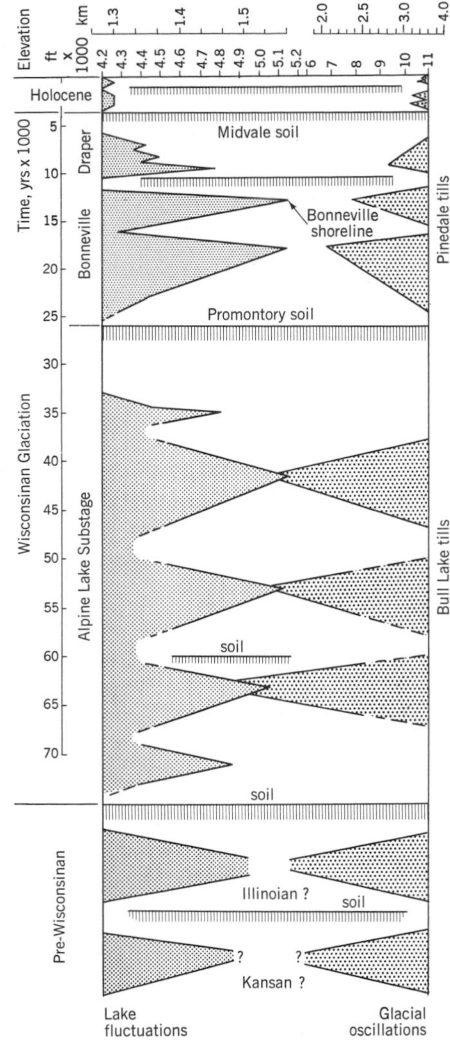


**FIGURE 41.12.** Fluctuations in Lake Bonneville levels (*left*) and corresponding episodes of glacial till deposition in the Wasatch Mountains (*right*). Note that two elevation scales are used. No time scale given for pre-Wisconsinan events. [After R. B. Morrison (1965), in *The Quaternary of the United States,* H. E. Wright, Jr., and D. G. Frey, Eds., Princeton, N.J., Princeton Univ. Press, p. 275, Figure 3.]

(Figure 41.13). This event is known as the *Provo still-stand.*

Again a dry episode occurred, coinciding with the brief Twocreekan Substage of glacial recession at about −12,000 years. There followed a final pluvial stage at about −10,000 years, corresponding with the Valders ice advance in the central United States.

This abbreviated statement of the history of Lake Bonneville does not express adequately the degree of complexity of the record, or the multiplicity of interpretations that have been derived from the ancient shorelines and associated lacustrine deposits. However, this account can serve to illustrate the general pattern of events and the close response of a pluvial lake to glacial and interglacial substages.

As shown in Figure 41.11, the highest shoreline of Lake Bonneville is now upwarped into a broad dome, the result of isostatic crustal rise following disappearance of Lake Bonneville. Similar crustal warpings in progress during the earlier lake history have made the identification of shorelines particularly confusing.

Second largest of the western pluvial lakes was Lake Lahontin (Figure 41.10). At least two periods of existence of a deep lake here are well established, and are marked by elevated shorelines carved into the mountain slopes. Death Valley, in southeastern California, was occupied by Lake Manly. The shoreline of this pluvial lake can be seen sharply marked by a color change along the base of the alluvial fan pictured in Figure 35.25.

## Pleistocene climatic zones and periglacial phenomena

As the Pleistocene ice sheets spread into lower latitudes and average atmospheric temperatures fell to lower levels, climatic zones were pushed equatorward

**FIGURE 41.13.** Former shorelines of glacial Lake Bonneville carved in the mountain base near Provo, Utah. (Photograph by A. K. Lobeck.)

and crowded more closely together. We can infer that the upper-air westerlies extended their influence into lower latitudes and that the subtropical belts of high pressure were also displaced into lower latitudes. As a result, the desert belts migrated to latitudes as low as perhaps 10° to 15°, compressing the wet equatorial climate into a narrow zone. It seems reasonable to conclude that lowered atmospheric temperature would have greatly reduced atmospheric moisture and precipitation generally in low latitudes. As evidence, we find relict landforms of aridity, such as sand dunes and pediments, in what are today areas of tropical forests.

Of particular interest to students of the Pleistocene Epoch are relict forms of arctic climates in unglaciated middle-latitude zones that bordered the southern limits of the ice sheets. Such features are described as *periglacial,* the prefix *peri* meaning "near," and implying that a cold environment existed near the ice sheets. Periglacial features consist of inactive structures or landforms of the kinds now found in the process of formation in tundra regions of the arctic and adjacent to the Greenland Ice Sheet. Examples are ice-wedge fillings, polygonal ground, and stabilized flowage structures produced by solifluction. Inactive talus slopes and boulder fields are other relict periglacial features produced by intensive frost-shattering in a colder climate. These features are described in Chapter 32.

## Pleistocene changes of sea level

One of the most important phenomena of the Pleistocene and Holocene epochs has been the changing of sea level with respect to the continents. Not only have sea-level changes caused the alternate exposure and inundation of continental margins, but also they have had many secondary effects relating to denudation of the continents and sedimentation upon the ocean floors.

It is well to keep in mind that changes of sea level relative to the land have a variety of causes, some of which act on a world-wide basis and others of which act locally. World-wide changes of sea level are related either to changes in the volume of ocean water or in the volume of the ocean basins. These changes are described as *eustatic.* Consider first the possible causes of changes in volume of the ocean basins. One cause is the extrusion of magma in the form of lava flows and volcanic ejecta upon the ocean floors. Another is the gradual accumulation of sediments brought from the lands. A third cause is crustal deformation, whether by tectonic processes of warping and faulting or by isostatic adjustments to the addition or removal of load.

Changes in total volume of ocean water also have more than one possible cause. We have already taken note of the gradual increase of ocean volume throughout geologic time through outgassing of volatiles from the earth's interior. This process acts so slowly that its effects would not be discernible in Pleistocene time.

Changes in water temperature cause water volume changes. It has been estimated that if all ocean water should undergo a temperature rise of 1.8 F° (1 C°) the ocean volume increase would cause a world-wide rise of sea level of 24 in. (60 cm). However, temperature changes of the vast bulk of deep ocean water are not likely to have ranged through more than about 3.6 F° (2 C°) from glaciations to interglaciations, so that eustatic sea level changes due to this cause would probably not exceed about 3 ft (1 m).

By far the most important single cause of ocean volume change in the Pleistocene Epoch has been the alternate accumulation and melting of glacial ice. Amounts of sea level change from this cause can be calculated from known volumes of existing ice masses and from estimates of volumes of former ice sheets. The Antarctic Ice Sheet alone holds sufficient water volume to provide a sea level rise of about 200 ft (60 m), should all of that ice be melted. Assuming that the added load of this water upon the oceanic crust caused an isostatic downwarping of 65 ft (20 m), the net sea level rise would still be about 135 ft (40 m). Estimates of the total sea level rise that would accompany the melting of all existing glacial ice run to 200 ft (60 m), or somewhat higher. The effects of a 200-ft rise of sea level upon the heavily populated lowlands of the Atlantic and Gulf coastal plain have been a favorite theme of journalists and writers, thus they can hardly have escaped the attention of the majority of laymen. Of more interest, scientifically, is the very real lowering of sea level that accompanied each glaciation as enormous ice sheets spread over the continents in middle latitudes.

The record of sea level lowering in the Wisconsinan Stage is now quite well documented by means of radiocarbon dating of samples taken from floors of the continental shelves. The principle is quite simple. Certain types of bottom materials are known to have been produced in very shallow water or at sea level. Examples of such materials are salt-marsh peat, oyster shells, oolites (spherical carbonate particles), corals,

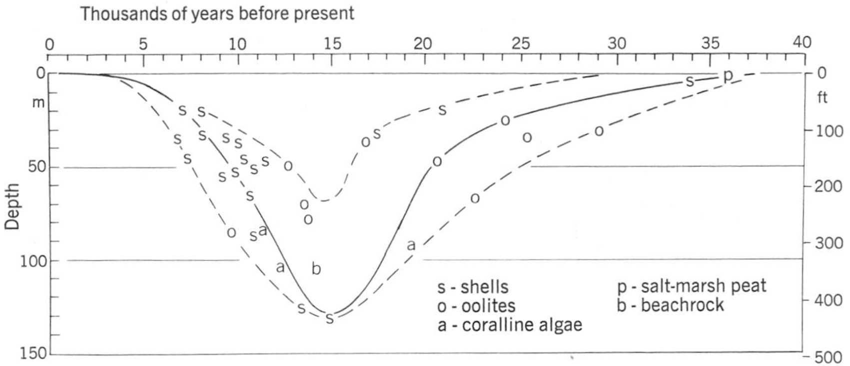


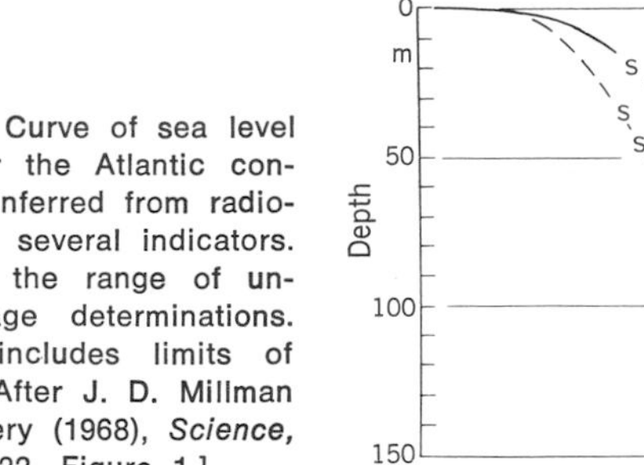
**FIGURE 41.14.** Curve of sea level (solid line) for the Atlantic continental shelf, inferred from radiometric ages of several indicators. Not shown is the range of uncertainty of age determinations. Dashed line includes limits of observations. [After J. D. Millman and K. O. Emery (1968), *Science,* vol. 162, p. 1122, Figure 1.]

algae associated with corals, and beachrock (lithified beach deposits). A radiocarbon date for such a sample establishes the presence of sea level at that time along that bottom contour. Many such dated samples are plotted in a diagram scaled in time units (horizontal scale) and depth (vertical scale) as shown in Figure 41.14. A line is then drawn to express the trend of the points. Various uncertainties exist in the record, including spurious radiometric ages and the possibility that crustal warping occurred during the period of record.

On the Atlantic continental shelf sea level at about −30,000 to −35,000 years stood close to its present position. This was a recessional substage and can be correlated with the Farmdalian Substage (Figure 41.3). Afterward sea level fell gradually until about −20,000 years, then dropped quite rapidly to a low point near −15,000 years. This minimum of −410 ft (−125 m) correlates with maximum ice advances of the Woodfordian Substage. There followed a rapid rise, which gradually tapered off until at −4000 years sea level stood only about 10 ft (3 m) below its present position. The curve of sea level for the same period of the Gulf Coast is essentially similar to that of the Atlantic coast.

Assuming that the order of magnitude of sea-level lowering in the last major glacial advance is at least 325 ft (100 m), we find that the Atlantic continental shelf was exposed out to a distance of 60 to 125 mi (100 to 200 km) beyond the present shoreline off the northeastern United States. To this figure we may add perhaps an additional 100 ft (30 m) of emergence due to isostatic rise in response to removal of water load. The shoreline may have reached a point close to the shelf break. It is interesting to note that analysis of pollen in freshwater peat samples far out upon the shelf indicate presence of a forest vegetation consisting of such trees as fir, spruce, pine, and oak. Teeth of Pleistocene elephants (mastodons and mammoths) have been dredged up from points far out upon the shelf. All of these indications point to the last glacial substage as providing here a vegetated landscape populated with animal life.

Carrying back the curve of sea level changes into earlier stages of the Pleistocene presents many difficulties because of limitations of radiometric age determinations and because the extent of crustal warping is very difficult to evaluate. The important point from the standpoint of geological interpretation is that during the maximum of each glacial stage sea level fell to a point that probably exposed almost the entire width of the continental shelves. Thus during this time wave and current action of the surf zone could have ranged over the entire width of the shelves, and this process, together with processes of fluvial erosion and deposition, are probably largely responsible for shaping the configuration of the shelves. Under this interpretation, the shelf break at about −600 ft (−180 m) is determined by shoreline processes acting at the time of lowest sea levels of the glacial stages and is not merely the outer limit of an embankment of sediments carried across the shelf by bottom currents in depths comparable to those existing today.

**Crustal rise and Pleistocene marine shorelines** Many coastal zones the world over exhibit elevated marine shorelines in the form of wavecut benches, coral reefs, and beach ridges (see Chapter 38). In fact, one might perhaps say that coasts with a history of crustal rise during the Pleistocene and Holocene epochs are the rule rather than the exception. Crustal sinking, producing shorelines of submergence, seems largely to be associated with areas of heavy ice loading.

As explained in Chapter 36, fluvial denudation of the continents must be accompanied by isostatic uplift to compensate for the removal of load. This isostatic uplift may account in part for the progressive rise of continental margins of stable crust. Tectonic processes would be expected to produce uplift of extensive marginal zones of rigid crustal plates, such as those surrounding the Pacific basin.

Whatever the causes of crustal uplift, there is abundant evidence that the eustatic rise and fall of sea level throughout the Pleistocene has been superimposed in many places on a persistent rise of the crust. Successive elevated shorelines, such as those pictured in Figure 38.19, are one manifestation of crustal rise. Along the United States coastal plain are found many less spectacular indications of former higher sea levels. These evidences take the form of low terrace scarps, broad beach ridges, and long narrow swamps occupying what were formerly lagoons behind barrier beaches.

A particularly interesting example of the relationship between glacially controlled eustatic changes of sea level and a rising crust is found in successions of elevated coral reefs. Along the coast of New Guinea at

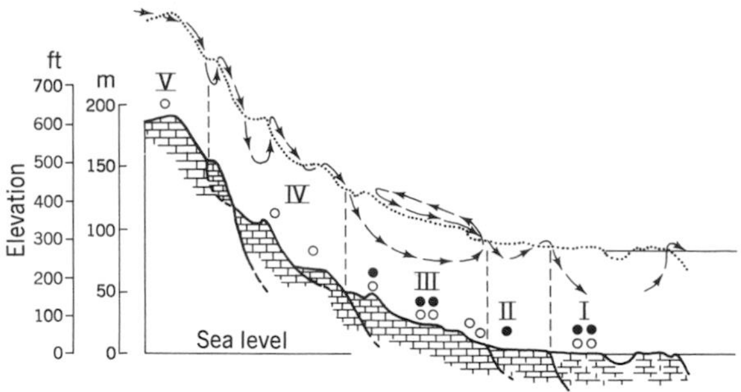


**FIGURE 41.15.** Cross section of coral reef deposits and terraces of northeast New Guinea coast. Arrows on upper profile show inferred positions of shoreline during falling and rising of sea level. Solid circles indicate carbon-14 dates, and open circles, thorium-230 dates. Compare with Figure 41.16. [After H. H. Veeh and J. Chappell (1970), *Science*, vol. 167, p. 863, Figure 1.]

about latitude 6° S., a succession of reef limestones is found from sea level up to an elevation of about 650 ft (200 m) (Figure 41.15). These represent five successive coral reef deposits, each resting upon the eroded surface of the next older deposit. They are designated by numerals from *V* through *I*, the highest numbered being the oldest. Dating of carbonate samples from these old reefs was done by carbon-14 and thorium-230 methods. The oldest reef proved to have an age of about −120,000 years. Figure 41.16 is a corresponding graph in which the elevations and dates are plotted and connected with a curve of sea level rise and fall (upper curve). A straight line indicates the estimated trend of crustal rise. When the crustal rise is subtracted from

**FIGURE 41.16.** Interpretation of data of Figure 41.15. Inferred sea level changes (*above*) are subtracted from estimated uniform crustal rise. Elevation difference (*below*) is attributed to eustatic sea level change. [Data of upper diagram from H. H. Veeh and J. Chappell (1970), *Science*, vol. 167, p. 864, Figure 2.]

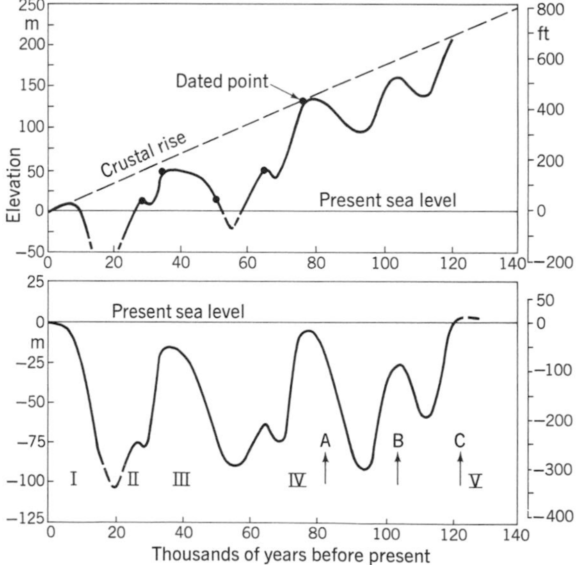


the observed curve heights, a curve of eustatic sea level changes remains (lower curve).

About two years before the results of the New Guinea investigation appeared (1970), similar studies were being carried out by a group of American scientists upon elevated coral reefs on the Island of Barbados, West Indies. Here the dates of three elevated reef terraces were determined by the thorium-230 method and found to be −82,000, −103,000, and −122,000 years from lowest to uppermost. These dates represent three periods of high sea levels. Positions of these dates are shown by capital letters *A*, *B*, and *C* in Figure 41.16. Notice that they correlate rather well with three periods of high sea level in the New Guinea curve.

Yet another type of crustal rise producing a succession of elevated shorelines is that of isostatic rebound of areas formerly depressed under the load of glacial ice and now continuing to rise long after the ice has disappeared. This subject has been discussed at earlier points in this chapter and in Chapter 25. Post-Pleistocene crustal rise of the arctic fringes of North America has resulted in spectacular successions of strandlines, each marked by a single beach (Figure 41.17).

**Sea level changes and fluvial processes** Greatly lowered sea level during glaciations had a strong influence upon the lower courses of major streams draining the continents. As explained in Chapter 36, the relative lowering of baselevel, whether by rise of the earth's crust (epeirogenic uplift) or by fall of sea level (nega-

**FIGURE 41.17.** Upraised marine shorelines bordering the shoreline of Hudson Bay. Snow bands lie in swales between beach ridges. (Photograph by Canadian Government Department of Energy, Mines, and Resources; National Air Photo Library.)

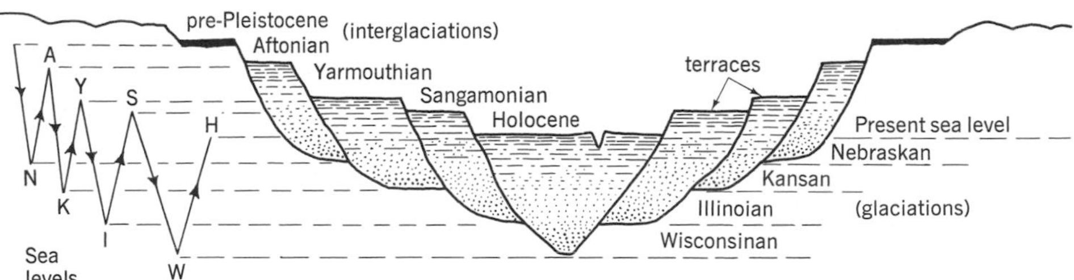


**FIGURE 41.18.** Highly diagrammatic representation of paired terraces and nested alluvial fills resulting from glacial-eustatic sea-level fluctuations superimposed upon persistent crustal uplift. Actual deposits would be fragmentary.

tive eustatic movement), causes a stream to degrade its channel. This action starts at the mouth and progresses upstream, in some cases eventually reaching points far up the tributaries.

Rejuvenation affected all large streams in their lower courses during periods of lowered sea level, causing valley deepening and an extension of the valley across the exposed continental shelf. A particularly good example is the Hudson River, which scoured a channel —in places cut 90 to 120 ft (25 to 37 m) below the floor of the adjacent shelf—across the inner shelf directly southeast of New York Harbor. This channel fed directly into the head of the Hudson Submarine Canyon, which was eroded deeply into the outer edge of the shelf by turbidity currents. Narrow axial channels exist today in the estuaries of the Susquehanna, Delaware, and other Atlantic rivers, representing entrenched courses of those rivers cut in the Wisconsinan and earlier glaciations.

Rising sea level during onset of an interglaciation constituted a rise of a stream's baselevel and brought on aggradation. We can visualize that the continental landscape in broad zones left uncovered by ice recession would have great quantities of loose glacial debris lying unprotected at the surface, perhaps with little or no vegetative cover to hold it in place. Streams draining such a land surface would have carried large quantities of coarse bed load in traction and this material would have been spread over the valley floors by braided streams. As a consequence, the lower courses of valley trenches were filled by gravels and sands. As sea level reached a nearly stable position in the interglaciation, alluvial deposition diminished because of the development of soils and vegetative cover, which hold back coarse debris. Stream deposits now changed to silts and clays. Stream channels became graded and developed the meandering form, along with construction of natural levees in flood stage and the cutoff and filling of oxbows. Such a sequence seems to have been the history of the Lower Mississippi River in its alluvial plain. If we dig beneath the modern floodplain materials we find a thick deposit of well-sorted sands and gravels deposited in the previous phase of rapid aggradation.

Assuming that epeirogenic crustal rise was persistent throughout the Pleistocene, and that each glaciation saw a drawdown of sea level followed by an interglacial high of sea level, we might expect to find a series of alluvial deposits and terraces nested one within the other. Figure 41.18 is a schematic diagram of this sequence of alternate valley erosion and alluvial deposition. Paired terraces mark the limit of aggradation in each interglaciation, while remnants of bedrock valley floors mark the limit of downcutting in glaciations. In order to represent each landform, the width of the valley is shown to be narrowed with each successive cycle. More realistically, the alluvial deposits and terraces of older interglaciations would be largely or entirely removed, but a few remnants might be expected to remain at various points along the valley. A sequence of erosion and deposition, basically similar in plan to that described above, has been unraveled in the valley of the lower Mississippi River and other stream valleys of the Gulf coastal plain.

Closer to the ice margin, and far from base level, streams draining the wasting ice mass aggraded continuously, tending to fill valleys for long distances downstream from the ice front. This aggradation was largely independent of baselevel changes and continued during the entire glaciation. Entrenchment of this alluvial deposit, with the formation of alluvial terraces, occurred in the interglaciations and in post-glacial time, following the details illustrated in Figure 35.26.

## Deep-sea sediments and the Pleistocene record[1]

We have seen that the record of Pleistocene events as read from glacial deposits on the continents is, at best, a fragmentary one. Weathering and erosion have altered or partially removed the older glacial deposits, while the deposits of successive ice advances have partly or largely covered those of earlier advances. Consequently we turn to the one environment in which a continuous and undisturbed depositional record of the Pleistocene can be found—the floors of the deep oceans. It is from the evidence of deep-sea sediment cores that a series of cold and warm episodes can be identified, dated, and perhaps correlated with glaciations and interglaciations. Determination of the age of the Pliocene-Pleistocene boundary seems to have been finally settled from the evidence of the deep-sea cores, bringing to a close a long period of speculation in which a wide spread of ages had been offered.

We shall review the methods and interpretations of deep-sea core analysis carried out by David B. Ericson, Goesta Wollin, and their coworkers at the Lamont-Doherty Geological Observatory of Columbia University, where a great core collection has been accumulated. Interpretation of the deep-sea sediment cores makes use of several forms of data determination progressively from top to bottom within the core,

[1] Based on data of D. B. Ericson and G. Wollin (1968), "Pleistocene Climates and Chronology in Deep-Sea Sediments," *Science*, vol. 162, pp. 1227–1234.

including the following: (1) radiometric age determination of core materials, (2) determination of paleomagnetic epochs, whether normal or reversed, recorded in the sediment layers, (3) determination of the sequences of abundances of microfossils—foraminifera and radiolaria, and (4) determination of lithologic sequences reflecting changes in terrigenous sediment sources.

The nature of deep-sea sediments has been discussed in Chapter 24. Cores suitable for determination of Pleistocene chronology consist of the biogenic-pelagic and pelagic-detrital sediments which have accumulated very slowly in locations far from the continents and free from disturbance by bottom currents (see Table 24.1). The materials in these cores consist partly of terrigenous matter that has settled out from the overlying water body, and partly of the tests of microorganisms which lived in the near-surface zone of the overlying ocean.

In the case of cores taken in low and middle latitudes, the microfossils are almost entirely foraminifera of calcareous composition. The tests of these organisms are coarser than 74 microns diameter, whereas the terrigenous mineral particles are smaller. Consequently a small sample of the core can be washed to remove the fine mineral particles, leaving only the tests for examination. Figures 41.19 and 41.20 show two important kinds of foraminifera that have proved of great value in interpreting water temperatures and hence in discriminating between periods of colder and warmer climates associated with glaciations and interglaciations.

*Globorotalia menardii,* shown in Figure 41.19, has been judged to be an especially sensitive indicator of temperature change. Actually, three subspecies are included within the one named spaces, but these are treated together here. In a particular washed sample of foraminera tests, the numbers of tests of the *G. menardii* complex are counted and the ratio of their number to the total population of foraminfera tests is computed. This ratio can range from almost zero to as high as 10 or 12. A very low ratio is associated with cold water of glacial stages, and a high ratio with warm water of interglacial stages. The words "cold" and "warm" will have different meanings, depending upon latitude of the sample area. (See Figure 14.13 for present-day sea surface temperatures at various latitudes.) For example, for surface water of the Caribbean Sea the present temperature of about 82° F (28° C) is considered "warm," whereas estimated minimum values of around 70° F to (21° C) for glacial stages would be described as "cold." As explained in ensuing paragraphs, oxygen isotope analysis suggests that a range of about 9 to 11 F° (5 to 6 C°) is reasonable for sea surface temperatures from the coldest periods to the warmest periods during the Pleistocene Epoch.

Another valuable climate indicator is *Globorotalia truncatulinoides,* shown in Figure 41.20. In any given core sample some of the tests show a left-hand direction of coiling, and the others a right-hand direction of

**FIGURE 41.19.** Calcareous tests of foraminifera, *Globorotalia menardii,* enlarged about 25 times. (Photograph by D. B. Ericson, Lamont-Doherty Geological Observatory of Columbia University.)

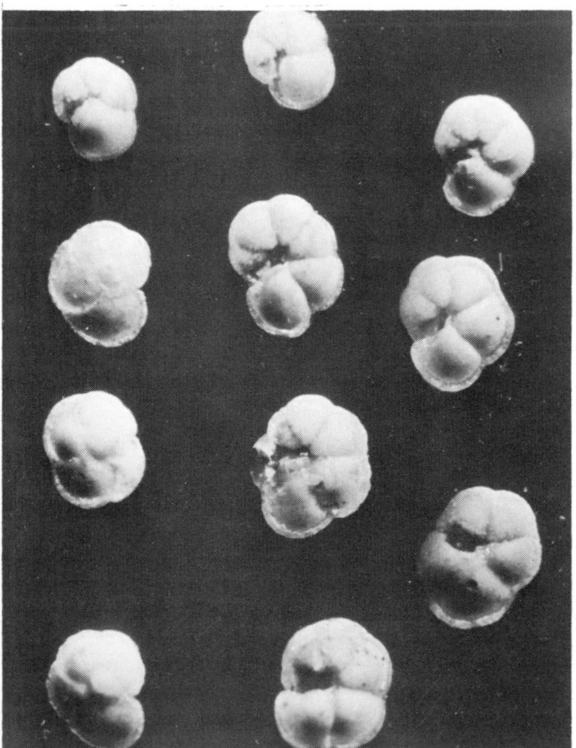

**FIGURE 41.20.** *Globorotalia truncatulinoides.* Left-coiling tests are on the left side, and right-coiling tests are on the right side. Enlargement about 50 times. (Photograph by D. B. Ericson, Lamont-Doherty Geological Observatory of Columbia University.)

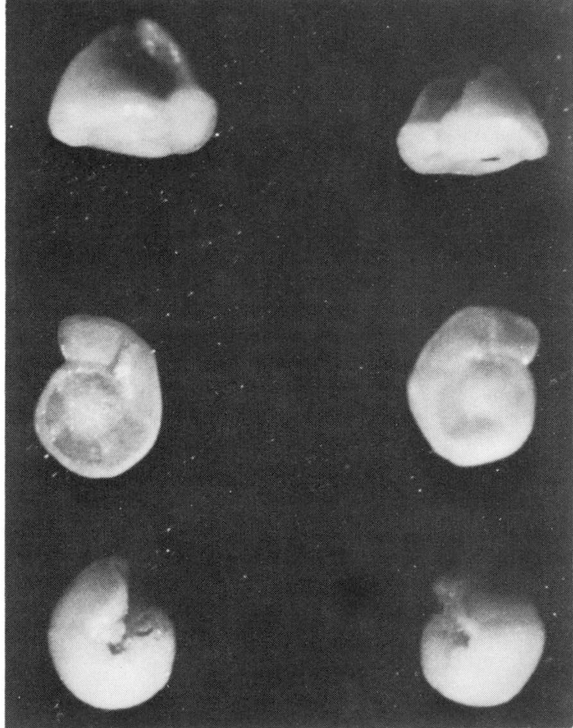

coiling. It has been established that left-coiling tests are dominant in periods of cold climate, while right-coiling tests are dominant in periods of warm climate. Ratios of the two coiling directions are observed to range from almost all left-coiling for cold water to almost all right-coiling for warm water.

Figure 41.21 shows the data of both *G. menardii* abundances and coiling directions of *G. truncatulinoides* for a single deep-sea core. The core was taken at about 25° S. latitude in the South Atlantic Ocean. Tests were counted in small samples taken at distances 4 in. (10 cm) apart along the length of the core. The records of the two forms of data are not in complete agreement, but the general correspondence is good. The data of many such cores must be averaged to establish the glacial and interglacial stages, since there are to be expected many local variations due to controls other than surface sea-water temperatures.

Radiometric ages of core materials can be made by the radiocarbon method, described earlier in this chapter, and by protactinium–ionium, protactinium, and thorium-230 methods. Unfortunately, use of the radiocarbon method does not extend much beyond 40,000 years, while the other methods are limited to about 175,000 years. Consequently, while the foraminifera show a record of temperature changes throughout the entire Pleistocene Epoch and into the Pliocene Epoch, the assignment of ages to the first three glaciations and to the Pliocene-Pleistocene boundary was for many years based on pure extrapolation and led to quite a wide range of figures. Estimates for the start of the Pleistocene Epoch have ranged from −300,000 years to −1.5 million years.

A dramatic improvement in dating of Pleistocene events was achieved in about 1966 by application of paleomagnetic polarity analysis to deep-sea cores. The determination of normal and reversed epochs of polarity has been explained in Chapter 25, along with the extension of this analysis to sediment in ocean bottom core samples (Figure 25.29).

There remained only the need to establish the points of polarity reversals within the cores for which foraminiferal data had already been obtained. Having independently established on the continent the radiometric dates for each polarity reversal, the entire record of any given deep-sea core can be given an age-scale. Figure 41.22 shows the paleomagnetic age scale applied to the Ericson-Wollin general curve of water temperature fluctuations based on the foraminifera abundances and coiling directions in many cores. Glaciations and interglaciations are shown with ages for the entire Pleistocene Epoch. Particularly surprising was the finding that the onset of the first glaciation occurred before the start of the Olduvai event at −1.8 m.y. Thus the beginning of the Pleistocene Epoch was pushed further back in time than had been called for by any earlier estimates.

Establishment of the Pliocene-Pleistocene time boundary is now based upon several criteria besides that of water temperature change. One criterion is the extinction of a distinctive group of planktonic organisms, the *Discoasteridae,* which secreted six-rayed star-shaped skeletal elements known as *discoasters.* This extinction occurred between −2.0 and −1.8 m.y. Other criteria relate to changes in the species and abundances of various foraminifera. Particularly important is

**FIGURE 41.21.** Interpretation of foramifera of a single deep-sea core (V 16-39) from the South Atlantic at about lat. 25° S., long. 5° W. Paleomagnetic polarity scale was determined from the core sediments. [After D. B. Ericson and G. Wollin (1968), *Science,* vol. 162, pp. 1231 and 1233, Figures 5 and 6.]

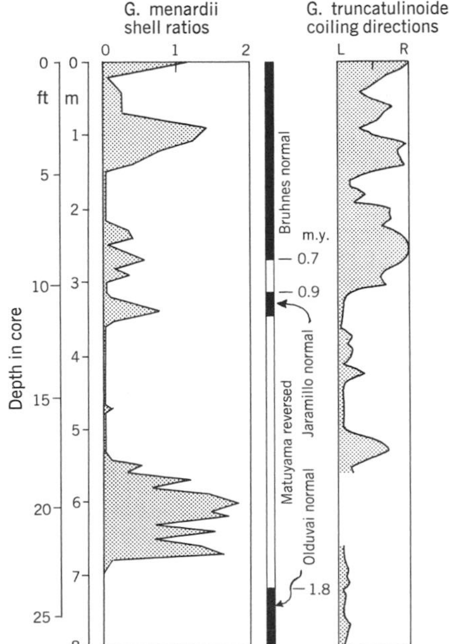


**FIGURE 41.22.** Generalized curve of ocean-water temperatures interpreted from data of foraminifera in deep-sea cores. [After D. B. Ericson and G. Wollin (1968), *Science,* vol. 162, p. 1233, Figure 7.]

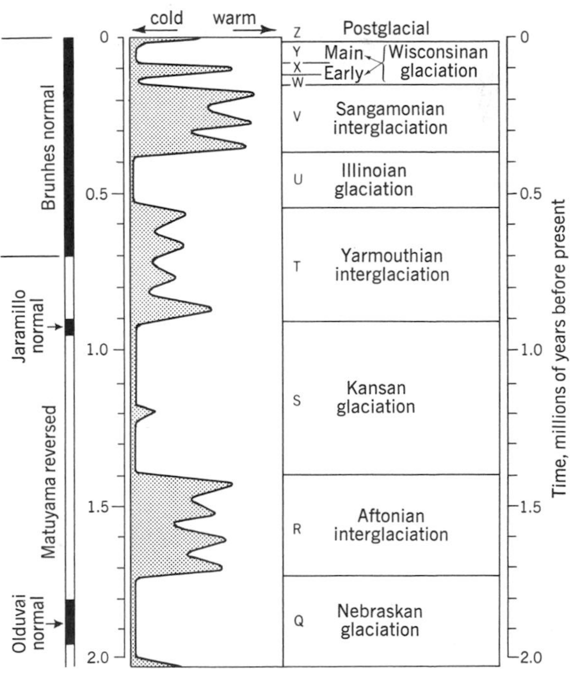

the first appearance of *Globorotalia truncatulinoides* at about −2.0 m.y., an event that has been proposed as a mark for the start of the Pleistocene Epoch.

Independent evidence for the start of the Pleistocene Epoch at about −2.0 m.y. has come from a study by James D. Hays, also of the Lamont-Doherty Geological Observatory. At a particular point in deep-sea cores of the Antarctic region—where the sediment changes from red clay to a diatom ooze—there is a marked change in the radiolarian faunas. According to the paleomagnetic scale, the point of change falls near the base of the Olduvai event. The faunal change is interpreted as marking the Pliocene-Pleistocene boundary and correlates closely with core data from middle and low latitudes.

Although final acceptance of the Pleistocene time scale based upon deep-sea cores must await further corroboration and may require some adjustments, the present indications are favorable to adoption of this time scale and the establishment of the Pliocene-Pleistocene boundary at close to −2.0 m.y. From the presence of ice-rafted glacial materials in cores of the southern Indian Ocean there is evidence of continental glaciation in progress as far back as −4.0 m.y. This debris probably came from Antarctica. The presence of an enormous ice sheet on Antarctica would be expected then, as now, in a time when the other continents were free of ice sheets.

Arctic deep-sea cores, taken from ice island T-3, show records of magnetic polarity reversal epochs back to more than −6.0 m.y. A marked change from brown clay to glacial-marine sediment was found in 1968 at a point in time judged to be about −4.0 m.y. This finding suggests that Northern Hemisphere glaciers came into existence at that time. The possibility of extending the onset of the Pleistocene Epoch to −4.0 m.y., if the presence of glaciers is to be the sole criterion for this time boundary, is thus suggested by the data from both arctic and antarctic oceans.

## Oxygen isotopes and paleotemperatures

Independent evidence of ocean-water temperature changes comes from an analysis of the ratio of abundances of isotopes of oxygen. (Refer to Chapter 23 for an explanation of isotopes.) In addition to the common form, *oxygen-16,* there exist two heavier oxygen isotopes, *oxygen-17* and *oxygen-18.* In 1947 Harold C. Urey reasoned that because the ratio of oxygen-18 to oxygen-16 in ocean water depends partly upon water temperature, the ratio of those isotopes in the carbonate shell matter of marine organisms should reflect the surrounding water temperature at the time that matter was secreted. Changes in water temperature should be reflected in changes in the oxygen isotope ratio. Through improvement in laboratory techniques it became possible in ensuing years to measure very small differences in oxygen-isotope ratios and to interpret these differences in terms of a relative tem-

**FIGURE 41.23.** (*A*) Paleotemperature curve based on oxygen-isotope ratios. [After C. Emiliani (1966), *Science,* vol. 154, p. 853, Figure 5.] (*B*) Curve of incoming solar radiation, scaled in equivalent latitude of present value at 65° N. [After A. Van Woerkom (1953), in *Climate Change,* Cambridge, Mass., Harvard Univ. Press, p. 147.] (*C*) Generalized climate curve based on data of foraminifera in deep-sea cores. [After D. B. Ericson and G. Wollin (1968), *Science,* vol. 162, p. 1233, Figure 7.]

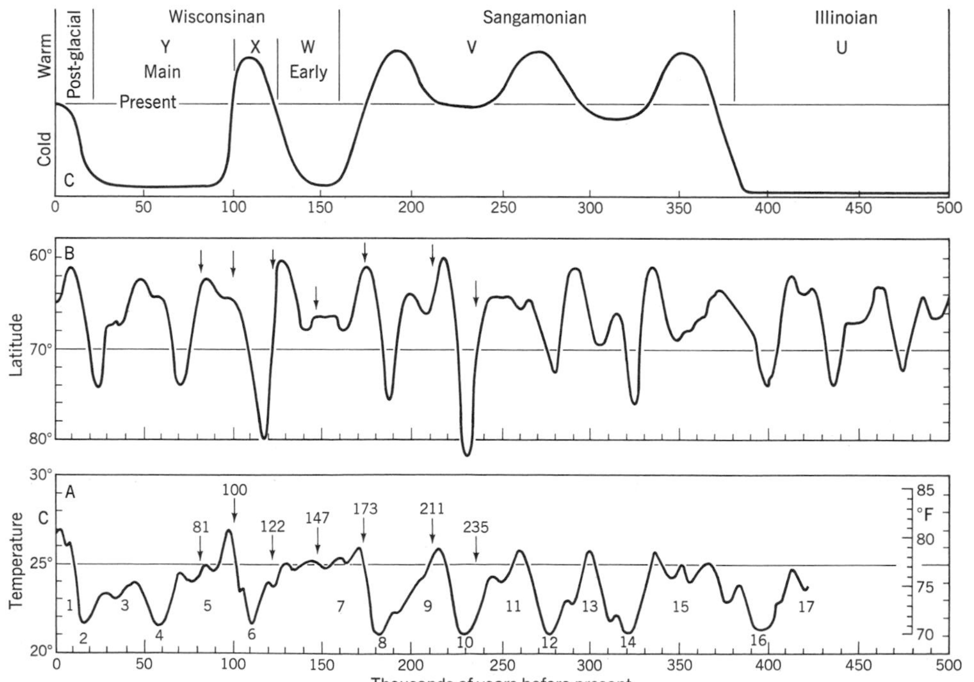

perature scale. Because other factors influence the isotope ratio, an absolute temperature scale cannot be applied, but the presence of temperature fluctuations and the magnitude of their range can be determined.

The oxygen-isotope method was applied to foraminifera tests by Cesare Emiliani, who had begun his research under Urey's direction. Oxygen-isotope ratios were determined at intervals along the lengths of deep-sea cores. Figure 41.23 shows Emiliani's 1966 temperature curve, scaled in *isotopic* temperature, which should be regarded as giving a close approximation to the actual surface water temperature. Above the Emiliani curve is a curve of solar radiation changes due to astronomical causes, referred to in later paragraphs of this chapter. The isotopic temperature curve is compared with the "warm–cold" climatic curve obtained by Ericson and Wollin in the manner explained in preceding paragraphs. The two curves are obviously very different. The oxygen-isotope curve shows a large number of short-term temperature fluctuations that are not shown in the Ericson climatic curve based upon his evaluation of foraminifera distributions. The Emiliani curve includes nine warm periods in the past 450,000 years—these are given odd integer numbers from 1 through 17 in Figure 41.23. Alternate cold periods are marked by prominent low points in the curve (even numbers). Radiometric dates of core material were used to establish ages as far back as about −170,000 years, but beyond that point age is estimated by extrapolation, assuming a uniform rate of sediment accumulation.

Emiliani concludes that instead of the supposed four glaciations, there was a considerably larger number of glaciations. He estimates that about 14 climatic cycles, each representing a glaclation and an interglaciation, occurred following the last reversal of magnetic polarity (about −700,000 years), and that there were 20 such glacial cycles in the past 1.0 m.y. Independent evidence of the occurrence of several stages of high sea level coinciding approximately with the peaks of higher temperature are cited by Emiliani in support of the validity of his curve. These high sea levels are shown by arrows in Figure 41.23. This subject, and that of the relationship of astronomical cycles to temperature cycles, are discussed in later paragraphs.

Although both Emiliani and Ericson's group have worked from similar deep-sea cores, their different methods of data analysis have led to very different conclusions concerning both numbers of glaciations and ages in the older parts of the record. Emiliani has stated his reasons for considering the relative abundance of *Globorotalia menardii* as derived by Ericson to be invalid as an indicator of paleotemperatures.

That the interpretations of two highly qualified groups of investigators should disagree to such a large extent may prove disconcerting to those who ask scientists for a set of unimpeachable interpretations of the world around them. Despite the advances of basic science, controversies such as this will not diminish in frequency. Each difference will, however, be settled in due time as the weight of evidence from new information dictates a conclusion.

A particularly interesting and informative application of the oxygen-isotope method has been to sample the isotope ratios in a core taken from the Greenland Ice Sheet and thereby to estimate atmospheric temperatures back as far as 100,000 years. In 1966 scientists of the U.S. Army Cold Regions Research and Engineering Laboratory drilled through the entire Greenland Ice Sheet, obtaining a core of ice for study. Oxygen-16/oxygen-18 ratios were measured from about 1600 ice samples over the core length, which is about 4600 ft (1400 m).

Atmospheric temperature at the time of the formation of snow is reflected in the concentration of oxygen-18. As snow layers accumulate and are buried to produce glacial ice, the deposit of a given year moves to progressively greater depths as well as outward from the center of the ice sheet. Although there is no effective method as yet for determining the age of the ice at points deep in the core, age can be estimated on the basis of certain assumptions concerning rates of ice accumulation and glacier flowage.

The result of this isotope analysis, reported in 1969 by a group of Danish and American scientists, is an interesting isotope-ratio curve for the past 100,000 years, corresponding with the Wisconsinan Glaciation and the Sangamonian Interglaciation (Figure 41.24). Plotted in the same diagram is the Emiliani paleotemperature curve for Caribbean Sea cores, as well as a

**FIGURE 41.24.** Climatic record shown by oxygen-isotope ratios in an ice core extracted from the Greenland Ice Sheet near Camp Century. Data are compared with record of ice advances and retreats in Great Lakes region (*center*) and with the Emiliani isotope paleotemperature curve (*right*). [After W. Daansgaard, and others (1969), *Science,* vol. 166, p. 380, Figure 5.]

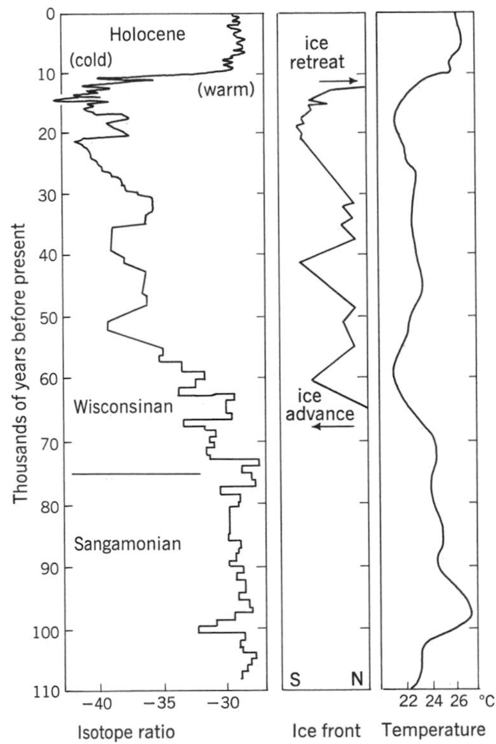

graph of glacial advances and retreats in the Great Lakes region as documented by carbon-14 dates. The oxygen-isotope ratios in the ice core show a good general correlation with glaciations and interglaciations. The sudden rise in atmospheric temperature at −10,000 years is particularly striking. In a later section of this chapter the temperature fluctuations of the last 10,000 years, or Holocene Epoch, will be considered in detail, for it is in this age range that the age of the ice in the core is most accurately estimated.

## Basic causes of continental glaciation

We know that glaciation has occurred a number of times in the geologic past. One of the best documented is the Permo-Carboniferous glaciation, from which there remains lithified glacial till, including striated and faceted stones and a striated surface of older rock upon which the indurated till rests. The hypothesis that this glaciation occurred while the Gondwana continent remained intact and was centered over the South Pole has been discussed in Chapter 29. Good geologic evidence is also available of glaciation in earliest Cambrian time. Any theory of glaciations must therefore account for occasional and seemingly sporadic repetitions of glaciation throughout all recorded geologic time.

A general requirement of glaciation is a lowering of the earth's average atmospheric temperature along with sustained or increased levels of precipitation. It is well established by world-wide evidence that during the Pleistocene Epoch the *snow line* (elevation above which snowbanks remain throughout the year) was lowered in elevation by about 200 ft (600 m) in equatorial latitudes and by 3000 to 4000 ft (900 to 1200 m) in middle and high latitudes. This world-wide phenomenon clearly indicates a generally colder climate for the earth as a whole at times of glaciation. This conclusion is strongly reinforced by the data of deep-sea cores. A reduced average temperature would, in general, reduce rates of ablation at those places where snow could accumulate in large quantities, thus causing growth of glacial ice bodies.

Another requirement of ice-sheet growth is that there be present an elevated landmass—a plateau or mountain range—favorably situated to receive snowfall derived from cyclonic storms into which maritime air masses are drawn (see Chapter 19). Low-lying continental plains would not be likely to accumulate enough snowfall to initiate ice-sheet growth, even if the climate were sufficiently cold.

Favorable topographic conditions are found in Greenland and Antarctica, where ice sheets exist today, and in the Labrador Highlands, the northern Cordilleran Ranges, Scandinavia, the Urals, and the southern Andes, where Pleistocene icecaps grew. Once formed, a small icecap might be expected to grow into a large ice sheet, the ice body itself functioning as a highland to induce the necessary orographic precipitation. Now, we know that Pliocene and early Pleistocene times saw great orogenic and volcanic activity, resulting in growth of mountain ranges. Epeirogenic upwarping of large parts of the more stable continental shields also occurred at this time. It is therefore reasonable to suppose that general uplift of the continents on a world-wide basis created topographic conditions favorable to the growth of Pleistocene ice sheets.

Assuming a favorable global topography, what mechanisms can be invoked for repeated cycles of atmospheric cooling and warming?

**Solar-topographic hypothesis** A supposed change in rate of output of solar energy has provided the basis for several hypotheses of glaciation. Although minor fluctuations are observed in incoming radiation, we do not as yet have evidence of any long-range trend of change in its value, hence the concept of a solar constant of 2 langleys per minute remains essentially valid. As noted in Chapter 13, the use of earth satellites to measure solar radiation beyond the limits of the earth's atmosphere may yield valuable new information. There is as yet no reason to doubt the constancy of the sun's energy output for the span of geologic time in which glaciations have left a record. We can, nevertheless, speculate that reductions of the sun's energy output have occurred and that the planetary temperature was correspondingly lowered, bringing on the growth of ice sheets.

When the hypothesis of fluctuation in solar-energy output is combined with the topographic effect of uplift of mountain and plateau areas in late Cenozoic time, there results an explanation of ice-sheet growth and disappearance that can be labeled the *solar-topographic hypothesis.* In essence, the hypothesis states that formation of highlands created a favorable topographic configuration for ice-sheet development, but that fluctuations in the sun's energy output, causing world-wide atmospheric temperature changes, governed the actual growth and disappearance of ice sheets.

In the complete absence of any time schedule of variations in solar radiation, should such variations have occurred, no further development of this hypothesis is possible.

**The astronomical hypothesis** A different approach to the possibility of variations in *insolation,* the intensity of solar energy received at the earth's surface, has been to invoke systematic changes in geometrical relations of the earth's axis and orbit known through astronomical observations.

Referring back to Chapters 1 and 2, we note that the precession of the equinoxes involves a 26,000-year cycle through which the axis completes a 360-degree change in orientation. Also mentioned is a precession of aphelion and perihelion in a cycle of 108,000 years duration. With respect to the equinoxes, the combined effect of both precessions is a cycle of 21,000 years. This means that every half-cycle (10,500 years) perihelion will coincide with summer in the opposite hemisphere, hence that a point in the middle or high latitudes will receive more intense insolation in summers coinciding with perihelion, less in summers coinciding with aphelion (the latter is the case today in the Northern Hemisphere). In addition, the eccentricity of the earth's orbit varies slightly in a cycle of about 92,000 years. The combined effects of precession and changes in eccentricity of orbit upon relative distance

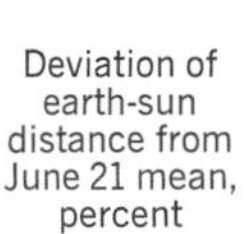


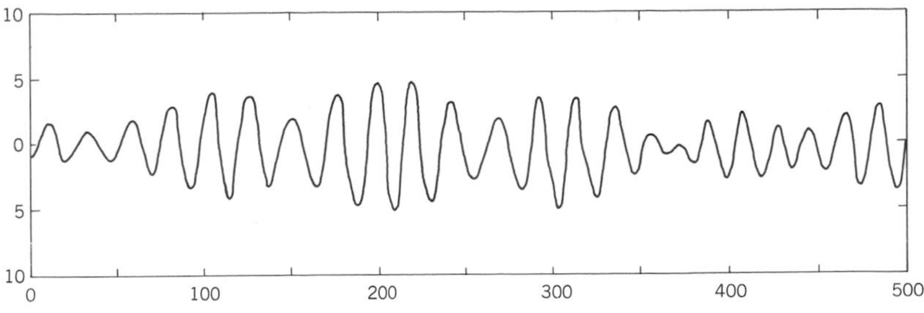


**FIGURE 41.25.** Changes in earth–sun distances due to precessional and eccentricity cycles over the past 500,000 years. [From W. Broecker and J. van Donk (1970), *Reviews of Geophysics,* vol. 8, p. 188, Figure 9.]

of earth from sun during summer solstice are shown in Figure 41.25.

There exists also a 40,000-year cycle of variation in the inclination of the earth's axis with respect to the plane of the ecliptic. This cycle is shown in Figure 41.26. Note that an increased tilt angle correspondingly increases summer insolation at middle and high latitudes.

When the effects of the two curves are combined in certain selected ratios it is possble to calculate variations in summer insolation at various latitudes and to translate this information into a temperature scale. Figure 41.23 shows one such curve scaled in equivalent latitude of existing insolation for the past 500,000 years. Because of the extreme precision of astronomical measurements, the age scale on this curve has a high order of accuracy. This type of curve is sometimes referred to as the *Milankovitch curve,* after the astronomer who first calculated the curves of variation. Also shown in Figure 41.23 is Emiliani's 1966 paleotemperature curve based on oxygen-isotope ratios. Recall that the age scale of this curve is largely extrapolated beyond −170,000 years from dates in the early part of the record. The extent to which a correlation exists between the two curves is largely a matter of opinion.

The Milankovitch curve has been used as the basis for an *astronomical hypothesis* of the cause of glaciation, based on the simple assumption that reduced summer insolation and air temperatures in middle latitudes triggered off glaciations, whereas increased insolation set off deglaciations. Because of the great difficulty of correlating the Milankovitch curve with Pleistocene events, and in view of doubts as to the sufficiency of the mechanism to initiate and terminate glaciation, the astronomical hypothesis long lacked wide general support. However, in 1966 it was revived by Wallace S. Broecker of Columbia University in an attempt to improve the effectiveness of the explanation. A revision by Broecker and J. van Donk followed in 1970.

Broecker and van Donk use a revised curve of Northern Hemisphere summer insolation based on calculations made in 1968 (Figure 41.27). The vertical scale in langleys per day gives the difference between insolation received at the specified latitude at summer solstice and the present daily value (900 ly/day at 45° N., 845 ly/day at 55° N., 775 ly/day at 65° N.). The greatest variations of the curve thus represent departures of about ±5% from present values.

The insolation cycle has a dominant period of about 20,000 years, but there is superimposed a longer cycle, averaging about 80,000 to 90,000 years, in which unusually high insolation peaks occur. Broecker and van Donk associate these high insolation peaks with rapid terminations of glaciations, since more rapid ice ablation is to be expected with warmer summers. During times of reduced summer insolation, ice sheets would tend to grow in volume. Ice volume increase takes place over a relatively long glaciation, but is terminated very rapidly. Terminations are shown by Roman numerals in Figure 41.27. Notice that terminations *I* through *IV* coincide with exceptional insolation maxima, whereas termination *V* does not. By increasing the Emiliani time scale 25%, Broecker and van Donk find a good correlation between oxygen-isotope paleotemperatures and the insolation cycle. Figure 41.28 summarizes their 1970 chronology—summer insolation variations, sea-level changes, and oxygen-isotope ratios are correlated for the past 140,000 years. Termination *II* occurred at about −130,000 years, giving an exceptionally high sea level (Barbados *C*). There followed two secondary cycles of ice growth represented by high sea levels (Barbados *B* and *A*). Then, at about −80,000 years, a major glaciation set in with increasing ice volume, culminating in the late Wisconsinan maximum at about −20,000 years.

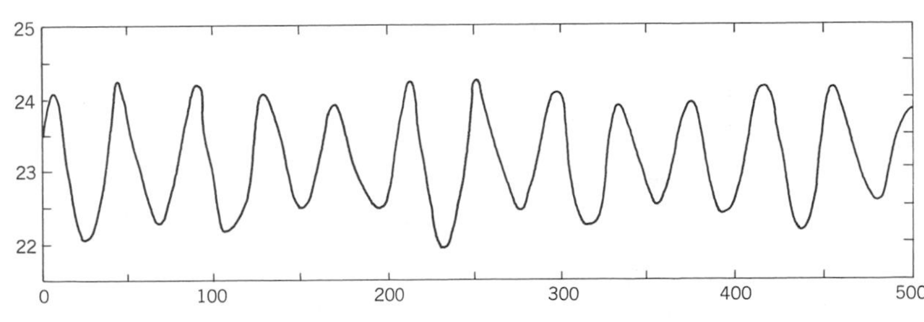


**FIGURE 41.26.** Changes in tilt of the earth's axis with respect to ecliptic during the past 500,000 years. [From W. Broecker and J. van Donk (1970), *Reviews of Geophysics,* vol. 8, p. 188, Figure 9.]

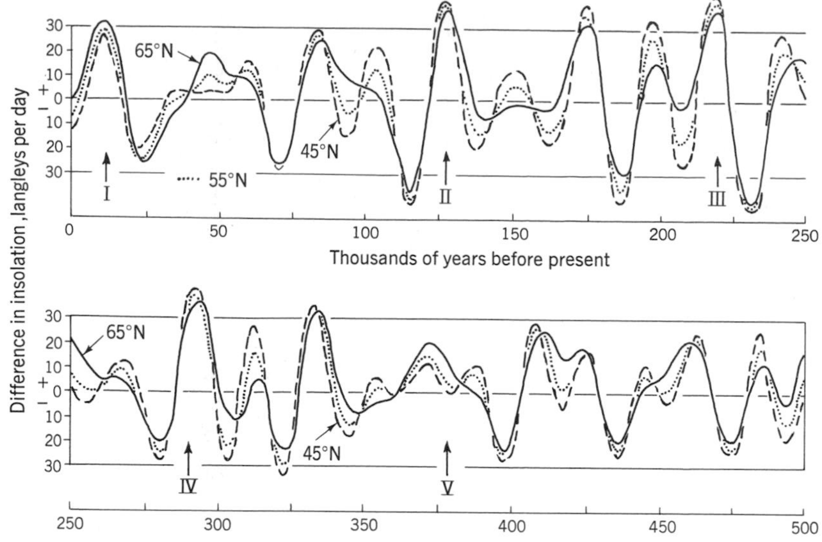


**FIGURE 41.27.** Fluctuations in summer daily isolation at three northern latitudes over the past 500,000 years based upon calculations made by A. D. Vernekar, 1968. The zero value represents the present solstice insolation for latitude 65° N. [From W. Broecker and J. van Donk (1970), *Reviews of Geophysics,* vol. 8, p. 190, Figure 10.]

Termination *I* followed abruptly at −11,000 years, bringing the Wisconsinan glaciation to a rapid close.

**Hypotheses of atmospheric changes** A widely supported hypothesis, relatively simple in concept, attributes world-wide temperature drop and ice-sheet growth to a decrease in the carbon dioxide content of the atmosphere. The average content (about 0.033 percent by volume), variations in content, and importance of carbon dioxide have been discussed in Chapters 12 and 13. Along with water vapor, carbon dioxide is an important gas in causing the greenhouse effect, in which terrestrial radiation is absorbed in the lower atmosphere and the average air temperature is thereby considerably increased over what it would be without these gases.

Estimates have been made to show that if the carbon dioxide content of the atmosphere were reduced to half of the existing quantity, the earth's average surface temperature would drop by about 7 F° (4 C°), enough to bring on the growth of ice sheets under favorable topographic conditions. Reduction of atmospheric carbon dioxide could occur through increased production of carbonate sediments (lime muds, limestones, coral reefs) in the world's oceans, but such a change would be relatively permanent in comparison with the rapid climate fluctuations shown by the records of glaciations.

The rapid growth of forests would be expected to withdraw carbon dioxide from the atmosphere, causing an initial drop in temperature. This process might also be rapidly reversed by disappearance of plant cover and consequent release of carbon dioxide to the atmosphere. It has been pointed out that the amount of carbon dioxide held in solution in sea water would increase as the water became colder, hence that a trend toward reduced atmospheric carbon dioxide would be self-perpetuating and would continue until the necessary drop in atmospheric temperature was achieved.

Whether or not the fluctuation in carbon dioxide is adequate to control glaciation, under any hypothesis its effect in reinforcing temperature fluctuation due to other controls must be taken into account.

Also involving change in atmospheric composition is the hypothesis of glaciation brought about by increase in quantity of volcanic dust in the upper troposphere. Should there be an episode of unusually great volcanic activity, the greatly increased atmospheric dust would reflect back into space a greater part of the incoming solar radiation, thus reducing the quantity of solar energy received at the earth's surface and consequently lowering the average atmospheric temperature. Reductions in quantity of solar radiation received at the ground have been observed for short periods immediately following great volcanic eruptions. Nevertheless, it is doubtful that volcanic eruptions have occurred on the scale needed to produce the growth of ice sheets. Moreover, periods of exceptional volcanic activity have not been shown to be correlated with periods of glaciation.

**Ewing-Donn hypothesis of glaciation** An explanation of the growth and disappearance of ice sheets of the Pleistocene Epoch was put forward by Maurice Ewing and William L. Donn of the Lamont-Doherty Geological Observatory in 1956 and considerably modified in 1966. It is based upon considerations of the energy and moisture balances affecting the atmosphere and oceans. Whereas the hypotheses of variations in solar radiation, insolation, and atmospheric composition provide only explanations of possible initial atmospheric temperature changes, the Ewing-Donn hypothesis provides a complete picture of ice-sheet growth and decay in relation to air and sea-surface temperatures, flux of water vapor, air masses, and the nourishment of the ice by precipitation.

It is first necessary to call upon polar wandering to bring the continents and oceans into essentially their present locations with respect to the poles. (This subject is discussed in Chapter 26.) Arrival of the Arctic Ocean basin and its surrounding continental masses in

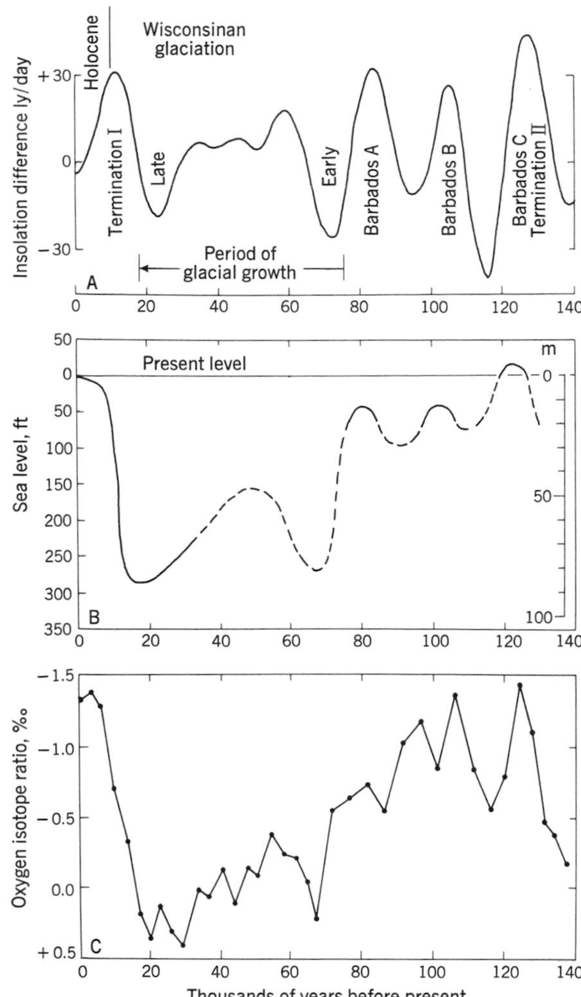


**FIGURE 41.28.** Correlation of summer insolation, sea level, and oxygen-isotope ratios for the past 150,000 years. (*A*) Insolation difference at lat. 45° N. (See Figure 41.27.) (*B*) Inferred changes in sea level. (*C*) Oxygen-isotope ratios, modified from Emiliani core data. [From W. Broecker and J. van Donk (1970), *Reviews of Geophysics*, vol. 8, pp. 184 and 195, Figures 7 and 13.]

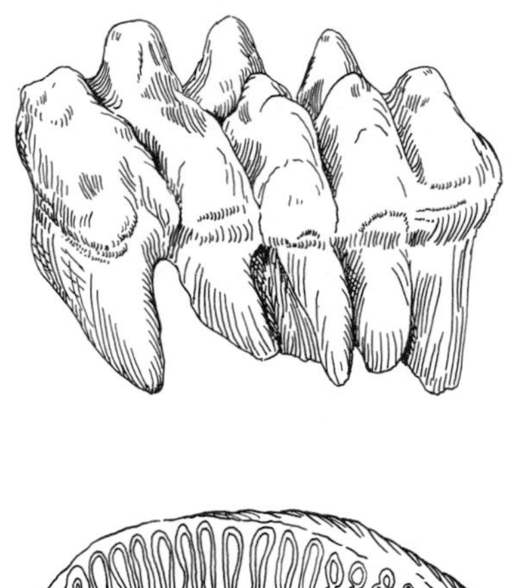

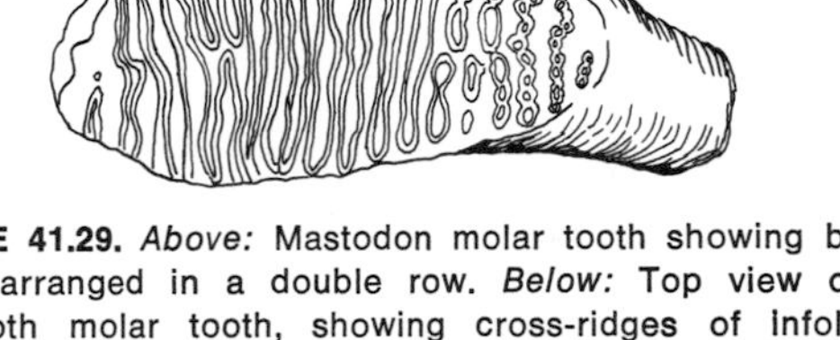

**FIGURE 41.29.** *Above:* Mastodon molar tooth showing blunt cusps arranged in a double row. *Below:* Top view of a mammoth molar tooth, showing cross-ridges of infolded enamel. The mastodon tooth is shown on about twice the scale of the mammoth tooth. [Upper drawing made from a photograph by Carl O. Dunbar of a specimen in the Yale Peabody Museum. Lower drawing after E. H. Colbert (1955), *Evolution of the Vertebrates,* New York, Wiley, p. 412, Figure 122*F*.]

the vicinity of the north geographical pole, and a corresponding arrival of Antarctica in a south polar location, are considered to have occurred in late Cenozoic time, possibly in the Miocene Epoch. As we have noted from the evidence of deep-sea cores of the Southern Ocean, glaciation of Antarctica probably began long before the Pleistocene Epoch started and has been continuous ever since. Thus by very late Cenozoic time the configuration of ocean basins and continents was favorable to a very strong climatic zonation grading from a warm and equable equatorial zone to cold arctic and polar regions. The high ice plateau of Antarctica serves to refrigerate the south polar zone, while the isolated Arctic Ocean hemmed in by lands intensifies the cold of the north polar zone.

Onset of a glaciation is considered to be initiated by melting of the sea-ice cover of the Arctic Ocean. Whereas the earlier version of the Ewing-Donn hypothesis proposed that warming of arctic water took place by influx of water from the warmer Atlantic Ocean during high stages of sea level, their more recent calculations of the heat balance have led them to conclude that a small change in the existing heat budget could permit melting of the sea ice, and that once the water

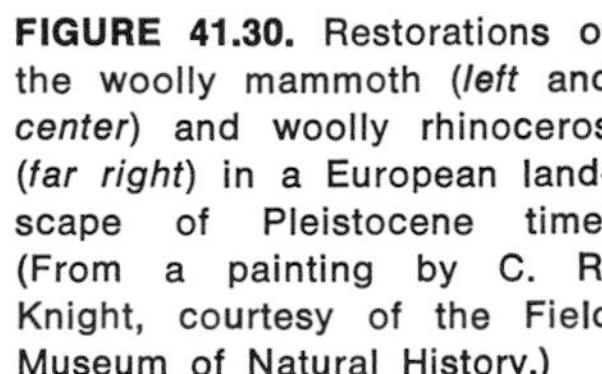

**FIGURE 41.30.** Restorations of the woolly mammoth (*left* and *center*) and woolly rhinoceros (*far right*) in a European landscape of Pleistocene time. (From a painting by C. R. Knight, courtesy of the Field Museum of Natural History.)

**FIGURE 41.31.** Reconstruction of a midsummer scene along the Missouri River in late Pleistocene time. From left to right are mastodon, royal bison, and horse. (Painting by C. R. Knight, courtesy of the American Museum of Natural History.)

surface is fully exposed a substantial warming of the surface water must occur.

Once free of ice, the Arctic Ocean supplied a large quantity of water vapor to the overlying atmosphere. Thus an important new source region of a maritime air mass came into existence. As explained in Chapter 19, polar and arctic air masses originating over snow-covered surfaces are extremely cold and have very low water vapor content. In contrast, maritime polar air masses hold substantial amounts of water vapor and cause heavy precipitation over windward continental margins. Largely supplied by moist air masses from the Arctic Ocean, lands in subarctic latitudes in North America and Eurasia received surplus accumulations of snow and began to develop icecaps. As these icecaps grew into ice sheets of great extent and high surface altitude, their cooling effects were increased and resulted in continued expansion. As the ice spread into middle latitudes, the principal sources of nourishment shifted from the ice-free Arctic Ocean to the moisture derived from air masses having source regions in the North Atlantic and North Pacific Oceans. The ice sheets now depressed the average atmospheric temperatures generally over the Northern Hemisphere, and the resultant cooling of the Arctic Ocean water caused it to freeze over. Although this source of moisture was now cut off, the ice sheets continued to grow through nourishment from other oceanic sources.

Under the Ewing-Donn hypothesis, deglaciation was initiated by the effects of cooling of the surface waters of the middle-latitude oceans, particularly the North Atlantic. Lowered water temperature resulted in a sharp decrease in evaporation and hence in greatly reduced atmospheric moisture. Gradually starved of nourishment, the ice sheets began to waste away. By the time the ice sheets had been reduced to about half their maximum extent, the process of wastage could not be reversed and so continued until the ice sheets completely disappeared.

Reduction in extent and elevation of the ice sheets would have led to a warming of average atmospheric temperatures, since the ice sheets were themselves the principal atmospheric refrigerators. As atmospheric temperatures rose during deglaciation, ocean temperatures should also have increased, allowing increased flux of water vapor into the atmosphere. This effect would have tended to nourish rather than to starve the ice sheets, halting their recession. However, the Ewing-Donn hypothesis relies on observations that the warming of the Atlantic Ocean lagged behind the phase of rapid ice wastage by some 5000 years, permitting the ice to reach a critical point in decline before the effect of increased precipitation could take hold.

The Ewing-Donn hypothesis thus accounts for a complete cycle of glaciation and deglaciation. A new cycle of glaciation would have begun when the Arctic Ocean again became ice-free. Perhaps the melting of the sea ice was caused by a small increase in insolation or by the effect of post-glacial rise in sea level. However, the important premise of the Ewing-Donn hypothesis is that increases and decreases in precipitation are the primary controls of the glacial cycle, whereas temperature changes are only secondary effects.

Validation or invalidation of the Ewing-Donn hypothesis may ultimately rest upon evidence from Arctic deep-sea cores. Several investigators have interpreted their core data to mean that ice-free periods are not shown in the Pleistocene record of the Arctic Ocean.

## Mammals of the Pleistocene

Mammalian development progressed from Pliocene into Pleistocene time with no evidence of evolutionary crisis as world temperatures fell and the first ice sheets began their spread. Shifting of climate zones into lower latitudes seems to have been met by migrations of floras and faunas, although extinctions occurred locally in special geographical traps, such as islands and peninsulas from which migration could not take place.

Throughout the Old World landmasses—Eurasia and Africa—migrations were continuously possible during the entire Cenozoic Era. Animals of Africa were able to migrate into Europe during warm interglaciations

of the Pleistocene. Moreover, Man evolved in the Old World and developed in continuous contact with the other mammals. In the New World, evolution was complicated by the separation of North and South America until the late Pliocene. As a result, mixing of grossly unlike faunas took place early in the Pleistocene in North America, yielding a mammalian assemblage somewhat different from that of the Old World.

**FIGURE 41.32.** *Above:* Dire wolf (*Canis dirus*) reconstructed from remains found in the La Brea, California, asphalt pits. This Pleistocene carnivore was about the same size as the modern timber wolf. *Below:* Reconstruction of the saber-toothed tiger (*Smilodon*) from the same locality; specimen about 3 ft (1 m) in height. The lower jaw could open much wider than shown to permit the upper teeth to be used for stabbing. (Sketched from photographs prepared by Carl O. Dunbar from models by R. S. Lull in the Yale Peabody Museum.)

In the Pleistocene of North America there lived a number of now-extinct mammals whose bones, teeth, and tusks are abundantly preserved in interglacial and post-glacial silts and peats. Undoubtedly the most spectacular were members of the elephant group, which were of two types. The *mastodons* were forest-dwellers having a distinctive tooth structure consisting of pairs of cusps. (Figure 41.29, upper.) Mastodon remains have been found widely distributed over the eastern United States and far out upon the now-submerged continental shelf. The true elephants, which arose from early mastodons, are represented by the *mammoths* of the Pleistocene and the modern elephants. Their tooth structure became highly specialized for grinding of coarse grasses (Figure 41.29, lower). The mammoths came to North America in the Pleistocene by way of the land bridge connecting Siberia with Alaska. Well-known to all is the woolly mammoth, which—along with the muskox and, in Europe, the woolly rhinoceros —was adapted to cold periglacial climates (Figure 41.30). Over the southwestern United States there roamed the great *imperial mammoth,* which attained a shoulder height of 14 ft (4.3 m).

Other grazing mammals of the Pleistocene Epoch in North America included the horse, bison, camel, and peccary (wild pig) (Figure 41.31). From South America there had emigrated the ground sloths, some of which were huge animals, and the glyptodonts.

Pleistocene carnivores, which are particularly well preserved in large numbers in the tar pits of Rancho La Brea in southern California, included a number of now-extinct species, among them the *saber-tooth tiger* (*Smilodon*) with teeth adapted to stabbing its prey, and the huge *dire wolf* (*Canis dirus*) (Figure 41.32). The list includes, of course, all of the living carnivores—wolf, fox, lynx, puma, badger, otter, skunk, and weasel.

It is particularly interesting to find that few mammalian extinctions occurred in North America until after the close of the Wisconsinan, about −10,000 years, at which time Man spread widely over the continent. The inference has been made that extinction of species, particularly the mastodons and mammoths, was through hunting by Man. If so, this event serves as an ominous presage to greater Man-caused extinctions of the present and the total extinction of planetary life which he seems destined ultimately to achieve as his supreme contribution to the evolutionary process.

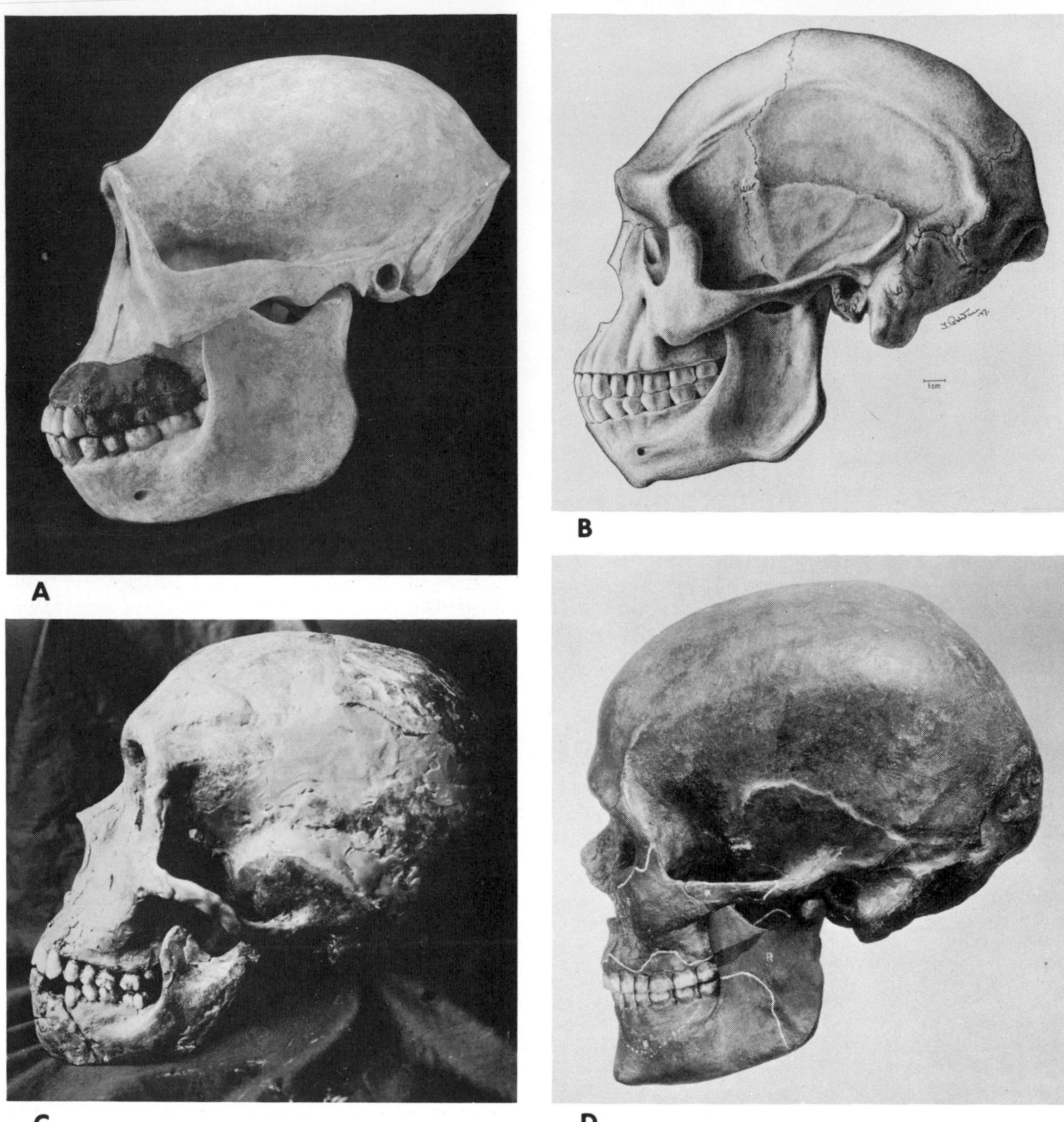


**FIGURE 41.33.** Skulls of hominids of the Pleistocene Epoch. (*A*) *Australopithecus;* a reconstructed skull about 11 in. (28 cm) high. (*B*) *Homo erectus;* reconstructed skull about 8 in. (21 cm) high. (*C*) *Neanderthal Man;* reconstructed skull from southwestern France. (*D*) *Cro-Magnon Man;* of late Wisconsinan age, from Europe. (Photographs by courtesy of the American Museum of Natural History.)

## The evolution of Man[2]

As we took leave of our hominoid menage in Chapter 30, evolutionary progress stood about as follows at the opening of the Pleistocene Epoch: Through the Pliocene Epoch the apes had evolved independently from primitive hominoid stocks going back into Miocene time (see Figure 30.26). From *Dryopithecus,* the common ancestor of hominids and apes, there had evolved in late Miocene time *Ramapithecus,* the hominid ancestor of fossil men. Although evidence from limb or pelvic bones is lacking, it is supposed that *Ramapithecus* was bipedal and lived on the ground. Because only jaw fragments are known, we do not know the size of the *Ramapithecus* brain, but it was probably small, comparable to that of the modern apes.

A second genus of hominids, *Australopithecus,* came on the scene about at the start of Pleistocene Epoch (−2 m.y.), although his evolution from *Ramapithecus* may have occurred in the late Pliocene. *Australopithecus* was named for a well-preserved skull found in South Africa in 1924. Subsequently, in the Olduvai Gorge of Tanzania, the skull of another species of *Australopithecus* was found. From associated volcanic rocks, dated by the potassium–argon method, this specimen

[2] Based on data of A. L. McAlester (1968), *The History of Life,* Englewood Cliffs, N.J., Prentice-Hall, Chapter 7.

**FIGURE 41.34.** Reconstruction of a group of individuals of *Australopithecus* in their African habitat in early Pleistocene time. [Reproduced by permission from J. Augusta and Z. Burian, *Prehistoric Man,* Prague, Artia.]

is assigned an age of not less than −1.75 m.y., which is close to the beginning of the Pleistocene Epoch.

From a large number of bones, including jaws, skulls, and limbs, it is known that *Australopithecus* walked upright, although in a slouched attitude. His size ranged from that of a chimpanzee in the smaller species to that of a gorilla in the larger. Although his limb bones closely resemble those of modern Man, the *Australopithecus* skull had only half the brain capacity of modern Man (Figure 41.33). With his erect stance, *Australopithecus* developed the ability to use bones, sticks, and stones as tools and weapons, although he had not learned to shape tools (Figure 41.34). Advanced arm and hand functions tended to place a premium upon intelligence, and promoted an evolutionary increase in brain size, the most important distinguishing characteristic setting Man apart from the apes.

*Australopithecus* spread widely over the Old World, for his remains have been found in Java. He became extinct some time in the middle Pleistocene, after giving rise to *Homo,* the third and final genus of hominids. Specimens of *Homo* found associated with those of *Australopithecus* in South Africa suggest that both hominids were in existence for a considerable span of time in the age range of −700,000 to −500,000.

*Homo erectus,* the earliest known species of *Homo,* was discovered in 1891 in Java, where he was named "Java Man." Since then many jaws, skulls, and limbs of *Homo erectus* have been found in the Old World, including localities in China, Europe, and Africa. It should be kept in mind that until recently various different names have been applied to specimens that are now placed in the single genus *Homo.* For example, "Peking Man," first described as *Sinanthropus,* is now considered a member of the species *H. erectus. Homo erectus* possessed a brain volume of about 900 to 1100 cc, which is intermediate between that of *Australopithecus,* 600–700 cc, and modern Man, 1400–1600 cc (Figure 41.33). The head of *Homo erectus,* with its protruding mouth and slanted forehead, jutted forward from a sloping neck with powerful muscles, giving him a distinctly ape-like appearance (Figure 41.35). *Homo erectus* became extinct some time in the late middle Pleistocene, but he had already given rise to *Homo sapiens,* the single species that includes all present-day races of the human family.

*Homo sapiens* appeared on the scene early in the middle Pleistocene, at about −500,000 years, and was for a long period a contemporary of *Homo erectus.* As with the latter species, *H. sapiens* includes a number of men formerly designated as separate species but now regarded as races within the species. One of these was *Neanderthal Man,* who inhabited Europe from about −100,000 until −40,000 years—late Sangamonian and early Wisconsinan (Figure 41.36). Because Neanderthal Man was short, stocky, and heavy-boned, he was

**FIGURE 41.35.** Reconstruction of a group of individuals of *Homo erectus* of middle Pleistocene time in a forest habitat in the Far East, perhaps on the island of Java. [Reproduced by permission from J. Augusta and Z. Burian, *Prehistoric Man,* Prague, Artia.]

formerly designated as a separate species. It is true that his skull seems to resemble that of *H. erectus* more than it does modern Man. However, his brain capacity was at least equal to that of modern Man and he made good stone tools, including stone axes, scrapers and points. In terms of culture, Neanderthal Man is said to belong to the *Middle Paleolithic* culture, or "Old Stone Age."

In Europe at about −35,000 years Neanderthal Man was replaced by a more advanced race of *H. sapiens.* This newcomer was represented by *Cro-Magnon Man,* among others. He was tall, straight, and long-legged. His skull was centered directly over the top of the spine and showed a high forehead and prominent chin (Figure 41.33). In these respects he strongly resembled modern Man. Cro-Magnon Man belonged to the final phases of the Paleolithic culture, but the quality of his stone implements was high, showing finely-chipped forms. In addition, Cro-Magnon Man shaped bone and ivory into tools, weapons, and ornaments. He had developed the use of the bow and arrow and dressed himself in furs. Cro-Magnon Man was succeeded in the Near East at about −10,000 years (start of the Holocene) by peoples of the Neolithic culture. These peoples learned to make pottery and to domesticate animals, then later turned to agriculture. At about −5000 years the introduction of use of metals brought on the Age of Metals, and shortly thereafter came the dawn of recorded human history.

It is well established that *Homo sapiens* originated in the Old World. It is supposed that he migrated to the New World by way of the Bering Strait very late in the Pleistocene. He may not have spread south to the contiguous United States from Alaska until ice recession of the late Wisconsinan opened up migration routes. Radiocarbon dates establish the presence of Man in a number of widely separate places in North America (Texas, Alabama, Mexico City) at around −9000 to −10,000 years. Association of human bones and weapon points with bones of the mastodon, mammoth, and saber-tooth tiger suggest that those animals were living at the time Man occupied North America and, as already noted, their extinction was due in part to hunting by Man.

## The Holocene environment

Onset of the Holocene Epoch is rather clearly marked by a rapid rise in ocean temperatures starting about −10,000 years. As would be expected, climate zones on the continents shifted rapidly poleward as the periglacial tundra climates of North America and Europe gave way successively to subarctic climates and ulti-

**FIGURE 41.36.** Reconstruction of Neanderthal Man. (Courtesy of Field Museum of Natural History.)

mately to present-day middle-latitude climates. Soil-forming processes began the development of soil profiles, and vegetation became reestablished.

The first climatic stage of the Holocene in middle latitudes is known as the *Boreal Stage.* "Boreal" is an adjective referring to the present subarctic latitudes in which needle-leaf forests are the dominant vegetation. Much can be learned about post-glacial history of climate and vegetation through the science of *palynology,* the study of fossil spores and pollens found in sedimentary deposits. Identification of pollens in post-glacial bogs, together with radiocarbon dating, furnishes a record of the compositions of surrounding forests. Pollens of the Boreal Stage indicate a vegetation similar to that of present subarctic regions, spruce being a dominant tree.

A general warming of climate continued until, at about −8000 years, the *Atlantic* climatic stage was reached. This was a period in which temperatures averaged somewhat higher than those of the present, perhaps on the order of 4.5 F° (2.5 C°) higher. This period, which lasted about 3000 years, is described as the *climatic optimum,* so far as Holocene climates of North American and European latitudes are concerned. There followed a period of lower-than-average temperatures, the *Subboreal* climatic stage, in which winters seem to have been colder and alpine glaciers showed a phase of readvance. By this time (−5000 to −2000 years) sea level had risen to almost its present position and existing submergence of coastal fringes was largely complete.

Even the last two millennia (0 to 2000 A.D.) show a sequence of marked climatic cycles. Particularly striking is a cycle of lower temperatures that reached its low point in the eighteenth century and persisted until late in the nineteenth century. General advance of alpine glaciers during this cycle has led to its designation as a "Little Ice Age."

## Interdependence in the earth sciences[3]

It is fashionable to close a textbook on the earth sciences with a chapter that tells what modern Man has done to his environment. Many in the natural sciences share the conviction that Man's destruction and contamination of the biosphere is fast approaching a point at which wholesale elimination of life segments is certain to result. Throughout this book there are a number of examples of Man's role in environmental change—for example, by burning of fossil fuels, by inducing soil erosion and floods, and by excessive pumping of ground water. However, the content of this book serves a more fundamental purpose with respect to the science of the environment; it furnishes the basic facts and the understanding of terrestrial processes necessary to solve certain physical aspects of our environmental problems.

Turning to another matter, I recall that a colleague of mine once praised a competitive earth-sciences textbook by saying that the several parts of the book were completely unrelated to one another and this enabled him to present the subjects in any order he chose and to omit any topics he chose. If such compartmentalization of knowledge was possible in past decades, it is intolerable today. As current research in various fields of the earth sciences is reviewed, one is struck by the interdependence of the natural and physical sciences. In solving many of the most complex and difficult problems of earth processes and earth history it is absolutely necessary to call for help from colleagues in a diverse range of sciences. Nowhere is this cooperation better demonstrated than in the final chapter on the Pleistocene Epoch. In trying to work out the chronology of Pleistocene events it has been necessary to call together astronomers, geochemists, geophysicists, and biologists. Perhaps after finishing with the astronomical facts about the earth's rotation and revolution in Chapters 1 and 2, you expected that they would be of no further value, yet in the final chapter these same facts reappear as the basis for a Milankovitch insolation curve and a theory of glaciation. A quarter of a century ago the subject of terrestrial magnetism was probably not mentioned in a single introductory geology course in any college in the United States, except for a brief note on the correction of the compass for declination. In treating this topic in Chapter 7,

[3] An editorial commentary expressing the author's personal viewpoints.

I did not intend that the information should be laid to rest thereafter. Now it reappears in "fossil" form as a chronology of polarity reversals by which we can date layers of sediment taken from the floor of the ocean. Thus the gap of irrelevance between dynamo theory of the earth's dipole field and age of the Pliocene-Pleistocene boundary has been eliminated in only a decade.

For a long time it seemed that fragmentation and compartmentalization of science were increasing in an irreversible trend. Yet that trend has been sharply reversed in the earth sciences in the past two decades through the need to bring diverse disciplines together to solve difficult problems. If this book has served to bring you a greater awareness of the trend toward unification in the fast-growing body of our knowledge of planet Earth, I shall feel amply rewarded.

## References for further study

Flint, R. F. (1957), *Glacial and Pleistocene Geology,* New York, Wiley, 553 pp.

Hough, J. L. (1958), *Geology of the Great Lakes,* Urbana, Univ. of Illinois Press, 313 pp.

Wright, H. E., Jr., and D. G. Frey, Eds. (1965), *The Quaternary of the United States,* Princeton, N.J., Princeton Univ. Press, 922 pp.

McAlester, A. L. (1968), *The History of Life,* Englewood Cliffs, N.J., Prentice-Hall, 151 pp., chap. 7.

Dunbar, C. O., and K. M. Waage (1969), *Historical Geology,* 3rd ed., New York, Wiley, 556 pp., chaps. 18, 19, 20.

# Appendixes

# I

# Maps for the data of the earth sciences

MANY FORMS OF EARTH-SCIENCE data require presentation on a map showing all or a large part of the globe. Every such map must be based upon a *map projection,* which is an orderly system of parallels and meridians drawn upon a flat surface to represent the earth's geographic grid. Because it is impossible to transfer the ellipsoidal earth grid to a plane surface without grossly distorting either the areal scale or the shapes of surface features, no single map projection gives a true picture of the earth's surface.

When a scientist is faced with the problem of selecting a map projection upon which to depict his data, he has before him two basic choices: (1) a *conformal* projection, on which the shape of any small area is correctly shown, or (2) an *equal-area* projection, on which a constant scale of areas is preserved over the entire map. The conformal projection always shows a right-angle (orthogonal) intersection of any parallel with any meridian, just as holds true for all corresponding intersections of parallels and meridians on the globe. On an equal-area projection a small square or circle, representing a given number of square miles, may be moved about over the map and will delimit the same area of ground surface wherever it is placed.

It is impossible to devise a map projection that is both conformal and equal-area. All conformal projections suffer from severe scale changes so that areas are not correctly represented. All equal-area projections suffer from serious distortions of shapes. Therefore a scientist wishing to depict the areal extent of some surface property (such as relative areas of oceans and continents) will select an equal-area projection, while a scientist wishing to show the configuration of a given linear property (such as isobars or weather fronts on a weather map) will choose a conformal projection.

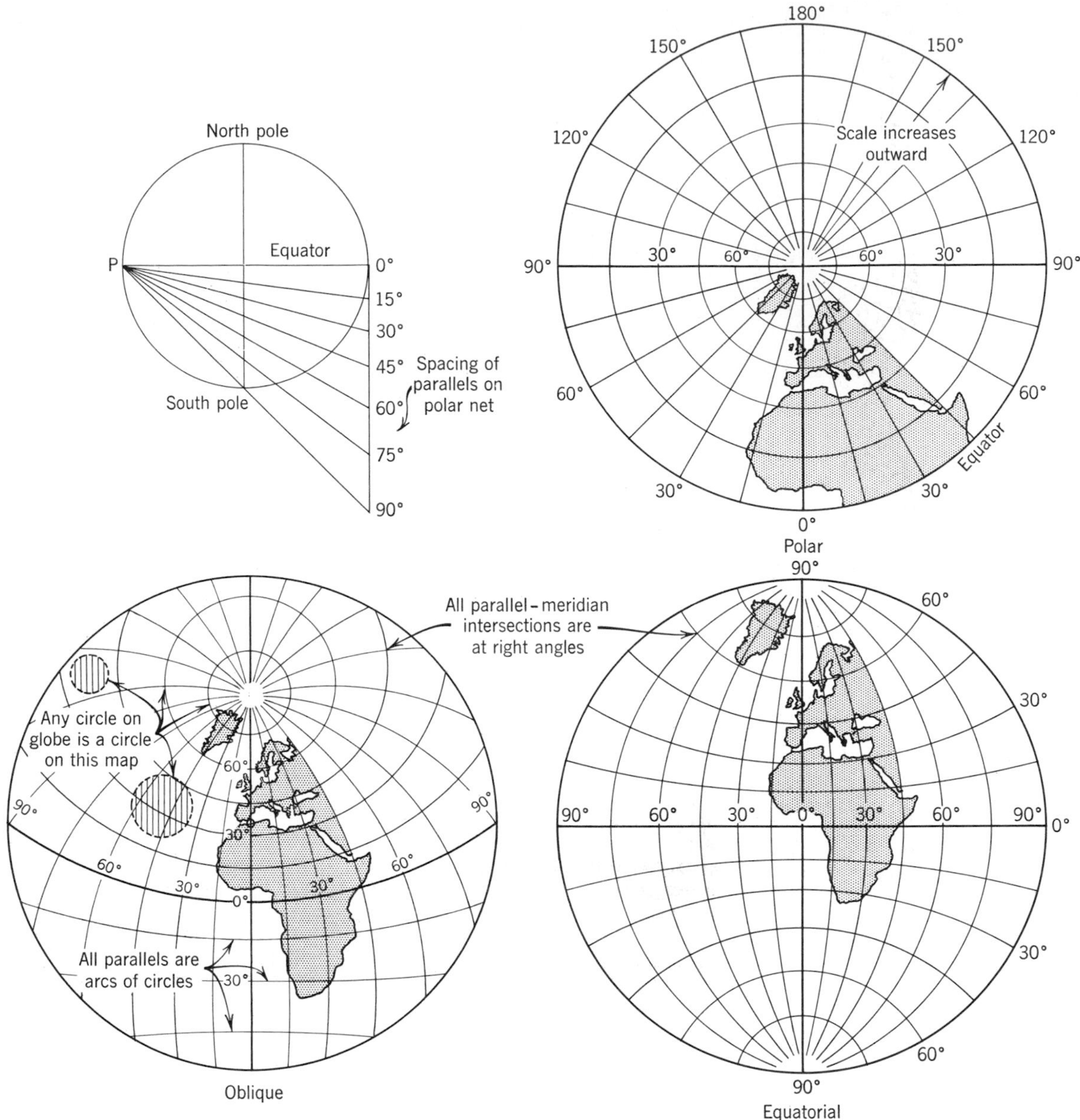


**FIGURE I.1.** Stereographic projection. (© 1960, John Wiley & Sons, New York.)

Several useful map projections are neither equal area nor conformal, but possess some unique property that dictates their selection for a specific use.

In this appendix only a few of the important projections are illustrated. The serious student of the earth sciences will need to go much further in his study of the principles and varieties of map projections.

## Conformal projections

One of the most important projections for scientific uses is the *stereographic projection,* a perfect conformal network (Figure I.1). In concept, the intersections of meridians and parallels are projected upon a tangent plane from a point source lying diametrically opposite to the point of tangency, as shown in the construction diagram. Any point of tangency may be selected. *Polar* projections result when either pole is selected as the point of tangency, and *equatorial* projections when a point on the equator is selected. An *oblique,* or *tilted,* projection results from selection of a point between equator and poles. All three positions are illustrated in Figure I.1.

In the stereographic projections, all lines are either straight lines or arcs of circles. Any small circle on the globe is represented as a true circle on the projection. Map scale increases radially outward from the center of

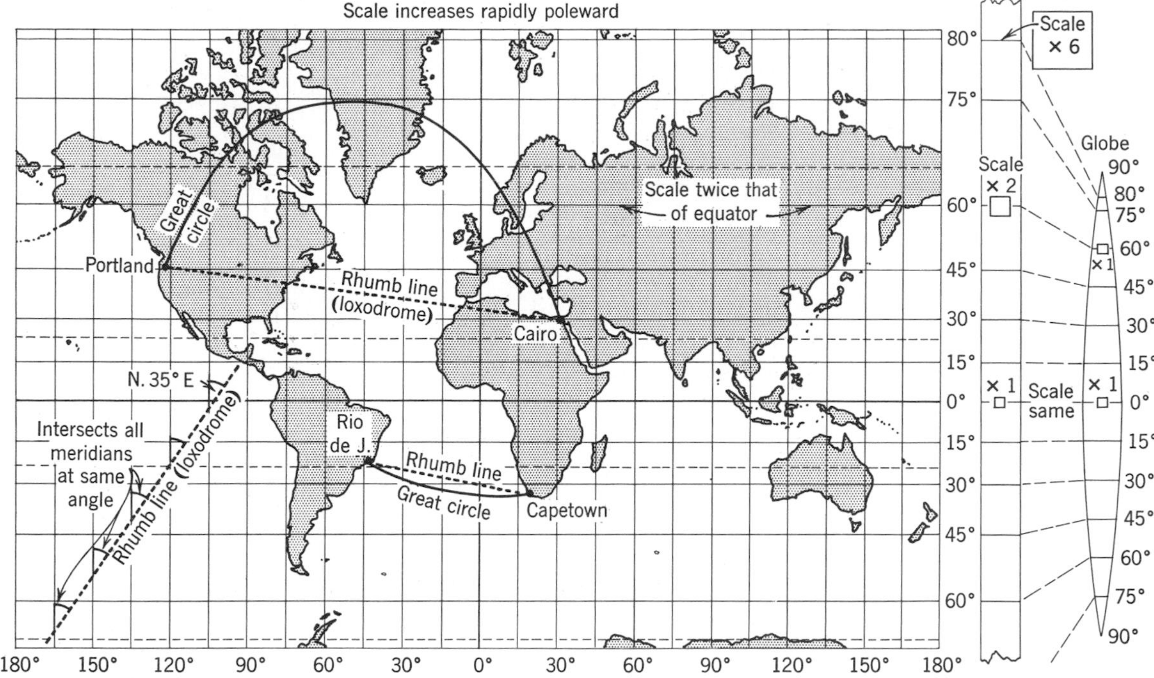


**FIGURE I.2.** Equatorial Mercator projection. (© 1960, John Wiley & Sons, New York.)

projection. It is impossible to show the entire globe on this projection.

The polar stereographic projection is generally selected for scientific maps of the polar regions, serving as the base of the Universal Polar Stereographic (UPS) Military Grid System for latitudes between 80° and 90°. The U.S. Weather Bureau uses a stereographic projection as the base for its surface-weather maps and upper-air charts. In seismology and geology, stereographic projections are useful to show the true patterns of island and mountain arcs and their associated earthquake epicenters. The stereographic network is also useful in the geometrical solution of problems in structural geology and in crystallography.

The *Mercator projection,* in its various forms, is perhaps the most useful of the true conformal projections for scientific purposes. In concept the network of parallels and meridians is drawn upon a cylinder enveloping the globe and tangent to it along a great circle. The cylinder is then imagined to be cut parallel to its axis and unrolled into a flat sheet. The Mercator projection thus has a single reference line—a great circle—along which the scale is constant. Scale decreases away from this line in both directions.

The classic equatorial projection invented by Gerardus Mercator in 1569 is perhaps the best known of all map projections (Figure I.2). Meridians and parallels are straight lines forming a rectangular grid. Meridians are equidistantly spaced, while parallels are spaced at distances increasing rapidly away from the equator. To produce a true conformal projection, Mercator introduced exactly the right degree of north-

**FIGURE I.3.** (*A*) Tangent cylinder and (*B*) secant cylinder for transverse Mercator projection. (© 1960, John Wiley & Sons, New York.)

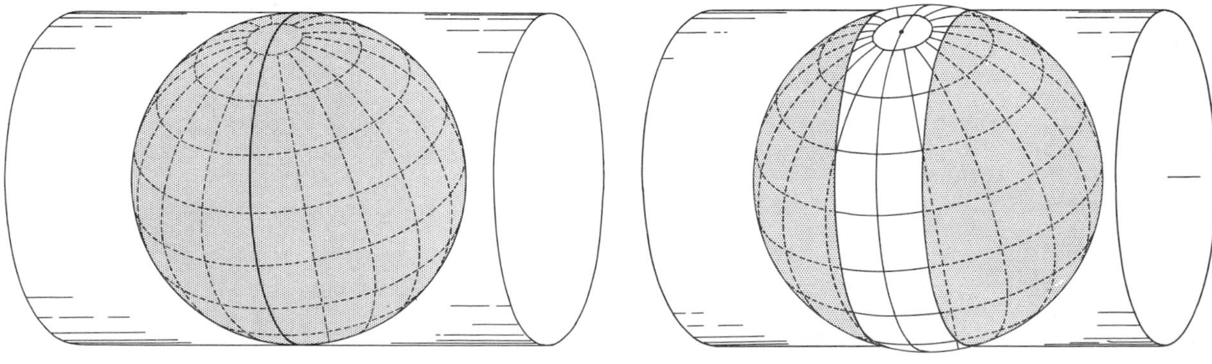

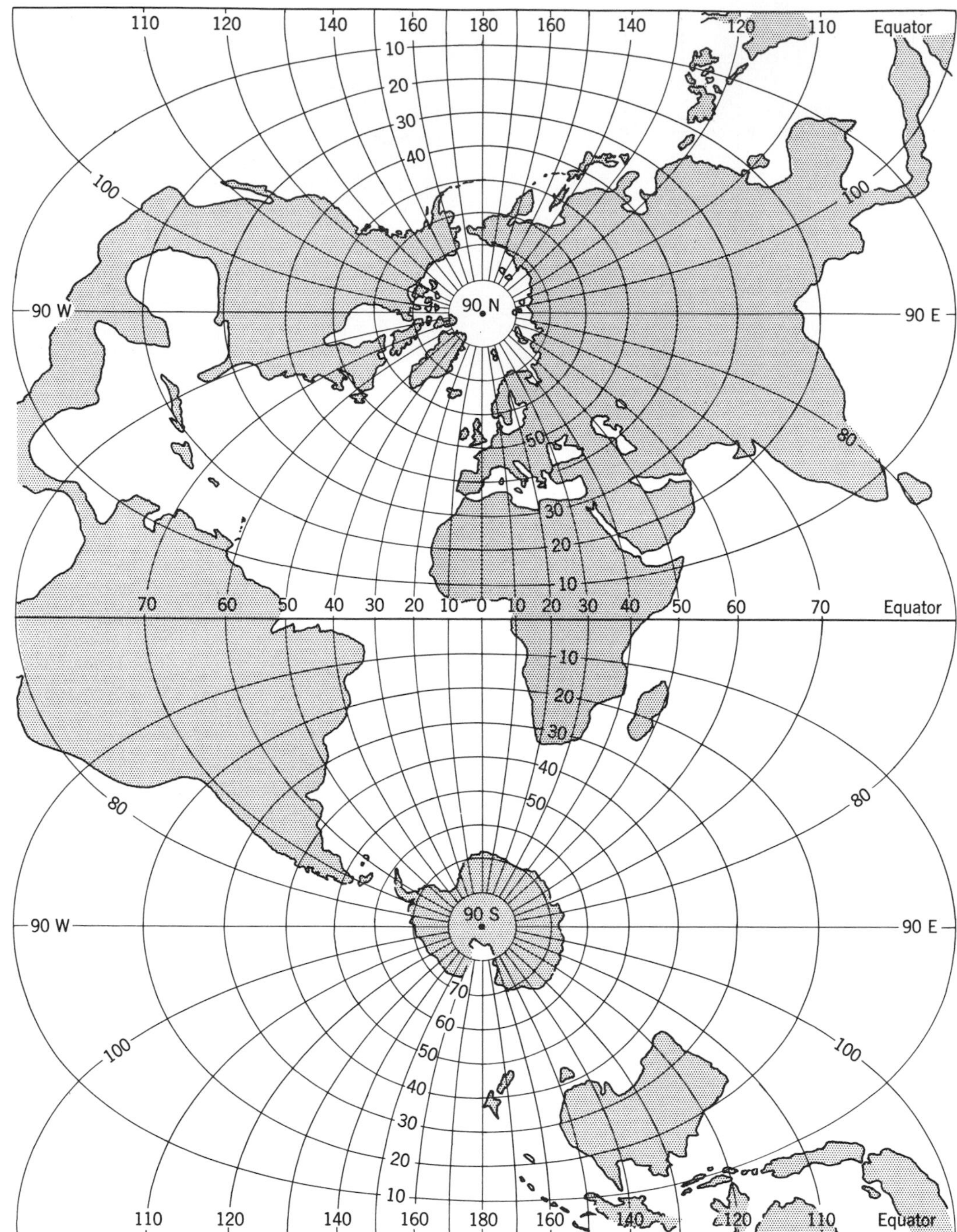


**FIGURE I.4.** Transverse Mercator projection. (© 1960, John Wiley & Sons, New York.)

south increase in scale needed to match the east-west increase in scale resulting from maintaining parallel meridians. Thus at 60° the east-west scale has been increased to twice that at the equator. (The 60th parallel of latitude is one-half as long as the equator.) Correspondingly, the north-south scale must be doubled. At 80° the scale increase is about sixfold. In mathematical terms, the scale on a Mercator projection increases poleward as the secant of the latitude. It is obvious that so rapid a scale increase makes it impractical to show regions poleward of, say, 85° and impossible to show the poles.

Although it is a true conformal projection depicting any small part of the earth's surface without shape distortion, the equatorial Mercator projection suffers from the vast increase in scale at high latitudes. Thus Greenland appears larger than South America, whereas it is actually only one-eighth as large.

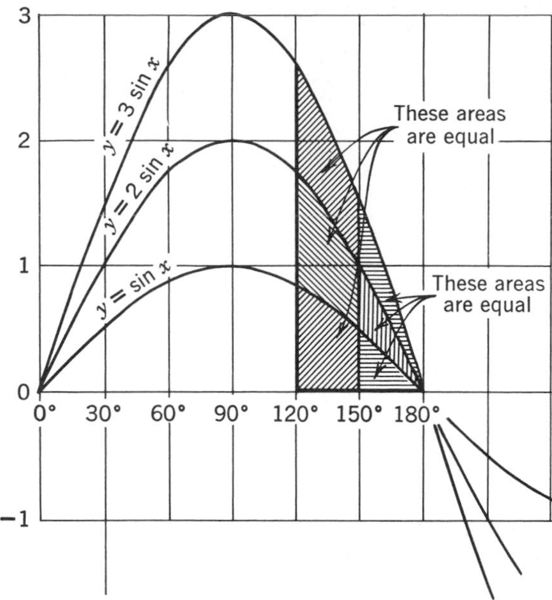


**FIGURE I.5.** Sine curves as meridians in the sinusoidal projection. (© 1960, John Wiley & Sons, New York.)

A remarkable and unique quality of the equatorial Mercator projection is that any straight line drawn upon the map is a line of constant compass direction. Such a line is called a *rhumb line,* or *loxodrome* (Figure I.2). Plotting of a rhumb line between any two points is, on the Mercator projection, a simple matter of drawing a straight line connecting those points.

The *transverse Mercator projection* has in recent years come into prominence as a world-wide standard for plotting military maps. As shown in Figure I.3*A,* the cylinder is imagined to be tangent along a pair of opposing meridians. The resulting map is shown in Figure I.4. Any pair of meridians may be selected, depending upon the zone of interest. An improvement of the tangent cylinder is the secant cylinder, shown in Figure I.3*B,* which minimizes scale errors along a narrow zone.

The Mercator projection is used in the earth sciences as a base for showing the geographic variations of some physical property, such as magnetic declination (isogonic map), in which the azimuth of the lines is to be measured by protractor at various points. Another use is to plot the earth track of satellites in oblique orbits. The Mercator projection is commonly misused, as when areal surface distributions are shown on it or when the geographic relations among points in the high latitudes are referred to it.

## Equal-area projections

Equal-area projections are used to show the areal extent of some property of the earth's surface. For example, a world map of mean annual precipitation (Figure 18.28) uses an equal-area base map because emphasis is upon the quantity of area lying between successive isohyets or within a single closed isohyet, while on the other hand the compass direction taken by the isohyets is of only secondary importance, thus the map need not be conformal.

The *sinusoidal projection* is a true equal-area projection, making use of *sine curves* for meridians (Figure I.5). Parallels are equidistantly spaced on this map, just as they are equally spaced on the globe. The sinusoidal projection can show the entire globe, but it suffers from extreme distortion of shapes in marginal zones at high latitudes (Figure I.6).

*Mollweide's homolographic projection* uses ellipses to form the meridians. Spacing of parallels is adjusted

**FIGURE I.6.** Sinusoidal projection. (© 1960, John Wiley & Sons, New York.)

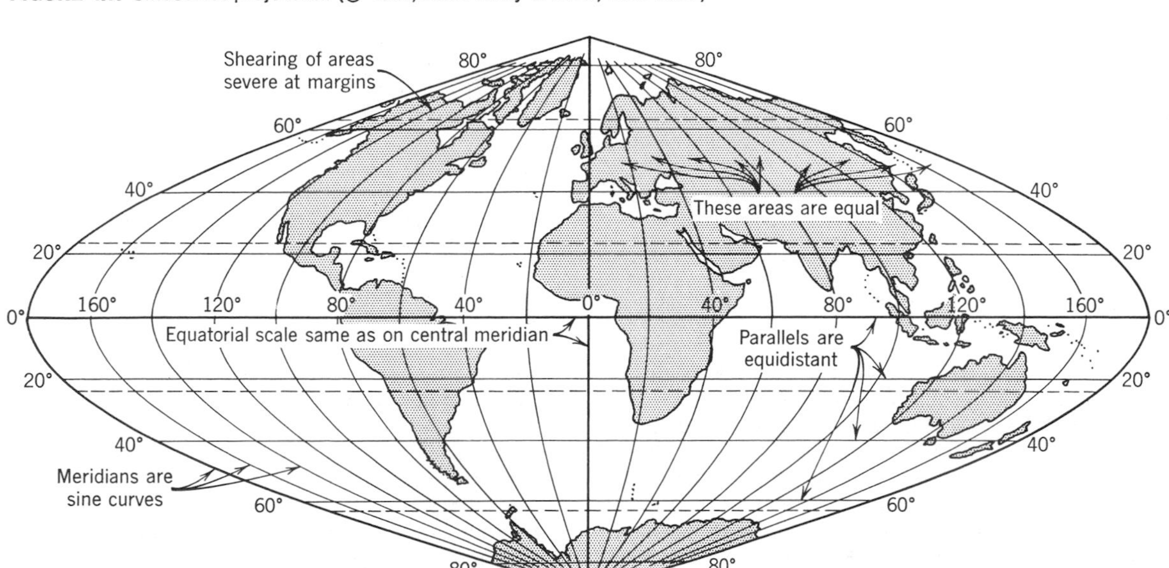

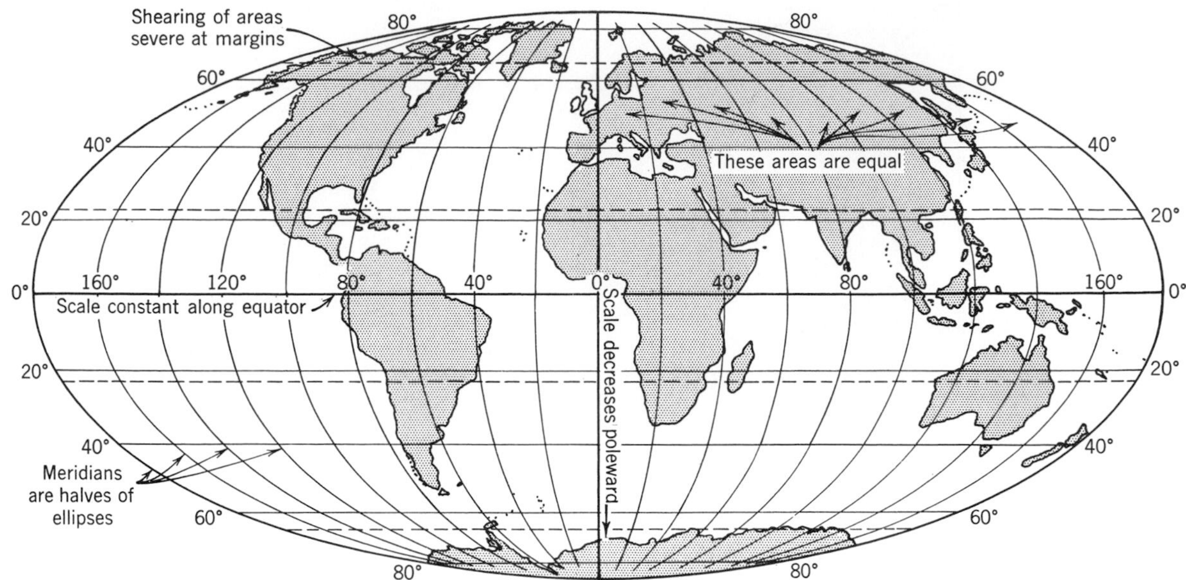


**FIGURE I.7.** Mollweide homolographic projection. (© 1960, John Wiley & Sons, New York.)

to produce a true equal-area net (Figure I.7). Parallels become more closely spaced toward the poles. Distortion in marginal areas is a serious defect in this projection, as it is in the sinusoidal projection. Data cannot easily be plotted or interpreted where the net is strongly sheared into narrow parallelograms.

The problem of marginal distortion in both sinusoidal and homolographic projections can be largely solved by splitting apart the global network into sectors along certain meridians. The result is an *interrupted* map projection—an example is the *interrupted sinusoidal projection* shown in Figure I.8. When the map is designed for showing continents to best advantage, interruption is made along meridians passing largely through oceans. Straight central meridians are chosen to be approximately centered upon each major landmass. Polar areas suffer badly from fragmentation, but low and middle latitudes have good continuity and excellent depiction of shapes.

Examples of use of the interrupted sinusoidal projection are found in Figures 13.8, 13.10, 13.12, and 13.18, all of which show global distribution of radiation phenomena. It is essential to be able to compare accurately the sizes of areas receiving or returning given

**FIGURE I.8.** Interrupted sinusoidal projection, designed in 1970 by A. N. Strahler. Interruption of Eurasia on the 60th meridian east minimizes distortion in eastern Asia.

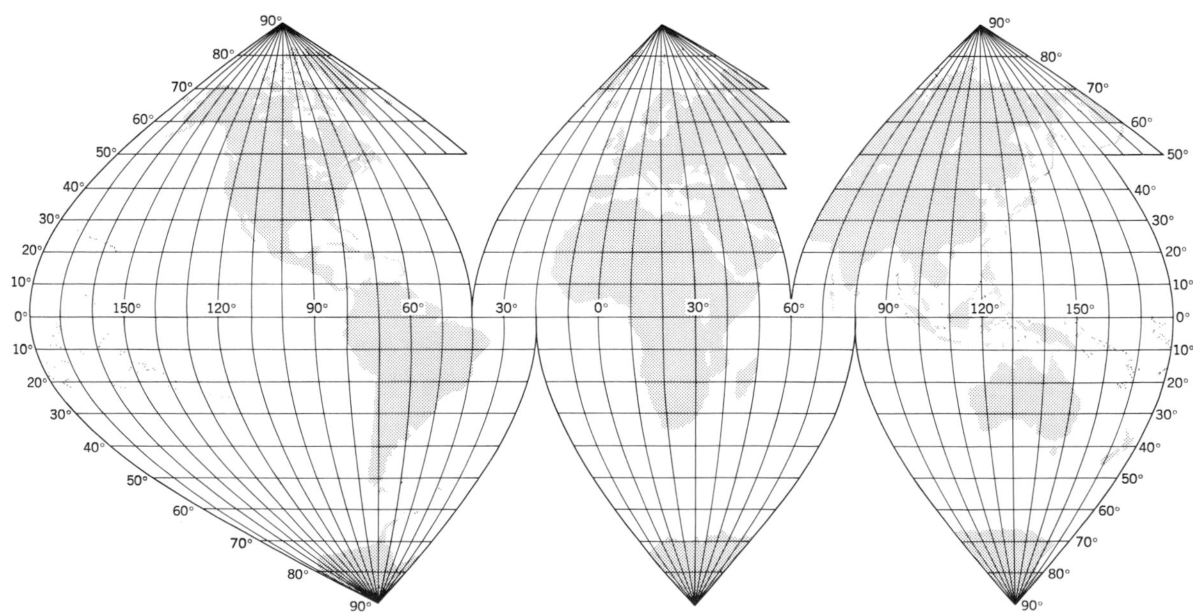

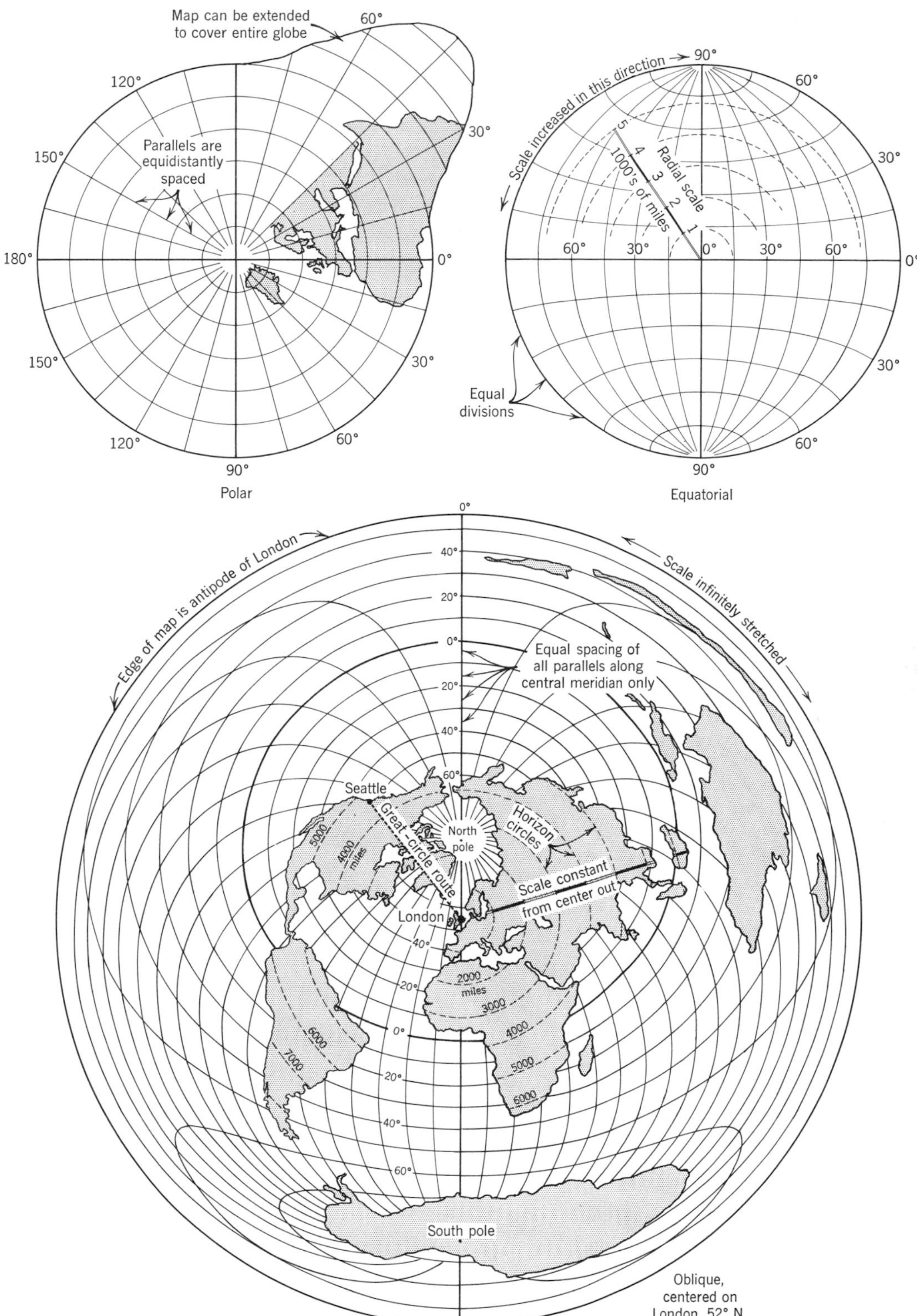


**FIGURE I.9.** Azimuthal equidistant projection. (© 1960, John Wiley & Sons, New York.)

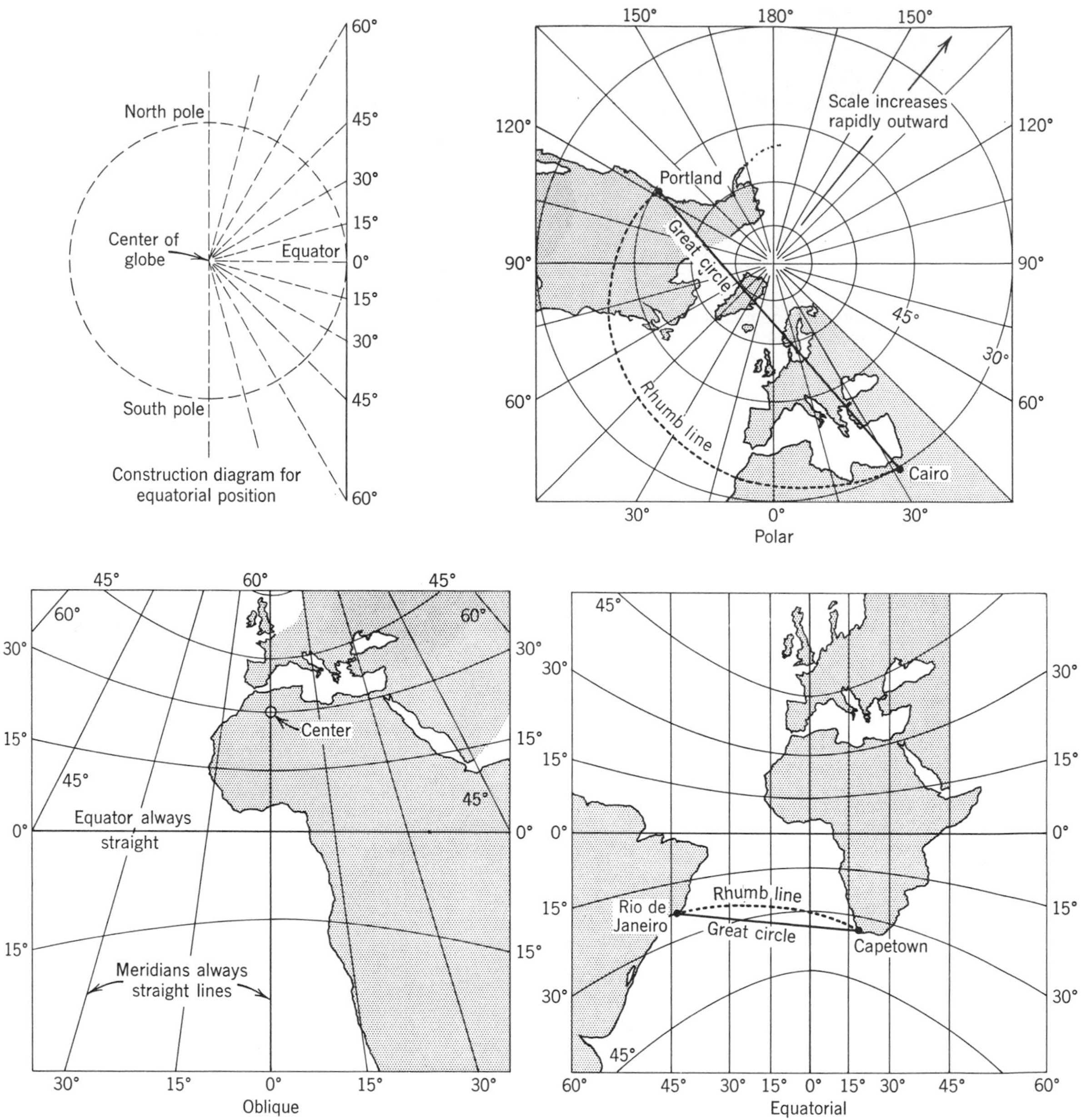


**FIGURE I.10.** Gnomonic projection. (© 1960, John Wiley & Sons, New York.)

quantities of radiation. At the same time, because latitude is a primary control of radiation phenomena, the projection used must have straight horizontal parallels spaced equidistantly, as on the globe itself.

Equal-area projections can also be interrupted in ways that present the oceans most favorably. An excellent example is Figure 14.13, based upon *Goode's homolosine projection,* which is a combination of sinusoidal projection (between 40° S. and 40° N.) and homolographic projection (poleward of 40°). Central meridians are located in midocean, while separation occurs on meridians running through the continents.

For showing areal data of arctic and polar regions, the *azimuthal equal-area projection* is used. Examples are shown in the world temperature maps of Figures 14.27 and 14.28. In addition to being a true equal-area net, this projection has only minor shape distortion poleward of the fortieth parallels. Map scale along the meridians decreases gradually from pole toward equator, whereas scale of the polar stereographic projection increases gradually in the same direction.

## Other projections

Many map projections are neither equal area nor conformal, but have some other unique and useful property. Two are of particular interest in the earth sciences.

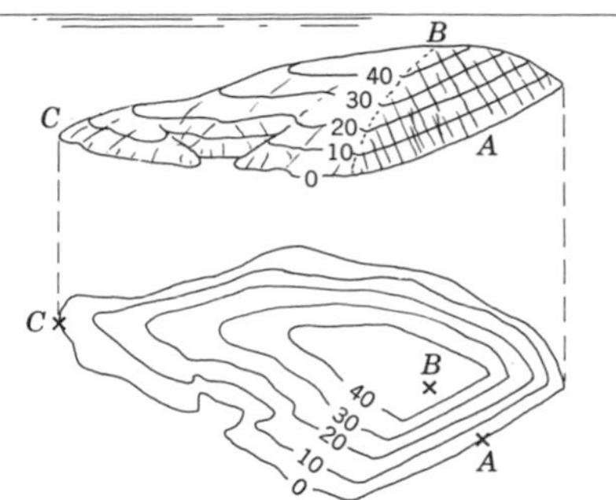


**FIGURE I.11.** Principle of the topographic contour map. (© 1960, John Wiley & Sons, New York.)

The *azimuthal equidistant projection* has the unique property that the linear scale (scale of distance) is constant from the center radially outward in all directions (Figure I.9). Any point on the globe may be placed at the center of the projection. For example, if the projection is drawn to be centered on a seismological observatory, all possible locations of an epicenter of known distance can be drawn by means of a circle, termed a *horizon circle*. Similarly, the limits of direct straight-line visibility or radio-wave transmission from a point at given height above the earth (as from a satellite) can be shown by a horizon circle.

The *gnomonic projection* is unique in that any straight line drawn on the map represents a true great circle on the earth's surface (Figure I.10). All meridians and the equator appear as straight lines on the gnomonic projection. The arc of a great circle represents the shortest surface distance between any two points on the globe, hence the gnomonic projection is of use in air and marine navigation and in any other use requiring rapid plotting of great-circle courses.

## Map scale

Globes and maps represent the features of the earth's surface on a much smaller size than the actual features. *Scale* is the ratio of length of a given line segment as measured on a globe or a map to the true length of that line on the earth's surface. Scale is given in terms of a *representative fraction* (*R.F.*).

**FIGURE I.12.** Relation of contour spacing to surface gradient.

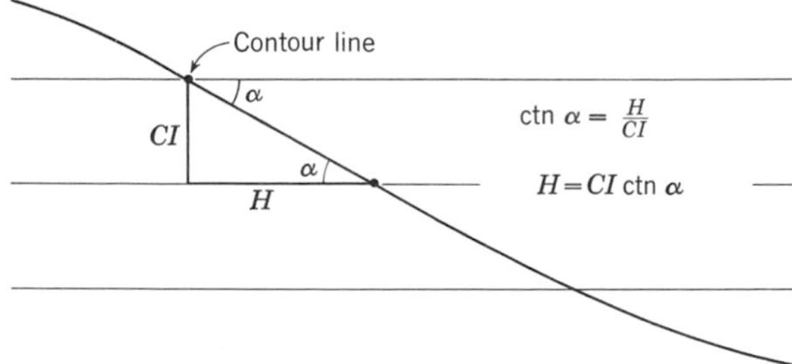


$$\frac{1}{100{,}000}$$

The fraction may also be written as 1:100,000. Any desired units of length may be used with the representative fraction. For example,

$$\frac{1}{100{,}000} = \frac{1\text{ cm on map}}{100{,}000\text{ cm on ground}} = \frac{1\text{ cm}}{1\text{ km}}$$

The scale may now be stated as "one centimeter represents one kilometer." Should English units of inches and miles be desired, the denominator is divided by 63,360, which is the number of inches in one mile, thus:

$$\frac{1\text{ in.}}{100{,}000\text{ in.} \div 63{,}360} = \frac{1\text{ in.}}{1.57\text{ mi}}$$

or "one inch represents 1.57 miles." The advantages of the metric system are obvious.

To estimate distances on a map a *graphic scale* is used; it is a line marked off into equal length units and numbered in distance units. Graphic scales in both English and metric units are illustrated in Figure I.15 and will be found on all maps of small areas shown in this book except where the map is purely schematic.

Maps showing a large part or all of the earth's surface will have no graphic or fractional scales attached, for the reason that the scale changes greatly from one part of the map to another. Only a globe is a true-scale replica of the earth, therefore only a globe can possess a single scale ratio applicable to the entire surface. World maps, such as those used to illustrate map projections, have varying scales because the spherical surface of the earth must be distorted by areal expansion or contraction when transformed to a plane surface.

Each map projection has its particular scale properties. For example, the azimuthal equidistant projection (Figure I.9) has a constant scale on all radial lines

**FIGURE I.13.** Hills and depressions shown by contour lines. (© 1960, John Wiley & Sons, New York.)

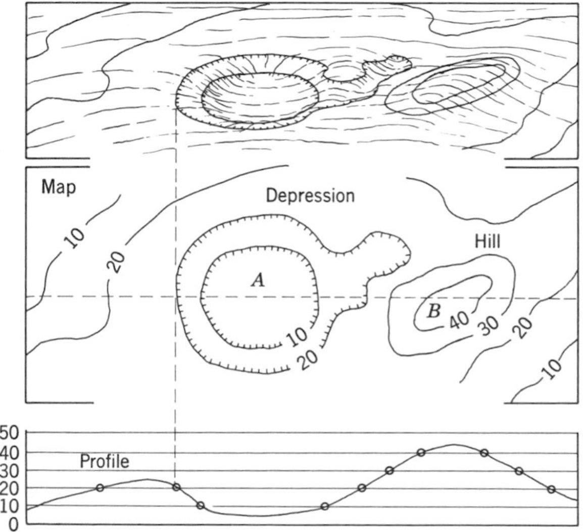

emanating from the center of the projection. However, the scale changes continuously with latitude in the east-west direction over the entire map. In the sinusoidal projection (Figure I.6) scale is constant and the same along both the equator and the central meridian, but only on those two lines. In the equatorial Mercator projection (Figure I.2) scale is constant along any given parallel of latitude. On large Mercator charts graphic scales are shown for various latitudes, enabling east-west distances to be estimated. In view of the unique and varied scale properties of individual map projections, together with the shape distortions caused by scale changes, it is advisable to use a good globe in conjunction with any world map whenever relationships between continental and oceanic units are under study.

## Isopleth maps

In almost every branch of the earth sciences it is necessary to show the distribution of some physical property over an area of the earth's sea-level datum or at some given level above or below that surface. Such maps consist of lines connecting all points having the same quantity or value. The lines are in general referred to as *isopleths* (from the Greek *isos,* equal, and *plēthos,* fullness or quantity), and the maps are known as *isopleth maps.* The term *isarithm* (from the Greek *arithmos,* number) is also used in scientific writing in essentially the same sense as isopleth.

The technique of constructing, reading, and interpreting isopleth maps may be illustrated by study of the *topographic contour map,* familiar to many persons because of its widespread use to depict the relief features of the landscape. A *contour line* is a line drawn on the map through all points having equal elevation above a *datum,* usually mean sea level (Figure I.11). A contour line is therefore an *isohypse* (from the Greek *hypso,* height), but this term is little used in English writing. If in the case of the island shown in Figure I.11 the sea level were to rise exactly 10 feet, the water would come to rest on the line of the 10-foot contour line, a second rise of 10 more feet would bring the water line to the 20-foot contour line, etc. Successive contour lines have a constant unit of vertical separation, the *contour interval.*

A most important property of isopleth maps is that the relative horizontal spacing of successive isopleths indicates the *gradient,* or rate at which the value is changing with respect to horizontal distance. In the

**FIGURE I.14.** Principle of construction of an isohyetal map from rainfall data. (© 1960, John Wiley & Sons, New York. Data from D. W. Mead.)

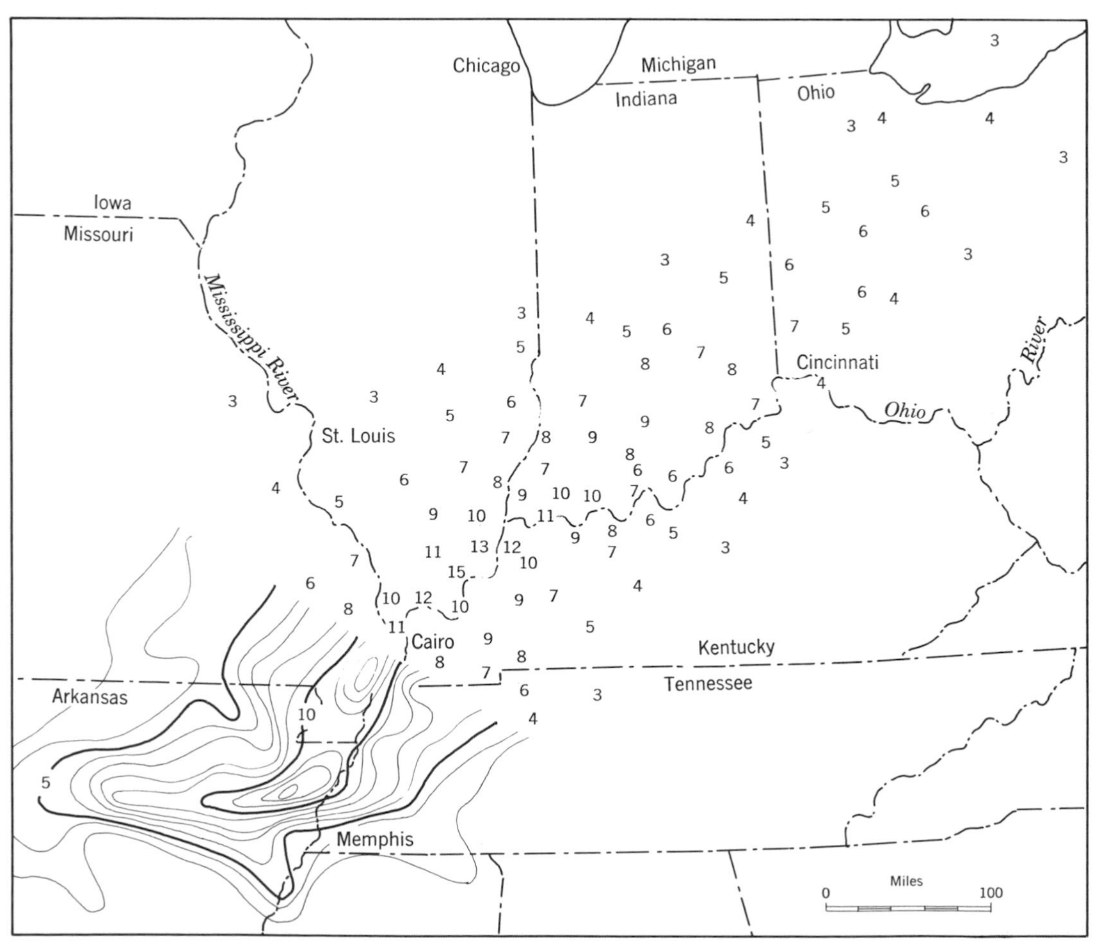

example of the island (Figure I.11) the gradient of the ground surface is steep on the right-hand side, hence the contours are closely spaced in descending from *B* to *A*. By contrast, the ground slope from *B* down to *C* is gentle, hence the contours there are spaced widely apart.

To be exact about the relation of gradient to spacing of isopleths, refer to Figure I.12. The angle of surface slope, or gradient, is represented by the angle $\alpha$, which is one acute angle of a right triangle whose legs are the contour interval, *CI,* and the horizontal spacing, *H,* between successive contours. The *tangent* of angle $\alpha$ is defined as *CI* divided by *H.* Hence the horizontal distance, *H,* is equal to *CI* times the cotangent of the angle $\alpha$. From this observation we derive the general statement that the horizontal spacing between isopleths is directly proportional to the cotangent of the gradient measured in degrees.

On a topographic contour map, a hilltop is represented by a contour that forms a continuous loop (*B* in Figure I.13). A hollow, known as a *topographic depression,* is also delineated by a contour forming a closed loop (*A* in Figure I.13). A special type of contour line, the *hachured line,* is conventionally used to show a depression, as at *A* of Figure I.13.

Construction of an isopleth map is illustrated in Figure I.14 by a partially completed isohyetal map. As a first step, the data are plotted on the map. A line is then drawn to connect those points bearing the same value. Where the plotted values do not coincide with that of the isopleth, its position is estimated at proportionate distances between points.

Table I.1 lists a variety of isopleths encountered in various branches of the earth sciences. Examples are found in the text.

**FIGURE I.15.** A simple geologic map. Below is a structure section drawn along the lower edge of the map area. (© 1960, John Wiley & Sons, New York.)

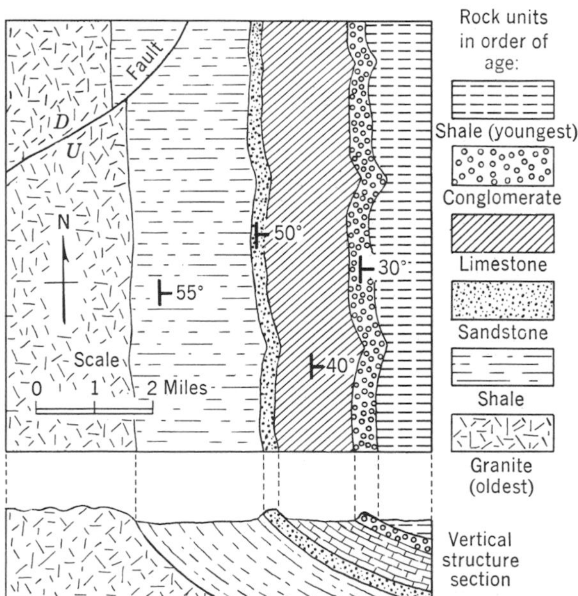


**TABLE I.1. EXAMPLES OF ISOPLETHS**

| Name of Isopleth | Greek Root | Property Described | Examples in Text |
|---|---|---|---|
| Isobar | *baros,* weight | Barometric pressure | 15.3, 15.32 |
| Isotherm | *therme,* heat | Temperature of air, water, or soil | 14.26, 14.27 |
| Isotach | *tachos,* swift | Fluid velocity | 15.29 |
| Isohyet | *hyetos,* rain | Precipitation | 18.25, 18.28 |
| Isohypse | *hypso,* height | Elevation | 40.17 |
| Isopach | *pachys,* thick | Thickness, as of a rock stratum, or glacial ice | 40.21 |
| Isobath | *bathos,* depth | Depth, of water | 24.11 |
| Isocline | *clino,* slope | Magnetic dip | 7.8, 7.9 |
| Isogonic line, or isogone | *gonia,* angle | Magnetic declination | 7.11 7.12 |
| Isodyne | *dynamis,* power | Magnetic intensity | 7.6 |

## Geologic maps and structure sections

The surface distribution of rock varieties or of rock units differentiated according to age is shown by means of the *areal geologic map* (Figure I.15). Each rock variety or unit is assigned a distinctive color or pattern. Interest centers upon the lines of contact, which may represent the disconformities between essentially parallel strata or the unconformities between rock bodies of grossly different structures and geologic age. Also represented are contacts between igneous bodies and the surrounding rocks which they have invaded, or the effects of juxtaposition of unlike rock masses by movement on faults. Faults are shown by heavy lines. In general, contacts and faults are shown by continuous lines where their existence is known with certainty from direct observations on outcrops, and by dotted or broken lines where their presence is suspected or inferred but not confirmed by direct observation.

In mapping and reporting upon geologic relations, it is necessary to describe the attitude of various natural rock planes, including planes of stratification (bedding planes), planes of foliation and cleavage, fault planes, joint planes, planar igneous contacts, and surfaces of

**FIGURE I.16.** Strike and dip illustrated by strata at the shore of a lake. (© 1960, John Wiley & Sons, New York.)

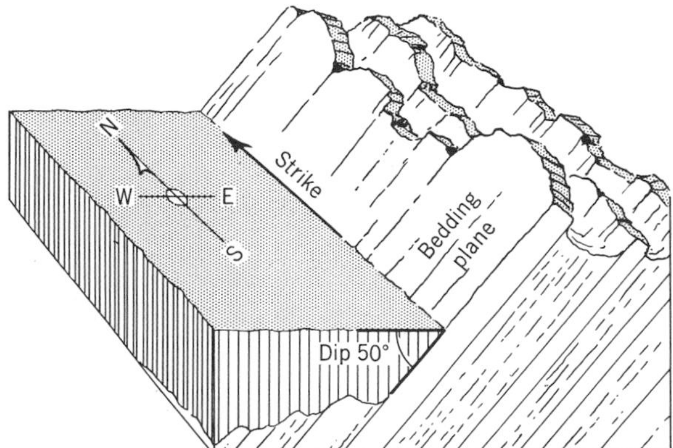

unconformity. The *dip* of a natural rock plane is the acute angle formed between the rock plane and an imaginary horizontal plane of reference (Figure I.16). Dip is stated in degrees and ranges from zero for a horizontal plane to 90° for a vertical plane. Instruments for measurement of dip normally use a level bubble for determination of the horizontal. The direction of dip may also be stated, using compass-quadrant bearings or azimuths, as explained in Chapter 11. The *strike* of an inclined rock plane is the direction assumed by the line of intersection between the rock plane and a horizontal plane of reference (Figure I.16). Geologists conventionally state strike in terms of compass-quadrant bearings (Chapter 11). Any horizontal line has two directions, but it is conventional to give strike with reference to geographic north, for example, N. 25° E., or N. 67° W. Strike and dip are indicated on a geologic map by T-shaped symbols. The crossbar of the T shows strike, and the other bar shows direction of dip (Figure I.15).

Distribution of rock bodies at depth is shown by means of the *structure section,* representing the configuration of the rocks as they would appear upon the walls of a straight vertical trench cut to the desired depth (Figure I.15). The uppermost line of the structure section is a topographic profile upon the ground surface. Considerable vertical exaggeration is commonly used, resulting in the exaggeration of dips from their true values. Structure sections may be drawn by inference based on surface observations or may be based upon rock cores or cuttings brought to the surface by drilling of holes. Seismic refraction and reflection data (Chapter 23) and observations by magnetometer (Chapter 7) and gravimeter (Chapter 10) constitute geophysical methods of obtaining information for construction of structure sections.

# World climates, soils, and vegetation

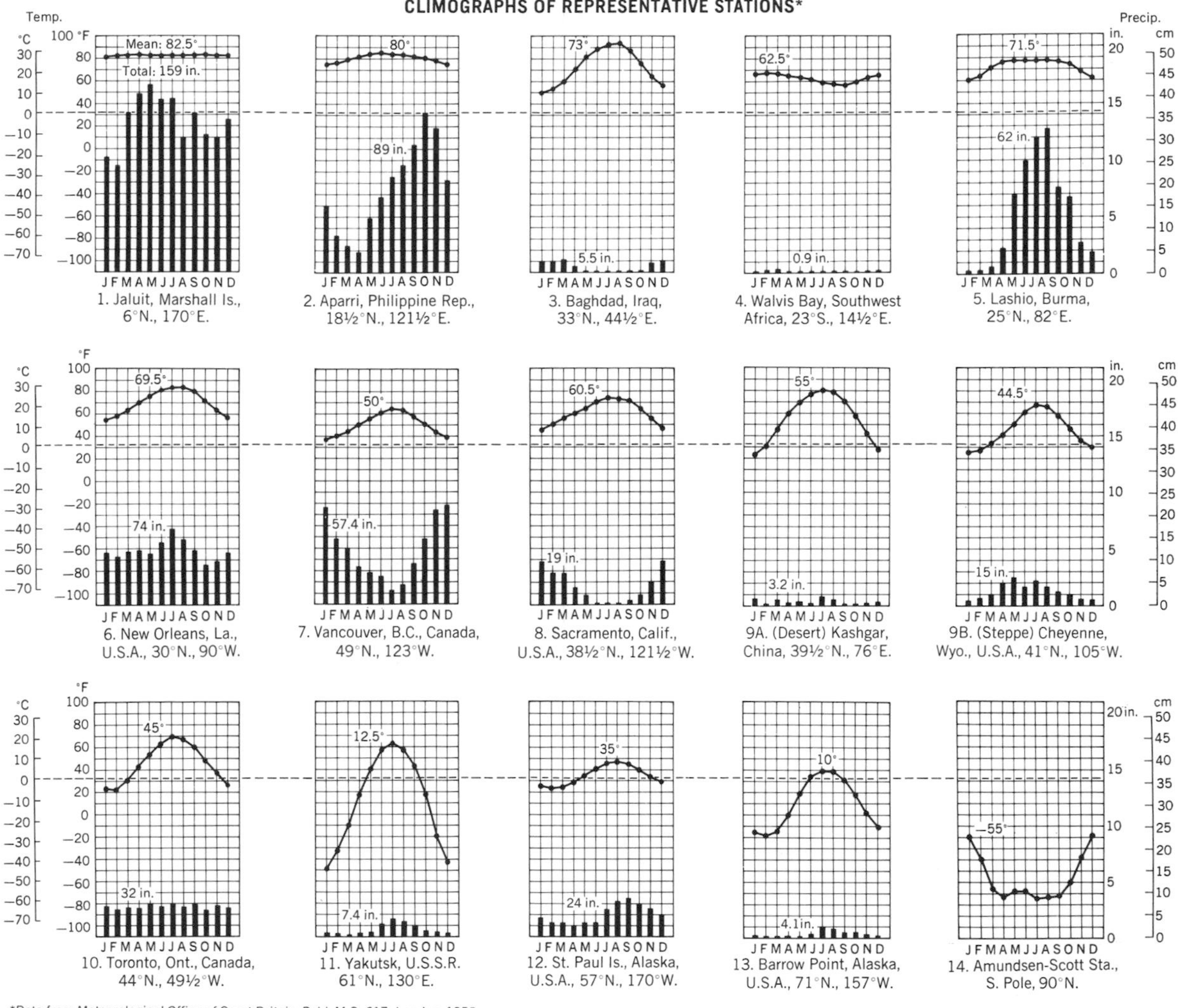


*Data from Meteorological Office of Great Britain, Publ. M.O. 617, London, 1958

## WORLD CLIMATES*

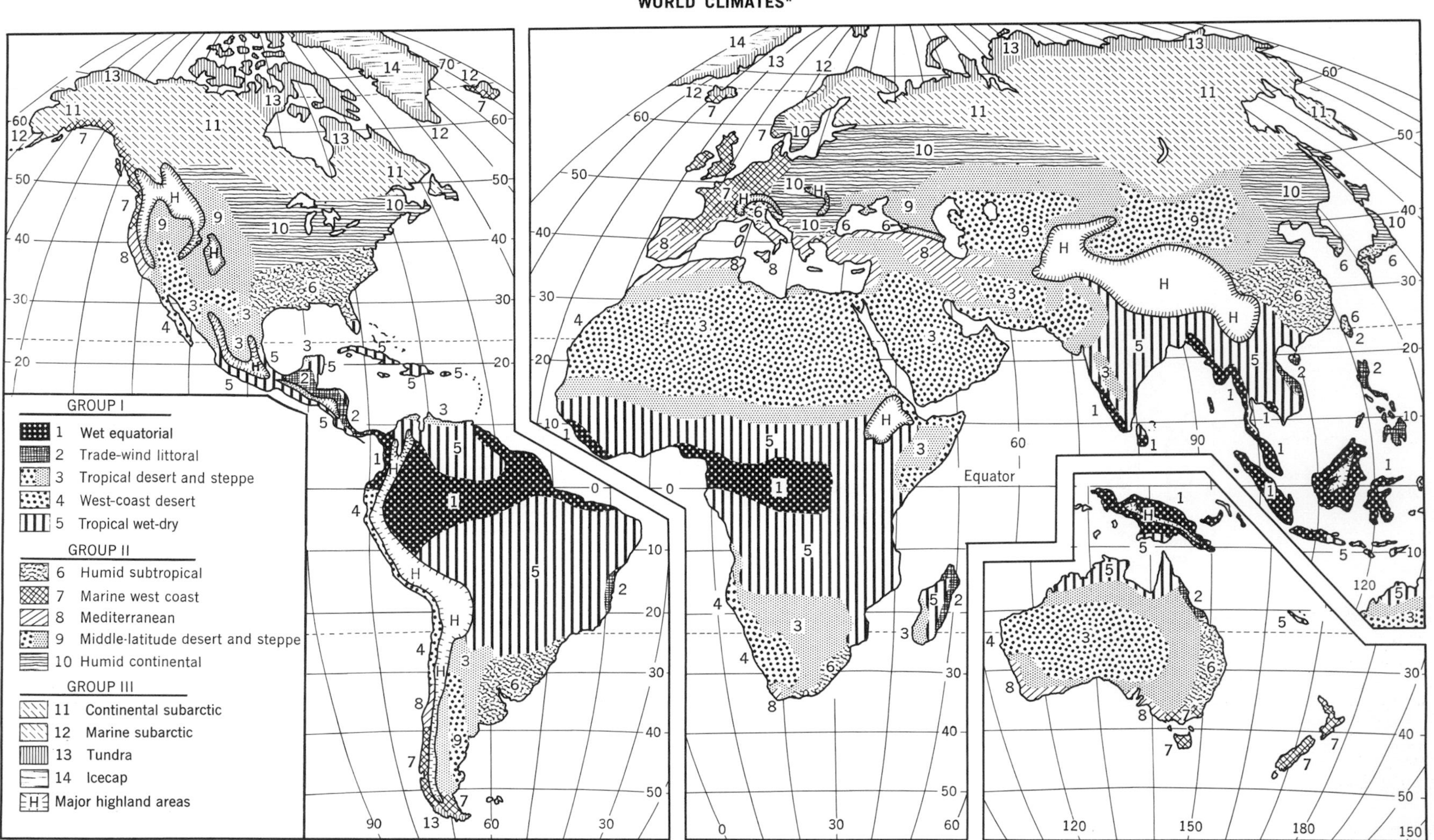


*From A. N. Strahler, 1969, Physical Geography, 3rd edition, John Wiley & Sons, New York.

# SUMMARY OF WORLD CLIMATES*

## GROUP I: CLIMATES DOMINATED BY TROPICAL AIR MASSES

**1. Wet Equatorial Climates 10° N.–10° S. lat. (Asia 10°–20° N.)**
Equatorial trough (convergence zone) climates dominated by warm, moist tropical maritime (mT) and equatorial (mE) air masses yielding heavy rainfall through convectional storms. Remarkably uniform temperatures prevail throughout the year.

**2. Trade Wind Littoral Climates 10°–25° N. and S. lat.**
Tropical easterlies (trades) bring maritime tropical (mT) air masses from moist western sides of oceanic subtropical high-pressure cells to give narrow east-coast zones of heavy rainfall and uniformly high temperatures. Rainfall shows strong seasonal variation.

**3. Tropical Desert and Steppe Climates 15°–35° N. and S. lat.**
Source regions of continental-tropical ($cT_S$) air masses in high-pressure cells at high level over lands astride the Tropics of Cancer and Capricorn give arid to semiarid climate with very high maximum temperatures and moderate annual range.

**4. West Coast Desert Climates 15°–30° N. and S. lat.**
On west coasts bordering the oceanic subtropical high-pressure cells, subsiding maritime tropical ($mT_S$) air masses are stable and dry. Extremely dry but relatively cool foggy desert climates prevail in narrow coastal belts. Annual temperature range is small.

**5. Tropical Wet-Dry Climates 5°–25° N. and S. lat.**
Seasonal alternation of moist mT or mE air masses with dry cT air masses gives climate with wet season at time of high sun, dry season at time of low sun.

* From A. N. Strahler (1969), *Physical Geography,* 3rd ed., New York, Wiley. 

## GROUP II: CLIMATES CONTROLLED BY BOTH POLAR AND TROPICAL AIR MASSES

**6. Humid Subtropical Climates 20°–35° N. and S. lat.**
Subtropical eastern continental margins dominated by moist maritime (mT) air masses flowing from the western sides of oceanic high-pressure cells. In high-sun season, rainfall is copious and temperatures warm. Winters are cool with frequent continental polar (cP) air mass invasions. Frequent cyclonic storms.

**7. Marine West Coast Climates 40°–60° N. and S. lat.**
Windward middle-latitude west coasts receive frequent cyclonic storms with cool moist maritime polar (mP) air masses. These bring much cloudiness and well-distributed precipitation with winter maximum. Annual temperature range is small for middle latitudes.

**8. Mediterranean-type Climates 30°–45° N. and S. lat.**
Wet-winter, dry-summer climate results from seasonal alternation of conditions causing climates 4 and 7—mP air masses dominate in winter with cyclonic storms and ample rainfall, $mT_S$ air masses dominate in summer with extreme drought. Moderate annual temperature range.

**9. Middle-Latitude Desert and Steppe Climates. 35°–50° N. and S. lat.**
Interior middle-latitude deserts and steppes of regions shut off by mountains from invasions of maritime air masses (mT or mP), but dominated by continental tropical (cT) air masses in summer and continental polar (cP) air masses in winter. Great annual temperature range—hot summers, cold winters.

**10. Humid Continental Climate 35°–60° N. lat.**
Located in central and eastern parts of continents in middle latitudes, these climates are in the polar front zone, the battle ground of polar and tropical air masses. Seasonal contrasts are strong and weather highly variable. Ample precipitation throughout the year is increased in summer by invading maritime tropical (mT) air masses. Cold winters are dominated by continental polar (cP) air masses invading frequently from northern source regions.

## GROUP III: CLIMATES DOMINATED BY POLAR AND ARCTIC AIR MASSES

**11. Continental Subarctic Climates 50°–70° N. lat.**
This climate lies in the source region of continental polar (cP) air masses, which in winter are stable and very cold. Summers are short and cool. Annual temperature range is enormous. Cyclonic storms, into which maritime polar (mP) air is drawn, supply only light precipitation, but evaporation is small and the climate is therefore effectively moist.

**12. Marine Subarctic Climates 50°–60° N., 45°–60° S. lat.**
Located in the arctic frontal zones of the winter season, these windward coasts and islands of subarctic latitudes are dominated by cool mP air masses. Precipitation is relatively large and annual temperature range small for so high a latitude.

**13. Tundra Climates North of 55° N., South of 50° S. lat.**
The arctic coastal fringes lie along a frontal zone in which polar (mP, cP) air masses interact with arctic (A) air masses in cyclonic storms. Climate is humid and severely cold with no warm season or summer.

**14. Icecap Climates (Greenland, Antarctica)**
Source regions of arctic (A) and antarctic (AA) air masses situated upon the great continental icecaps have climate with annual temperature average far below all other climates and no above-freezing monthly average. High altitudes of ice plateaus intensify the cold of their air masses.

## WORLD SOILS*

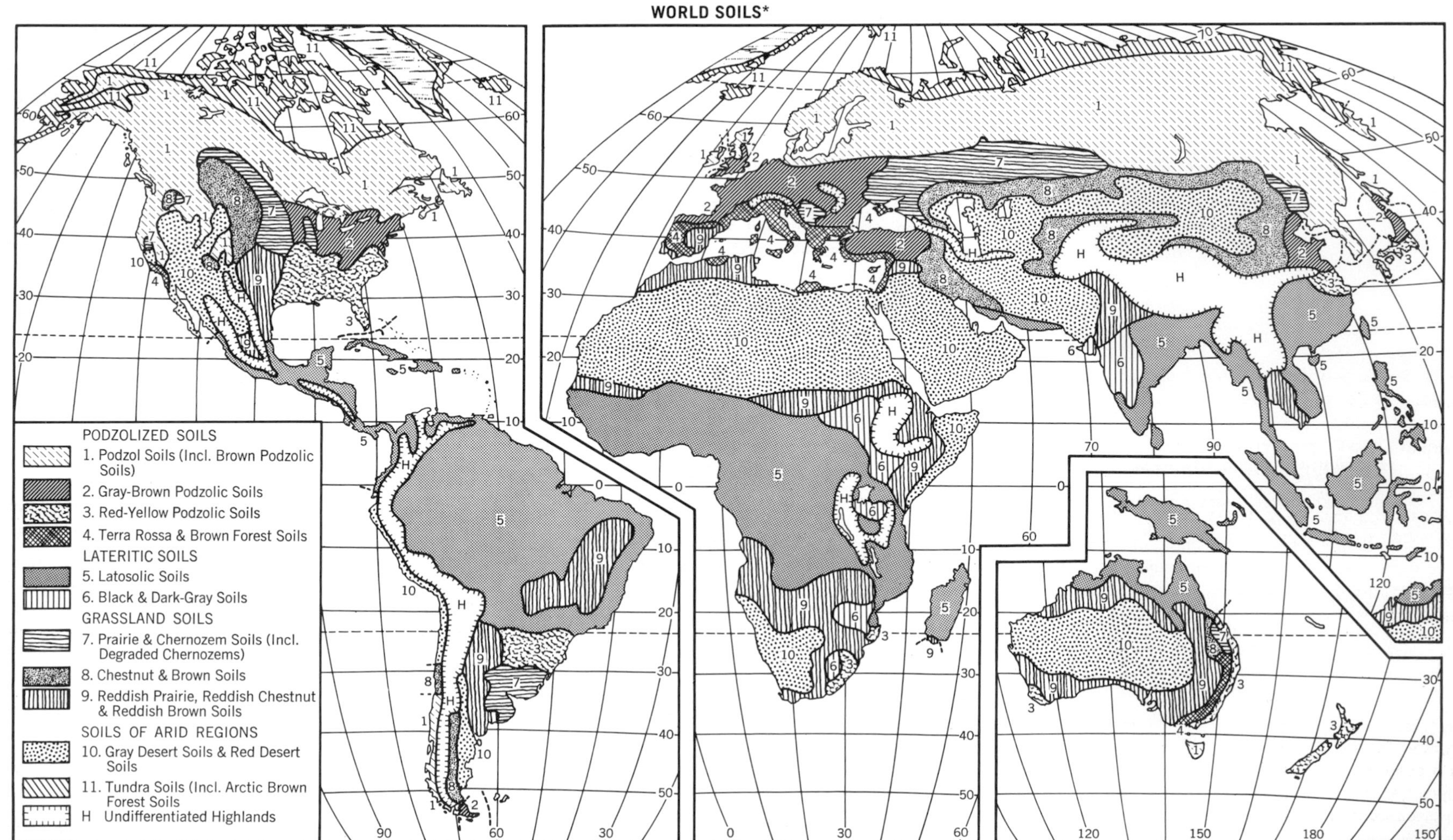


*Based on a world map of soils by A. C. Orvedal in Goode's *World Atlas*, 11th Edition, 1960. E. B. Espenshade, Jr. Editor Used by permission of Rand McNally & Co., Chicago, Ill.

## SUMMARY OF WORLD SOILS

The accompanying map is a highly generalized and schematic representation of the distribution of great soil groups, as classified by the Soil Survey Division of the U.S. Department of Agriculture, following a system developed earlier by C. F. Marbut. Only groups of the zonal order are shown. They represent idealized conditions of favorable soil texture and good drainage. Many areas of intrazonal soils (poorly drained environments) and azonal soils (lithosols and regosols) exist within map areas shown as zonal.

### PODZOLIZED SOILS

Light-colored soils of forested regions in which organic acids remove soil bases (eluviation). Typically, a leached $A_2$ horizon lies above a dense *B* horizon of colloid accumulation. A regime of podzolization is favored by a large excess of precipitation over evaporation in cold and cool humid climates.

**1. Podzol Soils (Including Brown Podzolic Soils).** Profile: $A_0$—raw humus; $A_1$—thin, acid, gray to brown; $A_2$—ash-gray, strongly leached; *B*—brownish, dense, clayey, with hardpan. Climate: continental subarctic; colder parts of humid continental; marine west-coast.

**2. Gray-Brown Podzolic Soils.** Profile: $A_1$—moderately acid, humus-rich; $A_2$—grayish brown, leached; *B*—thick, dense, yellowish brown to reddish brown. Climate: humid continental; marine west-coast (Europe).

**3. Red-Yellow Podzolic Soils.** Profile: $A_1$—pale red or yellowish, low in humus; $A_2$—very pale reddish or yellowish, weakly developed; *B*—reddish, dense. Transitional to latosols. Climate: humid subtropical.

**4. Terra Rossa and Brown Forest Soils.** Terra rossa: red color, deficient in humus, rich in sesquioxide of iron. Origin uncertain. Climate: Mediterranean-type. Brown Forest Soils: Very dark brown, friable, grading down to lighter brown. Illuviation weak. Calcification dominant, podzolization weak. Climate: Mediterranean-type.

### LATERITIC SOILS

Soil of humid equatorial and tropical regions with prevailingly high temperatures and a large precipitation surplus either year-around or in a rainy season. Chemical alteration of parent matter complete, silica largely removed, sesquioxides of iron and aluminum abundant.

**5. Latosolic Soils.** Red-brown upper zone, deep red *B* horizon. Nodules of sesquioxides. Rests on deeply altered bedrock. Associated with accumulations of laterite. Climate: Wet equatorial; monsoon; tropical wet-dry.

**6. Black and Dark-Gray Soils.** Upland soils in India and Africa, locally associated with basaltic bedrock. Climate: Tropical wet-dry.

### GRASSLAND SOILS

Soils of subhumid and semiarid climates in which annual evaporation balances or exceeds precipitation and with seasons of prolonged drought and high temperatures. Calcium carbonate occurs in excess. Leaching is absent. Humus is well distributed throughout the *A* and *B* horizons. Pedogenic regime of calcification dominates.

**7. Prairie and Chernozem Soils.** Chernozem: Profile: *A*—thick, rich in humus, dark brown, crumb or nut structure; *B*—brown to yellow-brown, contains precipitated calcium carbonate. Widely developed on loess. Climate: Humid continental (arid side). Prairie Soils: Profile: resembles chernozem. Lacks excess calcium carbonate. Climate: Humid continental (subhumid portions).

**8. Chestnut and Brown Soils.** Chestnut soils: Profile resembles chernozem, but not as dark. Excess calcium carbonate. Climate: Transition from humid-continental to middle-latitude steppe. Brown soils: Profile lighter brown than chestnut soils. Prismatic structure in *B* horizon. Climate: Middle-latitude steppe.

**9. Reddish Prairie, Reddish Chestnut, and Reddish Brown Soils.** Reddish brown upper zone grading downward into dull-red lower zone, overlying a zone of calcium carbonate accumulation. Widely distributed in climates having seasonal aridity and high heat.

### SOILS OF ARID REGIONS

Soils of dry climates lacking in humus and with weakly developed profile horizons. Calcification is the dominant pedogenic process. Salinization in poorly drained areas (playas), producing saline soils of intrazonal classification (not differentiated on map).

**10. Gray Desert Soils and Red Desert Soils.** Gray desert soils, or sierozem: Light gray to grayish brown, horizons poorly developed. Excessive calcium carbonate; forms nodules and layers of lime crust (caliche). Climate: Middle-latitude continental deserts. Red desert soils: Pale reddish gray to deep red. Horizons poorly developed. Abundant excess calcium carbonate. Climate: Tropical deserts.

### SOILS OF COLD REGIONS

Soils of climates lacking a summer season. Chemical alteration slight, frost action intense. Pedogenic regime of gleization dominates.

**11. Tundra Soils (Including Arctic Brown Forest Soils).** Tundra soils: Profile consists of layers of sandy clay and raw humus. Shallow active layer thaws in summer. Moisture remains frozen below (permafrost). Climate: Tundra. Arctic Brown Forest Soils: Thick profile. Dark $A_1$ horizon rich in organic matter, grading down into lighter brown horizons. Found in central Alaska in continental subarctic climate.

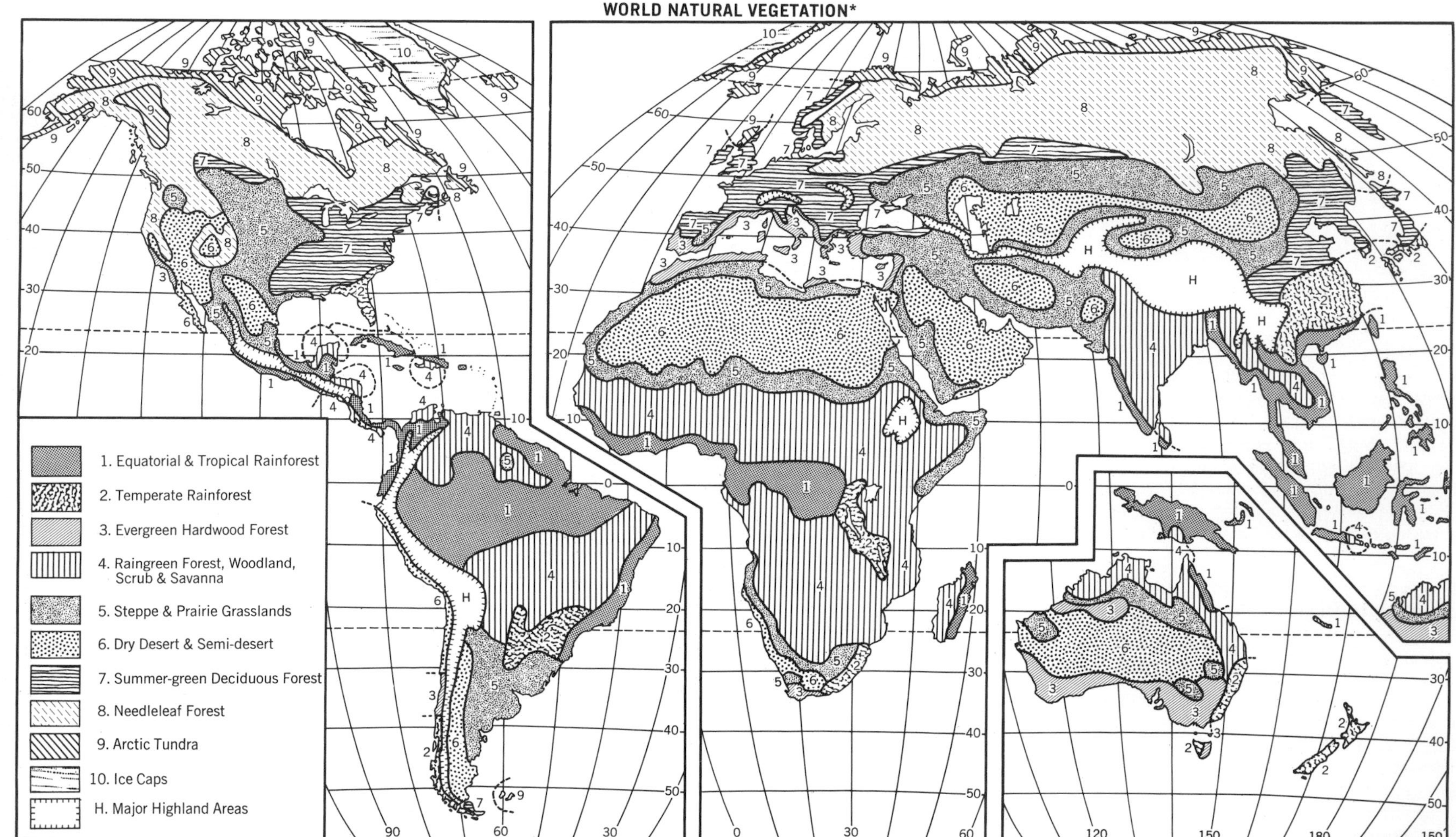


*Modified and simplified from a world map by H. Brockman Jerosch, 1951, following Rübel's classification

Aitoff's Equal-Area Projection. Adapted by V. C. Finch

## SUMMARY OF WORLD NATURAL VEGETATION

Natural vegetation is described and classified in terms of *formation classes,* of which some 18 to 20 are recognized according to systems developed by A. F. W. Schimper (1903), Eduard Rübel (1930), F. C. von Faber (1935), and Pierre Dansereau (1957). A formation class describes the physical structure of a natural plant assemblage that has achieved a climax state on a well-drained upland surface. The accompanying map is a largely schematic plan of world areas in which the formation classes may be expected to exist under favorable conditions. Deforestation, cultivation, and urbanization, presence of excessively wet or dry habitats, or unfavorable terrain or soils have precluded development of the idealized vegetation formation class over large parts of the map.

Structural description of vegetation takes into account life-form (tree, shrub, liana, herb, bryoid, epiphyte), plant size, stratification (tree layer, shrub layer, herb layer, moss layer), coverage (continuous, discontinuous, sparse), function (deciduous, evergreen), leaf shape and size (broadleaf, needleleaf, graminoid), and leaf texture (membranous, sclerophyllous, succulent).

**1. Equatorial and Tropical Rainforest.** Forest of tall closely-set trees whose crowns form a continuous canopy of foliage, providing dense shade. Trees broadleaved evergreen. Lianas abundant. Large numbers of tree species. Climate: wet equatorial, trade-wind littoral. Pedogenic regime: laterization. Soils: latosols.

**2. Temperate Rainforest (also Laurel Forest).** Forest of evergreen trees, such as oak, laurel, magnolia, or beech; elsewhere of conifers. Large tree-ferns abundant; epiphytes numerous. Found at high altitudes in equatorial and tropical zones; along eastern continental margins with a humid subtropical climate; along west coasts with marine west-coast climate. Pedogenic regime: laterization at low latitudes; podzolization in middle latitudes.

**3. Evergreen Hardwood Forest (also Sclerophyll Forest).** Forest of low trees with small, hard, leathery leaves. Trees typically low-branched and gnarled, with thick bark. Map class includes large areas of woodland and scrub. Associated with Mediterranean-type climate having a long dry (and often hot) summer with large water deficit. Soils: *terra rossa* (Mediterranean lands), or reddish chestnut, reddish-prairie, and reddish-brown groups.

**4. Raingreen Forest, Woodland, Scrub, and Savanna.** Includes open monsoon forest and tropical savanna woodland (park-like). Trees and shrubs shed leaves in dry season of low sun. During rainy season in high-sun period tree foliage and grasses grow profusely. Climate: tropical wet-dry. Pedogenic regime: laterization.

**5. Steppe and Prairie Grasslands.** Steppe, or short-grass prairie, is associated with semi-arid climates ranging from tropical to middle-latitude zones and associated with brown soils under a pedogenic regime of calcification. Prairie, consisting of tall grasses, is associated with subhumid middle-latitude continental climate under a pedogenic regime of calcification. Soils: prairie and chernozem.

**6. Dry Desert and Semidesert.** Dry desert consists of widely dispersed shrubs (typically spiny or succulent) or hard grasses; semidesert (half-desert) of low shrubs and grasses in less arid desert margins. Climates: continental and west-coast deserts, wide latitude range. Pedogenic regime: calcification. Soils: gray and red desert.

**7. Summergreen Deciduous Forest.** Forest of tall broad-leaved deciduous trees which shed leaves in winter. May include needleleaf evergreen trees. Climates: humid continental, marine west-coast (Europe). Pedogenic regime: podzolization. Soils: gray-brown and red-yellow podzolic.

**8. Needleleaf Forest.** Usually a dense forest consisting of straight-trunked conical trees with needle-like leaves. Map class includes cold woodland (taiga). Trees are conifers which may be evergreens—typically spruce, fir, pine or larch. Climate: subarctic, colder parts of humid-continental, marine west-coast. Pedogenic regime: podzolization. Soils: podzols.

**9. Arctic tundra.** Grassy tundra of low herbaceous plants, also mosses and lichens. Map class includes arctic fell field of sparse vegetation on rocky surfaces. Associated with tundra and marine subarctic climate. Pedogenic regime: gleization. Soils: tundra. Permafrost layer beneath.

**10. Icecaps.** Areas of permanent ice and snow, devoid of plants.

# Conversion graphs

1. Units of Length
   Metric to English Units

   Equivalents of length:

   1 micron ($\mu$) = 0.001 millimeter (mm) = 0.00004 inch (in.)
   1 mm = 0.1 centimeter (cm) = 0.03937 in.
   1000 mm = 100 cm = 1 meter (m) = 39.37 in. = 3.2808 foot (ft)
   1 m 0.001 kilometer (km) = 1. 0936 yard (yd)
   1000 m = 1 km = 0.62137 mile (mi)
   1 in. = 2.54 cm
   12 in. = 1 ft = 0.3048 m
   63,360 in. = 5280 ft = 1 mi = 1.60935 km

   Equivalents of area:

| | |
|---|---|
| 1 mm$^2$ = 0.00155 in.$^2$ | 1 in.$^2$ = 6.452 cm$^2$ |
| 1 m$^2$ = 10.764 ft$^2$ | 1 ft$^2$ = 0.09290 m$^2$ |
| 1 km$^2$ = 0.3861 mi$^2$ | 1 mi$^2$ = 2.5800 km$^2$ |

   Equivalents of volume:

| | |
|---|---|
| 1 mm$^3$ = 0.000061 in.$^3$ | 1 in.$^3$ = 16.387 cm$^3$ (cc) |
| 1 cm$^3$ (cc) = 0.0610 in.$^3$ | 1 ft$^3$ = 0.02832 m$^3$ |
| 1 m$^3$ = 35.315 ft$^3$ | 1 mi$^3$ = 4.1682 km$^3$ |
| 1 km$^3$ = 0.239911 mi$^3$ | |

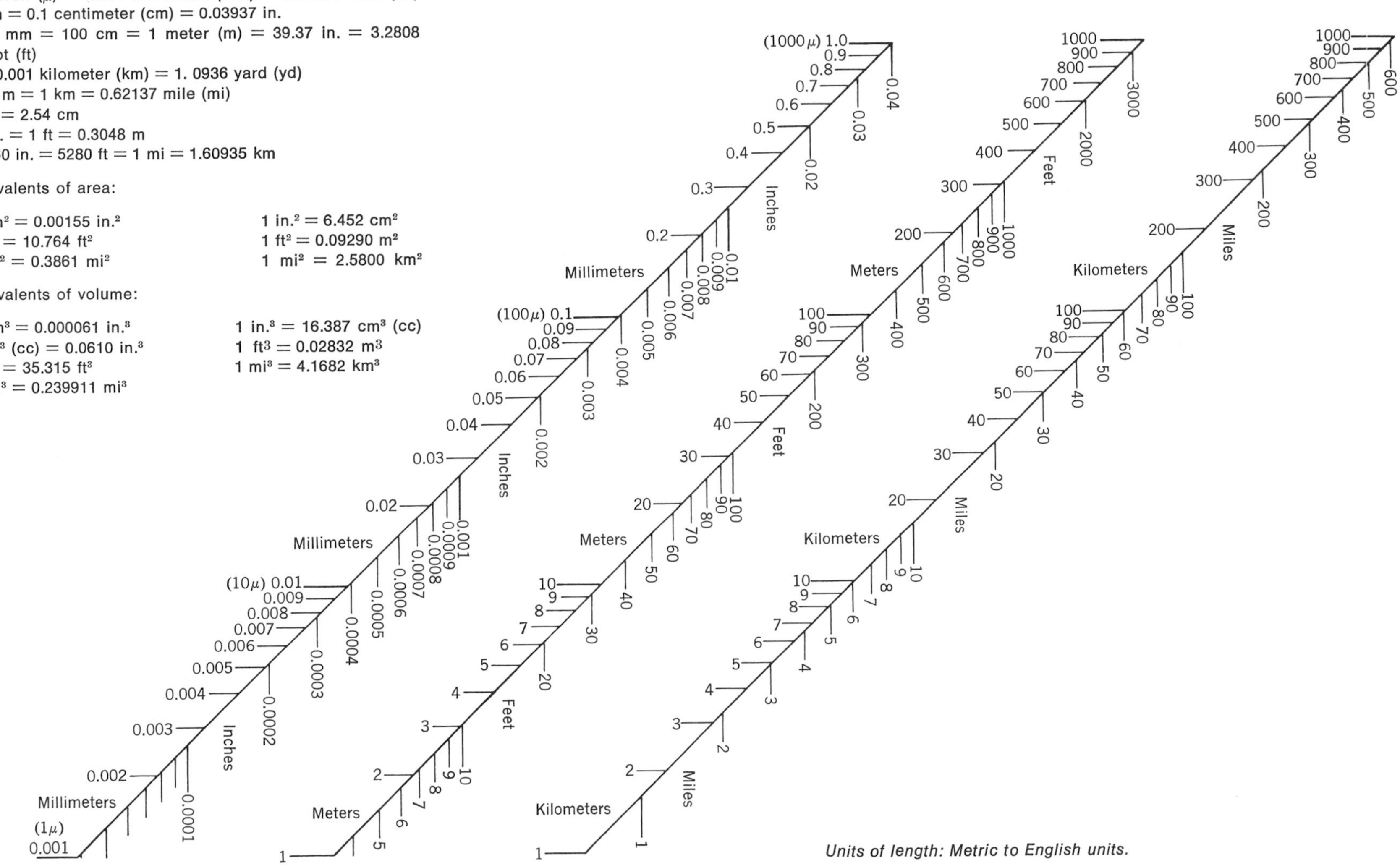


*Units of length: Metric to English units.*

2. Temperature Scales
Centigrade (Celsius) to Fahrenheit

Equivalents:

1 C° = 1.8 F°
1 F° = 0.5556 C°
1 K° (Kelvin) = 1 C°
−273° C = −459.4° F = 0° K

Conversion formulas:

°F = 9/5 °C + 32
°C = 5/9 (°F − 32)

Note: °F is read "degrees Fahrenheit."
F° is read "Fahrenheit degrees."
°C is read "degrees Centigrade, or Celsius."
C° is read "Centigrade, or Celsius, degrees."

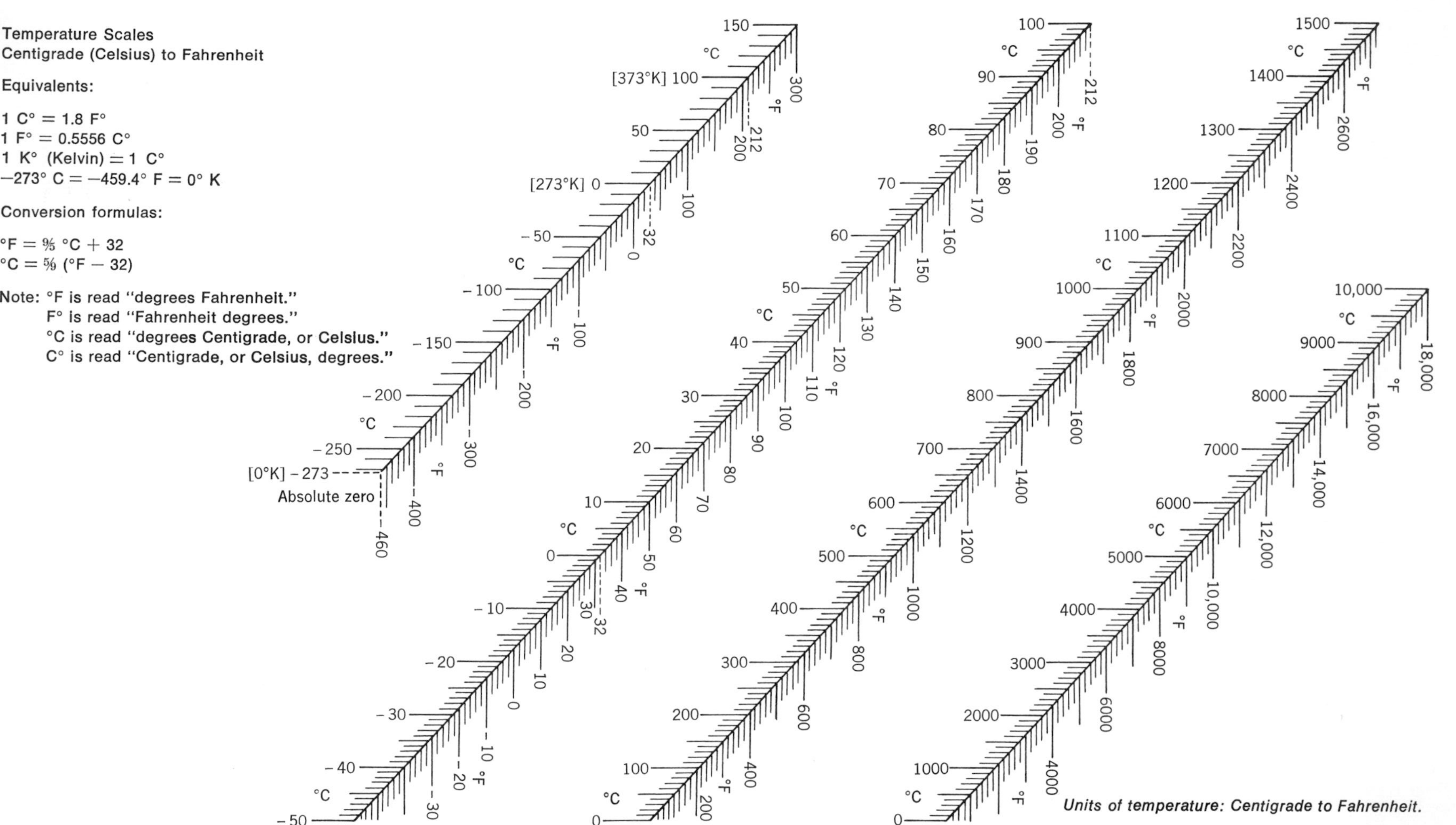


*Units of temperature: Centigrade to Fahrenheit.*

# Index